First printing, June 1986
Second printing, October 1988
Third printing, February 1992

ASM Handbook is a collective effort involving thousands of technical specialists. It brings together in one book a wealth of information from world-wide sources to help scientists, engineers, and technicians solve current and long-range problems.

Great care is taken in the compilation and production of this volume, but it should be made clear that no warranties, express or implied, are given in connection with the accuracy or completeness of this publication, and no responsibility can be taken for any claims that may arise.

Nothing contained in the ASM Handbook shall be construed as a grant of any right of manufacture, sale, use, or reproduction, in connection with any method, process, apparatus, product, composition, or system, whether or not covered by letters patent, copyright, or trademark, and nothing contained in the ASM Handbook shall be construed as a defense against any alleged infringement of letters patent, copyright, or trademark, or as a defense against any liability for such infringement.

Comments, criticisms, and suggestions are invited, and should be forwarded to ASM International.

Library of Congress Cataloging in Publication Data

American Society for Metals

Metals handbook.

Includes bibliographies and indexes.
Contents: v. 1. Properties and selection—v. 2. Properties and selection—nonferrous alloys and pure metals—[etc.]—v. 10. Materials characterization

1. Handbooks, manuals, etc. I. Title: American Society for Metals. Handbook Committee.
TA459.M43   1978   669   78-14934
ISBN 0-87170-007-7 (v. 1)

SAN 204-7586

Printed in the United States of America

ASM Handb

Formerly Ninth Edition, Meta

Volume 10
Materials
Characterizatio

Prepared under the direction of
the ASM Handbook Committee

Ruth E. Whan, Coordinator

Kathleen Mills, Manager of Editorial Operation:
Joseph R. Davis, Senior Technical Editor
James D. Destefani, Technical Editor
Deborah A. Dieterich, Production Editor
George M. Crankovic, Assistant Editor
Heather J. Frissell, Assistant Editor
Diane M. Jenkins, Word Processing Specialist

William H. Cubberly, Director of Publications
Robert L. Stedfeld, Associate Director of Publicati

Editorial Assistance
Esther Coffman
Robert T. Kiepura
Bonnie R. Sanders

**The Materials
Information Society**

Foreword to the Third Printing

With the third printing of this Volume, it takes its place in the new *ASM Handbook* series. The *ASM Handbook* was established to build upon the proud tradition of the *Metals Handbook* and to position the series to meet the needs of future engineers, researchers, technicians, and students. The *ASM Handbook* series will encompass volumes from both the 9th and 10th Editions of *Metals Handbook*—as well as new and revised Volumes as they are released—in order to establish one comprehensive set of reference materials. This will allow a much more flexible approach to updating information: technological advances will be the impetus behind Volume revisions or the addition of new Volumes to the series. The title of the new *ASM Handbook* series reflects the increasingly interrelated nature of materials technology and emphasizes the position of ASM International as the premier source of authoritative materials information.

The Editors

Foreword to the First and Second Printings

When the Volume 10 Organizing Committee first met in 1983 to begin planning a brand-new *Metals Handbook* on materials characterization, much of the discussion centered on the needs of the intended audience and how to most effectively meet those needs. In a subsequent report sent to Volume 10 authors, committee chairman Dr. Ruth E. Whan summarized the consensus:

"The committee feels strongly that the target audience should be individuals who are involved in materials work and need characterization support, but who are not themselves materials characterization specialists. . . . In general, these people will not be required to personally carry out the required materials characterization tasks, but they will have to interact with organizations and individuals who specialize in various aspects of materials characterization. The goal of the Handbook, then, will be to facilitate these interactions between materials engineers and characterization specialists, i.e., to help the materials engineer use characterization specialists effectively in the solution of his problems. . . .

"The Handbook should be assembled . . . in a way that will enable the materials engineer to make a fairly quick decision about what type of characterization specialist to see, and will also enable him to gain an elementary-level knowledge of how this technique works, how it might provide the information he needs, what types of specimens are needed, etc. The committee feels that if we provide a Handbook that can be easily used by the target audience to help them interact effectively with the appropriate materials specialists, the Handbook will be widely used and we will have performed a worthwhile service."

The tireless efforts by Dr. Whan and her committee, the authors and reviewers, the ASM Handbook Committee, and the ASM Handbook staff have indeed been worthwhile. This volume is one of the few basic reference sources on the subject of materials characterization; it cuts through the confusing and at times intimidating array of analytical acronyms and jargon. We believe that readers will find the format convenient and easy to use.

Dr. Whan and the Volume 10 section chairmen (listed in the Table of Contents) are to be congratulated for recruiting the top analytical specialists from this country and others to contribute to this Handbook. One of our authors, Jerome Karle of the Naval Research Laboratory, was the co-winner of the 1985 Nobel Prize for Chemistry. Karle and Herbert Hauptman of the Medical Foundation of Buffalo shared the award for their revolutionary development of direct determination methods for the crystal structure of chemicals, drugs, hormones, and antibiotics.

The American Society for Metals is honored by the opportunity to work with individuals of such caliber. We thank all of them for making this Handbook possible.

John W. Pridgeon
President

Edward L. Langer
Managing Director

The Ninth Edition of Metals Handbook
is dedicated to the memory of
TAYLOR LYMAN, A.B. (Eng.), S.M., Ph.D.
(1917–1973)
Editor, Metals Handbook, 1945–1973

Policy on Units of Measure

By a resolution of its Board of Trustees, the American Society for Metals has adopted the practice of publishing data in both metric and customary U.S. units of measure. In preparing this Handbook, the editors have attempted to present data primarily in metric units based on Système International d'Unités (SI), with secondary mention of the corresponding values in customary U.S. units. The decision to use SI as the primary system of units was based on the aforementioned resolution of the Board of Trustees, the widespread use of metric units throughout the world, and the expectation that the use of metric units in the United States will increase substantially during the anticipated lifetime of this Handbook.

For the most part, numerical engineering data in the text and in tables are presented in SI-based units with the customary U.S. equivalents in parentheses (text) or adjoining columns (tables). For example, pressure, stress, and strength are shown both in SI units, which are pascals (Pa) with a suitable prefix, and in customary U.S. units, which are pounds per square inch (psi). To save space, large values of psi have been converted to kips per square inch (ksi), where 1 kip = 1000 lb. Some strictly scientific data are presented in SI units only.

Both nanometers (nm) and angstrom units (Å) have been used in the text (1 nm = 10 Å). Angstroms are often used as a unit of measure in x-ray crystallography, while nanometers are preferred in the measurement of light wavelengths.

On graphs and charts, grids correspond to SI-based units, which appear along the left and bottom edges; where appropriate, corresponding customary U.S. units appear along the top and right edges.

Data pertaining to a specification published by a specification-writing group may be given in only the units used in that specification or in dual units, depending on the nature of the data. For example, the typical yield strength of aluminum sheet made to a specification written in customary U.S. units would be presented in dual units, but the thickness specified in that specification might be presented only in inches.

Data obtained according to standardized test methods for which the standard recommends a particular system of units are presented in the units of that system. Wherever feasible, equivalent units are also presented.

Conversions and rounding have been done in accordance with ASTM Standard E 380, with careful attention to the number of significant digits in the original data. For example, an annealing temperature of 1575 °F contains three significant digits. In this instance, the equivalent temperature would be given as 855 °C; the exact conversion to 857.22 °C would not be appropriate. For an invariant physical phenomenon that occurs at a precise temperature (such as the melting of pure silver), it would be appropriate to report the temperature as 961.93 °C or 1763.5 °F. In many instances (especially in tables and data compilations), temperature values in °C and °F are alternatives rather than conversions.

The policy on units of measure in this Handbook contains several exceptions to strict conformance to ASTM E 380; in each instance, the exception has been made to improve the clarity of the Handbook. The most notable exception is the use of $MPa\sqrt{m}$ rather than $MN \cdot m^{-3/2}$ or $MPa \cdot m^{0.5}$ as the SI unit of measure for fracture toughness. Other examples of such exceptions are the use of "L" rather than "l" as the abbreviation for liter, the use of g/cm^3 rather than kg/m^3 as the unit of measure for density (mass per unit volume), and the use of A/cm^2 rather than A/m^2 as the unit of measure for electric current density.

SI practice requires that only one virgule (diagonal) appear in units formed by combination of several basic units. Therefore, all of the units preceding the virgule are in the numerator and all units following the virgule are in the denominator of the expression; no parentheses are required to prevent ambiguity.

Organizing Committee

Ruth E. Whan
Chairman
Sandia National Laboratories

Ray W. Carpenter
Arizona State University

Paul T. Cunningham
Los Alamos National Laboratory

William H. Dingledein
Carpenter Technology Corporation

Kenneth H. Eckelmeyer
Sandia National Laboratories

Dean A. Flinchbaugh
Bethlehem Steel Corporation

Raymond P. Goehner
Siemens Corporation

J.I. Goldstein
Lehigh University

Merton Harrington
Special Metals

Harris L. Marcus
University of Texas

Carolyn McCrory-Joy
AT&T Bell Laboratories

David A. Smith
IBM Thomas J. Watson Research Center

Suzanne H. Weissman
Sandia National Laboratories

Authors and Reviewers

Brent L. Adams
Brigham Young University

R.W. Armstrong
University of Maryland

Mark A. Arnold
University of Iowa

Roger A. Assink
Sandia National Laboratories

Raghavan Ayer
Exxon Research & Engineering
Company

Delbert S. Barth
University of Nevada

Larry H. Bennett
National Bureau of Standards

S.M. Bhagat
University of Maryland

J.C. Bilello
State University of New York at Stony
Brook

Jack Blakely
Cornell University

George A. Blann
Buehler Ltd.

G. Dana Brabson
University of New Mexico

S.S. Brenner
University of Pittsburgh

Chris W. Brown
University of Rhode Island

Elliot L. Brown
Colorado School of Mines

D.R. Browning
Consultant

Richard R. Buck
University of North Carolina

Robert W. Buennecke
Caterpillar Tractor Company

Merle E. Bunker
Los Alamos National Laboratory

Frank B. Burns
Sandia National Laboratories

Thomas A. Cahill
University of California—Davis

Alan Campion
University of Texas—Austin

Martin J. Carr
Sandia National Laboratories

Joel A. Carter
Oak Ridge National Laboratory

Anders Cedergren
University Umea

M.B. Chamberlain
Sandia National Laboratories

W.F. Chambers
Sandia National Laboratories

K.L. Cheng
University of Missouri—Kansas City

Gary D. Christian
University of Washington

Wei-Kan Chu
University of North Carolina

M.J. Cieslack
Sandia National Laboratories

William A.T. Clark
Ohio State University

Stephen P. Clough
Perkin-Elmer Corporation

Dick Crawford
Lawrence Livermore National
Laboratory

Nelda A. Creager
Sandia National Laboratories

Stanley R. Crouch
Michigan State University

D.R. Crow
The Polytechnic, Wolverhampton

A.W. Czanderna
Solar Energy Research Institute

P. D'Antonio
Naval Research Laboratory

David L. Davidson
Southwest Research Institute

Barry Diamondstone
National Bureau of Standards

David L. Donahue
Oak Ridge National Laboratory

Elsie M. Donaldson
Canmet

Thomas R. Dulski
Carpenter Technology Corporation

James R. Durig
University of South Carolina

Gareth R. Eaton
University of Denver

Kenneth H. Eckelmeyer
Sandia National Laboratories

T. Egami
University of Pennsylvania

Robert Ellefson
Monsanto Research Corporation

Loren Essig
Leco Corporation

Deon G. Ettinger
Argonne National Laboratories

Lynda M. Faires
Los Alamos National Laboratory

Horatio A. Farach
University of South Carolina

Paul B. Farnsworth
Brigham Young University

B. Fleet
Imperial College

D.M. Follstaedt
Sandia National Laboratories

Ronald L. Foster
Allied Bendix Corporation

James C. Franklin
Oak Ridge Y-12 Plant
Wolfgang Frech
University of Umea
R.B. Fricioni
Leco Corporation
William G. Fricke, Jr.
Alcoa Technical Center
Stephen W. Gaarenstroom
General Motors Research Laboratory
Mary F. Garbauskas
General Electric R&D
S.R. Garcia
Los Alamos National Laboratory
Anthony J. Garrett-Reed
Massachusetts Institute of Technology
John V. Gilfrich
Naval Research Laboratory
Ernest S. Gladney
Los Alamos National Laboratory
Raymond P. Goehner
Siemens Corporation
J.I. Goldstein
Lehigh University
Michael Gonzales
Sandia National Laboratories
John T. Grant
University of Dayton Research Institute
Robert B. Greegor
The Boeing Company
Q.G. Grindstaff
Oak Ridge Y-12 Plant
Anita L. Guy
University of Arizona
D.M. Haaland
Sandia National Laboratories
Richard L. Harlow
E.I. DuPont de Nemours
Jackson E. Harrar
Lawrence Livermore National
Laboratory
W.W. Harrison
University of Virginia
Fred M. Hawkridge, Jr.
Virginia Commonwealth University
T.J. Headley
Sandia National Laboratories
G. Heath
University of Edinburgh
Kurt F.J. Heinrich
National Bureau of Standards
Michael B. Hintz
Michigan Technological University
Paul F. Hlava
Sandia National Laboratories
Paul Ho
IBM Thomas J. Watson Research Center
David H. Huskisson
Sandia National Laboratories
Hatsuo Ishada
Case Western Reserve University
Michael R. James
Rockwell International Science Center

A. Joshi
Lockheed Palo Alto Research Laboratory
Silve Kallmann
Ledoux and Company
J. Karle
Naval Research Laboratory
Michael J. Kelly
Sandia National Laboratories
Lowell D. Kispert
University of Alabama
David B. Knorr
Olin Corporation
John H. Konnert
Naval Research Laboratory
Jiri Koryta
Czechoslovak Academy of Sciences
Byron Kratochvil
University of Alberta
Aaron D. Krawitz
University of Missouri—Columbia
G.R. Lachance
Geological Survey of Canada
Max G. Lagally
University of Wisconsin
D.G. LeGrand
General Electric Company
Donald E. Leyden
Colorado State University
Eric Lifshin
General Electric R&D Center
J.S. Lin
Oak Ridge National Laboratory
MacIntyre R. Louthan, Jr.
Virginia Polytechnic Institute and State
University
Jesse B. Lumsden
Rockwell International Science Center
C.E. Lyman
Lehigh University
Curtis Marcott
The Proctor & Gamble Company
J.L. Marshall
Oak Ridge Y-12 Plant
George M. Matlack
Los Alamos National Laboratory
James W. Mayer
Cornell University
M.E. McAllaster
Sandia National Laboratories
Gregory J. McCarthy
North Dakota State University
Linda B. McGown
Oklahoma State University
N.S. McIntyre
University of Western Ontario
T. Mehrhoff
General Electric Neutron Devices
D.M. Mehs
Fort Lewis College
Louis Meites
George Mason University
C.A. Melendres
Argonne National Laboratory

Raymond M. Merrill
Sandia National Laboratories
M.E. Meyerhoff
University of Michigan
J.R. Michael
Bethlehem Steel Corporation
A.C. Miller
Alcoa Technical Center
Dennis Mills
Cornell University
M.M. Minor
Los Alamos National Laboratory
Richard L. Moore
Perkin-Elmer Corporation
Gerald C. Nelson
Sandia National Laboratories
Dale E. Newbury
National Bureau of Standards
John G. Newman
Perkin-Elmer Corporation
Monte C. Nichols
Sandia National Laboratories
M.A. Nicolet
California Institute of Technology
M.R. Notis
Lehigh University
M.C. Oborny
Sandia National Laboratories
John Olesik
University of North Carolina
Mark Ondrias
University of New Mexico
David G. Oney
Cambridge Instruments Inc.
Robert N. Pangborn
Pennsylvania State University
Carlo G. Pantano
Pennsylvania State University
Jeanne E. Pemberton
University of Arizona
William M. Peterson
EG&G Princeton Applied Research
Corporation
Bonnie Pitts
LTV Steel Company
Charles P. Poole, Jr.
University of South Carolina
Ben Post
Polytechnic Institute of New York
Paul S. Prevey
Lambda Research, Inc.
William C. Purdy
McGill University
R. Ramette
Carleton College
Leo A. Raphaelian
Argonne National Laboratory
Julian L. Roberts, Jr.
University of Redlands
Philip J. Rodacy
Sandia National Laboratories
Alton D. Romig, Jr.
Sandia National Laboratories

Contents

Introduction

R.E. Whan, Materials Characterization Department, Sandia National Laboratories

Scope

Materials Characterization has been developed with the goal of providing the engineer or scientist who has little background in materials analysis with an easily understood reference book on analytical methods. Although there is an abundance of excellent in-depth texts and manuals on specific characterization methods, they frequently are too detailed and/or theoretical to serve as useful guides for the average engineer who is primarily concerned with getting his problem solved rather than becoming an analytical specialist. This Handbook describes modern analytical methods in simplified terms and emphasizes the most common applications and limitations of each method. The intent is to familiarize the reader with the techniques that may be applied to his problem, help him identify the most appropriate technique(s), and give him sufficient knowledge to interact with the appropriate analytical specialists, thereby enabling materials characterization and troubleshooting to be conducted effectively and efficiently. The intent of this Handbook is *not* to make an engineer a materials characterization specialist.

During the planning of this Handbook, it became obvious that the phrase "materials characterization" had to be carefully defined in order to limit the scope of the book to a manageable size. Materials characterization represents many different disciplines depending upon the background of the user. These concepts range from that of the scientist, who thinks of it in atomic terms, to that of the process engineer, who thinks of it in terms of properties, procedures, and quality assurance, to that of the mechanical engineer, who thinks of it in terms of stress distributions and heat transfer. The definition selected for this book is adopted from that developed by the Committee on Characterization of Materials, Materials Advisory Board, National Research Council (Ref 1): "Characterization describes those features of composition and structure (including defects) of a material that are significant for a particular preparation, study of properties, or use, and suffice for reproduction of the material." This definition limits the characterization methods included herein to those that provide information about composition, structure, and defects and excludes those methods that yield information primarily related to materials properties, such as thermal, electrical, and mechanical properties.

Most characterization techniques (as defined above) that are in general use in well-equipped materials analysis laboratories are described in this Handbook. These include methods used to characterize materials such as alloys, glasses, ceramics, organics, gases, inorganics, and so on. Techniques used primarily for biological or medical analysis are not included. Some methods that are not widely used but that give unique or critical information are also described. Techniques that are used primarily for highly specialized fundamental research or that yield information not consistent with our definition of materials characterization have been omitted. Several techniques may be applicable for solving a particular problem, providing the engineer, materials scientist, and/or analyst with a choice or with the possibility of using complementary methods. With the exception of gas chromatography/mass spectroscopy, tandem methods that combine two or more techniques are not discussed, and the reader is encouraged to refer to the descriptions of the individual methods.

Organization

The Handbook has been organized for ease of reference by the user. The article "How To Use the Handbook" describes the tables, flow charts, and extensive cross-referenced index that can be used to quickly identify techniques applicable to a given problem. The article "Sampling" alerts the reader to the importance of sampling and describes proper methods for obtaining representative samples.

The largest subdivisions of the Handbook have been designated as Sections, each of which deals with a set of related techniques, for example, "Electron Optical Methods." Within each Section are several articles, each describing a separate analytical technique. For example, in the Section on "Electron Optical Methods" are articles on "Analytical Transmission Electron Microscopy," "Scanning Electron Microscopy," "Electron Probe X-Ray Microanalysis," and "Low-Energy Electron Diffraction." Each article begins with a boxed summary of general uses, applications, limitations, sample requirements, and capabilities of related techniques, which is designed to give the reader a quick overview of the technique, and to help him decide whether the technique might be applicable to his problem. This summary is followed by text that describes in simplified terms how the technique works, how the analyses are performed, what kinds of information can be obtained, and what types of materials problems can be addressed. Included are several brief examples that illustrate how the technique has been used to solve typical problems. A list of references at the end of each article directs the reader to more detailed information on the technique.

Following the last Section is a "Glossary of Terms" and appendices on metric conversion data and abbreviations, acronyms, and symbols used throughout the Volume. The Handbook concludes with a detailed cross-referenced index that classifies the entries by technique names, types of information or analyses desired, and classes of materials. This index, combined with the tables and flow charts in the article "How To Use the Handbook," is designed to enable the user to quickly determine which techniques are most appropriate for his problem.

REFERENCE

1. *Characterization of Materials*, prepared by The Committee on Characterization of Materials, Materials Advisory Board, MAB-229-M, March 1967

How To Use the Handbook

R.E. Whan, K.H. Eckelmeyer, and S.H. Weissman, Sandia National Laboratories

Effective Analytical Approach

The key to the successful solution of most materials problems is close interaction between the appropriate engineers, materials scientists, and analytical specialists. Engineers and other applications-oriented personnel are often the first to encounter material failures or other problems. When this occurs, consultation with a materials specialist is an essential first step in the troubleshooting process. By virtue of his knowledge of materials, the materials specialist can help the engineer define the problem, identify possible causes, and determine what type of information (analytical or otherwise) is needed to verify or refute each possible cause. Once a decision has been made regarding the information needed, they must determine which analytical techniques appear most applicable to the problem.

With the large number of techniques available, it is often difficult to identify the best method or methods for a given problem. The goal of this Handbook is to help engineers and materials scientists identify the most applicable analytical methods and interact effectively with the appropriate analytical specialists, who can help define the analytical test matrix, determine sampling procedures, take the data, and assist in interpreting the data. Together, these workers can solve problems much more effectively than could be done by any one, or even any two, of them.

This collaborative approach to solving a problem has many benefits. When the analyst is fully informed about the nature of the problem and its possible causes, he is much more likely to understand what to look for and how best to look for it. He may be able to suggest complementary or alternative techniques that will yield supplemental and/or more useful information. He will also be better equipped to detect features or data trends that are unexpected and that can have substantial impact on the problem solution. In short, involving the analyst as a fully informed member of the team is by far the most effective approach to solving problems.

Tools for Technique Selection

To facilitate the technique identification process, this Handbook contains several reference tools that can be used to screen the analytical methods for applicability. The first of these tools is a set of tables of common methods for designated classes of materials. In the next section of this article, a separate table has been developed for each of several classes of materials: inorganic solids (metals, alloys, and semiconductors; glasses and ceramics; minerals, ores, etc.), inorganic liquids, inorganic gases, organic solids, organic liquids, and organic gases. The most common methods (not necessarily all-inclusive) for analyzing a particular class of materials are listed on the left. The kinds of information available are listed as column headings. When a particular technique is applicable, an entry appears in the appropriate column. It should be emphasized that lack of an entry for a given technique does not mean that it cannot be adapted to perform the desired analysis; it means simply that that technique is not usually used and others are generally more suitable. Because there are always situations that require special conditions, the entries are coded according to the legend above each table. For example, an "●" indicates that the technique is generally usable, whereas an "N" indicates that the technique is usable only for a limited number of elements or groups.

As a simple example of how to use the tables, suppose that an engineer has a bar of material labeled only "18-8 stainless steel," and he wants to know whether it can be welded. Through consultation with a welding metallurgist he would find that weldable stainless steels contain very small amounts of carbon or alloying elements, such as niobium or titanium, that tie up carbon in order to avoid formation of chromium car-

bides at the grain boundaries during cooling. In addition, stainless steels that contain selenium or sulfur to improve their machinability are extremely difficult to weld. Therefore, to determine whether the steel is weldable, quantitative analyses for niobium, titanium, selenium, sulfur, and carbon should be performed, as well as for chromium and nickel to document that the material really is an 18-8 type of stainless.

Referring to the table "Inorganic Solids: Metals, Alloys, and Semiconductors," then, the engineer can look down the list of analytical methods for one having "●"s under the "Macro/Bulk" column, the "Quant" column, and the "Major" and "Minor" columns. This quickly shows that optical emission spectroscopy, spark source mass spectrometry, and x-ray spectrometry are potentially useful methods. The engineer can then refer to the boxed summaries in the individual articles on these methods to check limitations. For instance, he would find that x-ray spectrometry cannot generally analyze for elements with atomic numbers less than 11, so if this method was selected for analysis of niobium, titanium, selenium, sulfur, chromium, and nickel, another technique, such as high-temperature combustion, inert gas fusion, or vacuum fusion analysis (all having "G"s in the appropriate columns) would have to be employed for carbon determination. The boxed summaries in the articles "Optical Emission Spectroscopy" and "Spark Source Mass Spectrometry," however, indicate that these methods can analyze for all the elements of interest; therefore, one of these would be a logical choice.

Another method for selecting analytical methods is by use of the flow charts shown under the tables. Again, a separate chart for each of the different classes of materials has been developed. The charts are based on the type of analyses and/or the type of information desired. The subdivisions separate the analyses into several different categories, depending on the class of materials. For example, the flow chart for "Inorganic Solids: Metals, Alloys, and Semiconductors'' is divided into bulk/elemental analysis, microanalysis/structure, and surface analysis. Each of these categories is then further subdivided so that the user can follow the flow to exactly the kinds of information or analyses that he needs. Under each category only the most commonly used techniques are listed, in order to keep the flow chart readable. Several other methods may be adapted for use under special conditions or with special attachments or modifications as described in the individual articles.

Taking the stainless steel example discussed above, the engineer could examine the flow chart for ''Inorganic Solids: Metals, Alloys, and Semiconductors,'' follow the flow to ''Bulk/Elemental—Quantitative,'' and look for entries under ''Major/Minor.'' The same techniques identified in the table are cited in the chart, leading the engineer to the appropriate articles in the Handbook.

Finally, the detailed cross-referenced index at the back of the Handbook can be consulted under any or all of the pertinent categories cited above. In this index, techniques are listed not only by categories such as qualitative vs quantitative, macro vs micro, and major vs minor vs trace, but also by typical ways in which they are applied to the solution of materials problems. For example, under the heading ''Twinning,'' the entries listed are metallography, by which twinning can be detected; x-ray diffraction, by which twinning in single crystals can be character-

ized; and transmission electron microscopy, by which twinning in polycrystalline samples can be characterized. Similarly, under the heading ''Inclusions,'' the entries listed are metallography, by which inclusion morphology can be documented; image analysis, by which inclusion numbers, spacings, and morphologies can be quantified; and scanning electron microscopy, transmission electron microscopy, electron probe x-ray microanalysis, and Auger electron spectroscopy, by which inclusion chemistries can be determined.

Again, it should be emphasized that this Handbook is meant as a tool to familiarize the nonanalytical specialist with modern analytical techniques and to help him identify techniques that might be applied to his problems. The Handbook is not meant to be an analytical textbook or to replace indispensable consultation with materials and analytical specialists.

Tables and Flow Charts

The tables and flow charts in this section have been developed as tools to provide information about the most widely used methods of analysis for different classes of materials. These tables and charts are *not* intended to be all-inclusive but to identify the most commonly used techniques for the types of materials to be characterized and the types of information needed. As a result,

many techniques that require special modifications or conditions to perform the desired analysis are omitted. The previous section of this article describes how to use these tools. After examining the tables or charts, the reader is encouraged to refer to the appropriate articles in the Handbook for additional information prior to consultation with an analytical specialist.

Abbreviations used in the headings of the tables and charts are:

Elem	Elemental analysis
Alloy ver	Alloy verification
Iso/Mass	Isotopic or mass analysis
Qual	Qualitative analysis (identification of constituents)
Semiquant	Semiquantitative analysis (order of magnitude)
Quant	Quantitative analysis (precision of $\pm 20\%$ relative standard deviation)
Macro/Bulk	Macroanalysis or bulk analysis
Micro	Microanalysis ($\leq 10~\mu m$)
Surface	Surface analysis
Major	Major component (>10 wt%)
Minor	Minor component (0.1 to 10 wt%)
Trace	Trace component (1 to 1000 ppm or 0.0001 to 0.1 wt%)
Ultratrace	Ultratrace component (<1 ppm or <0.0001 wt%)

The acronyms listed below are used in the tables and charts (for additional acronyms and abbreviations, see the section ''Abbreviations and Symbols'' in this Volume).

AAS	Atomic absorption spectrometry	ICP-AES	Inductively coupled plasma atomic emission spectroscopy	RBS	Rutherford backscattering spectrometry
AES	Auger electron spectroscopy	IGF	Inert gas fusion	RS	Raman spectroscopy
COMB	High-temperature combustion	IR	Infrared spectroscopy	SAXS	Small-angle x-ray scattering
EFG	Elemental and functional group analysis	ISE	Ion selective electrode	SEM	Scanning electron microscopy
EPMA	Electron probe x-ray microanalysis	LC	Liquid chromatography	SIMS	Secondary ion mass spectroscopy
ESR	Electron spin resonance	LEISS	Low-energy ion-scattering spectroscopy	SSMS	Spark source mass spectrometry
FT-IR	Fourier transform infrared spectroscopy	MFS	Molecular fluorescence spectroscopy	TEM	Transmission electron microscopy
GC/MS	Gas chromatography/mass spectrometry	NAA	Neutron activation analysis	UV/VIS	Ultraviolet/visible absorption spectroscopy
GMS	Gas mass spectrometry	NMR	Nuclear magnetic resonance	XPS	X-ray photoelectron spectroscopy
IA	Image analysis	OES	Optical emission spectroscopy	XRD	X-ray diffraction
IC	Ion chromatography	OM	Optical metallography	XRS	X-ray spectrometry

INORGANIC SOLIDS: Metals, alloys, semiconductors

Wet analytical chemistry, electrochemistry, ultraviolet/visible absorption spectroscopy, and molecular fluorescence spectroscopy can generally be adapted to perform many of the bulk analyses listed. ● = generally usable; N or † = limited number of elements or groups; G = carbon, nitrogen, hydrogen, sulfur, or oxygen: see boxed summary in article for details; S or * = under special conditions; D = after dissolution; Z or ** = semiconductors only

Method	Page	Elem	Alloy ver	Iso/Mass	Qual	Semi-quant	Quant	Macro/Bulk	Micro	Sur-face	Major	Minor	Trace	Phase ID	Struc-ture	Mor-phol-ogy
AAS	43	D					D	D			D	D	D			
AES	549	●			●	●			●	●	●	●	S			S
COMB	221	G	G				G	G			G	G				
EPMA	516	●	S		●	●	●			●	●	●	N	S		●
ESR	253	N			N	N	N	N				N	N		N	●
IA	309								●	●						
IC	658	D, N			D, N	D, N	D, N	D, N			D, N	D, N	D, N			
ICP-AES	31	D	D		D	D	D	D			D	D	D			
IGF	226	G	G				G	G			G	G				
IR/FT-IR	109	Z			Z	Z	Z	Z				Z	Z			
LEISS	603	●			●	●				S	●	●	●			
NAA	233	●		N	●	●		●			●	●	●			
OES	21	●	●		●	●	●	●			●	●	●			
OM	299								●	●						●
RBS	628	●			●	●	●			●	●	S	S			
RS	126	Z			Z	Z	Z	Z			Z	Z	Z			●
SEM	490	●			●	●	S		●		●	●		S		●
SIMS	610	●		●	●	●				●	●	●	S			
SSMS	141	●	●	●	●	●	●	●			●	●	●			
TEM	429	●			●	●	S		●		●	●		●	●	●
XPS	568	●			●	●				●	●	●				
XRD	325	●			●	●	S	●			●	●		●	●	
XRS	82	●	●		●	●	●	●			●	●	N			

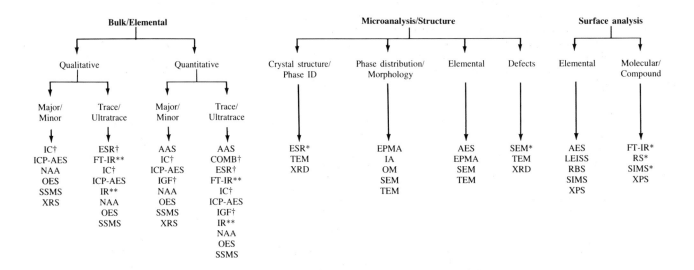

Bulk/Elemental
- Qualitative
  - Major/Minor: IC†, ICP-AES, NAA, OES, SSMS, XRS
  - Trace/Ultratrace: ESR†, FT-IR**, IC†, ICP-AES, IR**, NAA, OES, SSMS
- Quantitative
  - Major/Minor: AAS, IC†, ICP-AES, IGF†, NAA, OES, SSMS, XRS
  - Trace/Ultratrace: AAS, COMB†, ESR†, FT-IR**, IC†, ICP-AES, IGF†, IR**, NAA, OES, SSMS

Microanalysis/Structure
- Crystal structure/Phase ID: ESR*, TEM, XRD
- Phase distribution/Morphology: EPMA, IA, OM, SEM, TEM
- Elemental: AES, EPMA, SEM, TEM
- Defects: SEM*, TEM, XRD

Surface analysis
- Elemental: AES, LEISS, RBS, SIMS, XPS
- Molecular/Compound: FT-IR*, RS*, SIMS*, XPS

INORGANIC SOLIDS: Glasses, ceramics

Wet analytical chemistry, ultraviolet/visible absorption spectroscopy, and molecular fluorescence spectroscopy can generally be adapted to perform many of the bulk analyses listed. ● = generally usable; N or † = limited number of elements or groups; S or * = under special conditions; D = after dissolution

Method	Page	Elem	Speci-ation	Iso/Mass	Qual	Semi-quant	Quant	Macro/Bulk	Micro	Sur-face	Major	Minor	Trace	Phase ID	Struc-ture	Morphol-ogy
AAS	43	D					D	D			D	D	D			S
AES	549	●			●	●			●	●	●	●	S			S
EPMA	516	●			●	●	●		●		●	●		S		●
IA	309								●							
IC	658	D, N			D, N	D, N	D, N	D, N			D, N	D, N	D, N			
ICP-AES	31	D			D	D	D	D			D	D	D			
IR/FT-IR	109	S	S		S	S	S	S			S	S	S	S	S	
LEISS	603	●			●	●			S	●	●	●	●			
NAA	233	●		N	●	●	●	●			S	●	●			
OES	21	●			●	●	●	●			●	●	●			
OM	299								●	●						●
RBS	628	●			●	●	●			●		S	S			
RS	126	S	S		S	S	S	S	S		S	S	S	S		●
SEM	490				●	●			●		●	●		S		●
SIMS	610	●		●	●	●				●		●	S			
SSMS	141	●		●	●	●	●						●			
TEM	429	●			●	●	S				●	●		●	●	●
XPS	568	●	N		●	●				●	●	●				
XRD	325				●	●	S	●			●	●		●	●	
XRS	82	●			●	●	●	●			●	●	N			

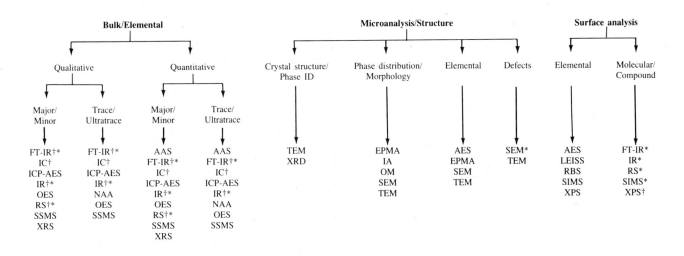

Bulk/Elemental

- Qualitative
  - Major/Minor: FT-IR†*, IC†, ICP-AES, IR†*, OES, RS†*, SSMS, XRS
  - Trace/Ultratrace: FT-IR†*, IC†, ICP-AES, IR†*, NAA, OES, SSMS
- Quantitative
  - Major/Minor: AAS, FT-IR†*, IC†, ICP-AES, IR†*, OES, RS†*, SSMS, XRS
  - Trace/Ultratrace: AAS, FT-IR†*, IC†, ICP-AES, IR†*, NAA, OES, SSMS

Microanalysis/Structure

- Crystal structure/Phase ID: TEM, XRD
- Phase distribution/Morphology: EPMA, IA, OM, SEM, TEM
- Elemental: AES, EPMA, SEM, TEM
- Defects: SEM*, TEM

Surface analysis

- Elemental: AES, LEISS, RBS, SIMS, XPS
- Molecular/Compound: FT-IR*, IR*, RS*, SIMS*, XPS†

INORGANIC SOLIDS: Minerals, ores, slags, pigments, inorganic compounds, effluents, chemical reagents, composites, catalysts

Wet analytical chemistry, electrochemistry, ultraviolet/visible absorption spectroscopy, and molecular fluorescence spectroscopy can generally be adapted to perform many of the bulk analyses listed. ● = generally usable; G = carbon, nitrogen, hydrogen, sulfur, or oxygen: see boxed summary in article for details; N or † = limited number of elements or groups; S or * = under special conditions; D = after dissolution

Method	Page	Elem	Speci-ation	Iso/Mass	Qual	Semi-quant	Quant	Macro/Bulk	Micro	Sur-face	Major	Minor	Trace	Com-pound/Phase	Struc-ture	Mor-phol-ogy
AAS	43	D					D	D			D	D	D			
AES	549	●			●	●			S	●	●	●	S			S
COMB	221	G				G	G	G			G	G	G			
EPMA	516	●			●	●	●			●	●	●	S	S		●
ESR	253	N	N		N	N	N	N				N	N		N	
IA	309							●	●							●
IC	658	D	S		D	D	D	D			D	D	D			
ICP-AES	31	D			D	D	D	D			D	D	D			
IGF	226	G						G	G			G	G			
IR/FT-IR	109	S, D			S, D	S, D	S, D	S, D		S	S, D	S, D	S, D	S, D	S, D	
ISE	181	D, N				D, N	D, N	D, N			D, N	D, N	D, N			
LEISS	603	●			●	●				●	●	●	●			
NAA	233	●		N	●	●	●	●			●	●	●			
OES	21	●			●	●	●	●			●	●	●			
OM	299							●	●							●
RBS	628				●	●	●	●		●	●					
RS	126	S, D			S, D	S, D	S, D	S, D		S	S, D	S, D	S	S	S, D	S, D
SEM	490	●			●	●			●	●	●	●	●		S	●
SIMS	610	●		●	●					●	●	●	S	S		●
SSMS	141	●		●	●			●		●	●	●	S	S		
TEM	429	●			●		S				●	●		●	●	●
XPS	568	●	●		●	●				●	●	●	●	●	●	●
XRD	325	●			●	●	S	●			●	●	●	S	●	
XRS	82	●			●	●	●	●			●	●	N			

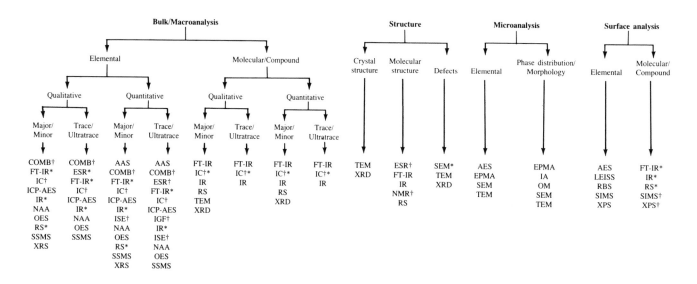

INORGANIC LIQUIDS AND SOLUTIONS: Water, effluents, leachates, acids, bases, chemical reagents

Wet analytical chemistry, electrochemistry, ultraviolet/visible absorption spectroscopy, and molecular fluorescence spectroscopy can generally be adapted to perform the bulk analyses listed. Most of techniques listed for inorganic solids can be used on the residue after the solution is evaporated to dryness. ● = generally usable; N or † = limited number of elements or groups; S = under special conditions; V or * = volatile liquids or components

Method	Page	Elem	Speci-ation	Com-pound	Iso/Mass	Qual	Semi-quant	Quant	Macro/Bulk	Major	Minor	Trace	Struc-ture
AAS	43	●						●	●	●	●	●	
EFG	212	N	N	N			N	N	N	N	N	N	
ESR	253	N	N			N	N	N	N		N	N	N
GC/MS	639	V, N		V	V	V	V	V	V		V	V	
GMS	151	V, N		V	V	V	V	V	V	V	V	V	
IC	658	●	●	S		●	●	●	●	●	●	●	
ICP-AES	31	●				●	●	●	●	●	●	●	
IR/FT-IR	109	●		●			●	●	●	●	●	●	
ISE	181	●	S				●	●	●	●	●	●	
NAA	233	●			N	●	●	●	●	●	●	●	
NMR	277	N		N		N	N		N		N	●	N
RS	126	●		●		●	●	●	●	●	●	S	
XRS	82	●				●	●	●	●	●	●	N	

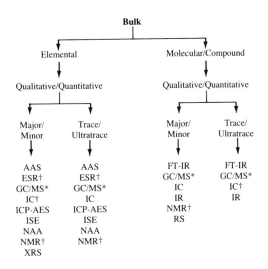

Bulk

Elemental — Molecular/Compound

Qualitative/Quantitative — Qualitative/Quantitative

Major/Minor	Trace/Ultratrace	Major/Minor	Trace/Ultratrace
AAS	AAS	FT-IR	FT-IR
ESR†	ESR†	GC/MS*	GC/MS*
GC/MS*	GC/MS*	IC	IC†
IC†	IC	IR	IR
ICP-AES	ICP-AES	NMR†	
ISE	ISE	RS	
NAA	NAA		
NMR†	NMR†		
XRS			

INORGANIC GASES: Air, effluents, process gases

Most of the techniques listed for inorganic solids and inorganic liquids can be used if the gas is sorbed onto a solid or into a liquid. ● = generally usable

Method	Page	Elem	Speci-ation	Com-pound	Iso/Mass	Qual	Semi-quant	Quant	Macro/Bulk	Major	Minor	Trace
GC/MS	639	●		●	●	●	●	●	●	●	●	●
GMS	151	●		●	●	●	●	●	●	●	●	●
IR/FT-IR	109	●	●	●		●	●	●	●	●	●	●
RS	126	●	●	●		●	●	●	●	●	●	

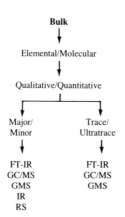

Bulk
↓
Elemental/Molecular
↓
Qualitative/Quantitative
|

Major/Minor — Trace/Ultratrace
↓ ↓
FT-IR   FT-IR
GC/MS   GC/MS
GMS   GMS
IR
RS

ORGANIC SOLIDS: Polymers, plastics, epoxies, long-chain hydrocarbons, esters, foams, resins, detergents, dyes, organic composites, coal and coal derivatives, wood products, chemical reagents, organometallics

Most of the techniques for inorganic solids and inorganic liquids can be used on any residue after ashing. ● = generally usable; N or † = limited number of elements or groups; S or * = under special conditions; D = after dissolution/extraction; V = volatile solids or components (can also be analyzed by GC/MS), pyrolyzed solids; C = crystalline solids

Method	Page	Elem	Speci-ation	Com-pound	Iso/Mass	Qual	Semi-quant	Quant	Macro/Bulk	Micro	Sur-face	Major	Minor	Trace	Struc-ture	Mor-phol-ogy
AES	549	●				●	●			●	●	●	●			
COMB	221	N						N	N			N	N	N		
EFG	212	●		●		●	●	●	●			●	●			
EPMA	516	N				N	N	N		N			N	N	N		N
ESR	253	N	N			N	N	N	N					N	N	N	
GC/MS	639	V		V	V	V	V	V	V				V	V	V		
IA	309								●	●						●
IC	658	D, N		D, N		D, N	D, N	D, N	D, N				D, N	D, N	D, N		
IR/FT-IR	109	D, N	D, ●	D, ●		D, ●	D, ●	D, ●	D, ●		D, S	D, ●	D, ●	D, ●	D, S		
LC	649			D		D	D	D	D			D	D	D		
LEISS	603	●				●	●				●	●	●	S		
MFS	72	D, N	D, N	D, N		D, N	D, N	D, N	D, N				D, N	D, N	D, N		
NAA	233	N			N	N	N	N	N				N	N	N		
NMR	277	N		N		N	N		N				N	N		N	
OM	299								●	●						●
RS	126	D, N	D, ●	D, ●		D, ●	D, ●	D, ●	D, ●		S	D, ●	D, ●		D, S	
SAXS	402	●		●		●			●						●	
SEM	490	N				N	N			●			N	N		●
SIMS	610	●		S	●					●	●	●	●	●		●
TEM	429	S		C		N	N			●			N	N		C	●
UV/VIS	60	D, ●	D, ●	D, ●		D, ●	D, ●	D, ●	D, ●				D, ●	D, ●	D, ●		
XPS	568	●	N	S		●	●				●	●	●	●		
XRD	325			C		C	C	C, S	C				C	C	C	
XRS	82	N				N	N	N	N				N	N	N		

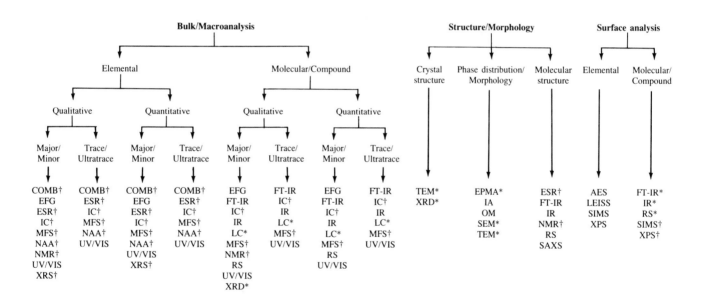

ORGANIC LIQUIDS AND SOLUTIONS: Hydrocarbons, petroleum and petroleum derivatives, solvents, reagents

Most of the techniques listed for inorganic solids and inorganic liquids can be used on any residue after ashing. Many wet chemical techniques can be adapted to perform the analyses listed. ● = generally usable; N or † = limited number of elements or groups; S = under special conditions; V or * = volatile liquids

Method	Page	Elem	Speci-ation	Com-pound	Iso/Mass	Qual	Semi-quant	Quant	Macro/Bulk	Major	Minor	Trace	Struc-ture
EFG	212	●		●		●	●	●	●	●	●	●	
ESR	253	N	N			N	N	N	N		N	N	N
GC/MS	639			V	V	V	V	V	V	V	V	V	
GMS	151			V	V	V	V	V	V	V	V	V	
IR/FT-IR	109	S	S	●		●	●	●	●	●	●	●	●
LC	649			●		●	●	●	●	●	●	●	
MFS	72	N		N		N	N	N	N	N	N	N	
NAA	233	N			N	N	N	N	N	N	N	N	
NMR	277	N		N		N	N	N	N	N	N		N
RS	126	S	S	●		●	●	●	●	●	●		●
UV/VIS	60			●		●	●	●	●	●	●	●	
XRS	82	N				N	N	N	N	N	N	N	

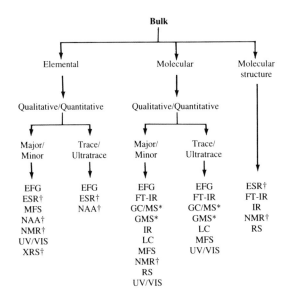

ORGANIC GASES: Natural gas, effluents, pyrolysis products, process gas

Most of the techniques listed for organic solids and organic liquids can be used if the gas is sorbed onto a solid or into a liquid. ● = generally usable; S = under special conditions; L = after sorption onto a solid or into a liquid

Method	Page	Elem	Speci-ation	Com-pound	Iso/Mass	Qual	Semi-quant	Quant	Macro/Bulk	Major	Minor	Trace	Struc-ture
GC/MS	639	●		●	●	●	●	●	●	●	●	●	
GMS	151	●		●	●	●	●	●	●	●	●	●	
IR/FT-IR	109	●	S	●		●	●	●	●	●	●	●	●
LC	649			L		L	L	L	L	L	L	L	
RS	126	●	S	●		●	●	●	●	●	●		●

General analyses
↓
FT-IR
GC/MS
GMS
IR
LC
RS

Sampling*

John K. Taylor, Center for Analytical Chemistry, National Bureau of Standards
Byron Kratochvil, Department of Chemistry, University of Alberta

Introduction

Sampling is the selection for testing of a portion of a population. Portions are used for economic and technical reasons for the chemical and physical measurement of raw materials, plant process streams, and the final products and wastes produced by industry. Many industrial decisions relating to quality control of raw materials and end products and to environmental monitoring are based on such measurements.

The reliability of any measurement depends on sample quality. A poorly devised sampling plan or uncertainties in the sampling process, in sample storage, preservation, or pretreatment may obscure results or prevent their interpretation. This article will primarily consider the problem of sampling bulk materials, including minerals, metals, environmentally important substances, and industrial raw materials and waste products.

The design of bulk sampling programs involves:

- Identifying the population from which the sample is to be obtained
- Selecting and withdrawing valid gross samples of this population
- Reducing each gross sample to a laboratory sample suitable for the analytical techniques to be used

Inherent in the design should be an effort to maintain sampling conditions that yield accurate results rapidly and economically. Commonly used terminology is defined in the section "Glossary of Terms" in this Volume.

Preliminary Considerations in Sampling

Many sources of error, such as contaminated apparatus or reagents, biased methods, or operator errors, can be controlled by proper use of blanks (a measurement involving addition of all the reagents, but not the sample), standards, and reference materials. However, controls and blanks will not be useful if the sample is invalid. Accordingly, sampling uncertainty is often treated separately from other uncertainties. For random errors, the overall standard deviation, s_o, is related to the standard deviation for the sampling operations, s_s, and to that for the remaining analytical operations, s_a, by: $s_o^2 = s_a^2 + s_s^2$. Whenever possible, measurements should be conducted so that sample variability and measurement variability can be separately evaluated. For a measurement process in statistical control where s_a is known, s_s can be evaluated from s_o, which is determined by analysis of the samples. Alternatively, an appropriate series of replicate measurements or samples can be devised to evaluate both standard deviations.

Further reduction in measurement uncertainty is unimportant once it is one third or less of the sampling uncertainty (Ref 1). Therefore, if the sampling uncertainty is large and cannot be reduced, a rapid, approximate analytical method may be sufficient, and further refinements in measurement may not significantly improve the overall results. In such cases, a rapid method of low precision that permits more samples to be examined may reduce the uncertainty in the average value.

Types of Samples

Random Samples. Sampling is occasionally directed at obtaining an extreme value, such as the best or worst case. However, a sample usually is collected to determine the distribution of some characteristic among the population. To obtain the best estimate of this distribution, random sampling may be performed. In random sampling, every part of the population has an equal chance of being included in the sample, regardless of the location or nature of that part.

The distinction between the target population to which conclusions should apply and the parent population from which these samples are actually drawn is important. In practice, these are rarely identical, although the difference may be small. This difference may be minimized by random selection of portions for examination, in which each part of the population has an equal chance of selection. Generalizations based on mathematical probability can be made from such random samples.

A random sample is obtained by basing sample collection on a table of random numbers; it is not selected haphazardly. However, samples selected using a defined protocol tend to reflect biases brought about by decisions of the sampler and the equipment used. In addition, individuals who obtain samples must understand that the apparently unsystematic collection pattern must be followed closely to be valid.

In random sampling of an entire lot of bulk material, the material is divided into a number of real or imaginary segments. For example, a bin of raw material can be conceptually subdivided horizontally and vertically into cells. Each segment is then assigned a number. Segments from which sample increments will come are selected by starting in an arbitrary place in a random number table (Ref 2) and choosing numbers according to a preset pattern, such as adjacent, alternate, or nth entries, then sampling those segments for the determined number of samples. Because of its simplicity, sampling at evenly spaced intervals over the bulk is often used instead of random sampling, although results must be closely monitored to prevent errors from periodicity in the material.

Systematic Samples. Each sample collected systematically and analyzed to re-

*Pages 12 to 15 adapted from Sampling Bulk Materials for Chemical Analysis, *Anal. Chem.*, Vol 53 (No. 8), 1981, p 924A, with permission

Fig. 1 Sequence for an overall operation to estimate a property of a system

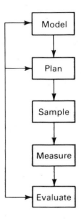

flect or test some systematic hypothesis, such as changes in composition with time, temperature, or spatial locations, should be considered representative of a separate, discrete population under the existing conditions. However, the results may still be statistically tested for the significance of any apparent differences.

A carefully designed sampling plan includes the possibility of unanticipated events or phenomena that could prejudice the analyses. For example, measurements at timed intervals are sometimes made with random start or other superimposed random time element. The less known about a given process, the more randomness is merited. Conversely, the more fully a process is understood, the more efficient is a systematic approach to data acquisition.

Representative sample frequently connotes a single sample of a universe or population expected to exhibit average properties of the population. It is not possible to select such a sample by a random process, or to verify if it is representative. A truly representative sample seems valid only if the sample is defined *a priori* as representing a specific purpose, such as the Hazardous Waste Management System, which prescribes seven protocols for obtaining samples that "will be considered by the agency [Environmental Protection Agency] to be representative of the waste" (Ref 3), or if truly homogeneous materials are sampled.

Although it may reduce costs, measurement of samples defined as representative yields information not equaling that from valid random samples of the population, except when the population is homogenized before sampling to produce a number of similar subsamples. A properly designed and executed random sampling plan provides sample mean and variation between members, neither of which can be obtained by analysis of one "representative sample."

A composite sample may be considered a special type of representative sample. Many sampling procedures assume that only average composition is desired, such as bulk, time-weighted, or flow-proportional averages, and specify collection or preparation of a suitable composite. Elaborate crushing, grinding, mixing, and blending procedures have been developed and standardized for preparing solid composites (see the articles "Milling of Brittle and Ductile Materials" and "Blending and Premixing of Metal Powders" in Volume 7 of the 9th Edition of *Metals Handbook*). Sampling systems have been developed to obtain liquid (especially water) composites (Ref 4, 5).

Analysis of individual samples permits determination of the average (at the expense of additional analytical effort), of the distribution of samples within the population (between-sample variability), and of within-sample variability (if replicate analyses are conducted). Composite samples provide limited information, and the consequences should be carefully considered before deciding between this approach and the analysis of individual samples.

Subsampling is necessary, because the sample received by the analytical laboratory is usually larger than that required for a single measurement. Test portions taken for replicate measurements or for measurement of different constituents by several techniques must be sufficiently alike so that results are compatible. The effort necessary to reduce particle size, mix, or otherwise process the laboratory sample before withdrawing portions (subsamples) for analysis depends on the homogeneity of the original sample.

The Sampling Plan

Before sampling begins, a model of the overall operation should be established (Fig. 1). The model should define the objectives of the study, although multiple objectives may compete for limited resources. Typical objectives include estimation or evaluation of the average of characteristics in a population and their variability or distribution and determination of whether characteristics of interest in the population meet specified standards or pre-established criteria (Ref 6).

The model should also define the population studied, substance(s) to be measured, extent of speciation and distribution within the population, and precision required as well as identify all assumptions about the population. Once the model is complete, a sampling plan can be established.

The plan should specify the size, number, and location of the sample increments, the extent of compositing, if applicable, and procedures for reducing the gross sample to a laboratory sample and to test portions. Before work begins, this should be written as a detailed protocol that includes procedures for all steps, from sampling to sample treatment, measurement, and data evaluation. It should be revised as necessary for new information.

The protocol dictates when, where, and how to take the sample increments and will establish on-site criteria for collection of a valid sample. Decisions about whether a component is foreign (not part of the population) often must be made at the time of sampling. If possible, criteria for such decisions should be established logically and systematically before sampling begins. The type of container, cleaning procedure, protection from contamination before and after sampling, storage conditions and possible addition of preservatives should be specified.

The analyst should perform or supervise the sampling operation or should provide a written protocol to well-trained individuals aware of the importance of minimizing bias and contamination. Also important are careful labeling and recording of samples. A chain of custody to ensure the integrity of the samples from source to measurement is essential. Details such as temperature position of the collecting probe in the sample stream and flow velocity of the stream should be recorded when the sample is taken. Omission or loss of such information may greatly decrease the value of a sample or render it worthless.

Sampling Bulk Materials. Once the substances to be determined and the precision desired have been specified, a sampling plan can be designed that considers:

- Quantity of samples to be taken
- Their sizes
- Location in the bulk material (population) from which they should be taken
- Whether individual samples should be analyzed or a composite prepared

The relative homogeneity of the system affects sample size. Gross samples should be unbiased with respect to the different sizes and types of particles present in the bulk material. The size of the gross sample is often a compromise between the heterogeneity of the bulk material and the cost.

When the properties of a material to be sampled are unknown, a useful approach is to collect a small number of samples, using experience and intuition as a guide to make them as representative of the population as possible, then to analyze for the component of interest. From these preliminary analyses, the standard deviation s_s of the individual samples can be calculated, and confidence limits for the average composition established using:

$$\mu = \bar{x} \pm \frac{ts_s}{\sqrt{n}} \qquad \text{(Eq 1)}$$

where μ is the true mean value of the population, $\bar{x}$ is the average of the analytical measurements, and t is obtained from statistical tables for n measurements (often given as $n - 1$ degrees of freedom) at the desired level of confidence, usually 95%. Tables of t values are provided in Ref 2 and 11.

On the basis of this preliminary information, a more refined sampling plan can be devised. After one or two cycles, the parameters should be known with sufficient confidence to estimate the optimum size and number of the samples with a high level of confidence. Considerable savings in time and cost result from optimizing the sample program.

Minimum Size of Individual Increments. There are several methods for estimating the amount of sample required in a given increment so as not to exceed determined sampling uncertainty. One method uses Ingamells' sampling constant (Ref 7-9). Because the between-sample standard deviation, s_s, decreases with increasing sample size, the following relation is often valid:

$$wR^2 = K_s \qquad \text{(Eq 2)}$$

where w is the weight of sample analyzed, R is the relative standard deviation (in percent) of sample composition, and K_s is the sampling constant, corresponding to the weight of a single sample required to limit the sampling uncertainty to 1% with 68% confidence; K_s may be determined by estimating s_s from a series of measurements of samples of weight w. Once K_s is evaluated for a given sample, the minimum weight w required for a predetermined maximum relative standard deviation of R percent can be readily calculated. This method applies only to subsampling of well-mixed samples and cannot be used if segregation is present.

Minimum Number of Individual Increments. Unless the population is known to be homogeneous, or unless an analytical problem necessitates a representative sample, sufficient replicate samples (increments) must be analyzed for the component under study. The minimum number of sample increments necessary to achieve a given level of confidence can be estimated from:

$$n = \frac{t^2 s_s^2}{E^2} \qquad \text{(Eq 3)}$$

where t is the Student's t-table value for the level of confidence desired (Ref 2, 11), s_s^2 is estimated from preliminary compositional measurements on, or from previous knowl-edge of, the bulk material, and E is the standard deviation acceptable in the average. Initially, t can be set at 1.96 for 95% confidence limits, and a preliminary value of n calculated. The t value for this n can then be substituted and the system iterated to constant n. The expression applies if the sought-for component is distributed in the population in a positive binomial, or Gaussian, distribution, which is characterized by an average, μ, larger than the variance of the mean, σ_s^2.

Values of σ_s (and s_s) may depend greatly on the size of the individual samples. The value of σ_s may also depend on concentration. If the relative standard deviation is constant with respect to concentration, relative standard deviation and relative error may be substituted for s_s and E.

Sampling a Segregated (Stratified) Material. Special care must be taken when assessing the average amount of a substance distributed nonrandomly throughout a bulk material. Such segregation may be found, for example, in ore bodies, in different production batches in a plant, or in samples in which settling produces variable composition. To obtain a valid sample of a stratified material:

- Divide the material into real or imaginary segments (strata) based on the known or suspected pattern of segregation
- Further divide the major strata into real or imaginary subsections and select the required number of samples randomly (preferably with the aid of a table of random numbers)
- Take samples proportional in number to the size of each stratum if the major strata are not equal in size

In general, stratified random sampling is preferred to unrestricted random sampling if the number of strata is kept sufficiently small that several samples can be taken from each. In this way, possible variations within the parent population can be detected and assessed without increasing the standard deviation of the sampling step.

Minimum Number of Individual Increments in Segregated Material. When a bulk material is highly segregated, many samples must be taken from different segments. A useful guide to estimating the number of samples needed is cited in Ref 10. The variance in sample composition depends on the degree of homogeneity within a given sample increment and the degree of segregation between sample increments (Ref 10):

$$s_s^2 = \frac{A}{wn} + \frac{B}{n} \qquad \text{(Eq 4)}$$

where s_s^2 is the variance of the average of n samples using a sample increment weight w, and A and B are constants for a given bulk material; A is a homogeneity constant, and B a segregation constant.

Values for A and B can be obtained experimentally for a bulk population in two ways. In the first, two sets of increments are collected, one with w as small and the other as large as feasible. The component of interest is measured and a sampling variance calculated for each set. Values for A and B can be calculated from $A = w_L w_S (s_S^2 - s_L^2)/w_L - w_S$ and $B = S_L^2 - (A/w_L)$. A second approach, applicable only to material for which the reciprocal of the average particle mass m can be estimated, is to collect a series of pairs of increments, each member of a pair being of weight w and collected from near its partner. The increments are then analyzed or tested, and an intraclass correlation coefficient r is calculated (Ref 11). Values for A and B are then calculated using Eq 4 and the relationship $r = B/Am$.

Sampling Materials in Discrete Units. If the lot of material under study occurs in discrete units, such as truckloads, drums, bottles, or tank cars, the variance of the analytical result is the sum of the variance between units in the lot, the average variance of sets of samples taken from within one unit, and the variance of the analytical operations. The contribution from each depends on the number of units in the lot and the number of samples taken (Ref 6):

$$\sigma_{\bar{x}}^2 = \frac{\sigma_b^2}{n_b} \frac{(N - n_b)}{N} + \frac{\sigma_w^2}{n_b n_w} + \frac{\sigma_t^2}{n_t} \qquad \text{(Eq 5)}$$

where $\sigma_{\bar{x}}^2$ is variance of the mean, σ_b^2 is variance of the units in the lot, σ_w^2 is average variance of the samples taken from a segment, σ_t^2 is variance of the analytical operations, N is number of units in the lot, n_b is number of randomly selected units sampled, n_w is number of randomly drawn samples from each unit selected for sampling, and n_t is total number of analyses, including replicates, run on all samples.

If stratification is known to be absent, preparing a composite sample saves measurement time and effort. Equation 5 also applies to this situation. If the units vary significantly in weight or volume, results should be weighted accordingly.

For homogeneous materials, including many liquids and gases, σ_w^2 is zero, and the second term on the right side of Eq 5 drops out. If all units are sampled, $n_b = N$, and the first term on the right of Eq 5 also drops out.

Optimizing Sampling Resources

Sampling plans must include minimizing the cost of determining an estimation of the population mean to within a specified variance or minimizing the variance for a given allocation of funds. For a stratified sampling plan, assuming the strata to be equal in size and in variance within strata, the total cost c is:

$$c + c_o + n_1c_1 + n_1n_2c_2 + n_1n_2n_3c_3 \qquad (Eq\ 6)$$

where c_o is the overhead cost, c_1 is the cost of selecting each of the n_1 strata, c_2 is the cost per sample of collecting n_2 samples within each strata, and c_3 is the cost per analysis for n_3 analyses per sample (Ref 12). For example, if an analysis of variance has provided estimates of σ_1^2, σ_2^2, and σ_3^3 for the selection of strata, the sampling within each strata, and the measurement, each contributes to the overall variance by:

$$\sigma^2 = \frac{\sigma_1^2}{n_1} + \frac{\sigma_2^2}{n_1n_2} + \frac{\sigma_3^2}{n_1n_2n_3} \qquad (Eq\ 7)$$

The minimum cost c for a fixed value of σ^2 is obtained (Ref 13):

$$n_1 = \frac{\sqrt{\sigma_1^2/c_1}}{\sigma^2}(\sqrt{\sigma_1^2c_1} + \sqrt{\sigma_2^2c_2} + \sqrt{\sigma_3^2c_3}) \qquad (Eq\ 8)$$

$$n_2 = \sqrt{\frac{\sigma_2^2c_1}{\sigma_1^2c_2}} \qquad (Eq\ 9)$$

and

$$n_3 = \sqrt{\frac{\sigma_3^2c_2}{\sigma_2^2c_3}} \qquad (Eq\ 10)$$

Because n_2 and n_3 are not affected by the value selected for σ^2, if σ^2 is to be reduced, the number of strata n_1 sampled should be reduced while holding n_2 and n_3 constant.

For a fixed total cost c, the optimum values of n_1, n_2, and n_3 are:

$$n_1 = \frac{c\sqrt{\sigma_1^2/c_1}}{\sqrt{\sigma_1^2c_1} + \sqrt{\sigma_2^2c_2} + \sqrt{\sigma_3^2c_3}} \qquad (Eq\ 11)$$

$$n_2 = \sqrt{\frac{\sigma_2^2c_1}{\sigma_1^2c_2}} \qquad (Eq\ 12)$$

$$n_3 = \sqrt{\frac{\sigma_3^2c_2}{\sigma_2^2c_3}} \qquad (Eq\ 13)$$

For this system, the optimum allocation beyond the first stage of sampling is the same for fixed total cost as for fixed total variance.

Example 1. In sampling a trainload of metal pipe for the percentage of an alloying element, the standard deviation is 0.25 between cars, 0.15 within a car, and 0.08 for a determination. The relative costs of the operation are 5:4:1. The overall standard deviation σ_o in the result is not to exceed 0.10. The optimum sampling scheme is:

$$n_1 = \left[\frac{\sqrt{0.25^2/5}}{0.10^2}\right]\left[\sqrt{(0.25^2)(5)} + \sqrt{0.15^2)(4)} + \sqrt{(0.08^2)(1)}\right] = 10.5 \qquad (Eq\ 14)$$

$$n_2 = \sqrt{\frac{(0.15^2)(5)}{(0.25^2)(4)}} = 0.67 \qquad (Eq\ 15)$$

$$n_3 = \sqrt{\frac{(0.08^2)(4)}{(0.15^2)(1)}} = 1.07 \qquad (Eq\ 16)$$

Taking $n_1 = 11$, $n_2 = 1$, and $n_3 = 1$, $\sigma_o^2 = 0.25^2/11 + 0.15^2/11(1) + 0.08^2/11(1)(1) = 0.008$, and $\sigma_o = 0.09$. The cost $= (11 \times 5) + (1 \times 4) + (1 \times 1) = 60$ on the relative scale.

If the costs were fixed at, for example, 40 times that of a single determination on the relative scale, the minimum standard deviation that could be obtained would be:

$$n_1 = 40\sqrt{\frac{0.25^2}{5}} \div [\sqrt{(0.25^2)(5)} + \sqrt{(0.15^2)(4)} + \sqrt{(0.08^2)(1)}] = 4.8 \qquad (Eq\ 17)$$

$$n_2 = \sqrt{\frac{(0.15^2)(5)}{(0.25^2)(4)}} = 0.67 \qquad (Eq\ 18)$$

$$n_3 = \sqrt{\frac{(0.08^2)(4)}{(0.15^2)(1)}} = 1.07 \qquad (Eq\ 19)$$

Taking $n_1 = 5$, $n_2 = 1$, and $n_3 = 1$, $c = (5)(5) + (5)(1)(4) + (5)(1)(1)(1) = 50$ and $\sigma_o^2 = 0.25^2/5 + 0.15^1/5(1) + 0.08^2/5(1)(1) = 0.018$, then $\sigma_o = 0.14$.

Calculating Statistical Sampling Uncertainties. Sampling is most impor-

tant when significant heterogeneity or segregation exists. When $\bar{x}$, s, K_s, A, and B are known exactly, it is easy to calculate the statistical sampling uncertainty and to determine the number and size of the samples needed for a given precision. If, as is more usual, these quantities are known only approximately or not at all, preliminary samples and measurements must be taken, and from these more precise sampling procedures developed.

Practical Aspects of Sampling

Chemical analysis is typically performed on a material that is a subset of some other material or even of a system of materials of interest. Although the actual sample analyzed may be so small that its ratio to its parent is almost infinitesimal, for example, a few milligrams of sample as related to thousands of tons of an ore, it must represent the population of interest.

All aspects of the sample must be considered in relation to the model of the analytical problem (Ref 14). It must be taken according to a specific strategy, preserved to minimize deterioration, contained to prevent intrusion of foreign substances or to minimize escape of constituents of interest, processed to retain its integrity, and subsampled as necessary, while maintaining its correspondence to other members of its immediate family. Because all these aspects cannot be guaranteed, it may be necessary to analyze a number of subsamples, to perform related measurements to evaluate the magnitude of any actual or potential complication, or both.

For example, the appearance of a lump of ore under analysis may suggest heterogeneity and that care should be exercised in sampling it. A sample such as a piece of metal may appear uniform and provide no indication of microheterogeneity. Even if the material is uniform in structure, different sized particles or chips obtained by crushing or machining may have significantly different compositions.

Sampling Protocol. The model of the problem and planning of the measurement program should specify the location of sampling sites, the number of samples required, and how the actual samples are to be taken. There should be no uncertainty as to what the sample is, which requires that it be taken according to a protocol ideally codeveloped by the problem-area specialist, the analyst, and a statistician. Therefore, a minimum of these three disciplines must be represented in planning.

In many cases, such as failure analysis, field examination of the material or structure being analyzed is required. Such on-site examination frequently reveals information essential to problem solving that may either go undetected or be permanently lost if the description of the incident and sample-taking are left to personnel who are not familiar with metallugical, analytical, and statistical principles.

Mechanism of Field Sampling. Sampling usually requires equipment. Buckets, scoops, or shovels are useful for fluid or granular materials (Ref 15). Special devices called thieves are used to sample granular materials at various levels within a container or mound (Ref 15). The use of thieves is discussed in the article "Sampling of Metal Powders" in Volume 7 of the 9th Edition of *Metals Handbook*. Dredges, drills, saws, cutting torches, augers, or corers may be needed to obtain samples from massive materials. In some cases, the sample may be extracted using filters, sieves, or absorption devices. It may be obtained in a form ready for analysis or may require further extraction or processing in the laboratory.

Samples must be taken in a way that does not influence the measurements to be made. For example, the use of cutting for removing samples from metal structures for metallographic examination should be avoided, because the heat generated by cutting can significantly alter the microstructure. If cutting torches must be used, large samples should be taken and subsequent metallography performed at locations where microstructural alteration from the cuts has not occurred.

Similarly, gas samples must be taken in uncontaminated containers that can be subsequently sealed to prevent material leakage into or out of the container before analysis. Many incorrect conclusions have been drawn because samples were altered during sampling. To prevent this, knowledgeable metallurgical and analytical personnel must be involved in sampling.

Any device used for sampling must conform to the sampling protocol. Sampling devices may have critical dimensions or operational parameters, such as those used for sampling respirable matter, or filters used to separate "dissolved" or particulate fractions, or in isokinetic sampling. Failure to conform to critical dimensions or operational parameters can produce erroneous results. Sampling equipment such as pumps and sieves may require calibration to verify their performance characteristics at the time of use. Sampling devices ideally should not be made of or contain the analyte of interest. Therefore, plastic scoops are more suitable when taking metal samples, but metal scoops may be more appropriate for sampling organic materials.

Preservation of the sample may be required unless it is measured immediately.

Changes in sample composition can result from oxidation, radiation, differential evaporation, loss of volatile constituents, thermally induced degradation, and interaction with other constituents of the sample or the container. Contamination from airborne dust can be important, and the introduction of foreign substances can occur. Protection from airborne contamination may require handling of samples in ultra-clean rooms (Ref 16). Preservation techniques include addition of preservatives, low-temperature storage, enclosure in inert atmospheres, hermetic sealing, and the use of nonactinic glass or opaque containers.

The concept of holding time can be applied to evaluating preservation techniques. Samples preserved in a given way can be analyzed periodically to determine the interval that occurs before a tolerable amount of deterioration has taken place. If this is considered the first indication of significant deterioration, it is equivalent to three standard deviations of the measurement technique used to evaluate it (corresponding to a confidence level of 95%). If unknown, the standard deviation of measurement may be evaluated concurrently with the holding time evaluation by duplicate measurement of subsamples. For some samples, the holding time may be so short as to require field analysis or at least measurement on a rigid time schedule.

Discrimination. Decisions should be made that define whether certain constituents of a population should be included or rejected. A particular material may be a foreign object (rejected) or a constituent (included). The model should anticipate such situations and provide the basis for decision, depending on the use to be made of the data. Thus, sieves may be specified to separate coarse objects or materials from fines if the former are believed to be foreign.

Moisture. If the original population contains water, the model should define if the analytical result should be reported on a dry or "as-received" basis. Moisture loss or gain from the time of sampling to analysis also can introduce problems. When different laboratories treat the question of moisture differently (and sometimes in an unspecified manner), disparity in results can occur.

The moisture content may not be theoretically defined, but based on arbitrary considerations. Arbitrary drying procedures must be described or documented. Above all, the basis for the analytical result, such as "as-received," or dried by a specific procedure, must be stated whenever the moisture content of a sample is a significant consideration (Ref 17).

Because of moisture problems, analytical results on solid materials are frequently re-

ported on a dry-weight basis. The sample may be dried before analysis, or the wet sample may be analyzed and corrected for its moisture content, which is measured independently (Ref 17). The nature of the sample may dictate the procedure. Whenever significant volatile components could be lost, the latter approach may be necessary.

Homogenization or blending procedures may be required in subsampling and field sampling. Because it may sometimes be difficult or impossible to blend in the field, final homogenization is left to laboratory personnel.

Liquid samples may require only mixing before analysis. However, if immiscible components of differing densities are present, blending may be required continuously during subsampling. The shape of the container and type of mixer may be important in ensuring a proper blending of the constituents.

When the sample contains liquid and solid constituents, the phases may be separated and analyzed separately, in which case the amount and the composition of each phase present may need to be known. Complete separation of the phases could be a problem, and the definition of dissolved and suspended matter may be arbitrary, for example, based on separability by a filter of specified porosity. Filtered solids may contain absorbed or occluded liquids that may be difficult to remove. The alternative of analyzing a suspension could cause even greater problems if any difficulties of maintaining suspendibility are expected.

Blending of heterogeneous solids is frequently performed. Such samples are often crushed to obtain small particle sizes that promote improved mixing. Crushers can range from the familiar mortar and pestle to specially designed mills. They must be made of noncontaminating materials harder than the materials processed to minimize abrasion and should have chemical resistivity to the samples. The fineness of grinding required will depend on the heterogeneity of the sample, but fine grinding is ordinarily preferred. Sieving may be performed at intermediate stages to separate fines and coarses that are later reground. When the coarses differ in composition from the fines, each may be ground using a different process, then combined to compose the analytical sample.

The grinding of soft materials, especially those with appreciable water content, may require special grinders. Special mills have been developed for such materials as food samples and feeds. Cryogenic grinding and blending may also be used (Ref 18). In such cases, prevention of condensation of atmospheric moisture may be a problem. Caking and electrostatic clinging of material to parts of grinders and blenders can cause mixing problems as well.

Blending is often necessary after grinding. Blenders include rifflers in which the sample emerges from a container in preset fractions. Cone and V-blenders have been designed for mixing materials. Cones are often double and joined at their bases. Rotation produces swirling or tumbling. V-blenders achieve the same result by alternately pouring their contents from one arm to the other as the device is rotated. For best results, mixers should not be overloaded and should be operated slowly enough to produce alternate interchanges of the contents. Holdup due to caking can decrease their efficiency. The number of cycles required must be determined empirically.

In the simple process of quartering, the sample is placed on a sheet of suitable material, and alternate edges are pulled together to achieve mixing. Shoveling from the edges of a cone of material to the top is sometimes effective.

Quality Assurance for Sampling

Many sampling errors can be eliminated or minimized by an appropriate quality-assurance program (Ref 19). Quality control may be achieved by following standard operating procedures and recommended laboratory and measurement practices. Protocols should be developed as part of the planning program to define how each aspect of sampling will be executed. They should specify related calibration procedures and schedules and provide for controls such as field blanks and for the container cleaning process.

Training of personnel should provide a thorough knowledge of the elementary statistics of sampling. Specific training should be devoted to the operation concerned with each specific measurement program, including a thorough review of the protocols to be followed. Critical steps should be identified and explained, and any special documentation reviewed.

Sample uncertainties, random or systematic, result from the sample or from the sampling operation. Population-related variability has been discussed above. However, unless the entire sample is analyzed, a subsample may be required that may have some of the problems encountered in the original considerations. Thus, subsampling may be considered as sampling the sample. Unless proven otherwise, subsampling error should be assumed to be present (Ref 20).

Sampling can introduce uncertainties superimposed on that of the sample variability. Faulty calibration of sampling equipment,

introduction of contamination, malfunction of equipment, and differences between equipment used can introduce systematic errors, and variation of these factors can produce random errors.

Rigorous cleaning of equipment between samples may be necessary to minimize error from contamination or carryover problems. Evaluating the effectiveness of cleaning may be difficult. Containment may contribute to contamination, especially in trace analysis. Virgin containers usually require cleaning. If containers are to be reused, cleaning may need to be monitored. It may be necessary to restrict reuse to a certain class of samples and even to restricted levels within such classes if memory or cross contamination is a possibility.

Rigid calibration programs and checks may be necessary to ensure proper functioning of some sampling equipment. If calibration is performed in the laboratory, periodic field checks may be required to confirm retention of calibration, especially if the usage is severe.

Sample Identification. Definite procedures may be required to ensure the identity of samples that are analyzed. Well-designed labels can document the details of sample location and of the sampling operation. Critical aspects of their transport and storage can also be attested. Breakage-proof containers and tamper-proof closures may be required. A sample custodian may be necessary in some cases. There should be no reasonable doubt about the identity and the integrity of any sample analyzed.

Sampling Specific Materials. The general principles discussed above apply to the major problems of sampling for chemical analysis. Sources of information on procedures for sampling specific materials are cited in Ref 15 and 21 to 25.

REFERENCES

1. W.J. Youden, The Roles of Statistics in Regulatory Work, *J. Assoc. Off. Anal. Chem.*, Vol 50, 1967, p 1007
2. M.G. Natrella, *Experimental Statistics*, National Bureau of Standards Handbook 91, U.S. Government Printing Office, Washington, Aug 1963, p 2-13
3. Hazardous Waste Monitoring System, General, *Fed. Regist.*, Vol 45 (No. 98), 1980, p 33075-33127
4. "Standard Practices for Sampling Water," ASTM D 3370, Vol 11.01, *Annual Book of ASTM Standards*, ASTM, Philadelphia, 1984, p 85-94
5. "Standard Practice for Manual Sampling of Petroleum and Petroleum Products," ASTM D 4057, Vol 05.03, *Annual Book of ASTM Standards*, ASTM, Philadelphia, 1984, p 663-686
6. "Standard Practice for Sampling Industrial Chemicals," ASTM E 300, Vol 15.05, *Annual Book of ASTM Standards*, ASTM, Philadelphia, 1984, p 410-443
7. C.O. Ingamells and P. Switzer, A Proposed Sampling Constant for Use in Geochemical Analysis, *Talanta*, Vol 20, 1973, p 547
8. C.O. Ingamells, New Approaches to Geochemical Analysis and Sampling, *Talanta*, Vol 21, 1974, p 141
9. C.O. Ingamells, Derivation of the Sampling Constant Equation, *Talanta*, Vol 23, 1976, p 263
10. J. Visman, A General Sampling Theory, *Mat. Res. Stand.*, Nov, 1969, p 8
11. G.W. Snedecor and W.G. Cochran, *Statistical Methods*, 7th ed., Iowa State University Press, 1980, p 243
12. H.A. Laitinen and W.E. Harris, *Chemical Analysis*, McGraw-Hill, 1975, p 576
13. C.A. Bennett and N.L. Franklin, *Statistical Analysis in Chemistry and the Chemical Industry*, John Wiley & Sons, 1954, p 62, 482
14. J.K. Taylor, Quality Assurance of Chemical Measurements, *Anal. Chem.*, Vol 53, 1981, p 1588A-1595A
15. C.A. Bicking, in *Treatise on Analytical Chemistry*, 2nd ed., Vol 1, I.M. Kolthoff and P.J. Elving, Ed., John Wiley & Sons, 1979, p 299-359
16. J.R. Moody, NBS Clean Laboratories for Trace Elemental Analysis, *Anal. Chem.*, Vol 54, 1982, p 1358A-1376A
17. "Standard Practice for Preparation of Sediment Samples for Chemical Analysis," D 3976, *Annual Book of ASTM Standards*, ASTM, Philadelphia, 1984, p 673-676
18. R. Zeisler, J.K. Langland, and S.H. Harrison, Chemical Homogenization of Biological Tissues, *Anal. Chem.*, Vol 55, 1983, p 2431
19. J.K. Taylor, *Principles of Quality Assurance*, NBSIR 85-3105, National Bureau of Standards, Gaithersburg, MD, 1985
20. G.E.F. Lundell and J.I. Hoffman, *Outlines of Methods of Chemical Analysis*, John Wiley & Sons, 1938
21. B.G. Kratochvil and J.K. Taylor, "A Survey of the Recent Literature on Sampling for Chemical Analysis," NBS Technical Note 1153, National Bureau of Standards, Gaithersburg, MD, 1982
22. B.G. Kratochvil, D. Wallace, and J.K. Taylor, Sampling for Chemical Analysis, *Anal. Chem. Rev.*, Vol 56, 1984, p 113R

23. ''Methods for Sampling Chemical Products,'' Parts 1, 2, 3, 4, BS 5309, British Standards Institution, London, 1976

24. ''General Rules for Methods of Sampling Bulk Materials,'' Japanese Industrial Standard (JIS) M1800-1973, Japanese Standards Association, Tokyo, 1975 (in English)

25. Subject Index: Alphanumeric List, Vol 00.01, *Annual Book of ASTM Standards*, ASTM, 1984, p 1-726

Optical
and X-Ray
Spectroscopy

Optical Emission Spectroscopy

Paul B. Farnsworth, Department of Chemistry, Brigham Young University

General Uses

- Quantitative determination of major and trace elemental constituents in various sample types
- Qualitative elemental analysis

Examples of Applications

- Rapid determination of concentrations of alloying elements in steels and other alloys
- Elemental analysis of geological materials
- Determination of trace impurity concentrations in semiconductor materials
- Wear metals analysis in oils
- Determination of alkali and alkaline earth concentrations in aqueous samples
- Determination of calcium in cement

Samples

- *Form*: Conducting solids (arcs, sparks, glow discharges), powders (arcs), and solutions (flames)
- *Size*: Depends on specific technique; from approximately 10^{-6} g to several grams
- *Preparation*: Machining or grinding (metals), dissolution (for flames), and digestion or ashing (organic samples)

Limitations

- Some elements are difficult or impossible to determine, such as nitrogen, oxygen, hydrogen, halogens, and noble gases
- Sample form must be compatible with specific technique
- All methods provide matrix-dependent responses

Estimated Analysis Time

- 30 s to several hours, depending on sample preparation requirements

Capabilities of Related Techniques

- *X-ray fluorescence*: Bulk and minor constituent elemental analysis; requires sophisticated data reduction for quantitative analysis; not useful for light elements (atomic number ≤ 9)
- *Inductively coupled plasma emission spectroscopy*: Rapid quantitative elemental analysis with parts per billion detection limits; samples must be in solution; not useful for hydrogen, nitrogen, oxygen, halides, and noble gases
- *Direct-current plasma emission spectroscopy*: Similar in performance to inductively coupled plasma emission spectroscopy
- *Atomic absorption spectroscopy*: Favorable sensitivity and precision for most elements; single-channel technique; inefficient for multielement analysis

Introduction

Optical emission spectroscopic methods originated in experiments performed in the mid-1800s, yet they remain some of the most useful and flexible means of performing elemental analysis. Free atoms, when placed in an energetic environment, emit light at a series of narrow wavelength intervals. These intervals, termed emission lines, form a pattern, the emission spectrum, that is, characteristic of the atom producing it. The intensities of the lines are usually proportional to the number of atoms producing them. The presence of an element in a sample is indicated by the presence in light from the excitation source of one or more of its characteristic lines. The concentration of that element can be determined by measuring line intensities. Thus, the characteristic emission spectrum forms the basis for qualitative elemental analysis, and the measurement of intensities of the emission lines forms the basis of quantitative elemental analysis.

General Principles

The characteristic spectrum an atom produces reflects the electronic structure of the atom. Changes in the energy of the valence or outer shell electrons result in the atomic lines used in emission spectroscopy. Each atom has a ground state in which all of its electrons occupy positions of minimum potential energy. As an atom absorbs energy, one or more of the outer electrons may be promoted to higher energies, producing an excited state. The energy of an atomic state is a function of the energies of the individual electrons and of energy changes resulting from interactions among the electrons. Each possible combination of electron configurations produces a spectroscopic term that describes the state of the atom.

Electronic Energy Levels. The simplest atoms, such as hydrogen and the alkali metals, have only one electron outside a filled shell. The simple electron configurations of these atoms produce several possible terms, as illustrated by the energy-level diagram for lithium in Fig. 1. Atomic emission lines result when the atom undergoes a spontaneous transition from one excited state to another lower energy state. Not all possible combinations of states produce emission lines. Only transitions obeying quantum mechanically derived selection rules occur spontaneously. Diverse factors control the relative intensities of the lines. Those transitions between a low excited state and the ground state, termed resonance transitions, generally yield the most intense emission.

The energy of the excited electron increases with decreasing spacing between excited states until it reaches an ionization limit. At this point, the electron is no longer bound to the atom and may assume a continuous range of energies. Such unbound electrons may undergo transitions to bound states. Because the upper state of the transition is not limited to discrete values, the light from such transitions is spread continuously over a range of wavelengths.

The ionization limit for the atom corresponds to the ground state of the singly charged ion. Excitation of the remaining

Fig. 1 Energy level diagram for lithium

With the exception of the s states, each horizontal line corresponds to two closely spaced energy levels. The numbers and letters to the left of the lines are designations for the orbitals that the single electron can occupy. Transitions from the two 2p states to the ground 2s state produce a pair of closely spaced resonance lines at 670.785 nm.

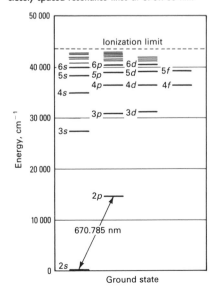

Fig. 2 Example of spectral complexity exhibited in a small section of the iron emission spectrum

bound electrons yields a new term system and a new set of lines. Ionization and excitation may continue until an atom is completely stripped of its electrons. In practical emission sources, ionization rarely proceeds beyond removal of two electrons, and in most cases, only the first stage of ionization need be considered. However, a line from the first ion spectrum is commonly used in analysis instead of a neutral atomic line.

Spectral Overlap. The use of atomic emission for elemental analysis requires measurability of the emission intensity from a line of interest independent of overlapping emission from other species in the sample. The probability of undesired overlap depends on the number of lines in the spectrum and on the wavelength spread or linewidth of each transition. If all atomic term systems were as simple as that shown for lithium in Fig. 1, the probability of spectral overlap would be low. However, lithium is one of the simplest atoms.

Atoms with more complex electronic structures produce correspondingly complex emission spectra. The iron spectrum, a small section of which is shown in Fig. 2, exemplifies such spectral complexity. The spectrum from one ionization stage of a single element may, given sufficient excitation energy, consist of hundreds of emission lines. The complexity is compounded when several elements are present in a sample, each generating neutral and ionic spectra.

Line Broadening. Spectral complexity would not be a problem if, in practice, each emission line were strictly monochromatic and instruments were available with infinite spectral resolution. The energy associated with an electronic term is not defined exactly, but spread over a range of values. The uncertainty in the energy levels appears in the emission spectrum as wavelength broadening of the emission lines. Several factors dictate the magnitude of the energy spread. The most important for emission spectroscopy are frequent collisions of the emitting atom or ion with other species in the excitation source and placement of the emitter in an inhomogeneous electric field. The first type of line broadening is collisional broadening; the second, Stark broadening.

A third type, Doppler broadening, results from motion of the emitting species relative

to the device detecting the emission. For a fixed transition energy, the emission recorded from an atom moving toward the detector is at shorter wavelengths than that recorded from an atom at rest. The emission from an atom moving away from the detector is at longer wavelengths.

The relative magnitude of these three line-broadening contributions depends strongly on the type of source exciting the emission. The collisional contribution to linewidth is primarily a function of source pressure. The Doppler contribution for a given element depends on source temperature. The magnitude of the Stark contribution depends on the density of charged species near the emitter.

Self-Absorption. Atomic line profiles produced by any of the above effects can be altered by self-absorption. At high concentrations of atoms in the spectroscopic source, the probability is reasonable that the radiation an atom emits will be absorbed by another atom of the same type. The probability of absorption is greater at wavelengths near the center of the line profile than at wavelengths near the wings. The emission profiles observed under such conditions are flatter and broader than those observed in the absence of self-absorption. If the absorbing atoms are at lower temperatures than the emitting atoms, a line profile similar to that illustrated in Fig. 3 results. The Doppler absorption profile of low-temperature absorbers is narrower than the emission profile of the hotter emitters. This is called self-reversal.

Molecular Emission. The energetic emitting volume of a spectroscopic source may contain small molecules in addition to free atoms. Like the atoms, the molecules produce optical emission that reflects change in the energies of the outer electrons of the molecule. Unlike the atoms, the molecules have numerous vibrational and rotational levels associated with each electronic state. Each electronic transition in the molecule

Fig. 3 Emission profile of a self-absorbed line

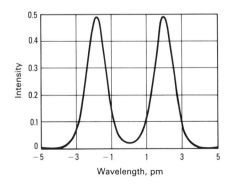

produces an emission band composed of individual lines reflecting the vibrational and rotational structure of the electronic states involved in the transition.

Molecular bands appear in a recorded spectrum as intense edges, out of which develop at higher or lower wavelengths less intense lines with a spacing that increases with distance from the edge. The edge is the band head. Composed of many closely spaced lines, molecular bands may dominate a region of the spectrum, complicating detection of emission from other species in that region. Emission sources are often designed to minimize molecular emission. Less frequently, band intensities are used in place of atomic line intensities to measure concentration.

Optical Systems

Atomic emission is analytically useful only to the extent that the emission from one atomic species can be measured and its intensity recorded independent of emission from other sources. This detection and quantification demands high-resolution wavelength-sorting instrumentation. Further, before the light can be sorted, it must be collected efficiently, sometimes only from an isolated region in a spatially heterogeneous emission source. Background information on optical systems is cited in Ref 1 and 2.

Wavelength Sorters. The key element in modern wavelength-sorting instruments is the diffraction grating, a precisely shaped reflective surface having many closely spaced parallel grooves. Figure 4 shows a partial cross section of a diffraction grating. Parallel rays of light strike adjacent grooves on the grating. The incident rays are in phase with each other. The rays scattered from the grating have traversed different paths. The difference in the path lengths is AB + BC. At angles producing a path difference that is an integral number of wavelengths, the exiting rays are in phase, and light is diffracted at that angle. At other angles, the exiting rays are out of phase, and destructive interference occurs. The angles at which diffraction takes place for a given wavelength can be determined by noting that $AB = d \sin \alpha$ and $BC = d \sin \beta$, where d is the diffraction grating groove spacing, α is the angle of incidence, and β is the angle of diffraction. The diffraction condition is:

$$m\lambda = d(\sin \alpha \pm \sin \beta) \qquad \text{(Eq 1)}$$

The minus sign enters when the incident and diffracted beams are on opposite sides of the grating normal.

Fig. 4 Partial cross section of a plane diffraction grating

α and β are the angles of incidence and diffraction, respectively. d is the groove space.

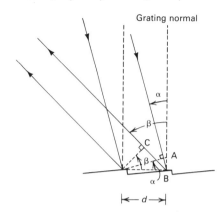

Two types of wavelength-sorting devices are most commonly used for emission spectroscopy. The first, the grating monochromator, is used for single-channel detection of radiation. Figure 5 shows the light path through a Czerny-Turner monochromator, a typical configuration. Light enters the monochromator through the entrance slit and passes to the collimating mirror. The collimated light strikes the plane diffraction grating and is diffracted at an angle dependent on its wavelengh. Some of the light is diffracted at angles such that it strikes the focusing mirror. It is then focused to form an array of entrance slit images in the focal plane of the monochromator. The position in the array of a slit image depends on the angle at which the light that forms it exited the grating. The wavelength of the image centered on the exit slit is:

$$m\lambda = 2d \sin \theta \cos \phi \qquad \text{(Eq 2)}$$

where θ is the angle through which the grating is rotated, and ϕ, the instrument angle, is the angle that a line through the center of the grating and the center of either mirror makes with the centerline of the instrument. The relationships between θ and ϕ and the angles α and β used in Eq 1 are shown in Fig. 5. As the grating is rotated, images from different wavelengths pass sequentially through the exit slit and are detected by a photomultiplier tube.

The second general type of wavelength sorter is the polychromator. Most polychromators are variations on the Rowland circle mount (Fig. 6). The diffraction grating is concave, with a radius of curvature R. If an entrance slit is located on a circle of radius $R/2$ tangent to the grating face, the diffracted images of the slit are focused around the circle. Exit slits and photomultiplier tubes may be placed at positions on the focal curve corresponding to wavelengths of lines from various elements. Line intensities from 40 to more than 60 elements, depending on instrument capability, can be determined simultaneously.

Alternatively, a strip of film or a photographic plate may be positioned in the focal curve in place of the slits and photomultiplier tubes, converting the polychromator into a spectrograph. An entire emission spectrum can be recorded in a short time on a plate or piece of film. Photographic detection allows more flexibility in line selection and provides more information than the combination of fixed slits and photomultiplier tubes. However, the time required to process the photographic medium, locate the lines of interest, and record their intensities makes

Fig. 5 Light path through a Czerny-Turner monochromator

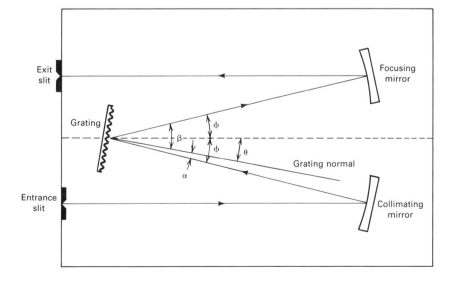

Fig. 6 Light path through a Rowland circle grating mount

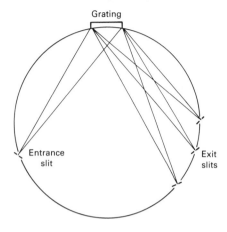

the use of photographic instruments tedious. Advancements in the data acquisition and processing capabilities of computerized polychromators are edging spectrographic instruments into disuse.

Collection optics for a spectroscopic instrument must transfer radiant power from the source to the detector with maximum efficiency and resolve or, in some cases, scramble spatial heterogeneities in the emission from the source. The first requirement is met if radiation from the source fills the entrance slit and the collimating optic of the spectrometer. A simple lens of appropriate size may be used to image the source on the entrance slit with sufficient magnification to fill it.

The size of the lens is selected such that radiation passing through the slit just fills the collimating optic. The entrance slit, then, defines the area of the source viewed by the system, and any source nonuniformity within that area is transferred to the detector. Photographic detection often requires spatial uniformity of the slit images. The desired uniformity is obtained if the source is imaged onto the collimating optic by a lens near the slit. Other lenses are then used to generate an intermediate image of the source at an aperture to provide spatial resolution.

Emission Sources

An emission light source must decompose the sample from some easily prepared form into an atomic vapor, then excite that vapor with sufficient efficiency to produce a measurable emission signal from the sample components of interest. Each of the four types of emission sources—arcs, high-voltage sparks, glow discharges, and flames—has a set of physical characteristics with accompanying analytical assets and liabili-

ties. Background information on excitation mechanisms is cited in Ref 3.

Excitation Mechanisms. The property of an emission source most closely linked to its excitation characteristics is temperature. Temperature indicates the amount of accessible energy in the source. Because energy can be partitioned variously among different species, different temperatures may reflect that partitioning.

Gas kinetic temperature and electron temperature indicate the kinetic energies of heavy particles and electrons, respectively. Excitation and ionization temperatures reflect the electronic energy content of atomic and molecular species. In addition, molecules store energy in rotational and vibrational modes, which is expressed as vibrational and rotational temperatures. In many source environments, excess energy in one mode is rapidly exchanged, or transferred, to another. In such cases, all the above temperatures are equal, and the source is in local thermodynamic equilibrium (LTE). When LTE exists, excitation conditions may be described without an understanding of the microscopic mechanisms of energy transfer. The population distribution among the possible excited states for a given species is given by the Boltzmann equation:

$$\frac{n_q}{n} = \frac{g_q \exp \dfrac{-E_q}{kT}}{\displaystyle\sum_{m=0}^{j} g_m \exp \dfrac{-E_m}{kT}} \qquad \text{(Eq 3)}$$

Equation 3 gives the fraction of the total population of a given species that is in excited state q. If, for example, the species is a neutral atom, n_q is the number density of atoms in state q and n is the number density of atoms in all states. E is the energy above the ground state of state q, g values are statistical weights reflecting the fact that different combinations of quantum numbers can give rise to states with the same energy, j (the limit for the summation in the denominator) is the number of possible excited states of the atom, k is the Boltzmann constant, and T is the absolute temperature.

Examination of Eq 3 illuminates several important characteristics of thermal excitation. At the high-temperature limit, the population n is distributed nearly equally among all the possible excited states. The populations of the individual states depend only on their statistical weights. At practical temperatures, the distribution favors states with low excitation energies. Therefore, the quantum mechanically allowed resonance transitions from low-lying excited states almost always

produce the most intense emission. The higher the energy of such transitions, the hotter the source required for efficient excitation. The denominator on the right-hand side of Eq 3 is the partition function for the species. The value of the partition function increases with the number of excited states. This implies that thermal excitation of a given level is more efficient for a simple atom with few excited states than for a complex atom with many excited states.

Equation 3 alone does not characterize excitation completely, because it describes only the distribution among excited states of the atom or ion in question, omitting the equilibrium among the possible stages of ionization. That equilibrium is described by the Saha equation:

$$S = \frac{n_i n_e}{n_a} = 4.83 \times$$

$$10^{15} T^{3/2} \frac{Z_i}{Z_a} \times 10^{-(5040/T)V_i} \qquad \text{(Eq 4)}$$

where n_i, n_e, and n_a are the number densities of the ions, electrons, and atoms, respectively; Z_i and Z_a are the partition functions of the ion and atom; and V_i is the ionization potential in volts. This function reaches large values at temperatures routinely generated by analytical excitation sources; therefore, ionization of some atomic species is virtually complete. The emission spectra from the ionic forms of an element are useful in such cases, but emission from neutral atomic species is weak or absent.

When LTE does not exist, Eq 3 and 4 are not rigorously applicable. A complete description of excitation in such cases must account for microscopic collisional processes that may excite or deexcite a given energy level with an efficiency far different from that predicted using LTE. For example, in low-pressure discharges, a small portion of the electron population may have a temperature far higher than the gas temperature in the discharge. These fast electrons may produce highly excited atoms or ions in much greater numbers than would be generated under LTE conditions. The excitation efficiency in non-LTE sources often depends on close matches in the kinetic or internal energy of colliding species and therefore displays sharp variations as the chemical composition of the excitation region changes.

The ideal emission source would sample all materials efficiently regardless of form and would deliver vapor to the excitation zone with a composition directly proportional to the sample composition. Excitation would be uniformly efficient for all elements. It would produce simple spectra, with all the excitation energy concentrated in a few excited states. The source would generate no background spectrum. Therefore, the analytical results for equal concentrations of elements in two samples would be identical, regardless of differences in the concentration of other sample constituents. That is, sampling and excitation would have no matrix dependence.

Arc Sources

The term arc describes various electrical discharges; this discussion will focus on the direct-current (dc) arc. Figure 7 shows a circuit for generating a dc arc, defined as a self-maintaining dc discharge (Ref 4). Direct-current arcs are operated at voltages below that required to break down the gap between the electrodes; therefore, they must be started by touching the electrodes together or by ionizing the gas in the gap with a transient high-voltage discharge. Once current begins to flow, the motion of the electrons heats the electrodes and the gas in the gap. This heating increases the number of charged species in the gap and thus reduces gap resistance.

This reduction in resistance with increased current necessitates the resistor in the circuit. Without it, the current would increase rapidly to the capacity of the source, with catastrophic results. For a given value of ballast resistance, the gap resistance depends on the composition of the arc plasma. To minimize the effect of changes in plasma composition on arc current, the ballast resistor should be selected as the major source of resistance in the discharge circuit. Typical operating currents for the dc arc are 5 to 20 A. This current range can be obtained from sources operating at 250 V, with ballast resistances from 10 to 50 Ω.

Electrodes for a dc arc are arranged coaxially on a vertical axis with a separation of a few millimeters. They are most commonly machined from graphite or amorphous carbon. The lower electrode, usually the anode, has a cup machined in it to hold

Fig. 7 Direct-current arc source

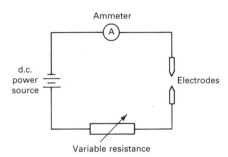

the sample. Heating of the anode vaporizes the material in the cup into the interelectrode region, where it is heated to 5000 to 7000 K in a generally LTE environment. At these temperatures, ionization of most elements is minimal, and neutral atomic lines dominate the spectrum. Therefore, neutral emission lines are traditionally designated as arc lines.

Analysis Limitations. Sampling and excitation in the dc arc are far from ideal. Sample components vaporize from the cup electrode at different rates, depending on their volatility. The arc tends to anchor to spots on the electrode that wander about the electrode surfaces during a burn (the time of emission source excitation). This wandering causes erratic and irreproducible sampling. Excitation conditions in the arc are not uniform spatially and tend to change with the composition of the material introduced from the sample cup. The hot cylindrical region between the two electrodes, the positive column, is surrounded by a cooler region, the mantle. These conditions produce the self-reversed lines often characteristic of arc spectra. The background spectrum from the arc consists predominantly of molecular emission bands from the cyanogen (CN) molecule. These bands are in the violet region of the spectrum and may interfere with detection of atomic emission in that region.

Minimizing Undesirable Characteristics. The dc arc is used extensively for its ability to sample and excite diverse samples with favorable sensitivity. Careful sample preparation, electrode design, and selection of arcing atmosphere minimize the impact of some of the undesirable characteristics of the arc. One approach to the problem of selective vaporization involves advantageous use of time-dependent vaporization by recording emission from a species of interest only during evaporation from the sample cup. This minimizes spectral interferences from sample components with different volatility and optimizes signal-to-background ratios by recording spectral information only when signal from the sample is significant. A second approach is to integrate emission during consumption of the entire sample.

Both approaches require uniform and reproducible vaporization of the sample. Uniformity and reproducibility result from mixing powdered samples with some combination of powdered graphite, carriers, and buffers. The powdered graphite promotes a smooth burn. The carrier contributes to rapid vaporization of the trace components of the sample. The buffer provides the arc with a steady, high concentration of an element having desirable ionization properties. The high concentration of the buffer in the arc column controls the arc voltage and current.

The effect of changes in the concentrations of other species with varying ionization potentials is comparatively small.

Control of the atmosphere in which the arc is burning minimizes the problems of self-reversal and CN emission. The arc may be burned in a quartz enclosure or in a sheath of nitrogen free gas generated in a device such as the Stallwood jet. The exclusion of nitrogen from the arcing atmosphere prevents formation of CN molecules. The flowing sheath gas sweeps away cool atomic vapor from the arc mantle and decreases self-reversal. The flowing gases also help to stabilize the arc.

Direct current arc emission spectroscopy is not precise. Its primary value is in qualitative or semiquantitative analysis of samples not easily dissolved in preparation for analysis using a more precise but less flexible emission source, such as the inductively coupled plasma (ICP), or when a more precise source is not available (see the article ''Inductively Coupled Plasma Atomic Emission Spectroscopy'' in this Volume).

Spark Sources

The high-voltage spark is an intermittent electrical discharge characterized by operating voltages sufficient to cause spontaneous breakdown of an analytical gap and high currents resulting from capacitively stored energy in the discharge circuit. Figure 8 shows a controlled waveform spark source consisting of a high-voltage charging circuit, an inductor-capacitor tank circuit with a high-voltage switch, and waveshaping circuitry incorporating the analytical gap.

The circuit generates series of identical spark discharges with precise control over current magnitude and direction as well as discharge duration. In practice, the charging section of the circuit is simply a high-voltage transformer and full-wave rectifier. The spark is triggered at times delayed from the zero-crossing of the alternating current (ac) charging waveform selected to produce the same capacitor voltage at the beginning of each discharge. The trigger is usually a hydrogen thyratron or a high-voltage silicon-controlled rectifier.

For a given discharge voltage, the relative values of the inductances and capacitance in the tank and waveshaping sections of the circuit dictate the shape and amplitude of the current waveform. For analytical operation, the component values are usually selected to provide a unidirectional discharge current with peak amplitudes from 50 to 200 A and durations from 50 to 150 μs.

Analysis Limitations. The analytical spark gap consists typically of a tungsten pin anode and a cathode of the material to be analyzed. Because the sample forms one of

Fig. 8 Controlled waveform spark source
Source: Ref 5

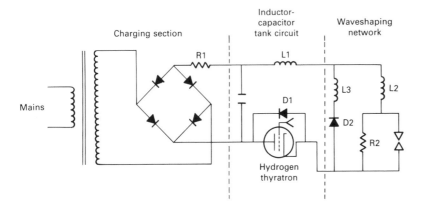

the electrodes, analysis by spark emission spectroscopy is limited to samples that are conductive or can be made so. The analysis is usually carried out in an inert atmosphere, which, as with the dc arc, is provided in a closed chamber or as a flowing sheath of gas. Unless stabilized, the individual sparks in a train strike different locations on the sample electrode, generating a several millimeter wide burn pattern on a planar sample. With a sheath of argon flowing from the anode to the cathode, the sparks strike much more reproducibly, and the burn area is reduced by a factor of ten.

When a spark strikes the sample electrode, rapid local heating ejects electrode material into the spark gap. In an unstabilized spark, the trajectory of the ejected material is random. In a stabilized spark, the material propagates upward through the gap as an expanding cylinder about the interelectrode axis. In either case, the vapor is subjected to various excitation conditions during a single spark. It first passes through the energetic cathode spot, where it may undergo several stages of ionization. As it continues upward, the vapor in the current-conducting spark channel remains highly excited; the vapor removed from the interelectrode axis experiences much less energetic conditions. Coincident in time with the movement of sample vapor through the gap, the current in the discharge increases and decreases, altering the excitation conditions markedly.

The temporal and spatial inhomogeneity of the spark preclude its characterization in terms of an excitation temperature. Emission is generated at different times and places from several stages of ionization of the sample material and the atmospheric gas. The dominant form of emission is often the first ion spectrum. Lines from the singly charged ion are traditionally termed spark lines.

Changes in spark emission occur within microseconds. The emission from a spark train also varies within minutes. This long-term change in emission intensity, the sparking-off effect, is primarily a reflection of change in the sample electrode caused by repeated sparking at its surface. Chemical and physical changes in the electrode contribute to the sparking-off effect. Therefore, the exact nature of the sparking-off curves depends strongly on experimental conditions.

Spark source parameters (capacitance, voltage, inductance, repetition rate), sample composition, sample phase structure, sample surface condition, sparking atmosphere, and burn area must be considered in describing sparking-off behavior. Of particular importance are the dependencies on sample composition and phase structure, indicating that the emission results for an element are strongly matrix dependent. This is important when the spark is used as an analytical emission source.

Minimizing Undesirable Characteristics. Diverse procedures have been adopted in spark analysis to minimize the effect of source nonidealities. Sparking-off effects are traditionally dealt with by recording emission only after the largest intensity changes associated with a burn have occurred. Light to the detector is blocked during a preburn period typically lasting approximately 1 min, during which the spark conditions the fresh electrode surface. If the spark is unstable positionally and samples a large area, the emission following the preburn period, for most elements, remains fairly constant for the 30 s required to record an emission spectrum.

Positionally stable sparks generate sparking-off curves compressed in time compared to those produced by unstable discharges. Instead of increasing to a steady state value,

the emission intensity increases to a maximum within a few seconds, then decreases to a relatively low value. The emission becomes progressively more erratic as the burn continues. The emission peak during the first 2 min of the burn contains information on the concentration of an element in a sample and the type of matrix in which the element is found (Ref 6).

An additional compensation for the non-ideality of the spark source is use of intensity ratios rather than unmodified emission intensities to indicate elemental concentration. The intensities of lines from minor constituents are ratioed with intensities from a major matrix constituent. For example, in steel analysis, the line intensities from the alloying elements are ratioed with the intensity of an iron line. This procedure compensates somewhat for variations in sampling and excitation efficiency from one sample to another. It involves the implicit assumption that sampling and excitation of the reference component represent the same processes for the minor constituents. This may not always be the case, especially if the sample contains inclusions that differ significantly in concentration from the bulk of the sample.

The above measures do not produce satisfactory analytical results unless the spark spectrometer is calibrated using standards that match the unknown sample closely in chemical composition and physical form. Laboratories using the spark for analysis must have sets of standards for each type of material to be analyzed. Standards for spark investigations are not easily produced and generally must be purchased from the National Bureau of Standards (Ref 7) or from private companies.

Glow Discharges

Glow discharges are dc low-pressure discharges that are distinguished from arcs primarily by the current density in the discharge and by the mechanism of electron production at the cathodic electrode. Current conduction in an arc is confined to a well-defined channel that tends to anchor itself to the cathode, causing intense local heating. Electrons are thermally ejected from the cathode. In contrast, current conduction in a glow discharge is diffuse, and the cathode is maintained at relatively low temperatures. Thermionic emission of electrons from the cathode is unimportant. Rather, bombardment of the cathode by high-energy photons and ions ejects electrons.

The glow discharges used as spectroscopic emission sources are operated in the current-voltage domain characteristic of "abnormal" glow discharges. The conducting region in such discharges envelopes the entire cathode. Increases in current necessarily increase current density and thus discharge voltage. The increase in voltage with increasing current continues until the cathode becomes sufficiently hot to emit electrons thermally and an arc forms. Decreases in the current below a threshold value contract the conducting region; current density and voltage remain constant. This constant voltage discharge is a "normal" glow discharge. The values of the current at which the transitions from "normal" to "abnormal" glow discharge and from abnormal glow discharge to arc occur depend on electrode geometry, gas pressure, and electrode cooling efficiency.

At typical operating pressures of a few torr, 10- to 500-mA currents produce an "abnormal" glow discharge. For a given electrode configuration, current, voltage, and fill-gas pressure regulate operation of a glow discharge. The values of two of these may be varied independently, fixing that of the third. At a fixed current, an increase in pressure decreases voltage. As with the dc arc, the current in a glow discharge is not self-regulating. A ballast resistor must be included in the discharge circuit to limit the current.

Glow discharges are inhomogeneous spatially, particularly in the region near the cathode. Most of the voltage applied between the electrodes is dropped across a layer near the cathode surface, because electrons are repelled from the cathode faster than the heavier positive ions are attracted to it and a positive space charge develops. Electrons exiting the cathode are accelerated through this region of high electric field, termed the cathode fall, and acquire sufficient energy to ionize the buffer gas. The buffer gas ions are in turn accelerated toward the cathode, gaining sufficient energy to eject atoms of the cathode material when they strike its surface. The sputtered atoms diffuse from the cathode surface and may then be excited by the energetic electrons produced in the cathode fall. The most intense emission from a glow discharge originate from a region termed the negative glow. Electron energies in this region are optimum for excitation of buffer gas atoms and atoms sputtered from the cathode.

The Grimm Emission Source. Glow discharges have become popular as emission sources only since Grimm's development of a source for use with various planar samples that enables rapid sample changeover (Ref 8). Figure 9 shows the Grimm source. The flat sample surface seals a cylindrical opening in a water-cooled cathode block. The sample is in electrical contact with the block and is thus cathodic. A portion of the anode

is machined to a cylinder that fits into the opening in the cathode block opposite the sample; spacing between the face of the anode cylinder and the sample surface is only 0.2 mm (0.008 in.).

The source uses a flowing gas system; an inert buffer gas enters the source near the quartz window and exits through one of two independently pumped vacuum ports. The annular region between the anode and cathode is pumped to maintain the pressure in that region lower than the pressure in the main body of the source. This pressure differential ensures confinement of the discharge to the small cylindrical section of the anode and the circular portion of the cathodic sample surface opposite the end of the cylinder.

Sampling in the Grimm emission source is by cathodic sputtering. Because sputtering is nonthermal, the problems of selective vaporization in other electrical discharges are not present. The circular area on the cathode to which the discharge is confined erodes at a rate that depends on discharge current, voltage, and pressure and on the composition of the buffer gas and cathode (Ref 9). Argon is used as a buffer gas in most practical work, because it is inexpensive and sputters efficiently.

Minimizing Undesirable Characteristics. Although free of the problems caused by thermal sampling, sampling by sputtering is not ideal. The dependence of sputtering rate on sample composition is a serious matrix effect that must be considered in any emission experiment in which the glow discharge is used as an excitation source.

One approach to compensating for changes in sputtering with changes in sample composition involves use of a weighted sum of emission intensities from all sample constituents as an internal standard (Ref 10). A sputtering rate is calculated for each sample using:

Fig. 9 Grimm glow discharge source

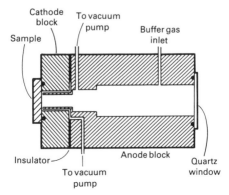

$$S = a \times I_1 + b \times I_2 + c \times I_3 \ldots$$

where the I_1, I_2, I_3, and so on, are the raw intensities measured for each component in the sample. The coefficients a, b, c, and so on, are determined from a standard using:

$$a = \frac{C_1}{I_1} ; b = \frac{C_2}{I_2} ; \ldots$$

where C_1, C_2, and so on are the concentrations of the components in the standard. Normalized intensities, $a \times I_1/S$, $b \times I_2/S$, and so on, are then used to generate analytical working curves. This method reduces but does not eliminate the effect of matrix on analytical results. It requires detailed knowledge of the sample composition, because failure to include even a minor constituent in the sputtering rate calculation may bias severely the results of a measurement. As with the spark, optimum analytical results are obtained if the standards are well matched to the samples.

Sample excitation in the glow discharge source differs significantly from that provided by arcs or sparks. The glow discharge is a non-LTE source. The gas kinetic temperature is relatively low (Ref 11), but the excitation temperatures some species exhibit are high. This is an ideal combination, because elements with high excitation potentials are excited efficiently without the line broadening that occurs in hot dense plasmas. The high excitation energies are attributable to a small population of fast electrons generated in the cathode fall. These electrons excite analyte atoms directly to energetic neutral or ionic states. They also produce energetic buffer gas atoms and ions that may in turn excite cathode vapor by various collisional routes.

The line intensities produced by the discharge do not remain constant during a burn. These variations have been attributed to changes in excitation conditions as sputtering of the cathode surface creates a crater and alters electrode geometry (Ref 9). Glow discharges yield burnoff curves that are in many ways analogous to the spark-off curves produced by high-voltage sparks. The intensities of most lines increase sharply at the beginning of a burn, then, under appropriate conditions, level out to near steady state values. If burn conditions are not selected correctly, emission intensities never reach a steady value. Because of this dependence of emission intensity on time, fresh electrode surfaces are preconditioned by a brief burn before recording analytical data.

Self-absorption of resonance radiation from major constituents may be a problem for samples excited using the Grimm discharge. This can be minimized by judicious selection of excitation conditions and by use of nonresonance radiation as an indicator of concentration. Examples of the effects of self-absorption are cited in Ref 12.

Applications for the glow discharge are similar to those for the high-voltage spark. Because, like the spark, the glow discharge requires a conducting sample, the source is most readily applied to samples of metals and alloys, which are conductors. Glow discharges have been used to analyze ferrous (Ref 13) and nonferrous (Ref 12, 14, 15) alloys with favorable results and have performed favorably in comparison to spark sources in the analysis of steels (Ref 16). The glow discharge source generates working curves that are more linear than those produced by the spark and less matrix dependent. The glow discharge source is simpler electronically than the spark source and does not generate its characteristic radio frequency (RF) noise. The glow discharge source produces clean spectra with narrow lines.

However, it must operate in a low-pressure environment on a clean sample that has been ground smooth enough to provide a vacuum between the O-ring and the sample. The spark source operates at atmospheric pressure on samples that have been only coarse sanded or surface ground. Both sources will doubtless find continued application in metallurgy.

Flame Sources

Flames were the emission sources for emission spectroscopy as it evolved into an analytical science in the last half of the nineteenth century. Flame emission sources differ significantly from other sources in that the energy required for the decomposition and excitation of the sample derives from chemical combustion rather than an electrical discharge. Analytical flames are generated by the burning of a mixture of two gases—a fuel and an oxidant—in a burner arrangement that allows introduction of the sample as a fine aerosol.

Burner Selection. Total consumption and premix burners are the two types in common use. In the total consumption burner (Fig. 10), tubing connected to a central capillary is placed in a vessel containing a sample solution. Oxidant exits the top of the burner from an annular opening that surrounds the sample capillary. The flow of gas past the tip of the capillary reduces the pressure at the tip, and atmospheric pressure on the solution vessel forces solution through the capillary. Exiting the capillary, the solution is broken into a fine

mist, which may be further decomposed into free atoms in the flame environment. Fuel is provided for the flame through a second annular opening that surrounds the opening for the oxidant.

The fuel and oxidant for the premix burner (Fig. 11) are mixed in a chamber below the burner head before combustion occurs. The fuel enters the chamber directly. The oxidant aspirates and nebulizes the sample, then transports the aerosol through a spray chamber to the premix chamber. The spray chamber removes the largest droplets from the aerosol; they fall to the bottom of the chamber and are drained off as waste. This separation is inefficient. Less than 5% of the aspirated sample typically reaches the flame. The nebulizer shown in this diagram is a concentric nebulizer. Several other nebulization techniques are possible using premix burners (Ref 17, 18).

Both types of burners have advantages and disadvantages. Premix burners cannot be used with some combinations of fuel and oxidant, because the burning velocity of the gas mixture exceeds the velocity of the gas exiting the burner head. Under such conditions, the flame enters the confined space of the mixing chamber, and an explosion or flashback results. Flashback does not occur in total consumption burners, because the gases are mixed above the burner head. The openings in premix burners promote laminar flow of the gases through the burner head. As a result, premix flames burn stably and

Fig. 10 Total consumption burner

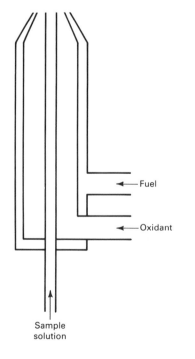

are acoustically and optically quiet. However, the gas flow from total consumption burners is turbulent. The flames are spatially unstable and are acoustically and optically noisy. The capillary tips in total consumption burners are close to the hot flame environment and are prone to clogging by salt deposits. This is less of a problem with premix burners.

Neither burner is efficient. Only 5% of the sample solution enters the flame in a premix burner. Although the entire sample passes through total consumption flame, much of it is in the form of droplets too large to be broken down during their short time in the flame.

Factors for Consideration. The formation of an aerosol in either type of flame is only the beginning of sampling. Once in the flame, the droplets follow the sequence illustrated in Fig. 12. The free atoms are excited in an environment that in most cases is in LTE. Therefore, the most important factors controlling the efficiency with which an atom is excited are the flame temperature and the excitation potential of the first excited state of the atom in question. Table 1 lists temperatures for several combinations of fuel and oxidant. The flame temperature should be hot enough to excite the atoms of interest efficiently but not cause excessive ionization. Even the hottest flames do not excite elements with high excitation potential efficiently. Flames are best suited for determination of elements with low-lying excited states. Flame spectroscopy is among the most sensitive means available for determining alkali metals.

The number of photons detected from M (neutral atom) in the flame depends ideally only on its concentration in the sample solution and on the flame operating conditions. In practice, several other factors affect the concentration of M in the flame, the efficiency with which it is excited, and the magnitude of the recorded emission signal. Such factors may be categorized as solvent and nebulization effects, spectral interferences, vaporization interferences, and ionization interferences.

Fig. 11 Premix burner

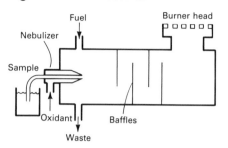

Fig. 12 Droplet sequence during flame emission spectroscopy

M, the cation; *X*, the anion

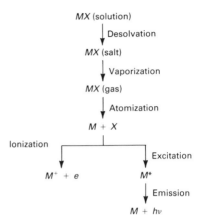

Table 1   Temperatures of commonly used premix flames

Fuel	Oxidant	Temperature °C	°F
Acetylene	Air	2125-2400	3855-4350
Acetylene	Oxygen	3060-3135	5540-5675
Acetylene	Nitrous oxide	2600-2800	4710-5070
Hydrogen	Air	2000-2050	3630-3720
Hydrogen	Oxygen	2550-2700	4620-4890
Methane	Air	1875	3405
Methane	Oxygen	2670	4840

Source: Ref 19

The rate at which solution is aspirated through the nebulizer capillary and the droplet size distribution depend on the viscosity of the solution. Dilute solutions are aspirated at higher rates than solutions having high salt content. Organic solutions generally provide higher aspiration rates than aqueous solutions. Care must be taken in sample preparation to avoid changes in viscosity from one sample to the next.

Solvent composition also affects desolvation rate and the amount of flame cooling that occurs during desolvation. Most organic solvents are combustible and may provide additional fuel for the flame during their evaporation. Water offers no such contribution. Consequently, aqueous solutions cool the flame to a greater extent than organic solutions.

Spectral interferences result when a flame background feature or an emission line from another element cannot be resolved spectroscopically from the emission from the element of interest. The flame background consists of molecular band emission and a continuum. The continuum is a combination of black body emission from hot particles in the flame and emission from nonquantized molecular recombination processes. The hottest flames generally produce the most intense and complex background spectra. This liability must be weighed against the advantages for many applications of high temperatures. For a given flame type, spectral interferences decrease with the spectral bandwidth of the wavelength sorting device until that bandwidth matches the width of the narrowest emission feature.

Vaporization interferences result from the dependence of vaporization and atomization rates on the nature of *X* (the anion in the salt *MX*). For example, calcium phosphate is less

volatile and more stable than calcium chloride. The presence of large amounts of phosphorus in a sample containing calcium reduces severely the density of free calcium atoms. A similar problem occurs when *MX* is an oxide that has formed in a lean flame. Addition to the sample of an excess (more than a stoichiometric amount) of a releasing agent, such as lanthanum or strontium, prevents phosphate formation. These elements prevent combination of the available phosphate with the analyte. Use of fuel-rich flames prohibits oxide formation. The magnitude of either problem decreases with increasing temperature of the flame.

Some elements with low ionization potentials are ionized to a large extent in the hotter analytical flames, reducing the neutral atom population and thus the analytical signal. Addition of an excess of an easily ionizable element, or ionization buffer, to the sample increases the electron density in the flame. The increased electron density shifts the ionization equilibrium to favor the neutral atom.

Applications

Arc Sources. Direct current arc excitation was used to determine 12 trace metal impurities present in phosphor grade calcium tungstate ($CaWO_4$) from 5 to 250 ppm. A precision of ±15% was reported. These results were obtained only after careful development of the method, which involved (1) selection of appropriate buffering and sample dilution agents, (2) selection of an appropriate internal standard, and (3) selection of a burn duration that would provide acceptable sensitivity and reproducibility.

First, 20 combinations of graphite diluent, carriers, and buffers were tested. Combination of one part sample with three parts powdered graphite without a carrier or a buffer yielded optimum results. Second, scandium, gallium, and germanium were tested as internal standards. Of these, scandium exhibited behavior most like the trace impurities under analysis. Finally, the time-dependent emission from the trace elements and the standard was recorded. The important emission signals all occurred during the

first 35 s of the burn, and a burn duration for the analyses of 35 s was selected. Details of this procedure are given in Ref 20.

Spark Sources. Spark source excitation is the most rapid method of obtaining an elemental analysis of a metal or alloy. Speed is critical in the steel industry, for which a melt from a production furnace must be sampled and analyzed and the concentrations of alloying elements adjusted to within predetermined ranges. During the production of a heat of steel, the metal is sampled, and the molten sample is cooled. A flat surface is ground or sanded on the cooled sample then placed with no additional preparation into a spark source. The analysis is performed, and the results are sent immediately to the furnace, where appropriate adjustments are made in the composition of the heat. Sampling and analysis requires at most a few minutes.

Glow discharge sources may be used to determine carbon, phosphorus, and sulfur in low-alloy steels and cast iron (Ref 21). The resonance emission lines for these elements are all in the vacuum ultraviolet and are usually detectable only using expensive vacuum spectrometers. In this application, the concentrations of three elements were determined sequentially by focusing the emission from the steel sample into an auxiliary glow discharge with cathode composed partially of the element of interest. Fluorescence from that element in the auxiliary discharge was detected at right angles to the primary emission beam. Detection limits using this approach ranged from 0.002% for sulfur to 0.014% for carbon.

Flame Sources. Flames are among the most efficient sources for excitation of spectra from alkali metals and have their greatest utility in the trace determination of these elements. Nitrous oxide-acetylene and air-acetylene flames were used to excite dissolved samples of various standard materials, including feldspar, firebrick, magnetite, limestone, portland cement, and spodumene. Lithium was determined from 0 to 2 ppm, sodium from 0 to 50 ppm, and potassium from 0 to 150 ppm. Spectral interferences were avoided by use of a monochromator with moderate resolution, and ionization was suppressed by addition of 4000 ppm cesium to each sample. Because of the excellent sensitivity the flame provides for alkali metals, samples could be diluted, without compromising determination of less abundant constituents, until the concentration of the most abundant of the three elements was in a linear working range. The agreement between measured and certified concentrations of lithium, sodium, and potassium in the standard material listed above was generally excellent. This application is described in Ref 22.

REFERENCES

1. R.M. Barnes and R.F. Jarrell, in *Analytical Emission Spectroscopy*, Vol 1, Part I, E.L. Grove, Ed., Marcel Dekker, 1971
2. H.T. Betz and G.L. Johnson, in *Analytical Emission Spectroscopy*, Vol 1, Part I, E.L. Grove, Ed., Marcel Dekker, 1971
3. P.W.J.M. Boumans, in *Analytical Emission Spectroscopy*, Vol 1, Part II, E.L. Grove, Ed., Marcel Dekker, 1971
4. *Compilation of ASTM Standard Definitions*, 5th ed., ASTM, Philadelphia, 1982, p 39
5. D.M. Coleman and J.P. Walters, *Spectrochim. Acta*, Vol 31B, 1976, p 547
6. D. Ekimoff and J.P. Walters, *Anal. Chem.*, Vol 53, 1981, p 1644
7. Standard Reference Materials Catalog, NBS special publication 260, National Bureau of Standards, Washington, Feb 1984
8. W. Grimm, *Spectrochim. Acta*, Vol 23B, 1968, p 443
9. P.W.J.M. Boumans, *Anal. Chem.*, Vol 44, 1972, p 1219
10. H. Jager, *Anal. Chim. Acta*, Vol 58, 1972, p 57
11. N.P. Ferreira, H.G.C. Human, and L.R.P. Butler, *Spectrochim. Acta*, Vol 35B, 1980, p 287
12. H. Jager, *Anal. Chim. Acta*, Vol 71, 1974, p 43
13. H.W. Radmacher and M.C. de Swardt, *Spectrochim. Acta*, Vol 30B, 1975, p 353
14. R.A. Kruger, L.R.P. Butler, C.J. Liebenberg, and R.G. Böhmer, *Analyst*, Vol 102, 1977, p 949
15. N.P. Ferreira and L.R.P. Butler, *Analyst*, Vol 103, 1978, p 607
16. J. Durr and B. Vandorpe, *Spectrochim. Acta*, Vol 36B, 1981, p 139
17. R.F. Browner and A.W. Boorn, *Anal. Chem.*, Vol 56, 1984, p 787A
18. R.F. Browner and A.W. Boorn, *Anal. Chem.*, Vol 56, 1984, p 875A
19. R.N. Knisely, in *Flame Emission and Atomic Absorption Spectrometry*, Vol 1, J.A. Dean and T.C. Rains, Ed., Marcel Dekker, 1969
20. H.G. Kamat, V. Sughandi, and T.R. Saranathan, *Anal. Lett.*, Vol 14, 1981, p 933
21. H.G.C. Human, J.A. Strauss, and L.R.P. Butler, *Spectrochim. Acta*, Vol 35B, 1980, p 207
22. M.A. Hildon and W.J. Allen, *Analyst*, Vol 96, 1971, p 480

SELECTED REFERENCES

- C.Th.J. Alkemade, Tj. Hollander, W. Snelleman, and P.J.Th. Zeegers, *Metal Vapours in Flames*, Pergammon Press, 1982
- P.W.J.M. Boumans, *Theory of Spectrochemical Excitation*, Plenum Press, 1966
- G. Herzberg, *Atomic Spectra and Atomic Structure*, Dover, 1944
- M. Slavin, *Emission Spectrochemical Analysis*, Wiley-Interscience, 1971
- J.P. Walters, *Science*, Vol 198, 1977, p 787

Inductively Coupled Plasma Atomic Emission Spectroscopy

Lynda M. Faires, Analytical Chemistry Group, Los Alamos National Laboratory

---

General Use

- Simultaneous multielement analysis
- Quantitative and qualitative analysis for over 70 elements with detection limits in the parts per billion (ng/mL) to parts per million (μg/mL) range
- Determination of major, minor, and trace elemental components

Examples of Applications

- Composition of metal alloys
- Trace impurities in alloys, metals, reagents, and solvents
- Analysis of geological, environmental, and biological materials
- Water analysis
- Process control

Samples

- *Form*: Liquids, gases, and solids; liquids are most common
- *Size*: 5 to 50 mL of solution, 10 to 500 mg of solids
- *Preparation*: Most samples are analyzed as solutions; solutions can be analyzed as received, diluted, or preconcentrated as required; solids must usually be dissolved to form solutions; gases may be analyzed directly

Limitations

- Detection limits parts per billion to parts per million
- Cannot analyze for noble gases
- Halogens and some nonmetals require vacuum spectrometer and optics
- Sensitivity poor for alkali elements, especially rubidium; cannot determine cesium

Estimated Analysis Time

- Dissolution of solids in sample preparation may require up to 16 h
- Analysis may require minutes to several hours

Capabilities of Related Techniques

- *Direct-current arc emission spectrography*: Samples may be analyzed directly as solids; sensitivity and quantitative precision poorer; longer analysis time required
- *Atomic absorption spectroscopy*: Single-element analysis; better sensitivity for most elements, especially by using electrothermal atomization, but not as good for refractory elements; more limited dynamic range

Introduction

Inductively coupled plasma atomic emission spectroscopy (ICP-AES) is an analytical technique for elemental determinations in the concentration range of major to trace based on the principles of atomic spectroscopy. In theory, the technique applies to all elements except argon, and samples may be introduced as liquids, gases, or solids. In practice, favorable analytical results are obtained for approximately 70 elements, with detection limits usually attainable at the parts per billion level, and most samples are introduced in liquid form as aqueous solutions. The technique has found widespread application in the metallurgical, geological, environmental, agricultural, industrial, and biological fields and is an important technique in the modern analytical laboratory.

The first developmental research on the ICP as an excitation source for optical analytical atomic spectroscopy was published in 1964 (Ref 1) and 1965 (Ref 2). The first commercial instrumentation for analytical laboratories began to appear in the mid-1970s. In subsequent years, the success of the technique renewed interest in analytical atomic emission, which had been largely supplanted by developments in atomic absorption instrumentation in the 1950s and 1960s (see the article "Atomic Absorption Spectrometry" in this Volume). The success of the ICP was due to its ability to perform multielement analysis and to determine a wide concentration range in the same sample—two important characteristics atomic

Fig. 1 Electric and magnetic fields of the inductively coupled plasma

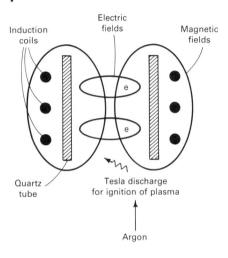

absorption could not match. The high-temperature and inert argon atmosphere of the plasma also greatly lessened the chemical and matrix interferences of flame emission techniques.

Principles of Operation

The ICP is an excitation source for atomic emission spectroscopy. It is an argon plasma operated at atmospheric pressure and sustained by inductive coupling to a radio frequency (RF) electromagnetic field. Argon gas flows axially through a quartz tube surrounded by three or four turns of an induction or work coil connected to an RF generator. The standard frequencies of operation are 27.12 MHz or, less commonly, 40.68 MHz, the frequencies allowed by the

Fig. 2 Structure of ICP plasma torch

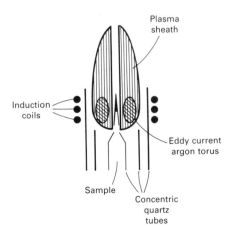

Federal Communications Commission for scientific and medical instrumentation. Power output is generally 1 to 5 kW.

The high-frequency current of up to 100 A flows in the water-cooled copper induction coils, generating oscillating magnetic fields whose lines of force are oriented axially inside the quartz tube and follow closed elliptical paths outside the tubes. If free electrons are present inside the tube, the induced magnetic fields cause the electrons in the gas to flow in oscillating closed annular paths inside the quartz tube space. This electron flow is termed the eddy current, and the electrons are accelerated by the time-varying magnetic field, causing collisions that result in further ionization of the argon gas and resistive heating. These electrical and magnetic fields responsible for the plasma are represented in Fig. 1.

The energy transmission in the plasma is similar to an electrical transformer in which the induction coils are the primary winding and the ionized gas is the secondary. Because the argon gas is initially neutral and nonconducting, the plasma must be initiated by seed electrons, usually generated by a brief tesla discharge. With RF power applied, the plasma ignites instantaneously, then is self-sustaining. The resulting plasma is a highly ionized gas with temperatures in the proximity of 10 000 K.

The plasma torch is not a single quartz tube but three concentric tubes (Fig. 2). The high temperatures of the plasma require protective isolation from the quartz walls. This is accomplished by a tangential flow of coolant gas between the two outer tubes at a rate of about 15 L/min. This isolates the plasma from the torch walls and stabilizes and centers the plasma. This is sometimes referred to as Reed's vortex stabilization technique. An auxiliary gas flow known as the plasma gas is sometimes used during ignition of the plasma or with organic solutions. The plasma gas flows between the two inner tubes at 1 to 5 L/min. A small-diameter central tube is used to introduce the analytical sample into the plasma, usually as a fine liquid aerosol transported by a carrier gas flow at approximately 1 L/min.

Careful design of the torch enables the sample carrier gas to penetrate the base of the plasma so that the sample passes through a channel in the plasma central axis. The hot plasma is then toroidal, and the sample experiences a cooler central channel, with temperatures of 5000 to 8000 K. During a transit time of 2 to 3 ms in this central channel, the sample aerosol is desolvated, volatilized, dissociated, atomized, and, to varying degrees, ionized; the free atoms and ions are electronically excited. Radia-

Fig. 3 Nomenclature of the zones of the inhomogeneous plasma

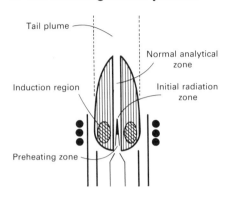

tion of varying wavelengths in the ultraviolet and visible portion of the spectrum is emitted on the nanosecond time scale as the electrons return to lower energy levels. The wavelength of this emitted radiation is characteristic of the atomic species present in the plasma and the intensity of the emitted radiation is proportional to the quantities of each atomic species present. Thus, analysis of the emitted radiation provides qualitative and quantitative elemental analysis.

The ICP has a distinct structure (Fig. 3), and a nomenclature system has been derived to describe the zones of the plasma (Ref 3). Low in the plasma, predominantly atomic emission is observed. This initial radiation zone extends approximately 0 to 10 mm (0 to 0.4 in.) above the induction coils. Vertically higher, another region exists where predominantly ionic emission is observed. This normal analytical zone, the region most commonly used for spectroscopic measurements, extends approximately 10 to 20 mm (0.4 to 0.8 in.) above the induction coils. Higher still, the tail plume of the plasma extends 30 to 100 mm (1.2 to 4 in.) above the induction coils, where atomic and some molecular emission will be observed.

In the excitation temperature profile in the plasma, the temperature is moderate (~5000 K) in the lower zone, reaches a maximum (~6000 to 8000 K) in the normal analytical zone, then drops rapidly to lower values (<5000 K) in the tail plume (Ref 4). Because a temperature gradient exists in the plasma, different elements will reach their maximum emission intensity at different heights above the induction coils according to differences in excitation energies of the different atoms and ions (Ref 5). Therefore, in simultaneous multielement analysis, a compromise viewing height must be selected.

Basic Atomic Theory

An atom consists of a nucleus composed of protons (positively charged particles) and neutrons (neutral particles). The nucleus is surrounded by electrons (shells of negative charge). In a neutral atom, the positive and negative charges are equal. The electrons are characterized by energy levels related to the radii of the shells from the atomic nucleus, and these energy levels are quantized or have discrete allowed values. If the atom absorbs energy from an external source, the electrons may be raised to higher energy levels or excited states. These allowed energy levels of the electrons have discrete values, depending on the atomic structure of the particular element. Energy of exactly the quanta of energy separating the states must be absorbed for these transitions to occur.

The electronically excited atom is inherently unstable. Within nanosecond time frames, the excess energy will be re-emitted as photons of light as the electrons return to their lower and more stable energy levels. The emitted photons are also characterized as quanta of energy, and the energy of the photons will exactly correspond to the differences in the quantized electronic energy levels in the atom. Because most atoms have many such possible electronic energy levels, many transitions are possible as the electrons absorb and re-emit the corresponding quanta of energy so that atoms of a single element may emit photons of several different energies. Thus, the photons that atoms in the excited state emit are distinctly characteristic of the type of atom, and the quantity of photons, or the light intensity, emitted will be proportional to the number of atoms in the excited state.

The energy, E, of an emitted photon is proportional to the frequency, v, of the corresponding light wave:

$$\Delta E = hv \qquad \text{(Eq 1)}$$

where h is Planck's constant. The frequency of the light is related to its wavelength, λ:

$$\lambda = \frac{c}{v} \qquad \text{(Eq 2)}$$

where c is the velocity of light. Therefore, the energy of the photon can be expressed in terms of its wavelength:

$$\Delta E = \frac{hc}{\lambda} \qquad \text{(Eq 3)}$$

The energies of the photons emitted by excited atoms in spectroscopic sources, such as the inductively coupled plasma, corre-

Fig. 4 Calibration curve for ICP analysis showing detection limits and concentration of analyte in sample

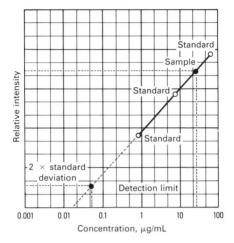

spond to wavelengths in the ultraviolet and visible region of the electromagnetic spectrum. A spectrometer is used to disperse such emitted radiation into its component wavelengths and to measure the intensity of each component.

Analytical Characteristics

The ICP as an analytical technique provides the capability of performing simultaneous multielement analysis for as many as 60 elements within 1 to 2 min; applicability to most elements in the periodic table; a large linear dynamic range (calibration curves that are linear over three to six orders of concentration magnitude), enabling determination of trace, minor, and major components in a single analysis; detection limits in the parts per billion (ng/mL) range for most elements; precision and accuracy on the order of 1%; and relative freedom from chemical interferences.

Detection limits for the ICP are determined by first establishing a calibration curve (plot of signal intensity at a given wavelength versus concentration for a series of standard solutions). The detection limit is calculated as the concentration that would correspond to an analytical signal equal to two (or three, according to choice of definition) times the standard deviation (noise) of repeated measurements of a blank at that wavelength (Fig. 4). This concentration is the lowest value measurable with any certainty as present in the sample. These detection limit values must be considered extreme limits, because they are determined under

ideal situations. Practical detection limits will be somewhat higher. Some sample preparation procedures, such as dissolution and dilution, necessarily degrade the achievable detection limits of the elements in the original sample material.

Precision and Accuracy. The precision of the ICP technique is usually determined by making several consecutive measurements, then calculating the standard deviation of the replicates as a percentage of the mean value. Major causes of signal fluctuations in the ICP are small variations in the RF power applied to the plasma and changes in the nebulization process. Precision can be increased to less than 1% by close regulation of the RF power (most new instrumentation accomplishes this to $\pm 0.1\%$), by improved nebulization techniques, or by use of an internal standard. Nebulization is stabilized by using a mass flow controller to regulate the nebulizer gas flow and by use of improved nebulizer designs, such as the high-pressure crossflow nebulizer. The accuracy of the ICP technique is essentially limited by the precision and by systematic errors, such as interference effects, but is usually shown to be comparable to the precision.

Interference effects, sometimes termed matrix effects or interelement effects, are any phenomenon that interferes with the intensity versus concentration relationship of the analyte due to the presence of other components in the sample. Interference effects may be classified as spectral, vaporization-atomization, and ionization. Some causes in the latter categories may be physical or chemical.

Spectral interferences, a basic problem in any emission technique, arise from the incomplete isolation of radiation emitted by the analyte from other radiation as detected by the instrument. The emission spectra of many elements are complex, and the high temperatures of the ICP allow transitions from many excited states of the atom. Thus, the wavelength of the emission line selected for analysis may coincide with that of a line emitted by another component of the sample (direct spectral overlap), or the two lines may be so close in wavelength that they partially overlap (partial or wing overlap). If these close or coincident lines are not resolved at the detector, spectral interference occurs, and the intensity reading is erroneously high for the true concentration level.

Spectral interferences are fundamental problems in emission spectroscopy and will still occur for the ICP. Although partial overlaps may be reduced by using high-resolution spectrometers, direct spectral overlap necessitates selection of alternative analytical wavelengths. The system computer, using interelement correction factors previously determined, can sometimes mathematically compensate for partial spectral overlap. The use of computer graphics in most new instrumentation assists detection and evaluation of spectral interferences. Using a graphics package, the immediate vicinity of an analytical line can be scanned and displayed on the computer terminal. Repetitive scans of analyte and suspected interferents at the wavelength of interest can be graphically overlaid and usually inspected for potential problems. Stray light in the spectrometer can also produce spectral interferences, but the use of holographic gratings and improved spectrometer design have greatly reduced this problem in new instruments.

Another type of spectral interference is continuum overlap caused by the electron recombination continuum that is part of the ICP background emission. This can be corrected by background subtraction from the analytical signal. However, one significant advantage of the ICP over flame and arc-spark techniques is the great reduction, due to high temperatures and inert argon atmosphere, in background emission arising from flame gases, combustion products, and molecular species.

Vaporization-atomization interference processes reduce the free atom population in the vapor phase and thus reduce the intensity of the emission signal. These can arise from various effects, such as the formation of refractory compounds, formation of metal oxides, or occlusion of analyte in refractory compounds formed by matrix components. These are major problems in flame spectrometry. The predominant absence of these interferences is a major advantage of ICP. The relatively long residence time of 2 to 3 ms combined with the high-temperature and argon atmosphere result in complete dissociation and atomization of the sample. Change in sample solution viscosity due to differing matrices or differing acid concentrations affect nebulization and alter the observed signal intensities. The chemical composition of the standards should be matched to those of the sample solutions to compensate for these interferences.

Ionization interferences result from a shift in the ionization equilibrium of the analyte or a modification of the excitation mechanisms due to the presence of other sample components, especially the easily ionized alkali elements. This is a common problem in flame systems. These effects are less severe but not absent (Ref 6) in the ICP, indicating the need to match standards and samples for optimum results.

Analytical Procedure

Inductively coupled plasma is, in practice, essentially a solution technique. Therefore, the sample to be analyzed must be prepared as a solution unless it originated as such (waters, and so on). The volume of solution required for analysis depends on the type of spectrometer to be used and the number of elements to be determined. For a polychromator, as many as 60 elements can be determined with less than 5 mL of solution, although replicate measurements or longer integration times will require correspondingly more solution. For a monochromator, determination of each element requires approximately 2 to 5 mL of solution; correspondingly more solution is required for replicates or longer integrations. Smaller sample volumes may be analyzed using such specialized techniques as discrete sample introduction.

Once the sample has been prepared for analysis, it is necessary to calibrate the instrument by using a set of standard solutions of known concentration for each element to be determined. More than one element may be combined in a standard solution for efficiency if no interference effects are observed for the combination. In principle, it is possible to establish a calibration curve of signal intensity versus concentration using only a blank and one moderate concentration standard. However, use of a blank and two or three standard solutions that encompass the range of the expected sample values is preferable.

Calibration curves for the ICP are generally linear from approximately 10 ppb (ng/mL) to 1000 ppm (μg/mL), although self-absorption effects will cause curvature of the calibration curves for the alkali elements and some alkaline earths at 100 ppm and greater. These calibration curves remain analytically useful if enough standards were used to define the curves sufficiently. The instrument must be calibrated at least once daily; high precision and accuracy require more frequent calibration. In some cases, the alternation of samples and standards throughout the analysis is recommended for optimum results.

The sample is now analyzed by recording the signal intensity at the analytical wavelength for each element. In some cases, background subtraction is applied to correct for continuum radiation or sloping baseline in the spectrum. In other cases, interelement correction factors are applied for partial spectral overlap. These corrections and the final calculation of concentration from the predetermined calibration curves (Fig. 4) are done by the system computer.

Each element will have its own unique

Fig. 5 Components in an ICP analytical system

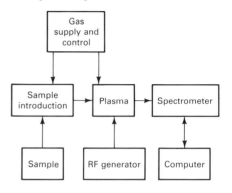

position of emission intensity maximum in the plasma. Further, each element will respond and optimize differently to changes in plasma parameters, such as power and gas flows. Nevertheless, an advantage of the ICP technique is that compromise conditions, which have become standard operating conditions in most analytical laboratories, exist that provide high-quality results for most elements simultaneously. The alkali elements, being the primary exception to this, may require special conditions for optimum results (Ref 6).

System Components

The principal components of an analytical ICP system are (1) the sample introduction system, (2) the ICP torch and argon gas supplies, (3) the RF generator and associated electronics, (4) the spectrometer, (5) the detection electronics and interface, and (6) the system computer with appropriate hardware and software. The relationships among these components is shown in Fig. 5.

Sample Introduction

Although, in principle, samples for the ICP may be liquid, gas, or solid, in practice the predominant form of sample introduction into the plasma is solution. The most common method of introducing the solution is a fine aerosol of solution droplets generated by a pneumatic nebulizer.

Several nebulizer designs are used for the ICP. The two most frequently used pneumatic types are the concentric (Ref 7, 8) and the crossflow (Ref 9). Both designs depend on a high-velocity argon gas flow, termed the nebulizer or carrier gas, to create a low-pressure zone into which sample solution is drawn or pumped through a capillary tube and subsequently atomized into fine droplets of varying sizes by the force of the flowing gas. The size distribution of the droplets generally ranges from 0.1 to 100 μm in diameter. Only 10-μm or smaller

Fig. 6 Concentric or Meinhard nebulizer for ICP sample introduction

(a) Side view. (b) End view

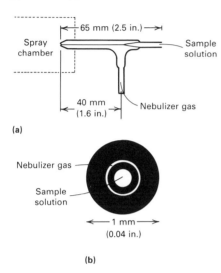

(a)

(b)

diameter droplets can be effectively desolvated, dissociated, atomized, and excited in the residence time of a few milliseconds in the plasma. Larger droplets contribute to excessively noisy analytical signals and cool the plasma by the introduction of too much water; they must be removed by passing the aerosol through a spray chamber after nebulization and before transport into the plasma by the carrier gas.

The concentric nebulizer, or Meinhard nebulizer, is illustrated in Fig. 6. It is constructed of borosilicate glass. Although variations are available, the basic model uses an argon flow of 1.0 L/min at a line pressure of approximately 275 kPa (40 psi) through an outer annulus as low pressure draws the sample solution through the inner capillary tube at approximately 1-2 mL/min. Even

Fig. 7 Crossflow nebulizer for ICP sample introduction

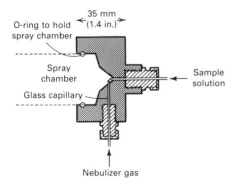

though these nebulizers perform well over extended times with dilute aqueous solutions, the fine dimensions of the sample capillary and the gas annulus make the nebulizer prone to blockage by small particles in the sample solution or the argon gas supply. Such blockages may stop sample and gas flows entirely or alter the flows, making detected signals erroneous in comparison to previous calibrations.

Another potential problem in using the concentric nebulizer involves sample solutions of high salts content. A phenomenon know as "salting up" may occur by which aspirated droplets deposit on the exterior of the nebulizer tip and evaporate, accumulating a dry deposit that partially blocks the tip and changes sample and gas flows. Many instruments incorporate means of reducing this problem by humidifying the nebulizer gas and washing the tip between samples. Stabilization of the analytical signal after beginning aspiration of a given solution requires approximately 20 s, known as the uptake delay. A 20-s delay is also required after stopping aspiration of the solution to clear the nebulizer and spray chamber.

The crossflow nebulizer is the other most common pneumatic nebulizer design (Fig. 7). The sample capillary and the nebulizer gas capillary are mounted at right angles. The mounting may be fixed or adjustable. The adjustable mounting allows for optimization, but may be difficult to maintain for long-term stability or reproducibility. The horizontal gas flow creates a low-pressure zone over the tip of the vertical sample tube, drawing up sample solution that is shattered into fine droplets. Crossflow nebulizers are generally less subject to salting up than concentric nebulizers. The gas flow and solution uptake rates are similar, as is analytical performance. A fixed crossflow MAK nebulizer operated at 1380 kPa (200 psi) back pressure provides improved precision (Ref 10).

Use of Peristaltic Pumps. Concentric nebulizers can initiate and sustain aspiration simply by the action of the nebulizer gas flow. This is true of some crossflow nebulizers. A peristaltic pump is commonly used to supply sample solution to either type of nebulizer. The peristaltic pump uses small-gage tubing to pass the solution along by a series of rollers on a rotating head. Typical rates are 0.8- to 2.0-L/min solution uptake and 2-Hz pump pulsation. Without use of the pump, the uptake rate of the sample solution will depend on the viscosity of the solution and the nebulizer gas flow rate. Changes in either will alter the amount of analyte reaching the plasma and can cause errors in the analytical measurement. The peristaltic pump will deliver solution to the nebulizer at

Fig. 8 Spray chamber for ICP sample introduction

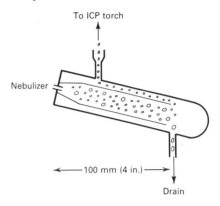

a fixed volume rate and eliminate some of these errors.

Spray Chambers. Once generated by the nebulizer, the aerosol passes into a spray chamber mounted just below the torch. The most common design is the Scott type illustrated in Fig. 8 (Ref 11). The spray chamber removes the larger droplets from the aerosol by forcing the aerosol to travel around a sharp bend in its path to the plasma. The larger, heavier droplets fall out or collide with the chamber walls and flow out of the drain in the bottom of the chamber. Because of the large distribution of droplet size, much of the aerosol flows out of the drain instead of upward into the plasma. The efficiency of a nebulizer is defined as the percent of aerosol reaching the plasma compared to the total solution uptake. For the pneumatic nebulizers described above, this efficiency is 1 to 5%.

Another design of spray chamber less frequently used causes the aerosol to strike a large impact bead placed in front of the nebulizer tip. This causes large droplets to fall out or break into smaller ones. Because pressure fluctuations in the spray chamber will change the observed analytical signal, a liquid trap must be provided in the drain line from the spray chamber and smooth flowing of the condensed liquid out of the chamber must be ensured.

Corrosion-resistant nebulizers and spray chambers are also available for analysis of solutions in concentrated acids, including hydrofluoric acid. Although most sample solutions for the ICP are prepared in aqueous or acidic mediums, such applications as extraction procedures in the sample preparation require the use of organic solvents. Introduction of organic solvents into the plasma can be accomplished with some modifications of the operating parameters, for example, operating at higher powers and use of the auxiliary plasma gas.

The ultrasonic nebulizer exhibits favorable performance characteristics, but is not commonly used (Ref 12). The sample solution is passed over the surface of an ultrasonic transducer. A fine aerosol of predominantly small droplets breaks away from the liquid surface. Nebulizer efficiency is high because of the small droplets, and the sample solution is delivered to the plasma at a high rate, providing the potential for lower detectivity. However, greater quantities of water are also delivered to the plasma, having a cooling effect. Therefore, it is necessary to desolvate the aerosol before delivery to the plasma by passing it through a heated spray chamber to evaporate the water, then through a cooled condensing chamber to remove the water molecules. Another problem is a memory effect (persistence of a signal after removing the sample) caused by some difficulty in effective cleaning of the nebulizer between solutions. These disadvantages and a relatively high price have hindered acceptance of this technique.

Alternate Designs. Other principal types of nebulizers include the Babington type, of which many variations have been developed. The sample solution flows freely over a small orifice through which the high velocity nebulizer gas flows, producing an aerosol. The major advantage is that the solution does not travel through a capillary, and higher salt or dissolved solids content can be nebulized without blocking or salting up. Babington-style nebulizers may also be used to nebulize slurries of solid samples.

Fritted disk nebulizers have also been developed in which the solution is pumped onto the surface of a fine glass frit, and nebulizer gas from the back side of the frit generates the aerosol (Ref 13, 14). High efficiencies are obtained due to small droplet size, allowing analysis of small solution volumes, but a memory effect due to difficulty of cleaning the frit between solutions is a problem.

Hydride-Generation Systems. The introduction of gas phase samples into the plasma would make nebulization unnecessary and allow 100% efficiency of sample introduction. However, most sample materials are not originally in the gas phase or not easily volatilized. One useful approach is the generation of gaseous hydrides of arsenic, antimony, bismuth, lead, tin, tellurium, and selenium from acidic solutions by the addition of sodium tetrahydroborate. This method was originally developed for atomic absorption spectroscopy to improve detection limits for these elements. A commercial hydride generator for ICP spectrometers is available.

Solid-Sample Analysis. The techniques for efficient, simple, and reliable introduction of solid samples into the plasma remain predominantly experimental. Methods currently under investigation include electrothermal vaporization, direct insertion into the plasma, laser ablation, and spark volatilization of conductive solids.

Electrothermal vaporization of analyte from the surface of resistively heated graphite tubes, graphite rods, and tantalum filaments is another technique that originated for atomic absorption spectroscopy, enabling analysis of μL volume samples and providing some of the best detection limits reported in analytical atomic spectroscopy due to the efficiency of sample utilization. This method has been adapted to ICP for volatilization of smaller volumes of liquid sample, for solid residues of solutions, and for solids (Ref 15, 16). In each case, the electrothermal device is used only to vaporize the sample material, which is then transported by the argon carrier gas into the plasma, where atomization and excitation occur.

The analytical signal produced is now a transient signal, because a pulse of analyte material is swept into the plasma. This transient signal must be integrated by the detection electronics and the total peak area used for the quantitative measurement. Determination of more than one element in the sample requires use of a polychromator spectrometer. The pulsed heating of the electrothermal device can also produce an undesirable pressure pulse in the plasma. This effect can be damped out by use of a long length of tubing to connect the vaporization chamber to the plasma torch or by proper vaporization chamber design, inlet configurations, and the use of smaller heating elements. Loss of material during transport over lengths of a few meters is not a problem if the volatilized material has condensed into a particulate aerosol before contact with any surfaces.

The direct sample insertion device (DSID) is another means of introducing solids or discrete small amounts of liquid samples into the ICP (Ref 17). A rod with a graphite electrode cup or a tantalum wire loop is attached to the upper end of a rod that is pneumatically raised up the central channel of the plasma torch. Preconcentration steps, such as electrodeposition, may be used in the sample preparation. By stopping the rod at a position just below the plasma, radiant heat can be used to dry or ash the sample before injection into the plasma for vaporization and excitation. Selective volatilization such as occurs in the dc arc methods may be observed. This may be advantageous or adverse, depending on the application (Ref 18).

Laser ablation has also been investigated as a means of solid sampling (Ref 19, 20). This method is a modification of the laser

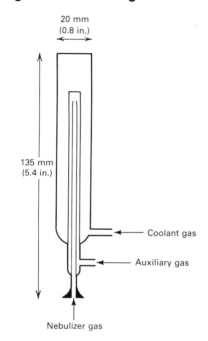

Fig. 9 ICP torch design

20 mm (0.8 in.)

135 mm (5.4 in.)

Coolant gas

Auxiliary gas

Nebulizer gas

microprobe, in which the spark source is replaced by the ICP. The pulse of focused laser energy samples only a small area on the sample surface. High temperatures achieved by the laser indicate that refractory components are also vaporized. As in the electrothermal case, the condensed aerosol can be transported through several meters of tubing to the plasma. The longer the tubing, the greater the delay in arrival of the analyte signal, and the more spread out is the observed signal peak. Integration of peak area during the transient signal is used. The sample can be rotated under repetitive laser pulses, and the resulting signal time-averaged.

Spark Volatilization. One commercially available solids sampling device is the conductive solids nebulizer (CSN). Disks or pellets of a conducting sample are rotated under the electrode of a spark, which generates a sample vapor that is subsequently swept into the plasma for analysis.

Torch and Gas Supplies

Favorable analytical performance of the ICP is critically dependent on the torch design and dimensions. Most importantly, the design must ensure that the nebulizer gas punches through the base of the plasma to carry the sample up a central channel. The design most often used is referred to as the Fassel torch (Fig. 9).

The Fassel torch consists of three concentric quartz tubes. Total torch length is approximately 135 mm (5.4 in.). The outermost tube diameter measures 20 mm (0.8 in.) and extends approximately 20 mm (0.8 in.) above the upper level of the two inner tubes. The annular gap between the outer tube and the middle tube is 1 mm (0.04 in.), and the diameter of the tip of the inner tube is 1.5 mm (0.06 in.). The coolant gas, which is the primary plasma supply, flows tangentially in the annular gap between the outer and middle tubes at 10 to 20 L/min. An auxiliary gas flowing the gap between the middle and inner tubes is used at approximately 1 L/min during ignition of the plasma to hold the plasma up off the ends of the inner tubes, or it is used continuously in the case of nebulizing organic solvents. The nebulizer gas flows up the central tube at approximately 1 L/min, carrying the sample material into the plasma. The plasma operating with this torch design at usual power levels does not tolerate injection of air and will usually extinguish if the nebulizer operates in air for more than a few seconds during changes of solutions. Use of a quartz bonnet greatly reduces arcing between the induction coils and the outer surface of the torch.

During operation of the plasma, the central tube tip will gradually deteriorate, degrading analytical performance. The first signs of usage of a torch will include a brownish coloration on the inside of the central tube at the tip and extending a few millimeters downward on the inside and a whitish coloration of the middle tube. These effects do not necessarily impair analytical performance, but the continued nebulization of sample solutions may cause a gradual accumulation of deposit at the tip of the central tube that may impede the gas flows and alter the analytical signals being measured if not totally prevent sample introduction into the plasma. Periodic cleaning of the torch in nitric acid or aqua regia is recommended for optimum results and service life.

Stability of the gas flows in the torch is also critical for precision of analytical measurements. Especially important is the flow rate of the nebulizer gas, which controls the amount of analyte introduced into the plasma. The use of mass flow controllers to regulate the gas flows provides the most reliable performance of the system. Low-flow, low-power torches (Minitorches) for the ICP to reduce operating costs by consuming less argon are also available (Ref 21). These devices, which may operate with only a few liters per minute total argon flow, require less power, and solid-state RF generators providing approximately 1 kW of power are sufficient.

Radio-Frequency

The RF generator supplies the high-frequency alternating current in the induction coil that initiates and sustains the inductive coupling of energy into the plasma. The current of up to 100 A can have frequencies of 1 to 60 MHz or higher (Ref 22), but commonly available instrumentation operates at 27.12 or 40.68 MHz. The input or forward power to the plasma generally varies from 1 to 5 kW, with most analytical argon plasmas operating near 1 kW. The induction coil consists of two to five turns with an inside diameter of approximately 25 mm (1 in.). The copper coils are water cooled to dissipate excess heat.

The free-running generator that allows the frequency of the oscillating current to vary with plasma impedance and the crystal-controlled generator that uses a piezoelectric crystal to regulate a constant frequency of the current are the two major types available. The latter version is more common in modern instrumentation. The generator may provide the current with vacuum tube or solid-state electronics using a positive feedback from the output to the input.

Stability of the frequency is less critical than stability of the power to the plasma. Small changes in the power delivered to the plasma significantly alter the observed emission intensities. These changes are element dependent. Therefore, optimum analytical results require power regulation of ±0.05%. Generators on commercial analytical systems may be low power (less than 2 kW) or high power (up to 5 kW). Signal intensities increase with power level until concomitant increases in background intensity overcome the advantage. The higher powers are required when organic solutions are nebulized into the plasmas and for operating with mixed gas or diatomic gas plasmas, such as argon, helium, and nitrogen mixtures, or pure nitrogen (Ref 23-26). These mixed gas plasmas are currently being evaluated for improved precision and sensitivity in analysis.

Detection Instrumentation

Inductively coupled plasma atomic emission spectrometry is inherently a multielement technique, and two types of spectrometer configurations are typically used to detect the atomic emission of interest: polychromators for simultaneous multielement analysis and monochromators for sequential multielement analysis.

The polychromator, or direct-reading spectrometer, has been in use in analytical atomic spectroscopy for many years in conjunction with arc and spark excitation

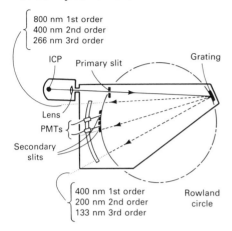

Fig. 10 Polychromator or direct-reader spectrometer for ICP

sources. It consists of a focusing lens, a primary or entrance slit, a concave diffraction grating to disperse the incident light into component wavelengths, secondary or exit slits to isolate the resolved spectral lines, and individual electronic detection channels to detect and measure the intensity of those spectral lines. The spectrometer is designed following the principles of the Paschen-Runge design (Fig. 10).

The primary slit, diffraction grating, and secondary slits are mounted on the Rowland circle. Its diameter of typically 1 m is equal to the radius of curvature of the concave grating. The diffracted spectral lines then focus on the Rowland circle, and the secondary slits are positioned according to the wavelengths to be detected. The spectrometer components are mounted in a light-tight box that must be carefully temperature controlled for instrument stability. For vacuum spectrometers, the box must be airtight as well.

The usual range of wavelength coverage for polychromators is 200 to 800 nm. Vacuum or inert gas-purged spectrometers are required to detect analytical wavelengths from 170 to 200 nm (Ref 27). Important lines in this region include phosphorus (178.2 nm), sulfur (180.7 nm), and carbon (193.1 nm). The diffraction grating that disperses the light is a mirror surface finely lined with closely spaced parallel grooves, for example, 1200 grooves per millimeter. The finer the ruling spacing of the grating, the higher its light-dispersing ability or resolution.

Gratings may be replicas of mechanically ruled master gratings or may be holographically produced by photographic processes and laser light. Holographic gratings can be produced less expensively, with fewer imperfections producing spurious spectral lines, and larger for higher resolution. Advantages of replica gratings include the ability to "blaze" the angle of the grooves on the grating for optimum efficiency at certain wavelengths and the ability to use higher orders of spectral lines effectively for wider wavelength coverage.

The lens, usually quartz, is mounted between the ICP source and the spectrometer primary slit and focuses the emitted radiation onto the slit. In a vacuum spectrometer, the lens will also be part of the airtight seal of the spectrometer box, and the optical path between the lens and the plasma must also be purged.

Most polychromator designs also provide a quartz refractor plate, sometimes termed a spectrum shifter, situated just behind the primary or entrance slit. Slight rotation of this refractory plate displaces the incident beam and enables scanning of the spectrum at each analytical wavelength over a small range of approximately 1 nm. This option is used to investigate the spectral vicinity of each line for performing background corrections or identifying spectral interferences.

The secondary slits that isolate the spectral lines may be permanently fixed on a single metal mask along the Rowland circle or may be individual, adjustable assemblies. The space required for each slit and associated electronics limits the number of spectral lines that can be simultaneously detected; 20 to 60 lines are usually observed. A spectral bandpass of approximately 0.05 nm will typically pass through the 50-μm width of the secondary slit. This light is then focused, sometimes using a small secondary mirror, onto the cathode of a photomultiplier tube (PMT). The PMT is an excellent detector as the light-measuring device for the ICP spectrometer, because it can provide linear response over a light intensity range as great as 10^8. The PMT generates a current proportional to light intensity. This photocurrent is converted into a voltage, amplified, and recorded over preselected integration times by the system computer for data handling of the analytical information.

The principal advantage of the polychromator configuration is the simultaneous detection of up to 60 analytical wavelengths within 1 min. This is useful in routine determinations of large numbers of samples having similar compositions, as in geological, metallurgical, or some environmental and biological applications. Addition of an auxiliary monochromator that can operate simultaneously with the polychromator but at any preselected wavelength often alleviates the lack of flexibility in changing or adding analytical wavelengths. The electronics of the monochromator detector are coupled with the main spectrometer so that the

Fig. 11 Monochromator of Czerny-Turner design for ICP

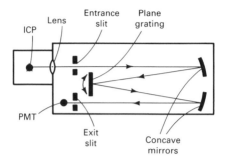

monochromator provides one channel of variable wavelength in combination with the several fixed-wavelength channels of the polychromator. This is sometimes referred to as the $n + 1$ channel.

The scanning monochromator is the alternate major spectrometer configuration for detecting ICP radiation. The Czerny-Turner optical design is the most common (Fig. 11). The monochromator consists of a focusing lens, a concave mirror to collimate the incident light onto a plane grating, a second concave mirror to focus the dispersed light onto the secondary slit, and a photomultiplier detector with associated electronics. Only a single wavelength can be detected at a time, and wavelength selection at the detector is accomplished by rotating the plane grating by a computer-controlled stepper motor. In sequential multielement analysis, the grating is driven at a fast slew rate to a position near each of the preselected analytical wavelengths. The grating drive must then scan more slowly across the estimated position of the desired wavelength, recording integrated light intensities at each step—for example, nine steps across a 0.05-nm scan.

Because of unavoidable mechanical and thermal instabilities in the instrument, a peak-seeking routine must be performed at each analytical wavelength to ensure that the analytical measurement is made at the proper wavelength. The peak is located by fitting the intensities recorded during the stepwise scan of the estimated position of the analytical wavelength to a mathematical model of spectral line. The peak intensity is calculated as the maximum value in the mathematically fitted curve through the three to five highest measurements in the scan. Background intensities can be measured on either side of the peak for simple background correction by subtraction from the peak intensity.

An alternative to the Czerny-Turner design is a scanning monochromator that uses a fixed grating and a focal curve along which a

mask of equally spaced secondary slits is placed. The photodetector moves behind this mask on a computer-controlled carriage. Selection of a given wavelength involves rapid movement of the carriage to the secondary slit closest to the selected wavelength on the focal curve, and fine tuning of the selection is accomplished by precise and small movement of the primary slit. This provides rapid and precise wavelength selection.

The scanning monochromator offers freedom of choice in analytical wavelengths for each analysis. This is valuable in research and development or in an analytical laboratory where the elements to be determined and the sample types are variable, requiring a high level of flexibility. The major disadvantage of this type of spectrometer is the increased amount of time necessary for each analysis. Because each measurement at each wavelength will require approximately 20 s or longer, determination of several elements will require several minutes and more sample. Therefore, the choice between instrument configurations involves a compromise between flexibility and speed. Some instrument manufacturers offer a combination of simultaneous and sequential spectrometers in one system.

Alternate Designs. One approach to detecting all the wavelengths of the emitted radiation simultaneously involves replacing the photomultiplier tubes of conventional spectrometers with photodiode arrays (PDA) (Ref 28). PDA is a linear array of usually 1024 small, individual light-sensing detectors. The diodes are set on 25-μm centers, and the total array is only 25 mm (1 in.) long. Light intensity on each diode is measured in sequence during a single scan of the array, providing 1024 spectral resolution elements.

Depending on the compromise between resolution and spectral range, a spectral window of approximately 20 nm can be observed at moderate resolution on one PDA, and all the emission lines and spectral background simultaneously monitored. One arrangement is to use a single PDA at the exit plane of a monochromator to observe such a spectral window; the wavelengths under observation are then selectable by rotating the grating. Another arrangement is to mount several PDAs along the focal curve of a polychromator to cover several such spectral windows. However, use of the PDA involves a loss of sensitivity by a factor of 10 compared to PMTs used as the light detectors.

Another approach to simultaneous detection of wavelengths of the emitted radiation is the use of Fourier transform spectrometers (FTS) as the detection instrumentation (Ref 29-37). Such spectrometers are based on the

Fig. 12 Basic design of a Fourier transform spectrometer

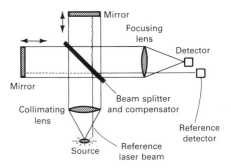

principles of the Michelson interferometer illustrated in Fig. 12 (Ref 38, 39). Light from the source enters the circular spectrometer aperture, is collimated by a lens, and divided into two beams by a beam splitter. The two beams travel in the two arms of the interferometer, being reflected by the mirrors back onto the beam splitter, where they recombine and are focused onto a single detector. If one or both of the mirrors move while the light is being detected, a path difference exists in the two arms, and the recombined beams will interfere constructively or destructively according to the path difference and the wavelengths of the light. The effect is a changing signal at the detector termed an interferogram.

An associated computer must perform a mathematical Fourier transform to convert the observed interferogram of signal versus mirror movement into an analytically useful spectrum of intensity versus wavelength. The resolution of the spectrum is determined by the extent of mirror movement in the interferometer. Use of FTS as a detection system for the ICP provides simultaneous and comprehensive detection for an entire selected spectral region. Although Fourier transform spectroscopy has found widespread application in infrared spectroscopy, this approach is experimental for atomic spectroscopy in the ultraviolet and visible light wavelength range, and no commercial instrumentation is yet available.

Detection Electronics and Interface

The wavelengths and intensities of the light emitted by the atoms and ions in the plasma contain the analytical information. Wavelength separation and selection take place in the spectrometer. The light intensity at the analytical wavelengths is detected and measured by converting photon flux at the detector into electrical signals the system computer can acquire and process. The PMT

detector used in most spectrometer configurations responds to photons at the cathode to produce an electrical current at the anode of approximately 10^{-9} to 10^{-6} A. Because the photon flux at the detector is discrete and statistical, measuring the current over an integration time of 5 to 20 s and storing the charge on a microfarad capacitor enhance precision.

At the end of the integration period, an analog-to-digital converter (ADC) reads and digitizes the charge on the capacitor. The digital value is now transferred to the computer for data management. In the polychromator, all the wavelength channels integrate their signals simultaneously. At the end of the integration period, the ADC reads the integrators in sequence. In the monochromator, integration of signal followed by conversion to the digital value is accomplished in sequence at each selected wavelength.

System Computer

A dedicated system computer is required for an analytical ICP to control and monitor instrument functions and to process, store, and output analytical data. A minicomputer with floppy or removable hard disks is usually used. The analytical software is most often written in Fortran or Basic, and source codes are typically provided on request to enable modification of the programs for specific applications. The instrument control function drivers are usually written in assembly or machine language.

Analytical programs should include:

- An instrument configuration program that stores such information as the individual channel numbers, corresponding wavelengths and elements, and predefined detection limits
- Individual task file programs tailored to specific analytical jobs that include the elements to be determined, wavelengths to be used, signal integration times for each wavelength, concentrations of the standards solutions to determine the calibration curves, and interelement or interference corrections to be made on the analytical data
- A calibration program that establishes calibration curves for concentration determinations using intensities measured from a set of two or more standard solutions of known concentration for each element to be determined and calculates detection limits from this data
- A background-correction option that allows for subtraction of background emission intensity from the peak of the analytical line
- The analysis routine in which intensities of selected wavelengths are measured

over the predefined integration times and compared to the calibration curves to determine concentrations of elements in the sample

- Data storage and reporting of analytical results in a variety of formats

A useful option is the graphic display of the spectra obtained by the stepwise scanning of the monochromator through a wavelength window or the scanning of the refractor plate of the polychromator across the analytical line. This provides visual display of the background structure and facilitates identification of interelement interferences.

New Developments

The ICP, long recognized as an efficient means of vaporizing, atomizing, and ionizing sample materials, may be used as the ion source for traditional quadrapole inductively coupled plasma mass spectrometry (ICP-MS) (Ref 40-42). Development of this technique began in 1980, and the instrumentation was commercially available in 1983.

The ICP source is mounted horizontally, and the sample is introduced into the plasma as a solution by standard ICP nebulization processes. Inductively coupled plasma mass spectrometry is the only method that allows continuous introduction of solutions into a mass spectrometer. This is a simple means of sample introduction for mass spectroscopy, with subsequent improvements in speed of analysis and the ability to apply modern automation procedures for sample handling. The mass spectrum can be recorded in approximately 1 min, enabling analysis of samples at a much faster rate than conventional mass spectrometric techniques. Other sample-introduction techniques under development or currently available for ICP-MS include hydride generation, electrothermal vaporization, and laser ablation.

The free ions produced in the plasma are then admitted into the mass spectrometer through a 1-mm (0.04-in.) diam water-cooled orifice. The technological advance that made ICP-MS possible was the design of the interface between the atmospheric pressure plasma and the vacuum spectrometer. This is accomplished by a two-stage pumping process; the first differentially pumped stage operates at approximately 130 Pa (1 torr), and the second high-vacuum stage is sustained at 13 mPa (10^{-4} torr) by a high-speed cryogenic pump. The quadrapole mass filter allows the mass range of 3 to 300 to be scanned in under 1 s with high resolution and sensitivity. The ions are detected by a high-gain single-channel electron multiplier using fast counting techniques. Final data management is performed

Fig. 13 Inductively coupled plasma mass spectrometry instrumentation

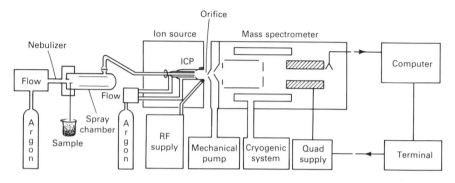

by an associated computer system. The instrumentation is shown in Fig. 13.

Inductively coupled plasma mass spectrometry complements the optical spectroscopy techniques originally developed for the ICP. Inductively coupled plasma mass spectrometry provides increased sensitivity, with detection limits in the subparts per billion range for most elements. Conversion of analytical information into the mass spectral domain simplifies or eliminates many spectral overlap and interference problems observed in the optical spectral domain. This is particularly useful in the analysis of such samples as rare earths and actinides that produce complex optical spectra. Some minor mass interferences are observed, particularly in the low to mid mass range, due to doubly charged ions, metal oxide ions, and molecular fragments that are originally present in the plasma or formed at the orifice and interface.

Natural applications of the ICP-MS technique include isotope ratio measurements and isotope dilution analysis. In the latter case, an enriched stable isotope of the ele-

Fig. 14 Direct-current plasma or plasmajet

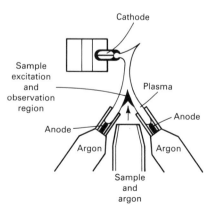

ment to be determined is added to the sample, providing an absolute internal standard; the original concentration can be determined from the altered isotope ratio relative to the natural abundance of the element. Multielement isotope dilution can be performed by adding stable isotope mixtures to the samples.

Direct Current Plasma

A spectroscopic technique similar to the ICP is direct-current plasma (DCP), also called the plasmajet (Ref 43). This is a three-electrode plasma source, in which the plasmajet is formed between two spectrographic carbon anodes and a tungsten cathode arranged in an inverted Y configuration (Fig. 14). The plasma requires approximately 1 kW and operates at an argon consumption of approximately 8 L/min: 2 L/min for the cathode, 1 L/min for each of the anodes, and 4 L/min for the nebulizer. A dc power supply provides a regulated current of approximately 7 A. The plasma is ignited by contacting the three electrodes. The excitation temperature of the plasma is estimated at 6000 K, which is similar to the ICP. An argon carrier gas introduces the sample into the region under the two arms of the plasmajet as a solution aerosol at an uptake rate of 1 to 2 mL/min. The sample excitation and spectroscopic observation region is just below the crook of the Y where the plasma continuum emission is minimal.

The DCP can detect essentially the same set of 60 to 70 elements detected by the ICP. Analytical performance of the plasmajet results in detection limits of parts per million to parts per billion in some cases, with precision of 1 to 4%. The dynamic range of the plasmajet is more limited than the ICP, with analytical curves that are linear over three orders of magnitude for most elements. Matrix interference effects may be a problem, especially for alkali and alkaline earth

elements as the interferent, and the matching of standards and samples is recommended in these cases. This plasma exhibits good stability in the presence of different solvents, including high dissolved solids, high acid concentrations, and organic solvents.

The plasma jet is usually combined with an echelle grating spectrometer (Fig. 15). An echelle grating is a coarsely ruled grating (typically 79 grooves per millimeter) used at high angles of incidence (Ref 44). Echelle gratings are typically used at spectral orders of 40 to 120. When used with an auxiliary dispersing element, such as a prism, the echelle grating can provide resolution power of an order of magnitude greater than a conventional grating spectrometer within a compact focal length instrument. Cross dispersion by the grating and the prism achieves resolution of the spectrum in two dimensions at the focal plane of the spectrometer. Spectral orders are separated in one direction, and wavelengths within an order are dispersed in the other direction.

An optical cassette or mask enables simultaneous detection of approximately 20 elements (Fig. 16). This optical mask is drilled to allow light from the selected positions of the two-dimensional wavelength array to pass through to fixed-position photomultiplier detectors. The electric signal may be processed in a direct-read or time-integrate mode. A simple change of cassettes or masks allows the detection of an alternate set of elements. The spectrometer may be operated in a sequential mode by positioning a single exit slit in the focal plane. Some instruments also allow the use of a photographic attachment for qualitative analysis of the entire spectrum. The DCP has provided good-quality multielement analysis at a lower instrumentation price than the ICP and has found application, for example, in metallurgy, oil and photography industries, and biological and environmental analysis.

Fig. 15 Echelle spectrometer design for direct-current plasma

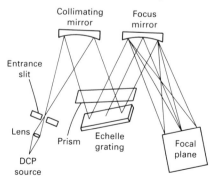

Fig. 16 Optical mask and photodetectors for echelle spectrometer

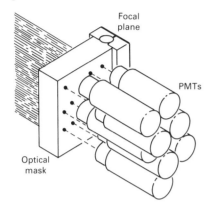

Applications

Example 1: Analysis of Silver Scrap Metal. The metal content in silver scrap metal used in the refining industry was analyzed using an ICP polychromator. The elements determined included gold, platinum, nickel, iron, chromium, zinc, and copper. The weighed solid sample (0.1 g) was dissolved in 20 mL 1:1 nitric acid and water by reflux heating 30 to 45 min. Concentrated hydrochloric acid (30 mL) was then added, and the solution again heated 30 to 45 min. The solution was then diluted to a known volume (200 mL). Sample preparation time totaled approximately 2 h. Reference standards were dilutions of 1-, 10-, 100-, and 1000-ppm (μg/mL) solutions of the desired elements prepared from high-purity stock standard solutions.

Sample analysis involved:

1. Calibration of the spectrometer by measuring the emission intensities of each of the standard solutions and a blank for each of the desired elements. Calibration curves were calculated using a linear least squares program and stored in the computer
2. Computer recording and storage of emission intensities of each of the desired elements in each sample solution. Integration times for each measurement were set at 10 s, and measurements were made in triplicate
3. Computer calculation of elemental concentrations from recorded emission intensities and weight and dilution factors and printing of analytical results, including concentration of each element for each integration, average concentration of each element for triplicate, and standard deviation of concentrations for triplicate

4. Repeat analysis for copper because concentration exceeded the upper limit of the calibration curves. Sample solutions were diluted by a factor of 100 and reanalyzed for copper according to steps 2 and 3
5. Analysis time for 12 samples of 4 h, including sample preparation

Example 2: Analysis of Plant Tissues. Agricultural samples of plant tissues were analyzed using an ICP sequential monochromator. The elements determined included calcium, magnesium, aluminum, cadmium, chromium, lead, zinc, iron, copper, and manganese. Weighed portions (2 g) of plant tissue were allowed to stand overnight in nitric acid. Perchloric acid was added, and the mixture slowly heated to near dryness. Because the addition of perchloric acid can lead to explosions, standard operating procedures for safety should be followed. When complete digestion was apparent, nitric acid was again added, and slow heating to near dryness repeated. The sample solution was then diluted to a known volume (200 mL). An NBS certified reference material was included to provide a check on accuracy of the analytical method. Reference standards were dilutions of 1-, 10-, and 1000-ppm (μg/mL) solutions of the desired elements prepared from high-purity stock standard solutions.

Spectral scans of the analytical wavelengths of each element to be determined were performed in the presence of the 10- and 1000-ppm standard solutions of each of the other elements. The contribution of the matrix elements to the signal intensities of the other analytes were calculated by the computer, and the appropriate interelement correction factors were calculated and stored by the computer. Programming time totaled approximately 2 h.

Sample analysis involved:

1. Entering the analytical wavelengths and desired integration period to be used in this analysis into the computer control program of the spectrometer
2. Calibration of the spectrometer by measuring the emission intensities of each of the standard solutions and a blank for each of the desired elements. Calibration curves were calculated and stored by the computer using a linear least squares program
3. Measuring emission intensities of each of the desired elements in each sample solution in sequence by the scanning monochromator. Measurements at each wavelength were made in triplicate
4. Computerized interelement corrections from stored data, calculation of elemental concentrations from recorded emis-

sion intensities and weight and dilution factors, and printing of analytical results as average concentration of each element from triplicate and standard deviation of concentration from triplicate
5. Analysis time for six samples of 4 to 5 h after overnight digestion

Example 3: Analysis of Natural Waters. Natural waters were analyzed for possible pollution using an ICP vacuum polychromator. The elements determined included sulfur, phosphorus, selenium, and arsenic. Natural water samples were collected from lakes and streams. These samples were filtered, acidified with 2 to 5 mL concentrated mineral acid per liter of sample to attain a pH less than 2.0, then refrigerated in polyethylene bottles. Reference standards were dilutions of 1- and 100-ppm (μg/mL) solutions of the desired elements prepared from high-purity stock standard solutions.

Sample analysis involved:

1. Use of a vacuum spectrometer to detect the low UV analytical lines of sulfur, phosphorus, selenium, and arsenic
2. Calibration of the spectrometer by measuring the emission intensities of each of the standard solutions and a blank for each of the desired elements. Calibration curves are calculated using a linear least squares program and stored by the computer
3. Analysis of water samples without further treatment. Emission intensities of each of the desired elements in each sample solution were recorded and stored by the computer. Measurements were made in duplicate
4. Computer calculation of elemental concentrations from the recorded emission intensities and printing of analytical results
5. No detection of arsenic or selenium. Analysis was repeated for these elements using a hydride generation system to increase sensitivity
6. Analysis time for 12 samples of 3 to 4 h

REFERENCES

1. S. Greenfield, I.L. Jones, and C.T. Berry, *Analyst*, Vol 89, 1964, p 713
2. R.H. Wendt and V.A. Fassel, *Anal. Chem.*, Vol 37, 1965, p 920
3. S.R. Koirtyohann, J.S. Jones, and D.A. Yates, *Anal. Chem.*, Vol 52, 1980, p 1965
4. L.M. Faires, B.A. Palmer, R. Engleman, and T.M. Niemczyk, *Spectrochim. Acta*, Vol 39B, 1984, p 819
5. M.W. Blades, G. Horlick, *Spectrochim. Acta*, Vol 36B, 1981, p 861
6. L.M. Faires, T.M. Bieniewski, C.T.

Apel, and T.M. Niemczyk, *Appl. Spectrosc.*, Vol 37, 1983, p 558

7. J.E. Meinhard, *ICP Info. Newslet.*, Vol 2 (No. 5), 1976, p 163

8. J.E. Meinhard, in *Applications of Plasma Emission Spectrochemistry*, R.M. Barnes, Ed., Heyden and Sons, 1979

9. S.E. Valente and W.G. Schrenk, *Appl. Spectrosc.*, Vol 24, 1970, p 197

10. H. Anderson, H. Kaiser, B. Meddings, in *Developments in Atomic Plasma Spectrochemical Analysis*, R.M. Barnes, Ed., Heyden and Sons, 1981

11. R.H. Scott, V.A. Fassel, R.N. Kniseley and D.E. Nixon, *Anal. Chem.*, Vol 46, 1974, p 76

12. K.W. Olson, W.J. Haas, and V.A. Fassel, *Anal. Chem.*, Vol 49, 1977, p 632

13. C.T. Apel, T.M. Bieniewski, L.E. Cox, and D.W. Steinhaus, Report LA-6751-MS, Los Alamos National Laboratory, 1977

14. R.R. Layman and F.E. Lichte, *Anal. Chem.*, Vol 54, 1982, p 638

15. M.W. Tikkanen and T.M. Niemczyk, *Anal. Chem.*, Vol 56, 1984, p 1997

16. D.R. Hull and G. Horlick, *Spectrochim. Acta*, Vol 39B, 1984, p 843

17. E.D. Salin and G. Horlick, *Anal. Chem.*, Vol 51, 1979, p 2284

18. A.G. Page, S.V. Godbole, K.H. Madraswala, M.J. Kulkarni, V.S. Mallapurkar, and B.D. Joshi, *Spectrochim. Acta*, Vol 39B, 1984, p 551

19. J.W. Carr and G. Horlick, *Spectrochim. Acta*, Vol 37B, 1982, p 1

20. T. Ishizuka and W. Uwamino, *Spectrochim. Acta*, Vol 38B, 1983, p 519

21. R.N. Savage and G.M Hieftje, *Anal. Chem.*, Vol 51, 1980, p 408

22. B. Capelle, J.M. Mermet, and J. Robin, *Appl. Spectrosc.*, Vol 36, 1982, p 102

23. S. Greenfield and D.T. Burns, *Anal. Chim. Acta*, Vol 113, 1980, p 205

24. A. Montaser, V.A. Fassel, and J. Zalewski, *Appl. Spectrosc.*, Vol 35, 1981, p 292

25. M.H. Abdallah and J.M. Mermet, *J. Quant. Spectrosc. Radiat. Trans.*, Vol 19, 1978, p 83

26. R.M. Barnes, *ICP Info. Newslet.*, Vol 8 (No. 3), 1982, p 171

27. T. Hayakawa, F. Kikui, and S. Ikede, *Spectrochim. Acta*, Vol 37B, 1982, p 1069

28. G. Horlick, *Appl. Spectrosc.*, Vol 30, 1976, p 113

29. G. Horlick, R.H. Hall, and W.K. Yuen, *Fourier Transform Infrared Spectroscopy*, Vol 3, Academic Press, 1982, p 37-81

30. L.M. Faires, B.A. Palmer, R. Engleman, and T.M. Niemczyk, *Proceedings of the Los Alamos Conference on Optics*, SPIE Vol 380, 1983, p 396-401

31. L.M. Faires, B.A. Palmer, R. Engleman, and T.M. Niemczyk, *Spectrochim. Acta*, Vol 39B, 1984, p 819

32. L.M. Faires, B.A. Palmer, and J.W. Brault, *Spectrochim. Acta*, Vol 40B, 1985, p 135

33. L.M. Faires, B.A. Palmer, R. Engleman, and T.M Niemczyk, *Spectrochim. Acta*, Vol 40B, 1985, p 545

34. E.A. Stubley and G. Horlick, *Appl. Spectrosc.*, Vol 39, 1985, p 805

35. E.A. Stubley and G. Horlick, *Appl. Spectrosc.*, Vol 39, 1985, p 811

36. L.M. Faires, *Spectrochim. Acta*, Vol 40B, 1985

37. L.M. Faires, *Anal. Chem.*, Vol 58, 1986

38. G. Horlick, *Appl. Spectrosc.*, Vol 22, 1968, p 617

39. E.A. Stubley and G. Horlick, *Appl. Spectrosc.*, Vol 39, 1985, p 800

40. R.S. Houk, V.A. Fassel, G.D. Flesch, H.J. Svec, A.L. Gray, and C.E. Taylor, *Anal. Chem.*, Vol 52, 1980, p 2283

41. A.R. Date and A.L. Gray, *Analyst*, Vol 106, 1981, p 1255

42. A.R. Date and A.L. Gray, *Analyst*, Vol 108, 1983, p 1033

43. R.J. Decker, *Spectrochim. Acta*, Vol 35B, 1980, p 19

44. P.N. Keliher and C.C. Wohlers, *Anal. Chem.*, Vol 48, 1976, p 333A

SELECTED REFERENCES

- R.M. Barnes, *CRC Crit. Rev. Anal. Chem.*, 1978, p 203
- P.W.J.M. Boumans, *Optica Pura Aplicada*, Vol 11, 1978, p 143
- P.W.J.M. Boumans, *Spectrochim. Acta*, Vol 35B, 1980, p 57
- V.A. Fassel and R.N. Kniseley, *Anal. Chem.*, Vol 46, 1974, p 1110A, 1155A
- V.A. Fassel, *Pure Appl. Chem.*, Vol 49, 1977, p 1533
- V.A. Fassel, *Science*, Vol 202, 1978, p 183
- S. Greenfield, *Analyst*, Vol 105, 1980, p 1032
- J.P. Robin, *Prog. Anal. At. Spectrosc.*, Vol 5, 1982, p 79
- M. Thompson and J.N. Walsh, *A Handbook of Inductively Coupled Plasma Spectrometry*, Blackie and Son, 1983

Atomic Absorption Spectrometry

Darryl D. Siemer, Westinghouse Idaho Nuclear Company

General Use

- Quantitative analyses of approximately 70 elements

Examples of Applications

- Trace impurities in alloys and process reagents
- Water analysis
- Direct air sampling/analysis
- Direct solids analysis of ores and finished metals

Samples

- *Form*: Solids, solutions, and gaseous (mercury)
- *Size*: Depends on technique used—from a milligram (solids by graphite furnace atomic absorption spectrometry) to 10 mL of solution for conventional flame work
- *Preparation*: Depends on the type of atomizer used; usually a solution must be prepared

Limitations

- Detection limits range from subparts per billion to parts per million
- Cannot analyze directly for noble gases, halogens, sulfur, carbon, or nitrogen

- Poorer sensitivity for refractory oxide or carbide-forming elements than plasma atomic emission spectrometry
- Basically a single-element technique

Estimated Analysis Time

- Highly variable, depending on the type of atomizer and technique used
- Sample dissolution may take 4 to 8 h or as little as 5 min
- Typical analysis times range from approximately 1 min (flames) to several minutes (furnaces)

Capabilities of Related Techniques

- *Inductively coupled plasma atomic emission spectrometry and direct current plasma atomic emission spectrometry* are simultaneous multielement techniques with a wider dynamic analytical range and sensitivities complementing those of atomic absorption spectrometry. They cost considerably more to set up and require more expert attention to potential matrix interference (spectral) problems

Introduction

Atomic absorption spectrometry (AAS) originated in the 1850s and 1860s (Ref 1, 2). It was recognized that the positions (wavelengths) of the dark lines in the solar spectrum matched those of many of the bright (emission) lines seen in laboratory flames "salted" with pure compounds. It was deduced that the dark lines were caused by the extremely selective absorption of the bright continuum radiation emitted from the inner regions of the sun by free atoms in the cooler, less dense upper regions of the solar atmosphere. The qualitative spectral analysis technique that resulted from this research remains the most important tool for astrophysical research. However, as a routine chemical laboratory analysis technique,

AAS was often overlooked in favor of atomic emission techniques until relatively recently.

The first important use of AAS as a routine laboratory technique for quantitative analysis dates from a description of a mercury vapor detection instrument in 1939 (Ref 3). This development did not greatly affect the chemical analysis field, because the procedure was useful only for mercury, an element whose physical properties make it a special case. The potential value of AAS as a general-purpose metallic-element analysis method was not realized until 1955, when a more flexible technique was discovered (Ref 4). These instruments combined the two basic components found in most modern spectrometers: a simple flame atomizer to

dissociate the sample solutions into free atoms and sealed atomic line source spectral lamps. Early papers stressed the theoretical advantages of absorption as compared to emission methods of spectrochemical analyses; that is, atomic absorption is independent of the excitation potential of the transition involved, and analytical methods based on absorption should be less subject to some types of interferences, making these techniques more rugged.

The technique remained largely a laboratory curiosity for a few more years until instrument companies began to manufacture first-generation instruments for routine analytical work. By the early 1960s the practical analytical advantages of AAS over the other spectrochemical methods had become appar-

Fig. 1 Energy-level transitions of the atomic spectrometries

(a) Atomic emission spectrometry. (b) Atomic absorption spectrometry. (c) Atomic fluorescence spectrometry. N^*, number of atoms in the excited state; N_0, number of atoms in the ground state; I_0, light intensity measured without the analyte present; I, light intensity measured with the analyte present

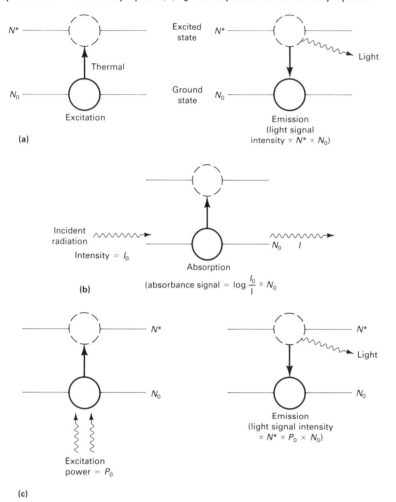

transition between electronic energy levels of the outer electrons of the selected analyte element. The third component is the light intensity-to-electrical signal transducer, usually a photomultiplier tube (PMT). Finally, an electronic data-reduction system converts this electrical signal to an analytical response proportional to the concentration of analyte in the sample solution.

It should be noted that within typical atmospheric pressure atomizers, the intrinsic width of the absorption/emission lines of the elements are typically from 0.002 to 0.008 nm. A comparison of these linewidths with the approximately 600 nm-wide working range of the spectrometers normally used in atomic spectroscopy indicates that approximately 10^5 resolution elements are potentially available to determine the approximately 100 elements of the periodic table. The relatively high ratio of the number of possible resolution elements to the number of chemical elements (approximately 1000:1) explains why atomic spectroscopic methods tend to be more specific than most other analysis techniques. The ease of applying this intrinsic specificity in actual practice differs substantially among the three types of atomic spectroscopy.

In atomic emission spectrometry (Fig. 1a and 2a), the flame serves an additional function not required in AAS or AFS: excitation. To produce the desired signal, hot flame gases must thermally (collisionally) excite a significant fraction of the free atoms produced by dissociation in the atomizer from the relatively populous ground-state level to one or more electronically excited states. The excited atoms emit light at discrete wavelengths corresponding to these differences in energy levels when they spontaneously relax back to the lower states. That is, the instrument "sees" the excited-state population of analyte atoms, not the ground-state population.

The ratio of the population of atoms in a thermally excited state to that in a lower energy state follows the Boltzmann distribution; that is, the logarithm of the ratio is directly proportional to the absolute temperature and inversely proportional to the difference in energy between the states. Therefore, the absolute magnitude of emission signals is temperature dependent. At typical atomizer temperatures, only a small fraction of atoms are excited to levels capable of emitting visible or ultraviolet radiation; most remain at or very near to the ground-state energy level.

Because flames do not specifically excite only the element of interest, a monochromator able to resolve close lines while maintaining a reasonable light intensity throughput must be used to reduce the probability of

ent, providing nonspecialists with a simple, reliable, and relatively inexpensive method for trace-metal analyses.

Atomic absorption spectrometry is generally used for measuring relatively low concentrations of approximately 70 metallic or semimetallic elements in solution samples. The basic experimental equipment used is essentially the same as that of 30 years ago—enhanced by modern electronics, background-correction schemes, and alternate types of atomizers. The predominance of AAS in general-purpose trace-metal analysis has recently been somewhat eclipsed by modern atomic emission spectrochemical methods designed to permit solution analysis. However, its ruggedness and relatively low equipment costs keep AAS competitive. Atomic absorption spectrometry performed using the graphite-tube furnace atomizer

usually remains the method of choice for ultra-trace-level analysis.

Principles and Instrumentation

Figures 1 and 2 show the relationship between the flame atomizer versions of AAS and the related techniques of atomic fluorescence spectrometry (AFS) and atomic emission spectrometry (AES). Several features are common to all three techniques. The first is a sample-introduction/atomization system consisting of a sample sprayer (referred to as the nebulizer) and the flame. The flame desolvates, vaporizes, then atomizes (dissociates to free atoms) the fine sample droplets produced by the nebulizer. Next is the monochromator, which isolates a wavelength of light characteristic of a particular quantized

Fig. 2 Comparison of (a) flame atomic emission spectrometry, (b) flame atomic absorption spectrometry, and (c) flame atomic fluorescence spectrometry

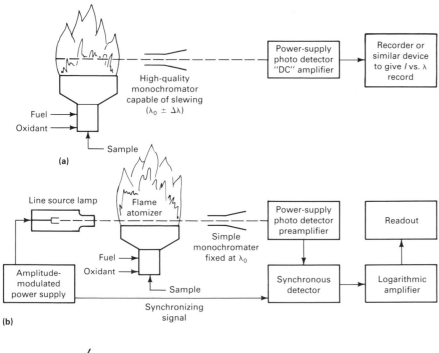

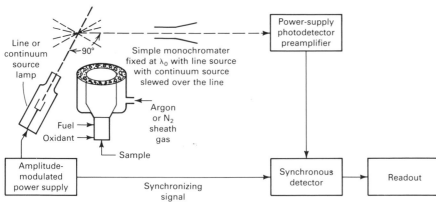

The absorption lines have a bandwidth approximately twice as wide as the emission profiles of the same elements in the low-pressure source lamp. In contrast to AES, ground-state (not excited state) atomic populations are observed.

The source light not absorbed in the atomizer passes through the monochromator to the light detector, and the data reduction/display system of the spectrometer outputs an absorbance response directly proportional to the concentration of analyte in the sample solution. Absorbance is the logarithm (base 10) of the ratio of the light intensities measured without (I_0) and with (I) the analyte atoms present in the light path (absorbance = $\log I_0/I$). In practice, the intensity of the source lamp is amplitude modulated at a specific frequency to permit subsequent electronic isolation of the "AC" light signal of the lamp from the "DC" light caused by the emission from species thermally excited by the atomizer. DC light is invariant relative to time.

Only the relatively highly populated ground-state population of the same element in the atomizer that is in the source lamp can contribute to the signal. Therefore, the analytical response of atomic absorption spectrometers is element-selective and not as sensitive to atomizer temperature variations as that of atomic emission spectrometers. In addition, the electronic lamp modulation/signal demodulation system renders the spectrometer blind to extraneous light sources. The monochromator serves only to isolate the desired analytical line from other light emitted by the one-element source lamp. Consequently, a less sophisticated monochromator suffices in AAS than is usually required for general-purpose AES. The major error signal encountered in AAS is the nonselective absorption or scattering of source-lamp radiation by undissociated molecular or particulate species within the atomizer. Several different types of background correction systems will be discussed later in this article.

Atomic fluorescence spectrometry (Fig. 1c and 2c), an emission technique, relies on an external light beam to excite analyte atoms radiatively. The absorption of light from the light source creates a higher population of excited-state atoms in the atomizer than that predicted by the Boltzmann equation at that temperature. Consequently, the absolute sizes of the atomic emission signals detected are larger than those seen in AES experiments performed with the same concentration of analyte atoms within the atomizer. A source-lamp modulation/signal demodulation scheme similar to that applied in atomic absorption spectrometers isolates the atomic fluorescence response from that

spectral interferences. Additional broad band-like light emitted by similarly thermally excited molecular species, for example, OH or CH flame radicals or matrix-metal oxides, complicates isolation of the desired signal from the background.

Atomic emission spectrometry usually necessitates scanning the monochromator completely over the analytical spectral line to obtain the background signal values necessary for the calculation of a correct analytical response. Reasonably inexpensive high-resolution monochromators capable of automatic correction of background emission

using Snellemans's wavelength modulation system have become available only recently.

In atomic absorption spectrometry (Fig. 1b and 2b), radiation from a lamp emitting a discrete wavelength of light having an energy corresponding to the difference in energies between the ground state and an excited state of the analyte element is passed through the atomizer. This light is generated by a low-pressure electrical discharge lamp containing a volatile form of the analyte element. Free analyte atoms within the atomizer absorb source-lamp light at wavelengths within their absorption profiles.

emitted by thermally excited analyte, flame, or matrix species.

Atomic fluorescence spectrometry spectra tend to be much simpler than AES spectra. This is true even when bright continuum light sources, such as xenon-arc lamps, are used instead of line sources for excitation, because only those atomic emission lines originating from energy levels whose populations are enhanced by the initial atomic absorption step can contribute to an AFS response. When line-source excitation lamps are used, this initial excitation step is very selective, and the AFS spectrum becomes extremely simple. Monochromators are often not used; the only concession to spectral isolation is the use of a photomultiplier insensitive to room light (Ref 5).

Atomic fluorescence spectrometry has two major sources of error. The first is chemical scavenging or de-excitation (termed quenching) of the nonequilibrium excited-state analyte atom population (that in excess of the thermally excited population) before a useful light signal can be emitted. The magnitude of this error signal depends on the concentration of the quenchers in the gas phase, which depends on the chemical makeup of the sample matrix accompanying the analyte element. Consequently, quenching introduces a potential source for matrix effects in AFS not found in AAS.

The second source of error is scatter of the exciting radiation by particulate matter within the atomizer. Some refractory metals, such as zirconium and uranium, if present in high concentrations in the sample, are apt to be incompletely dissociated or even gassified in conventional atomizers. This scatter signal is sometimes compounded with molecular fluorescence emission signals from naturally present gaseous flame species, a condition especially troublesome when continuum-type excitation sources are used.

Advantages of Atomic Absorption Spectrometry. During the past 25 years, AAS has been one of the most widely used trace element analysis techniques, largely because of the degree of specificity provided by the use of an analyte-line light source. This reduces the probability of "false positives" caused by matrix concomitants and serves to enhance greatly the reliability of AAS determinations performed on "unknown" samples. A background-corrected atomic absorption instrument is also one of the most reliable, albeit slow, tools available for qualitative analysis. The need for simple monochromators has maintained the cost of AAS equipment well below that of AES instrumentation having similar capabilities.

Line-excited AFS has the specificity of AAS as well as other desirable characteristics, such as a greater dynamic range and

potentially better detection limits. However, obtaining appreciable improvement over AAS detection capabilities with AFS usually requires more attention to optimizing the optics, atomizer, and electronics of the system. In addition, because correction for "scatter" signals is fundamentally more important and more difficult to accomplish than is background absorption correction in AAS, no flame- or furnace atomizer-based AFS unit is commercially available.

Atomic emission spectrometry has found limited acceptance in the instrument marketplace. Although most of the better atomic absorption instruments sold during the 1960s and 1970s could be used for flame-excited AES, the instrument requirements for the two techniques are so different that the results achieved using these spectrometers did not reflect the true potential of the method. Only the recent introduction of electrical plasma emission sources, such as inductively coupled plasma (ICP) or direct current plasma (DCP), designed for the routine analyses of solution samples has prompted commercial production of fairly inexpensive and compact spectrometers optimized for AES (see the article "Inductively Coupled Plasma Atomic Emission Spectrometry" in this Volume). However, these instruments remain considerably more expensive than basic atomic absorption spectrometers.

Atomic Absorption Spectrometry Sensitivities. The periodic table shown in Fig. 3 lists typical analytical sensitivities obtained using representative atomic absorption spectrometers with either a flame or the more sensitive graphite furnace atomizer. The entries in Fig. 3 represent the magnitude of the atomic absorbance signal expected when a 1-ppm solution of the element is continuously aspirated into a flame atomizer or introduced as a discrete 25-μL aliquot into a graphite furnace.

In practice, the performance of reliable analysis requires signal magnitudes ranging from 0.01 to 1.0 absorbance unit. This is a consequence of the signal-to-noise considerations involved in measuring small differences in two relatively large light signals. This rather limited dynamic analytical range often necessitates the concentration or dilution of sample solutions before analysis.

The reasons for the extreme differences in AAS sensitivities noted in Fig. 3 can be divided into three basic categories, the first two of which affect AAS, AFS, and AES nearly equally. First, because the number of atoms within the light path at a given time fundamentally determines the instantaneous signal, the mass-based sensitivities in Fig. 3 are biased in favor of the lighter elements.

Second, a substantial number of elements do not possess ground-state lines in a region of the spectrum that is accessible with normal spectrometers and to which the gases present within normal atomizers are transparent. Less sensitive alternative analytical lines may sometimes be used, for example, with mercury and phosphorus; for other elements (most of the fixed gases), no good lines are available. Further, many elements possess a multitude of atomic energy states near the absolute ground-state level. These low-lying levels are thermally populated to some degree at the working temperature of the atomizer, which tends to reduce the fraction of analyte atoms available at any one energy level to absorb a specific wavelength of light emitted by the source lamp. This reduces the sensitivity achievable by any atomic spectroscopic technique for many of the transition, lanthanide, and actinide elements.

Lastly, none of the atomizers commonly used in atomic absorption spectrometers provides conditions capable of substantially dissociating some of the more commonly encountered forms of some chemically reactive analyte elements. For example, boron forms stable nitrides, oxides, and carbides. No practical adjustment of the operating conditions of any of the conventional atomic absorption atomizers can provide an environment that is simultaneously sufficiently free of nitrogen, oxygen, and carbon to give a favorable degree of boron dissociation. However, the combination of the much higher temperatures and inert gas environments found in electrical plasma AES sources makes boron one of the most sensitive elements determined by modern AES instruments.

Atomizers

The sensitivity of AAS determinations is determined almost wholly by the characteristics of the light source and the atomizer, not by the optics or electronics of the spectrometer. Simple, inexpensive AAS instruments have the same sensitivity as more sophisticated models. Because the line-source lamps used in AAS have essentially the same line widths, most of the sensitivity differences noted between instruments can be attributed to differences in the atomizers.

Table 1 lists the more important characteristics of the three most common AAS atomizers. The values listed for the dilution factor (Df) represent an estimate of the degree to which an original liquid sample is diluted (or lost) by the time it passes through the optical path of the spectrometer. Furnaces are more sensitive than flame atomizers primarily because the volatilized analyte

Fig. 3 Typical analytical sensitivities obtained using flame or graphite furnace atomic absorption spectrometry

(a) Results obtained by Varian Techtron Ltd., Melbourne, Australia. (b) Results obtained by Allied Analytical Systems, Waltham, MA

Legend: top number = Absorbance of 1 µg/mL solution with flame atomizer (a); bottom number = Absorbance of a 25-µL aliquot of a 1 µg/mL solution with furnace atomizer (b). Each box shows the top number (a), the Element symbol, and the bottom number (b).

0.26 **Li** 37	0.26 **Be** 1100											0.0005 **B** –	**C** –	**N** –	**O** –		
1.5 **Na** 275	1.5 **Mg** 157											0.006 **Al** 275	0.003 **Si** 3.7	0.00003 **P** –	**S** –		
0.44 **K** 19	0.21 **Ca** 2.8	0.013 **Sc** –	0.003 **Ti** 3.7	0.005 **V** 7.3	0.08 **Cr** 220	0.18 **Mn** 110	0.071 **Fe** 366	0.067 **Co** 37	0.066 **Ni** 44	0.11 **Cu** 137	0.49 **Zn** 550	0.004 **Ga** 210	0.003 **Ge** 277	0.006 **As** 18	0.009 **Se** 11		
0.11 **Rb** –	0.10 **Sr** 110	0.0009 **Y** –	0.0005 **Zr** –	0.0002 **Nb** –	0.013 **Mo** 18	**Tc** –	0.006 **Ru** –	0.029 **Rh** 11	0.048 **Pd** 5.5	0.122 **Ag** 220	0.40 **Cd** 366	0.012 **In** 10	0.009 **Sn** 18	0.015 **Sb** 14	0.017 **Te** 16		
0.04 **Cs** –	0.022 **Ba** 27		0.0004 **Hf** –	0.0004 **Ta** –	0.0008 **W** –	0.0004 **Re** –	0.004 **Os** 0.41	0.006 **Ir** 0.65	0.004 **Pt** 2.4	0.034 **Au** 110	0.020 **Hg** 11	0.016 **Tl** 23	0.04 **Pb** 61	0.02 **Bi** 22	**Po** –		

Lanthanides:

0.0009 **La** 1.9	**Ce** –	0.0002 **Pr** –	0.0005 **Nd** –	**Pm** –	0.0006 **Sm** –	0.011 **Eu** 12	0.002 **Gd** –	0.0004 **Tb** –	0.007 **Dy** 2.1	0.005 **Ho** 1.2	0.007 **Er** 2.4	0.015 **Tm** –	0.057 **Yb** 85	0.0006 **Lu** –

Actinides:

Ac –	**Th** –	**Pa** –	0.00004 **U** –

is diluted with far less extraneous gas. Because the magnitude of an atomic absorption signal is proportional to the number of atoms present within a unit cross section of the light path at a given instant, the product of the dilution factor and the path length of the atomizer ($Df \times L$) provides the best indication of the relative analytical sensitivities expected for elements atomized with equal efficiencies.

When the sensitivity figures listed in Fig. 3 are combined with the dilution factor estimates of Table 1 to estimate molar extinction coefficients of gas phase atoms, figures of approximately 10^8 (in the usual units of liters per mole per centimeter) are typical. In conventional spectrophotometry of dissolved molecular species, extinction coefficients for strong absorbers are at best three orders of magnitude lower. This extremely high absorption coefficient enables AAS performed using atomizers with high Df factors to have sensitivities competitive with other analytical techniques.

Flame atomizers are usually used with a pneumatic nebulizer and a premix chamber (Fig. 4). The fuel/oxidant/sample droplet mixtures are burned in long, narrow slot burners to maximize the length of the atomization zone within the light path of the spectrometer. The premix chamber is designed to discard the sample droplets produced by the sprayer, which are larger than a certain cutoff size, and to mix the remaining droplets with the fuel and oxidant gases before they reach the burner.

Because the larger droplets are discarded, the sample uptake rate is usually 10 to 35 times greater than the flux (mass flow per unit time) of sample actually entering the flame. Organic-solvent sample solutions generally yield better analytical sensitivities than do aqueous solutions, because they possess less surface tension than aqueous solutions, which results in smaller mean droplet sizes when they are sprayed.

The reason for this deliberate size discrimination is that oversized droplets containing a great amount of dissolved matrix salts will leave large solid particles after evaporation of the solvent in either the hot burner head or in the lower millimeter or two of the flame. These larger particles may not decompose completely by the time they reach the optical path. This lessens the degree of analyte dissociation in those droplets compared to similarly sized droplets that do not contain as much total dissolved salt. This constitutes the mechanism for the vaporization-interference matrix effect. Smaller aerosol droplets result in smaller desolvated particles that have a better chance to dissociate completely before they reach the light path of the spectrometer.

The ability of a nebulizer/premix chamber system to supply the flame with a copious supply of small droplets determines the analytical sensitivity achievable and the degree of immunity of the overall analytical procedure to matrix effects. The design of the premix chamber for use with a given nebulizer involves a compromise between maximizing analytical sensitivity in matrix-free samples, which is favored by allowing passage of a larger fraction of the sample droplets, and minimizing potential interferences when analyzing complex samples. Common practice is to use sample pickup rates of 5 to 10 mL/min and to discard most of the sample spray. If optimum sensitivity is required and only small volumes of sample are available, fritted disk or ultrasonic nebu-

Table 1 Atomizer characteristics

Atomizer	Temperature, K	Sample volumes, mL	Atomizer path length, cm	Dilution factor(a)	Atomizer path length × dilution factor
Air-acetylene flame	2500	0.1–2	10	2×10^{-6}	2×10^{-5}
Nitrous oxide-acetylene flame	3000	0.1–2	5	1.7×10^{-6}	8.5×10^{-6}
Graphite furnace	300–3000	0.001–0.05	2.5	0.02	0.05
Quartz tube (hydride generator)	800–1400	1–40	15	0.007	0.1

(a) Dilution factor (Df) assumptions: Flames—20 L/min of fuel/oxidant, 7 mL/min sample aspiration rate (5% actually introduced); furnace—maximum furnace diameter of 0.6 cm (0.25 in.), gaseous analyte atom containment efficiency of 30%, 50-μL sample aliquot; quartz tube—20-mL sample, a gas/liquid separation efficiency giving 10% of analyte in the light path within 2 s at signal maximum, 1200 K

Fig. 4 Typical flame atomization system

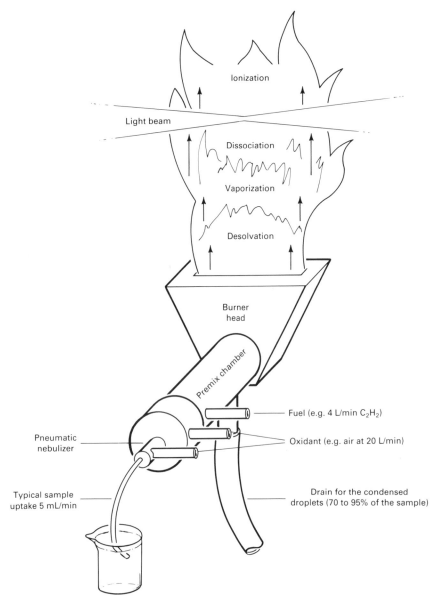

lizers are preferable to conventional pneumatic types because they produce a spray with a finer mean droplet size.

For the more easily atomized elements, such as lead and cadmium, the air-acetylene flame is preferred because it is less expensive to operate, more sensitive (higher $Df \times L$ product), and safer to use than high-temperature flames. Automated flame lighting and extinguishing systems enhance safety.

The higher temperature, fuel-rich nitrous oxide/acetylene flame is used to enhance the extent of dissociation of refractory compounds that are initially formed when certain analytes, such as lanthanides, titanium, or aluminum are sprayed into the flames. This type of matrix effect can sometimes be controlled without using the hotter flame by adding to the sample solution a concomitant, or releasing agent, that chemically competes with the analyte for the particular interferent. An example is the addition of excess lanthanum to sample solutions in which the common matrix component phosphorus may interfere with the determination of alkaline-earth analytes.

Because the gaseous species constituting most of the flame volume have high ionization energies, the free electron concentration of "unsalted" flames is low. This lack of electron buffering capacity may cause readily ionized analyte atoms to be thermally ionized to an appreciable degree. This depletes the ground-state atomic population and reduces the response. To correct for this, it is common practice to add a relatively large concentration of some easily ionized nonanalyte element, for example, lanthanum or potassium, to all the sample and standard solutions. The electrons produced by these ionization suppressants in the flame buffer the electron concentration and make the degree of analyte ionization constant regardless of the concentration of ionizable concomitant elements in the sample solutions.

Because sample solutions are usually aspirated into flame atomizers for at least 10 s, a steady-state signal is produced. Because such signals can be extensively low-pass filtered to reject AC noise, flame atomization AAS is usually more precise than AAS performed with atomizers that produce only transient signals. Consequently, the detection limit capability of flame atomizers relative to the other atomizers is somewhat better than the relative $Df \times L$ products shown in Table 1 would indicate.

One of the first attempts to improve the sensitivity of flame atomizers was the Fuwa tube (Ref 6). In this device, the flame was directed through long ceramic or quartz tubes aligned with the optical path. The longer path length increased the $Df \times L$

Fig. 5 Essential components of a graphite furnace atomizer

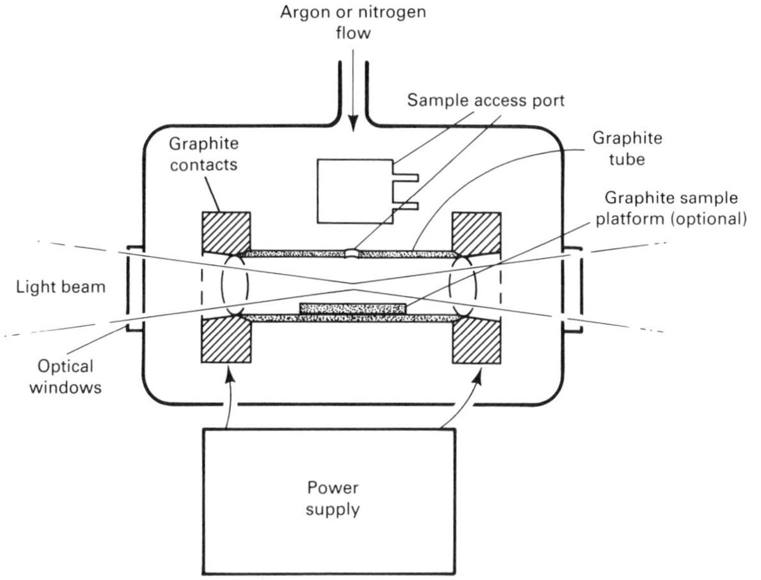

product and therefore the sensitivity. However, because these systems had poor light throughput and consequently noisier signals, detection capabilities were not enhanced proportionately. A more fundamental limitation was that they were applicable only to volatile analytes because the tubes significantly cooled the gas relative to that in unconfined flames.

Another early device, which is used for biological fluid analyses, is the sampling boat (Ref 7). It consists of a small metal (usually nickel) "boat" or "cup" into which discrete aliquots of sample are pipetted. After the sample has been dried, the cup is rapidly inserted directly over a conventional air-acetylene burner for the analysis. Relatively volatile analyte metals, such as lead and cadmium, are rapidly and quantitatively introduced into the flame without the wasteful droplet-size segregation process that takes place in conventional flame AAS.

Furnace Atomizers. A typical graphite furnace atomizer (Fig. 5) consists of a 2.5-cm (1-in.) long, 0.6-cm (0.25-in.) internal diameter graphite tube that is resistively heated by the passage of electrical current (typically 300 A, 10 V) through it lengthwise. Although furnaces with different geometries were sold during the early 1970s, most of the furnaces currently available are variations of this basic Massmann design (Ref 8).

Sample aliquots are generally placed into the furnace tube through a hole drilled through the wall, or the aliquot can be placed onto a small graphite planchet, or L'vov platform, situated at the inside center of the tube. An analysis is performed by heating the tube in three distinct steps to dry, pyrolyze, then atomize the sample aliquot. The resulting atomic absorbance signal typically lasts approximately 1 s. Because the residence time of individual atoms within the light path is generally considerably less than the time necessary to volatilize all the analyte, the signal never achieves a steady state.

In contrast to the conditions obtained in flame atomizers, the temperatures experienced by gaseous analyte species in furnace atomizers depend on the volatilization characteristics of the analyte, which depend on the chemical and physical composition of the sample matrix remaining at the conclusion of the pyrolysis step. If the analyte is trapped in a solid, nonvolatile salt matrix at the conclusion of pyrolysis, it will eventually volatilize at higher temperatures than if originally introduced into the furnace in a low-salt sample solution.

Differentials between the mean gas phase temperatures experienced by the analyte element in the samples and standards will vary mean residence times (usually diffusion controlled) of gaseous atoms in the light path. This affects instrument response per unit mass of the analyte regardless of whether peak or area signals are recorded. These matrix-induced temperature differentials may also result in differing degrees of analyte dissociation from sample to sample and from samples to standards.

Volatile analytes, such as mercury or cadmium, evaporated from the tube walls of typical Massmann furnaces, may experience

mean gas temperatures as much as 500 to 1000 °C (900 to 1800 °F) lower than in the "cool" air-acetylene flame atomizer, regardless of the nominal furnace temperature setting. Placing the sample aliquot on a L'vov platform instead of on the wall of the tube retards analyte volatilization until the gas-phase temperature within the tube is considerably higher (typically by 400 °C, or 720 °F). Additions of large amounts of volatilization-retarding salts (matrix modifiers) to the samples and standards normalize the volatilization characteristics of the analyte and raise the effective atomization temperature.

Moreover, the small Df factor responsible for the excellent sensitivity obtainable with furnace atomizers often increases the amount of covolatilized matrix material present in the light path along with the analyte. Some of the more common concomitant elements, such as chlorine, often cause gas-phase matrix effects due to their ability to form strong chemical bonds with many analyte atoms.

In addition, these furnaces typically have large thermal gradients from the center of the tube (the hottest point) to the ends. This causes a rapid transfer of volatilized material (both analyte and matrix) from the center to the ends of the tube during atomization. This material tends to accumulate in these cooler zones, and is the source of potential memory effects and high background absorption error signals. Because of these problems, considerable sample-specific *in situ* sample pretreatment is often necessary before atomization can be attempted. These additional steps make AAS using a graphite furnace atomizer (GFAAS) considerably more time consuming than flame AAS.

Hydride-Generation Systems. Quartz tube atomizers are used to determine mercury and such elements as selenium, antimony, arsenic, germanium, bismuth, tin, lead, and tellurium that readily form volatile hydrides under suitable aqueous reaction conditions. Figure 6 depicts a typical hydride-generation AAS system. A chemical reductant, such as sodium borohydride, is mixed with the sample solution in a separate reaction chamber to produce the hydrides. A carrier gas removes the hydride from the solution and transfers it into the flame-heated quartz tube atomizer. Because the reductant produces mercury atoms directly for determination of that element, the quartz tube acts as a cuvette and needs to be heated only enough to prevent the condensation of water vapor on the glass.

Hydride-generation systems produce a transient signal similar to that in GFAAS, but from 10 to 30 s in duration. Higher and narrower signals can be obtained if the metal hydride is frozen in a cold trap during

Fig. 6 Hydride-generation atomic absorption spectrometry system

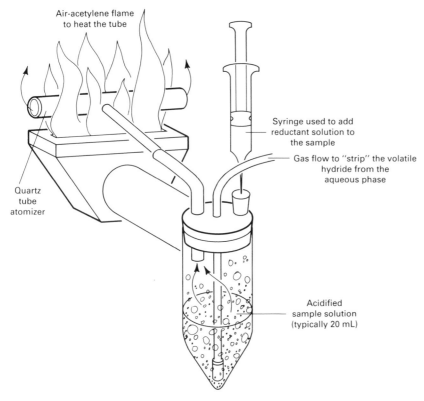

Fig. 7 Double-beam atomic absorption spectrometer

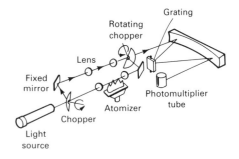

reduction and is then suddenly released by subsequent rapid heating of the trap.

A similar system has been described for the determination of nickel (Ref 9). An acidic sample solution is continuously sparged with a gas stream containing carbon monoxide. When the borohydride reductant is added, the elemental nickel produced is converted to the volatile nickel carbonyl, which is then swept into the atomizer by the gas stream.

Analytical sensitivities—based on concentration, not the absolute mass of analyte—achievable with these systems are outstanding, because essentially all (not the 1 to 10% passing through the premix chamber of typical flame units) of the analyte element in a large sample volume is effectively removed from the solution and swept as a slug into the atomizer. A well-designed hydride-generation atomic absorption spectrometer can better the GFAAS sensitivities given in Fig. 3 by at least an order of magnitude.

A variation (Ref 10) of the hydride-generation system consists of a conventional flame atomizer/nebulizer with a simple Y in the sample pickup tube leading to the nebulizer. The sample solution is drawn through one "leg" of the Y and mixed with a borohydride solution through the other. The rapid hydride generation reaction converts essentially all of the hydride-forming analyte in the mixed stream to a gas in the spray chamber. Because gaseous analyte is not subject to the wasteful sample droplet size segregation mechanism in conventional flame atomization, the analytical sensitivity is considerably enhanced. Similar Y-tube sample pickup tubes have been used for the cointroduction of ionization suppressants and releasing agents, but none of these reagents so directly affects sensitivity (Ref 11, 12).

Spectrometers

Most atomic absorption spectrometers use sealed hollow cathode lamps (HCL) or electrodeless discharge lamps (EDL) as light sources. These light sources differ in the type of power supply needed and in how the atomic vapor is produced, but their spectral characteristics are similar in that the emission lines have approximately the same widths. Therefore, AAS analytical sensitivities are similar with either source. However, the usually greater intensity of the EDL may result in superior analytical detection limits, especially if the optical system of the spectrometer is not very efficient at conveying light to the detector. This is because smaller electronic gains are needed, lessening amplifier noise during measurement.

Most atomic absorption spectrometers are double beam instruments that automatically compensate for variations in the output of the source lamp by splitting the beam and passing half of it around rather than through the atomizer. The beam passing around the atomizer is used as a reference for the other. An example is shown in Fig. 7. The different ways instrument manufacturers accomplish this are essentially equivalent. However, the need for double-beam instrumentation in most AAS applications is questionable because modern source lamps are quite stable.

The monochromators used in atomic absorption spectrometers generally have unsophisticated optics unless the instrument was also designed for AES. This is because the narrow line-light source and the lamp modulation/signal demodulation system handle most of the spectral selection. Although a dual-monochromator, dual-source lamp instrument is commercially available, most atomic absorption spectrometers are single-channel instruments.

The degree of automation incorporated into the instrument varies widely among atomic absorption spectrometers. Some instruments require only the pouring of samples/standards into an automatic sampler approximately every hour; a dedicated computer and commercial (preset) programs control other operations. These instruments save much time and effort in performing many routine analyses, but tend to take longer to set up for a single analysis, are more expensive than less sophisticated atomic absorption spectrometers, and are ineffective as teaching tools because the automation conceals operation principles.

If the instrument is to be used for GFAAS using state-of-the-art furnaces, an automated system can produce results superior to those of manual instruments. Automated systems can more accurately reproduce the multiple *in situ* sample pretreatment steps often necessary to avoid possible matrix effect prob-

Fig. 8 Continuum-source background-correction system (a) with absorption/emission profile (b)

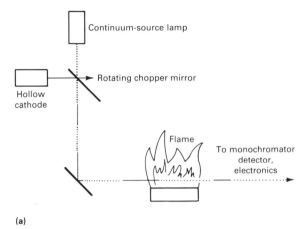

(a)

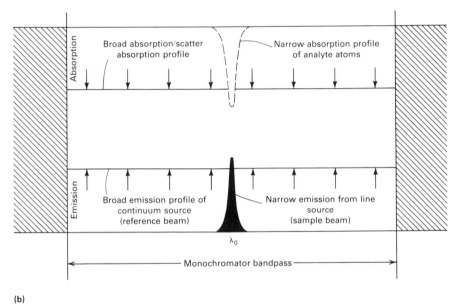

(b)

width of free atoms is so narrow (perhaps 0.005 nm) relative to the bandpass of the monochromator (typically 1 nm) that, regardless of their concentration in the light path, purely atomic absorption of the light of the continuum source is negligible.

The primary advantage of this system is that essentially no analytical sensitivity is lost; other correction systems often significantly reduce the analytical response of the instrument. Another advantage is that most of these instruments can be converted for general-purpose ultraviolet-visible solution spectrophotometry analysis by moving the continuum lamp over to the position normally occupied by the line source lamp. The only additional instrument modification needed is a small bracket on the burner head to hold the cuvette in the light path.

Disadvantages of this system include potentially serious lamp alignment problems and overcorrection of the signal. Overcorrection occurs when small analyte signals are accompanied by large concomitant (nonanalyte) atomic or sharp molecular-band absorption signals within the bandpass of the monochromator but not coincident with the analyte line. If the two light beams do not "see" exactly the same portion of the atomizer, any mismatch of the spatial distributions of the absorbing species may cause errors.

Zeeman background correction (Ref 14) relies on the principle that if sufficiently strong magnetic fields are imposed around the atomizer, the absorption lines of the atoms will be divided into two components. In the case of spectral lines that exhibit an anomalous Zeeman effect, each of these components may consist of a group of closely grouped lines. In addition, each of these components can absorb only light having a plane of polarization at right angles to that absorbed by the other component. In contrast to the Koirtyohann/Pickett system, a single conventional HCL or EDL source lamp is used.

One of the two components can also be divided into two subcomponents (individual lines or groups of lines) symmetrically shifted to each side of the normal line position. Using various combinations of polarizers and magnets (ac or dc fields) or geometries (magnetic fields parallel with or at right angles to the light path), several ways to separate the absorption signals of the shifted and unshifted line components have been devised (Ref 14). Figure 9 shows a schematic diagram of a Zeeman-corrected spectrometer. Because the molecular absorption bands responsible for background absorption signals generally do not similarly split in strong magnetic fields, their contribution to the total absorption signal can be

lems. Other than the degree of automation, the data processing capabilities of atomic absorption spectrometers are equivalent for routine analysis. Early instruments often required modification of their electronics to hasten transient signal response for accurate GFAAS.

However, the performance of the background-correction systems provided by different manufacturers varies significantly. Background absorbance (or scattering) signal correction usually is necessary only when graphite furnace atomization is used. This is because the relatively small degree of sample dilution in the furnace causes the gas-phase concentrations of interfering species to be higher than they are in flames. Background correctors are sometimes used with flame or quartz-tube atomizers at wavelengths below

220 nm, where normal flame gas components begin to absorb appreciably.

Continuum-Source Background Correction. The first method devised to accomplish background correction was the Koirtyohann/Pickett system (Ref 13), which uses light from an auxiliary continuum source lamp as a reference beam (Fig. 8). A low-pressure, molecular hydrogen (D_2 or H_2) lamp is used for the ultraviolet range, and a tungsten-iodide lamp for the visible range. These background-correction systems extract an atomic absorbance-only signal by subtracting the absorbance noted with the broadband (continuum) source from that seen with the line source. The physical principle is that broadband absorbers (or scatterers) absorb light from both sources equally well. However, the absorption band-

Fig. 9 Zeeman background-correction spectrometer

P, polarized light

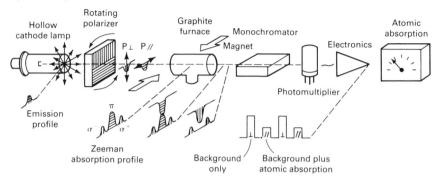

easily distinguished from the atomic absorption signals.

The primary advantage of Zeeman-corrected instruments relative to those using the Koirtyohann/Pickett system is that the signal and reference channel light measurements are performed at the exact wavelength of the analytical line. Consequently, the simultaneous presence of large concentrations of concomitant free atoms having absorption lines within the bandpass of the monochromator but not exactly coincident with the line of the analyte cannot cause overcorrection errors. In addition, misalignment problems are far less likely with a single source lamp than with two lamps. Lastly, use of a single lamp eliminates having to balance the intensities of the signal and reference beams so that the electronics of the spectrometer can compare them accurately.

Disadvantages include the necessity of a large, expensive magnet system. The correction systems generally cannot be used with standard atomizers; that is, producing a high magnetic field strength requires the use of specially designed furnace atomizers or burner heads. Further, the analytical curves often roll over; that is, two different analyte concentrations can produce the same analytical response. Lastly, a significant loss of sensitivity and nonlinear calibration curves are observed for those elements having complex Zeeman splitting patterns. The curve straightening software in the data-acquisition systems of these instruments can compensate for nonlinearity.

The Smith/Hieftje system (Ref 15) uses a single conventional hollow cathode lamp to produce a broadened, self-absorbed atomic line reference beam as well as the usual narrow-line sample beam (Fig. 10). This is typically accomplished by momentarily pulsing the operating current of the lamp to a level perhaps a hundred times higher than usual. The high concentration of cool sputtered atoms that rapidly accumu-lates in front of the cathode of the lamp selectively absorbs the central wavelengths of the light emitted from the rear of the cathode—a process analogous to that observed in the solar atmosphere (Ref 1).

Because the outer edges of the emission profile of this broadened line now largely lie outside the absorption profile of the atoms within the atomizer, the reference light beam is not absorbed by atoms as strongly as the narrow-line sample beam produced under low lamp current conditions. The difference in the absorbance signals measured with the two beams is output as the background-corrected AAS signal.

Advantages of the system include easy but not necessarily perfect lamp alignment. The probability of encountering overcorrection errors is low, because the effective bandpass of the instrument is limited to the width of the atomic line of the broadened reference beam—typically two orders of magnitude narrower than the bandpass of the monochromator. Further, constraints on the configuration of the atomizer are nonexistent. Finally, because no high power magnets or special source lamps are needed, there is an inherent simplicity to these systems that should be consistent with producing low-cost equipment.

The primary disadvantage is a substantial loss of sensitivity for elements whose hollow cathode emission lines do not broaden significantly when the lamp current is raised. The elements most strongly affected possess resonance lines already intrinsically broad due to hyperfine and/or isotopic line-splitting.

Research and Future Trends

The use of discrete atomic line-source lamps in AAS is responsible for two of the fundamental limitations of the technique as well as for most of its strengths. First, because the emission lines from these lamps are very narrow and at fixed wavelengths, it is not possible to scan the absorbance line of the analyte element. Consequently, in contrast to solution spectrophotometry, the sensitivity of the determination cannot be changed by moving the wavelength setting of the spectrometer slightly off the center of the analytical line.

This severely limits the upper range of concentrations that can be measured using a single dilution of the sample unless the atomizer configuration is changed. The simplest of these changes—turning the slot burner at right angles to the light path—will typically reduce sensitivity by approximately one order of magnitude. Second, the need for a separate line source lamp for each analyte element in the sample characterizes conventional AAS as a single-channel analytical approach. Although difficult, multielement line-source AAS instruments may be pieced together in the laboratory.

Continuum-Source AAS Systems. The development of atomic absorption spectrometers that combine a high-resolution AES-type spectrometer with a xenon-arc continuum source lamp (Ref 16, 17) indicates that sensitive, multielement atomic absorption spectrometers with a wide dynamic range can be manufactured. In these instruments, the xenon lamp is used unmodulated, and the bandpass of the spectrometer is repetitively scanned to 60 Hz over the absorption line of the analyte element (wavelength modulation). Many individual intensity measurements are recorded at closely adjacent wavelength intervals across the line during each scan.

Subsequently, several calibration curves of differing sensitivities can be plotted using data obtained at various distances from the center of the absorption profile of the analyte element. This broadens the dynamic analytical range from approximately two to approximately four orders of magnitude by extending it to higher analyte concentrations.

Another advantage is that data from 40 elements can be simultaneously measured if a sufficiently powerful computer is available for data storage. Finally, because absorbance calculations are based on the light intensities simultaneously measured over the analytical line, the response of the instrument is inherently background corrected.

Although the mechanical, optical, and electronic requirements of these instruments are stringent compared to those of conventional atomic absorption spectrometers, their manufacture in commercial quantities is well within the capabilities of current technology. Such instruments have not been built and distributed commercially probably because readily available inductively coupled plasma

Fig. 10 Smith/Hieftje background-correction system

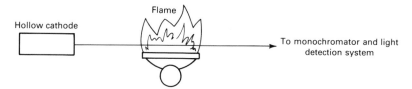

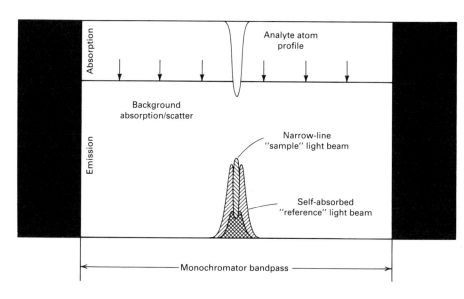

atomic emission spectrometry (ICPAES) systems perform most of the same analytical functions equally well.

Several alternate atomic absorption spectrometer designs with versatile continuum-type sources have been devised. One involves interposing a modulator flame into the light path between the source and the monochromator (Fig. 11a). Periodic injection of solutions of the analyte element into this flame at a specific frequency enables selective modulation of its transparency to the emission of the xenon lamp over the atomic absorption profile of the selected element. The response of an ac amplification system tuned to this frequency is a measure of the transmittance of the analytical flame over the same wavelength interval. Although the slopes of the analytical curves obtained using these systems approach those of line-source instruments, the signal-to-noise ratio and therefore the detection capabilities are inferior.

Another way to use continuum sources in AAS involves implementing resonance detectors (Fig. 11b), which consist of an integral source of atoms, a light filter, and a PMT. The PMT is usually situated at right angles to the optical path so that it "sees" only the atomic fluorescence excited in its integral atom source by the source light

traveling to the detector. The source light is amplitude modulated, or chopped, before it is passed through the atomizer. The bandpass of the system and therefore the sensitivity of the detector are determined by the element present in the atom source of the detector. If a flame atomizer is used as this atom source, the detector is versatile and different solutions can be aspirated into it as necessary. The fact that instruments using resonance detectors are still laboratory curiosities reflects the lack of interest among instrument manufacturers and users in alternatives to line-source AAS.

Flame atomizer technology has not changed substantially for several years. Use of chemical flames has largely been limited to the two fuel-oxidant combinations discussed above, because other chemical flames examined over the past 20 years do not offer substantially improved characteristics for general-purpose AAS work. Similarly, major changes in the introduction of solution samples into flames are not expected. This is because alternative nebulizers offer no advantages over the simple and reliable pneumatic types, except in situations in which the amount of sample available is limited. One area that could be improved is the design of the premix chambers used with pneumatic nebulizers. Systematic optimization of the

number, position, and shape of impact surfaces in these chambers may simultaneously increase the analytical sensitivity and the ruggedness of AAS determinations.

In certain instances, analytes have been introduced into flame atomizers by means other than direct nebulization or hydride generation. One of these techniques involves converting relatively refractory metals to their volatile chlorides by passing HCl over sample aliquots that have first been dried in electrically heated quartz test tubes (Ref 18). The volatile chloride salts are then carried directly into the flame by the flowing gas stream. Another method uses the derivitization techniques of gas chromatography to form volatile metallo-organic compounds (Ref 19).

Graphite furnace atomizers will probably undergo a major change in design in the future in that instrumentation manufacturers will switch to the 25-year-old L'vov furnace design (Ref 20) instead of the mechanically simpler Massmann type currently used. Although use of L'vov platforms and matrix modifiers has greatly enhanced the analytical utility of Massmann furnaces, they still have serious deficiencies not evident in the L'vov furnace. Figure 12 depicts several versions of the L'vov furnace.

Modern versions of L'vov furnaces are superior because they rigorously separate volatilization from atomization. This is accomplished by performing each process in two separately heated, spatially separated zones. Regardless of the volatilization characteristic of the analyte element in a particular sample matrix, its vapor is subjected to precisely the same temperature while passing through the lightpath of the spectrometer. In the case of volatile analyte elements, this atomization temperature can be much higher than that possible with Massmann furnaces. Although L'vov-type furnaces have repeatedly been shown to simplify analysis of complex samples (Ref 21-23), instrumentation manufacturers have been reluctant to abandon the simpler furnace design.

Electrical plasma atomizers may be used to eliminate the chemical and temperature limitations of conventional AAS atomizers (Ref 24). The ICP is an efficient sample atomizer because of its high temperature and inert gas environment, but gaseous sample atom density per unit light-path cross section is so low that the analytical sensitivities achieved for most elements are much lower than those obtained using conventional flame atomizers. There are three reasons for this. First, the ability of the ICP to tolerate molecular gases is so limited that very little solution sample can be introduced (unless the droplets produced by the nebulizer are

Fig. 11 Alternate continuum-source spectrometer designs

(a) Use of a modulator flame, which is placed between the light source and the monochromator.
(b) Resonance detection system

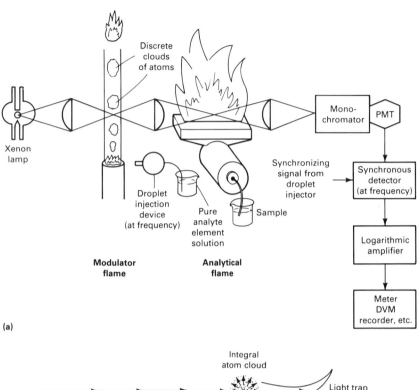

(a)

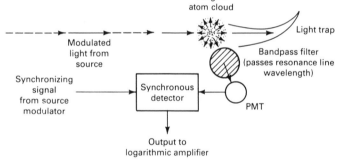

(b)

desolvated by a separate add-on device). Second, the geometry (round) of the ICP is poor for absorption work. Finally, the plasma is often so hot that most of the analyte is present as ions, not as ground-state atoms.

Low-pressure sputter chambers sometimes used in atomic emission spectroscopy may be effective AAS atomizers in such specialized applications as solid metal analysis (Ref 25). Atomic absorption analyses may also be performed on plumes of sample gas generated by discharging a large capacitor through a fine wire or thin metallic film on which the sample has been deposited or by directing high-power laser beams at a solid sample surface.

The Langmuir Torch atomizer to date remains untried as an atomizer in AAS (Ref 26). Hydrogen gas is first dissociated by passage through an atmospheric-pressure ac or dc arc discharge. The recombination of the hydrogen atoms downstream of the arc produces a highly reducing flame having a considerably higher temperature than typical chemical flames. Sample introduction into the hydrogen stream is probably best accomplished using an ultrasonic nebulizer followed by a desolvation system. The chemical simplicity and high temperature of this flame may help enhance AAS sensitivities for elements such as boron.

Sample introduction/atomization systems that combine a simple graphite furnace used only as a volatilizer and a conventional flame used as the atomizer are inexpensive to manufacture and can handle solid and liquid samples. The analytical sensitivities achieved are between those of conventional flame and furnace atomizers. Flame modification, that is, "salting" it with selected reagents sprayed into the air stream, and selective volatilization of the sample by the furnace can be used to control matrix effects.

Fig. 12 L'vov-type furnace design

(a) L'vov furnace (Ref 20). (b) Frech/Lundburg furnace (Ref 22). (c) Siemer furnace (Ref 21). PS_1, atomization power supply connection; PS_2, volatilization power supply connection

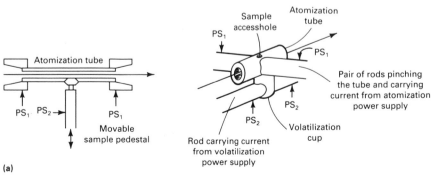

(a)

(b)

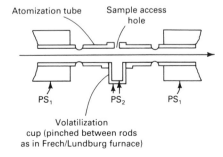

(c)

AAS Accessory Equipment. Such aspects of AAS instrumentation as data handling capabilities, and automation, have been developed past the point of diminishing financial return. Further improvements in these ancillary areas should be directed at lowering the cost of AAS instrumentation. Additional price increases will direct purchase decisions toward alternate analytical equipment.

Applications*

Applications of conventional AAS equipment routinely include most of the types of samples brought to laboratories for elemental analyses. The limitations of the method include inadequate or nonexistent sensitivity for several elements, an analytical range covering only two orders of magnitude in concentration under a single set of experimental conditions, and a single-channel characteristic that limits analytical throughput. Although the latter feature is less important in highly automated systems, AES and continuum-excited AFS systems are better suited to high-volume routine analyses.

The use of AAS instruments as detectors for other analytical equipment, such as flow injection analyzers (FIA) and ion or liquid chromatographs, is an important area of application. Flame atomizers interface easily with these instruments and, when their sensitivity is adequate, relatively trouble-free, highly specific metal detection systems are feasible. Ultrasonic or "fritted disk" nebulizers are ideal for these applications. Continuously heated graphite furnaces can also be used for such applications; however, the gas generated when the solvent (eluent) evaporates sweeps the analyte out of the light path so rapidly that it reduces analytical sensitivity to flame-atomizer levels.

Elemental Analysis. Flame AAS is a reliable technique for routine elemental analysis. It can be relatively inexpensive because the basic equipment needed is not complex and because the intrinsic specificity of the technique eliminates the need for expertly trained operators. Flame AAS is especially well suited to laboratories whose anticipated sample loads cannot justify the purchase and maintenance cost of ICP-AES spectrometers. Instrument manufacturers can supply literature on applications. In many cases, only sample dissolution and/or dilution is required. In more complex instances, an extraction procedure may be used to remove

*Example 2 in this section was supplied by Suzanne H. Weissman and Michael Gonzales, Sandia National Laboratories. Example 4 was provided by Suzanne H. Weissman. This work was performed at Sandia National Laboratories and supported by the U.S. Department of Energy under Contract No. DE-AC04-76DP00789.

the bulk of interfering salts and/or to concentrate the analyte. Unless there is an insufficient original sample to prepare a suitable sample solution, the use of flame AAS instead of a graphite furnace technique is recommended for routine analysis.

The sensitivity of GFAAS enables performance of analyses that are virtually impossible using other analytical technique. Applications include:

- Lead or cadmium in a drop of blood
- Several metals in a needle tissue biopsy sample
- Rubidium in an insect egg (solid sampling)
- Silver in cloud-seeded rainwater
- Lead at the part per million concentration level in a steel chip (solid sampling)

The predilection of conventional GFAAS equipment to matrix interferences generally requires that considerable attention be paid to preparing the sample aliquot before atomization. This often involves adding matrix modifiers to the sample aliquot to enhance the efficiency of *in situ* pyrolysis heating step(s). Modifiers include:

- Ammonium nitrate and/or nitric acid to saline water samples to remove (volatilize) chlorine
- A mixture of magnesium nitrate and ammonium phosphate to retain volatile analytes such as cadmium and lead by entrainment so that the matrix can be suitably "ashed"
- Nickel to prevent arsenic and selenium from volatilizing in molecular forms during the atomization heating cycle, before gas-phase temperatures high enough to efficiently atomize them are reached
- Phosphoric acid to convert all forms of lead in air particulate samples to a single chemical species

In conventional furnaces, superior results are usually obtained when sample aliquots are deposited on a L'vov platform rather than the inner wall of the tube. The delay in evaporation of the analyte accompanying the use of a platform results in higher effective analyte gas phase temperatures and reduces the fraction of sample vapor removed from the optical path by rapidly expanding inert gas. L'vov platforms are generally most helpful with volatile analyte metals, but their use is recommended for all but the most refractory analyte metals.

The integral of the entire transient GFAAS signal is often a better measure of the amount of analyte in the sample aliquot than the maximum peak height signal, especially when differences in matrix composition may

change the volatilization characteristics of the analyte in the standards and samples. When the analyte element has a considerably different volatility than that of the bulk of the matrix, solid samples may be analyzed without prior dissolution. If the matrix covolatilizes with the analyte, the large amount of gas created may sweep the analyte out of the light path and/or chemically react with the analyte in the gas phase.

In one class of direct solid sample analyses, the matrix is volatilized before the analyte during ashing. Examples include determinations of trace metals in plant or animal tissue samples. The addition of oxygen to the gas surrounding the furnace during ashing often facilitates removal of the organic matrix. In the second class of solid sample analyses, the temperature is regulated so that the analyte volatilizes before the matrix. Examples include the determination of silver, lead, and cadmium in ground glass or steel chips.

Certain trace metals at part per million concentrations can adversely affect the physical properties of steel products. Conventional flame AAS analyses of these trace metals generally requires a preparative extraction/concentration sample workup with the attendant risk of contamination. A modified graphite "cup" atomizer for direct metal chip analyses has been used (Ref 27). The cup is first preheated to the desired atomization temperature by passing electrical current through its walls, then small pieces of the sample are dropped into it. The optical beam is passed through a pair of holes drilled through the cup.

Adding the sample after the cup is hot renders the gas phase temperatures experienced by the analyte independent of the volatilization characteristics of the analyte in the sample matrix. Results are generally favorable for trace analyte metals that are not highly soluble in the bulk matrix metal, for example, bismuth or lead in iron-based alloys. However, when analytes are highly soluble in the matrix, for example, lead in an alloy containing a high amount of tin, it is impossible to volatilize the analyte completely within a reasonable time.

A commercially available furnace atomizer for trace characterization of steel and nickel-base alloys has also been used (Ref 28). This design differs from the Massmann type in that the L'vov platform, or miniboat, used is readily removed and replaced through a slot cut in the side of the tube. Although most published research discusses the use of conventional Massmann furnaces (Ref 29), the miniboat-equipped furnace is better suited to direct solid sample analysis. The integrals of the analytical signals seen for volatile analyte metals are independent of the specific type of matrix alloy, and the

Table 2 Parameters for the flame AAS determination of alloying elements in steels

Analyte	Maximum concentration in steel(b), %	Maximum standard solution concentration(c), ppm	Spectral line, nm	Bandpass, nm	Flame(d)
Aluminum	2	200	309.3	0.2	N
Cobalt	0.5	50	240.7	0.1	AO
Chromium	0.5	50	357.9	0.2	N
Copper	0.2	20	324.7	0.2	A
Magnesium	0.2	2	285.2	0.5	N
Manganese	0.2	20	279.5	0.2	AO
Molybdenum	0.5	50	313.3	0.2	N
Nickel	0.6	60	352.4	0.2	AO
Lead	0.4	40	283.3	0.2	AO
Tin	0.8	80	286.3	0.2	N
Titanium	2.5	250	364.3	0.2	N
Vanadium	1	100	318.4	0.1	N
Tungsten(a)	4	400	255.1	0.1	N

(a) Samples containing more than 0.5% W will require the addition of 5 mL each of concentrated phosphoric and sulfuric acids to facilitate dissolution. (b) If the anticipated concentration is greater than given in this table, dilute an aliquot of the dissolved sample with the 5% Fe solution and water to 1% Fe level. (c) Prepare several standards covering the range from 0 (the blank) to the values given in this table in a 1% iron-matrix solution. (d) N, reducing nitrous oxide/acetylene flame; A, stoichiometric air/acetylene flame; AO, oxidizing (lean) air/acetylene flame.

overall precision of the analyses is favorable (approximately 6% RSD) at part per million analyte levels. Sample inhomogeneities in the sample chips are not a problem.

Example 1: Determination of Alloying Elements in Steels by Flame AAS. Manganese, magnesium, chromium, copper, nickel, molybdenum, vanadium, cobalt, titanium, tin, aluminum, and lead in iron-base alloys can be readily determined using flame AAS. One-gram samples are first dissolved in 15 mL of a 2:1 hydrochloric/nitric acid mixture. Then, 10 mL perchloric acid are added, and the solution is heated to drive off most of the more volatile acids. After approximately 5 min of moderate heating following the first appearance of perchloric acid fumes, the salts are dissolved, then diluted to 100 mL with water. Elemental standards containing iron at the 1% concentration level are prepared by adding suitable amounts of various 1000-ppm stock solutions and water to a 5 wt% stock solution of high-purity iron dissolved in the same manner as the samples. Having iron at approximately the same concentration level in all of the solutions exerts a leveling effect on nebulization/atomization.

The instrument conditions are those usually recommended by the manufacturer for the particular analyte. Table 2 outlines the more important instrument parameters. A reducing nitrous oxide/acetylene flame can be used for all these analyte metals if the resulting simplification of the analytical procedure is more important than the loss of sensitivity for some of the elements that results from using this type of flame. If the analyte concentration level in a particular steel sample is greater than the maximum listed for the standard solution in Table 2, a suitable aliquot of the sample solution can be added to some of the 5% pure-iron stock solution and diluted to an approximately 1% total dissolved-iron level.

Example 2: Analysis of Thermite by Flame AAS. Flame atomic absorption spectroscopy is widely used to determine major and minor elements in various chemical compounds. The analysis of thermite illustrates the use of flame AAS. Thermites are a mixture of iron oxide and finely divided aluminum powders used in welding iron and steel, for incendiary bombs, and other applications requiring generation of high temperatures. Thermite reacts exothermally upon

ignition, developing temperatures from 1100 to 2700 °C (2010 to 4890 °F), depending on such factors as the mole ratio present and particle size. The thermite reaction is:

$$8Al + 3Fe_3O_4 \rightarrow 9Fe + 4Al_2O_3 + heat$$

In this example, a set of thermite samples that would not ignite is analyzed. In addition to the determination of aluminum and iron oxide (Fe_3O_4), quantification of the amount of alumina (Al_2O_3), which will suppress ignition, was necessary. The amounts of Fe_3O_4 and aluminum in several unreacted thermite samples were determined by measuring iron and aluminum in the samples using flame AAS after dissolution in hydrochloric acid; the amount of Al_2O_3 was calculated by weighing the insoluble residue. The samples (approximately 150 mg) were heated in 27 mL of concentrated high-purity hydrochloric acid and 10 mL of water to dissolve the Fe_3O_4 and aluminum. Each solution was filtered through a tared 1 A3 Berlin crucible. Solutions were diluted so that aluminum concentrations ranged from 5 to 50 μg/mL. To each, hydrochloric acid was added to obtain a final acid concentration of 2 wt%. Iron and aluminum were determined from the same solution, to which 0.1 wt% potassium (as potassium chloride) was added as an ionization buffer for suppression of the ionization interference for aluminum.

The resulting dilutions were analyzed using an atomic absorption spectrometer. Manufacturer's recommendations (Ref 30) on instrument conditions were followed, optimizing flame conditions for each element (Table 3). Aluminum and iron were determined quantitatively by comparing the concentration readout on the instrument against an internal linear standard curve generated by analyzing aqueous calibration solutions (Fig. 13). Absorbances ranged to 0.21 for 50-μg Al/mL and 0.22 for 5-μg Fe/mL. The amount of Fe_3O_4 was calculated with assumption of stoichiometric proportions, and the amount of Al_2O_3 was determined by weighing the insoluble residue (Table 4). Estimated uncertainties of these numbers are ±5% (relative). The desired composition of a thermite mixture is 23.7% Al and 76.3% Fe_3O_4. These samples were depleted in aluminum and contaminated with Al_2O_3, which accounted for their failure to ignite. Consequently, this material was discarded and replaced with material of the correct composition.

Flame AAS is useful for determining major, minor, and trace levels of elements in samples that can be dissolved. Following dissolution, sample solutions are diluted to a

Table 3 Instrument conditions for determining aluminum and iron in a thermite sample

Element	Lamp current, mA	Wavelength, nm	Slit width, μm	Bandpass, nm	Flame
Aluminum	8	309.3	320	1	Nitrous oxide/acetylene, reducing, fuel-rich, red
Iron	8	248.3	80	0.3	Air/acetylene, oxidizing, fuel-lean, blue

Fig. 13 Calibration curve for the determination of aluminum in thermite by flame AAS

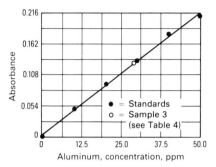

Table 4 Thermite analysis results

	Element, wt%			
Sample	Al(a)	Fe(a)	Fe₃O₄(b)	Al₂O₃(c)
1	16.5	56.4	77.8	6.0
2	20.0	52.9	72.9	5.0
3	19.5	52.1	71.8	5.9
4	20.8	53.3	73.6	5.0
5	20.8	54.5	75.2	4.5

(a) Determined by flame AAS. (b) Calculated from column 3 (Fe, wt%). (c) Determined gravimetrically, assuming residue was Al₂O₃.

useful working range (generally 1 to 50 μg/mL, depending on the element) and a concomitant added if necessary, for example, an ionization suppressor. Various samples, including metals, electrolytes, and reagents, can be analyzed. Flame AAS is preferable to graphite furnace AAS when element concentrations are sufficient because it is faster and more precise. Instrument conditions and potential interferences for each element are well documented and vary little from one instrument to another.

Example 3: Determination of Bismuth in Nickel by GFAAS. Like some of its neighbors in the periodic table, such as arsenic, antimony, tellurium, and selenium, bismuth is more easily determined using GFAAS by implementing nickel as a matrix modifier. The nickel tends to prevent volatilization of the analyte until higher furnace-tube temperatures are reached. This increases the efficiency of the pyrolysis clean-up step and the degree of atomization of the analyte when it finally volatilizes. When determinations of these elements in nickel-base alloys are attempted, the modifier is naturally present in solutions of the samples and needs only to be added to the standards at approximately the same level.

Solution preparation. First, 1 g of metal sample (drill chips or turnings) is dissolved in a Teflon beaker with 15 mL of 1:1:1 mixture of water/nitric acid/hydrofluoric acid. A moist salt is then evaporated and dissolved in 25 mL of a 1:10 nitric acid/water solution. This solution is diluted to exactly 50 mL with water and mixed well. Lastly, bismuth standards and a blank are prepared in 2% Ni.

Experimental Procedure. Because GFAAS determinations of trace metals in pure-metal alloys without prior separation of the bulk of the matrix tends to be a worst-case situation regarding potential background over-correction problems, an instrument having a Smith-Hieftje or a Zeemann-type

background-correction system is recommended. To enhance further the reliability of the procedure, the sample aliquot should be deposited on a L'vov platform, and the integral of the signal—not its peak height—should be used for calibration and measurement.

The first step in preparing reasonable conditions for the analysis is to calculate a suitable sample volume to be taken for each analysis. Figure 3 shows that under ideal conditions, a 1-ppm bismuth solution would provide an absorbance of approximately 22 if 25 μL of the solution were taken. That is, the absolute sensitivity to be expected is on the order of 0.88 absorbance units per nanogram of bismuth. Because sample dissolution entails a 50-fold dilution of the original 1-ppm bismuth concentration of the raw sample, 25 μL of the solution should contain approximately 0.5 ng of bismuth. This is sufficient to provide a response on the order of 0.45 absorbance units, optimum for AAS.

Next, an atomization temperature sufficient to volatilize the bismuth rapidly, but not high enough to covolatilize the nickel matrix, must be selected. This temperature can be determined experimentally, but the necessary information is usually available in the literature of the instrument manufacturer. In this case, 1900 °C (3450 °F) was recommended for bismuth, and 2400 °C (4350 °F) for nickel. Consequently, a 1900-°C (3450-°F) atomization was selected; during which the signal was to be measured, followed by a burnout step at 2400 °C (4350 °F) to remove the nickel matrix before beginning the next determination.

Aliquots of one of the standards are then subjected to a series of drying/pyrolysis/atomization steps using succeedingly greater pyrolysis temperatures until significant loss of analyte response is first noted. In this case, that temperature was approximately 1000 °C (1830 °F). Therefore, a conservative pyrolysis temperature of approximately 850 °C (1560 °F) was selected for the actual analyses.

Finally, 25-μL aliquots of the sample(s), standards, and blank(s) are analyzed using the conditions decided upon, and the concentration of the bismuth in the unknowns is calculated from the calibration graph. In this case, because a convenient standard reference material was available, (NBS SRM 898), verification of the entire procedure was facile.

Example 4: Determination of Trace Tin and Chromium in H₂O₂ by GFAAS. Graphite furnace atomic absorption spectroscopy is useful for quantifying trace and ultratrace levels of contaminants in various chemical reagents. One example of its use was analysis of hydrogen peroxide (H₂O₂),

which was used in the production of hybrid microcircuits.

The failure of a hybrid microcircuit was attributed to delamination of a gold-to-gold thermal compression bond on one of the integrated circuits. Auger analysis of the part correlated the problem with tin and chromium contamination, which occurred after production parts were cleaned in a H₂O₂/H₂O mixture. The problem appeared to be related to use of specific lots of H₂O₂. Trace amounts of tin are often used by manufacturers as H₂O₂ stabilizers. Trace analysis of several H₂O₂ solutions was necessary to determine the source of contamination. Tin and chromium concentrations were too low for analysis by flame AAS; therefore, GFAAS was used.

Twenty-milliliter aliquots of the H₂O₂ solutions were placed in platinum crucibles and decomposed by gentle heating. The platinum serves as a catalyst for the reduction. Each solution was diluted to 25 mL final volume and analyzed by GFAAS using an atomic absorption spectrometer with graphite furnace and an automatic sampler. Chromium and tin were quantified by comparing absorbances for the samples with those for aqueous standards (0.25 to 0.99 μg tin and chromium per milliliter), prepared by diluting 1000-μg/mL standards. Further sample dilutions were conducted as necessary so that tin concentrations were in the same ranges as for the standards.

Instrument conditions were optimized individually for the determination of tin and chromium (Table 5). For each element, the temperature program recommended by the manufacturer for ultrapure water (Ref 31) was adjusted to accommodate the instrument used in this example and to adjust for higher volatilities at the high altitude (1645 m, or 5400 ft). With these instrument conditions, the automatic sampler sprayed each solution into the pyrolytically coated graphite cuvette, which was held at the temperature selected in the first step of the temperature program (Table 5). The graphite cuvette was heated in six steps: the sample was dried in steps 1 and 2, pyrolyzed in steps 3 and 4, and

Table 5   Instrument conditions for trace-element content in H₂O₂

Element	Delay, s	Sample decomposition Deposition, s	Replicates	Integration Mode	Integration time, s
Chromium	5	20	2	Peak area	4
Tin	5	20	2	Peak height	1.5

Element	Step 1	2	3	4	5	6	Wavelength, nm	Bandpass, nm	Slit width, nm
Chromium	100 (212) 10	125 (255) 15	800 (1470) 15	900 (1650) 10	2100 (3810) 0	2100 (3810) 10	357.9	1	320
Tin	75 (165) 10	100 (212) 15	450 (840) 10	800 (1470) 10	2100 (3810) 0	2100 (3810) 10	235.5	0.5	160

(column groups: Temperature program(a), °C (°F), s — steps 1–6; Spectrometer conditions — Wavelength, Bandpass, Slit width)

(a) The time stated for the temperature program indicates the time to ramp to the stated temperature (0 s indicates a rapid temperature increase in <1 s) or the time that temperature remains constant (i.e., for step 6).

Table 6   Results of trace-element GFAAS analysis of H₂O₂

Sample Manufacturer	Lot	Bonding failure	Element concentration, μg/mL Cr	Sn
1	...	ID(a)	<0.001	0.32
2	...	Yes	0.002	3.7
3	...	ID(a)	0.072	3.0
4	A	No	0.049	0.10
4	B	Yes	<0.001	0.24

(a) Insufficient data

atomized in steps 5 and 6. No absorbance was observed before step 5 for either element. For chromium, the absorbance was integrated by the microprocessor beginning with the atomization stage (step 5). For tin, better precision was obtained by measuring the maximum absorbance (peak-height method) rather than by integrating the absorbance (peak-area method). Because of the simple matrix and ease in matching blanks and standards to the sample, background correction was not necessary. Absorbances (integrated absorbance for chromium) were linearly dependent on concentration and ranged to 0.75 for 0.50 μg Cr/mL and 0.35 for 0.99 μg Sn/mL.

Table 6 lists the resultant data, expressed as μg/mL of the original H₂O₂ sample. Estimated uncertainties in these data are ±10% (relative). These results show that tin and chromium contamination varied by several orders of magnitude and were independent. Although there were not enough data to correlate bonding performance with tin and chromium concentrations, these results, together with related data, were used to establish chromium and tin maximum limts for H₂O₂ used in future production development.

Graphite furnace atomic absorption spectrometry is useful for determining trace and ultratrace levels of elements in solutions. It is particularly useful for analyzing contaminants in chemical reagents, pollutants in environmental samples, and low-level dopants in materials. Because use of a graphite furnace is time consuming and the resultant data are less precise than with a flame, GFAAS should be reserved for those instances in which element concentrations are too low for flame AAS. Determining the optimum instrument conditions, especially the temperature program, is matrix dependent and must be considered individually for each sample type. Useful starting points are

the conditions suggested by instrument manufacturers and those listed in articles noted in the annual review issue of *Analytical Chemistry*.

Direct Solid-Sample AAS Analysis. Research on a general-purpose direct solid-sample AAS analysis system has been performed using a capsule-in-flame atomizer (Ref 32). The sample (ore samples, minerals, dried tissue, and so on) is ground in graphite powder, then packed into a graphite tube that is placed over a conventional analytical flame and resistively heated using the same type of power supply used in GFAAS. Analyte vapors diffusing through the relatively porous walls of the graphite tube enter the flame and are observed in the surrounding flame approximately 1 cm (0.4 in.) above the tube.

This system permits the controlled, rapid volatilization of 5- to 50-mg samples into a stable flame. The large volume of flame gas buffers the atomization conditions in the light path, making the technique less sensitive to matrix-effect problems than other GFAAS techniques. Detection levels range from 10^{-5}% for titanium to 10^{-7}% for cadmium. Determination of the same metals at comparable concentration levels using conventional flame AAS would require the dissolution of more sample as well as extensive analyte separation and preconcentration.

Air Filters. Another application of GFAAS has been the use of the porous graphite atomizers, or removable portions of them, as filters for air particulates (Ref 33). Air filters can be readily machined from several of the conventional types of graphite used to make dc arc spectroscopic electrodes. These filters are highly retentive but porous enough to permit reasonable air sampling rates. In addition, graphite filters can be cleaned before sampling by preheating in the same atomizer workhead used for the final analysis.

After sample collection, the graphite filter is placed in the atomizer workhead. When the power is applied, the particulates are atomized and the resulting atomic gas is analyzed as in typical GFAAS. The technique permits rapid spot air pollutant determinations on air-sample volumes of only a few cubic centimeters.

REFERENCES

1. G. Kirchoff, *Pogg. Ann.*, Vol 109, 1860, p 275
2. G. Kirchoff and R. Bunsen, *Philos. Mag.*, Vol 22, 1861, p 329
3. T.T. Woodson, *Rev. Sci. Instrum.*, Vol 10, 1939, p 308
4. A. Walsh, *Spectrochim. Acta*, Vol 7, 1955, p 108
5. J.D. Winefordner and R. Elser, *Anal. Chem.*, Vol 43 (No. 4), 1971, p 24A
6. K. Fuwa and B. Vallee, *Anal. Chem.*, Vol 35, 1963, p 942
7. H.L. Kahn, G.E. Peterson, and J.E. Schallis, *At. Absorp. Newslet.*, Vol 7, 1968, p 35
8. H. Massmann, *Spectrochim. Acta*, Vol 23B, 1968, p 215
9. P. Vijan, *At. Spectrosc.*, Vol 1 (No. 5), 1980, p 143
10. Yu Xian-an, D. Gao-Xian, and Li Chun-Xue, *Talanta*, Vol 31, 1984, p 367
11. I. Rubeska, M. Miksovsky, and M. Huka, *At. Absorp. Newslet.*, Vol 14, 1975, p 28
12. M.C. Cresser and A. Edwards, *Spectrochim. Acta*, Vol 39B, 1984, p 609
13. S.R. Koirtyohann and E.E. Pickett, *Anal. Chem.*, Vol 38, 1966, p 585
14. M.T.C. de Loos-Vollebrgt and L. de Galan, *Prog. Analyt. At. Spectrosc.*, Vol 8, 1985, p 47
15. S. Smith and G. Hieftje, *Appl. Spectrosc.*, Vol 37, 1983, p 552
16. A. Zander, T. O'Haver, and T. Keliher, *Anal. Chem.*, Vol 48, 1976, p 1166
17. J.D. Messman, M.S. Epstein, and T. Raines, *Anal. Chem.*, Vol 55, 1983, p 1055

18. R.K. Skogerboe, D.L. Dick, D.A. Pavlica, and F.E. Lichte, *Anal. Chem.*, Vol 47, 1975, p 568

19. D.R. Jones and S.E. Manahan, *Anal. Chem.*, Vol 48, 1976, p 502

20. B.V. L'vov, *Atomic Absorption Spectrochemical Analysis*, Chapter 5, Adam Hilger, 1970

21. D.D. Siemer, *Anal. Chem.*, Vol 55, 1983, p 693

22. W. Frech, A. Cedergren, E. Lundberg, and D.D. Siemer, *Spectrochim. Acta*, Vol 38B, 1983, p 1438

23. G. Lundgren and G. Johansson, *Talanta*, Vol 21, 1974, p 257

24. B. Magyar, *Guidelines to Planning Atomic Spectrometric Analysis,* Chapter 5, Elsevier, 1982

25. B.M. Gatehouse and A. Walsh, *Spectrochim. Acta*, Vol 16, 1960, p 602

26. R. Mavrodineanu and H. Boiteux, *Flame Spectroscopy*, John Wiley & Sons, 1965

27. W. Frech, E. Lundberg, and M. Barbooti, *Anal. Chim. Acta*, Vol 131, 1981, p 42

28. S. Backmann and R. Karlsson, *Analyst*, Vol 104, 1979, p 1017

29. F.J. Langmyhr, *Analyst*, Vol 104, 1979, p 993

30. J.J. Sotera and R.L. Stux, *Atomic Absorption Methods Manual*, Vol 1, *Standard Conditions for Flame Operation*, Instrumentation Laboratory Report No. 42208-01, Sandia National Laboratories, Albuquerque, June 1979

31. *Atomic Absorption Methods Manual*, Vol 2, *Flameless Operations*, Instrumentation Laboratory Report No. 42208-02, Sandia National Laboratories, Albuquerque, Dec 1976

32. B.V. L'vov, *Talanta*, Vol 23, 1976, p 109

33. D. Siemer, *Environ. Sci. Technol.*, Vol 12 (No. 5), 1978, p 539

Ultraviolet/Visible Absorption Spectroscopy

G. Dana Brabson, Department of Chemistry, University of New Mexico

General Uses

- Quantitative analysis
- Qualitative analysis, especially of organic compounds
- Fundamental studies of the electronic structure of atomic and molecular species

Examples of Applications

- Quantitative determination of the principal and trace constituents in metals and alloys
- Quantitative determination of trace constituents in environmental (air and water) samples. These determinations are often conducted on site
- Measurement of the rates of chemical reactions
- Identification of the functional groups in organic molecules
- Detection of species in the effluent of liquid chromatographs
- On-line monitoring of species in process streams
- Quantitative analysis of electroplating and chemical treatment baths
- Analysis of wastewater streams before and after treatment

Samples

- *Form*: Gas, liquid, or solid. Analyses are most commonly performed on liquid solutions
- *Size*: For solutions, typical sample volumes range from approximately 0.1 to 30 mL
- *Preparation*: Often quite complex. Complexity increases with the difficulty of placing the analyte in solution and the number of interferences

Advantages

- For quantitative analysis of inorganic ions, spectroscopic samples may contain as little as 0.01 mg/L in the case of species that form highly absorbing complexes
- For qualitative analysis of organic compounds, concentrations of spectroscopic samples may be as small as 100 nanomolar
- The initial capital outlay for ultraviolet/visible spectrophotometric techniques is usually far less than that for related techniques

Limitations

- The analyte must absorb radiation from 200 to 800 nm, or be capable of being converted into a species that can absorb radiation in this region
- Additional steps are often necessary to eliminate or account for interferences by species (other than the analyte) that also absorb radiation near the analytical wavelength

Estimated Analysis Time

- The actual time required to analyze each sample is a matter of minutes. However, it may take several hours to prepare the sample, make the standards, and create a calibration curve

Capabilities of Related Techniques

- *Molecular fluorescence spectroscopy*: For molecules that fluoresce strongly, this technique offers significantly greater sensitivities and freedom from interferences
- *Atomic absorption spectroscopy, optical emission spectroscopy*: For quantitative analysis of metals and some nonmetals, these techniques usually offer better sensitivity and almost complete freedom from interferences

Introduction

Ultraviolet/visible (UV/VIS) absorption spectroscopy, despite the emergence of newer techniques, remains a powerful and important tool. In addition, the instrumentation for UV/VIS spectrophotometry is for the most part relatively inexpensive and widely available. Some instruments are designed specifically to be taken in the field for on-site analyses.

Ultraviolet/visible absorption spectroscopy can be used as a qualitative tool to identify and characterize molecular species (including solvated molecular ions) and as a quantitative tool to assess the quantities of inorganic, organic, and biochemical species present in various samples. Of the many applications of this technique, this article will emphasize the quantitative analysis of elements in metals and metal-bearing ores. Additional applications can be found in the References in this article.

Principles

Light, Energy, and Molecular Structure. Ultraviolet/visible absorption spectroscopy is almost exclusively the spectroscopy of molecules dissolved in solvents (most atoms in the gas phase also absorb in this spectral region; however, this is the province of atomic absorption spectroscopy, as described in the article "Atomic Absorption Spectrometry" in this Volume). The spectral region of interest extends from 200 to 800 nm. The short-wavelength (200 nm) high-energy end of this spectral region is defined by the fact that below 200 nm oxygen and nitrogen in the atmosphere begin to absorb the radiant energy. The region below approximately 185 nm is termed the vacuum ultraviolet; the optical paths for experiments in the vacuum ultraviolet are evacuated or purged with a nonabsorbing gas, such as helium. The long-wavelength low-energy end of the spectral region is defined by the fact that the eye can no longer detect light at wavelengths longer than the red end of the visible spectrum, near 700 nm.

The quantitative relationship between the energy of a photon of light and its wavelength is:

$$E = \frac{hc}{\lambda} \qquad \text{(Eq 1)}$$

where h is 6.63×10^{-34} J · s (Planck's constant), c is 3.00×10^{17} nm/s (speed of light), and λ is the wavelength of the photon in nanometers.

For a molecule to absorb energy of a specific wavelength, the molecule must have two energy levels separated exactly by

Fig. 1 Absorption of a photon
(a) Ground state. (b) Transition. (c) Excited state

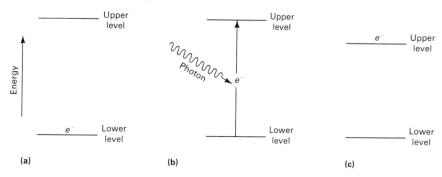

Fig. 2 Absorption of light by samples of thickness *b*
(a) Sample placed in a light path that absorbs half of the incident light. (b) A second sample (identical to the first) in the light path that passed through the first sample

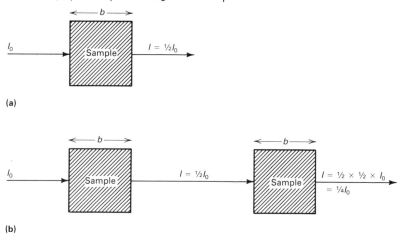

the energy equal to the energy of the photon that will be absorbed; one of these energy levels must be occupied by an electron, and the second energy level must have a vacancy that can accept the electron (Fig. 1a). Upon absorption of the photon (Fig. 1b), the electron makes the transition (jumps) from the lower energy level to the upper. Although the outcome of the excited molecule (Fig. 1c) will not be detailed in this article, the electron eventually must return to the lower energy level. A common result of this return to the ground state is the emission of a photon, again of precisely the same energy as the difference in energy between the two states (energy is always conserved). This phenomenon gives rise to other spectroscopic techniques, including molecular fluorescence spectroscopy (see the article "Molecular Fluorescence Spectroscopy" in this Volume).

Certain symmetry conditions must also be satisfied before a molecule can absorb energy of a specific wavelength. If these con-

ditions are not met, the probability of absorption of the photon by the molecule may be small, and it would be difficult or impossible to observe the spectroscopic transition experimentally.

Beer's law is the quantitative relationship that describes the quantity of light absorbed by a sample (a more rigorous derivation of Beer's law can be found in Ref 1). Suppose, for example, that a sample of thickness b (Fig. 2a) is placed in a light path and that this sample absorbs half of the light incident on it. If a second sample identical to the first is then placed in the path of the light that passed through the first sample (Fig. 2b), the second sample will absorb half of the light incident on it, and the number of photons passing through both samples will be one-fourth the number of photons incident on the first sample.

This process could be continued indefinitely; each time another sample is added, the radiant power will be reduced by a factor of two. The radiant power is the rate of

Fig. 3 Exponential decay of radiant power as a function of path length

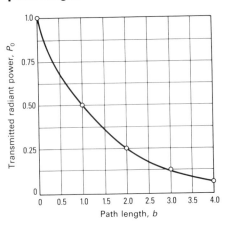

transfer of radiant energy and is therefore proportional to the number of photons passing through a unit area per second. Many older texts use the term intensity instead of radiant power. Table 1 lists and defines terms and symbols used in UV/VIS absorption spectroscopy. Plotting the radiant power of the light that is transmitted as a function of the number of samples placed in the light path yields an exponential decay curve (Fig. 3). This exponential decrease in radiant power can be expressed as:

$$\frac{P}{P_0} = e^{-kb} \qquad \text{(Eq 2)}$$

where P is the radiant power transmitted (not absorbed) by a sample of thickness b, P_0 is the radiant power incident on the sample, and k is a constant.

Note that the exponential decrease of the intensity is exactly like the exponential decay of a radioactive sample. After one half-life, half of the radioactive sample remains; after the second half-life, one quarter remains, and so forth. The mathematical equation for this decay has the same form as Eq 2:

$$\frac{N}{N_0} = e^{-kt} \qquad \text{(Eq 3)}$$

where N is the number of radioactive atoms remaining after time t, N_0 is the initial number of radioactive atoms, and k is a constant (related to the inverse of the half-life).

To this point, only one experimental variable (the thickness of the sample) has been discussed. The concentration of molecules in the sample will be examined next. As before, it is assumed initially that the sample absorbs half of the radiant energy incident

upon it and that the number of molecules through which the light must pass is doubled. In this instance, however, the number of molecules is increased by doubling the concentration of the sample instead of doubling the path length through which the light must pass. Nevertheless, the result is the same: each time the concentration is increased by one unit, the amount of light passing through the sample is decreased by a factor of two. Figure 4 illustrates this exponential decrease in the radiant power.

Thus, there are two important experimental variables, and the radiant power transmitted by the sample depends exponentially on each of them. This can be expressed mathematically by modifying Eq 2 to include the concentration, c, of the sample:

$$\frac{P}{P_0} = e^{-2.303abc} \qquad \text{(Eq 4)}$$

where P is the radiant power transmitted (not absorbed) by a sample of thickness b and concentration c, P_0 is the radiant of power incident on the sample, and $2.303a$ is a constant. The ratio P/P_0 is the fraction of incident radiation transmitted by the sample and is set equal to T, the transmittance of the sample. Many spectrophotometers are designed to read $\%T$ ($= 100 \times T$) directly.

Inverting Eq 4 and then taking the logarithm of both sides yields the following transformations:

$$\frac{P_0}{P} = \frac{1}{T} = e^{+2.303abc} \qquad \text{(Eq 5)}$$

and

$$\log_{10}\left(\frac{P_0}{P}\right) = \log_{10}\left(\frac{1}{T}\right) = abc \qquad \text{(Eq 6)}$$

Finally, the absorbance, A, is defined as follows: $A = \log_{10}(1/T)$. This yields the final form of Beer's law:

$$A = abc \qquad \text{(Eq 7)}$$

where A is the absorbance, a is the absorptivity (liters per gram centimeter), b is the optical path length through the sample (cen-

Fig. 4 Exponential decay of radiant power as a function of concentration

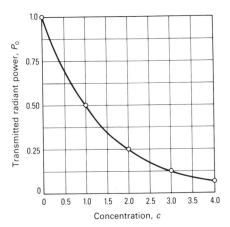

timeters), and c is the sample concentration (grams per liter). The absorbance, an experimentally measurable quantity, is a linear function of the path length, b, and of the concentration, c, of the sample. Thus, if for a fixed path length the absorbance of several solutions were measured as a function of concentration, a linear calibration curve similar to that shown in Fig. 5 would result. To determine the concentration of an unknown solution, it is necessary only to measure the absorbance of the solution, then read the concentration directly from the calibration curve.

The absorptivity, a, is the proportionality constant in Eq 7. Its units are selected so that the absorbance, A, is a unitless quantity. The absorptivity depends on the nature of the molecule, the wavelength at which the measurement is made, and, to a lesser degree, the solvent in which the molecule is dissolved.

Especially for the spectroscopy of organic molecules, Beer's law is often expressed as:

$$A = \epsilon bc \qquad \text{(Eq 8)}$$

where A is the absorbance, ϵ is the molar absorptivity (liters per mole centimeter), b is the optical path length through the sample (centimeters), and c is the sample concentration (moles per liter). Again, the units have

Table 1   Terms and symbols used in UV/VIS absorption spectroscopy

Term and symbol	Definition	Alternative
Radiant power, P	Energy per unit area per unit time	Intensity, I
Absorbance, A	$\log_{10}(P_0/P) = \log_{10}(1/T)$	Optical density, OD, or D; extinction, E
Transmittance, T	P/P_0	Transmission, T
Path length, b	...	l, d
Absorptivity, a	A/bc	Extinction coefficient, k
Molar absorptivity, ϵ	A/bc	Molar extinction coefficient

Fig. 5 Calibration curve showing absorbance as a function of sample concentration

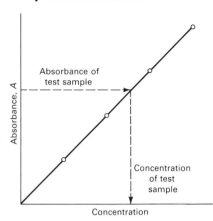

Fig. 6 Absorbance as a function of wavelength for a $Cu(H_2O)_4^{2+}$ complex ion

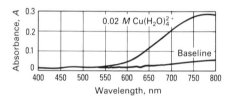

been selected so that the absorbance is unitless. The conversion factor between the absorptivity, a, and the molar absorptivity, ϵ, is simply the molecular weight of the absorbing species:

$$\epsilon a MW \qquad \text{(Eq 9)}$$

where MW is the molecular weight (grams per mole).

Figure 6 shows a typical absorption spectrum, that of the cupric (Cu^{2+}) ion dissolved in water. The actual absorbing species is the tetra-aquocopper(II) complex ion, $Cu(H_2O)_4^{2+}$, a square planar complex consisting of four water molecules bonded to a Cu^{2+} ion. Like many other compounds of copper, the $Cu(H_2O)_4^{2+}$ ion is blue-green, because it absorbs light in the orange and red portions of the spectrum and reflects (and transmits) light in the blue-green portion.

It is important to note that the absorbance (and hence the absorptivity) is a strong function of the wavelength at which the absorbance is measured. Thus, for maximum sensitivity in an analysis, the absorbance of the analyte is normally measured at the wavelength at which the absorptivity is greatest, the absorbance maximum. The notations λ_{max}, a_{max}, and ϵ_{max} are used in the

literature to represent the wavelength, absorptivity, and molar absorptivity, respectively, for the analyte-complex at the wavelength at which the absorbance is a maximum. In Fig. 6, for example, it can be estimated that $\lambda_{max} = 780$ nm.

Qualitative Analysis

A primary application of UV/VIS absorption spectroscopy is the identification of organic molecules. In principle, because no two molecules have exactly the same electronic distribution, the absorption maxima and molar absorptivities should be uniquely characteristic of each compound, and it should be possible to identify a compound uniquely from its UV/VIS spectrum. In practice, however, the quantity of molecules with absorption maxima at the same wavelength precludes a unique identification. Reference 2 lists no less than 85 compounds with absorption maxima at 260 nm.

Nevertheless, the UV/VIS spectrum of a molecule remains a useful piece of information, and when used in conjunction with other pieces of evidence, such as the infrared spectrum, the mass spectrum, the nuclear magnetic resonance (NMR) spectrum, and the physical properties, it can lead to the identification of the molecule. Moreover, molecules having the same functional groups usually have absorption maxima at approximately the same wavelengths. That is, the wavelength of the absorption maximum of a compound may indicate the functional groups and the structure of the molecule. To illustrate, Table 2 lists data for isolated chromophores (color-producing groups).

Reference 2 provides the physical constants for 21 000 common organic compounds and tabulates infrared (IR), Raman, UV/VIS, proton NMR, and carbon-13 NMR spectral data for these compounds. Volume 1 of Ref 2 contains information designed to aid interpretation of the UV/VIS absorption data. The tables of UV/VIS bands are provided in Vol VI. Reference 3 provides descriptions of the common techniques used in organic chemistry (mass, infrared, ^{1}H NMR, ^{13}C NMR, and UV spectrometry) and illustrates how the data from these techniques can be integrated to identify and characterize the unknown compound.

Quantitative Analysis

Ultraviolet/visible absorption spectroscopy is widely used to measure the concentrations of materials present in samples. For example, the concentrations of many organic molecules present in solutions can be measured easily. Similarly, the concentrations of various elements in metals, alloys, ores, and so on can be measured. To illustrate the

Fig. 7 Comparison of 0.02 M $Cu(H_2O)_4^{2+}$ and 0.02 M $Cu(NH_3)_4^{2+}$

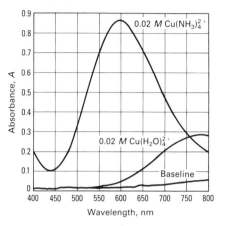

capabilities and limitations of this experimental technique, this article will focus on the latter applications.

Two principal conditions must be satisfied to achieve a successful analysis. First, the species of interest must absorb light in the spectral range from 200 to 800 nm, or it must be converted to some other molecule that absorbs in this region. Second, other species in the samples that absorb light at the same wavelength as the species of interest must be considered and accounted for.

Sensitivity. The absorptivity, a, and the molar absorptivity, ϵ, of a molecule are measures of the probability that, when a photon encounters the molecule, the photon will be absorbed by the molecule. Molecules with small values of a and ϵ absorb photons infrequently and therefore do not absorb much of the light incident on them. Consequently, relatively high concentrations of such molecules are necessary to achieve measurable absorbance, and the technique will not be very sensitive for these molecules. For example, in the spectrum of the $Cu(H_2O)_4^{2+}$ ion shown in Fig. 6, the molar absorptivity, ϵ, is calculated from the concentration and path length to be approximately 12. If a value of 0.01 is set arbitrarily for the absorbance of a molecule whose concentration can be mea-

Table 2 Absorption data for isolated chromophores

Chromophore	Structure	λ_{max}, nm	ϵ_{max}
Carbonyl (ketone)......	–CO–	188	900
		279	15
Carboxyl............	.–COOH	204	60
Nitro...............	–NO$_2$	271	19
Carbonyl (aldehyde)....	–CHO	290	16
Azo...............	.–N=N–	347	4
Source: Ref 2			

Table 3 Photometric methods for analysis of metals and metal-bearing ores

Element	Method	ASTM standard(s)
Aluminum	Aluminum	E 31:205, E 107:57
	8-hydroxyquinoline	E 350:76, E 360:20
Antimony	Rhodamine B	E 37:27, E 396:61
	Brilliant green	E 350:180
	Iodoantimonite	E 62:70
Arsenic	Molybdenum blue	E 46:14, E 57:17, E 360:9, E 361:9, E 364:8
Beryllium	Aluminon	E 106:19
Bismuth	Thiourea	E 46:33
Boron	Carmine	E 34:30
	Curcumin	E 350:257
Chromium	Dichromate	E 30:18
	Diphenylcarbazide	E 34:39, E 120:39, E 146:27, E 439:9
Cobalt	Nitroso-R-salt	E 39:7, E 75:29, E 76:30, E 106:36, E 107:25, E 350:53
Copper	Neocuproine	E 35:21, E 39:18, E 107:79, E 146:135, E 350:125, E 396:9
	Cupric bromide	E 35:30, E 46:22, E 107:8
	Cuprizone	E 120:58
	Diethyldithio-carbamate	E 120:68
	Oxaldihydrazide	E 478:8
Iron	1,10-phenanthroline	E 34:73, E 35:39, E 46:41, E 120:85, E 146:8, E 315:19, E 439:19, E 478:17, E 581:8
	Thiocyanate	E 39:29, E 40:34, E 76:41, E 106:44, E 107:16
Lead	Dithizone	E 35:48, E 40:25, E 361:20, E 363:20, E 368:9, E 396:19
Magnesium	8-hydroxyquinoline	E 107:93
Manganese	Periodate	E 34:293, E 35:57, E 39:40, E 75:59, E 76:53, E 107:33, E 120:102, E 146:49, E 314:13, E 350:8, E 352:8, E 439:29
Molybdenum	Thiocyanate	E 120:127, E 120:222, E 350:190, E 351:196, E 352:162, E 353:190, E 354:153
Nickel	Dimethylglyoxime	E 35:66, E 62:7, E 106:27, E 146:18, E 315:9, E 439:39, E 478:35
Nitrogen	Nessler reagent	E 146:58, E 350:63
Palladium	1-nitroso-2-naphthol	E 120:161
Phosphorus	Vanadate-molybdate	E 156:8, E 278:12, E 581:25
	Molybdenum blue	E 350:18, E 1070:1
Silicon	Molybdosilicic acid	E 34:118, E 35:93
	Molybdenum blue	E 107:49, E 120:171, E 146:154, E 315:30, E 350:114
Tantalum	Pyrogallol	E 367:9
Thallium	Rhodamine B	E 396:29
Tin	Phenylfluorone	E 62:80
	8-hydroxyquinoline	E 396:72
Titanium	Pertitanate	E 30:62, E 367:9
	Tiron	E 107:41
	5-sulfosalicylic acid	E 146:79
	Diantipyrylmethane	E 878:1
Tungsten	Dithiol	E 120:197
	Thiocyanate	E 146:102
Zirconium	Alizarin red-S	E 35:128

Note: The ASTM standard number and the pertinent section of the standard are listed above; for example, E 31:205 represents ASTM Standard E 31, Section 205.
Source: Ref 6

sured reliably, concentrations less than 0.005 g/100 mL cannot be measured using a cell with a path length of 1 cm.

Fortunately, however, the $Cu(H_2O)_4^{2+}$ ion can be converted into another ion that absorbed light more strongly, adding a few drops of concentrated ammonium hydroxide to the sample changes the color from a pale sky blue to a rich deep blue. In essence, an ammonia molecule replaces each of the water molecules in the $Cu(H_2O)_4^{2+}$ complex ion; the result is the tetra-amminecopper(II) ion

$Cu(NH_3)_4^{2+}$ (Fig. 7). The absorbance is approximately four times as great for the same concentration of copper. Consequently, it is possible to measure the concentration of more dilute solutions of the $Cu(NH_3)_4^{2+}$ ion than of the $Cu(H_2O)_4^{2+}$ ion. The sensitivity of the analysis can be increased tenfold by using the tetra-amminecopper(II) absorption band at 220 nm, because the peak absorbance of this band is approximately ten times the absorbance of the band at 590 nm. The rising portion of the spectrum of the $Cu(NH_3)_4^{2+}$ ion spec-

trum at 400 nm shown in Fig. 7 is actually the edge of the 220-nm band.

Finally, if this process is taken one step further by reducing the cupric (Cu^{2+}) ion to the cuprous (Cu^+) ion and converting the cuprous ion to the neocuproine complex, an additional 20-fold increase in the analytical sensitivity can be achieved (Ref 4):

$$2 \text{ neocuproine } + Cu^+ \rightarrow Cu(neocuproine)_2^+$$

$$\lambda_{max} = 455 \text{ nm}$$

$$\epsilon_{max} = 7950 \text{ L/mol} \cdot cm$$

neocuproine =

2,9-dimethyl-1,10-phenanthroline

The nature of the complexing reagent can have a tremendous impact on the intensity of the color of the analyte-complex and therefore on the sensitivity (and detection limits) of the analysis. The molar absorptivity of the analyte-complex is a useful index of the potential sensitivity of a particular technique.

Although some ions, such as the cupric and ferric ions, are colored in aqueous solutions (that is, their aquo complexes are colored), other ions are colorless in aqueous solutions. Nevertheless, satisfactory photometric analyses can be performed after the ions have been reacted with an appropriate organic molecule to form brightly colored complex ions. An example is the aluminum ion, Al^{3+}, which is colorless in aqueous solutions (Ref 5):

$$Al^{3+} + 3 \text{ oxine} \rightarrow Al(oxinate)_3 + 3 H^+$$

$$\lambda_{max} = 386 \text{ nm}$$

$$\epsilon_{max} = 6640 \text{ L/mol} \cdot cm$$

oxine =

8-hydroxyquinoline (8-quinolinol)

The American Society for Testing and Materials (ASTM) has approved photometric tests for 25 elements in metals, alloys, and ores (Ref 6). Table 3 lists these elements and provides references to the 1985 ASTM standards. Additional tests may be found elsewhere in the 1985 ASTM standards. For example, ASTM has approved photometric tests for 18 elements in water (Ref 7). Except for the inert gases (helium, neon, argon, krypton, xenon, and radon), photometric analyses have or at least in principle could be developed for all the elements in the periodic table. Additional information is available in Ref 8 to 11.

Fig. 8 Comparison of spectra from aqueous solutions containing nickel and cobalt ions

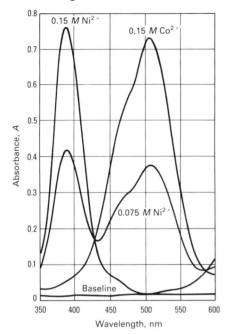

Interferences. If the analyte were the only species present in the sample (except for a solvent that is transparent at the wavelength at which the analysis is to be conducted), the analysis would be straightforward. Because few samples are so well behaved, interferences (other molecules that absorb radiation at the same wavelength as the analyte) must be considered.

Consider the analysis of a solution containing cobalt (Co^{2+}) and nickel (Ni^{2+}) ions. Figure 8 shows the spectra of aqueous solutions of these ions. The cobalt solution has a broad band centered at 510 nm, and the nickel solution has a broad band centered at 395 nm. Although the nickel solution does not absorb at the wavelength at which the cobalt solution has its absorption maximum (510 nm), both the nickel solution and the cobalt solution have significant absorbances at 395 nm. Consequently, if the analytical sample contains both ions, the nickel in the sample will not interfere with the analysis for the cobalt, but the converse is not true. In the presence of cobalt ions, high readings will be obtained for the nickel ion concentration unless specific measures are taken to account for or to remove this interference.

There are several methods for dealing with interferences. The following samples are illustrative.

Simultaneous Determination. When there are only two species in the sample, it is possible to determine the concentrations of both by solving two simultaneous equations (in principle, three species can be simultaneously analyzed for by solving three simultaneous equations, and so on). For example, the simultaneous analysis for nickel and cobalt can be accomplished by taking advantage of two features of Beer's law. First, Beer's law applies at all wavelengths, and, second, absorbances are additive. Thus, equations for the total absorbances at 510 and 395 nm can be expressed as:

$$A_{510} = a_{Co,510}bc_{Co} + a_{Ni,510}bc_{Ni} \quad (Eq\ 10)$$

$$A_{395} = a_{Co,395}bc_{Co} + a_{Ni,395}bc_{Ni} \quad (Eq\ 11)$$

The four absorptivities, $a_{Co,510}$, $a_{Ni,510}$, $a_{Co,395}$, and $a_{Ni,395}$, can be determined experimentally by measuring the absorbances of Co^{2+} and Ni^{2+} at 510 and 395 nm and by preparing a Beer's law plot for each ion at each wavelength. The concentrations of Ni^{2+} and Co^{2+} can now be determined in any solution. First, the absorbance is measured at 510 and 395 nm. These values are inserted into Eq 10 and 11. The two equations are then solved simultaneously for the two unknowns, c_{Co} and c_{Ni}. Another example of simultaneous determination is the carbamate method for analysis of nickel in water (Ref 12).

Selected Complexation. Occasionally, a complexing reagent is found that forms a colored complex with the analyte, but not with any of the potentially interfering species. An example of this method is the analysis for copper in iron and steel alloys by the neocuproine method (Ref 13). Neocuproine is essentially uniquely selective for copper. Because of its unique shape and size, neocuproine can form a highly colored complex with the Cu^+ ion (two neocuproine molecules per Cu^+ ion). Although neocuproine forms complexes with a few other ions, these are not highly colored and rarely interfere with the analysis for copper.

Separation by Complexation. It is sometimes possible to find a reagent that ties up potentially interfering ions by forming stable complexes that do not interfere with the analysis. To be effective, these complexing reagents must not form complexes with the analyte, and they must form colorless complexes with the interfering ions—that is, complexes that do not absorb at the analytical wavelength. An example of this method is the analysis for beryllium in copper-beryllium alloys by the aluminon method (Ref 14). Typical interfering elements in copper-beryllium alloys include aluminum, iron, and copper. To remove these interferences, ethylenediaminetetraacetic acid (EDTA) is added to the solution, along with the aluminon. The EDTA forms complexes with the potentially interfering elements, but not with the beryllium. The aluminon is then free to react with the beryllium alone, forming the characteristic red color (λ_{max} = 515 nm). The importance of adding EDTA is apparent in light of the use of aluminon in ASTM E 107 (Ref 15) to form a red complex (λ_{max} = 525 nm) with the aluminum in the photometric method for analysis of aluminum in electronic nickel.

Direct Chemical Separation. Often the most desirable method of eliminating interferences is to separate the analyte chemically from the interferences. In general, this is achieved by adding a reagent that reacts selectively with the analyte. An example of this method is the analysis for copper in magnesium alloys by the hydrobromic acid/phosphoric acid method (Ref 16).

In this method, iron and nickel interfere if they are present in amounts comparable to the amount of copper in the alloy. Consider the following list of electrochemical reduction potentials:

$$Cu^{2+}(aq) + 2e^- \rightarrow Cu(s) \quad E^\circ = 0.337\ V$$

$$Pb^{2+}(aq) + 2e^- \rightarrow Pb(s) \quad E^\circ = -0.126\ V$$

$$Ni^{2+}(aq) + 2e^- \rightarrow Ni(s) \quad E^\circ = -0.250\ V$$

$$Fe^{2+}(aq) + 2e^- \rightarrow Fe(s) \quad E^\circ = -0.440\ V$$

As this list suggests, lead is a stronger reducing agent than copper, but is a weaker reducing agent than nickel or iron. Accordingly, if lead is added to a solution containing Cu^{2+}, Ni^{2+}, and Fe^{2+} ions, it will reduce the Cu^{2+} ions to copper, but will not react with the Ni^{2+} or Fe^{2+} ions. Thus, in ASTM E 35, finely granulated low-copper lead is added to the analytical solution (Ref 16). The copper is removed from solution by the oxidation-reduction reaction with the lead:

$$Cu^{2+}(aq) + Pb(s) \rightarrow Cu(s) + Pb^{2+}(aq)$$

The aqueous phase containing the potentially interfering elements is discarded, the solid phase containing copper and residual lead is brought back into solution, hydrobromic and phosphoric acids are added, and the colored solution is analyzed photometrically (the Pb^{2+} ions do not interfere).

Electrodeposition of Interferences. If the reduction potential of the analyte is so negative that the analyte is not reduced in

Fig. 9 Schematic of Nessler tube colorimetry

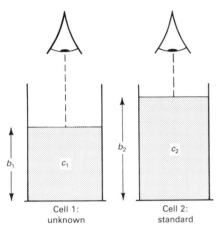

Cell 1: unknown   Cell 2: standard

aqueous electrolytic cells, it may be possible to remove the interferences by electrodeposition while allowing the analyte to remain in solution. An example of this method is the analysis for aluminum in electronic nickel by the aluminon method (Ref 15). When locating traces of aluminum in nickel alloys, advantage can be taken of the fact that the nickel ions (reduction potential = −0.250 V) can be reduced electrochemically to nickel metal while aluminum ions (reduction potential = −1.662 V) remain in solution:

$$Ni^{2+}(aq) + 2e^- \rightarrow Ni(s)$$

In this method, the solution containing aluminum, nickel, and other ions is poured into a beaker containing a pool of mercury (the cathode) and a platinum anode. Current is applied to the cell until the pale green color due to the Ni^{2+} ions has disappeared. With the nickel thus removed by reduction at the mercury cathode, the aluminon can then be added to the solution to make the characteristic bright red complex with the aluminum ions.

Ion exchange is one of the most effective techniques for separating ions. Because the ions of different analytes have different affinities for the exchange resin on the column, it is often possible to elute the ions from the column selectively, usually by adjusting the pH of the eluant. An example of this method is the analysis for niobium, tantalum, and titanium in ferroniobium alloys (Ref 17). After the sample has been dissolved in a hydrochloric-hydrofluoric (HCl-HF) acid mixture, the solution is passed through a column containing an anion-exchange resin. The niobium, tantalum, and titanium ions are retained by the column. The first eluant used is an ammonium chloride-hydrochloric-hydro-

fluoric (NH_4Cl-HCl-HF) mixture, which selectively removes the titanium ions from the column. An NH_4Cl-HF solution is then used to remove the niobium ions. Finally, an NH_4Cl-NH_4F (ammonium fluoride) solution removes the tantalum ions. Thus, three solutions, each containing one analyte, have been prepared, and each can be subjected to analysis for the specific ion it contains.

Use of Excess Reagent. The interference is sometimes more subtle in that the interfering species uses up the color-forming reagent and thus depletes the supply of reagent that would normally react with the analyte. This interference can be eliminated by adding sufficient excess reagent so that the demands of the interfering species and the analyte are satisfied. An example of this method is the analysis for iron in lead alloys by the 1,10-phenanthroline method (Ref 18). In this method, copper tends to interfere with the analysis for iron by forming a complex with the 1,10-phenanthroline. Although the copper-1,10-phenanthroline complex does not interfere with the photometric determination of the iron, the presence of the copper prevents complete color development of the iron by depleting the available supply of 1,10-phenanthroline. The solution is to use an appropriate excess of 1,10-phenanthroline.

Intentional Addition of Interfering Species. Accepting the presence of an interfering species and ensuring that the same amount of interfering species is present in all samples is sometimes more practical. This method may require the intentional addition of interfering species to ensure that the contribution due to the interference is the same in all samples. An example of this method is the analysis for nickel in copper alloys by the dimethylglyoxime method (Ref 19). In this method, each solution (the test solution and each calibration solution) is prepared to contain exactly 1 g of copper.

Instrumentation

The instrumentation for UV/VIS absorption analyses ranges from the simple to the sophisticated. The three key components are a light source, a wavelength selector to isolate a narrow band of wavelengths near the desired analytical wavelength, and a detector to measure how much of the light incident on the sample is transmitted by the sample. The most common light sources are the hydrogen (or deuterium) lamp in the ultraviolet region and the tungsten lamp in the visible region of the spectrum. These lamps are termed white light sources because they emit light at all wavelengths within their spectral ranges. The analytical wavelength may be selected by a filter that allows passage of only those wave-

lengths near the analytical wavelength or by a monochromator that disperses the white light, then selects a narrow band of wavelengths from the dispersed spectrum. The most commonly used detector is the photomultiplier tube (PMT), a current source that typically yields 10^4 to 10^6 electrons for each photon striking the photocathode. Upon impact on the photocathode, the photons eject small showers of electrons from the photosensitive surface. The electrons are electrostatically accelerated to the first dynode, where each electron ejects several additional electrons; these are accelerated to the second dynode, where the process is repeated. After several stages of amplification in the PMT, the current is measured, and the resulting signal is used to drive a meter, strip-chart recorder, or microprocessor.

Nessler (color comparison) tubes, named after the German agricultural chemist Julius Nessler, represent perhaps the oldest and simplest technique still used today. In this technique (Fig. 9), a solution of unknown concentration is placed in cell 1, and a solution of known concentration in cell 2. The amount of standard solution in cell 2 is adjusted until the intensity of the color in the two cells, when observed from above the cells, appears the same to the eye. In terms of Beer's law, the absorbance is the same in the two cells; this relationship can be expressed as:

$$A_1 = ab_1c_1 = A_2 = ab_2c_2 \qquad (Eq\ 12)$$

where a is a constant for this experiment because the same molecule is absorbing light in both cells. Equation 12 can be simplified as follows:

$$b_1c_1 = b_2c_2 \qquad (Eq\ 13)$$

Because c_2 is known, it is necessary only to measure b_1 and b_2, then to calculate the concentration, c_1, in cell 1. Typical Nessler tubes have flat bottoms, and graduations are often etched on their sides to allow direct reading of b_1 and b_2. Analytical techniques using Nessler tubes are simple and effective, but are suitable only if the analyte makes a colored solution, and if there are no interfering substances in the sample that also absorb light in the visible portion of the spectrum.

Color-Comparison Kits. Commercially available color-comparison kits also involve visual comparison of the intensity of the color in the analytical sample with a standard. In this case, the standard is a colored strip of paper or transparent plastic (often a disk). The hue of the standard is the same as that expected for the analytical sample. The intensity (brightness) of the color of the standard changes continuously from light (colorless) at one end of the scale to dark at the other end. It is a simple matter to find that location on the standard for which the intensity of the color is the same as that in the analytical sample. A digital scale on the standard provides a numerical value that is easily converted to the concentration of the analyte. As in the case of the Nessler tubes, color-comparison kits may not be suitable if the sample contains optically interfering substances.

Filter Photometers. Although the eye can achieve credible results when comparing the intensities of the colors in two samples, filter photometers provide greater precision and improved performance in the presence of interferences. These improvements are achieved by incorporating an electro-optical detector (more capable than the eye for distinguishing small changes in intensity) and an optical filter that selects a narrow band of wavelengths (usually at the absorption maximum of the analyte) and rejects wavelengths at which interfering species absorb. Absorption and interference filters are commonly used for this task.

Absorption filters are colored pieces of glass or quartz that selectively transmit wavelengths of one color while absorbing wavelengths at shorter and longer wavelengths. Typically, the band of wavelengths passed by an absorption filter is quite broad. Interference filters, in contrast, reject wavelengths on either side of the transmission notch rejected by destructive interference. These filters are made by depositing several layers of transparent dielectric materials of different indexes of refraction on a transparent substrate. The thicknesses of dielectric layers are selected so that the incident light destructively interferes with itself at all wavelengths except those near the desired transmission notch. The selectivity (narrowness of the band pass) of an interference filter increases with the number of layers. Interference filters with transmission notches and band passes designed for many analytical applications are commonly available, and when circumstances dictate, an interference filter can be manufactured with parameters tailored to the specific application.

Typical filter photometers are single-beam instruments. Because, as indicated by Eq 5 and 6, determination of the absorbance of a sample requires measurement of the radiant power incident on the sample, P_0, and of the radiant power exiting the sample, P, two separate measurements must be made for each sample. The first measurement (of P_0) is made using a blank containing no analyte; the blank is replaced by the solution containing the analyte for the second measurement (of P). Filter photometers are particularly suitable for applications involv-

Fig. 10 Schematic of a dispersive single-beam spectrophotometer

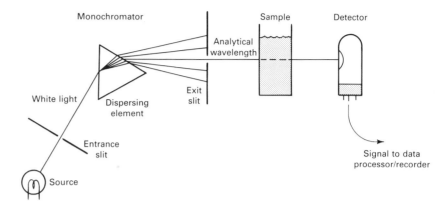

Fig. 11 Block diagram of a double-beam spectrophotometer

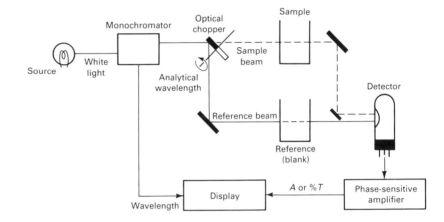

ing infrequent changes of the analytical wavelength.

Dispersive Single-Beam Spectrophotometers. Figure 10 shows a schematic of a simple dispersive single-beam spectrophotometer. In contrast with filter photometers, which permit use of only one or perhaps a few fixed analytical wavelengths, dispersive spectrophotometers contain monochromators that permit selection from among a continuous choice of wavelengths.

The key components in a monochromator are the dispersing element and the slits. The dispersing element (typically a grating or a prism) separates the white light into its individual wavelengths and projects the dispersed light onto the exit plane of the monochromator. The exit slit, basically a narrow opening in the exit plane of the monochromator, allows a narrow band of wavelengths to exit the monochromator and pass through the sample. By varying the position of the grating or prism, the color (wavelengths) of the light leaving the monochromator can be adjusted to the band of wavelengths required for the analysis. As in the case of filter photometers, the absorb-

ance of the sample is determined by comparing the intensity of light that passes through a blank with the intensity of light that passes through the analytical sample.

The dual-beam dispersive spectrophotometer, the most complex and expensive of the instruments, makes separate measurements of P_0 and P for each sample unnecessary. Figure 11 shows a block diagram illustrating the key elements of a typical double-beam spectrophotometer. In this diagram, the optical beam is mechanically chopped by a rotating half-silvered mirror; the beam passes alternately through the blank and the sample. The output from the detector, alternately proportional to P_0 and P, is processed by a phase-sensitive amplifier, which in turn generates signals proportional to the absorbance, A, and the transmittance T. The output is usually displayed as a function of wavelength on an x-y plotter or a strip-chart recorder.

Because a double-beam instrument continuously ratios the light transmitted by the sample against the light transmitted by the blank, two advantages result. First, the instrument continuously compensates for slow drifts in instrumental parameters such as the source intensity. Second, the instrument automatically compensates for the fact that the intensity of the source and the response of the detector are functions of the wavelength. Consequently, a double-beam instrument is ideally suited for scanning the spectrum of a substance and is the instrument of choice for qualitative analysis of unknown materials and the development of new analytical methods.

Pseudo Double-Beam Spectrophotometers. With the advent of high-speed microprocessors and high-capacity inexpensive digital storage devices, it has been possible to introduce single-beam spectrophotometers that emulate nearly all the features of the classical double-beam instruments. First, the instrument scans the blank as a function of wavelength, digitizes the data, and stores the data in memory. Second, the instrument scans the sample. Finally, the instrument electronically compares the data for the two scans and produces a spectrum. These instruments offer the advantages of inherent mechanical simplicity and a high performance-to-cost ratio.

Experimental Parameters (Ref 20)

Selection of Optical Cells. Ultraviolet/ visible absorption spectrophotometry depends on measuring the fraction of the incident beam of light transmitted through the sample. However, absorption of photons by the analyte is not the only phenomenon that can reduce the radiant power of the incident beam. Other phenomena include reflection of the incident beam at the interfaces between the air and the sample cell and at the interfaces between the sample cell and the sample, absorption by the solvent, and absorption by the sample cell itself. The following suggestions will minimize the effects of these phenomena:

- For single-beam experiments, use the same cell for the blank and for the sample, or use matched cells
- Especially for spectrophotometers using test-tube sample cells, that is, cells without flat optical surfaces, place the sample cell in the sample compartment in precisely the same orientation each time
- For dual-beam experiments, use matched pairs of cells

Preparation of the Blank. As mentioned above, the solvent and other reagents used to prepare the sample may absorb some of the light at the analytical wavelength. Potential problems due to this fact can be minimized if the sample and the blank are as similar as possible. The same reagents (amounts and concentrations, except for the analyte) should be used to prepare the blank and the sample. This precaution can be relaxed if the blank has been shown not to absorb at the analytical wavelength.

Optimum Absorbance. For optimum results, the absorbance of the sample should be between 0.1 and 1.0 absorbance units. This corresponds to a transmittance between 80 and 10%. Samples outside this range may be diluted or concentrated, or a shorter or longer sample cell can be used. The most common sample cells have a path length of 1 cm. Cells with path lengths as short as 0.1 cm and as long as 10 cm are also available.

Slit Width and Signal-to-Noise Ratio. As indicated in the section "Instrumentation" in this article, the dispersed light in the monochromator falls on the exit plane of the monochromator, and the exit slit in the exit plane selects a portion of this light for transmission to the sample. Consequently, as the slit width is increased, the amount of light that passes through the sample and arrives at the detector is increased, and the signal-to-noise ratio is improved.

Slit Width and Selectivity. The width of the exit slit in the monochromator determines the amount of light and the purity of the radiation leaving the monochromator. The wider the slit, the greater the range of wavelengths of light. A wide slit is rarely a problem if the analyte is the only absorbing species in the sample, that is, if there are no interferences. However, if the sample contains an interfering species with an absorption maximum near that of the analyte, a wide slit can result in absorption of light by the analyte and by the interfering species. To minimize this problem, it is necessary to narrow the slit sufficiently so that the band of wavelengths transmitted by the monochromator overlaps the absorption band of the analyte, but not the absorption band of the interfering species.

An example of the application of this precaution is the analysis for manganese in iron and steel alloys by the periodate method (Ref 21). In this method, the manganese is oxidized to the permanganate ion, which has an absorption maximum at 545 nm. If the sample contains chromium in addition to manganese, as is often the case, the chromium is oxidized to the chromate ion. Because the chromate ion absorbs appreciably at wavelengths shorter than 530 nm, the monochromator must transmit wavelengths near 545 nm, but not near 530 nm. Therefore, for this analysis, ASTM E 350 recommends use of a narrow-band spectrophotometer (with a bandwidth of 10 nm or less)

and care in centering the band pass at 545 nm. Similarly, if a filter photometer is used, the filter must have a narrow band pass, and transmission maximum for the filter should be between 545 and 565 nm.

Development and Stability of Color. Although the colors of some analytes develop almost instantly and are stable almost indefinitely, this is not universally true. Examples of illustrative situations follow:

- *Analysis for boron in aluminum alloys by the Carmine method* (Ref 22): Development of the color is slow. Accordingly, the color is permitted to develop for at least 45 min before the photometric measurements are made
- *Analysis for chromium in beryllium by the diphenylcarbazide method* (Ref 23): The color develops almost immediately, but begins to fade after approximately 10 min. Therefore, the procedure recommends that the measurements be made within 5 min after the diphenylcarbazide is added to the sample
- *Analysis for antimony in copper alloys by the iodoantimonite method* (Ref 24): The pitfall in this analysis is exposure of the analytical sample to air. Air slowly oxidizes the iodide present in the sample to iodine, which in aqueous solutions forms a yellow-brown complex that interferes with the analysis for antimony at 420 nm
- *Analysis for aluminum in ferrosilicon/ferroboron by the aluminon method* (Ref 25): Because the intensity of the aluminum-aluminon complex has a strong temperature coefficient, this method recommends that all measurements be made within ±1 °C (1.8 °F) of a convenient temperature. To achieve this accuracy, many of the more sophisticated spectrophotometers have temperature-controlled sample compartments and sample holders
- *Analysis for iron in copper-beryllium alloys by the thiocyanate method* (Ref 26): The analyte-complex, like those in many analyses, is photosensitive; the color fades upon exposure to light. Accordingly, the procedure recommends protection of the photometric samples from direct sunlight

Purity of Solvents and Reagents. Because most of the UV/VIS absorption methods are quite sensitive, it is important to pay careful attention to the purity of the reagents used in the analyses. In some cases, it will be necessary to use distilled water instead of deionized water. Common organic solvents are available in various purities. As a minimum, reagent-grade solvents should be used; in many cases, use of specially

Table 4 Analysis for manganese in zirconium alloys by the periodate method

In the left-hand column, Sections 49–56 of ASTM E 146 (Ref 31) have been reproduced. Explanatory notes have been added in the right-hand column.

Method E 146	Notes
49. Summary of Method 49.1 Manganese in an acid solution is oxidized to permanganate by means of potassium periodate. Photometric measurement is made at approximately 525 nm.	49.1 The permanganate, $KMnO_4^-$, ion gives the solution a deep red-purple color that absorbs in the green portion of the spectrum.
50. Concentration Range 50.1 The recommended concentration range is from 0.01 to 0.20 mg of manganese in 100 mL of solution, using a cell depth of 10 cm. (Note) This procedure has been written for a cell having a 10-cm light path. Cells having other dimensions may be used, provided suitable adjustments can be made in the amounts of sample and reagents used.	50.1 As long as the concentration of manganese in the optical sample is held within these limits, the recorded absorbance will be within reasonable bounds. If the absorbance of the test solution is found to exceed 1.0, it will be necessary to take a smaller sample in Step 55.1. Avoid the temptation simply to dilute the test solution with distilled water.
51. Stability of Color 51.1 The color is stable for at least 24 h.	
52. Interferences 52.1 The interference of residual or alloying iron, chromium, and nickel is eliminated by discharging the permanganate color in a portion of the sample with sodium azide and using this as a reference solution.	52.1 The solution mentioned in this step is actually used as a blank (See Steps 55.4 and 56.1) rather than as a reference solution (the reference solution is distilled water).
53. Reagents 53.1 *Manganese, Standard Solution* (1 mL = 0.01 mg Mn)—Dissolve 0.5000 g of electrolytic manganese in 10 mL of $HNO_3(1+1)$. Boil to remove the oxides of nitrogen. Cool and dilute to 1 L in a volumetric flask (1 mL = 0.500 mg Mn). Dilute 20 mL of this solution to 1 L with water in a volumetric flask. 53.2 *Potassium Periodate* (KIO_4) 53.3 *Sodium Azide* (NaN_3)	53.1 The ASTM standards use the following convention to express dilution of reagents: (volume of reagent + volume of water). Thus, in this section, the notation (1 + 1) means that one volume of concentrated HNO_3 is to be diluted with one volume of water.
54. Preparation of Calibration Curve 54.1 *Calibration Solutions*—Transfer 0.0, 2.0, 5.0, 10.0, and 20.0 mL of manganese solution (1 mL = 0.01 mg) to five 250-mL chemical-resistant glass beakers. Dilute to approximately 50 mL with water and add 40 mL of $H_2SO_4(1+1)$. 54.2 *Reference Solution*—Use distilled water as the reference solution. 54.3 *Color Development*—Add 0.3 g of KIO_4. Bring to a boil and maintain at boiling for at least 15 min. Cool in a water bath, transfer to 100-mL volumetric flasks, and dilute to the mark with water. 54.4 *Photometry*—Transfer a suitable portion of the reference solution to an absorption cell and adjust the photometer to the initial setting, using a light band centered at approximately 525 nm. While maintaining this photometer adjustment, take the photometric readings of the calibration solutions. 54.5 *Calibration Curve*—Plot the photometric readings of the calibration solutions against the micrograms of manganese per 100 mL of solution.	54.4a This step is written for a single-beam spectrophotometer. With the reference solution in the sample compartment, the instrument is adjusted to read 0.000 absorbance units (100% transmittance). This adjustment is not disturbed throughout the remainder of the analysis. The same (or a matched) cell is used for the rest of the analysis. 54.4b If a dual-beam instrument is used, the reference solution is placed in the reference compartment and remains there throughout the analysis. A matched cell is used for the calibration and test solutions. 54.5 This is the Beer's law plot. Draw the best straight line through the origin and the data points.
55. Procedure 55.1 *Test Solution*—Weigh 1.0 g of the sample into a platinum beaker. Add 40 mL of $H_2SO_4(1+1)$ and then add HF dropwise (about 2 mL) until solution is complete. Add 4 to 5 drops of HNO_3 and evaporate to dense white fumes. Cool, rinse down the sides of the beaker with water, and fume again. Allow to cool. To the cool H_2SO_4 solution, carefully add about 50 mL of water, and transfer to a 250-mL beaker. 55.2 *Reference Solution*—Use distilled water as the reference solution. 55.3 *Color Development*—Proceed as directed in 54.3. 55.4 *Photometry*—Take the photometric reading of the test solution as described in 54.4. To the remaining portion of the test solution contained in the volumetric flask, add approximately 10 mg of NaN_3. Warm gently for several minutes. When cool, read the absorbance of the solution as described in 54.4. Use this absorbance as a blank.	55.4 The NaN_3 destroys the MnO_4^- ion without destroying the color of the interfering ions (Fe^{3+}, CrO_4^{2+}, Ni^{4+}). Thus, the residual absorbance in the blank is due solely to the interfering ions and can be subtracted from the total absorbance of the test solution. The difference is the absorbance due to the MnO_4^- ion alone.
56. Calculation 56.1 Correct the absorbance readings for the blank and determine the micrograms of manganese present from the calibration curve. Calculate the parts per million of manganese as follows: $$Manganese, ppm = A/B$$ where: A = micrograms of manganese corrected for blank, and B = grams of sample used.	56.1 The correction for the blank is applied to the measured absorbance of the test solution, not to the absorbances of the calibration solutions.

purified spectroscopic-grade materials is appropriate.

Cleanliness of Glassware. Related to the requirement for the use of pure reagents is the requirement to use carefully cleaned glassware. The analysis for phosphorus in iron and steel alloys by the molybdenum blue method (Ref 27) will serve as an example. In this method, the phosphorus is oxidized to the phosphate ion, which is converted in two steps to a deeply colored blue complex. The method is so sensitive that as little as 0.005 mg of phosphorus per 100 mL of sample can be observed spectrophotometrically. Therefore, the method includes this comment: ''Glassware must be phosphorus- and arsenic-free. Boil the glassware with hydrochloric acid and rinse with water before use. It is recommended that glassware used for this determination be reserved for this use only. Many detergents contain phosphorus and must not be used for cleaning purposes.''

Sensitivity and Detection Limits. For quantitative analysis, the absorbance of the analyte normally should be between 0.1 and 1. With somewhat degraded results, the range may be expanded from 0.05 to 1.50 absorbance units. However, when the detection of trace amounts of a substance is the first priority (and quantification the second priority), the useful range can be extended to much smaller absorbances. A practical lower limit is an absorbance of approximately 0.001 (Ref 28). With consideration of this value, Eq 8 can be used to place a lower boundary on the detection limits for an analysis:

$$c_{min} = \frac{0.001}{\epsilon b}$$ (Eq 14)

where $b = 10$ cm (the longest cell that can fit into most commercial instruments); values for the molar absorptivity, ϵ, often can be found in such sources as Ref 9.

Precision and Accuracy. For qualitative analysis, the accuracy of the wavelength determination is of principal interest. A typical value of wavelength accuracy for a moderately priced double-beam instrument is ± 0.5 nm. Numerous wavelength standards are available for the calibration of spectrophotometers. A low-pressure mercury arc has numerous emission lines throughout the ultraviolet and visible regions of the spectrum. Alternatively, a holmium oxide glass filter or a 4% solution of holmium oxide in 1.4 M perchloric acid may be used; each has several narrow absorption bands with well characterized absorption maxima (Ref 29).

For quantitative analysis, the emphasis shifts to the precision and accuracy of the measured absorbance, A. Typical instrumental values are $\pm 0.002 A$ and $\pm 0.005 A$ for the precision and accuracy, respectively. However, the values of which the instrument is capable rarely represent the overall precision or accuracy of the analysis. Such factors as sample preparation, interferences, and experimental technique are key. A reasonable expectation is a relative error of 1 to 5%, but even this may not be achievable in some cases.

Deviations from Beer's Law. Beer's law predicts a linear relationship between the measured absorbance and the concentration of the analyte. Deviations from this linear relationship are of two types: real or apparent. Real deviations from Beer's law are rare in the quantitative analysis of analytes dissolved in solvents if (1) the band pass of the monochromator is narrow relative to the width of the absorption band, and (2) the analytical wavelength coincides with the wavelength of the absorption maxima (Ref 30). The spectrum should be scanned near the nominal analytical wavelength, and the wavelength set at the experimentally observed absorption maximum. Circumstances occasionally arise—for example, the presence of an interfering species that absorbs at a nearby wavelength—that make it desirable to select an analytical wavelength other than that at the absorption maximum. In such cases, real deviations from Beer's law may be anticipated.

Apparent deviations from Beer's law are more common and are often attributable to the fact that the various samples at different concentrations are not truly chemically identical. The analysis for chromium as the dichromate ion, $Cr_2O_7^{2-}$, is an example. The dichromate ion is in equilibrium with other chromium containing ions that absorb at different wavelengths:

$$H_2O + Cr_2O_7^{2-} \rightleftarrows 2HCrO_4^- \rightleftarrows$$
$$2CrO_4^{2-} + 2H^+$$

Consequently, of the total chromium in solution, the fraction present as the dichromate ion depends on the pH and on the concentration of the solution. To avoid the concomitant apparent deviations from Beer's law in this example, the pH must be controlled with an appropriate buffer.

Applications

A traditional quantitative investigation involving analysis for manganese in zirconium alloys by the periodate method is outlined in Table 4. This is one of many applications of UV/VIS absorption spectroscopy. The following discussions indicate the applicability of UV/VIS absorption spectroscopy to a variety of problems.

Determination of the Number of Ligands in a Complex. An experiment in which the concentration of a metal ion is held constant as the concentration of the reagent that forms a colored complex with that metal ion is slowly increased will serve as an example. As the concentration of the complexing reagent is increased, more and more metal ions pick up complexing groups (ligands), and the intensity of the color of the solution increases. This process can be followed spectrophotometrically. The process

continues until all the available metal ions have reacted to form colored complexes; at this point, the intensity of the color ceases to increase. By comparing the initial concentration of metal ions with the amount of complexing reagent added, the number of complexing groups per metal ion can be calculated.

Spectrophotometric Titrations. Many titrations—for example, acid-base titrations using acid-base indicators and oxidation-reduction titrations with iodide or permanganate ions—are characterized by distinct color changes at their end points. Ultraviolet/visible absorption spectroscopic techniques are well suited to accurate determination of the end points in these reactions.

Assay of Enzyme Activity. Serum glutamate pyruvate transaminase (SGPT), an enzyme found especially in the heart, converts a mixture of L-alanine and α-ketoglutarate into a mixture of pyruvate and L-glutamate. The rate of this reaction depends on the concentration of SGPT; thus, the concentration of SGPT in a sample can be determined if the amount of pyruvate formed in a unit of time, for example, 10 min, can be measured. Because pyruvate forms a yellow-orange complex with salicylaldehyde, the amount of pyruvate formed is measured easily using conventional UV/VIS absorption techniques.

Indirect Determinations. The enzyme assay referred to above is an example of an indirect spectrophotometric method in that the substance under assay is not measured directly. A similar example involves the determination of bromine based on the fact that traces of bromine catalyze the oxidation of iodine to iodate by the permanganate ion in sulfuric acid solutions (Ref 32). At the beginning of the experiment, known amounts of iodine and potassium permanganate are added to the sample containing traces of bromine. After exactly 10 min, the remaining (unreacted) iodine in the solution is extracted with carbon tetrachloride (CCl_4); the amount of iodine in the CCl_4 is then determined spectrophotometrically at 515 nm. The quantity of iodine that was oxidized during the 10-min interval is determined by subtraction; the rate at which the iodine was oxidized is proportional to the amount of bromine in the original sample.

Characterization of Surfaces. Many spectrophotometers have specular reflectance accessories that permit characterization of the surfaces of nontransparent samples. In a specular reflectance accessory, a mirror is used to intercept the sample beam and bring the light to the surface of the sample. A second mirror captures the specularly reflected light (at an angle of reflection equal to the angle of incidence) and returns it to the optical path of the instrument. The information thus obtained can be used to characterize the state of the surface, for example, the oxidation, or the coatings on the surface.

REFERENCES

1. D.J. Swinehart, *J. Chem. Educ.*, Vol 39, 1962, p 333
2. J.G. Graselli and W.M. Ritchey, Ed., *Atlas of Spectral Data and Physical Constants for Organic Compounds*, Vol 1-6, 2nd ed., CRC Press, 1975
3. R.M. Silverstein, G.C. Bassler, and T.C. Morrill, *Spectrometric Identification of Organic Compounds*, 4th ed., John Wiley & Sons, 1981
4. E.B. Sandell and H. Onishi, *Photometric Determination of Traces of Metals: General Aspects*, 4th ed., John Wiley & Sons, 1978, p 367
5. E.B. Sandell and H. Onishi, *Photometric Determination of Traces of Metals: General Aspects*, 4th ed., John Wiley & Sons, 1978, p 432
6. *Annual Book of ASTM Standards*, Vol 03.05, ASTM, Philadelphia, 1985
7. *Annual Book of ASTM Standards*, Vol 11.01, ASTM, Philadelphia, 1985
8. E.B. Sandell, *Colorimetric Determination of Traces of Metals*, Part II, 3rd ed., John Wiley & Sons, 1959
9. E.B. Sandell and H. Onishi, *Photometric Determination of Traces of Metals: General Aspects*, 4th ed., John Wiley & Sons, 1978
10. F.D. Snell, *Photometric and Fluorometric Methods of Analysis: Metals*, Parts 1 and 2, John Wiley & Sons, 1978
11. F.D. Snell, *Photometric and Fluorometric Methods of Analysis: Nonmetals*, John Wiley & Sons, 1981
12. "Standard Test Methods for Nickel in Water," D 1886, Sections 7-15, *Annual Book of ASTM Standards*, Vol 11.01, ASTM, Philadelphia, 1985
13. "Standard Methods for Chemical Analysis of Carbon Steel, Low-Alloy Steel, Silicon Electrical Steel, Ingot Iron, and Wrought Iron," E 350, Sections 125-134, *Annual Book of ASTM Standards*, Vol 03.05, ASTM, Philadelphia, 1985
14. "Standard Methods for Chemical Analysis of Copper-Beryllium Alloys," E 106, Sections 19-26, *Annual Book of ASTM Standards*, Vol 03.05, ASTM, Philadelphia, 1985
15. "Standard Methods for Chemical Analysis of Electronic Nickel," E 107, Sections 57-64, *Annual Book of ASTM Standards*, Vol 03.05, ASTM, Philadelphia, 1985
16. "Standard Methods for Chemical Analysis of Magnesium and Magnesium Alloys," E 35, Sections 30-38, *Annual Book of ASTM Standards*, Vol 03.05, ASTM, Philadelphia, 1985
17. "Standard Methods for Chemical Analysis of Ferrocolumbium," E 367, *Annual Book of ASTM Standards*, Vol 03.05, ASTM, Philadelphia, 1985
18. "Standard Methods for Chemical Analysis of Lead- and Tin-Base Solder," E 46, Sections 41-51, *Annual Book of ASTM Standards*, Vol 03.05, ASTM, Philadelphia, 1985
19. "Standard Methods for Chemical Analysis of Copper Alloys," E 478, Sections 35-44, *Annual Book of ASTM Standards*, Vol 03.05, ASTM, Philadelphia, 1985
20. A. Knowles and C. Burgess, Ed., *Practical Absorption Spectrometry, Ultraviolet Spectrometry Group*, Chapman and Hall, 1984
21. "Standard Methods for Chemical Analysis of Carbon Steel, Low-Alloy Steel, Silicon Electrical Steel, Ingot Iron, and Wrought Iron," E 350, Sections 8-17, *Annual Book of ASTM Standards*, Vol 03.05, ASTM, Philadelphia, 1985
22. "Standard Test Methods for Chemical Analysis of Aluminum and Aluminum Base Alloys," E 34, Sections 30-38, *Annual Book of ASTM Standards*, Vol 03.05, ASTM, Philadelphia, 1985
23. "Standard Methods for Chemical Analysis of Beryllium," E 439, Sections 9-18, *Annual Book of ASTM Standards*, Vol 03.05, ASTM, Philadelphia, 1985
24. "Standard Methods for Chemical Analysis of Copper and Copper Alloys (Photometric Methods)," E 62, Sections 70-79, *Annual Book of ASTM Standards*, Vol 03.05, ASTM, Philadelphia, 1985
25. "Standard Methods for Chemical Analysis of Ferroalloys," E 31, Sections 205-215, *Annual Book of ASTM Standards*, Vol 03.05, ASTM, Philadelphia, 1985
26. "Standard Methods for Chemical Analysis of Copper-Beryllium Alloys," E 106, Sections 44-51, *Annual Book of ASTM Standards*, Vol 03.05, ASTM, Philadelphia, 1985
27. "Standard Methods for Chemical Analysis of Carbon Steel, Low-Alloy Steel, Silicon Electrical Steel, Ingot Iron, and Wrought Iron," E 350, Sections 18-29, *Annual Book of ASTM Standards*, Vol 03.05, ASTM, Philadelphia, 1985
28. E.B. Sandell and H. Onishi, *Photometric Determination of Traces of Metals: General Aspects*, 4th ed., John Wiley & Sons, 1978, p 191
29. J.G. Graselli and W.M. Ritchey, Ed., *Atlas of Spectral Data and Physical Constants for Organic Compounds*, Vol 1, 2nd ed., CRC Press, 1975, p 403-404
30. D.A. Skoog and D.M. West, *Principles of Instrumental Analysis*, 2nd ed., Saunders College, Philadelphia, 1980, p 153-157
31. "Standard Methods for Chemical Analysis of Zirconium and Zirconium Alloys," E 146, Sections 49-56, *Annual Book of ASTM Standards*, Vol 03.05, ASTM, Philadelphia, 1985
32. "Standard Test Methods for Iodide and Bromide in Water," D 1246, Sections 16-24, *Annual Book of ASTM Standards*, Vol 11.01, ASTM, Philadelphia, 1985

Molecular Fluorescence Spectroscopy

Linda B. McGown, Department of Chemistry, Oklahoma State University

General Uses:

- Fundamental studies of electronic transitions of organic and inorganic fluorescent molecules as well as of some atomic species
- Qualitative and quantitative chemical analysis

Examples of Applications

- Correlation of structural features of crystalline materials with their fluorescence spectral properties to study the nature of the interactions between lattice constituents
- Spectral fingerprinting for oil spill identification
- Determination of carcinogenic polynuclear aromatic compounds in environmental and biological samples
- Use of fluorescent labels for immunoassays
- Determination of metals that exhibit native fluorescence or that can induce fluorescence in appropriate crystallophor matrices
- Determination of electronic excited-state lifetimes
- Studies of protein dynamics, protein-ligand interactions and transport, and membrane structure and function
- Detection for high-performance liquid chromatography

Samples

- *Form:* Gas, liquid, or solid. Analyses are most commonly performed on liquid solutions
- *Size:* For solutions, sample size ranges from several milliliters to subnanoliter volumes using laser excitation
- *Preparation:* Requirements are often minimal and may include extraction, addition of reagents to induce or modify fluorescence, and so on. Special techniques, such as matrix isolation or Shpol'skii spectroscopy, require more complex sample preparation

Limitations

- The molecular (or atomic) species of interest must exhibit native fluorescence or must be coupled to or modified by chemical or physical interactions with other chemical species
- Detection limits for intensely fluorescent chemical species can extend from nanomolar to subpicomolar levels, depending on the type of instrumentation used

Estimated Analysis Time

- Usually ranges from minutes to hours. Actual measurement time per sample is generally on the order of seconds or less per measurement, and the analysis time depends on the number of measurements conducted per wavelength and the number of wavelengths used as well as other experimental variables and data-analysis requirements

Capabilities of Related Techniques

- *Ultraviolet/visible absorption spectroscopy:* Directly applicable to a wider range of molecules because fluorescent and nonfluorescent absorbers can be studied, but absorption is therefore less selective. Absorption spectra are more featureless than fluorescence spectra, and absorption detection limits are at least three orders of magnitude poorer and linear dynamic ranges much shorter than those of fluorescence
- *Atomic absorption and emission techniques (flame, furnace, inductively coupled plasma):* For atomic species, these techniques often afford improved detection limits and applicability to a wider range of elements.

Introduction

Molecular fluorescence spectroscopy has fundamental applications that include studies of electronic properties of organic and inorganic molecules in gas, liquid, and solid phases. Fluorescence spectroscopy is routinely used for chemical analysis of various samples, including those of forensic, environmental, toxicological, clinical, biochemical and biological, and industrial importance. Fluorimetric measurements have been used in kinetic and enzymatic methods as well as flow systems.

The emission of photons from molecules that have been excited electronically by absorption of photons in the ultraviolet/visible (UV/VIS) region is referred to as molecular luminescence and includes fluorescence and phosphorescence. This article will discuss the theory of fluorescence and its application to chemical analysis.

Theory

Figure 1 shows the processes involved in molecular fluorescence. When a molecule in its ground electronic singlet state (S_0, vibrational level $v = 0$) absorbs (process A, for absorption) a photon of an appropriate UV/VIS frequency, it is elevated to a higher electronic singlet energy state (for example, S_1). The molecule rapidly de-excites by vibrational relaxation (VR) to the lowest vibrational level ($v = 0$) of S_1. The molecule may then de-excite back down to S_0 by one of several competitive routes. De-excitation by emission of a photon is referred to as fluorescence (F). Alternatively, the molecule may undergo nonradiative (NR) transfer of energy as heat to the surroundings. Finally, if a triplet state (T_1) of somewhat lower but overlapping energy is available, intersystem crossing (IX) may occur. In the triplet state, the molecule relaxes vibrationally to the lowest vibrational level ($v = 0$) of T_1, from which it may de-excite by photon emission, referred to as phosphorescence (P), or by NR de-excitation. Once returned to S_0, the molecule relaxes vibrationally to the lowest vibrational level ($v = 0$).

The fluorescence quantum yield Φ_F is the efficiency of fluorescence de-excitation:

$$\Phi_F = \frac{\text{No. of photons emitted as fluorescence}}{\text{No. of photons absorbed}} \quad \text{(Eq 1)}$$

The overall rate of de-excitation, k, of the molecule population from S_1 to S_0 is the sum of the rates of each of the de-excitation processes:

$$k = k_F + k_{NR} + k_{IX} \quad \text{(Eq 2)}$$

Fig. 1 Jablonsky diagram indicating molecular absorption and de-excitation processes

See text for explanation

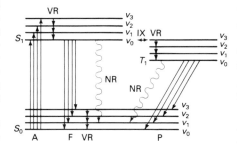

and the fluorescence quantum yield is:

$$\Phi_F = \frac{k_F}{(k_F + k_{NR} + k_{IX})} \quad \text{(Eq 3)}$$

The mean radiative lifetime of the excited state, τ_F, is inversely proportional to the de-excitation rate:

$$\tau_F = \frac{1}{k} \quad \text{(Eq 4)}$$

Fluorescence lifetime is the time required for the fluorescence emission to be reduced to 1/e of its initial intensity following excitation by a pulse of light with negligible duration. It is characteristic of the molecule and depends on the environment of the molecule. The inherent fluorescence lifetime, τ_F^0, is the mean radiative lifetime in the absence of competing de-excitation processes ($\Phi_F = 1$, $k_{NR} = k_{IX} = 0$). Therefore, the fluorescence quantum yield can also be expressed as $\Phi_F = \tau_F/\tau_F^0$.

Delayed Fluorescence. If a molecule undergoes IX from the S_1 to the T_1 state, it may then undergo a second IX and return to the S_1 state. The net rate of $S_1 \rightarrow T_1$ intersystem crossing (k_{IX} in Eq 2 and 3) is then:

$$k_{IX} = k(S_1 \rightarrow T_1) - k(T_1 \rightarrow S_1) \quad \text{(Eq 5)}$$

If the molecule subsequently de-excites by photon emission, fluorescence spectrally similar to prompt fluorescence is observed, but the mean radiative lifetime is much longer, reflecting the additional time consumed by the IXs.

Quenching of fluorescence refers to any process that lowers the fluorescence quantum yield of a fluorophore. Quenching processes can generally be classified as collisional or complexational. Collisional quenching lowers Φ_F to a degree determined by the concentration of the quencher [Q]:

$$\frac{\Phi_F^0}{\Phi_F} = 1 + k_c\,[Q]\,\tau_0 \quad \text{(Eq 6)}$$

where Φ_F^0 and Φ_F are the quantum yields in the absence and presence of quencher Q, respectively; k_c is the collisional quenching rate constant; and τ_0 is the fluorescence lifetime in the absence of quencher. The effect of collisional quenching on fluorescence intensity is:

$$\frac{F_0}{F} = 1 + k_c[Q]\tau_0 \quad \text{(Eq 7)}$$

where F_0 and F are the fluorescence intensities in the absence and presence of quencher, respectively.

As the rate of collisional quenching increases, the observed radiative lifetime of the fluorophore decreases, because:

$$\tau_F = \frac{1}{k_F + k_{NR} + k_{IX} + k_c[Q]} \quad \text{(Eq 8)}$$

where the rate of collisional quenching has been added to the possible de-excitation processes.

Complexation quenching involves the reduction of fluorescence quantum yield due to the formation of a complex between the fluorophore and the quencher. The equation for complexation quenching is:

$$\frac{F_0}{F} = 1 + K[Q] \quad \text{(Eq 9)}$$

where K is the dissociation constant of the complex. Because complexation quenching is a static rather than dynamic process relative to the time scale of fluorescence, the observed fluorescence lifetime is independent of concentration of quencher.

Fluorescent Molecules

Organic Compounds. The first requirement for fluorescence is that a molecule absorb UV/VIS radiation. The best candidates are polyaromatic molecules with highly delocalized π electrons and low-energy π-π* transitions (* denotes the excited state), combining high molar absorptivities with high fluorescence efficiencies. Molecules containing heteroatoms may also exhibit fluorescence corresponding to n-π* transitions, but the fluorescence emission will be much lower due to low molar absorptivities combined with relatively poor fluorescence efficiencies. Structural rigidity favors fluorescence because radiationless deactivation by internal conversion is difficult in rigid molecules. Linear planar structures favor fluorescence (Table 1). Substituents that increase delocalization of the

Table 1 Structural effects on fluorescence quantum yields for some polynuclear aromatic hydrocarbons

Hydrocarbon	Structure	Quantum yield, Φ_F
Anthracene		0.36
Phenanthrene		0.13
p-terphenyl		0.93
m-terphenyl		0.29
Triphenylene		0.08
Chrysene		0.14
Pyrene		0.32

Source: Ref 1

Table 2 Substituent effects on fluorescence quantum yields for monosubstituted benzene derivatives

Substituent	Quantum yield, Φ_F
$-H$	0.07
$-F$	0.13
$-CH_3$	0.17
$-C_2H_5$	0.18
$-OH$	0.08
$-OCH_3$	0.29
$-NH_2$	0.08
$-NO_2$	0
$-Br$	~0
$-I$	~0

Source: Ref 1

Table 3 Minimum detectable quantities for fluorescent metals

Metal	Minimum detectable quantity, µg
Praseodymium	2.5×10^{-4}
Neodymium	0.5
Samarium	5×10^{-5}
Europium	2.5×10^{-4}
Gadolinium	1
Terbium	2.5×10^{-3}
Dysprosium	2.5×10^{-3}
Erbium	5×10^{-3}
Thulium	5×10^{-3}

Source: Ref 2, 3

Table 4 Crystallophosphor host matrices and metals that can be determined by inducing fluorescence

Matrix	Metals
Vanadates	Samarium, europium, dysprosium, holmium, erbium, thulium, gadolinium, terbium, neodymium, ytterbium
Oxyhalides: GdOX	Samarium, europium, praseodymium, neodymium, dysprosium, terbium
LaOCl, YOF	Praseodymium, terbium, dysprosium, holmium, neodymium, samarium, europium, erbium, thulium, ytterbium
CaF_2	Thulium, neodymium, europium, lanthanide (III) ions
CeO_2	Neodymium, europium, holmium, erbium
Y_2O_3	Praseodymium, samarium, europium, gadolinium, dysprosium, holmium, erbium, thulium
NaF	Uranium

Source: Ref 4

Table 5 Organic complexing agents and metals that can be determined fluorimetrically by complexation

Organic complexing agent	Metals
8-hydroxyquinoline	Aluminum, calcium, cadmium, cesium, gallium, indium, potassium, lithium, magnesium, sodium, rubidium, tin, strontium, yttrium, zinc, zirconium
8-hydroxyquinoline-5 sulfonic acid	Silver, aluminum, cadmium, gallium, indium, magnesium, manganese, tin
Calcein	Barium, calcium, cadmium, magnesium, strontium
Rhodamine 6-G	Gallium, antimony, rhenium
Rhodamine B	Gold, gallium, thallium, rhenium
Morin	Aluminum, boron, beryllium, cadmium, gallium, hafnium, indium, lutetium, magnesium, molybdenum, tin, antimony, thorium, uranium, tungsten, zirconium
Flavonol	Boron, hafnium, tin, thorium, tungsten, zinc, zirconium
Benzoin	Boron, beryllium, germanium, antimony, zinc

Many metals form fluorescent complexes with organic complexing agents (Table 5). The fluorescence results from the greater structural rigidity of the complex relative to the individual ligand, which may be non- or weakly fluorescent. In addition, the nonbonding electron energy level of the ligand may be lowered due to the association of the nonbonding electrons with the metal cation, resulting in a greater n-π^* transition energy. The lowest energy singlet-singlet transition may then become the π-π^*, promoting fluorescence.

Complex formation does not necessarily promote fluorescence. Complexation of a highly fluorescent ligand may quench its fluorescence. Complexation with certain metals may also increase the rate of IX, increasing phosphorescence probability and decreasing fluorescence efficiency.

Excitation and Emission Spectra and Qualitative Analysis

Under normal conditions, ground-state molecules generally are excited from the lowest energy vibrational level ($v = 0$) upon

π-electron system also favor fluorescence; substituents that diminish the delocalized system due to steric interference or electron withdrawal decrease fluorescence. High atomic weight (heavy) atoms increase the triplet character of the excited state, increasing the rate of IX and decreasing fluorescence efficiency. Table 2 lists substituent effects on fluorescence quantum yields.

Inorganic Atoms and Molecules. Rare-earth elements exhibiting native fluorescence of their ions in solution include cerium, praseodymium, and neodymium, which have broad-band fluorescence due to $5d$-$4f$ transitions, and samarium, europium, gadolinium, terbium, dysprosium, erbium, and thulium, which have narrow fluorescence bands due to $4f$ transitions. Table 3

lists minimum detectable quantities for some of these elements. Some salts of La^{3+} fluoresce, with radiative lifetimes on the order of microseconds, and have therefore been used to label immunoassay reagents to provide discrimination based on the lifetime difference between the label and the much shorter-lived sample background emission. Uranyl compounds fluoresce from 520 to 620 nm, and various methods have been described for the fluorimetric determination of U(IV) salts.

Multicomponent inorganic crystalline materials known as crystallophosphors fluoresce due to the presence of an activating impurity in the crystal lattice. Table 4 lists crystallophosphor host matrices along with the elements that can activate fluorescence and thus be determined fluorimetrically.

Fig. 2 Absorption and fluorescence emission spectra of N-phenyl carbazole

Source: Ref 1

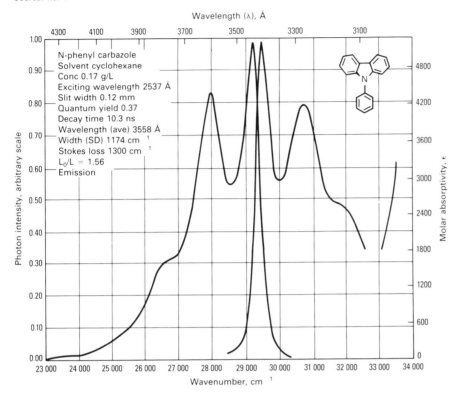

Table 6   Approximate excitation and emission maxima and fluorescence lifetimes for molecules with overlapping fluorescence spectra(a)

Molecule	Excitation maximum, nm	Emission maximum, nm	Fluorescence lifetime (τ_F), ns
Fluoranthene	360	460	53.0
3-phenylfluoranthene	370	475	34.5
3,3′-bifluoranthenyl	372	463	7.8
1,1,4,4-tetraphenylbutadiene	346	455	1.76
1,6-diphenylhexatriene	354	453	12.4
1-aminoanthracene	390	470	22.8

(a) The emission and excitation spectra of these compounds consist of broad bands, resulting in a high degree of spectral overlap.
Source: Ref 1

photon absorption. Fluorescence emission generally occurs from molecules in the $v = 0$ vibrational level of the excited state. Therefore, fluorescence emission spectra are Stokes-shifted, that is, appear at longer wavelengths, from the corresponding absorption spectra. Due to the similarity between the vibrational transitions of the ground and excited states, emission spectra are often approximate mirror images of the absorption spectra. Figure 2 shows the absorption and emission spectra of N-phenyl carbazole.

Excitation spectra correspond to the same spectral information contained in absorption spectra, but are collected using the fluores-

cence instrumental configuration rather than the 180° instrumental configuration used to obtain absorption spectra.

Emission and excitation spectral information can be used to identify fluorescent components in samples. Excitation spectra are acquired by scanning the excitation monochromator at a constant emission wavelength, λ_{em}, and emission spectra are acquired by scanning the emission wavelength at constant excitation wavelength λ_{ex}. In general, the emission spectrum is independent of the excitation wavelength used, and the excitation spectrum is independent of the emission wavelength monitored. This provides two independent dimensions of spec-

tral information that can be exploited for qualitative analysis in contrast to the single spectral dimension available in absorption spectroscopy.

Peaks due to scattered light appear centered around $\lambda_{ex} = \lambda_{em}$ and may conceal fluorescence emission. Scattered light can be reduced by using polarizers, one in the emission beam and one in the excitation beam, positioned perpendicular to each other. Each polarizer reduces the beam intensity by approximately 50%; therefore, polarizers are used only when necessary.

Other types of fluorescence information can sometimes be used in addition to spectral information to help identify the emitter(s) in a sample. Fluorescence lifetimes of species with highly overlapping spectra often vary greatly (Table 6). Other fluorescence experiments involving selective quenching and polarization measurements can also be useful for qualitative purposes.

Quantitative Analysis

The fluorescence emission intensity I_F for a particular species is directly proportional to its molar concentration, c, according to:

$$I_F = I_0 k \Phi_F \, \epsilon bc \qquad \text{(Eq 10)}$$

where I_0 is the intensity of the incident excitation beam, ϵ is the molar absorptivity, k is a constant for instrumental and geometric factors, and b is the sample thickness in the direction of absorption.

Negative deviations from linear response occur at high concentrations of total absorbing species in the sample due to deviations from Beer's law of absorption behavior. Even below these concentrations, deviations may occur due to the inner-filter effect, in which most of the incident beam is absorbed near the front of the sample, significantly attenuating the beam as it traverses the sample. Therefore, I_0 is no longer essentially constant throughout the sample, and emission may appear to decrease as concentration increases at these levels. Self-absorption, in which the emitting species subsequently reabsorbs emitted radiation, may also occur at high concentrations.

Dimerization (P + P = P₂), excimer formation (P + P* = PP*), and exciplex formation (P* + N = P*N) cause deviations from linearity, where P is the fluorescent monomer with excited state P*, and N is a different molecular species. For example, pyrene is soluble in water at micromolar levels, above which excimer formation predominates. Figure 3 shows the emission spectra of pyrene monomer and excimer. Because formation of the excimer decreases fluorescence intensity due to the monomer

Fig. 3 Fluorescence emission spectra of pyrene monomer (solid spectrum) and excimer (dashed spectrum) in water

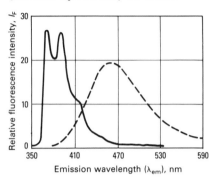

Fig. 4 Single-beam fluorometer with 90° configuration

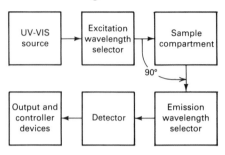

Fig. 5 Spectral output of typical xenon (dashed spectrum) and mercury (solid spectrum) lamp sources

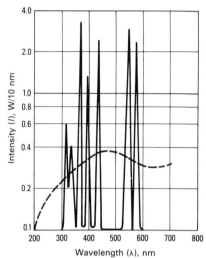

species, care must be taken in quantification of pyrene. Determinations can be simplified if an auxiliary reagent is added to the solutions, such as a micelle-forming species or albumin, that can prevent excimer formation.

The emission intensity from a sample containing multiple emitters equals the sum of the intensity contributions from each species if the total concentration of absorbing species is sufficiently low and if the emitters are noninteracting. Energy transfer, complex or exciplex formation, and any other chemical interactions between the species can cause deviations from additivity and linearity. Again, such auxiliary reagents as micellar species can sometimes be used to prevent (or promote) intermolecular interactions to simplify determination.

Selectivity. Fluorescence analysis offers inherent selectivity and therefore limited applicability due to the nonfluorescence of many molecules. Selectivity can be improved by use of fluorescence lifetimes and selective quenching or enhancement as well as other properties in addition to emission and excitation spectral characteristics. Physical separations can be used, for example, in high-performance liquid chromatography (HPLC) with fluorescence detection, to simplify multicomponent analysis of complex samples. The combination of circularly polarized excitation with fluorescence detection offers highly selective determination of chiral fluorescent molecules.

Detection Limits and Dynamic Range. Due to the direct dependence of fluorescence intensity on the concentration of the emitter(s), fluorescence detection limits are on the order of nanomolar to picomolar for efficient fluorescers. This is at least 10^3-fold lower than the micromolar limits obtained using UV/VIS absorption spectrophotometry, in which absorbance, derived from the ratio of two measured intensities, is

proportional to the concentration of absorber(s). Therefore, detection limits can be improved for fluorimetric determinations by increasing the source intensity, but such an increase will not directly affect absorption detection limits. Furthermore, dynamic ranges for fluorimetric determinations generally extend over four to five orders of magnitude, compared to two or three orders of magnitude for absorption experiments.

Indirect Determinations. Molecular and atomic species that do not fluoresce can be determined indirectly if their presence changes the fluorescence properties of another chemical species. For example, Br^-, I^-, and dissolved O_2 gas in solution can be determined from their collisional quenching effects. Fluorescence-enhancement effects can be used similarly. In indirect kinetic and enzymatic fluorimetric methods, the nonfluorescent analyte participates in a rate-determining capacity in reactions involving fluorescent reagents.

Instrumentation

Figure 4 shows the basic instrumental configuration for fluorescence instruments. Emission is measured at 90° to the excitation beam to avoid background from nonabsorbed radiation. Angles other than 90° are sometimes used for specific applications.

Radiation Sources. Relatively high intensity sources are used for fluorescence to exploit the direct dependence of emission intensity on source intensity. The most common continuum source is the xenon arc lamp, ranging from 150 to 450 W or more. Figure 5 illustrates the spectral distribution of the emission of a typical xenon lamp. Excitation-beam intensity can be increased further by using mirrored backing in the source compartment to redirect emitted light in the direction of the excitation beam. High-pressure mercury lamps are also common sources that provide high-intensity line emissions (Fig. 5).

The continuum output of the xenon arc lamp makes it suitable for scanning instru-

ments with monochromator wavelength selectors. The line emission of the mercury lamp is better suited to nonscanning filter instruments.

Lasers are also used in fluorescence experiments in which scanning of excitation is not required. Tunable lasers can be used to provide some multiwavelength excitation capabilities. Improvements in detection limits can sometimes be obtained using lasers, although the increased emission signal is accompanied by an increase in light scatter and localized heating effects. In addition, the excitation beam often must be attenuated greatly to avoid photodecomposition of the sample constituents. Lasers are frequently used for time-resolved fluorimetry and other specialized applications.

Wavelength Selectors. Filters or monochromators can be used for wavelength selection. Filters offer better detection limits, but do not provide spectral scanning capabilities. A filter will often be used in the excitation beam along with a monochromator in the emission beam to allow acquisition of emission spectra. Full emission and excitation spectral information can be acquired only if monochromators are used in the excitation and emission beams; therefore, two monochromators are necessary for such techniques as synchronous excitation and total luminescence spectroscopy.

Sample Holders. Liquid samples are contained in glass or quartz cuvettes for visible region or UV/VIS investigations, respectively. For measurements from 340 to 800 nm with appropriate solvents, disposable polyethylene cuvettes are convenient. Disposable acrylic cuvettes are also available for investigations from 275 to 350 nm, suitable for measurements of native protein fluorescence.

Fluorescence cuvettes are usually rectangular, with at least two transparent adjacent faces. The remaining two faces may also be transparent, or may have reflective surfaces to direct more of the fluorescence emission to the detector. Various modified cuvettes, including microvolume and flow cells, are also available.

Detectors. Photomultiplier tubes (PMTs) are the most commonly used detectors, and various types are available for different applications. In general, they are sensitive from 200 to 600 nm, with maximum sensitivity from 300 to 500 nm. Red-sensitive PMTs are also available for investigations beyond 600 nm.

Photomultipliers can be operated as analog detectors, in which the generated current is proportional to the incident radiative intensity, or as photon counters, in which the current pulses generated by individual incident photons are counted. A preset threshold value allows noise and other low-energy events to be disregarded. Single-photon detection offers greatly improved detection limits and is used to measure very low intensity emission signals. The linear-response range is much narrower than that of the analog detector, being limited on the low end by signal-to-noise deterioration and on the high end by the time response of the counter.

Use of two-dimensional multichannel imaging detectors for the simultaneous acquisition of emission and excitation spectra has increased the applications of total luminescence experiments, that is, those involving acquisition of an emission-excitation matrix, to include real-time experiments, kinetic measurements, and on-line detection for chromatography and other flow systems. The ability to acquire complete spectral information essentially instantaneously has also greatly facilitated qualitative analysis by reducing experiment times from hours to minutes. Among the more commonly used detectors are diode arrays, vidicons, silicon-intensified vidicons, charge-coupled and charge-injection devices, and numerous other devices implementing recent technological advances.

Computers are frequently interfaced with fluorometers to control data acquisition and to facilitate data analysis. For large data matrices, such as those acquired for an excitation-emission matrix (EEM) generated in total luminescence spectroscopy, and specialized experiments, such as those involving dynamic measurements of excited-state lifetimes, computerized data collection and analysis is almost indispensable.

Fig. 6 Double-beam spectrofluorometer

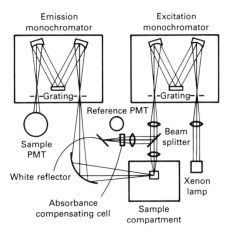

Ratiometric Instruments. Double-beam fluorometers (Fig. 6) are used to enable the simultaneous or near-simultaneous comparison of the sample emission to the signal from an appropriate reference. The ratio of the two emissions is measured to minimize the effects of source output fluctuations and drift.

Practical Considerations

Solvent Effects. According to the Franck-Condon principle, absorption of a photon is too rapid to allow rearrangement of the nuclear centers of the molecule. Therefore, upon entering the excited state, the solvated molecule has retained the geometry of its ground state, and only the electron distribution has been altered. Subsequent reorientation of the geometry of the solvated molecule to a more stable excited-state configuration can then occur. Upon emission of a photon as fluorescence, the molecule enters a Franck-Condon ground state that retains the nuclear configuration of the equilibrium excited state, followed by relaxation to the equilibrium ground-state configuration (Fig. 7). The time required for relaxation (on the order of 10^{-12} to 10^{-11} s following excitation) and the resulting effect on spectral properties depend on the nature of the solvent.

Such physical properties as polarity, dielectric constant and polarizability, and chemical interactions with the fluorescent molecules can contribute to modification of spectral properties. For example, the dipole moments of aromatic compounds are generally greater in the excited state than in the ground state. Therefore, as solvent polarity increases, the fluorescence spectrum shifts to lower energies (red-shift). Shifts in absorp-

Fig. 7 Energy-level diagram showing solvent-relaxation effects

S_0, equilibrium ground state; S_1, Franck-Condon excited state; S_1', equilibrium excited state; S_0', Franck-Condon ground state

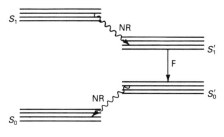

tion spectra may also occur, although fluorescence spectral shifts are not always accompanied by absorption shifts.

Corrected Spectra. Excitation and emission spectra contain distortions due to instrumental factors arising from nonlinear dependence of source output, monochromator efficiency, and detector response on wavelength. Spectra can be corrected to eliminate these distortions within experimental error. Various methods have been described for spectral correction, including use of thermopiles, quantum counters, calibrated phototubes with factory-supplied spectral response curves, and solutions of appropriate standard fluorescent compounds.

Wavelength Calibration. Instrumental emission wavelength settings can be calibrated periodically using a standard source, such as mercury arc lamp. The mercury emission lines (first and second order) from 253.65 to 809.32 nm offer a wide range of accurate calibration points. Excitation wavelength settings can then be calibrated against the calibrated emission wavelengths using a scattering solution.

Temperature. Fluorescence intensity generally decreases with increasing temperature, and the dependence is dramatic for some compounds. Many types of fluorescence experiments are conducted at 77 K or lower. Special dewars and sample container or mounting arrangements are available for low-temperature investigations.

Even for solution emission at room temperature, maintaining the sample compartment at a constant temperature is often desirable because heat from the source and heat generated by irradiation of the sample solution can cause intensity drift and fluctuations.

Scattered Light. Scattered light refers to light emitted from the sample due to nonquantized interactions between the exciting radiation and sample constituents. That is, the radiation is not absorbed, and elec-

Fig. 8 Total luminescence spectrum (EEM) of a mixture of naphthalene and anthracene

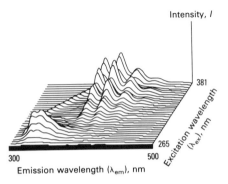

Fig. 9 Spectra of a synthetic five-component mixture

(a) Conventional emission spectrum.
(b) Synchronous excitation spectrum. Source: Ref 5

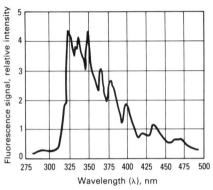

(a)

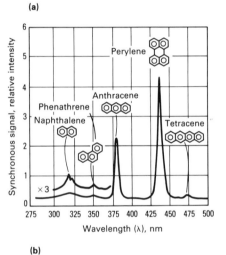

(b)

tronic transitions do not result from the interaction. Large particles, such as dust and macromolecular sample constituents, cause particulate scattering. These scattering peaks occur at $\lambda_{em} = \lambda_{ex}$. Rayleigh scattering, also observed at $\lambda_{em} = \lambda_{ex}$, results from elastic scattering interactions with molecules. Particulate and Rayleigh scattering blanks are troublesome when fluorescence emission is measured at wavelengths near the excitation wavelength.

Raman scattering is observed at $\lambda_{em} < \lambda_{ex}$ and $\lambda_{em} > \lambda_{ex}$ and is usually not sufficiently intense to cause significant blank problems when lamp sources are used. However, use of laser excitation frequently results in non-negligible Raman blanks from solvent as well as sample constituents and must be dealt with. The Raman bands, being excitation wavelength dependent, must be recognized in a particular experiment. Because scattering occurs on a much faster time scale than fluorescence, scattered-light signals can be distinguished from fluorescence emission by the differences in their respective decay times.

Special Techniques

Total Luminescence Spectroscopy. The total luminescence technique fully exploits the excitation and emission dimensions to improve the selectivity of fluorescence analysis for multicomponent samples. A total EEM is generated, in which fluorescence intensity is shown as a function of emission wavelength on one axis and excitation wavelength on the other. Figure 8 shows an EEM for a multicomponent sample.

An EEM can be acquired in several ways. Using a conventional scanning instrument, emission or excitation can be scanned at appropriate excitation (or emission) wavelength intervals. Alternatively, the emission and excitation monochromator exit slits can

be removed and the full EEM simultaneously acquired using a two-dimensional multichannel imaging detector.

Synchronous Excitation Spectroscopy. A synchronous excitation spectrum is obtained by scanning emission and excitation monochromators synchronously such that $\lambda_{em} = \lambda_{ex} + \Delta\lambda$. If a constant interval, $\Delta\lambda$, is maintained during the scan, the resulting spectrum corresponds to a diagonal slice through the total EEM. An appropriately selected $\Delta\lambda$ can greatly simplify the spectrum relative to conventional emission and excitation spectra, as shown in Fig. 9 for a mixture of polynuclear aromatic hydrocarbons. Synchronous excitation has been applied to the analysis of forensic, oil, environmental, and other complex samples.

Derivative and Wavelength-Modulation Techniques. Derivatives of emission and/or excitation spectra and of synchronously scanned spectra can be useful in detecting and measuring minor spectral features that may be overshadowed in the

nonderivative spectrum by broad spectral bands or background due to scattered light. Derivative spectra can also be used for multicomponent determinations. As with all derivative techniques, error propagation generally precludes use of derivatives higher than first or second order. The derivative spectra may be obtained using post-acquisition numerical techniques or real-time instrumental techniques, such as electronic differentiation or wavelength modulation.

Wavelength modulation has also been applied successfully to the determination of mixtures containing two or three components with highly overlapping excitation and emission spectra. Appropriate choice of the modulation interval, $\Delta\lambda$, allows selective detection of the modulated emission response of one component with minimal interference from the other(s).

Low-Temperature Techniques. Several techniques have been developed to exploit the improved spectral resolution and quantum efficiencies obtained at low temperatures and to alleviate collisional quenching and inner-filter effects encountered in solutions. One technique is based on the Shpol'skii effect, in which high-resolution spectra can be obtained in certain solvents (usually n-alkanes) at low temperatures ($\leq$77 K). The solvent and temperature used are major factors in determining the degree of spectral resolution obtained. Sufficient spectral resolution and detail are often obtained to permit the use of Shpol'skii spectra as fingerprints for qualitative investigation, and applications have included analysis of such samples as coal and coal tar pitch, organic extracts from geological samples, engine emissions, carbon black, crude oil, and marine sediments. Sample extracts are sometimes separated chromatographically, and the Shpol'skii spectra are then obtained for the appropriate fractions (Fig. 10).

In matrix isolation, another low-temperature technique, the sample is vaporized and the vapor mixed with a large excess of an appropriate diluent gas. The vapor mixture is then deposited on a solid surface at a low temperature (10 to 15 K or lower) for spectroscopic analysis. Deposition at low temperatures from the vapor phase is preferable to simply freezing liquid samples, because deposition from a thoroughly mixed vapor in which the diluent matrix gas is in large excess relative to the sample constituents minimizes aggregation and quenching effects. Special techniques include matrix isolation in Shpol'skii mediums to provide their increased spectral resolution and laser-induced matrix isolation to achieve selective excitation with high source power.

Fig. 10 Fluorescence spectrum of a liquid-chromatographic fraction of an automobile exhaust extract

The sample was frozen in n-hexane at 63 K; excitation wavelength was 313 nm. Source: Ref 6

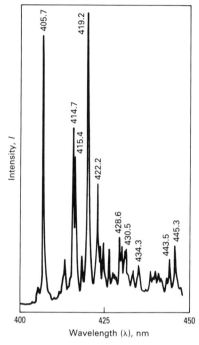

Fluorescence lifetimes (dynamic measurements) can be determined in two basic ways. First, in pulsed methods, the sample is excited with a pulse of radiation (using a laser or lamp source), and the subsequent emission decay is observed. The pulse should be brief relative to the emission-decay response, and the detector response must be suitably rapid. Optimum results have generally been obtained using laser instruments, and radiative displays in the nanosecond to picosecond range or lower can be determined. A repetitively pulsed source can be used in conjunction with time-correlated single-photon counting to determine fluorescence lifetimes.

The second approach to fluorescence lifetime determinations involves the use of an alternating current (ac) modulated excitation beam with phase-sensitive detection. In this phase-modulation technique, the emission-response function is demodulated and phase-delayed to an extent determined by the fluorescence lifetime of the emitter(s). Modulation frequencies from 1 to 100 MHz are used to determine lifetimes from several hundred nanoseconds to several hundred picoseconds.

Heterogeneous decay due to the emission from species with different fluorescence life-

times can be resolved into the individual lifetime components using pulsed or phase-modulation techniques. The phase-modulation approach also is the basis for phase-resolved fluorescence spectroscopy, in which the ac modulated emission function is integrated over a variable phase π-interval to produce phase-resolved intensities that are a function of the spectral characteristics, fluorescence lifetime(s), and concentration(s) of the emitting component(s).

The instrumentation and techniques for dynamic fluorescence measurements are useful for the direct determination of fluorescence lifetimes and for the incorporation of fluorescence lifetime as an independent selectivity parameter for fluorimetric analysis of multicomponent samples.

Fluorescence Enhancement Using Organized Mediums. Such reagents as micelles, cyclodextrins, and vesicles can be used to complex with fluorescent molecules, altering the fluorescence spectral and lifetime properties of the molecules. Fluorescence enhancement often results from the increased rigidity of the complex relative to the free molecule, although quenching can also occur due to specific chemical interactions. Collisional quenching may be retarded due to the relative isolation of the complexed molecule from the solvent unless the quencher is co-complexed, in which case quenching may actually increase. Micelles are also useful for solubilizing fluorescent molecules in various solvents by normal or reversed-phase micelle formation, allowing more flexibility in experimental design and sample preparation.

The wide variety of anionic, cationic, nonionic, and zwitterionic micelle-forming species affords much flexibility in designing experiments to improve detection limits and selectivity of fluorimetric determinations. Use of other reagents, such as cyclodextrins and vesicles, also holds promise for special applications. For example, the ability of cyclodextrins to induce chirality in some nonchiral molecules by the formation of inclusion complexes may allow for the selective determinations of these species using circularly polarized exciting light in conjunction with fluorescence detection.

Applications*

Example 1: Direct Determination of Benzo(a)pyrene.
Determination of benzo(a)pyrene (BaP), a potent carcinogen, in environmental water samples provides an

*Example 3 was provided by S.H. Weissman, Sandia National Laboratories. This work was supported by the U.S. Department of Energy under Contract No. DE-AC04-76DP00789.

example of direct fluorimetric determination. The BaP is first extracted from the sample into an appropriate organic solvent. If necessary, the fluorescent polynuclear aromatic hydrocarbons are separated into chromatographic fractions using HPLC with a reversed-phase C18 column. The BaP can then be determined in the appropriate fraction with a minimum of interferences.

To obtain emission and excitation spectra of the BaP sample or fraction, the appropriate wavelengths for excitation and emission, respectively, must be determined. If the spectra are unknown, the approximate excitation maximum can be located by removing the lid from the sample cuvette and scanning the excitation monochromator manually while observing the cuvette solution. The excitation wavelength at which light is observed to be emitted with maximum intensity is an approximate excitation maximum, and the color of the emitted light indicates an approximate emission maximum. Ultraviolet emission maxima must be located using the detector rather than this visual shortcut. Once the approximate excitation maximum is located, an emission spectrum is obtained using this excitation wavelength. The emission monochromator is then set to an emission maximum indicated by the emission spectrum, and the excitation monochromator scanned to obtain the excitation spectrum.

Once the spectra of the BaP are known (or verified), quantitative analysis is accomplished using measurements at the appropriate emission and excitation wavelength maxima. The wavelengths are selected to minimize interferences, if present, while maximizing sensitivity. Standard solutions of BaP are used to generate a calibration curve (relative fluorescence intensity versus BaP concentration), and the concentration of BaP in the unknown sample determined from its relative intensity using the curve.

Detection limits (in cuvette) in the nanomolar or subnanomolar range can be achieved, depending on the instrument used. The fluorescence lifetime of BaP is sufficiently long (approximately 14 ns) to render it slightly susceptible to quenching by dissolved oxygen in solution. Therefore, purging with nitrogen or helium gas can be used to improve detection limits slightly, although the minimal advantage may be outweighed by irreproducibility in purging from sample to sample. Purging of oxygen becomes more beneficial with increasing fluorescence lifetime of the emitting species.

Example 2: Enzymatic Determination of Glucose Using Oxygen Quenching of Fluorescence.
Numerous kinetic, enzymatic techniques have been developed that use fluorescence measurements of the analyte itself or of a reagent that has a

Fig. 11 Flow diagram for the quantification of uranium

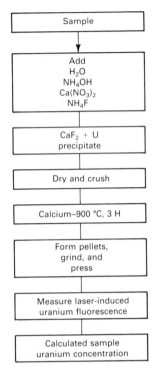

Fig. 12 Schematic diagram of laser-induced fluorescence spectroscopy instrumentation

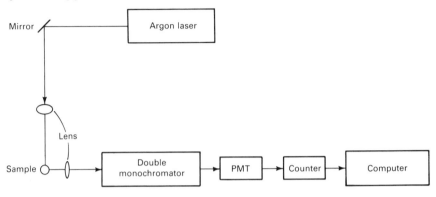

concentration dependence upon the analyte. An example of the latter approach is the use of collisional oxygen quenching of a fluorescent indicator to determine glucose using the enzymatic reaction:

$$Glucose + O_2 \underset{\rightleftharpoons}{\overset{GO}{}}$$

$$D\text{-}glucono\text{-}\delta\text{-}lactone + H_2O_2$$

where GO is the enzyme glucose oxidase, and O_2 is dissolved oxygen in the solution (typically approximately 1 mM) (Ref 7). The reaction is carried out in a fluorescence cuvette also containing pyrene butyric acid (PBA), a fairly efficient fluorescence emitter with a relatively long fluorescence lifetime (approximately 10^2 ns), rendering it susceptible to collisional quenching by dissolved oxygen in the solution. As the enzymatic reaction proceeds, dissolved oxygen is consumed, and the PBA is dequenched. The initial rate of dissolved oxygen consumption—observed as an increase in the relatively fluorescence intensity of the PBA—is directly proportional to the initial concentration of glucose in the solution. Fluorescence intensity is monitored as a function of time at the excitation and emission maxima of PBA, and the initial reaction rate is determined from the maximum slope of the time-dependent intensity curve. A calibration

curve of the initial rate of PBA signal increase versus glucose concentration is used to determine the glucose concentration in unknown samples.

Example 3: Determination of Ultratrace Uranium by Laser-Induced Fluorescence Spectroscopy. As part of a study to evaluate the safety of casks designed for transporting special nuclear materials, fixtures were designed that would allow leak testing of O-ring seals. Uranium dioxide (UO$_2$) powder was added to one side of the O-ring seal, and the seal was pressurized with helium. A cavity on the low-pressure side of the seal was sampled using nitric acid (HNO$_3$) to recover any UO$_2$ powder leaking through the O-ring seal (Ref 8). To detect small quantities of UO$_2$ powder leaking around the O-ring seal, it was necessary to develop a sensitive method of measuring uranium in HNO$_3$ solutions. The concentration of uranium was determined by co-precipitation of UO$_2^{+2}$ ion in a calcium fluoride (CaF$_2$) matrix followed by laser-induced fluorescence spectroscopy using a modification of Perry's procedure (Ref 9).

Calcium fluoride was precipitated from the test solutions, which were 2.3 M in HNO$_3$, using the procedure shown in Fig. 11. Aqueous uranium standards (prepared from uranyl nitrate), reagent blanks, and test samples were processed in the same manner. The acid concentrations of all standards and reagent blanks were matched to that of the sample. To achieve partial neutralization of the acid, 2 mL of 5 M NH$_4$OH was added to a 15-mL aliquot of each solution. One milliliter of 2.5 M Ca(NO$_3$)$_2$ and 30 mL of 0.3 M NH$_4$F were added to precipitate CaF$_2$. The precipitate was isolated by centrifugation, dried, and crushed. Each precipitate was transferred to a platinum crucible and fired 3 h at 900 °C (1650 °F). After cooling, the precipitate was ground into a fine powder

Fig. 13 Uranium laser-induced fluorescence spectra for a sample found to contain 8 ng U

Individual spectra are offset vertically for clarity; however, the vertical scale is constant. Peak A is the CaF$_2$ Raman peak; peak B is the uranium fluorescence peak. Spectra are shown for three of the six standards used in this analysis. cps, counts per second

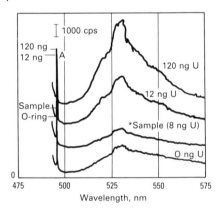

and pressed into pellets. All reagents used were ultrapure grade.

The fluorescence instrumental arrangement is shown in Fig. 12. Samples and standards, mounted as pellets, were irradiated with 488-nm light from an argon ion laser. The sample position was adjusted to maximize the intensity of the CaF$_2$ Raman band, which occurs at 496 nm, corresponding to a Raman shift of 322 cm^{-1}. The uranium occurs at 530 nm. Fluorescence spectra were recorded from 495 to 575 nm (Fig. 13).

The net intensity of the uranium band was determined by subtracting a baseline value from the band maximum (at approximately 530 nm). This baseline was determined by drawing a straight line from the valley after the CaF$_2$ Raman band to the fluorescence level at the maximum recorded wavelength.

Difficulties in positioning the pellets with reproducibility in the laser beam, coupled with differences in the optical characteristics of the pellets (reflectivity, surface roughness, and even absorption of the laser beam due to colored contaminants), generally precluded the reliable reproduction of absolute fluorescence intensities. Therefore, the net intensity of the CaF_2 Raman band was used as an internal standard and was divided into the net intensity of the uranium fluorescence band to obtain a figure of merit for the uranium concentration.

The figure of merit generally increased linearly with uranium concentration, although "bendover" at the higher concentrations was sometimes observed. The amount of uranium leaking around the O-ring seal was calculated from the amount of uranium measured on the low-pressure side of the O-ring seal and the fraction of sampling liquid recovered. Measurements from 8 to 250 ng of uranium—average uncertainty: $\pm 25\%$ (relative)—in seven of the test samples showed leakage of some UO_2 powder around the O-ring seals. For an additional two tests, no uranium was detected in the samples, with a detection limit of 13 ng.

The primary interferences to the method, in addition to direct contamination from ambient uranium, are substances that yield broad-band fluorescence profiles. Such broad-band fluorescence tends to obscure the uranium fluorescence band and, at the very least, complicates the measurement of the uranium fluorescence intensity. Organic species are not likely to be the source of this fluorescence, because they would not survive the firing procedure. Common transition elements, such as chromium, manganese, iron, and cobalt, are more likely to cause broad-band fluorescence. Rigorous sample handling procedures that minimize ambient contamination are needed. A cleanroom environment is strongly recommended for sample processing, but is not necessary for the measurement step. If such contamination is unavoidable, broad-bend fluorescence may often be minimized relative to sample fluorescence by using pulsed excitation (Ref 9, 10).

Most lanthanide and actinide elements are amenable to analysis by methods involving coprecipitation and laser-induced fluorescence (Ref 11). These methods are generally highly specific and capable of measuring ultratrace levels of material.

REFERENCES

1. I.B. Berlman, *Handbook of Fluorescence Spectra of Aromatic Molecules*, 2nd ed., Academic Press, 1971
2. V. Fassel, R. Heidel, and R. Huke, *Anal. Chem.*, Vol 24, 1952, p 606
3. V. Fassel and R. Heidel, *Anal. Chem.*, Vol 26, 1954, p 1134
4. S.G. Schulman, Ed., *Molecular Luminescence Spectroscopy: Methods and Applications, Part I*, Vol 77, *Chemical Analysis*, Wiley-Interscience, 1985, p 378-384
5. T. Vo-Dinh, *Anal. Chem.*, Vol 50, 1978, p 396
6. A. Colmsjo and U. Stenberg, *Anal. Chem.*, Vol 51, 1978, p 145
7. L.B. McGown, B.J. Kirst, and G.L. LaRowe, *Anal. Chim. Acta*, Vol 117, 1980, p 363-365
8. W.B. Leisher, S.H. Weissman, D.R. Tallant, and M. Kubo, in *Proceedings of the Seventh International Symposium on Packaging and Transportation of Radioactive Materials*, CONF-830528, Vol 1, 1983, p 655-663
9. D.L. Perry, S.M. Klainer, H.R. Bowman, F.P. Milanovich, T. Hirschfeld, and S. Miller, *Anal. Chem.*, Vol 53, 1981, p 1048-1050
10. M.V. Johnston and J.C. Wright, *Anal. Chem.* Vol 53, 1981, p 1050-1054
11. J.C. Wright, D.R. Tallant, F.J. Gustafson, M.V. Johnston, M.P. Miller, D.S. Moore, L.C. Porter, and J.R. Akse, *Angew. Chem. Int. Ed. Engl.*, Vol 18, 1979, p 738-752

SELECTED REFERENCES

- J.B. Birks, *Photophysics of Aromatic Molecules*, Wiley-Interscience, 1970
- J.N. Demas, *Excited State Lifetime Measurements*, Academic Press, 1983
- D. Eastwood, Ed., *New Directions in Molecular Luminescence*, STP 822, ASTM, Philadelphia, 1983
- P. Goldberg, Ed., *Luminescence of Inorganic Solids*, Academic Press, 1966
- G.G. Guilbault, *Practical Fluorescence: Theory, Methods and Techniques*, Marcel Dekker, 1973
- D.M. Hercules, *Fluorescence and Phosphorescence Analysis: Principles and Applications*, Interscience, 1966
- J.R. Lakowicz, *Principles of Fluorescence Spectroscopy*, Plenum Press, 1983
- C.A. Parker, *Photoluminescence of Solutions with Applications to Photochemistry and Analytical Chemistry*, Elsevier, 1968
- A.J. Pesce, C-G Rosen, T.L. Pasby, Ed., *Fluorescence Spectroscopy: An Introduction for Biology and Medicine*, Marcel Dekker, 1971
- E.L. Wehry, Ed., *Modern Fluorescence Spectroscopy*, Vol 1 to 4, Plenum Press, 1981
- C.E. White, and R.J. Argauer, *Fluorescence Analysis: A Practical Approach*, Marcel Dekker, 1970
- J.D. Winefordner, S.G. Schulman, and T.C. O'Haver, *Luminescence Spectrometry in Analytical Chemistry*, Vol 38, *Chemical Analysis*, Wiley-Interscience, 1972

X-Ray Spectrometry

Donald E. Leyden, Department of Chemistry, Colorado State University

General Use

- Qualitative and quantitative elemental determination in solids and liquids
- Applications to materials and thin films

Examples of Applications

- Qualitative identification of elemental composition of materials for elements of atomic number greater than 11; identification at concentrations greater than a few ppm requires only a few minutes
- Support of phase identification using x-ray powder diffraction patterns
- Selection of alternate methods of quantitative analysis
- Quantitative determination of elements without regard to form or oxidation state in various solid and liquid materials and compositions
- Determination of thickness of thin films of metal on various substrates

Samples

- *Form*: Samples may be bulk solids, powders, pressed pellets, glasses, fused disks, or liquids
- *Size*: Typical samples are 32 mm (1¼ in.) in diameter or placed in special cups, holders, and mounts
- *Sampling depth* may range from a few micrometers to a millimeter or more, depending on x-ray energy used and matrix composition of the sample
- *Sample preparation* may involve none, polishing to obtain a flat surface, grinding and pelletizing, or fusion in a flux

Advantages

- Applicable to various samples, including solids
- Relatively rapid and easy to learn
- Semiquantitative results can be obtained from many samples without use of standards; most standards may be kept for long periods of time, because most applications are for solids
- Instrumentation is relatively inexpensive

Limitations

- Detection limits for bulk determinations are normally a few ppm to a few tens of ppm, depending on the x-ray energy used and the sample matrix composition
- For thin-film samples, detection limits are approximately 100 ng/cm^2
- Not suitable for elements of atomic number less than 11 unless special equipment is available, in which case elements down to atomic number 6 may be determined

Capabilities of Related Techniques

- *Inductively coupled plasma optical emission spectroscopy* and *atomic absorption spectrometry* have better detection limits for most elements than x-ray spectrometry and are often better choices for liquid samples; elements of low atomic number can be determined using these techniques

Introduction

X-ray spectrometry, or x-ray fluorescence, is an emission spectroscopic technique that has found wide application in elemental identification and determination. The technique depends on the emission of characteristic x-radiation, usually in the 1- to 60-keV energy range, following excitation of atomic electron energy levels by an external energy source, such as an electron beam, a charged particle beam, or an x-ray beam. In most sample matrices, x-ray spectrometry can detect elements at concentrations of less than 1 μg/g of sample (1 ppm); in a thin film sample, it can detect total amounts of a few tenths of one microgram. Initially, x-ray spectrometry found wide acceptance in applications related to metallurgical and geochemical analyses. More recently, x-ray spectrometry has proved valuable in the analysis of environmental samples, in the determination of sulfur and wear elements in petroleum products, in applications involving forensic samples, and in measurements of electronic and computer-related materials.

Roentgen discovered x-rays in 1895. H.G.J. Moseley developed the relationships between atomic structure and x-ray emission and in 1913 published the first x-ray spectra, which are the basis for modern x-ray spectrometry. Moseley recognized the potential for quantitative elemental determinations using x-ray techniques. The development of routine x-ray instrumentation, leading to the x-ray spectrometer known today, took place over the following decades. Coolidge designed an x-ray tube in 1913 that is similar to those currently used. Soller achieved collimation of x-rays in 1924. Improvements in the gas x-ray detector by Geiger and Mueller in 1928 eventually led to the design of the first commercial wavelength-dispersive x-ray spectrometer by Friedman and Birks in 1948.

More recently, other detectors, such as the germanium and the lithium-doped silicon semiconductor detectors, have resulted in modified x-ray spectrometer designs. Modern energy-dispersive instrumentation facilitates qualitative identification of elements in various samples. The information content of an energy dispersive x-ray spectrum is among the highest obtainable from inorganic materials in a single measurement. The position and intensity of the spectral peaks provide qualitative and quantitative information, and the intensity of the background yields information on bulk composition of the sample matrix.

X-ray spectrometry is one of the few techniques that can be applied to solid samples of various forms. Although most x-ray spectrometers are in laboratories, many are finding application in routine analyses for production and quality control and in specialized tasks. Growth in the capability and economy of microcomputer technology will enhance these applications. Many of these same principles, practices, and instrumentation developments are common to electron microscopy and electron microprobe analysis.

Electromagnetic Radiation

Electromagnetic radiation is an energy form that may be propagated through space and may interact with atoms and molecules to alter their energy state. Both properties are important to spectroscopy. Electromagnetic radiation exhibits behavior that requires two theories to explain. The wave theory describes behavior of electromagnetic radiation, such as refraction, reflection, diffraction, and scatter. Radiation is defined as an energy form consisting of two orthogonal waves, each having the same frequency and wavelength. One is an oscillating electric field, and the other an oscillating magnetic field, thus producing the term electromagnetic radiation. In a vacuum, the velocity of propagation of the wave through space is the

speed of light ($c = 3 \times 10^{10}$ cm/s). This leads to an important fundamental relationship:

$$\lambda v = c \qquad \text{(Eq 1)}$$

This expression states that the product of the wavelength (λ) of electromagnetic radiation and its frequency (v) is equal to its velocity. The wavelength of electromagnetic radiation varies over many orders of magnitude. For example, radio waves in the normal AM broadcast band have wavelengths of several hundred meters. By contrast, x-rays useful in spectroscopy range from 0.01 to 10 nm.

Not all properties of x-rays can be adequately described by the wave theory. As physicists began to understand the quantum nature of the energy levels of atoms and molecules, the requirement for a different description of electromagnetic radiation became increasingly clear. The basic need was to describe the energy content of radiation that could interact with matter to cause the observed discrete energy changes. The energy content of electromagnetic radiation is proportional to frequency:

$$E = hv \qquad \text{(Eq 2)}$$

where the proportionality constant, h, is known as Planck's constant. Because the relationship in Eq 1 also holds, substitution of:

$$v = \frac{c}{\lambda} \qquad \text{(Eq 3)}$$

in Eq 2 yields:

$$E = hv = \frac{hc}{\lambda} \qquad \text{(Eq 4)}$$

Substitution of numerical quantities for h and c results in:

$$E = \frac{12.396}{\lambda} \qquad \text{(Eq 5)}$$

where E is in keV, and λ in angstroms (1 Å = 0.1 nm). This expression relates the energy content of photon quanta to the wavelength of the corresponding electromagnetic radiation. For example, a rhodium Kα x-ray has a wavelength of 0.0614 nm (0.614 Å), which corresponds to an energy of 20.2 keV. As a result of Eq 5, radiation may be discussed in terms of wavelength or energy interchangeably. For wavelength-dispersive spectrometry, it is often more convenient to use wavelength units, but for energy-dispersive x-ray spectrometry (EDS), the energy description is more convenient. Clearly, interconversion is simple.

Several commonly used descriptions of the characteristics of x-rays are significant. The proper meaning of the intensity of elec-

tromagnetic radiation is the energy per unit area per unit time; however, the number of counts per unit time from the detector is frequently used as intensity. Because the area is the active area of the detector used, and time is an adjustable parameter, the use of counts is a practical description of x-ray intensity. The terms hard or soft x-rays are often used to differentiate x-rays of short (0.01 to 0.1 nm, or 0.1 to 1 Å) and long (0.1 to 1 nm, or 1 to 10 Å) wavelengths, respectively.

X-radiation falls in the high-energy region of the electromagnetic spectrum. Although modern commercial x-ray spectrometers incorporate many safety features, awareness of proper procedures (Ref 1, 2) as well as local and national codes for installation, inspection, and safety precautions is necessary.

X-Ray Emission

X-rays are generated from the disturbance of the electron orbitals of atoms. This may be accomplished in several ways, the most common being bombardment of a target element with high-energy electrons, x-rays, or accelerated charged particles. The first two are frequently used in x-ray spectrometry—directly or indirectly. Electron bombardment results in a continuum of x-ray energies as well as radiation characteristic of the target element. Both types of radiation are encountered in x-ray spectrometry.

Continuum. Emission of x-rays with a smooth, continuous function of intensity relative to energy is called continuum, or bremsstrahlung, radiation. An x-ray continuum may be generated in several ways. However, the most useful is the electron beam used to bombard a target in an x-ray tube (tubes used in x-ray spectrometry will be discussed below). The continuum is generated as a result of the progressive deceleration of high-energy electrons impinging on a target, which is a distribution of orbital electrons of various energies. As the impinging electrons interact with the bound orbital electrons, some of their kinetic energy is converted to radiation; the amount converted depends on the binding energy of the electron involved. Therefore, a somewhat statistical probability exists as to how much energy is converted with each interaction.

The probability of an impinging electron interacting with an orbital electron of the target element should increase with the atomic number of the element; thus, the intensity of the continuum emission should increase with the atomic number of the target element. Further, the probability of an interaction increases with the number of electrons per unit time in the beam, or flux. Therefore, the intensity of the continuum increases with electron beam current (I), expressed in milliamperes.

Moreover, the ability of the impinging electrons to interact with tightly bound electrons of the target element increases with the kinetic energy of the bombarding electrons. Because the kinetic energy of the electrons in the beam increases with acceleration potential, the integrated intensity of the continuum should increase with electron acceleration potential (V), expressed in kilovolts. Finally, the maximum energy manifested as x-ray photons equals the kinetic energy of the impinging electron, which in turn relates to acceleration potential. These concepts can be approximated quantitatively (Ref 1, 2):

$$I_\lambda = K_i Z \left(\frac{\lambda}{\lambda_{\min} - 1} \right) \lambda^{-2} \qquad \text{(Eq 6)}$$

$$I_{\text{int}} = (1.4 \times 10^{-9}) I Z V^2 \qquad \text{(Eq 7)}$$

Other relationships have been proposed. Differentiation of an expression given by Kulenkampff (Ref 3) yields an expression that demonstrates that the energy of the maximum intensity in the continuum lies at approximately two thirds the maximum emitted energy. The shape of the continuum predicted by Eq 6 and 7 is approximate. These functions do not include the absorption of x-rays within the target material or absorption by materials used for windows in the x-ray tube and detectors. Therefore, some modification of the intensity distribution may occur—especially at low x-ray energies.

Characteristic Emission. Most of the electrons impinging on a target interact with the orbital electrons of the target element in nonspecific interactions and result in little or no disturbance of the inner orbital electrons. However, some interactions result in the ejection of electrons from these orbitals. The resulting vacancies, or holes, represent high-energy unstable states. If the orbital vacancies are in the innermost shells, electrons from outer shells cascade to fill them, resulting in a lower energy and more stable state.

The energy released by the process may be manifested as x-rays. Each of the transitions that may occur lead to the emission of sharp x-ray lines characteristic of the target element and the transition involved. These characteristic radiation lines are emitted with the continuum. The relationship between the elements and the characteristic spectrum will be discussed below.

X-Ray Absorption

X-rays impinging on a specimen undergo two important interactions with the elements of the specimen: absorption and scatter. Absorption of the radiation may occur by

specific interactions that are significant in sample excitation in x-ray spectrometry or by more general interactions that influence the emitted x-ray intensity from the sample. Scatter of x-rays leads to background intensity in the observed spectra.

Mass Absorption. When an x-ray beam passes through a material, the photons (electromagnetic fields) may interact in nonspecific ways with electrons in the orbitals of the target elements, attenuating the intensity of the x-ray beam. The interactions may lead to photoelectric ejection of electrons or scatter of the x-ray beam. In either case, the overall result is frequently described in terms of an exponential decrease in intensity with the path length of the absorbing material:

$$I_\lambda = I_0 \cdot \exp - \left[\left(\frac{\mu}{\rho} \right) \rho x \right] \qquad \text{(Eq 8)}$$

where I_λ is the intensity of a beam of wavelength λ after passing through a length x (cm) of an absorber, I_0 is the initial intensity of the beam, μ/ρ is the mass absorption coefficient of the absorber (cm^2), and ρ is the density of the absorber (g/cm^3). The mass absorption coefficient is characteristic of a given element at specified energies of x-radiation. Its value varies with the wavelength of the x-radiation and the atomic number of the target element. These relationships will be discussed in the section "Mass Absorption Coefficients."

The photoelectric effect is the most important of the processes leading to absorption of x-rays as they pass through matter. The photoelectric effect is the ejection of electrons from the orbitals of elements in the x-ray target. This process is often the major contributor to absorption of x-rays and is the mode of excitation of the x-ray spectra emitted by elements in samples. Primarily as a result of the photoelectric process, the mass absorption coefficient decreases steadily with increasing energy of the incident x-radiation. The absorption versus energy curve for a given element has sharp discontinuities. These result from characteristic energies at which the photoelectric process is especially efficient. Energies at which these discontinuities occur will be discussed in the section "Absorption Edges" in this article.

Scatter. When x-ray photons impinge on a collection of atoms, the photons may interact with electrons of the target elements to result in the scatter of the x-ray photons, as illustrated in Fig. 1. Scatter of x-rays from the sample is the major source of background signal in the spectra obtained in x-ray spectrometry. The scatter of x-rays is caused mainly by outer, weakly held electrons of the elements. If the collisions are elastic, scatter occurs with no loss of energy and is known as Rayleigh scatter; if inelastic, the x-ray

photon loses energy to cause the ejection of an electron, and the scatter is incoherent. The path of the x-ray photon is deflected, and the photon has an energy loss or a longer wavelength. This is Compton scatter.

Scatter affects x-ray spectrometry in two ways. First, the total amount of scattered radiation increases with atomic number because of the greater number of electrons. However, samples with low atomic number matrices exhibit a larger observed scatter because of reduced self-absorption by the sample. Second, the ratio of Compton-to-Rayleigh scatter intensity increases as the atomic number of the sample matrix decreases.

The energy loss associated with Compton scatter results in a predictable change in the wavelength of the radiation:

$$\Delta\lambda_{\text{cm}} = \left(\frac{h}{m_e c} \right) (1 - \cos \phi) \qquad \text{(Eq 9)}$$

where $\Delta\lambda_{\text{cm}}$ is the change in wavelength (cm), h is Planck's constant (6.6×10^{-27} erg · s), m_e is the electron mass (9.11×10^{-28} g), c is the velocity of electromagnetic radiation (3×10^{10} cm/s), and ϕ is the angle between the scattered and incident x-ray paths. Substitution of the above values into Eq 9 yields:

$$\Delta\lambda = 0.0243(1 - \cos \phi) \qquad \text{(Eq 10)}$$

Because most x-ray spectrometers have a primary beam-sample-detector angle of approximately 90°, $\phi = 90°$ and $\cos \phi = 0$. Therefore, for many spectrometers:

$$\Delta\lambda = 0.024 \text{ Å} \qquad \text{(Eq 11)}$$

This is known as the Compton wavelength. In energy-dispersive systems, the Compton shift may be more conveniently represented:

$$E' = \frac{E}{1 + 0.00196E(1 - \cos \phi)} \qquad \text{(Eq 12)}$$

where E and E' are the x-ray energies in keV of the incident and scattered radiation, respectively. For a spectrometer with beam-sample-detector geometry of 90°, a Compton-scattered silver Kα line (22.104 keV) from a silver x-ray tube will be observed at 21.186 keV. The intensity of the Compton scatter of the characteristic lines from the x-ray tube can be useful in certain corrections for matrix effects in analyses.

Relationships Between Elements and X-Rays

Absorption. X-ray photons may interact with orbital electrons of elements to be absorbed or scattered. The relationship be-

Fig. 1 Rayleigh and Compton scatter of x-rays

K, L, and M denote electron shells of principal quantum number 1, 2, and 3, respectively; φ is the angle between the incident and scattered rays.

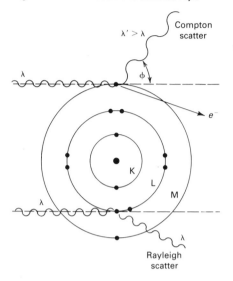

Fig. 2 X-ray absorption curve for uranium as a function of wavelength

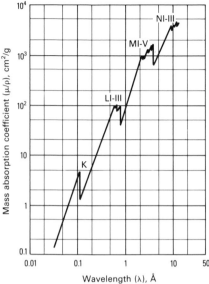

tween absorption and the atomic number of the element is important in selecting optimum operating conditions for x-ray spectrometry.

Mass absorption coefficients differ for each element or substance at a given energy of x-ray and at each energy of x-ray for a given element or substance. Because of the greater probability of interaction with orbital electrons, the mass absorption coefficient increases with the atomic number of the element of the target material. At a given atomic number, the mass absorption coefficient decreases with the wavelength of the x-radiation. This is illustrated in the log-log plot of mass absorption coefficient versus wavelength for uranium given in Fig. 2, which also shows discontinuities in the relationship at certain wavelength values. These result from specific energies required for the photoelectric ejection of electrons from the various orbitals of the atom and are characteristic of the element.

A detailed analysis of data similar to those shown in Fig. 2 for many elements confirms the relationship:

$$\frac{\mu}{\rho} = KZ^4\lambda_{cm}^3 \qquad \text{(Eq 13)}$$

where Z is the atomic number of the target element, λ is the wavelength of the incident x-ray, and K is the variable at each absorption edge of the target element.

Absorption edges, which are discontinuities or critical points in the plot of mass absorption versus wavelength or energy of incident x-radiation, are shown in Fig. 2.

Absorption-edge energy is the exact amount that will photoeject an electron from an orbital of an element. Figure 3 shows the electron shells in an atom. The familiar K, L, and M notation is used for the shells of principal quantum number 1, 2, and 3, respectively. The lower the principal quantum number, the greater the energy required to eject an electron from that shell. As shown in Fig. 3, the wavelength of an x-ray that can eject an L electron is longer (of less energy) than that required to eject an electron from the K shell. That is, the K-absorption edge energy (K_{abs}) is greater than the L-absorption edge energy (L_{abs}) for a given element.

Fig. 3 Photoejection of K electrons by higher energy radiation and L electrons by lower energy radiation

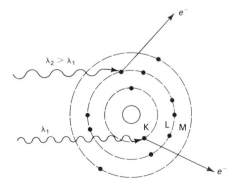

The photoelectric process leads to the unstable electronic state, which emits characteristic x-rays, as illustrated in Fig. 4. Figure 4(a) shows a plot of absorbance versus energy for radiation lower in energy than the x-ray region. In this case, photon energy is used to promote electrons from low-lying orbitals to higher ones. The transition is from a stable quantized state to an unstable quantized state. The atom, ion, or molecule that is the target defines the energy difference. The sample absorbs only photons with energy very close to this energy difference. The result is the familiar absorption peak found in visible, ultraviolet, and other forms of spectroscopy.

Figure 4(b) illustrates radiation in the x-ray energy range. The electron is ejected from a stable low-lying orbital of a given quantized energy level to the continuum of energy of an electron removed from the atom. Any excess energy in the x-ray photon is converted to kinetic energy of the ejected electron (measurement of the kinetic energy of these electrons is the basis of x-ray photoelectron spectroscopy). Therefore, instead of the absorption peak shown in Fig. 4(a), an absorption edge or jump is observed when the x-ray photon energy is sufficient to photoeject the electron. Selection of the x-ray photon energy for excitation of the elements in the sample will be based on these considerations. For example, 8.98-keV x-rays are required to photoeject the K (1s) electrons from copper, but x-rays of only approximately 1.1 keV are required for the 2s or 2p electrons. For magnesium, the values are 1.3 and 0.06 keV, respectively. The energy of the absorption edge of a given orbital increases smoothly with the atomic number of the target element.

Emission

The photoelectric effect is an x-ray absorption mechanism by which unstable states in the electron orbitals of atoms are created. Once the vacancies in the inner orbitals are formed, relaxation to the stable ground state may occur by the emission of x-rays characteristic of the excited element. Figure 5 illustrates excitation and emission for the photoejection of a K (1s) electron of copper. Figure 5(a) shows a plot of mass absorption coefficient of copper versus x-ray energy from 0 to 20 keV, with K_{abs} at 8.98 keV. Figure 5(b) depicts an electronic energy level diagram for copper. Irradiation of copper with an x-ray of just greater than 8.98 keV will photoeject an electron from the K shell. This is an ionization of the copper atom from the inner shell rather than the outer valence electrons, as is the case with chemical reactions. The energy of the 1s electron is

Fig. 4 Excitation of electronic energy levels

(a) Transition between two quantized energy levels. (b) Photoejection of electrons by x-radiation

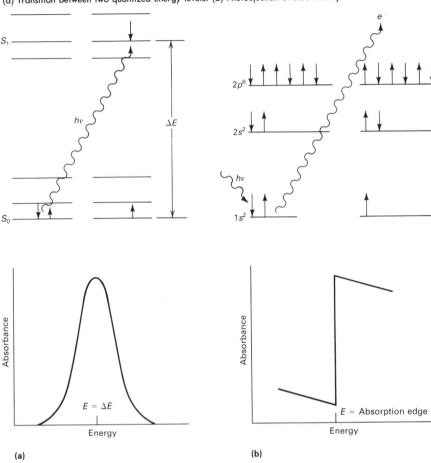

(a)

(b)

electrons. The observed 2:1 intensity ratio for the $K\alpha_1$ and $K\alpha_2$ lines results from the statistical probability of the transition. Although these two lines arise from different transitions, their energies are so similar that they are rarely resolved. It is common to report only a weighted average energy for these lines:

$$E_{\bar{\alpha}} = \frac{2E^{\alpha 1} + E^{\alpha 2}}{3} \qquad \text{(Eq 14)}$$

The $K\beta$ lines occur at an energy higher than the $K\alpha$ lines. The relative intensity of the $K\alpha$ to $K\beta$ lines is a complex function of the difference between the energy levels of the states involved in the transition; therefore, relative intensity varies with atomic number. However, as an example, the $K\beta$ lines for elements of atomic number 24 to 30 are approximately 10 to 13% of the total $K\alpha + K\beta$ intensity.

L Lines. Because the practical energy range for most wavelength-dispersive x-ray spectrometers is 0 to 100 keV, and 0 to 40 keV for energy-dispersive x-ray spectrometers, the use of emission lines other than the K lines must be considered. For a given element, L lines are excited with lower x-ray energy than K lines. Because there are three angular-momentum quantum numbers for the electrons in the L shell, corresponding to the $2s_{1/2}$, $2p_{1/2}$, $2p_{3/2}$ orbitals, respectively, there are three L absorption edges: L_I, L_{II}, and L_{III}. To excite all L lines, the incident x-ray photon energy must have a value greater than that corresponding to L_I. The use of L lines is particularly valuable for elements with atomic numbers greater than approximately 45.

M lines find limited application in routine x-ray spectrometry. The lines are not observed for elements with atomic numbers below approximately 57, and when observed, the transition energies are low. The only practical use for these lines is for such elements as thorium, protactinium, and uranium. They should be used only in these cases to avoid interferences with L lines of other elements in the sample.

Fluorescent Yield. An electron is ejected from an atomic orbital by the photoelectric process with two possible results: x-ray photon emission or secondary (Auger) electron ejection. One of these events occurs for each excited atom, but not both. Therefore, secondary electron production competes with x-ray photon emission from excited atoms in a sample. The fraction of the excited atoms that emits x-rays is termed the fluorescent yield. This value is a property of the element and the x-ray line under consideration. Figure 6 shows a plot of x-ray fluorescent yield versus atomic number of the elements for the K and L lines. Low atomic number elements

shielded from the state of the valence electrons such that the absorption-edge energy and the energy of the emitted x-rays are essentially independent of the oxidation state and bonding of the atom.

K Lines. Once the photoelectric effect creates a vacancy in the K shell, the excited state relaxes by filling the vacancy with an electron from an outer orbital. Only certain transitions are allowed because of quantum mechanical rules called selection rules. Some of these are:

$$\Delta n > 0$$

$$\Delta l = \pm 1$$

$$\Delta j = \pm 1 \text{ or } 0$$

where n is the principal quantum number, l is the angular quantum number, and $j = l + s$ is the vector sum of l and s (the spin quantum number). The transitions that follow the selection rules are termed allowed (diagram) lines, those that do not are called forbidden,

and those that result in atoms with two or more vacancies in inner orbitals at the time of the emission are called satellite (nondiagram) lines. The scheme of notation of x-ray spectral lines is unconventional; additional information is provided in Ref 4 and 5.

Figure 5(b) shows the transition for the K lines of copper. These are called the K lines because the original vacancy was created in the K shell of copper by photoejection. These examples may be related to the general transition diagrams for all elements. The number of K lines, and the exact one observed for an element, depends in part on the number of filled orbitals. The forbidden $K\beta_5$ line for copper is observed, because there are no $4p_{1/2,3/2}$ electrons to provide the $K\beta_2$ line of nearly the same energy that would obscure the much weaker $K\beta_5$ line.

The table in Fig. 5(b) shows some relationships among the relative intensities of the K lines. The $K\alpha_1$ and $K\alpha_2$ lines arise from transitions from the L_{III} ($2p_{3/2}$) and the L_{II} ($2p_{1/2}$) levels, respectively. The former orbital contains four electrons; the latter, two

Fig. 5 Transition diagram for copper

(a) Absorption curve. (b) Transitions

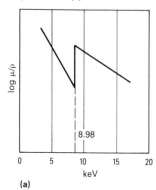

(a)

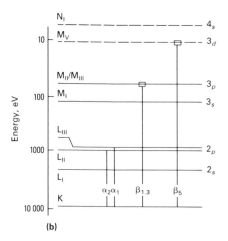

(b)

Line	Transition	Relative intensity	E, keV
$K\alpha_1$	$L_{III} \to K(2P_{3/2} \to 1S_{1/2})$	63	8.047
$K\alpha_2$	$L_{II} \to K(2P_{1/2} \to 1S_{1/2})$	32	8.027
$K\beta_1$	$M_{III} \to K(3P_{3/2} \to 1S_{1/2})$	10	8.903
$K\beta_3$	$M_{II} \to K(3P_{1/2} \to 1S_{1/2})$	10	8.973
$K\beta_5$	$M_V \to K(3D_{5/2} \to 1S_{1/2})$	<1(forbidden)	8.970

also have low fluorescent yield. Coupled with the high mass absorption coefficients that low-energy x-rays exhibit, the detection and determination of low atomic number elements by x-ray spectrometry is challenging.

Interelement Effects

For transitions in x-ray spectrometry, no emission line for a given series (K, L, M) of an element has energy equal to or greater than the absorption edge for that series. An important result is that the x-rays emitted from an element cannot photoeject electrons from the same orbital of other atoms of that element. For example, the most energetic K line of copper is below the K absorption edge for copper. This eliminates direct interaction of atoms of the same element in a sample.

However, a sample composed of a mixture of elements may exhibit interactions that are often called interelement effects. For example, the K_{abs} of chromium is 5.99 keV, but the Kα line for iron is at 6.40 keV. As a result, the x-ray intensities per unit concentration (sensitivity) from a sample containing chromium and iron will be affected by the composition. Because the x-radiation emitted from iron will photoeject K-shell electrons from chromium, the chromium x-ray intensity will be higher than expected. The chromium absorbs some of the Kα and Kβ x-rays from iron that would otherwise typically be detected, causing a lower intensity for iron than would be anticipated. Such interactions of elements within a sample often require special data analysis.

Instrumentation

Wavelength-Dispersive X-Ray Spectrometers. X-ray spectrometric instrumentation introduced commercially in the 1950s has been known as wavelength dispersive, denoting that the radiation emitted from the sample is collimated using a Soller collimator, then impinges upon an analyzing crystal. The crystal diffracts the radiation to different extents according to Bragg's law and depending on the wavelength or energy of the x-radiation. This angular dispersion of the radiation permits sequential or simultaneous detection of x-rays emitted by elements in the sample. Simultaneous instruments normally contain several sets of analyzing crystals and detectors; one is adjusted for each desired analyte in the sample. Although expensive, these instruments are efficient for routine determination of preselected elements, but are not easily converted to determine elements other than the ones selected at installation.

More common are sequential instruments that contain a mechanical system known as a goniometer that varies the angle among the sample, analyzing crystal, and detector. In this way, the desired wavelength of x-radiation may be selected by movement of the goniometer. Sequential wavelength-dispersive x-ray spectrometers may be computer controlled for automatic determination of many elements. Quantitative applications of automated wavelength-dispersive x-ray spectrometers are efficient, because the instrument can be programmed to go to the correct angles for desired determinations; however, qualitative applications are less efficient because the spectrum must be scanned slowly. Figure 7 shows a wavelength-dispersive spectrum of an AISI Type 347 stainless steel taken with a

Fig. 6 Fluorescent yield versus atomic number for K and L lines

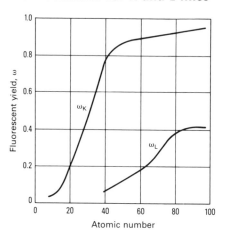

wavelength-dispersive x-ray spectrometer. Approximately 30 min were required to obtain this spectrum. Additional information on wavelength dispersive x-ray instrumentation and applications is available in Ref 4 to 8.

X-Ray Tubes. Various energy sources may be used to create the excited electronic states in the atoms of elements that produce x-ray emission. Among these are electron beams, charged particle beams, and x-radiation. Electron beams are directed on the sample in such techniques as scanning electron microscopy (SEM) and electron microprobe analysis. However, use of an electron beam requires a high vacuum to avoid energy losses of the electron. X-ray spectrometry is best used as a versatile analytical tool rather than as a specialty tool. Many samples are not suited for a high vacuum or are nonconductors, which causes problems of electrical charging when under an electron beam. Therefore, this energy source is not practical for x-ray spectrometry. In addition to the expense of a suitable accelerator, many of the same problems encountered using electron beams are associated with charged particle excitation. However, particle-induced x-ray emission (PIXE) is applied to special samples. Radioactive isotopes that emit x-radiation are another possibility for excitation of atoms to emit x-rays. However, the x-ray flux from isotopic sources that can be safely handled in a laboratory is too weak for practical use. Because these sources usually emit only a few narrow x-ray lines, several are required to excite many elements efficiently. The most practical energy source for x-ray spectrometry is an x-ray tube.

Wavelength-dispersive x-ray spectrometers require efficient high-power excitation

Fig. 7 Wavelength-dispersive x-ray spectrum of AISI type 347 stainless steel

Philips PW-1410 sequential x-ray spectrometer; molybdenum x-ray tube, 30 kV, 30 mA; P-10 flow proportional detector; LiF(200) analyzing crystal; fine collimation; 100 kcps full scale

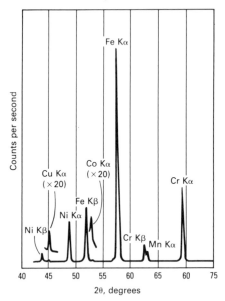

Fig. 8 Coolidge x-ray tube
(1) Filament; (2) target anode; (3) beryllium window

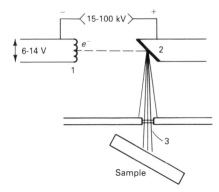

inner orbital electron from atoms of the target material, the tube will emit x-ray lines characteristic of the target element. Interaction of the electrons in the beam with electrons of the target element will also lead to emission of a continuum. The area of the continuum and the wavelength of maximum intensity will depend on the potential, current, and anode composition.

Analyzing Crystals. X-rays emitted by the x-ray tube are directed onto the sample. In most x-ray spectrometers, the sample is placed above the x-ray tube in what is known as inverted optics. This facilitates positioning the surface of a liquid using the bottom surface rather than the top. The x-radiation emitted from the sample is collimated and impinges on the surface of an analyzing crystal, which disperses the radiation. The parallel beam of polychromatic x-radiation from the sample is diffracted from different lattice planes in the crystal. Reinforcement occurs if the additional distance the radiation must travel by diffraction from different lattice planes equals an integer multiple of the wavelength. If this is not the case, destructive interference takes place. Bragg's law permits calculation of the angle θ at which a wavelength λ will be selected if the analyzing crystal has a lattice spacing of d; d and λ are in angstroms:

$$n\lambda = 2d \sin \theta \qquad \text{(Eq 15)}$$

to perform well; stability and reliability of the x-ray tube are important. The modern x-ray tube, a direct descendant of the Coolidge tube, is illustrated in Fig. 8. All components are in a high vacuum. A filament is heated by a filament voltage of 6 to 14 V. The heated filament thermally emits electrons. The flux of electrons that flows between the filament and the target anode must be highly regulated and controlled. This electron flow is electrical current (I) and is usually measured in milliamperes. The tube current is often referred to as the mA.

A potential of several kilovolts is applied between the filament (cathode) and the target anode, which serves as the acceleration potential for the electrons. This voltage is usually measured in kilovolts. The anode is usually copper, and the target surface is plated with high-purity deposits of such elements as rhodium, silver, chromium, molybdenum, or tungsten. X-ray tubes used for wavelength-dispersive x-ray spectrometry operate at 2 to 3 kW. Much of this power dissipates as heat, and provisions for water cooling of the x-ray tube are necessary. The power supplies and associated electronics for these x-ray tubes are large.

The electrons strike the target with a maximum kinetic energy equivalent to the applied tube potential. If the kinetic energy of the electron exceeds the absorption-edge energy corresponding to the ejection of an

Because the numerical value of $2d$ is needed for Bragg's law, the $2d$ value is often tabulated for analyzing crystals. Use of a goniometer permits precise selection of the angle θ. Because of the mechanical arrangement of the goniometer, it is convenient to use 2θ, rather than θ. The value of n can assume integer values 1, 2, 3, ... The resulting values of λ, λ/2, λ/3, . . . that solve Bragg's law are called first-order lines, second-order lines, and so on; any of these present in the sample will reach the detector. Table 1 shows some common analyzing crystals and their $2d$ spacing. Using the information in Fig. 5(b) and Table 1, the first-order Kα line for copper is determined to be at a 2θ angle of 44.97° if a LiF(200) analyzing crystal is used.

Detectors and associated electronics in wavelength-dispersive x-ray spectrometry detect x-rays diffracted from the analyzing crystal and reject undesired signals such as higher or lower order diffraction by the analyzing crystal or detector noise. Two detectors are commonly positioned in tandem. The first is a gas-filled or flowing-gas proportional detector. These detectors consist of a wire insulated from a housing. Thin polymer windows on the front and back of the housing permit entry and possible exit of x-radiation. A bias potential of a few hundred volts is applied between the wire and housing.

Although many gases may be used, the typical gas is P-10, a mixture of 90% argon and 10% methane. When x-rays enter the detector, the argon is ionized to produce many Ar^+-e^- pairs. The anodic wire collects the electrons, and the electrons at the cathodic walls of the housing neutralize the Ar^+ ions. The result is a current pulse for each x-ray photon that enters the detector. The P-10 filled proportional detectors are most efficient for detecting x-ray photons of energies less than approximately 8 keV (wavelengths greater than approximately 0.15 nm). More energetic x-radiation tends to pass through the proportional detector.

A second detector often located behind the proportional counter is usually a scintillation detector. This detector consists of a thallium-

Table 1 Common analyzing crystals

Chemical name [common name](a)	Chemical formula	$2d$, Å
Lithium fluoride [LiF(220)]	LiF	2.848
Lithium fluoride [LiF(200)]	LiF	4.028
Sodium chloride [NaCl]	NaCl	5.641
Germanium [Ge(111)]	Ge	6.532
Pentaerythritol [PET(002)]	$C(CH_2OH)_4$	8.742
Ammonium dihydrogen phosphate [ADP(101)]	$NH_4H_2PO_4$	10.640

(a) Numbers in parentheses are Miller indices to show the diffracting plane.

doped sodium iodide crystal [NaI(Tl)], which emits a burst of blue (410 nm) light when struck by an x-ray photon. The crystal is mounted on a photomultiplier tube that detects the light pulses. The number of light photons produced is proportional to the energy of the incident x-ray photon. After electronic processing, the scintillation burst is converted into a voltage pulse proportional in amplitude to the x-ray photon energy.

These two detectors may be operated independently or simultaneously. In simultaneous operation, the detector operating potential and output gain must be adjusted so that an x-ray photon of a given energy produces the same pulse-height voltage from both detectors. Both detector types require approximately 1 μs to recover between pulses. Some counts may be lost at incident photon rates greater than approximately 30 000/s. Pulse-height discrimination of the x-ray pulses from the detector(s) rejects higher or lower order x-rays diffracted from the analyzing crystal.

Fundamentals of Operation. When a sample is considered and the analyte element selected, the first decision is to select the emission line. In the absence of specific interferences, the most energetic line plausible is typically used. For elements with atomic numbers less than approximately 75, this will usually be the K line, because many wavelength-dispersive spectrometers can operate to 100-kV potentials for the x-ray tubes. When possible, an x-ray tube is selected that emits characteristic lines at energies just above the absorption edge for the line to be used for the analyte element. When such a tube is not available, the excitation must be accomplished by use of the continuum for an available x-ray tube.

The potential of the x-ray tube should be set approximately 1.5 times the absorption-edge energy or greater. The detector(s) must be selected based on the wavelength region to be used. The proportional counter should be used for x-rays longer than approximately 0.6 nm (6 Å), the scintillation detector for wavelengths shorter than approximately 0.2 nm (2 Å), and both for the overlapping region of 0.2 to 0.6 nm (2 to 6 Å). An analyzing crystal should be selected that allows the desired wavelength to be detected from 20 to 150° 2θ. In modern instruments, most parameter selections may be performed under computer control.

Energy-Dispersive X-Ray Spectrometers

Use of a goniometer in wavelength-dispersive x-ray spectrometers is based on the requirement to resolve into components the x-rays emitted by various elements in a sample. The use of a dispersion device is common in many types of spectroscopy to accomplish this task. Instruments without the mechanical components would be desirable if adequate resolution could be achieved. The development of lithium-drifted silicon detectors and their application to x-ray detection in the mid-1960s led to a field of spectroscopic analysis that became known as energy-dispersive x-ray spectrometry (EDS). Because of the tradition of the term x-ray fluorescence, the method is also known as energy-dispersive x-ray fluorescence (EDXRF).

Initially, these instruments were crude and inflexible. To function well, they required dedicated computer systems. Inexpensive microcomputer systems are available to fulfill the needs of data acquisition and analysis for EDS. Many software packages have been developed for data analysis, and suppliers continue to develop new detectors, electronics, and other hardware.

X-ray tubes used in wavelength-dispersive x-ray spectrometers are rated at 2 to 3 kW and must be water cooled. Those used in energy-dispersive x-ray spectrometers operate at much lower power and are usually air cooled. Typical tubes range from 9 to 100 W. Various anode materials are available, and each manufacturer of x-ray spectrometers offers special x-ray tube features. However, after many trials of tube design, most remain with the traditional "side window" design similar to the Coolidge tube shown in Fig. 8, although it is much smaller than those used in wavelength-dispersive systems. A major factor in the design of the tube and associated power supply is the stability of the tube and voltage.

An alternative to the direct x-ray tube excitation is the use of secondary-target excitation. In this mode, an x-ray tube is used to irradiate a secondary target, whose characteristic x-ray fluorescence is in turn used to excite the x-ray emission of the sample. Because of substantial efficiency loss when using a secondary target, higher wattage x-ray tubes are required than would be needed for direct excitation.

Secondary-target excitation sometimes affords significant advantages. For example, to determine the low concentration levels of vanadium and chromium in an iron sample, these elements could be excited with an iron secondary target without excitation of the iron in the sample. With direct-tube excitation this would be difficult. Several secondary targets would be required to cover a wide range of elements. Use of secondary-target excitation has been supported as a source of monochromatic radiation for excitation. The significance of this advantage is that many of the fundamental-parameter computer programs, used to compute intensities directly from the basic x-ray equations, require monochromatic excitation radiation.

In practice, secondary-target excitation only approaches the ideal monochromatic radiation. Direct-tube excitation with appropriate primary filters performs well when compared to secondary-target techniques (Ref 9). Therefore, direct x-ray tube excitation remains the most practical for the largest number of applications of EDS. The main strength of the energy-dispersive technique lies in its simultaneous multielement analysis capabilities. Although special cases will occur in which selective excitation is desirable, this often can be accomplished with intelligent use of an appropriate x-ray tube and filter. Any fundamental design features that limit the simultaneous multielement capability will diminish the advantage of the energy-dispersive spectrometer.

Because direct x-ray tube excitation is the most common method used in EDS, the factors governing the selection of an x-ray tube will be discussed. In wavelength-dispersive techniques, several x-ray tubes are usually available for the spectrometer. These may be changed for different applications. This is not commonly the case with energy-dispersive x-ray systems, because many wavelength-dispersive spectrometers have few if any choices of primary filters. In wavelength-dispersive techniques, it is customary to attempt to excite the desired element by the characteristic emission lines of the tube anode material, but the continuum is used more efficiently in energy-dispersive spectrometers. The use of energy-dispersive spectrometers has been enhanced by computer control of tube current and voltage and selection of the primary filter. Selection and efficient use of a single x-ray tube is important in the configuration of an energy-dispersive spectrometric system.

Characteristic lines emitted by an x-ray tube have much greater intensity at their maxima than the continuous radiation emitted. These lines should be used for excitation whenever possible. In addition, use of a primary filter between the x-ray tube and the sample can effectively approximate monochromatic radiation impinging on the sample from these characteristic lines. Commercial energy-dispersive x-ray systems usually offer various x-ray tube anode materials. To select the x-ray tube anode material, the applications most likely to be encountered should be considered.

The principal concern is to select an anode that has characteristic lines close to, but always higher, in energy than the absorption-edge energies to be encountered. None of the characteristic lines should create spectral interference with elements to be determined. This includes consideration of such details as the Compton scatter peak for the characteristic lines. In addition, it is difficult to perform determinations of the element of the anode material. This is especially true with samples having low concentrations of that element.

Rhodium is a favorable tube anode material for general-purpose use. The characteristic lines of this element are efficient for the excitation of elements with absorption edges to approximately 15 keV. The excitation efficiency for the K lines of the transition elements (Z = 22 to 30) is low; however, the continuum can be used efficiently in this region. Rhodium also has characteristic L lines at approximately 2.7 to 3.0 keV. These are efficient for the excitation of the K lines of low atomic number elements, such as aluminum, silicon, phosphorus, and sulfur. However, in these cases, a silver anode may be preferable because of the Compton scatter radiation from the rhodium lines. The characteristic lines and the continuum from the x-ray tube may be used for excitation.

Although the elements of many samples can be excited effectively using a combination of the characteristic x-ray lines from the tube anode element and the continuum, more monochromatic radiation is sometimes desired. One such situation involves enhancing the use of fundamental-parameter computations that permit quantitative determination of elements without the need for several concentration standards.

A more frequent situation is the need to reduce the background in the spectrum energy range to be used in the analysis. Use of primary filters placed between the x-ray tube and the sample can be effective in these cases and are usually incorporated under computer control in commercial spectrometers. The object is to filter the primary radiation from the x-ray tube and selectively pass the characteristic lines of the anode element. This is accomplished using a filter made of the same element as the tube anode. Because x-rays of a given line (K, L, and so on) of an element are lower in energy than the absorption edge for that element, the photoelectric component of the mass absorption coefficient is small. Such a filter does not efficiently absorb the characteristic line emitted by the x-ray tube. The higher energy x-rays from the continuum are efficient for the photoelectric process in the filter and are highly attenuated by absorption. X-rays of lower energy than the filter material absorption edge are absorbed more efficiently as the energy decreases.

The result is x-radiation striking the sample with an intensity that is largely deter-

mined by the characteristic lines of the tube anode and that approximates monochromatic radiation. Increasing the thickness of the filter decreases the total intensity, with further gain in the monochromatic approximation. Figure 9 shows the spectrum of a silver anode x-ray tube with and without a silver primary filter. The use of filters may be applied to the L lines and K lines. A filter with low mass absorption coefficient, such as cellulose, is required.

Detectors. The selective determination of elements in a mixture using x-ray spectrometry depends upon resolving into separate components the spectral lines emitted by the various elements. This process requires an energy-sorting or wavelength-dispersing device. For the wavelength-dispersive x-ray spectrometer, this is accomplished by the analyzing crystal, which requires mechanical movement to select each desired wavelength according to Bragg's law. Optionally, several fixed-crystal channels may be used for simultaneous measurement. In contrast, EDS is based on the ability of the detector to create signals proportional to the x-ray photon energy; therefore, mechanical devices, such as analyzing crystals, are not required.

Several types of detectors have been used, including silicon, germanium, and mercuric iodide.

The solid-state, lithium-drifted silicon detector [Si(Li)] was developed and applied to x-ray detection in the 1960s. By the early 1970s, this detector was firmly established in the field of x-ray spectrometry and was applied as an x-ray detection system for SEM and x-ray spectrometry. The Si(Li) detector, illustrated in Fig. 10, provides excellent resolution. It can be considered as a layered structure in which a lithium-diffused active region separates a p-type entry side from an n-type side. Under reversed bias of approximately 600 V, the active region acts as an insulator with an electric-field gradient throughout its volume.

When an x-ray photon enters the active region of the detector, photoionization occurs with an electron-hole pair created for each 3.8 eV of photon energy. Ideally, the detector should completely collect the charge created by each photon entry and result in a response for only that energy. Some background counts appear because of energy loss in the detector. Although these are kept to a minimum by engineering, incomplete charge

Fig. 9 Spectrum of silver x-ray tube emission

(a) Unfiltered. (b) Filtered with 0.05-mm (0.002-in.) thick silver filter

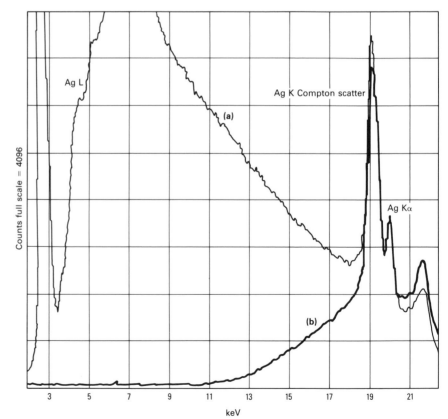

Fig. 10 Si(Li) solid-state x-ray detector

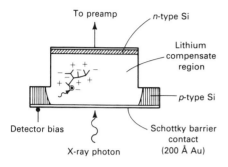

collection in the detector contributes to background counts.

From 1 to 20 keV, an important region in x-ray spectrometry, silicon detectors are efficient for conversion of x-ray photon energy into charge. Some of the photon energy may be lost by photoelectric absorption of the incident x-ray, creating an excited silicon atom that relaxes to yield a silicon Kα x-ray. This x-ray may "escape" from the detector, resulting in an energy loss equivalent to the photon energy; for silicon Kα, this is 1.74 keV. Therefore, an "escape peak" 1.74 keV lower in energy than the true photon energy of the detected x-ray may be observed for intense peaks. For Si(Li) detectors, these are usually a few tenths of one percent and never more than a few percent of the intensity of the main peak. The escape peak intensity relative to the main peak is energy dependent, but not count rate dependent. Precise quantitative determinations necessitate awareness of the possibility of interference by escape peaks.

Resolution of an energy-dispersive x-ray spectrometer is normally expressed as the full width at half maximum amplitude (FWHM) of the manganese x-ray at 5.9 keV. The resolution will be energy dependent and somewhat count rate dependent. Commercial spectrometers are routinely supplied with detectors that display approximately

145 eV (FWHM at 5.9 keV). The resolution of the system is a result of electronic noise and statistical variations in conversion of the photon energy. Electronic noise is minimized by cooling the detector and the associated preamplifier with liquid nitrogen. Half of the peak width is often a result of electronic noise.

As in x-ray tube selection, specification of the details of the detector to be supplied with the system requires consideration. In spectroscopy, there is a compromise between resolution and sensitivity. A detector with a large active surface area will collect x-rays from a large solid angle, resulting in good sensitivity. The large area leads to slightly lower resolution than that available from smaller-area detectors.

The detector must be in a vacuum because of the cryogenic temperatures. This requires a beryllium window on the detector housing. Thinner windows transmit x-rays more efficiently, especially at low x-ray energy, but are more susceptible to breakage. A system used for determinations of low atomic number elements, for which sensitivity and resolution are important, should have a thin window and small- or medium-area detector. In contrast, a system to be used in a factory for the determination of transition elements in alloys should have a thick window and larger-area detector. In the latter case, resolution usually is not a major factor.

Analyzer Systems. The x-ray spectrum of the sample is obtained by processing the energy distribution of x-ray photons that enter the detector. One x-ray photon entering the detector causes photoionization and produces a charge proportional to the photon energy. Numerous electrical sequences must take place before this charge can be converted to a data point in the spectrum. A detailed knowledge of the electronics is not necessary, although an understanding of their functions is important.

Upon entering the Si(Li) detector, an x-ray photon is converted into an electrical

charge that is coupled to a field effect transistor (FET), as shown in Fig. 11. The FET and the electronics comprising the preamplifier produce an output proportional to the energy of the x-ray photon. Using a pulsed optical preamplifier, this output is in the form of a step signal. Because photons vary in energy and number per unit time, the output signal, due to successive photons being emitted by a multielement sample, resembles a staircase with various step heights and time spacing. When the output reaches a determined level, the detector and the FET circuitry reset to their starting level, and the process is repeated.

The preamplifier output is coupled to a pulse processor that amplifies and shapes the signal into a form acceptable for conversion to a digital format by an analog-to-digital converter (ADC). Amplification is necessary to match the analog signal to the full-scale range of the ADC. This process involves the energy calibration of the spectrometer. Drift in the gain and/or offset (zero) of the amplification will result in errors in the energy assigned to the x-ray photons producing the signal. Therefore, these calibrations must be as stable as possible, and calibration must be routinely checked.

The energy calibration is important for qualitative identification of the elements and for precise quantitative results when using spectrum-fitting programs. The amplifier provides gain and zero controls for calibrations. A sample with two intense peaks of roughly equal magnitude, such as a mixture of titanium (Kα = 4.058 keV) and zirconium (Kα = 15.746 keV) metal powder cast in polyester resin, makes an excellent and convenient calibration standard. Software is usually supplied to facilitate the adjustment.

Normal operation in x-ray spectrometry is to set the time on the system clock to be used to acquire the spectrum. The processing of the pulses is not instantaneous. At high count rates, the time required may become significant. When a pulse is detected and process-

Fig. 11 Detector preamplifier and amplifier

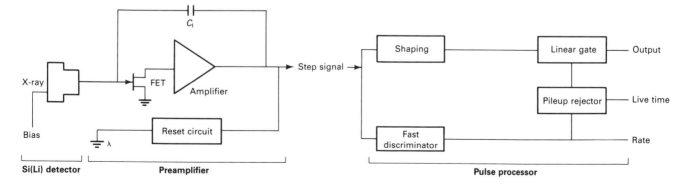

ing initiated, the clock is "stopped" until the system is ready to process a new photon. The length of time the clock is off is called dead time; the time the clock is on is called live time. Their total is real time. The system monitors live time. If the spectrometer is operated with a 50% dead time, the real time is twice the live time.

Processing of the pulse created by a photon must be complete before another pulse occurs. A pulse pileup rejector circuit blocks a pulse if it is received too soon. Once activated, the pulse pileup rejector will prevent the new signal from being processed if a second x-ray enters the detector before a prior pulse is fully processed. If analysis of the prior pulse had not yet been complete, it too would be blocked from further processing. If this blockage were not performed, pulse pileup would occur, resulting in an artifact that would appear at energies equal to the sum of the photon energy of the first and second photons to enter the detector. These are frequently called sum peaks.

Despite pulse pileup rejection circuitry, sum peaks are observed for intense peaks in the spectrum. This is the result of two photons entering the detector simultaneously or within a time difference faster than the fast discriminator can act. Sum peaks may be observed at twice the energy of an intense peak and/or at the sum of the energies of two intense peaks in the spectrum. Sum peaks decrease rapidly in intensity with count rate.

The importance of electronic pulse-processing components to system performance is easily overlooked in EDS. However, stability, linearity, and proper calibration of these components are important to use of a spectrometer.

Energy-dispersive x-ray spectrometers were among the first routine analytical instruments to require a dedicated computer system for data acquisition. Early spectrometers were heavy, unwieldy units that used hard-wired multichannel analyzers that could acquire data, but could do little to process it. Current spectrometer and data systems based on microprocessor technology are available as tabletop units.

In most data systems, the ADC converts the analog pulse height from the amplifier into an address in the computer memory, whose magnitude is proportional to the pulse height of the signal. The content of that address is incremented; that is, an address is identified by which calibration is equivalent to a given x-ray photon energy, and a count is added to the contents of that address. This can be performed by a system known as direct memory access (DMA).

Direct memory access can be accomplished without significant interruption of other computer routines that may be operating

during data acquisition. A spectrum will typically occupy 1024 or 2048 memory addresses, or channels. If a 0- to 20-keV spectrum is acquired with a 2048 channel memory range, the spectrum is plotted with an energy scale of approximately 9.8 eV/channel, and there will be approximately 15 points across the top half of each peak. In most systems, two memory "halves" may be operative. One half may be subtracted from or added to the other, or the two displayed on the screen simultaneously for comparison.

Although few options are normally available for the data system, a primary consideration is the amount of memory. Random access memory (RAM) is so inexpensive that it is advisable to obtain as much as possible on the system. Mass memory, such as floppy disks or hard disk drives, is also necessary. Floppy disks can contain only a fraction of the data of hard disks, but they are inexpensive and readily stored. Success in using EDS depends as much on the computer software available to process the spectral data as the hardware to acquire it.

Fundamentals of Operation. The simultaneous multielement capability of EDS complicates the selection of optimum conditions because of the factors to be considered for each element. The compromises in spectroscopy must be made, but the initial selection of instrument operating conditions can follow a logical sequence of decisions. Because of the variety of samples that may be encountered, the comments offered here must be taken as guidelines, and exceptions will challenge the rule. The comments are directed to quantitative determinations. Qualitative analysis will require similar procedures, usually with less stringent requirements. Experimentation is encouraged.

Once a sample is received for analysis and the elements to be determined by x-ray spectrometry are identified, the next decision is to ascertain which x-ray lines are to be used for the determinations. As a general rule, K lines are used up to a K absorption-edge energy a few keV below the characteristic line of the x-ray tube anode element. For example, operation of a rhodium x-ray tube usually necessitates using the K lines of the elements up to approximately atomic number 40 (zirconium; $K_{abs} = 18.0$ keV). The continuum may be used for excitation if the voltage to the x-ray tube is set sufficiently high to place the continuum maximum at an energy higher than the absorption edge and if a background filter is used. In these cases, K absorption-edge energies can be used up to approximately 66% of the maximum operating kV of the x-ray tube. However, the observed peaks will lie on a continuum background and reduce the signal-to-noise ratio.

For a 50-kV x-ray tube, absorption edges as high as 30 keV ($Z = 51$, antimony; $K_{abs} = 30.5$ keV) may be used if the element is present in sufficient concentration. For a 30-kV rhodium or silver tube, one is restricted essentially to excitation by the characteristic tube lines. This is of no great concern unless there is a special interest in the elements between atomic numbers 41 and 50 (niobium to tin).

Elements above atomic number 50 (40 for a 30-kV system) must generally be determined using the L lines of their x-ray spectra. To excite all L lines, the incident x-ray photon energy must exceed the L_l absorption edge. For practical use, the energy of the L lines must be greater than approximately 1 keV. For the L line spectra, this requires atomic numbers greater than 30 (zinc). At such low x-ray energies, absorption of the x-rays and low fluorescent yield in the L emission in this region require high concentration of the element to be determined and excellent sample preparation. Overlap of the K lines of the low atomic number elements in this region also causes difficulty. For example, the K lines of phosphorus overlap with the L lines of zirconium and the M lines of iridium at approximately 2.0 keV. These problems must be considered, but are to a large degree solved by careful use of processing software.

Once the x-ray spectral lines are selected for determination of the elements, the next step is to decide whether all analyte elements in the sample can be determined with one instrumental setting. Although the multielement capability of EDS is useful, all elements in every sample cannot be determined with a single set of instrument parameters. Some applications require more than one condition, such as a mixture of low atomic number elements and transition elements. The transition elements are best determined by excitation using the K lines of rhodium or silver and the low atomic number elements with the L lines or a properly adjusted continuum using a background filter. Computer control of instrument parameters facilitates changing the conditions. Whether automatic or manual control is used, all samples should be analyzed under one set of conditions, then analyzed again using the alternate set. This is preferred over changing conditions between samples.

X-ray tube operating voltage will affect the efficiency of excitation of each element in the spectrum and the integrated x-ray photon flux from the tube. The tube current will affect the flux only. Therefore, once the operating kV has been set, the tube current typically is adjusted until the system is processing counts efficiently. System dead time should be maintained below, but near, 50%.

The voltage and current settings for the x-ray tube have a surprisingly sensitive effect on the rate of information acquisition and count distribution among the respective spectral peaks for a given type of sample (Ref 10, 11).

Selection of primary tube filter thickness is important. If the filter is changed, the tube current, and sometimes the voltage, will often require resetting because the filter alters the intensity distribution of the x-rays striking the sample. When characteristic tube lines are used for excitation, the filter is usually made from the tube anode element. The intensity of the transmitted x-rays will decrease exponentially with increasing filter thickness. It is common to have two or three primary filters made from the tube anode element in the filter holder. The selection should reflect optimum count rate commensurate with reasonable current and voltage settings. Thicker filters will attenuate lower energy radiation more effectively and reduce the excitation efficiency for the element with low absorption coefficients.

The remaining decision is the choice of atmosphere in the sample chamber. If x-rays below approximately 5 keV are to be implemented, use of a vacuum may be advantageous. Intensity may increase sufficiently to reduce significantly the counting time required to obtain an adequate number of counts. If the concentration of elements yielding these x-rays is sufficiently high, the vacuum may not be needed. Because of the extra precautions required in sample criteria and handling, a vacuum path should not be used unless significant benefit is realized. Similar reasoning applies to the helium atmosphere.

These guidelines are useful for initial selection of operating conditions. The instrumental parameters are interactive, and a change in one parameter may dictate adjustment of another. For example, selection of a thicker primary filter or a decrease in the tube voltage may require an increase in the tube current. Subjective factors, such as the importance of a particular element of interest in a mixture, may alter the usual guidelines to enhance the intensity of x-rays from that element. For accurate results, reference spectra for spectrum fitting must be obtained under the same conditions as those for the analyses.

Sample Preparation

The care taken to determine the best method of sample preparation for a given material and careful adherence to that method often determine the quality of results obtained. Sample preparation is the single most important step in an analysis, yet it is all too often given the least attention. In most cases, the stability and overall reproducibility of commercial x-ray instrumentation is the least significant factor affecting the precision of analytical measurements. Too often, the precision of analytical results expected from x-ray spectrometric determinations is expressed in terms of the theoretical statistics of measurement of x-ray intensities.

When replicate samples are prepared and actual standard deviations measured, deviations are found to be larger than those predicted by counting statistics. If precision is poor, any one analytical result may also be poor, because it may differ substantially from the ''true'' value. The variety of sample types that may be analyzed using x-ray spectrometry necessitates various sample preparation techniques.

Samples are often classified as infinitely thick or infinitely thin based on measurement of the attenuation of x-rays. Samples are considered to be infinitely thick if further increase in the thickness yields no increase in observed x-ray intensity. The critical value for infinite thickness will depend on the energy of the emitted x-radiation and the mass absorption coefficient of the sample matrix for those x-rays. For pure iron, the critical thickness is approximately 40 μm for iron x-rays.

An infinitely thin sample is defined as one in which $m(\mu/\rho) \leq 0.1$, where m is the mass per unit area (g/cm^2) and μ/ρ is the sum of the mass absorption coefficients for the incident and emitted x-radiation (Ref 12). Although infinitely thin samples afford many advantages, it is rarely feasible to prepare them from routine samples. Many samples fall between these two cases and require extreme care in preparation.

In addition to preparation of the sample, precise positioning of the sample in the spectrometer is critical to quantitative determinations. Additional information is available in Ref 5.

Solid samples are defined as single bulk materials, as opposed to powders, filings, or turnings. Solid samples may often be machined to the shape and dimensions of the sample holder. The processing must not contaminate the sample surface to be used for analysis. In other cases, small parts and pieces must be analyzed as received. The reproducible positioning of these samples in the spectrometer will be critical. It is often useful to fashion a wax mold of the part that will fit into the sample holder. Using the mold as a positioning aid, other identical samples may be reproducibly placed in the spectrometer. This technique is especially useful for small manufactured parts.

Samples taken from unfinished bulk material will often require surface preparation prior to quantitative analysis. Surface finishing may be performed using a polishing wheel, steel wool, or belt grinder, with subsequent polishing using increasingly fine abrasives. Surface roughness less than 100 μm is usually sufficient for x-ray energies above approximately 5 keV, but surface roughness of less than 20 to 40 μm is required for energies down to approximately 2 keV.

Several precautions are necessary. Alloys of soft metals may smear on the surface as the sample is polished, resulting in a surface coating of the soft metal that will yield high x-ray intensities for that element and subsequently high analytical results. For matrices of low atomic number, such as papers and plastics, all samples should be infinitely thick for the most energetic x-ray utilized or should be the same thickness. Polishing grooves on the surface of the sample may seriously affect the measured intensity of low-energy x-rays. This can be examined by repetitive measurement of the intensity of a sample after 45° or 90° rotation. Use of a sample spinner reduces this effect. If a sample spinner is not available, the sample should be placed in the spectrometer such that the incident x-radiation is parallel to the polishing direction.

Powders and Briquets. Powder samples may be received as powders or prepared from pulverized bulk material too inhomogeneous for direct analysis. Typical bulk samples pulverized before analysis are ores, refractory materials, and freeze-dried biological tissue. Powders may be analyzed using the spectrometer, pressed into pellets or briquets, or fused with a flux, such as lithium tetraborate. The fused product may be reground and pressed or cast as a disk. For precise quantitative determinations, loose powders are rarely acceptable, especially when low-energy x-rays are used. Pressed briquets are more reliable. However, experience indicates that the best compromise is reground and pressed fusion products. This technique eliminates many problems associated with particle-size effects.

Particle-size effects result from the absorption of the incident and emitted x-rays within an individual particle. If the mass absorption coefficient of the sample matrix is high for the x-radiation used, particles even a few microns in diameter may significantly affect attenuation of the radiation within each particle. If the sample consists of particles of various sizes, or the particle size varies between samples, the resulting x-ray intensities may be difficult to interpret. This problem is compounded by the tendency of a material composed of a mixture of particle sizes to segregate when packed. Determination of elements using low-energy x-radiation may lead to errors from particle-size effects of as much as 50%.

If the required speed of analysis prohibits use of fusion techniques, direct determination from packed powders may be considered. The sample should be ground, if possible, to a particle size below the critical value. The grinding time required often may be ascertained by measuring the intensity from a reference sample at increasing grinding times until no further increase is observed. The lowest energy x-ray to be used in analysis should be selected for this test. Mathematical methods of correction for particle-size effects have been developed, but frequently are not useful because the particle-size distribution of the sample is required and not known.

Briquets or pressed powders yield better precision than packed powder samples and are relatively simple and economical to prepare. In many cases, only a hydraulic press and a suitable die are needed. In the simplest case, the die diameter should be the same as the sample holder so that the pressed briquets will fit directly into the holder. The amount of pressure required to press a briquet that yields maximum intensity depends on the sample matrix, the energy of the x-ray to be used, and the initial particle size of the sample. Therefore, prior grinding of the sample to a particle size less than 100 μm is advisable.

A series of briquets should be prepared from a homogeneous powder using increasing pressure. Safety precautions must be observed, because dies may fracture. The measured intensity of the x-ray lines to be used in the analysis are plotted versus the briqueting pressure. The measured intensity should approach a fixed value, perhaps asymptotically. Pressures of 138 to 276 MPa (20 to 40 ksi) may be required. For materials that will not cohere to form stable briquets, a binding agent may be required.

Acceptable binding agents include powdered cellulose, detergent powders, starch, stearic acid, boric acid, lithium carbonate, polyvinyl alcohol, and commercial binders. Experimentation is usually required with a new type of sample. Briquets that are not mechanically stable may be improved by pressing them into backing of prepressed binder, such as boric acid, or by the use of a die that will press a cup from a binding agent. The sample powder may then be pressed into a briquet supported by the cup. Metal cups that serve this purpose are available commercially. Improved results are often obtained if approximately 0.1 to 0.5 mm (0.004 to 0.020 in.) is removed from the surface of the briquet prior to measurement.

Fusion of materials with a flux may be performed for several reasons. Some refractory materials cannot be dissolved, ground into fine powders, or converted into a suitable homogeneous form for x-ray spectrometric analysis. Other samples may have compositions that lead to severe interelement effects, and dilution in the flux will reduce these. The fused product, cast into a glass button, provides a stable, homogeneous sample well suited for x-ray measurements. The disadvantages of fusion techniques are the time and material costs involved as well as the dilution of the elements that can result in a reduction in x-ray intensity. However, when other methods of sample preparation fail, fusion will often provide the required results.

Low-temperature fusions may be carried out using potassium pyrosulfate. More common are the glass-forming fusions with lithium borate, lithium tetraborate, or sodium tetraborate. Flux-to-sample ratios range from 1:1 to 10:1. The lithium fluxes have lower mass absorption coefficients and therefore less effect on the intensity of the low-energy x-rays. An immense variety of flux-additive recipes are reported for various sample types. Lithium carbonate may be added to render acidic samples more soluble in the flux; lithium fluoride has the same effect on basic samples. Lithium carbonate also reduces the fusion temperature. Oxidants, such as sodium nitrate and potassium chlorate, may be added to sulfides and other mixtures to prevent loss of these elements. Several detailed fusion procedures are provided in Ref 5. Routine production of quality specimens requires considerable practice.

Filters and Ion-Exchange Resins. Various filters, ion-exchange resin beads, and ion-exchange resin-impregnated filter papers have become important sampling substrates for samples for x-ray spectrometric analysis. Filter materials may be composed of filter paper, membrane filters, glass fiber filters, and so on. Filters are used in a variety of applications.

One widely used application is in the collection of aerosol samples from the atmosphere. Loadings of several milligrams of sample on the filter may correspond to sampling several hundred cubic meters of atmosphere. Such sampling may be performed in any environment. Many elements may be determined directly on these filters by x-ray spectrometric analysis. Particulate samples collected in this way present problems, stemming primarily from particle-size effects, which are reduced in part by the need to collect two particle-size regions using dichotomous samplers. With these units, particles are separated into those smaller and those larger than approximately 2 μm in

diameter. The smaller particles tend to represent man-made materials; the larger ones are of natural origin. The smaller particles exhibit fewer particle-size effects, and x-ray spectrometric determinations of even low atomic number elements, such as sulfur, is possible. Glass fiber filters are often used for this purpose. The Environmental Protection Agency has established guidelines for these determinations.

Filters may also be used for nonaerosol atmospheric components, such as reactive gases. Filter materials may be impregnated with a reagent reactive to the gas that will trap it chemically. Sampling is accomplished by conveying atmospheric gases through a treated filter under carefully controlled conditions. An example is a damp filter treated with ferric ion solution used to trap hydrogen sulfide (H_2S). The excess iron can be rinsed from the filter, but the precipitated ferrous sulfide (Fe_2S_3) will remain. The sulfur can be determined directly, or indirectly by measuring the iron x-radiation. The key to determining atmospheric components is the development of suitable standards. Some standards for aerosols are commercially available.

Filters can be used to determine solution components in ways parallel to those described for atmospheric components. Particulate materials may be filtered directly from solution. For example, particulate materials in environmental water samples are defined as that which is filtered using a 0.45-μm pore diameter membrane filter. Therefore, filtration of particles from water can be accomplished using such filters, and direct x-ray spectrometric analysis performed.

Application of filter sampling to dissolved elements in water is becoming more common. The principle is similar to the reactive reagent-impregnated filter application to atmospheric gases. In some cases, the filter may be impregnated with ion-exchange resins that will trap ions as the solution passes through the filter. Some varieties of these filters are commercially available.

Procedures using ion-exchange resin-impregnated filters must be carefully checked, because several passes of the solution may be required, and distribution of the ions across the paper thickness is seldom uniform. However, for solutions, a reaction may be performed prior to filtration. For example, many ions can be precipitated quantitatively from aqueous solution, even at parts per billion concentration levels. Commercially available or easily prepared reagents may be used (Ref 13, 14). The precipitates can be collected using 0.45-μm pore diameter membrane filters, which are then mounted between two Mylar sheets retained by ring clips on a standard plastic

Fig. 12 Spectrum of elements in a preconcentrated standard reference material for industrial effluent water

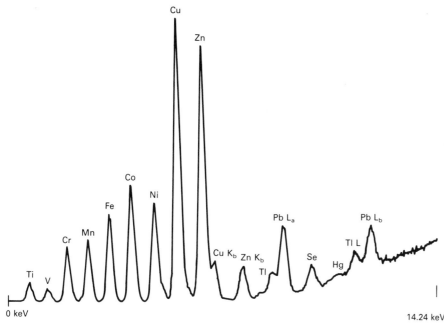

sample cup. Simultaneous multielement determinations are then performed using XRF.

Detection limits on the filters of as low as a few tenths of a microgram are common. If 100 g of sample solution is used, this corresponds to the detection limits of a few parts per billion in the sample. Standards are easily prepared as aqueous solutions. Standard Reference Materials (SRM) for environmental waters and industrial effluent water are available from the Environmental Protection Agency and commercial sources. The energy-dispersive x-ray spectrum of a precipitate of an SRM sample is shown in Fig. 12.

Thin-film samples are ideal for x-ray spectrometric analysis. The x-ray intensity of an infinitely thin sample is proportional to the mass of the element on the film, and the spectral intensities are free of interelement and mass absorption coefficient effects. However, in practice, perfect thin-film samples are rarely encountered. Powder samples of sufficiently small and homogeneous particle size may be distributed on an adhesive surface, such as cellophane tape, or placed between two drum-tight layers of Mylar film mounted on a sample cup.

More important thin-film types are platings and coatings on various substrates. Analysis of these sample types is increasingly important for the electronics industry. Of particular concern are measurements of film thickness and composition. Several techniques may be used, including the substrate intensity attenuation method, the coat-ing intensity method, various intensity ratio methods, and the variable takeoff angle method. The last method is not practical in most commercial spectrometers. These techniques are discussed in Ref 5. An example of thin-film applications is given in the section "Applications" in this article. To be infinitely thin to most x-rays used in x-ray spectrometric analyses, the specimen must be 10 to 200 μm thick.

Liquids may also be analyzed using x-ray spectrometry. The design of x-ray spectrometric instrumentation using inverted optics, in which the specimen is above the x-ray source and detector, facilitates the use of liquid samples. This convenient geometry demands caution in the preparation of liquid samples to avoid damaging the source or detector by such accidents as spills and leaking sample cups.

Quantitative standards are easily prepared for liquid samples. However, because solvents are usually composed of low atomic number elements, the Rayleigh and Compton scatter intensity is high, which increases background and leads to high limits of detection. These problems can be minimized by use of suitable primary tube filters, which reduce the scattered x-radiation in the analytically useful region.

Care must be taken with liquids containing suspended solids. If the suspension settles during the measurement time, the x-ray intensity of the contents of the sediment will be enhanced. The x-ray intensity from solution components or homogeneous suspension may decrease as a result of sediment absorption, which leads to erroneous results. This possibility is tested by brief, repetitive measurements, beginning immediately after a sample is prepared. Any observed increase or decrease in intensity with time indicates segregation in the sample. In these cases, an additive that stabilizes the suspension may be used, or the suspended content may be collected on a filter for analysis.

Special Sample Types. Applications of x-ray spectrometric analysis do not always provide convenient samples that can fit one of the above categories. Nondestructive analyses are occasionally required on production products that are not 32-mm (1.25-in.) diam circles of infinite thickness. Examples include computer disks, machined parts, and long, coated strips or wire. In these cases, a sample compartment that will accommodate the sample can often be designed. With the development of the mercuric iodide detector, which can provide adequate resolution for many analyses without a liquid nitrogen dewar, special analytical systems for on-line and nondestructive analysis of large samples may become increasingly feasible.

Qualitative Analysis

Energy-dispersive x-ray spectrometry is perhaps the most useful elemental qualitative analytical tool. The technique can qualitatively identify elements from atomic number 11 to the end of the periodic table at levels from a few hundred nanograms in thin films to a few parts per million in bulk samples. Liquids and solids may be analyzed directly, and, in some cases, gaseous materials may be collected for analysis on filters or in chemical traps. With few exceptions, x-ray spectrometry provides no information on the oxidation state, bonding, or other chemical properties of the element.

The primary basis of the identification of elements in a sample is the energy and relative intensity of the K, L, or M spectral lines. Elements can often be identified by simple use of "KLM markers" on the display screen. Precise energy calibration of the spectrometer is required, and the position and the relative intensity of the lines must be well matched with those displayed by the markers. This is because of coincidental overlap of Kα lines of an element of atomic number Z with the Kβ lines of element $Z - 1$ from 3 to 9 keV.

From 1 to 5 keV, L and M lines of high atomic number elements overlap with K lines of low atomic number elements. The data system will indicate the symbol for the element whose K, L, or M lines are shown. Similar procedures may be used for wavelength-dispersive spectrometers. However, the need to scan the spectrum impedes the process. Obtaining a suitable scan requires some prior knowledge of the composition to establish suitable operating conditions for the spectrometer.

X-ray spectrometry has good spectroscopic selectivity. That is, there are few circumstances in which spectral overlap of the x-ray energies cannot be adequately handled. For example, the lead L spectrum consists of an Lα line at 10.55 keV and Lβ lines at 12.6 keV. The arsenic K spectrum shows a Kα peak at 10.53 keV and Kβ at 11.73 keV. If the lead spectrum is not intense, the Lα peak at 14.76 keV may be missed. Using the KLM markers, the K spectrum of arsenic will not properly fit the L spectrum of lead, yet in a complex mixture, these may be misinterpreted.

Two alternatives remain. Lead will show an M line at approximately 2.3 keV, whereas arsenic L lines would appear at approximately 1.3 keV. The lead M lines will be weak because of low fluorescent yield. A remaining source of information is the absorption-edge energy values. If the x-ray tube voltage is decreased in steps and spectra acquired, the lead L spectrum will disappear at its L_{III} absorption-edge equivalent to 13.0-kV tube voltage. The arsenic K lines will persist to 11.9 kV. Rarely will such efforts be required for qualitative analysis.

Quantitative Analysis

The most important use of EDS is the quantitative determination of the concentration or amount of elements in a variety of materials. The qualitative information available from an x-ray spectrum is the energy or wavelength at which the x-ray emission lines appear in the spectrum. The quantitative information is the intensity of the emitted x-radiation. This intensity is normally expressed as the number of counts per second, I (cps), from the detector or the total number of counts, N, obtained in a fixed period of time, such as 100 s. Because x-ray emission is an example of a random-event process, the precision of intensity measurements can be predicted from theoretical considerations. These events follow Poisson statistics that enable calculation of the standard deviation in the number of counts:

$$\sigma = (N_t)^{1/2} \qquad \text{(Eq 16)}$$

where σ is the standard deviation in the counts, and N_t is the number of counts collected in the time t. The relative standard deviation (RSD) in percent is:

$$RSD = \left[\frac{(N_t)^{1/2}}{N_t} \right] \times 100 = \frac{100}{(N_t)^{1/2}} \quad \text{(Eq 17)}$$

This result is convenient. Unlike most spectroscopic techniques, instrument precision can be adjusted to some degree by the period of time t spent acquiring N_t counts from an x-ray line of intensity I. For example, an x-ray intensity of 100 counts per second counted 1 s gives $N_t = 100$, with RSD = 10%. If the same intensity is counted 100 s, $N_t = 10\,000$, and RSD = 1%. These statistics are for the counting process and represent only the theoretical instrumentation limit.

The electronics of most x-ray spectrometers are sufficiently stable that repetitive counting of an unmoved, stable specimen will result in a calculated standard deviation very close to the theoretical value. However, simply removing and replacing the sample will usually increase the standard deviation. The standard deviation obtained from replicate samples is even larger. In fact, the total variance (square of the standard deviation) is the sum of the variances of each step in the process of analyzing the sample:

$$V_{total} = V_{inst} + V_{pos} + V_{prep} +$$

$$V_{sampling} + \ldots \qquad \text{(Eq 18)}$$

where V_{total} is the total variance, and V_{inst}, V_{pos}, V_{prep}, and $V_{sampling}$ are the variances resulting from instrumentation, sample positioning, sample preparation, and sampling, respectively. Therefore, the total standard deviation in an analytical procedure is normally larger than that predicted by counting statistics alone.

In most determinations, the instrumentation contributes the least of all the above components to the total standard deviation. Precision for a procedure should not be suggested from the counting alone. It is more reliable to prepare replicate samples, measure the intensities, convert these to concentrations, and calculate precision from these data.

The lower limit of detection (LLD) of an element in a sample is a parameter important to the evaluation of instrumentation and the prediction of its applicability to certain analyses. The value of reported LLD frequently misleads because of lack of uniformity in the criteria for the definition. Calculation of an LLD value for x-ray spectrometry is simple. The lowest amount or concentration of an element that can be detected by the instrumentation and procedure used must be established. The magnitude of background in the region of the peak used is important.

If a total of N_b counts are taken in the background, the standard deviation in those counts is $(N_b)^{1/2}$. Assuming Gaussian statistics, 68% of a large number of replicate measurements would give background readings of $N_b \pm (N_b)^{1/2}$ (background ± one standard deviation). Therefore, if a net number of counts in excess of the background, $N_n = N_i - N_b$, is taken that equals one standard deviation, that is, $N_n = (N_b)^{1/2}$, these counts are expected to be greater than the background for only 68% of the measurements.

If the net counts are twice the background standard deviation, this probability increases to 95%, and for three times, the standard deviation increases to greater than 99% probability. The conservative definition of detection limit is often used as the quantity or concentration that yields a net signal equal to three times the standard deviation of the background. Using this definition, the minimum detectable concentration in a sample is:

$$C_{LLD} = \frac{3(I_b)^{1/2}}{M(t)^{1/2}} \qquad \text{(Eq 19)}$$

where C_{LLD} is the minimum detectable concentration, I_b is the intensity of the background (cps), M is the intensity per unit concentration of the analyte (cps/%), and t is the counting time. Such coefficients as 2 or $2 \times (2)^{1/2}$ may be used. Definitive work on the statistical basis of establishing detection limits for methods involving radiation counting is cited in Ref 15.

When comparing detection limits obtained using different spectrometers, it must be ascertained that the same method of computation is used. The detection limit for different elements depends on the instrument and excitation conditions as well as on the matrix composition of the sample. Criteria for establishing concentration levels required for quantitative determinations are also ambiguous. The criterion that the concentration must exceed three times the detection limit for quantitative measurements is often used.

Quantitative applications of x-ray spectrometry are based on the relationship between the intensity of the x-rays emitted by an element in the sample and the concentration of that element in a thick sample or on the total amount of the element in an infinitely thin sample. The intensities are measured using wavelength-dispersive x-ray spectrometry by setting the goniometer at the 2θ angle for the element of interest and counting x-ray pulses for a period of time to acquire sufficient counts to satisfy the statistical requirements discussed above. The background is taken in a similar way by carefully selecting an angle at which only background is measured.

Fig. 13 A second-order polynomial fit of intensity versus concentration

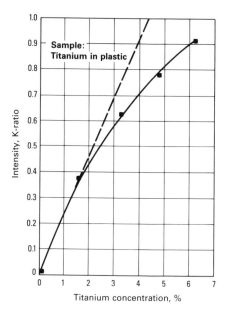

In EDS, the intensity is normally found by fitting the spectrum to a set of computer-generated peaks or to reference spectra of single elements previously acquired. The ratio of the area of the reference spectrum required to fit the experimental spectrum is used as the signal proportional to the intensity of x-ray emission by the element of interest. Instrument suppliers offer software for the fitting process.

Calibration Curves. Once the intensities of peaks in an energy-dispersive x-ray spectrum have been extracted, the data must be processed to relate the intensity of the respective peaks to concentration. This is most easily accomplished by plotting the x-ray counts (or counts per second) versus the concentration of the respective analyte element in standards. Such a plot is called a working curve or calibration curve and is the most fundamental way of relating the data to concentration. The relationship between intensity and concentration in x-ray spectrometry often depends on the total sample composition rather than only the element of interest; this is a result of matrix effects. Such cases require simultaneous or iterative computations of data for many elements in the sample. Use of the computer permits trying different mathematical models for the intensity-concentration relationships.

The ideal analytical relationship is one in which the signal or intensity is linearly related to concentration:

$$I_i = a_1 C_i + a_0 \qquad \text{(Eq 20)}$$

where I is the intensity and C is the concentration of the analyte element i. The coefficients a_1 and a_0 represent the slope (sensitivity) and intercept (blank + background), respectively. Taking a set of data from standards will result in random errors and a plot of the data scatter about a line. Therefore, a "best" line must be drawn using the data. Software using techniques known as least squares fit (LSQ), or linear regression, calculates the a_1 and a_0 values for this line.

Variations in the composition of a sample may cause deviations from linearity. Measurements of the intensity of K lines of titanium in a low atomic number matrix, such as a plastic material, represent a simple example. When the titanium concentration is low, the mass absorption coefficient at the energy of the titanium K lines is essentially that of the plastic. Therefore, the titanium concentration increases with the intensity of the titanium line and the mass absorption coefficient of the sample for the titanium K lines, resulting in a negative deviation from linearity, as shown in Fig. 13. In this example, the deviation is understood and can be corrected using mass absorption coefficients and iterative techniques. However, often it is easier to "fit" the curve with an empirical expression rather than use fundamental information that may not be readily available. For this purpose, polynomial regressions may be used:

$$I = a_n C^n + a_{n-1} C^{n-1} + \ldots a_0 \qquad \text{(Eq 21)}$$

If a high-degree polynomial, such as third or fourth order, is used, a good fit may be obtained. However, requiring polynomials higher than second order indicates the presence of several interacting processes. Figure 13 shows a second-order polynomial fit to the data. Whether a linear or polynomial regression is used, the concentration of analyte elements can be calculated from the measured intensities of lines from samples. Regression equations for several elements may be stored in the computer.

In many types of samples suitable for XRF, such as alloys, minerals and ores, and various composite materials, mass absorption coefficient changes resulting from sample composition are affected. Interelement effects may also result. These processes are based on the physics of the absorption-emission processes. The number of simultaneous processes occurring over a wide x-ray energy range complicates attempts to solve the corresponding mathematical relationships exactly. This is especially true when excitation is performed with polychromatic radiation, such as a continuum from an x-ray tube. It is often easier and

more effective to use model approximations of these processes. A variety of models have been proposed and applied to various circumstances and are described in Ref 5.

The basic processes that lead to interelement effects are absorption of x-rays emitted in a sample by another element in the sample and the resulting enhancement of the fluorescence of the latter element, thus often called "absorption/enhancement effects." Consider a stainless steel sample containing chromium, iron, and nickel in substantial amounts. Nickel x-rays from the K lines are above the K_{abs} of chromium and iron. Therefore, nickel x-rays traveling through the sample may be absorbed by chromium and iron as a result of the photoelectric process, thereby diminishing the nickel intensity. The probability of this happening will increase as the chromium and/or iron concentration increases. The nickel intensity will appear to decrease with increasing chromium and/or iron content in the sample even with constant nickel concentration. Except for the specific photoelectric absorption of nickel x-rays by iron and chromium, the three elements would have similar mass absorption coefficients. In the transition element series, it may be noticed that the K lines of an element with an atomic number Z are above K_{abs} for the elements with atomic number $Z - 2$ and below. This observation is useful in predicting absorption/enhancement possibilities.

In addition to the loss of intensity because of absorption of x-rays emitted by an element, the absorbing element may exhibit enhanced intensity. Absorption is significant because of the photoelectric effect. In the above example, the chromium atom with the nickel x-radiation will emit chromium x-rays. This extra mode of excitation enhances the chromium signal proportional to an increase in the nickel concentration.

The intensity of the nickel x-radiation will be proportional to the nickel concentration, but will be decreased by an amount proportional to the chromium concentration:

$$I_{Ni} = a_{1,Ni} C_{Ni} + a_{0,Ni} + b_{Ni,Cr} C_{Cr} \qquad \text{(Eq 22)}$$

where $b_{Ni,Cr}$ is the coefficient for the effect of chromium on the intensity of nickel x-rays and will have a negative value. The corresponding relationship for chromium is:

$$I_{Cr} = a_{1,Cr} C_{Cr} + a_{0,Cr} + b_{Cr,Ni} C_{Ni} \qquad \text{(Eq 23)}$$

where $b_{Cr,Ni}$ is the coefficient for the effect of nickel on the intensity of the chromium x-rays and will have a positive value.

In applying such relationships as Eq 22 and 23, the b coefficients are included to reflect the qualitatively known effects of x-ray absorption and emission. However, the degree of these effects is not easily computed from first principles. As a result, the coefficients are determined empirically by computation from intensity data taken from standards. Assuming the data are background corrected, the a_0 terms in Eq 22 and 23 can be assumed to be negligible. Using this assumption for two elements, there are four unknowns—$a_{1,Ni}$, $a_{1,Cr}$, $b_{Ni,Cr}$, and $b_{Cr,Ni}$—requiring four equations. The data for these four equations may derive from intensities measured from four standards.

Because of experimental errors, it is preferable to use an overdetermined system in which substantially more than the minimum required data are available. Least squares methods are used to obtain the coefficients. Obtaining reliable coefficients requires a minimum number of standards equal to the number of analyte elements plus the number of interactions to be considered.

Equations 21 and 22 are commonly written as:

$$\frac{C_i}{R_i} = 1 + a_{ij} \cdot C_j \qquad \text{(Eq 24)}$$

where R_i is the measured x-ray intensity of an element in a sample relative to that of the pure element under identical conditions; C_i is the concentration of the analyte i in the sample, a_{ij} values are termed alpha coefficients, and C_j is the concentration of the element j interacting with the analyte element i. Equation 24 represents a binary sample. For multicomponent cases, the relationship is:

$$\frac{C_i}{R_i} = 1 + a_{ij}C_j + a_{ik}C_k + \dots \qquad \text{(Eq 25)}$$

Equation 25 has become known as the Lachance-Traill equation. Other modifications of the basic equations are the Lucas-Tooth and Pyne model (Eq 26) and the Rasberry-Heinrich model (Eq 27):

$$C_i = B_i + I_i \left(K_0 + \sum_{j=1}^{j=n} K_{ij} I_j \right) \qquad \text{(Eq 26)}$$

$$\frac{C_i}{R_i} = 1 + \sum_{k \neq 1} A_{ik}C_k + \sum_{j \neq 1} \frac{B_{ij}}{1+C_i} \cdot C_j \qquad \text{(Eq 27)}$$

Equation 26 is based on intensities rather than concentrations and is especially useful when the concentration of interfering elements is not known in the standards. The basic empirical correction equations assume that an element pair exhibits only absorption or enhancement and treat enhancement as a "negative absorption." This is not the case with many types of samples.

Development of Eq 27 was based on analysis of chromium-iron-nickel alloy systems. The coefficients A_{ij} are absorption coefficients; B_{ij}, enhancement coefficients. Equation 27 permits independent and simultaneous consideration of absorption and enhancement. For example, in the determination of potassium, calcium, and titanium in paint, the L lines of barium in the paint enhance the potassium, calcium, and titanium intensity. The mass absorption coefficient of barium for the K lines of potassium, calcium, and titanium is large. Barium must be included as an enhancer and absorber for these elements. This increases the number of standards needed to determine the coefficients.

The algorithms proposed are based on a variety of assumptions, and none appears to work for all types of samples. Alpha coefficients are not constant over large changes in composition (concentration) when polychromatic radiation is used for excitation. Careful experimentation will reveal the model that provides optimum results for the sample types, analytes, and concentration range of concern. Software is available that allows selection of various models. Many of the models are described in Ref 6.

In using empirical corrections software, once the instrument conditions to be used are established, spectra of the standards are obtained. The software provides least squares solutions for the values of the coefficients. A minimum of one more standard than the number of coefficients to be calculated is required. More standards are required to use the full capability of Eq 27. Empirical parameter software has two parts. First, coefficients are calculated from the intensity and concentration data of the standards. Second, the coefficients are used to compute the concentration of the analyte elements in subsequent unknowns. The x-ray intensities of the unknowns must be measured under conditions identical to those used for the standards. These methods are only a best fit of a function to a set of standards and should not be used for samples whose composition falls outside the range represented by those standards.

Fundamental Parameters. The relative intensity of an x-ray spectral line excited by monochromatic radiation can be computed for a given element, specific transition, and known spectrometer geometry:

$$I_L = I_0 \, \omega_A g_L \, \frac{r_A - 1}{r_A} \, \frac{d\Omega}{4\pi}$$

$$\frac{C_A \mu_A(\lambda_{pri})\csc\phi}{\mu_M(\lambda_{pri})\csc\phi + \mu_M(\lambda_L)\csc\psi} \qquad \text{(Eq 28)}$$

where the terms are as defined in Table 2. However, if polychromatic excitation is

used, and if the sample has many elements to consider, Eq 28 becomes complex; such computations can be performed by computers and software is available (Ref 16, 17).

In principle, this software requires no standard. The intensities are computed from Eq 28 using the geometric factors of the instrumentation and detector efficiencies as a function of energy. However, it is more reliable if at least one standard similar to the unknown is used for instrument calibration. The software can function with filtered tube excitation (Ref 9) and is most useful in laboratories in which frequent quantitative or semiquantitative determinations are required on samples for which there are no standards.

Because the computations must involve the composition of the sample matrix to determine mass absorption coefficients, the interelement corrections are integral to the software. Fundamental parameter software will likely be improved in the future to the extent that quantitative determinations without the need for standards often will be possible. Fundamental parameter software written in C language for personal computers is available (Ref 18).

Special Methods. The lack of linear correlation between x-ray intensity and concentration of element in a sample matrix is sometimes more a result of general variation in mass absorption coefficient than specific interelement absorption/enhancement effects. These cases are especially prevalent in

Table 2   Definitions of symbols used in Eq 28

Symbol	Definition
I_L	Analyte line intensity
I_0	Intensity of the primary beam with effective wavelength λ_{pri}
λ_{pri}	Effective wavelength of the primary x-ray
λ_L	Wavelength of the measured analyte line
ω_A	Fluorescent yield of analyte A
g_L	Fractional value of the measured analyte line L in its series
r_A	Absorption-edge jump ratio of analyte A
C_A	Concentration of analyte A
$d\Omega/4\pi$	Fractional value of the fluorescent x-ray directed toward a detector
$\mu_A(\lambda_{pri})$	Mass absorption coefficient of analyte A for λ_{pri}
$\mu_M(\lambda_{pri})$	Mass absorption coefficient of the matrix for λ_{pri}
$\mu_M(\lambda_L)$	Mass absorption coefficient of the matrix for analyte line λ_L
ϕ	Incident angle of the primary beam
ψ	Takeoff angle of fluorescent beam

Fig. 14 Compton scatter for rhodium tube from iron and plastic

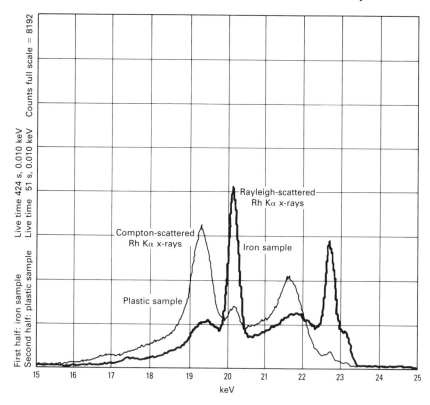

matrix by fusion of the sample with a flux often minimizes absorption/enhancement effects; a constant matrix is provided as well. Sample fusion is selected to provide accurate results. Although the mathematical manipulation of x-ray data is performed easily, use of proper sample preparation techniques to minimize the need for such processing frequently improves the quality of the analysis.

Applications

Cement can be analyzed using EDS, after being dried and ground to a fine particle size and prepared as pressed pellet specimens. NBS cement standards (633 to 639) were pressed into pellets as received at approximately 276 MPa (40 ksi). A rhodium x-ray tube was operated at 10 kV and 0.02 mA with no primary filter. A vacuum was used. The samples were irradiated for 200 s live time. Magnesium, aluminum, silicon, sulfur, calcium, iron, potassium, and titanium were determined in the samples. Reference files were created for spectra of these elements from their respective oxides, and intensity ratios were obtained using a fitting program. These ratios were related to the concentrations of the above elements (reported as oxides) in the NBS standards. The results are summarized in Table 3.

Table 3 shows a comparison of three methods of analysis of the data. For the empirical calculation, seven NBS standards were used to obtain the calibration curves and the empirical coefficients. NBS 634 was then analyzed again as an unknown. The data were treated using the empirical correction software. For the fundamental parame-

minerals and ores. Considerable improvement in results will often be observed if the mass absorption coefficient for the x-ray energy (excitation and emission) used is determined for the sample and this value used to correct the intensities for each sample. To do this rigorously would be tedious.

One of the simplest methods to approximate and simplify this measurement frequently provides surprisingly favorable results. The Compton scatter intensity measured for the characteristic lines of the x-ray tube increases as the mass absorption coefficient of the sample matrix decreases, as illustrated in Fig. 14. However, all else being equal, the intensity of emission lines of a sample increases as the mass absorption coefficient of the sample matrix decreases.

The ratio of the x-ray emission intensity to the intensity of the Compton scatter peak from the x-ray tube characteristic lines is often more linearly correlated to the concentration of analyte elements than the intensity alone. Figure 15(a) shows a plot of intensity versus concentration, and Fig. 15(b) the same concentration data plotted versus the ratio of the intensity to the Compton scatter peak of the x-ray tube. Although this procedure will not solve all problems, it can be easily tried.

Before the widespread use of personal computers associated with x-ray spectrometers, sample preparation techniques were frequently more practical for the reduction of matrix effects than application of mathematical models. Dilution of elements in a glass

Fig. 15 Ni Kα intensity versus percentage of nickel in nickel ores

(a) Nickel intensity. (b) Nickel intensity divided by scatter at 20 keV. Symbols represent iron concentration ranging from 10 to 65%.

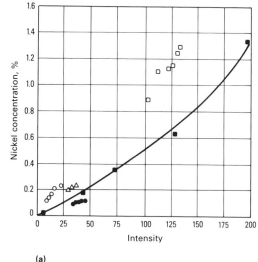

(a)

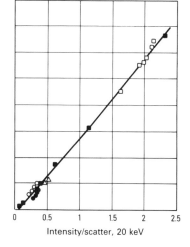

(b)

Table 3   Cement analysis for NBS 634

	Concentration, %			
Oxide	Given	Empirical corrections	XRF-11(a)	PC-XRF(b)
MgO 3.30		3.16	3.16	3.19
AlO 5.21		5.01	5.00	5.05
SiO$_2$ 20.73		20.45	20.10	20.35
SO$_3$ 2.21		2.54	2.30	2.32
K$_2$O 0.42		0.43	0.41	0.35
CaO 62.58		62.55	63.34	64.03
FeO 2.84		2.83	2.81	2.84
TiO$_2$ 0.29		0.29	0.29	0.30

(a) See Ref 17. (b) See Ref 18

ter methods, NBS 638 was used as a single standard for calibration of the instrument. The results show that for cement samples the fundamental parameters software performs exceptionally well.

Coal. The BTU and ash content of coal can be estimated from its mineral composition. X-ray spectrometry is a rapid and economical method for determining major and minor elements in coal. The coal may be dried and ground (<325 mesh), and specimens prepared as pellets. In the examples given below, a chromium x-ray tube was operated in the pulsed mode at 40 kV with no primary filter. Samples were irradiated 100 s live time. A set of well-characterized standards encompassing the range of concentrations found for each element in all unknowns were used. A typical set of results is given in Table 4; the values are expressed as percent of each element based on dry coal.

Stainless Steel. Each alloy type requires development of data-reduction procedures. The following example of the analysis of 300/400 series stainless steels illustrates options for data reduction and standardization. The samples were cut on a lathe with no further surface polishing. A silver x-ray tube was operated in the pulsed mode at 30 kV and 0.08 mA with a 0.05-mm (0.002-in.) silver primary filter. Samples were irradiated 256 s live time, with the dead time typically at 22%.

Several approaches to standardization and data reduction were implemented. A quadratic regression fit of each element to the intensity data of the standards was used, as was Eq 27 for absorption/enhancement effects. Finally, fundamental parameters software (Ref 17) was used with one standard. Table 5 lists a typical set of results for an AISI type 309 stainless steel sample for the various methods of data treatment.

Detailed evaluation of the data shows that none of the methods of data treatment is significantly better than the others. Equation 27 yields favorable results, but is sensitive to the quality of the data entered in the program. The fundamental parameters software outlined in Ref 17 works well and can accept

Table 4   Typical results for analysis of coal

	Concentration, %		
Element	Given	Found	Error
Na 0.070		0.153	0.083
Mg 0.100		0.176	0.076
Al 3.750		3.710	−0.040
Si 7.510		7.497	−0.013
S 0.720		0.662	−0.058
Cl 0.020		0.020	0.000
K 0.143		0.143	0.000
Ca 0.070		0.061	−0.009
Ti 0.249		0.247	−0.002
Fe 0.330		0.299	−0.031

more than one standard by using an adaptive regression technique. This option was not used in this example. Minimizing systematic errors in the software in Ref 17 depends on the quality of the standard selected. These analyses were performed using a system operated at 30 kV, indicating that the newer low-cost 30-kV power supplies and x-ray tubes are applicable.

Thin Films. The intensity of a characteristic x-ray line measured from a thin film depends on the thickness of the film or layer of material emitting the x-radiation. Figure 16 shows a plot of x-ray intensity versus thickness of such a film for a single element. The plot may be characterized by three regions. In the first region of very thin film thickness, the intensity of the x-radiation increases linearly with thickness of the film. In an intermediate region, the intensity varies exponentially with the thickness. At a higher film thickness, intensity of the emitted x-radiation does not change with increased film thickness. These are the regions of infinitely thin, intermediate thickness, and infinitely thick x-ray samples.

Table 5   Results of analysis of AISI type 309 stainless steel

	Concentration, %			
Element	Given	Quadratic	Eq 27	XRF-11(a)
Cr 23.8		23.5	23.7	23.5
Fe 59.8		59.1	56.7	58.1
Ni 13.5		14.5	16.4	15.6
Mn 1.83		1.80	2.09	1.81
Mo 0.19		0.24	0.24	0.18

(a) See Ref 17

The value of the film thickness for these regions depends on the composition of the film, geometric factors, and the energy of the x-radiation used. For chromium x-rays in a typical energy-dispersive spectrometer, an infinitely thin region is that below approximately 1 μm; the infinitely thick region is that above approximately 15 μm. If the thin layer on a dissimilar substrate is an alloy, interelement effects cause the measured intensity from the sample to deviate from the simple model. If a suitable set of standards is available, and if the measurements are applied to a small range of film thickness, an empirical, linear model can be used.

A set of standards of 20% Fe and 80% Ni (Permalloy) on a ceramic substrate was measured over a thickness range of 1.6 to 2.6 μm. A molybdenum x-ray tube was operated at 10 kV and 0.10 mA using a cellulose primary filter. The samples were irradiated 100 s live time. The software uses the intensity to compute the thickness of the alloy film, then utilizes this result to compute the composition of the alloy.

The results in Table 6 show that x-ray spectrometry is useful for rapid, on-line measurement to film thickness and composition in a variety of coating and plating products. Each case will require the development of data-treatment software and a set of well-characterized standards.

Petroleum Products. Energy-dispersive x-ray spectrometry, with its multielement capabilities, is ideally suited for many analyses of petroleum products. In the following examples the liquid sample was placed in a 32-mm (1.25-in.) diam sample cup with a polypropylene window. Polypropylene has better transmission characteristics for low-energy x-rays than Mylar and less interference with the low-Z

Fig. 16 Theoretical intensity versus thickness for a single element on a dissimilar substrate

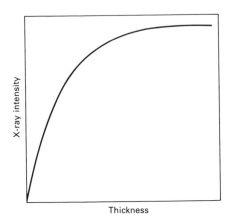

Table 6 Results of Permalloy film thickness determination on ceramic

Given	Calculated
Thickness, μm	
1.61	1.60
2.59	2.58
2.11	2.13
1.75	1.75
2.35	2.34
Iron concentration, %	
19.2	19.2
19.2	19.1
18.9	19.1
19.3	19.2
19.2	19.2

Table 7 Detection limits of minor elements in oil

Element	Detection limit, ppm
Ti	6.5
V	3.9
Cr	2.7
Mn	1.7
Fe	1.3
Ni	0.6
Cu	0.4
Zn	0.3
Pb	0.4

Table 8 Results of sulfur determination in oil

Concentration, %		Relative
Given	Found	error, %
0.010	0.007	29.5
0.141	0.156	10.4
0.240	0.249	3.7
0.719	0.691	−3.9
0.950	0.933	−1.7
1.982	2.008	1.3
4.504	4.499	0.1

elements. A silver x-ray tube was operated in the pulsed mode.

For the low-Z elements (aluminum, silicon, phosphorus, sulfur, calcium, and vanadium), the tube was operated at 8 kV, 0.4 mA, without a filter in a helium atmosphere, and the samples were irradiated 300 s live time. For the mid-Z and heavy elements (chromium, manganese, iron, nickel, copper, zinc, lead, and barium), the tube was operated at 21 kV, 0.8 mA, with a 0.05-mm (0.002-in.) silver filter and air path, and the samples were irradiated 100 s live time. The peak intensities were extracted using the XML software (Ref 18) and reference spectra of the elements required for the fit. The intensity and concentration data were correlated using a linear or quadratic function.

Analysis of Conostan C-20 100 ppm standard resulted in the calculation of detection limits for elements in oil, as shown in Table 7. Energy-dispersive x-ray spectrometry can perform rapid, accurate determinations of sulfur in oil. The results obtained from a set of standards and unknowns are shown in Table 8.

ACKNOWLEDGMENT

The author wishes to thank Tracor X-Ray Inc., Mountain View, CA, for permission to use material from "Fundamentals of X-Ray Spectrometry as Applied to Energy Dispersive Techniques" by D.E. Leyden.

REFERENCES

1. A.H. Kramers, *Philos. Mag.*, Vol 46, 1923, p 836
2. R.T. Beatty, *Proc. R. Soc. London, Ser. A*, Vol 89, 1913, p 314
3. H. Kulenkampff, *Ann. Phys.*, Vol 69, 1923, p 548
4. E.P. Bertin, *Introduction to X-Ray Spectrometric Analysis*, Plenum Press, 1978
5. E.P. Bertin, *Principles and Practice of X-Ray Spectrometric Analysis*, 2nd ed., Plenum Press, 1975
6. R. Tertian and F. Claisse, *Principles of Quantitative X-Ray Fluorescence Analysis*, Heyden and Son, 1982
7. H.K. Herglotz and L.S. Birks, Ed., *X-Ray Spectrometry*, Marcel Dekker, 1978
8. R. Jenkins, *An Introduction to X-Ray Spectrometry*, Heyden and Son, 1974
9. R.A. Vane, *Adv. X-Ray Anal.*, Vol 26, 1983, p 369
10. W. Wegscheider, B.B. Jablonski, and D.E. Leyden, *X-Ray Spectrom.*, Vol 8, 1979, p 42
11. B.B. Jablonski, W. Wegscheider, and D.E. Leyden, *Anal. Chem.*, Vol 51, 1979, p 2359
12. J.R. Rhodes, *Am. Lab.*, Vol 5 (No. 7), 1973, p 57
13. A.T. Ellis, D.E. Leyden, W. Wegscheider, B.B. Jablonski, and W.B. Bodnar, *Anal. Chim. Acta*, Vol 142, 1982, p 73
14. A.T. Ellis, D.E. Leyden, W. Wegscheider, B.B. Jablonski, and W.B. Bodnar, *Anal. Chim. Acta*, Vol 142, 1982, p 89
15. L.A. Currie, *Anal. Chem.*, Vol 40, 1968, p 586
16. J.W. Criss, L.S. Birks, and J.V. Gilfrich, *Anal. Chem.*, Vol 50, 1978, p 33
17. J.W. Criss, *Adv. X-ray Anal.*, Vol 23, 1980, p 93
18. Tracor X-Ray Inc., Mountain View, CA

SELECTED REFERENCES

- E.P. Bertin, *Introduction to X-Ray Spectrometric Analysis*, Plenum Press, 1978
- E.P. Bertin, *Principles and Practice of X-Ray Spectrometric Analysis*, 2nd ed., Plenum Press, 1975
- T.G. Dzubay, *X-Ray Fluorescence Analysis of Environmental Samples*, Ann Arbor Science Publishers, 1977
- K.F. Heinrich, D.E. Newbury, and R.L. Myklebust, Ed., *Energy Dispersive X-Ray Spectrometry*, National Bureau of Standards, (U.S.), Special Publication 604, June 1981
- H.K. Herglotz and L.S. Birks, Ed., *X-Ray Spectrometry*, Vol 2, *Practical Spectroscopy*, Marcel Dekker, 1978
- R. Jenkins, *An Introduction to X-Ray Spectrometry*, Heyden and Son, 1974
- R. Jenkins, R.W. Gould, and D. Gedcke, *Quantitative X-Ray Spectrometry*, Marcel Dekker, 1981
- R.O. Muller, *Spectrochemical Analysis By X-Ray Fluorescence*, Plenum Press, 1972
- J.C. Russ, *Fundamentals of Energy Dispersive X-Ray Analysis*, Butterworths, 1984
- R. Tertian and F. Claisse, *Principles of Quantitative X-Ray Fluorescence Analysis*, Heyden and Sons, 1982

Particle-Induced X-Ray Emission

Thomas A. Cahill, Crocker Nuclear Laboratory, University of California—Davis

General Uses

- Nondestructive multielemental analysis of thin samples, sodium through uranium, to approximately 1 ppm or 10^{-9} g/cm^2
- Nondestructive multielemental analysis of thick samples for medium and heavy elements
- Semiquantitative analysis of elements versus depth
- Elemental analyses of large and/or fragile objects through external beam proton milliprobe
- Elemental analyses using proton microprobes, spatial resolution to a few microns, and mass detection limits below 10^{-16} g

Examples of Applications

- Analysis of air filters for a wide range of elements
- Analysis of atmospheric aerosols by particle size for source transport, removal, and effect studies
- Analysis of powdered plant materials and geological powders for broad elemental content
- Analysis of elemental content of waters, solute, and particulate phases, including suspended particles
- Medical analysis for elemental content, including toxicology and epidemeology
- Analysis of materials for the semiconductor industry and for coating technology
- Archaeological and historical studies of books and artifacts, often using external beams
- Forensic studies

Samples

- *Form*: Thin samples (generally no more than a 10-mg/cm^2 thick solid) are analyzed in vacuum, as are stabilized powders and evaporated fluids. Thick samples can be any solid and thickness, but proton beam penetration is typically 30 mg/cm^2 or approximately 0.15 mm (0.006 in.) in a geological sample
- *Size*: The sample area analyzed is on the order of millimeters to centimeters, except in microprobes, in which beam spot sizes approaching 1 μm are available
- *Preparation*: None for air filters and many materials. Powders and liquids must be stabilized, dried, and generally placed on a substrate, such as plastic. Thick samples can be pelletized

Limitations

- Access to an ion accelerator of a few mega electron volts is necessary
- Generally, no elements below sodium are quantified
- Elements must be present above approximately 1 ppm
- Sample damage is more likely than with some alternate methods
- No chemical information is generated
- Computer codes are necessary for large numbers of analyses

Estimated Analysis Time

- 30 s to 5 min in most cases; thousands of samples can be handled in a few days

Capabilities of Related Techniques

- *X-ray fluorescence*: With repeated analyses at different excitation energies, essentially equivalent or somewhat superior results can be obtained when sample size and mass are sufficient
- *Neutron activation analysis*: Variable elemental sensitivity to neutron trace levels for some elements, essentially none for other elements. Neutron activation analysis is generally best for detecting the least common elements, but performs the poorest on the most common elements, complementing x-ray techniques
- *Electron microprobe*: Excellent spatial resolution (approximately 1 μm), but elemental mass sensitivity only approximately one part per thousand
- *Optical methods*: Atomic absorption or emission spectroscopy, for example, are generally applicable to elements capable of being dissolved or dispersed for introduction into a plasma

Introduction

Particle-induced x-ray emission (PIXE) is one of several elemental analyses based on characteristic x-rays. These methods can be classified by the method of excitation and the nature of x-ray detection. The excitation source creates inner electron shell atomic vacancies that cause x-ray emission when filled by outer electrons. X-ray fluorescence (XRF) uses x-rays for this purpose; electrons are used to cause vacancies in electron microprobes and some scanning electron microscopes. Particle-induced x-ray emission uses beams of energetic ions, normally protons of a few mega electron volts, to create inner electron shell vacancies. Regarding detection, the most widely used methods involve wavelength dispersion, which is scattering from a crystal, or energy dispersion, which involves direct conversion of x-ray energy into electronic pulses in silicon or germanium diodes.

These methods all provide quantitative analyses of elemental content, yet the differences between PIXE and other x-ray-based methods have favored PIXE in several specialized analytical applications, especially environmental and biological. Recent developments in focusing energetic proton beams (proton microprobes) have expanded the utility of PIXE in applications in geology and materials science, combining part per million elemental sensitivity and micron spatial resolution.

Fig. 1 Typical set-up for PIXE analysis

The entire apparatus is contained in a vacuum chamber. ρt_B, maximum target thickness; ρt_S, maximum sample thickness

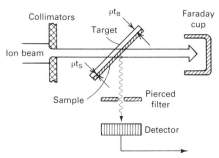

Table 1(a) Penetration of a 4-MeV proton in a low-Z matrix(a)

Target configuration	Thickness, mg/cm²
Thin target (10% energy loss)	5
Thick target (stopped beam)	28

(a) Effective atomic number, Z_{eff} = 9

Table 2   Typical loading and particle size diameter corrections for thin PIXE samples

Element	Kα x-ray energy, keV	Maximum sample thickness(a)	Loading correction(b) for ρt^S = 300 μg/cm²	Correction for particle size diameter 30 μm(c)	10 μm(d)	1 μm(d)
Sodium	1.041	150 μg/cm²	1.70	4.7	2.5	1.32
Magnesium	1.255	230 μg/cm²	1.39	4.2	2.0	1.22
Aluminum	1.487	390 μg/cm²	1.23	2.6	1.7	1.16
Silicon	1.739	640 μg/cm²	1.14	2.3	1.5	1.12
Phosphorous	2.014	1 mg/cm²	1.09	2.1	1.37	1.09
Sulfur	2.307	1.5 mg/cm²	1.06	1.9	1.26	1.07
Chlorine	2.622	2.2 mg/cm²	1.04	1.8	1.20	1.0
Potassium	3.312	4.3 mg/cm²	1.02	1.5	1.12	1.025
Calcium	3.690	(e)	1.02	1.4	1.09	1.02
Titanium	4.508	(e)	1.01	1.3	1.07	1.017
Iron	6.400	(e)	1.01	1.1	1.03	1.01

Note: maximum sample thickness denoted by ρt^S
(a) Assuming a 30% self attenuation correction at Z_{eff} = 9 for a target at 45° to the detector (Ref 1). (b) True value = correction × observed value. (c) Assumes earth crustal composition and ρ = 2.2 g/cm³. (d) Assumes Z_{eff} = 9 and ρ = 1.5 g/cm³. (e) Limitation set by energy loss in ion beam

Principles

Elemental analysis requires that some method of excitation reach the atom of interest and that the information obtained during de-excitation reach an appropriate detector. In the case of PIXE, the exciting radiation is an ion beam consisting of protons at an energy level of 2 to 5 MeV. These ions have a limited distance of penetration in a target material (Table 1). Table 1 lists the approximate stopping distance in milligrams per square centimeter for typical targets often encountered in PIXE analysis: low-Z (atomic number) targets, such as air filters and biological samples; medium-Z targets, such as silicon chips, rocks, and pottery; and high-Z targets, such as transition metals. In addition, the thicknesses of targets necessary to meet a thin-target criterion, selected in Table 1 to produce a 10% loss of primary beam energy or attenuation, are also given in milligrams per square centimeter.

Thin targets, in which corrections for primary beam excitation energy and secondary x-ray absorption and refluorescence are small and easily calculable, provide highly accurate, absolute values that compare well with the best alternate nondestructive elemental techniques, such as XRF and neutron activation analysis (NAA). Thus, many PIXE research programs have worked to prepare samples, such as thin air filters and powdered biological and geological samples, that meet these energy-loss criteria. Such thin-target analysis was not normally performed before development of intrinsic germanium, lithium-doped germanium, and lithium-doped silicon energy dispersive x-ray detectors, because wavelength dispersive x-ray detection is highly inefficient and generally uses more massive targets with significant and difficult correction factors. Figure 1 shows a typical PIXE setup in a thin-target mode.

Once inner-shell vacancies have been created in the atoms of interest, the resulting characteristic x-rays must be able to leave the sample and reach a detector to be useful. This poses severe problems even in thin samples (Table 2). Table 2 lists the transmission of radiation through a low-Z thin sample. The first type of required correction is a loading correction that reflects the passage of x-rays through a uniform layer of deposit. The second is a particle size diameter correction associated with a spherical particle of a given diameter and composition typical in ambient aerosol studies.

The severe limitations on sample thickness for low-Z elements are shown clearly in Table 2, and in practice this limits the utility of PIXE for such elements. X-rays of elements as light as those of boron are visible using windowless detectors, but results can never be more than qualitative for such elements. The lightest element normally reported and quantified is sodium (Z = 11), whose Kα x-ray energy is approximately 1 keV. The ability to observe and quantify every element from Z = 11 to 92 in a single analysis is the most important feature of a successful PIXE investigation. In some cases, nuclear methods such as Rutherford

Table 1(b)   Transmission of secondary radiation through a low-Z sample approximately 5 mg/cm² thick

Secondary radiation	Energy	Criterion
Photons	3 keV	10% attenuation
Electrons	140 keV	10% energy loss
Protons	4 MeV	10% energy loss
Deuterons	5.5 MeV	10% energy loss
Tritons	6.5 MeV	10% energy loss
³He	14.4 MeV	10% energy loss
⁴He	16 MeV	10% energy loss
Neutrons	Thermal	10% attenuation, good geometry

backscattering are used to measure elements lighter than sodium, down to and including hydrogen, allowing complete elemental analysis capable of direct comparison to total mass (determined by weighing the sample).

The ability of the incident ion to form a vacancy depends strongly on the energy of the ion. Although the process can be described in some detail by such models as the Plane Wave Born Approximation (Ref 2) and the Binary Encounter Model (Ref 3), realizing that the coulomb interaction that results in ionization depends heavily on the relative velocities of the ion and the electron yields considerable insight into vacancy formation. Thus, a very fast proton and a very slow electron behave much like a very fast electron and a very slow proton in that the probability of ionization in either case is low.

When the velocities are approximately matched, the cross section is maximum. This occurs for K-shell x-rays with a 2-MeV proton on aluminum and a 10-MeV proton on iron—and higher for heavier elements. Another insight is that, to a good approximation, electrons bound with equal energy have approximately equal velocities. Thus, x-ray production for the Kα x-ray of arsenic (per atom) occurs with approximately the same probability as that of an Lα x-ray of lead (per atom) because the Kα of arsenic and Lα of lead have the same energy. Obtaining the x-ray production versus mass requires factoring in the relative masses of arsenic and lead. Figure 2 illustrates x-ray production cross sections showing examples of such approximations.

Combining these cross-section curves with the range/energy relationship enables calculation of yield versus depth in thick samples. One difficulty in this calculation derives from the principle that protons lose energy as they penetrate the sample. The cross sections for x-ray production generally decrease, but this varies for each element. Another difficulty is that the attenuation of x-rays exiting the sample are also a function of depth in the sample, atomic number in the element, and the transition lines (K, L, M, . . .) used for identification and quantification. If the sample is nonuniform in depth or heterogeneous in structure, yield versus depth calculations may not be possible. These difficulties are less troublesome for uniformly deep or homogeneous samples. A corollary of the above approximate yield versus depth relationship is that only a correction factor scaled by the x-ray energy, E_x need be considered to first order, because the x-ray production and the mass attenuation of x-rays exiting the sample are similar for x-rays of the same energy (whether K, L, or M shell).

These concepts are useful in estimating x-ray production rates; however, approximations, published cross sections, and theoretical predictions are not adequate in practice to achieve the absolute accuracies (within a few percent) reported in analytical intercomparisons. This requires several gravimetric thin standards covering a range of atomic numbers. A fit to such multiple standards generally provides a better fit than any single standard alone.

Calculations of minimum detectable limits require evaluation of the characteristic x-ray production and the x-ray background (Fig.

Fig. 3 Portion of an x-ray spectrum from a sample layered on a supporting substrate

Characteristic x-rays from the substrate (blank contaminant) and the sample are shown superimposed on a characteristic smooth background of x-rays due to bremsstrahlung caused by scattered electrons. The number of x-rays due to elements with atomic number Z in the sample, $N_{x,z}$, must be statistically greater than the uncertainty or fluctuations in the background due to the substrate, N_B, and the sample, $N_{B,x}$, for detection and quantification.

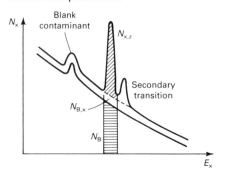

3). The standard relationship for identifying a peak as statistically significant is:

$$N_{x,z} \geq 3.3\sqrt{N_B + N_{B,x}} \qquad \text{(Eq 1)}$$

where $N_{x,z}$ is the number of x-rays, N_B is the number of background counts due to the substrate, and $N_{B,x}$ is the number of background counts due to the sample (Fig. 3). The quantity of background counts versus x-ray depends crucially on the matrix. If a low-Z matrix, such as a teflon air filter or a biological powder, is selected, the background is dominated by bremsstrahlung generated by "free" or loosely bound electrons. For a proton of E_p (MeV), these electrons can generate bremsstrahlung to approximately $2E_p$ (keV):

$$E_x \text{ (keV)} \simeq 2\, E_p \text{ (MeV)} \qquad \text{(Eq 2)}$$

The result is an 8-keV x-ray from a 4-MeV proton. This is approximately the point at which the bremsstrahlung curve flattens; it generally represents nearly optimum sensitivity of a PIXE system for a range of elements. Figure 4 illustrates theoretical and experimental background spectra for 3-MeV protons on transition metal substrates.

Approximately two-thirds of all PIXE analyses, standard or proton microprobe, operate with protons between 2 and 4 MeV, although energies as low as 0.15 MeV or as high as 50 MeV can be used (Ref 6). In addition, alpha particles with energies as high as 30 MeV are sometimes used. Figure

Fig. 2 (a) Kα x-ray production cross sections versus proton energy and atomic number and (b) L x-ray production cross sections versus proton energy and atomic number. Source: Ref 4

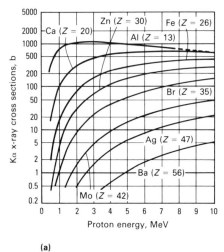

(a)

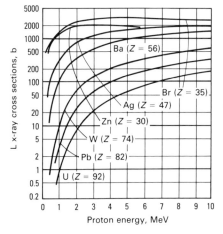

(b)

Fig. 4 Background spectra, experimental and theoretical, for 3-MeV protons on thin clean transition metal substrates

E_r is the energy of the electron recoil caused by a 3-MeV proton on carbon. Source: Ref 5

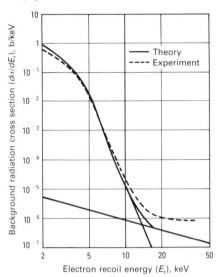

5 shows the elemental sensitivity of PIXE analysis based on typical parameters discussed in this article.

Data Reduction

Particle-induced x-ray emission analysis is normally used as a multielemental method because a single element in a well-specified matrix can be determined more conveniently by applying other techniques. When PIXE is used as a multielemental technique, accurate absolute values can be obtained for a wide range of elements (from $Z = 11$ to $Z = 92$), or firm, statistically sound upper limits obtained for elements not observed. Although the importance of the first case is recognized, that of the second is often overlooked, yet the absence of an element may clearly eliminate certain sources of air pollutants when used in statistical chemical mass balance studies. Data-reduction codes must identify, integrate, and reduce x-ray peaks into elemental concentrations (ideally automatically or semiautomatically) because so many peaks are present.

The HEX (Ref 7) and rapid acquisition and computer extraction (RACE) codes (Ref 8) have been developed to high degrees of sophistication. In the former, much x-ray information is incorporated into the program and used in the chi-squared fit to theoretical backgrounds shapes, peak widths, shapes, and locations and secondary transitions. One elemental value is obtained that includes all

available information. The codes require relatively large computers, careful control of detector gain shifts, sample matrix effects, and other factors, but work extremely well in the hands of trained scientists.

The RACE code is more traditional in that the search routine is a general correlation routine suitable for any relatively narrow peaks on top of any relatively smoothly varying background. Once all peaks have been found and integrated, a separate part of the code adds x-ray information. The RACE code uses a physical blank to remove most of the background. This blank includes contaminants, which are also subtracted. A polynomial fit then removes residual counts, and the peaks are integrated. Sum and escape peaks are removed; close peaks are identified and resolved (up to six at a time using chi-square fits). The code collects data on secondary x-ray transitions and upper limits, then delivers the results and uncertainties. The code can handle such phenomena as x-ray detector gain shifts and shape changes while identifying peak centroids to ± 5 eV. It is used on XRF and NAA spectra, with modification of the physics portion.

Calibration and Quality Assurance Protocols

Calibration for most PIXE analyses is performed using gravimetric standards thin enough to avoid serious absorption, refluorescence, or ion energy change corrections. Because the expected x-ray yields are well known and follow a smooth dependence from element to element, intervening elements are located with little additional uncertainty. Thus, in reality, the calibration

value should fall close to the yields predicted from the x-ray literature, or the presence of some error can be assumed. Once calibrated, a separate verification step is essential. This is ideally accomplished using thin multielement glass standards (Ref 9), but other standards can also be prepared. Because PIXE is nondestructive, a previously analyzed sample can be analyzed again as a secondary standard. Finally, participation in the difficult but useful formal intercomparisons is possible. In all cases, formal protocols must be established and adhered to strictly.

Comparison of Particle-Induced X-Ray Emission With X-Ray Fluorescence

Particle-induced x-ray emission and XRF are types of x-ray analysis. Although the excitation modes differ, neither generates the massive bremsstrahlung of the direct electron-beam excitation used in electron microprobes or scanning electron microscopes. Thus, both reach part per million detection levels, as opposed to 0.1% levels in electron excitation. In most modern systems, PIXE and XRF use energy dispersive lithium-doped silicon detectors. Although highly efficient, these detectors do not attain the energy resolution of wavelength dispersive systems. Data reduction codes can be essentially identical. Given these similarities, essentially equivalent detectable limits (in the part per million range) are achievable in the same amount of time (a few minutes). Figure 6 compares the detection limits for PIXE and XRF analysis.

Fig. 5 Sensitivity of PIXE analysis versus proton energy and atomic number based on typical parameter given in the text
Source: Ref 4

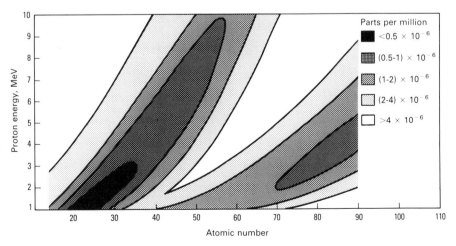

Fig. 6 Comparison of detection limits for PIXE and XRF analyses

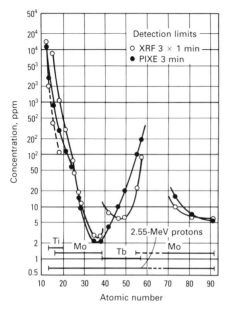

Particle-induced x-ray emission and XRF are also similar in that both have performed well in published interlaboratory and intermethod intercomparisons. Both methods can analyze samples "as received" or with such minimal preparation as grinding or evaporating. This allows both to operate in a truly nondestructive mode that separates these methods from any other elemental analysis technique in common use. Table 3 lists results of published interlaboratory intercomparisons using several elemental analysis procedures. Samples were prepared from solutions and placed in absorbant paper substrates, ground Canadian geological standard dusts, and ambient aerosols collected on filters. The standard deviation given in Table 3 represents the scatter of the ratio of the results to the "correct" value for many elements, ranging from aluminum to lead, and the scatter of the various reporting laboratories.

Results given in Table 3 compared reasonably well when standards were prepared from solutions. When ground rock and aerosol standards were used (such standards require the elements to be put into solution), results from atomic absorption (AA) and emission spectroscopy (ES) varied widely from correct values. Table 3 shows discrepancies as high as 47 standard errors from the correct value using AA and ES. After this test, one major environmental agency limited its use of AA spectrometry on environmental samples to species that go into solution easily, for example, lead and cadmium,

or those that x-ray or activation methods could not accommodate, such as beryllium.

Applications

Three areas in which PIXE has become a major analytical force are atmospheric physics and chemistry, external proton milliprobes and historical analysis, and PIXE microprobes. Two areas in which PIXE has not made any major analytical impact despite early promise are biological samples and materials science in the semiconductor industry. Additional information on the applications of PIXE is cited in Ref 10 to 12.

Atmospheric Physics and Chemistry. One of the earliest uses of PIXE, involving analysis of atmospheric particles for elemental content (Ref 13), is also its most common application. The problem of atmospheric particles entails personal health, atmospheric visibility, and ecological effects, including ties to acid rain. Because of the complexity of the particles, existing analytical methods were inadequate. Generally, only mass was measured (by weighing), and a few chemical compounds, such as nitrates, sulfates, organic species, and lead, were studied using AA spectrophotometry. Sampling was performed using high-volume samplers (Hi-Vols) that delivered a 20- by 25-cm (8- by 10-in.) sheet of fiberglass filter material for analysis. The complexity of the problem rendered such techniques as NAA and XRF ineffective.

Various elements are present in a given air sample; 22 elements occur at the 0.1% level in an average urban sample. Atmospheric variability demands timely information (sometimes as short as hours) and many analyses for statistical reliability. Particulate size is essential to understanding particulate sources, transport, transformation, effects on

health and welfare, and removal mechanisms. Although PIXE has reasonable success in analysis of such air samples, the parallel development of specialized air samplers has expanded the capabilities of PIXE for analyzing small amounts of mass in a small beam size.

Simultaneous size chemistry profiles are essential to atmospheric chemistry studies, spanning questions from particulate sources through transport to effects and health and safety. However, size-collecting devices are extremely limited in the amount of mass they collect. All elements in the atmosphere are important because they are part of the aerosol mass, and all results must be quantitative. These severe, simultaneous but important requirements demand the specialized capabilities of PIXE. Particle-induced x-ray emission spectroscopy "sees" more elements in a single analysis than any other method using microgram samples delivered by particulate collectors with sizing capabilities. Devices such as a solar-powered aerosol impactor and an 8-stage rotating-drum impactor have been designed and built for use in PIXE analysis of particulate matter. Because particle accelerators are used for PIXE (a limitation to PIXE's use), nuclear techniques, such as Rutherford backscattering, can be used in conjunction with PIXE to determine very light elements (down to hydrogen). This affords PIXE laboratories an advantage in some research efforts in that the sum of all elemental masses (hydrogen through uranium) can be compared with total particulate mass and determined by weighing the sample (Ref 14).

Biological Samples. The most successful applications involving multielemental analysis of powdered biological materials using PIXE are large, statistically based studies in medicine and the environment.

Table 3 Results of formal interlaboratory analyses comparing PIXE with other elemental analysis techniques

The values given represent the standard deviation (the ratio of the laboratory results to the established "correct" values)

Method	Number of groups reporting data(a)	Solution standards(b)	Ground rock standards(c)	Aerosol standards(d)	Aerosol samples(e)
PIXE.............	7	1.03 ± 0.16	0.99 ± 0.29	0.99 ± 0.19	0.98 ± 0.08; 1.01 ± 0.16
XRF	8	0.97 ± 0.12	1.07 ± 0.20	1.03 ± 0.14	0.97 ± 0.08; 1.08 ± 0.15
Wavelength XRF	3	1.19 ± 0.34	1.12 ± 0.47	1.37 ± 0.50	...
AA, ES(h)..........	3	0.88 ± 0.17	0.40 ± 0.31	0.47 ± 0.29	1.04(f); 0.84(g)
ACT(j)	...	...	...	...	0.76 ± 0.15(g)

(a) Each result represents the mean and standard deviation for all laboratories using the method for all elements quoted. (b) Two samples, each including aluminum, sulfur, potassium, vanadium, chromium, manganese, iron, zinc, cadmium, and gold. (c) Two samples, each including aluminum, silicon, potassium, calcium, titanium, manganese, and iron. (d) Two samples, each including aluminum, silicon, sulfur, potassium, calcium, titanium, manganese, iron, copper, zinc, selenium, bromine, and lead. (e) Three samples or more, including up to 20 elements, of which sulfur, calcium, titanium, iron, copper, zinc, selenium, bromine, and lead are intercompared. Each result represents a single laboratory, with the result being the mean and standard deviation for each element as compared to the referees. (f) Laboratory reported sulfur and lead results from AA only. (g) Laboratory reported sulfur only. (h) Results from atomic absorption and emission spectroscopies. (j) Charged particle activation analysis.
Source: Ref 6

Fig. 7 Comparison of (a) electron microprobe and (b) proton microprobe analyses of a biological sample

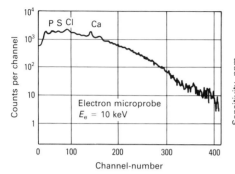

(a)

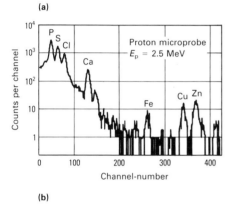

(b)

Fig. 8 Minimum detectable limits versus sensitivity and beam diameter for electron and PIXE microprobes

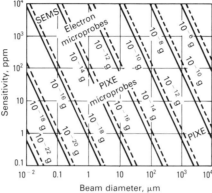

However, several handicaps have limited the applicability of PIXE. The ability of PIXE to handle small masses, based on sensitivity and proton beam size, has not been a great advantage in an area in which fractional mass sensitivity (parts per million) is valued highly. Unless sample preparation has been extensive, PIXE operates at the level of a few parts per million, but many important toxic elemental species are desired at the part per billion level. Elemental methods do not provide the important chemical nature of the materials. The nondestructive nature of PIXE is unimportant for such samples, and competitive methods are firmly established in the medical community. Therefore, PIXE programs in the biological sciences have met with limited success.

In other areas, the special characteristics of PIXE are making an impact. Tree ring analysis requires a small analytical area and a wide range of elements. Statistical studies in agriculture are also promising. These studies, which require low sensitivity (100 ppm) and the ability to handle large volumes of samples at low cost (a few dollars/sample), concentrate on the light, biologically important elements from sodium through zinc.

Materials Sciences in the Semiconductor Industry. This area was considered intensively in the first few years of the development of PIXE. An important advantage is that many of the laboratories conducting these analyses possess a particle accelerator for the Rutherford backscattering spectrometry (RBS) of layered semiconductor structures. Almost all such laboratories use PIXE, but it has not become the mainstay that had been predicted. One reason is that depth information is difficult to obtain from PIXE, but is essential to the semiconductor industry. In addition, the light element (sodium to calcium) capability of PIXE is not useful due to the dominance of the silicon x-ray peak in the middle of the range. The trace element capability of PIXE finds relatively little utility in materials carefully prepared from ultrapure and well-characterized sources.

Particle-Induced X-Ray Emission Milliprobe and Historical Studies. The external-beam PIXE milliprobe exemplifies an unanticipated successful application of PIXE. Low-energy proton beams are often brought out of vacuum into air or helium atmospheres to avoid the expense of large vacuum-tight chambers. The external proton beam collimated to millimeter size and closely coupled to an x-ray detector has revealed new opportunities in analysis of large and/or fragile objects that could not be readily placed in vacuum. The high x-ray cross sections in PIXE allow use of very low beam currents, 10^{-9} A or less, solving potential damage problems. Thus, a major use of PIXE has developed over the past few years in historical studies (Ref 15). Particle-induced x-ray emission has been successful because virtually no other nondestructive technique can provide part per million anal-

ysis of broad elemental range in minutes. A recent page-by-page analysis of a Gutenberg Bible proved the safety of the technique and revitalized an entire field of historical study (Ref 15).

The key advantage to these new uses is that external-beam PIXE does not require material removal from rare and/or fragile items; therefore, no damage to these objects results when the technique is used properly. As a result, much can be learned about the early history of printing and ancient techniques in ceramics and metallurgy. Particle-induced x-ray emission also offers a useful means of detecting forgeries.

Particle-Induced X-Ray Emission and the Proton Microprobe. Particle-induced x-ray emission has become the most important analytical method used with accelerator-based proton microprobes, which are low-energy accelerators modified to provide reasonably intense beams of protons with spatial dimensions of a few microns in diameter. Such beams can penetrate more deeply into a matrix than the standard electron microprobes while maintaining a small diameter versus depth. The beams of protons or other light ions allow use of several nuclear and atomic analytical methods, granting capabilities absent from electron microprobes.

Because proton beams have no primary bremsstrahlung background, unlike electrons, sensitivities are significantly better—parts per million with protons versus parts per thousand with electron beams. Figure 7 shows such a comparison for a biological matrix. The combination of high fractional mass sensitivity and small beam diameter results in minimum detectable limits of mass down to the 10^{-16}-g range and below (Fig. 8). Many microprobes have been constructed and used during the past few years to gain these advantages (Ref 6, 12, 16).

REFERENCES

1. T.A. Cahill, in *New Uses for Low Energy Accelerators*, J. Ziegler, Ed., Plenum Press, 1975
2. E. Merzbacher and H.W. Lewis, in *Encyclopedia of Physics*, S. Flugge, Ed., Springer Verlag, 1958
3. J.D. Garcia, R.D. Fortner, and T. Kavanaugh, *Rev. Mod. Phys.*, Vol 45, 1973, p 111
4. T.B. Johansson and S.A.E. Johansson, *Nucl. Instr. Meth.*, Vol 137, 1976, p 473
5. F. Folkmann, *J. Phys. E*, Vol 8, 1975, p 429
6. T.A. Cahill, *Ann. Rev. Nucl. Part. Sci.*, Vol 30, 1980, p 211

7. H.C. Kaufmann and R. Akselsson, *Adv. X-Ray Anal.*, Vol 18, 1975, p 353

8. J.F. Harrison and R.A. Eldred, *Adv. X-Ray Anal.*, Vol 17, 1973, p 560

9. Special Reference Material Catalog 1533, National Bureau of Standards, Gaithersburg, MD, 1984

10. K. Siegbahn, in *Proceedings of the International Conference on Particle Induced X-ray Emission and its Analytical Applications*, Vol 142 (No. 1 and 2), 1977

11. S.A.E. Johansson, in *Proceedings of the Second International Conference on PIXE and its Analytical Applications*, Vol 181, 1981

12. B. Martin, in *Proceedings of the Third International Conference on PIXE and its Analytical Applications*, Vol B3, 1984

13. T.B. Johansson, R. Akselsson, and S.A.E. Johansson, *Nucl. Instr. Meth.*, Vol 84, 1970, p 141

14. T.A. Cahill, R.A. Eldred, D. Shadoon, P.J. Feeney, B. Kusko, and Y. Matsuda, *Nucl. Instr. Meth.*, Vol B3, 1984, p 191

15. T.A. Cahill, B.H. Kusko, R.A. Eldred, and R.H. Schwab, *Archeometry*, Vol 26, 1984, p 3

16. J.A. Cookson, *Nucl. Instr. Meth.*, Vol 65, 1979, p 477

SELECTED REFERENCES

- J.R. Bird, P. Duerden, and P.J. Wilson, *Nucl. Sci. Applic.*, Vol 1, 1983, p 357
- T.B. Johansson, R. Akselsson, and S.A.E. Johansson, *Adv. X-ray Anal.*, Vol 15, 1972, p 373
- M.J. Owens and H.I. Shalgosky, *J. Phys. E*, Vol 7, 1974, p 593
- V. Volkovic, *Contemp. Phys.*, Vol 14, 1973, p 415

Infrared Spectroscopy

Curtis Marcott, The Procter & Gamble Company, Miami Valley Laboratories

General Uses

- Identification and structure determination of organic and inorganic materials
- Quantitative determination of molecular components in mixtures
- Identification of molecular species adsorbed on surfaces
- Identification of chromatographic effluents
- Determination of molecular orientation
- Determination of molecular conformation and stereochemistry

Examples of Applications

- Identification of chemical reaction species; reaction kinetics
- Quantitative determination of nontrace components in complex matrices
- Determination of molecular orientation in stretched polymer films
- Identification of flavor and aroma components
- Determination of molecular structure and orientation of thin films deposited on metal substrates (oxidation and corrosion products, soils, adsorbed surfactants, and so on)
- Depth profiling of solid samples (granules, powders, fibers, and so on)
- Characterization and identification of different phases in solids or liquids

Samples

- *Form*: Almost any solid, liquid, or gas sample
- *Size (minimum)*: Solids—10 ng if it can be ground in a transparent matrix, such as potassium bromide; 10-μm diameter for a single particle; 1 to 10 ng if soluble in a volatile solvent (methanol, methylene chloride, chloroform, and so on). Flat metal surfaces—1 by 1 cm (0.4 by 0.4 in.) or larger. Liquids—10 μL if neat, considerably less if soluble in a transparent solvent. Gases—1 to 10 ng
- *Preparation*: Minimal or none; may have to grind in a potassium bromide matrix or dissolve in a volatile or infrared-transparent solvent

Limitations

- Little elemental information
- Molecule must exhibit a change in dipole moment in one of its vibrational modes upon exposure to infrared radiation
- Background solvent or matrix must be relatively transparent in the spectral region of interest

Estimated Analysis Time

- 1 to 10 min per sample

Capabilities of Related Techniques

- *Raman spectroscopy*: Complementary molecular vibrational information
- *X-ray fluorescence*: Elemental information on bulk samples
- *X-ray photoelectron spectroscopy*: Elemental information on adsorbed species
- *High-resolution electron energy loss spectroscopy*: Molecular vibrational surface information
- *Mass spectrometry*: Molecular weight information
- *Nuclear magnetic resonance*: Additional molecular structure information

Introduction

Infrared (IR) spectroscopy is a useful technique for characterizing materials and providing information on the molecular structure, dynamics, and environment of a compound. When irradiated with infrared light (photons), a sample can transmit, scatter, or absorb the incident radiation. Absorbed infrared radiation usually excites molecules into higher-energy vibrational states. This can occur when the energy (frequency) of the light matches the energy difference between two vibrational states (or the frequency of the corresponding molecular vibration).

Infrared spectroscopy is particularly useful for determining functional groups present in a molecule. Many functional groups vibrate at nearly the same frequencies independent of their molecular environment. This makes infrared spectroscopy useful in materials characterization. Further, many subtle structural details can be gleaned from frequency shifts and intensity changes arising from the coupling of vibrations of different chemical bonds and functional groups.

Recent advances in computerized IR spectroscopy, particularly Fourier transform infrared (FT-IR) spectroscopy, have made it possible to obtain infrared spectra using various sampling techniques. Infrared spectra have traditionally been produced by transmission, that is, transmitting light through the sample, measuring the light intensity at the detector, and comparing it to the intensity obtained with no sample in the beam, all as a function of the infrared wavelength. Techniques such as attenuated total reflectance, diffuse reflectance, specular reflectance, reflection-absorption spectroscopy, and photoacoustic spectroscopy have recently become more common. This article will discuss the sampling techniques, applications, and the molecular structure information the resulting infrared spectra can provide.

Basic Principles

Infrared spectra are typically presented as plots of intensity versus energy (in ergs), frequency (in s^{-1}), wavelength (in microns), or wavenumber (in cm^{-1}). Wavenumber units are preferred, but several books of reference spectra are plotted in wavelength. Units can be converted easily using:

$$E = h\nu = \frac{hc}{\lambda} \qquad \text{(Eq 1)}$$

where E is energy in ergs, h is Planck's constant (6.63×10^{-27} erg $\cdot$ s), ν is the frequency in s^{-1}, λ is the wavelength in centimeters, and c is the velocity (speed) of light (3×10^{10} cm/s); and:

$$\bar{\nu} = \frac{1}{\lambda} \qquad \text{(Eq 2)}$$

where $\bar{\nu}$ is the wavenumber in cm^{-1}. When λ is expressed in microns (the unit normally used for wavelength), Eq 2 becomes:

$$\bar{\nu} = \frac{10\,000}{\lambda} \qquad \text{(Eq 3)}$$

In practice, wavenumber is often called frequency, and the symbol ν used instead of $\bar{\nu}$. Although, formally, the infrared region of the electromagnetic spectrum is between the wavelengths of 0.78 and 1000 μm (12 820 to 10 cm^{-1}), this article will consider the mid-infrared region from 2.5 to 25 μm (4000 to 400 cm^{-1}). This region, where most fundamental vibrational modes occur, is the most useful for materials characterization.

Intensity can be expressed as percent transmittance (%T) or absorbance (A). If I_0 is the energy, or radiant power, reaching the infrared detector with no sample in the

beam, and I is the energy detected with a sample present, transmittance is:

$$T = \frac{I}{I_0} \qquad \text{(Eq 4)}$$

and percent transmittance:

$$\%T = \frac{100I}{I_0} \qquad \text{(Eq 5)}$$

Absorbance is:

$$A = \log\left(\frac{1}{T}\right) = \log\left(\frac{I_0}{I}\right) \qquad \text{(Eq 6)}$$

Strong and weak bands are more easily visualized simultaneously without changing scale when spectra are plotted in transmittance, because the absorbance scale ranges from zero to infinity, while transmittance ranges from 0 to 100% T (0% T corresponds to an absorbance of infinity). For quantitative analyses (including spectral subtraction), absorbance or some other intensity scale proportional to concentration must be used.

The molecular geometry, atomic masses, and a complete description of the forces between the atoms (force field) are required to calculate the vibrational frequencies and describe the fundamental vibrations of a molecule. This is normal-coordinate analysis (Ref 1, 2). In practice, the molecular structure is usually not known, and the infrared spectra are used to assist in determining it. However, accomplishing this requires an understanding of how molecular vibrations contribute to the observed infrared spectrum. Molecular vibrations are complicated, because individual bond stretches or bond-angle bends are often highly coupled to each other. Progress in understanding the nature of molecular vibrations has derived mainly from empirical observation. Although of little practical use in materials characterization, normal-coordinate analysis reveals the nature of molecular vibrations, which can be useful in analyzing complicated infrared spectra.

Normal-coordinate analysis begins by describing a molecular structure as a collection of balls and massless springs. This is a reasonable model based on chemical intuition. The balls represent atoms, and springs the forces or chemical bonds between atoms. The problem would be simple if bonds stretched or bond angles bent independently, without affecting the motion of other atoms or bonds. Because this is seldom the case, there is the mechanical problem of solving for the normal modes of vibrations. The number of normal modes in a given molecule equals the total number of degrees

of freedom minus the number of rotational and translational degrees of freedom. For a nonlinear molecule, this number is $3N - 6$, where N is the number of atoms in the molecule. It is assumed that there is no coupling of the vibrational degrees of freedom with the rotations and translations.

Of the parameters necessary to begin a normal-coordinate analysis, only the atomic masses are always easily obtained. The molecular geometry can often be acquired from an x-ray structure or by using typical bond distances and angles from the literature. Problems can arise when several conformations are possible. Unfortunately, accurate force fields are usually unavailable, except for very simple molecules. Obtaining a force field requires knowing the potential energy of the molecule as a function of atomic displacements from the equilibrium geometry. These displacements are usually described relative to internal coordinates consistent with chemical intuition, such as bond stretches and angle bends. The potential energy (V) is usually expanded in a Taylor's series as a function of the internal coordinates (R_a):

$$V = V_0 + \sum_a \left(\frac{\partial V}{\partial R_a}\right)_0 R_a +$$
$$\left(\frac{1}{2}\right) \sum_{a,b} \left(\frac{\partial^2 V}{\partial R_a \partial R_b}\right)_0 R_a R_b + \ldots \qquad \text{(Eq 7)}$$

The derivatives of the potential energy with respect to the internal coordinates evaluated at the equilibrium geometry are the force constants. Force fields are typically derived empirically from the infrared frequencies they were designed to predict, and the number of parameters (force constants) often exceeds significantly the number of experimental frequencies. Therefore, a unique set of force constants that will predict the observed frequencies does not exist.

Most force-field (normal-coordinate) calculations of the vibrational frequencies are performed in the harmonic-oscillator approximation. Because the atomic displacements are considered to be small, the motions are approximated as harmonic. That is, the potential-energy function along an internal-displacement coordinate can be approximated as a parabola near its lowest potential energy.

In the harmonic-oscillator approximation, the only nonzero force constants are from the quadratic terms in Eq 7. The quadratic force constants are the second derivatives of the potential-energy function with respect to the internal coordinates. The harmonic-oscillator approximation reduces dramatically the number of force constants. The number number of parameters can be further lessened by assuming that force constants coupling internal coordinates more than one or two atoms apart are zero. That many force constants do not differ significantly from one molecule to another also helps in determining an initial set of quadratic force constants. Therefore, force constants can be transferred from simpler molecules containing the same functional groups.

The net result of a normal-coordinate analysis is a complete description of the atomic displacements for each normal mode, the vibrational frequency of that normal mode, and percentage contribution of each internal displacement coordinate to each vibration (potential-energy distribution). That is, a normal-coordinate analysis provides a complete picture (within the constraints of the initial model) of the molecular vibration responsible for each fundamental absorption band in an infrared spectrum of a pure compound.

Molecular Vibrations. Even with the approximations and assumptions discussed above, IR spectroscopy would be of limited practical use if it were necessary to rely completely on a normal-coordinate calculation for every structure identification or material characterization. Fortunately, certain functional groups consistently produce absorption bands in the same spectral regions independent of the remainder of the molecular structure. These molecular vibrations are known as group frequencies. For example, methylene stretching vibrations always occur from 3000 to 2800 cm^{-1}, methylene deformations from 1500 to 1300 cm^{-1}, and methylene rocking motions from 800 to 700 cm^{-1}. These relatively broad regions can be made more specific if the molecular environment of the CH_2 group is considered in more detail. Similar sets of rules for many other functional groups have been derived empirically and with the assistance of normal-coordinate calculations on simple molecules.

A few general rules are useful when applying the mechanical ball and spring model to molecular vibrations:

- Stretching vibrations generally have a higher frequency than bending vibrations
- The higher the bond order, the higher the stretching frequency
- The lighter the atoms involved in the vibration, the higher the vibrational frequency

The last two rules are apparent in the simple solution for the only molecular vibration of a diatomic molecule:

$$\nu = \left(\frac{1}{2}\pi c\right)\sqrt{k\left(\frac{1}{m_1} + \frac{1}{m_2}\right)} \qquad \text{(Eq 8)}$$

where ν is the frequency in cm^{-1}, m_1 and m_2 are the atomic masses in grams, and k is the Hooke's law force constant in dynes/cm. This is the solution that would result from a normal-coordinate calculation for a diatomic molecule. Vibrational frequency increases with the magnitude of the force constant, that is, bond order. As masses increase, vibrational frequency decreases.

For a molecular vibration to absorb infrared radiation, dipole moment must change during the vibration (Ref 2). The infrared photon frequency must resonate with the vibrational frequency to excite the molecule into the higher vibrational state. In addition, the electric dipole-transition moment associated with the molecular vibration being excited must have a component parallel to the polarization direction of the incident infrared photon. The dipole strength of the transition from vibrational state $|n>$ to vibrational state $|k>$, $D_{n,k}$, equals the square of the electric dipole-transition moment:

$$D_{n,k} = |<n|\vec{\mu}|k>|^2 \qquad \text{(Eq 9)}$$

where the electric dipole-moment operator, $\vec{\mu}$, is the sum over i of the charge multiplied by the position, $\sum_i q_i \vec{r_i}$, for each charged particle, i, relative to an arbitrarily selected origin fixed in the molecular frame. The electric dipole-transition moment is proportional to the first derivative of the electric dipole-moment operator with respect to the normal coordinate, that is, the motion of all atoms in the vibrational normal mode. Dipole strength can also be experimentally measured and is proportional to the frequency-weighted area under the absorption band for the transition:

$$D_{n,k} = K \int_{\text{Band}} \left[\frac{A(\nu)}{\nu}\right] d\nu \qquad \text{(Eq 10)}$$

where $A(\nu)$ is the absorbance at wavenumber ν, and K is a known constant. The observed infrared intensity contains contributions from the motions of all the atoms and electronic charges during molecular vibration. Infrared intensities have been studied for only 5 to 10 years; infrared frequencies, for more than 50. Although as much information may be in the intensities as in the frequencies, more study is necessary to exploit it fully.

Instrumentation

Obtaining an infrared spectrum necessitates detection of intensity changes as a function of wavenumber. Commercial infrared instruments separate light into single infrared wavenumber intervals using a dispersive spectrometer (prism, grating, or variable filter), a Fourier transform spectrometer, or a tunable infrared laser source.

In dispersive infrared spectroscopy, a monochromator separates light from a broad-band source into individual wavenumber intervals. The monochromator contains a dispersing element, such as a prism, diffraction grating, or variable filter, that rotates to enable a mechanical slit to select individual wavenumber regions sequentially. The spatial distance separating the individual wavelengths after dispersion and the mechanical slit width determine spectral resolution and optical throughput. For a given instrument, the higher the spectral resolution, the lower the signal-to-noise ratio of the spectrum. Figure 1 shows a typical double-beam grating spectrometer.

Fourier transform infrared spectroscopy uses an interferometer to modulate the intensity of each wavelength of light at a different audio frequency (Ref 3). A beam splitter divides the light from a broad-band infrared source into two optical paths. Recombination of the beams at the beam splitter generates a modulated optical path difference. The recombined beam undergoes constructive and destructive interference as a function of the instantaneous optical path difference. Several methods can be used to

Fig. 1 Optical diagram of a double-beam grating spectrometer
M, mirror; G, grating; S, slit. Courtesy of Perkin-Elmer

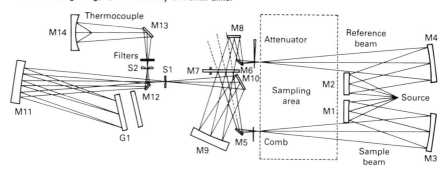

Fig. 2 Optical diagram of a FT-IR spectrometer
Courtesy of Digilab

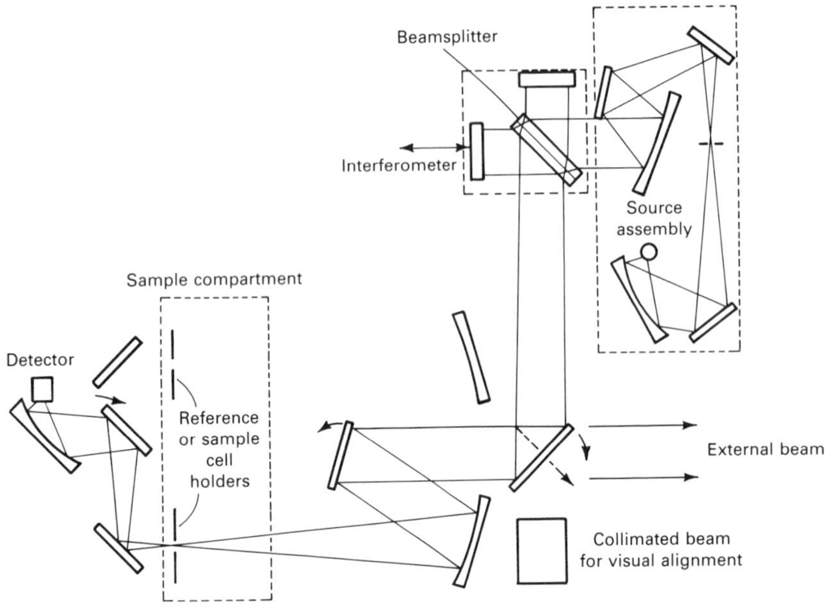

generate the modulated optical path difference. The most common is the Michelson interferometer (Ref 4, 5), as shown in Fig. 2.

After being split into two optical paths by the beam splitter, the light from each path strikes two flat mirrors, one fixed and one moving, that return it to the beam splitter. When the moving mirror is positioned so that the two optical paths are equal (zero path-difference position), all wavelengths of light simultaneously undergo constructive interference. At any other position of the moving mirror, a given wavelength of light may interfere constructively or destructively, depending on the phase relationship between the light rays in the two paths. For example, if the optical path difference is an integral multiple of the wavelength, constructive interference will result.

Spectrometer resolution equals the reciprocal of the distance the moving mirror travels. The modulation frequency for a particular wavenumber depends on mirror velocity. Modulation frequencies are typically from 50 Hz to 10 kHz. The detector signal, which is digitally sampled in fixed increments defined by interference fringes from a helium-neon laser, displays signal intensity as a function of moving mirror position. This signal is the interferogram. It must be Fourier transformed by a computer into the single-beam infrared spectrum.

Fourier transform infrared spectroscopy affords several advantages over dispersive IR spectroscopy. Information on the entire infrared spectrum is contained in an in-terferogram, which requires 1 s or less to collect. A spectrum with N resolution elements can be collected in the same amount of time as a single resolution element. This advantage is the multiplex, or Felgett's, advantage (Ref 6). Because the signal-to-noise ratio is proportional to the square root of the number of scans, the FT-IR time advantage can become a signal-to-noise ratio advantage of $N^{1/2}$ for the same data collection time as with a dispersive spectrometer. The greater the total number of resolution elements in the spectrum, the more important becomes Felgett's advantage.

Because no slit is required, FT-IR spectrometers have a light throughput advantage over dispersive spectrometers (Jacquinot's advantage) (Ref 7, 8). The helium-neon laser that controls sampling of the interferogram also provides precise calibration for the wavenumber position (Connes's advantage) (Ref 9). Finally, because a digital computer is used to perform Fourier transforms, it is available for data processing. A computerized dispersive spectrometer can also handle data processing.

Interferometers other than the Michelson design are also available (Ref 10-13). The Genzel interferometer is similar, except the light beam is focused at the beam splitter, and the moving mirror modulates the optical path length in both arms of the interferometer (Ref 10). In other interferometers, optical path length is changed by moving a refractive element in one of the arms of the interferometer (Ref 11-13).

Tunable infrared lasers can be used as an alternate method of obtaining single infrared wavenumber intervals (Ref 14). Although lasers can provide a tremendous amount of light intensity at each wavenumber compared to conventional broad-band infrared sources, their stability is generally not as favorable, and they are usually tunable over only short wavenumber ranges, limiting their general usefulness as a spectroscopic tool. Lasers are useful for specific applications in which high resolution or only a limited portion of the spectrum is required. For example, infrared diode laser systems are used in many process-monitoring situations in which the material of interest transmits almost no light.

Sample Preparation, Sampling Techniques, and Accessories

Sample preparation is usually necessary in obtaining the infrared spectrum of a material. Most materials are almost totally opaque in infrared light and must be dissolved or diluted in a transparent matrix before the transmittance spectrum can be obtained. Sampling techniques and accessories will be discussed below (Ref 15).

Nonvolatile liquid samples can often be deposited as a thin film spread between two infrared-transmitting windows. A drop or two of sample is placed on the face of one of the clean, polished windows, and the second window placed on top. All the air bubbles must be squeezed out, and the sample must cover the entire window area. The windows are clamped using a screw-down holder, and the path length adjusted, if necessary, so the absorbance maximum of the strongest band is approximately 5 to 10% T.

Solvent evaporation can be used to deposit as a film a nonvolatile liquid or solid sample that is soluble in a relatively volatile solvent whose absorption bands would mask or interfere with those of the sample. A few drops (depending on the sample concentration) of the sample solution are transferred to the face of a cleaned, polished window, and the solvent allowed to evaporate. When the solvent appears to have evaporated, the spectrum is obtained. If solvent bands are apparent, it may be necessary to continue drying the sample until they disappear.

Meltable solids, that is, samples with melting points under approximately 60 °C (140 °F) and that will not decompose upon heating, can be melted and pressed between two infrared-transmitting windows. Approximately 10 to 30 mg of sample are usually transferred to the face of one window and placed on or under a heating source. When the sample has melted, the top window is pressed down and the air bubbles squeezed out to distribute the melted sample over the entire area of the windows. The windows can then be clamped together, and the sample thickness adjusted as with the neat film.

Potassium bromide (KBr) pellets can often be prepared from solid samples that are difficult to melt or dissolve. The sample is dispersed in a KBr matrix and pressed into a transparent pellet. Approximately 0.4 to 1.0 mg of sample is usually ground in 200 to 400 mg of KBr or other infrared-transparent pressing powder. The sample and KBr must be ground so that the particle size is less than the wavelength of light, minimizing band distortion due to scattering effects. The matrix material must be pure and dry.

Preparing a mull is also an alternative for a grindable solid sample. The sample is ground with the mulling agent to yield a paste that is examined as a thin film between infrared-transmitting windows. As opposed to the pellet technique, mulling agents are not as hygroscopic as KBr and are less likely to react with some samples. However, mulling agents have some infrared absorption bands that can interfere with absorptions in the sample. This can be overcome by preparing a split mull. Half the spectrum is obtained in hydrocarbon oil, and the other half in fluorocarbon oil. The region of the spectrum below 1365 cm^{-1} is taken from the hydrocarbon oil spectrum and combined with the 4000- to 1365-cm^{-1} portion of the fluorocarbon oil spectrum, yielding a spectrum free of mulling-agent bands.

The diamond-anvil cell, a transmission accessory, is useful for very small single-particle samples or for obtaining infrared spectra under extremely high pressures (Ref 16). Beam-condensing optics are often necessary to focus the light beam on the sample, which is pressed between two small diamond windows. A screw and spring mechanism provides high pressures. The diamond cell is perhaps the best way to obtain a transmittance spectrum of samples such as a single hair. The sample size is well suited, and the high pressures can be used to compress the sample. This reduces the optical path length and prevents excessive intensity in the absorption bands. If thin Type II diamonds are used, only a small region of the infrared spectrum around 2000 cm^{-1} will be unusable due to absorption of the windows.

Gas Cells. Infrared spectra of gases can be obtained in vacuum-tight gas cells ranging in path length from a few centimeters to several meters. These glass or metal cells require valves to facilitate filling from an external vacuum system. Gas pressures necessary to obtain reasonable infrared spectra

Fig. 3 Top view of micro KRS-5 (thallium bromide/thallium iodide) IRE against which a solid is clamped

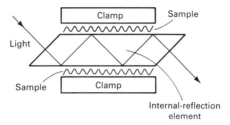

depend on the sample absorbance and the path length of the cell. Favorable spectra can usually be obtained with a partial pressure for the sample of approximately 6500 Pa (50 torr) in a standard 10-cm (4-in.) gas cell.

Attenuated Total Reflectance (ATR) Spectroscopy. Reflectance methods can also be used to obtain infrared spectra. One of the more useful reflectance techniques is attenuated total reflectance spectroscopy (Ref 17). An ATR plate or internal-reflection element (IRE) is constructed of an infrared-transparent material of high refractive index (usually greater than two). Light enters the IRE at near-normal incidence and is internally reflected at each sample/IRE interface. The sample can be a solution, a deposited film, or a solid pressed against the IRE. Figure 3 shows a solid sample clamped against a multiple-internal-reflection element. If the angle of incidence at the interface exceeds the critical angle, θ_c, the light will be totally internally reflected. At each internal reflectance point, a standing, or evanescent, wave is generated that penetrates a short distance (on the order of the wavelength of light) into the sample. The detector senses intensity loss due to absorption of the evanescent wave by the sample. Multiple internal reflections can be used to build up signal. Monolayer quantities of adsorbed material can be detected using this technique.

Internal-reflection elements are available in various shapes and sizes, depending on the geometry of the reflection optics and the number of internal reflections desired. Germanium, KRS-5, (a mixed crystal containing 42% thallium bromide and 58% thallium iodide), and zinc selenide are most commonly used as IREs; silver chloride, silicon, silver bromide, quartz, and sapphire have also been used. The depth of penetration of the evanescent wave into the sample depends on the angle of incidence at the interface (θ_i), the wavelength of light (λ), and the refractive indices of the sample and IRE (n_{sam} and n_{IRE}). Defining d_p as the distance re-

quired for the electric field amplitude to fall to e^{-1} of its value at the surface, the depth of penetration is (Ref 17):

$$d_p = \frac{(\lambda/n_{IRE})}{2\pi[\sin^2\theta_i - (n_{sam}/n_{IRE})^2]^{1/2}} \quad \text{(Eq 11)}$$

The depth of penetration can be decreased by increasing the angle of incidence or using an IRE with a higher refractive index. The depth of penetration will be greater at lower wavenumber than at higher wavenumber. Table 1 shows how changes in λ, n_{IRE}, and θ_i for an arbitrary sample with $n_{sam} = 1.5$ affect d_p. No values are entered for $\theta_i = 30°$ with the KRS-5 IRE, because $\theta_c = 40°$ in this case, and total internal reflection does not occur.

In extracting depth-profiling information from ATR spectra, the spectrum of the sample component closest to the interface is always weighted most heavily in ATR spectroscopy, regardless of the value of d_p. Contributions to the spectrum from beyond d_p are also present, although less heavily weighted. In addition, establishing favorable contact between the IRE and the sample is important, especially with solid samples. Further, the refractive index of the sample is not constant as a function of wavenumber and can change dramatically in the region of an absorption band. This can distort the ATR spectrum, particularly in regions in which the refractive index of the sample is close to that of the IRE. Moreover, in changing the depth of penetration by varying the angle of incidence, an IRE cut at the desired angle should be used at normal incidence, or the effective angle of incidence at the IRE/sample interface will vary only slightly.

When light enters a medium of high refractive index from air ($n_{air} = 1.0$) at non-normal incidence ($\theta_i \neq 0$), it is refracted according to Snell's law:

$$n_{air} \sin\theta_i = n_{IRE} \sin\theta_r \quad \text{(Eq 12)}$$

where θ_r is the angle of refraction. Because $(n_{air}/n_{IRE}) < 1$, the angle of incidence at the

Table 1 Depth of penetration, d_p, for a sample ($n_{sam} = 1.5$) as a function of ATR-plate material, angle of incidence, and wavenumber

Material	Wavenumber, cm^1	d_p, µm 30°	45°	60°
KRS-5(a)	3000	. . .	0.74	0.33
KRS-5(a)	1000	. . .	2.23	1.16
Germanium(b)	3000	0.40	0.22	0.17
Germanium(b)	1000	1.20	0.66	0.51

(a) Refractive index, $n = 2.35$. (b) Refractive index, $n = 4.0$

IRE/sample interface will not differ greatly from the $\theta_i = 0$ (normal incidence) case. Table 2 shows the angle of incidence achieved at the IRE/sample interface using 45° KRS-5 and germanium IREs at 30°, 45°, and 60°, along with the corresponding values of d_p (for $n_{sam} = 1.5$). This is not an effective technique for depth profiling a sample using IR spectroscopy. Perhaps the best overall method of depth profiling using only ATR is to alternate between two 45° IREs of germanium and KRS-5 (Table 1).

Attenuated total reflectance measurements can be performed on dispersive or Fourier transform instrumentation. When attempting ATR on a double-beam dispersive spectrometer, a matched pair of IREs and reflection optics are usually used to improve the baseline. A clean IRE is used as a reference in one beam, and the sample is placed on the IRE in the other beam path. With FT-IR spectrometers, the reference and sample are usually analyzed sequentially in the same beam using the same optics. Attenuated total reflectance spectra recorded on FT-IR instruments are generally superior to dispersive ATR spectra.

Diffuse reflectance spectroscopy (DRS) is another reflectance technique that has application in the infrared region of the spectrum (Ref 18). Until the advent of FT-IR spectroscopy, the technique had been used almost exclusively in ultraviolet (UV), visible (VIS), and near-infrared (NIR) regions of the spectrum, where brighter sources and more sensitive detectors exist.

Infrared radiation is focused on a cup filled with the sample; the resulting diffusely scattered light is collected and refocused on the detector. Although used in most UV-VIS-NIR applications to collect scattered radiation from the sample, integrating spheres are not very efficient in the mid-infrared region. Commercial attachments for FT-IR spectrometers typically incorporate large ellipsoidal mirrors for focusing and

collecting the light. The technique can be used on bulk samples or samples ground in a KBr or potassium chloride (KCl) matrix. Potassium bromide and KCl powders are excellent diffuse reflectors and are also used as reference standards. Spectra of matrixed samples are similar in appearance to KBr-pellet absorbance spectra when plotted in units proportional to concentration. Such units are log $(1/R)$ or $(1 - R)^2/2R$ (Kubelka Munk units) (Ref 19, 20), where $R = R(\text{sample})/R(\text{reference})$ is the sample reflectance measured relative to the reference standard. In DRS, the sample matrix need not be pressed into a transparent pellet, but simply packed loosely in a sample cup. Scattering artifacts that often occur in cloudy KBr pellets are not such a problem with matrixed diffuse reflectance samples.

Diffuse reflectance spectra collected on bulk, unmatrixed samples should be interpreted with extreme caution. Unless the diffuse reflectance accessory is designed and aligned so that little or none of the light reflected directly from the surface of the sample (specular component) reaches the detector, the observed spectrum will be a complicated combination of diffuse and specular components. Diffuse reflectance signals will appear as a decrease in reflected intensity versus a KBr or KCl reference standard, due to absorbance by the sample. However, specular reflectance signals can have a positive or negative sign, depending on the optical constants of the sample.

Diffuse reflectance spectroscopy can also be used to study adsorbed species on catalyst surfaces. This approach is suitable for high-surface-area infrared-transparent substrates. Evacuable cells that can be heated have been designed for observing catalysts under reaction conditions.

Infrared reflection-absorption spectroscopy (IRRAS) is a useful technique for studying material adsorbed on flat metal surfaces (Ref 21). Unlike many other surface techniques, IRRAS does not require ultra-high vacuum and provides more information on molecular structure and functional groups. Using a single external reflection at near-grazing angle of incidence, single monolayers adsorbed on low-area surfaces (flat metal plates) can be detected. Figure 4 illustrates a typical external reflectance attachment. Because the component of the incident light polarized parallel to the surface (perpendicular to the plane of incidence) has a node at the surface, only those dipole-transition moments of adsorbed molecules with a component perpendicular to the surface are observed. Therefore, information on the orientation of the adsorbed material can be obtained if the dipole-transition moment directions are known.

Fig. 4 Top view of a sample compartment containing a reflection-absorption attachment

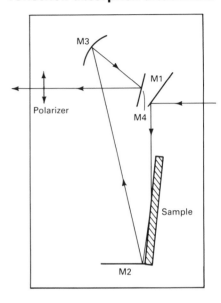

Infrared reflection-absorption spectroscopy experiments can be performed on dispersive and FT-IR spectrometers. When double-beam dispersive instruments are used, identical reflection devices are usually aligned in each beam path, one path containing a clean metal surface (reference) and the other the metal surface with the adsorbed film (sample). The difference signal due to the adsorbed film is then recorded directly.

Because commercial FT-IR spectrometers are single-beam instruments, the reference and sample metal surfaces must be analyzed sequentially, and the difference or ratio taken later. The signal difference of interest is usually extremely small compared to the size of the individual single-beam signals. Favorable signal-to-noise ratios and a stable interferometer are required to detect adsorbed monolayers on metals. Inserting a linear polarizer oriented to pass light polarized perpendicular to the surface (p-polarized component) in the beam path may improve sensitivity. Adsorbed films significantly thinner than the wavelength of light will not absorb the component of polarization oriented parallel to the surface (s-polarized component).

Polarization modulation can be used to measure infrared reflection-absorption spectra of adsorbed monolayers in a single-beam experiment (Ref 22, 23). A linear polarizer is oriented to pass p-polarized light and followed by a photoelastic modulator (PEM) oriented with the stress axis at 45° to the plane of polarization. The optical ele-

Table 2 Actual angle of incidence (at the interface between the ATR plate and sample) and depth of penetration at 1000 cm^{-1} as a function of ATR-plate material and apparent angle of incidence

Material	Apparent angle	Actual angle	d_p, μm
KRS-5	30°	38.7°	. . .
KRS-5	45°	45°	2.23
KRS-5	60°	51.3°	1.51
Germanium	30°	41.3°	0.73
Germanium	45°	45°	0.66
Germanium	60°	48.7°	0.61

ment of a PEM is a highly isotropic infrared-transmitting material, the most common being zinc selenide and calcium fluoride. Two piezoelectric drivers cemented to either side of the optical element induce a stress birefringence that rotates the plane of polarization 90° when the retardation is 180° or one half the wavelength of the incident light.

Photoelastic modulators typically modulate at approximately 50 kHz and flip the plane of polarization between the two perpendicular states at exactly twice that modulation frequency. Because monolayers adsorbed on metal substrates "see" only the p-polarized component, a spectrum attributable to the difference in reflectivity of the p and s components can be detected directly at twice the PEM modulation frequency. This polarization-modulation approach can also be used to measure linear dichroism of oriented samples and vibrational circular dichroism (VCD) of optically active compounds on dispersive or FT-IR spectrometers.

Specular reflectance refers to the component of incident light that bounces off the surface of the sample (Ref 24). Unlike reflection-absorption spectroscopy, in which the films are thin and the light reflects off a metal substrate, specular reflectance can be performed without a metal substrate on thick samples or films. Under these conditions, the incident electric field vectors do not have a node at the surface, and angles closer to normal incidence can be used. However, the sensitivity does not equal that of reflection-absorption spectroscopy, and spectra often contain a significant contribution from the refractive index of the sample. Extracting useful information from these spectra may be difficult.

Emission spectroscopy is another technique for obtaining infrared spectra of difficult samples (Ref 25). The principal applications are for remote samples, such as stars or smokestack emissions, and thin films adsorbed on metals. The sample becomes the source in emission spectroscopy. For weak emission signals, the spectrometer temperature should be less than the sample temperature, or infrared emission from the background and spectrometer optics may be larger than the source signal of interest. Heating the sample is usually more convenient than cooling the spectrometer. The sample is often placed on a heating element in a location optically equivalent to the normal source position. For remote emission studies, suitable optics direct the light into the interferometer or monochromator. A reference signal is obtained by positioning a blackbody, such as a metal plate painted black, in place of the sample and holding it at the same temperature as the sample to be

measured. The emission spectrum of the sample is the ratio of the emission of the sample and blackbody reference.

Emission signals can result when molecules in an excited vibrational state return to the ground state. Spectral emissivity equals spectral absorptivity. However, the observed emission spectrum of thick samples can become complicated when light emitted from the interior of the sample is self-absorbed by the outer part of the sample before detection.

Photoacoustic Spectroscopy (PAS). While in an excited vibrational state, a molecule can return to its ground vibrational state through the mechanism of emission, fluorescence, or nonradiative transfer of the vibrational energy to the lattice as kinetic energy. Fluorescence in the infrared is rare. Most molecules return to the ground state by the third mechanism. If the light that initially excited a molecule is modulated by a light chopper or interferometer, the kinetic energy in the lattice as a result of the nonradiative relaxation to the ground vibrational state is also modulated. This is the photoacoustic effect.

In PAS, a microphone or piezoelectric device detects the lattice modulations, and the signal amplitude is proportional to the amount of light the sample absorbs (Ref 26, 27). Photoacoustic spectroscopy is suitable for highly absorbing samples that are difficult to measure by transmission. In addition, because the PAS signal is proportional to the total amount of light absorbed, bulk samples can usually be analyzed without dilution or any other sample preparation. Modulation signals from solid samples are usually detected after the acoustic waves in the solid lattice are transferred to gas molecules. The microphone detects the acoustic wave in the gas. Photoacoustic spectroscopy is more sensitive to infrared absorbances by gases than solids, because the acoustic wave need not be transferred from the solid. The PAS sample cell must be carefully sealed, free of absorbing gases, and isolated vibrationally and acoustically from the environment.

Although PAS has been performed using dispersive spectrometers, it is far easier using FT-IR spectroscopy. On a FT-IR spectrometer, a modulated interferogram signal at the microphone is Fourier transformed in the usual manner. Each wavenumber is modulated at an independent frequency. The lower the modulation frequency, the deeper in the sample is the origin of the overall PAS signal. Thus, lower wavenumber absorbances come from deeper in the sample than higher wavenumber absorbances, and the resulting spectrum tends to be skewed in a manner similar to ATR spectra. Depth profiling can be achieved by varying mirror velocity. The depth of penetration depends

on the modulation frequency, the thermal diffusion length of the sample, and the extinction coefficient of the sample. This value can vary dramatically from one sample to another, but is typically between 10 and 100 μm.

Although suitable PAS spectra can be obtained within minutes on many FT-IR spectrometers, other techniques, such as ATR or diffuse reflectance, often yield higher quality spectra in less time. Photoacoustic spectroscopy is seldom the infrared technique of first choice, although it can be useful in specific applications such as analyses of optically thick samples (Ref 26, 27).

Chromatographic Techniques. The ability of Fourier transform spectrometers to obtain infrared spectra within 1 s allows interfacing FT-IR spectroscopy with various chromatographic techniques. The most advanced and useful of these techniques is gas chromatography-infrared (GC-IR) spectroscopy (Ref 28, 29). Although not as sensitive as the more widely used technique of gas chromatography/mass spectrometry (GC/MS), GC-IR spectroscopy can provide complementary information. Gas chromatography/mass spectrometry provides molecular-weight information, but cannot satisfactorily distinguish isomers. Gas chromatography-infrared spectroscopy can usually distinguish isomers effectively.

Using capillary columns and flow-through infrared cells (light pipes) consisting of gold-coated glass tubes 10 to 30 cm (4 to 12 in.) long with inside diameters of 1 to 2 mm (0.04 to 0.08 in.), 10 to 20 ng of typical infrared absorbers can be detected in real time ("on the fly") during gas chromatography. With some FT-IR systems, spectra may be stored every second during a GC-IR spectroscopy operation lasting 1 h or more. The infrared spectra of each of the chromatographic peaks, which can number 100 or more, can be searched against libraries of vapor-phase spectra or can be interpreted manually. Much of the computer software developed for GC-IR spectroscopy can be used to study the kinetics of such processes as chemical reactions, polymer curing, and adsorption on surfaces from solution.

Gas chromatography-infrared spectroscopy usage remains well below that of GC/MS primarily because of its relative lack of sensitivity. Although some small incremental improvements in GC-IR using light-pipe technology still occur, an approach that uses a matrix-isolation interface and is approximately two orders of magnitude more sensitive has been developed (Ref 30). Approximately 1.5% of an argon matrix gas is mixed with helium carrier gas in the gas chromatograph. The gas chromatograph effluent is frozen onto a rotating cryogenic (12 to 13 K) gold-coated disk surface. A gas chromatography peak can be concentrated in the argon matrix to an area less than 0.2 mm^2 (0.0003 in.^{2}) while the helium carrier gas is pumped away by the vacuum system. The infrared beam is focused onto the matrix band, reflected off the gold-coated disk, and refocused on an infrared detector after passing out of the vacuum system. The improved sensitivity of this approach derives from the reduced cross-sectional area of the sample, which results in a longer path length for the same amount of sample. In addition, matrix-isolation spectra generally have sharper bands with higher peak absorbances, the system has higher light throughput, and gas chromatography peaks can be held in the beam and scanned for much longer times.

High-performance liquid chromatography (HPLC) (Ref 31) and supercritical fluid chromatography (SFC) (Ref 32) are examples in which chromatographs have been interfaced with FT-IR spectrometers. Liquid flow cells are available for HPLC-IR interfaces. Unlike GC-IR spectroscopy, in which a nonabsorbing carrier gas (helium) is used, all liquid chromatography solvents absorb somewhere in the infrared region of the spectrum. Overlapping bands from the solvent often complicate interpretation of the spectra. One advantage of HPLC-IR over GC-IR spectroscopy is that effluent peaks of interest may often be isolated and analyzed later after elimination of the solvent. It is not as crucial that the spectra be taken in real time (''on the fly''). Although SFC-IR has potential, it is in an early stage of development. Carbon dioxide, a common SFC solvent, is transparent through the most critical portions of the infrared spectrum. It absorbs strongly only near 2350 and 667 cm^{-1}.

Infrared microsampling can be performed using many of the techniques discussed. Spectra of approximately 1 ng of sample are obtainable with diffuse reflectance and ATR, assuming the sample can be dissolved in a volatile solvent. The diamond-anvil cell can be used to obtain infrared spectra of single small particles. Infrared microsampling accessories are available (Ref 33). One design uses $32\times$ Cassegrainian optics to focus the light on the sample. Spectra of samples 15 μm in diameter can be obtained. The stage can be translated, and the exact area to be sampled viewed using normal microscope optics. Single small particles or a high-resolution infrared-spectral map can be measured.

Infrared Microscopes. Transmission and specular reflectance versions of the infrared microscope are available. The reflectance scope is designed for use when the sample of interest is optically too thick.

However, spectra recorded using the reflectance microscope exhibit potential optical artifact complications of regular specular reflectance spectra.

The ultimate spatial resolution of the infrared microscope is determined by the diffraction limit. When the aperture size is nearly the same as the wavelength of light, band shape distortions due to diffraction begin to occur. These distortions appear first in the lower wavenumber regions of the spectrum.

Qualitative Analysis

Qualitative identification is an important use of IR spectroscopy (Ref 34). The infrared spectrum contains much information related to molecular structure. The most positive form of spectral identification is to locate a reference spectrum that matches that of the unknown material. Many collections of reference spectra are published, and many of these volumes are being computerized. When an exact reference spectrum match cannot be found, a band-by-band assignment is necessary to determine the structure. In this case, the infrared spectrum alone will usually not be sufficient for positive identification. Nuclear magnetic resonance (NMR) and mass spectrometry (MS) measurements may often be necessary to confirm a molecular structure.

The interpretation of infrared spectra has recently become computerized. Vapor-phase spectral data bases have been used to assist identification of GC-IR spectra. Libraries of condensed-phase infrared spectra are also gradually being enlarged, although the number of compounds in the available data bases is only a small fraction of the total number of known compounds.

Infrared spectra data bases can be searched in several ways. The important factors are peak locations, band intensities, and band shapes. Because a typical infrared spectrum contains approximately 2000 data points, many data bases and their corresponding search strategies are designed to minimize the amount of data needed for searching without sacrificing a great deal of spectral selectivity. This can shorten search times and reduce the storge space required for the spectral libraries. It is more practical to search for unknown infrared spectra in laboratories in which large volumes of samples are analyzed daily and the compounds of interest are likely to be in existing data bases. Even when an exact match to an unknown spectrum cannot be found in a data base, search routines usually list the closest matches located. This can be useful in identifying at least the molecular type.

Absorbance-subtraction techniques, or spectral-stripping techniques, can be useful in interpreting spectra of mixtures or in removing solvent bands. Spectral subtraction should be attempted only when the spectrum is plotted in absorbance or some other units proportional to sample concentration. In addition, absorbance subtractions should be interpreted with extreme caution in any region in which sample absorbance exceeds approximately 0.6 to 0.8 absorbance units. Subtractions can be performed with or without scaling. An isolated band in the spectrum of the component to be subtracted out can often be minimized in intensity by interactively observing the difference between the two spectra as a function of scale factor. Subtraction of solid ATR spectra should be avoided because of the wavelength dependence of the depth of penetration and the difficulty in obtaining reproducible contact of the solid with the IRE. Absorbance subtractions are most effective when the optics are not perturbed between scans of the two spectra involved in the subtraction, for example, kinetic studies or flow cell systems.

Factor analysis is a mathematical procedure for determining the number of components in a set of mixtures (Ref 35). Knowledge of spectra of the pure components is unnecessary. A matrix of mixture spectra ($\mathbf{A}$) is constructed with each column vector representing the infrared spectrum of one mixture. This matrix is multiplied by its transpose ($\mathbf{A}^T$) to yield an $\mathbf{m} \times \mathbf{m}$ square matrix ($\mathbf{C}$), where $\mathbf{m}$ is the number of mixture spectra. The $\mathbf{C}$ matrix is then diagonalized, and the number of nonzero eigenvalues represents the number of independent components. Noise in the spectra can cause small eigenvalues, making it difficult to distinguish nonzero and zero eigenvalues. The presence of numerous components, some having similar infrared spectra, complicates factor analysis. Factor-analysis Fortran programs are available with many infrared software packages.

Resolution Enhancement Methods. Infrared spectra of condensed phases often contain many overlapping bands that cannot be resolved even by obtaining the spectra at high resolution, because the natural line widths of the spectra limit resolution. However, spectral lineshapes contain information on these broad overlapping bands. Several methods exist for enhancing the resolution of infrared spectra. Derivative spectroscopy can be used to determine the exact peak location of broad profiles. Second and fourth derivative spectra are much sharper, and more bands may appear; however, the signal-to-noise ratio deteriorates with each additional derivative.

Fourier self-deconvolution is another method of resolution enhancement (Ref 36). A region of an infrared absorption spectrum containing overlapping bands is Fourier transformed back to the time domain using the fast Fourier transform (FFT) algorithm. The resulting damped ringing pattern is multiplied by a function (usually containing an exponential term) that weights the tail portion of the pattern more heavily. The net effect is an interferogram whose tail extends farther in the direction of increasing time. This ringing pattern must be truncated before the noise becomes significant. The interferogram is Fourier transformed back to the frequency domain, where the resulting absorbance bands are now narrower.

Two parameters are varied during this procedure: the bandwidth and the number of points in the time domain spectrum retained before truncation. If the selected bandwidth is too broad, negative lobes will appear in the deconvolved spectrum. If too many points in the time domain spectrum are retained, noise will be deconvolved. Proper bandwidth selection is important. It is impossible to deconvolve bands of significantly different bandwidth simultaneously and completely.

Quantitative Analysis

The basis for quantitative analysis in infrared spectroscopy is Beer's law, which for a single compound at a single wavenumber is:

$$A = abc \qquad \text{(Eq 13)}$$

where A is the sample absorbance at a specific wavenumber, a is the absorptivity of the sample at that wavenumber, b is the pathlength, and c is the concentration. In practice, Beer's law may not hold due to matrix or concentration effects that change absorptivity. Calibration curves must be obtained to confirm linearity of the relationship between A and c.

As in spectral subtraction, derivative methods, and Fourier self-deconvolution, quantitative infrared analysis should not be attempted unless the spectra are plotted in absorbance units. Infrared intensity can be determined with favorable results by measuring peak height or the area under the absorption band. In either case, intensity measurements must be made relative to some baseline. Baseline determination can be subjective, particularly when there are overlapping bands, and can be a major source of error in intensity measurements. Consistent procedures for measuring intensities provide optimum results.

Before the concentration of a component in a mixture can be determined from the absorbance spectrum, the absorptivities of bands sensitive to the presence of that component must be known. This is usually accomplished by obtaining spectra of calibration standards for which the concentrations are known. Infrared bands sensitive to the presence of the component of interest are then determined. Linear plots of absorbance versus concentration indicate the validity of Beer's law over the concentration range of the calibration set for the bands selected. The path length is usually held constant or accurately measured. When the absorbance of a sample component of unknown concentration is measured, concentration is determined using the Beer's law plot.

Matrix methods are needed in analyzing complex mixtures. Computerized infrared spectrometers and commercial software packages facilitate multicomponent analysis on many instruments. A basic understanding of multicomponent analysis can help in avoiding errors. The **K**-matrix method is one approach to multicomponent analysis (Ref 37).

In the **K**-matrix method, absorptivity multiplied by the path length is defined as a single constant k, and Beer's law becomes:

$$A = kc \qquad \text{(Eq 14)}$$

Assuming Beer's law is additive, the absorbance at frequency i of sample j is:

$$a_{ij} = \sum_{l=1}^{n} k_{il}c_{lj} \qquad \text{(Eq 15)}$$

where the summation is over all components, l, from 1 to n. Equation 14 can be written in matrix form as:

$$A = \mathbf{KC} \qquad \text{(Eq 16)}$$

The **K** matrix is determined from the calibration spectra. The number of calibration samples and frequencies used should each exceed or equal the number of components, n. Solving for the **K** matrix yields:

$$\mathbf{K} = A\mathbf{C}^{\mathrm{T}}(\mathbf{CC}^{\mathrm{T}})^{-1} \qquad \text{(Eq 17)}$$

where the superscript T is the transform of the matrix, and the superscript -1 is the inverse of the matrix. The unknown concentrations of the components in the mixture can then be obtained from the absorbance spectrum of the mixture using:

$$\mathbf{C} = (\mathbf{KK}^{\mathrm{T}})^{-1}\mathbf{K}^{\mathrm{T}}A \qquad \text{(Eq 18)}$$

Sources of Error. Several potential sources of error may arise in quantitative infrared analysis. The matrix $(\mathbf{CC}^{\mathrm{T}})$ must be nonsingular to be inverted. Therefore, none of the rows or columns of **C** should be linear combinations of other rows or columns, that is, determinant $(\mathbf{CC}^{\mathrm{T}}) \neq 0$. The **K**-matrix method assumes that a linear relationship exists between the absorbances and the concentrations and that Beer's law is additive in the multicomponent case. The theory does not rigorously account for band shifts or absorptivity changes due to interaction of the components. The calibration data are always least squares fitted to the linear expression (Eq 16).

Other sources of error may occur during experimental measurement. The photometric accuracy of the instrument is important in quantitative analysis. Apparent breakdowns of Beer's law may result from spectrometer nonlinearities rather than sample component interactions. Many commercial infrared instruments become nonlinear when sample absorbances approach 1. Other instrument manufacturers claim ability to measure absorbances linearly to values as high as 3. Regardless of the photometric accuracy specification of the instrument, detection of stray light signals that do not pass through the sample can cause serious errors in absorbance measurements. For example, if during a transmittance measurement the sample solution contains an air bubble that allows passage of 1% of the total light, the largest absorbance that can be recorded at any frequency is 2. This will cause errors in the measured absorbance values that worsen progressively as sample absorbance increases.

Scattering artifacts, such as those described above, can severely affect quantitative accuracy and precision. Spectra that contain significant contributions from the refractive index can result in inaccurate peak heights or peak areas. Scattering effects can also cause sloped baselines that complicate intensity measurement. Noncontinuous samples can also lead to errors in quantification. Films that are not uniformly thick or inhomogeneous powders for which a representative aliquot is not collected can lead to absorbance spectra that do not reflect the average composition of the entire sample. Overlapping bands from atmospheric absorptions, such as water vapor and carbon dioxide, can also affect intensity measurements. Finally, sample temperature can affect band shapes and intensities due to phase transitions or changes in sample emission.

Curve fitting is a final alternate method of infrared quantitative analysis (Ref 38).

When the spectrum of a mixture is known to consist of specific pure components, and spectra of these components are available, it should be possible to generate a linear combination of the pure component spectra that reproduces the spectrum of the mixture. The coefficients then represent the amount of each pure component in the mixture. This is a specific case of the **K**-matrix approach in which the **C** matrix is a square matrix with ones along the diagonal and zeros elsewhere, and every frequency in the spectrum is used in the **K** and **A** matrices. Each mixture spectrum to be analyzed must contain only the pure components anticipated, and bands must not occur due to interaction of the components. Curve fitting usually is effective only with fewer than five components and with significantly differing pure component spectra.

Applications*

Example 1: Factor Analysis and Curve Fitting Applied to a Polymer Blend System.
Application of factor analysis and curve fitting to a polymer blend system of polystyrene (PS) and poly-2,6-dimethyl-1,4-phenylene oxide (2MPPO) has been documented (Ref 35). Five polymer blend (polyblend) films of PS and 2MPPO as well as the two pure-component films were prepared, and factor analysis was applied to the 3200- to 2700-cm^{-1} region of their infrared spectra. Figure 5 shows a plot of the log of the eigenvalue versus possible number of components. This plot indicates that the spectra of each of the several samples can be expressed as a linear combination of two spectra. By least squares curve-fitting the pure-component infrared spectra of PS and 2MPPO in the 3200- to 2700-cm^{-1} region, the composition of each polyblend film can be accurately determined (Table 3). Figure 6 illustrates the quality of the fit of the pure-component PS and 2MPPO spectra to the 1:3 PS/2MPPO polyblend.

Factor analysis applied to the 1800- to 1100-cm^{-1} region of the PS/2MPPO polyblend spectra indicated the presence of the independent components. This region of the infrared spectrum is evidently more sensitive to conformation effects, suggesting the occurrence of a conformation transition in one of the blend components.

Example 2: Examination of Structural Changes in Surfactant Molecules in Water.
Infrared spectroscopy can be used to study molecular aggregation in dilute aqueous solutions (Ref 39). Figure

*Examples 7 and 8 were supplied by D.M. Haaland, Sandia National Laboratories. Example 9 was supplied by M.C. Oborny, Sandia National Laboratories.

Fig. 5 Factor analysis from 3200 to 2700 cm^{-1} of PS/2MPPO polymer blend system
Source: Ref 35

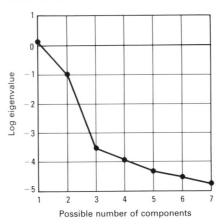

7 shows a transmittance spectrum in the CH-stretching region of a 10-mM solution of $C_{12}H_{25}N(CH_3)_3Cl$ in deuterium oxide (D_2O). A 50-μm calcium fluoride cell was used for the sample and reference (D_2O). As the surfactant concentration is increased, the bands shift to lower wavenumber and become narrower. The concentration at which the shift begins coincides with the known critical micelle concentration (cmc) of 21 mM (Fig. 8). Similar results were obtained in water. Problems with window solubility and/or adsorption onto the CaF_2 windows prevented obtaining data below 10 mM.

Similar, more recent experiments have been conducted with other surfactants using a cylindrical internal reflection cell (CIR-CLE) with a zinc selenide IRE (Ref 40, 41). Adsorption and solubility seem to be less of a problem with this device, and the lowest concentration for detection of spectrum with reasonable signal-to-noise ratios has been improved by an order of magnitude. The infrared transmission method has also been used to study structural changes in aqueous solution as a function of temperature and to characterize bilayer to nonbilayer transitions (Ref 42).

Fig. 6 Accuracy of fit of PS and 2MPPO spectra to a polymer-blend spectrum by least squares curve-fitting from 3200 to 2700 cm^{-1}

A, PS; B, 2MPPO; C, experimental PS/2MPPO polyblend spectrum (solid line). Best least squares fit of PS plus 2MPPO (dotted). Source: Ref 35

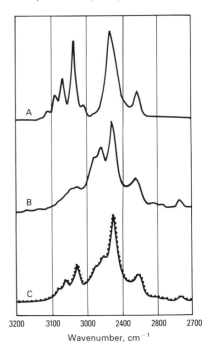

Example 3: Examination of Monolayers Adsorbed on Metal Surfaces.
Structure transformation similar to those observed in aqueous solution are apparent in the infrared reflection-absorption spectra of monolayer films adsorbed on metal surfaces. Figure 9 illustrates the CH-stretching region of $C_{14}H_{29}$dimethylammonium hexanoate ($C_{14}AH$) adsorbed on polished carbon-steel coupons. Spectrum A, of a dry coupon that had been soaked 5 days in a 0.1% aqueous solution of $C_{14}AH$, exhibits broad CH_2-stretching bands centered at 2925 and 2854 cm^{-1}. Spectrum B, of a dry coupon soaked 5 days in a 1.0% $C_{14}AH$ aqueous solution,

Table 3 Compositional analysis of PS/2MPPO polyblend films by least squares curve-fitting 3200 to 2700 cm^{-1}

Known		Calculated	
wt% PS	wt% 2MPPO	wt% PS	wt% PPO
50.0 ± 0.5	50.0 ± 0.5	50.00 ± 0.38	50.00 ± 0.54(a)
75.0 ± 0.5	25.0 ± 0.5	76.33 ± 0.52	23.67 ± 0.73
25.0 ± 0.5	75.0 ± 0.5	25.18 ± 0.50	74.82 ± 0.71
90.0 ± 0.5	10.0 ± 0.5	91.27 ± 0.30	8.73 ± 0.42
10.0 ± 0.5	90.0 ± 0.5	9.95 ± 0.63	90.05 ± 0.89

(a) Calibration
Source: Ref 35

Fig. 7 Infrared-transmittance spectrum of 10 mM C$_{12}$H$_{25}$N(CH$_3$)$_3$Cl in D$_2$O versus D$_2$O in a 50-μm CaF$_2$ cell

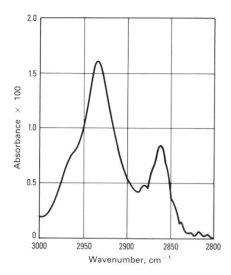

Fig. 8 Frequency of the CH$_2$ antisymmetric (top) and symmetric (bottom) stretching modes as a function of C$_{12}$H$_{25}$(CH$_3$)$_3$Cl concentration in D$_2$O

cmc, critical micelle concentration

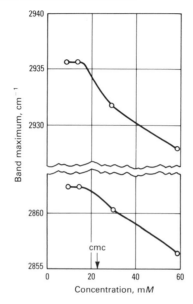

Fig. 10 Spectrum of bulk DTDMAC and DTDMAC adsorbed on metallic and nonmetallic substrates

A, ATR spectrum of bulk DTDMAC; B, infrared reflection-absorption spectrum of DTDMAC adsorbed on a 2-nm-thick film of cellulose acetate on copper; C, infrared reflection-absorption spectrum of DTDMAC adsorbed on copper

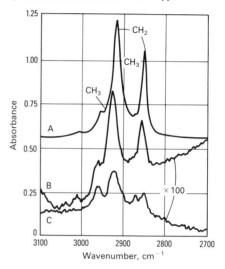

has much narrower bands that are shifted to 2920 and 2850 cm^{-1}. Spectrum B suggests a more ordered structure on the surface than spectrum A.

The IRRAS spectra in Fig. 9 do not clearly reveal any molecular orientation on the surface. Figure 10, however, shows spectral changes assignable to differences in molecular orientation. Spectrum A is an ATR spectrum of a randomly oriented evaporated film of ditallowdimethylammonium chloride (DTDMAC) adsorbed on a polished copper coupon in the CH-stretching region. It is shown to indicate the relative intensities of the methyl- and methylene-stretching bands in a randomly oriented situation. The spectrum confirmed the presence of 10 times more CH$_2$ than CH$_3$ groups in the molecule.

Spectrum C in Fig. 10 is of a polished copper coupon that had been soaked 30 min in a dilute aqueous solution of DTDMAC. The relative intensities of the methyl- and methylene-stretching modes suggest an attenuation of the CH$_2$ bands and a slight enhancement of the CH$_3$ bands. This result can be explained in terms of an orientation effect. A tendency of the hydrocarbon tails to orient vertically from the surface in an all-trans configuration would lead to significant attenuation of the CH$_2$ antisymmetric and symmetric stretching motions at 2920 and 2854 cm^{-1}. The dipole-transition moments for these molecular vibrations would lie in a plane parallel to the surface, making them inactive according to the surface selection rule. However, the methyl-stretching

vibrations would have significant components of their dipole-transition moments perpendicular to the surface for vertically oriented hydrocarbon chains.

Determining the orientation of DTDMAC on nonmetallic surfaces using IR spectroscopy presents two problems. First, nonmetallic substrates absorb infrared radiation,

Fig. 9 Infrared reflection absorption spectra of C$_{14}$AH adsorbed on steel from 1.0 (A) and 0.1% (B) aqueous solutions (soaked 50 days and dried)

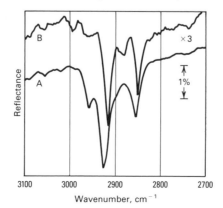

and the bulk substrate spectrum usually severely overlaps the desired surface spectrum of interest. Second, because the surface selection rule holds only for metallic substrates, if an infrared spectrum is obtainable, the orientation information is lost. One solution is to form a thin-film model substrate adsorbed on the metal surface and deposit the monolayer film of interest on top of this model surface. If the model substrate film is thin enough, its spectrum can often be completely subtracted without affecting the surface selection rule and orientation information about the top monolayer film.

Spectrum B in Fig. 10 shows the spectrum of DTDMAC deposited in the same manner as in spectrum C on a 2-nm-thick model surface of cellulose acetate adsorbed on copper. The cellulose acetate spectrum has been subtracted out. The relative intensities of the CH-stretching bands now match those observed in the randomly oriented case shown in spectrum A, suggesting that DTDMAC orients differently on cellulose acetate than on bare copper.

Figure 11 shows the orientation of a long-chain molecule on a model surface. The compound is dioctadecyldimethylammonium bromide (DODMAB), and the model surface is an 8-nm-thick film of keratin adsorbed on a polished copper coupon. The film represents three monolayers deposited using the Langmuir-Blodgett technique (Ref

Fig. 11 Three Langmuir-Blodgett monolayers of DODMAB adsorbed on an 8-nm-thick film of keratin on copper

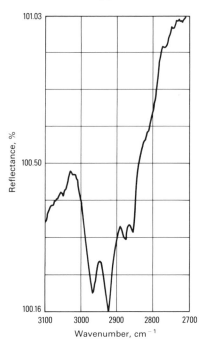

43-45). The relative intensities clearly indicated evidence of vertical orientation even on top of the 8-nm model protein surface.

Example 4: Depth-Profiling a Granular Sample Using ATR, Diffuse Reflectance, and Photoacoustic Spectroscopy. Although ATR and PAS can be used to depth-profile a sample, neither approach provides more than approximately one decade of dynamic range. The spectra shown in Fig. 12 illustrate how ATR, PAS, and DRS

Fig. 12 ATR, PAS, and DRS spectra of a granule containing DPDA, MPDA, and DA

The band at 1695 cm^{-1} (indicated by an asterisk) is due to carboxylic acid. The estimated depth of the infrared beam into the sample is shown in parentheses.

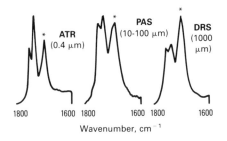

can be combined to depth-profile a granular sample. The spectra show the carbonyl-stretching region of a granule containing diperoxydodecanedioic acid (DPDA), monoperoxydodecanedioic acid (MPDA), and dodecanedioic acid (DA). The bands at 1753 and 1735 cm^{-1} are due to peracid groups, and the bands at 1695 cm^{-1} (labeled with an asterisk) are assigned to the carbonyl stretch of the carboxylic acid component. The estimated depth of penetration of the infrared beam into the sample for each experiment is shown in parentheses. Combining three infrared techniques enables acquisition of sample spectra from 0.4 μm to 1 mm (the diameter of the granule). Much more peracid is on the surface of the granule than in the interior. This result is more dramatic than that achieved using only one approach, in which dynamic range would have been narrower by at least a factor of 25.

Example 5: Determination of Molecular Orientation in Drawn Polymer Films. Infrared linear dichroism spectroscopy is useful for studying the molecular orientation in polymeric materials (Ref 46, 47). The ultimate properties of a polymer depend on the conditions under which it was formed. This study illustrates use of infrared linear dichroism to determine molecular orientation in a polymer film as a function of processing conditions.

When a polymer film is drawn, the macromolecular chains tend to align in a specific direction. The oriented film may then absorb, to different extents, incident infrared radiation polarized parallel and perpendicular to a reference direction usually defined as the drawing direction. The dichroic ratio, $R = A_{\parallel}/A_{\perp}$, associated with a specific absorbance band in the infrared spectrum can be used to assist determination of molecular chain orientation (Ref 46, 47). Absorbances of the components parallel and perpendicular to the reference direction are given by $A_{\parallel}$ and $A_{\perp}$, respectively. The farther from 1.00 that R is (greater or less), the greater the degree of orientation suggested.

Infrared spectra of eight samples of isotactic polypropylene were obtained with the

sample oriented parallel and perpendicular to a linear polarizer placed in the beam of the FT-IR spectrometer. The areas of the peaks at 528, 941, and 1104 cm^{-1} were measured, and the dichroic ratios calculated using the integrated intensities in place of the absorbance values. The results are shown in Table 4. The draw ratio and temperature at which the sample was drawn are indicated. Peak absorbances varied from near zero for parallel polarization of the 528-cm^{-1} band in the highly oriented samples to near 1.0 for the 1104-cm^{-1} band in the unstretched sample. Nevertheless, the same relative degree of orientation is predicted for the sample using each dichroic ratio. The 941-cm^{-1} band has a profile similar to band 2 in Fig. 13, and the baseline drawn from C to D was used to determine the peak area (Ref 47). The absorbance value A_2 could also be used in place of the peak area. The results in Table 4 indicate that the lower the temperature when stretching, the greater the orientation induced at a given draw ratio. At a given temperature, the greater the draw ratio, the greater the orientation induced.

Example 6: Monitoring Polymer-Curing Reactions Using ATR. Fourier transform infrared spectroscopy can be used to follow changes in polymer films as they cure. In this example, the polymer sample is a paint applied to a KRS-5 IRE. The method used is similar to a documented technique in which the paint samples were analyzed inside the instrument with a dry air purge infrared transmission (Ref 48). Use of a Wilks' ATR attachment (described below) enabled exposing the paint to ambient atmosphere. Absorbance subtraction was used to aid understanding of the chemical reactions. Subtraction is optimized, because the sample is not touched between analyses and the alignment of the ATR device remains constant.

The Wilks' ATR attachment used was designed as a skin analyzer for a dispersive spectrometer. When fitted into the front beam of the spectrometer, the attachment allows the sample to be exposed to the atmosphere during purging of the sample compartment with dry nitrogen. This avoids

Table 4 Order of samples according to degree of orientation ($R = A_{\parallel}/A_{\perp}$) for sample polypropylene bands at three wavenumbers

	Polypropylene sample	R at 528 cm^{-1}	R at 941 cm^{-1}	R at 1104 cm^{-1}
Most oriented	7× at 105 °C (225 °F)	0.017	0.049	0.161
	7× at 135 °C (275 °F)	0.027	0.070	0.188
	4× at 105 °C (225 °F)	0.030	0.070	0.190
	4× at 135 °C (275 °F)	0.046	0.075	0.205
	7× at 160 °C (325 °F)	0.130	0.147	0.263
	4× at 160 °C (325 °F)	0.250	0.244	0.340
Least oriented	Unknown at 150 °C (300 °F)	0.590	0.425	0.548
	Unstretched	1.020	1.059	1.092

Fig. 13 Synthetic spectrum showing baseline choices for two overlapping bands

The baseline from C to D is acceptable for band 2. The baseline drawn from A to B is correct for band 1, but if used for band 2 would give an incorrect value.

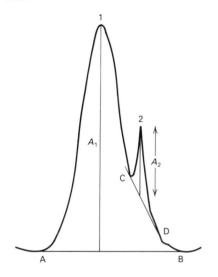

Fig. 14 KRS-5 ATR spectrum of paint

Spectrum after 15-min cure subtracted from spectrum after 30 min

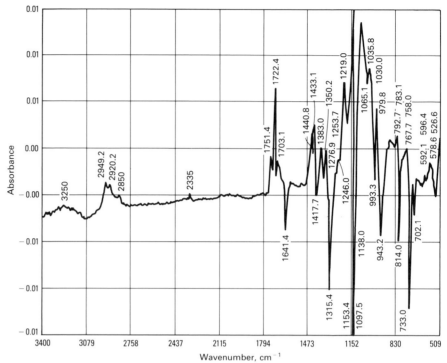

water vapor and carbon dioxide interference in the optical path while allowing oxygen to reach the sample. A paint sample was spread on the KRS-5 IRE, and spectra obtained every 15 min for the first 90 min and every hour thereafter for 5 h. A final measurement was taken after 24 h. Each spectrum was ratioed with a blank IRE reference spectrum that was converted to absorbance. Difference spectra were generated by subtraction of the most recent absorbance spectrum from the one immediately preceding it. The subtraction reveals the types of bonds forming or breaking. Bands that are positive in the difference spectra indicate functional groups forming, and those negative suggest disappearing functional groups.

Only the layer of paint next to the surface of the IRE is sampled in the ATR experiment. The depth of penetration of the infrared beam at 1000 cm^{-1} through a KRS-5 IRE is approximately 2 μm. Therefore, the spectra represent the innermost surface, away from the atmosphere.

These results are for paint dissolved in a methylene chloride solvent. The first part of the curing process involved loss of C=C and solvent with a gain of C=O and OH. Between 6 and 24 h, the OH, in the form of hydroperoxide, had disappeared. Subtraction of the 24-h spectrum from the time-zero spectrum did not reveal any hydroperoxide bands. Thus, the hydroperoxide is formed as an intermediate species. Figure 14 shows the result of subtracting a 15-min spectrum from

a 30-min spectrum. Table 5 summarizes band frequencies and their assignments.

Example 7: Quantitative Analysis of Hydroxyl and Boron Content in Glass. The properties of a seven-component glass were found to vary over a wide range of values. Careful study of the composition of the glass after preparation revealed that two components, boron oxide (B_2O_3) and hydroxyl groups, caused most of the variation in glass properties. These components were not well controlled because (1)

boron oxide is volatile, and some boron is lost during the melt preparation of the glass and (2) water in the atmosphere of the furnace can react with the glass to increase hydroxyl content. Because consistency of glass properties was required, the boron and OH content of each glass batch was monitored to identify proper melt operating conditions and to achieve better quality control of the final product. However, because of the large number of samples generated, a rapid method of analysis of the glass was

Table 5 Bands and assignments for difference spectrum

30-min spectrum minus 15-min spectrum

Band, cm^{-1}	Forming (F) or disappearing (D)	Assignment
3250	F	Hydroperoxide (O–H stretching)
1751	F	6-membered lactone (C=O stretching)
1722	F	Ketone or conjugated ester (C=O stretching)
1641	D	cis-vinyl or vinylidine (C=C stretching)
1437	F	Methylene adjacent to carbonyl (CH₂ deformation)
1417	D	Methylene adjacent to C=C (CH₂ deformation)
1315	D	Not assigned
1153	F	Ester (C–O stretching)
1138	D	Not assigned
993	D	Vinyl C=C (=CH₂ wagging)
943	D	Vinyl adjacent to ester (O–C–C=CCH₂ wagging)
814	D	R–O–CH=CH₂ (=CH₂ wagging)
733	D	Methylene chloride
702	D	Methylene chloride

Fig. 15 Typical FT-IR spectrum of a glass sample

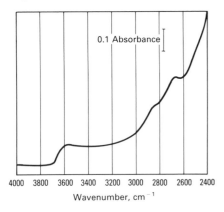

Fig. 16 Spectrum of a glass sample after pathlength normalization and linear baseline correction

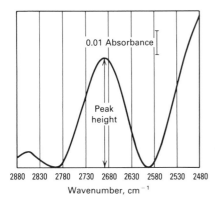

Fig. 17 Calibration of B_2O_3 concentration from ICE versus height of the B–O overtone band

The line drawn through the data is from the linear least squares fit of the data.

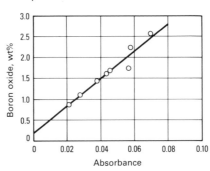

desired. Infrared spectroscopy was selected for its rapidity and accuracy for these two components in the glass.

Samples of 6-mm (0.24-in.) diam glass rod were poured from the original melt and cut into 5-mm (0.2-in.) thick samples for the infrared analysis. The samples were cleaned ultrasonically, but the faces of the samples were not polished. Spectra were taken using a FT-IR spectrometer at 4 cm^{-1} resolution (full-width at half maximum.). Figure 15 shows the infrared spectrum of a typical glass. The band at approximately 3560 cm^{-1} is due to the stretching vibration of OH groups. The band at approximately 2685 cm^{-1} has been assigned to the overtone band of the B–O stretching vibration. The peak intensities of these bands were found to follow Beer's law if the intensity was measured at the peak band position. The OH band remained at relatively constant frequency over the concentration range studied. The B–O band was found to shift to higher

energy with higher boron content. The OH content of the glass was determined on a relative basis, because there was no convenient method of absolute determination of OH in this glass. The boron oxide content of a set of glass samples used for infrared calibration was measured independently using ion chromatography exclusion (ICE). These samples covered the concentration range of B_2O_3 and OH expected in normal glass processing.

Because samples were not polished, spectra of the glass samples were sloped slightly. The sloping baseline, a result of scattered light from the rough glass surfaces, was removed using standard software to correct for linear baseline offsets. Sample thickness was measured accurately using a micrometer, and the spectrum was multiplied by the factor required to yield spectra in units of absorbance/5.0 mm (0.2 in.). Figure 15 shows a baseline-corrected and scaled spectrum. The OH content was then determined from the height of the 3560-cm^{-1} peak measured from the high-energy baseline.

For B_2O_3 determination, the spectra were further baseline corrected to facilitate measurement of the B–O overtone band (Fig. 16). The peak height of the baseline-corrected band was used to quantify the B_2O_3 content of the glass. Based on eight glass samples analyzed independently using ICE and covering the concentration range of 0.88 to 2.58 wt% B_2O_3, the infrared calibration for B_2O_3 was found to be linear (Fig. 17). The average relative percent error in determining boron content of the eight calibration samples using IR spectroscopy was 4.0%, which compares favorably with the 3% average relative error of the ICE analysis. The boron content of unknown glass samples was determined directly from the calibration shown in Fig. 17.

Following analysis of several glass batches, glass samples exhibiting the appropriate properties were found to have an OH content corresponding to a 3560-cm^{-1} band intensity less than 0.048 absorbance/mm and a B_2O_3 content from 1.0 to 1.4 wt%. Starting concentrations were then adjusted, and the humidity controlled for reproducibility of these ideal concentrations. Infrared spectroscopy was then used to monitor rapidly the quality of the final glass batches. Further details of the analysis are cited in Ref 49.

More accurate and automated analysis of the glass can be obtained with application of the **K**-matrix least squares approach. However, because the B–O band shifts with frequency, a nonlinear model (rather than the linear Beer's law model) must be used to achieve the higher accuracy and to model the frequency shift with boron concentration. Use of the **K**-matrix method for multicomponent quantitative analysis is discussed in the section "Matrix Methods" in this article. Additional information is cited in Ref 37.

Example 8: Quantitative Analysis of Oxygen Contained in Silicon Wafers. The oxygen content of silicon wafers can affect the properties, rejection rates, and long-term reliability of integrated circuits produced on the wafers. Therefore, rapid measurement of oxygen in silicon wafers is desired for quality control. Infrared spectroscopy is well suited to rapid and nondestructive analysis of oxygen in silicon wafers. The proper methods for infrared determination of interstitial oxygen in silicon are cited in Ref 50. However, because the methods were designed for dipersive spectrometers with silicon wafers 2 to 4 mm (0.08 to 0.16 in.) thick and polished on both sides, modifications are required when using FT-IR spectrometers applied to commercial silicon wafers approximately 0.5 mm (0.02 in.) thick that are normally polished on one side.

One possible procedure involves taking a spectrum of a float-zoned silicon wafer with negligible oxygen content as a reference. The spectrum of the sample to be analyzed is also obtained at the same spectral resolution. If interference fringes due to multiple reflections in the sample are observed, spectra taken at lower resolution may be obtained that exhibit reduced fringe intensity. Alternatively, the fringes can be removed with software processing (Ref 51). A scaled subtraction of the float-zoned and sample spectra is performed to yield the spectrum of the Si–O band in the absence of any silicon phonon band; the float-zoned silicon spectrum is scaled according to its thickness relative to the sample spectrum.

Figure 18 shows the spectra of the float-zoned material and the sample to be analyzed as well as the result of the scaled subtraction.

Fig. 18 FT-IR spectra of silicon

A, silicon wafer with oxygen content to be determined; B, float-zoned silicon wafer with negligible oxygen content; C, difference spectrum (A minus scaled B) showing the Si−O stretching band at 1105 cm⁻¹

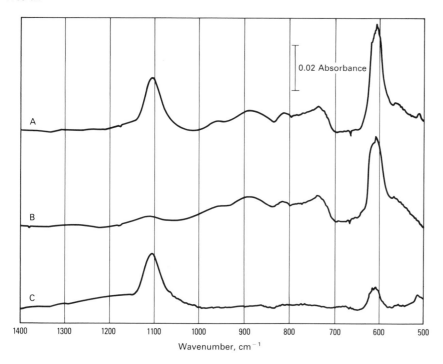

Fig. 19 Infrared spectrum of polymer material after subtraction of MEK spectrum

Residual artifact peaks are denoted by x.

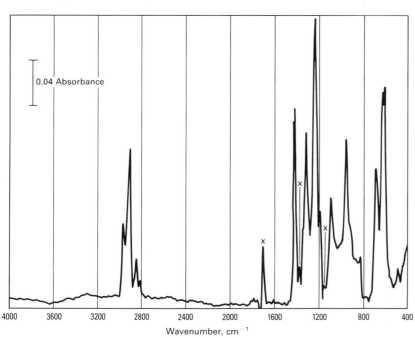

Conversion of absorbance to concentration in atomic parts per million for the 1105-cm⁻¹ band of Si−O uses the function 11.3 atomic ppm per cm⁻¹ at 300 K (Ref 50). The silicon sample with the Si−O band presented in spectrum C in Fig. 18 has an 1105-cm⁻¹ peak intensity of 0.0218 absorbance units; therefore, the oxygen content of this 0.50-mm (0.02-in.) silicon wafer as determined using IR spectroscopy is 4.9 atomic ppm. Further details of the oxygen analysis by FT-IR spectroscopy are cited in Ref 52 to 54. In addition, analysis of interstitial carbon impurities in silicon wafers can be determined using IR spectroscopy (Ref 52-54). With proper calibration, the **K**-matrix least squares method can also be used to achieve higher sensitivity for measurement of oxygen in the thin silicon wafers.

Example 9: Identification of Polymer and Plasticizer Materials in a Vinyl Film. A sheet of vinyl film was submitted for analysis to determine the identity of the polymer and any other information that might be available using IR spectroscopy.

A piece of the polymer approximately 25 by 10 mm (1 by 0.4 in.) was cut from the film, rinsed in methanol to remove surface contamination (fingerprints, and so on), then allowed to air dry. This sample was then soaked in acetone to extract the plasticizer from the sample. The acetone solution was retained to recover the plasticizer later. Being too thick for analysis, the film was prepared as a cast film on a KBr window. This was accomplished by dissolving the sample in methyl ethyl ketone (MEK) and adding several drops of the MEK solution to a KBr window. The MEK evaporated, leaving a cast film of the sample on the window. The KBr window was then placed in an appropriate sample holder, and the infrared spectrum taken. Because this spectrum exhibited MEK retention, a reference spectrum of an MEK capillary film was taken to subtract the spectrum of the MEK from the cast film spectrum (Fig. 19). Using a flow chart (Ref 55), the spectrum was identified as that of polyvinylchloride. This assignment was confirmed by comparison with published polyvinylchloride spectra.

The plasticizer material was recovered from the acetone extraction solution by evaporating the solution until only the viscous plasticizer remained. A small amount of the plasticizer was pressed between two KBr windows to form a thin film. Figure 20 shows the plasticizer spectrum. A computerized spectral search routine was used to identify the plasticizer. Although an exact match was not found, the compound was identified as a di-alkyl phthalate, a class of

Fig. 20 Infrared spectrum of plasticizer material

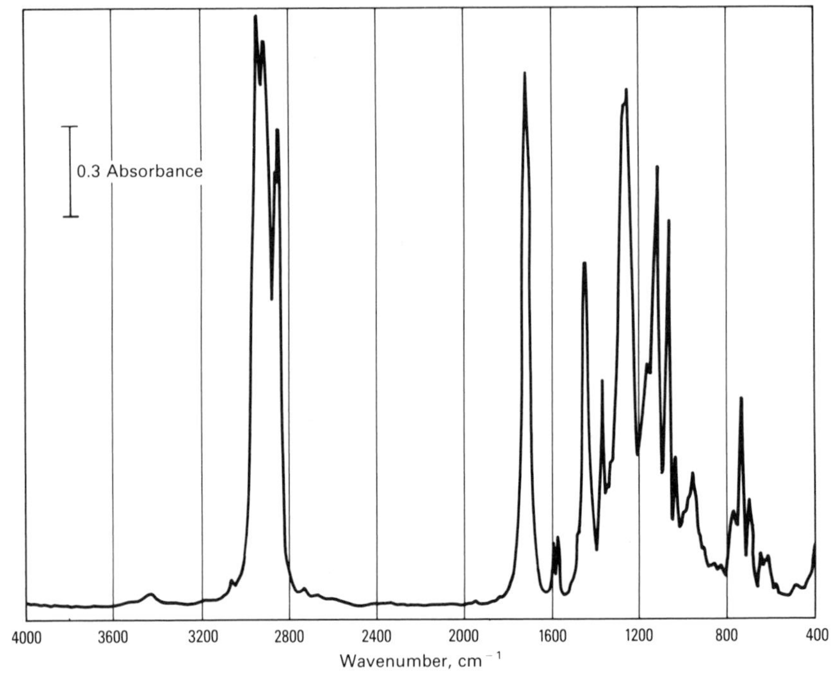

compounds commonly used as plasticizers in polymers.

REFERENCES

1. E.B. Wilson, J.C. Decius, and P.C. Cross, *Molecular Vibrations*, McGraw-Hill, 1955
2. P.C. Painter, M.M. Coleman, and J.L. Koenig, *The Theory of Vibrational Spectroscopy and Its Application to Polymeric Materials*, John Wiley & Sons, 1982
3. P.R. Griffiths, *Chemical Infrared Fourier Transform Spectroscopy*, John Wiley & Sons, 1975
4. A.A. Michelson, *Philos. Mag.*, Ser. 5, Vol 31, 1891, p 256
5. A.A. Michelson, *Philos. Mag.*, Ser. 5, Vol 34, 1892, p 280
6. P. Fellgett, *J. Phys. Radium*, Vol 19, 1958, p 187
7. P. Jacquinot and J.C. Dufour, *J. Rech. C.N.R.S.*, Vol 6, 1948, p 91
8. P. Jacquinot, *Rep. Prog. Phys.*, Vol 23, 1960, p 267
9. J. Connes and P. Connes, *J. Opt. Soc. Am.*, Vol 56, 1966, p 896
10. L. Genzel and J. Kuhl, *Appl. Opt.*, Vol 17, 1978, p 3304
11. W.M. Doyle, B.C. McIntosh, and W.L. Clark, *Appl. Spectrosc.*, Vol 34, 1980, p 599
12. R.P. Walker and J.D. Rex, in *Proceedings of the Society of Photo-Optical Instrumentation Engineers*, Vol 191, G.A. Vannasse, Ed., Society of Photo-Optical Instrumentation Engineers, Bellingham, WA, 1979
13. P.R. Griffiths, in *Advances in Infrared and Raman Spectroscopy*, Vol 10, R.J.H. Clark and R.E. Hester, Ed., Heyden, 1983
14. R.S. McDowell, in *Advances in Infrared and Raman Spectroscopy*, Vol 5, R.J.H. Clark and R.E. Hester, Ed., Heyden, 1980
15. W.J. Potts, *Chemical Infrared Spectroscopy*, Vol I, John Wiley & Sons, 1963
16. J.L. Lauer, in *Fourier Transform Infrared Spectroscopy, Applications to Chemical Systems*, Vol I, J.R. Ferraro and L.J. Basile, Ed., Academic Press, 1978
17. N.J. Harrick, *Internal Reflection Spectroscopy*, John Wiley & Sons, 1967
18. M.P. Fuller and P.R. Griffiths, *Appl. Spectrosc.*, Vol 34, 1978, p 1906
19. P. Kubelka and F. Munk, *Z. Tech. Phys.*, Vol 12, 1931, p 593
20. P. Kubelka, *J. Opt. Soc. Am.*, Vol 38, 1948, p 448
21. D.L. Allara, in *Characterization of Metal and Polymer Surfaces*, Vol II, Academic Press, 1977
22. L.A. Nafie and D.W. Vidrine, in *Fourier Transform Infrared Spectroscopy, Techniques Using Fourier Transform Interferometry*, Vol III, J.R. Ferraro and L.J. Basile, Ed., Academic Press, 1982
23. A.E. Dowrey and C. Marcott, *Appl. Spectrosc.*, Vol 36, 1982, p 414
24. W.W. Wendlandt and H.G. Hecht, *Reflectance Spectroscopy*, Interscience, 1966
25. J.B. Bates, in *Fourier Transform Infrared Spectroscopy, Applications to Chemical Systems*, Vol I, J.R. Ferraro and L.J. Basile, Ed., Academic Press, 1978
26. D.W. Vidrine, in *Fourier Transform Infrared Spectroscopy, Techniques Using Fourier Transform Interferometry*, Vol III, J.R. Ferraro and L.J. Basile, Ed., Academic Press, 1982
27. J.A. Graham, W.M. Grim III, and W.G. Fateley, in *Fourier Transform Infrared Spectroscopy, Applications to Chemical Systems*, Vol IV, J.R. Ferraro and L.J. Basile, Ed., Academic Press, 1985
28. P.R. Griffiths, in *Fourier Transform Infrared Spectroscopy, Applications to Chemical Systems*, Vol I, J.R. Ferraro and L.J. Basile, Ed., Academic Press, 1978
29. P.R. Griffiths, J.A. de Haseth, and L.V. Azarraga, *Anal. Chem.*, Vol 55, 1983, p 1361A
30. G.T. Reedy, S. Bourne, and P.T. Cunningham, *Anal. Chem.*, Vol 51, 1979, p 1535
31. D.W. Vidrine, in *Fourier Transform Infrared Spectroscopy, Applications to Chemical Systems*, Vol II, J.R. Ferraro and L.J. Basile, Ed., Academic Press, 1979
32. K.H. Shafer and P.R. Griffiths, *Anal. Chem.*, Vol 55, 1983, p 1939
33. K. Krishnan, *Polym. Prepr.*, Vol 25 (No. 2), 1984, p 182
34. N.B. Colthup, L.H. Daley, and S.E. Wiberley, *Introduction to Infrared and Raman Spectroscopy*, 2nd ed., Academic Press, 1975
35. M.K. Antoon, L. D'Esposito, and J.L. Koenig, *Appl. Spectrosc.*, Vol 33, 1979, p 351
36. J.K. Kauppinen, D.J. Moffatt, H.H. Mantsch, and D.G. Cameron, *Appl. Spectrosc.*, Vol 35, 1981, p 271
37. C.W. Brown, P.F. Lynch, R.J. Obremski, and D.S. Lavery, *Anal. Chem.*, Vol 54, 1982, p 1472
38. M.K. Antoon, J.H. Koenig, and J.L. Koenig, *Appl. Spectrosc.*, Vol 31, 1977, p 518
39. J. Umemur, H.H. Mantsch, and D.G. Cameron, *J. Colloid Interface Sci.*, Vol 83, 1981, p 558

40. A. Rein and P.A. Wilks, *Am. Lab.*, Oct 1982
41. P.A. Wilks, *Ind. Res. Dev.*, Sept 1982
42. H.H. Mantsch, A. Martin, and D.G. Cameron, *Biochemistry*, Vol 20, 1981, p 3138
43. I. Langmuir, *J. Am. Chem. Soc.*, Vol 39, 1917, p 1848
44. K.B. Blodgett, *Phys. Rev.*, Vol 55, 1939, p 391
45. K.B. Blodgett, *J. Chem. Rev.*, Vol 57, 1953, p 1007
46. R.J. Samuels, *Structured Polymer Properties*, John Wiley & Sons, 1974
47. B. Jasse and J.L. Koenig, *J. Macromol. Sci.-Rev. Macromol. Chem.*, Vol C17 (No. 2), 1979, p 61
48. J.H. Hartshorn, *J. Coatings Technol.*, Vol 54, 1982, p 53
49. M.C. Oborny, "Quantitative Analysis of Hydroxyl and Boron in S Glass-Ceramic by Fourier Transform Infrared Spectroscopy," SAND85-0738, Sandia National Laboratories, Albuquerque, July 1985
50. "Standard Test Method for Interstitial Atomic Oxygen Content of Silicon by Infrared Absorption," F 121, *Annual Book of ASTM Standards*, Vol 10.05, ASTM, Philadelphia, p 240-242
51. F.R.S. Clark and D.J. Moffatt, *Appl. Spectrosc.*, Vol 32, 1978, p 547
52. D.G. Mead and S.R. Lowry, *Appl. Spectrosc.*, Vol 34, 1980, p 167
53. D.G. Mead, *Appl. Spectrosc.*, Vol 34, 1980, p 171
54. D.W. Vidrine, *Anal. Chem.*, Vol 52, 1980, p 92
55. R.E. Kagarise and L.A. Weinberger, "Infrared Spectra of Plastics and Resins," Report 4369, Naval Research Laboratory, Washington, DC, 1954

Raman Spectroscopy

Jeanne E. Pemberton and Anita L. Guy, Department of Chemistry, University of Arizona

General Uses

- Molecular analysis of bulk samples and surface or near-surface species as identified by their characteristic vibrational frequencies
- Low-frequency vibrational information on solids for metal-ligand vibrations and lattice vibrations
- Determination of phase composition of solids

Examples of Applications

- Identification of effects of preparation on glass structure
- Structural analysis of polymers
- Determination of structural disorder in graphites
- Determination of surface structure of metal oxide catalysts
- Identification of corrosion products on metals
- Identification of surface adsorbates on metal electrodes

Samples

- *Form*: Solid, liquid, or gas
- *Size*: Single crystal of material to virtually any size the Raman spectrometer can accommodate

Limitations

- *Sensitivity*: Poor to fair without enhancement
- Raman spectroscopy requires concentrations greater than approximately 1 to 5%
- Analysis of surface or near-surface species difficult but possible
- Sample fluorescence or impurity fluorescence may prohibit Raman characterization

Estimated Analysis Time

- 30 min to 8 h per sample

Capabilities of Related Techniques

- *Infrared spectroscopy and Fourier-transform infrared spectroscopy*: Molecular vibrational identification of materials; lacks sensitivity to surface species; difficult on aqueous systems
- *High-resolution electron energy loss spectroscopy*: Vibrational analysis of surface species in ultrahigh-vacuum environment; extremely sensitive; requires ultrahigh-vacuum setup; low resolution compared to Raman spectroscopy; cannot be used for *in situ* studies

Introduction

Raman spectroscopy is a valuable tool for the characterization of materials due to its extreme sensitivity to the molecular environment of the species of interest. Information on molecular vibrations can provide much structural, orientational, and chemical information that can assist in defining the environment of the molecule of interest to a high degree of specificity. The materials applications for which Raman spectroscopy can be used continue to expand with improvements in requisite instrumentation and methodology.

This article will introduce principles of Raman spectroscopy and the representative materials characterization applications to which Raman spectroscopy has been applied. The section "The Raman Effect" includes a discussion of light-scattering fundamentals and a description of the experimental aspects of the technique. Emphasis has been placed on the different instrument approaches that have been developed for performing Raman analyses on various materials. The applications presented reflect the breadth of materials characterization uses for Raman spectroscopy and highlight the analysis of bulk material and of surface and near-surface species.

The Raman Effect

Fundamentals. Raman spectroscopy is one of many light-scattering phenomena. All these phenomena originate from the principle that the intensity of a beam of light decreases measurably when it passes through a nonabsorbing medium. The energy lost is not significantly degraded to heat. Rather, some of the light energy is scattered into the space surrounding the sample.

The Raman effect is named after C.V. Raman, who, with K.S. Krishnan, first observed this phenomenon in 1928 (Ref 1). It belongs to the class of molecular-scattering phenomena. The molecular-scattering phenomena that must be considered are Rayleigh scattering, Stokes scattering (the normal Raman effect), and anti-Stokes scattering. The nature of this scattered radiation is predicted by quantum theory and classical electromagnetic theory.

The quantum theory of Raman scattering involves consideration of radiation of frequency ν_0 as consisting of photons that have energy $h\nu_0$. Scattering of this radiation oc-

Fig. 1 Energy-level diagram of molecular light-scattering processes

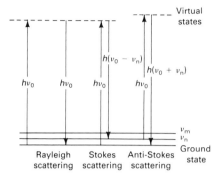

curs when these photons undergo two types of collisions with the molecules of a medium. These collisions are shown as energy-level diagrams in Fig. 1. Elastic collisions are those in which the energy of the scattered photon, $h\nu_s$, is unchanged relative to the initial energy of the incident photon; that is, $h\nu_s = h\nu_0$. This is known as Rayleigh scattering and is the most probable scattering that will occur in a molecular system.

Much less probable is the inelastic collision of a photon with a molecule. In this case, energy is exchanged between the photon and the molecule such that the scattered photon is of higher or lower energy than the incident photon. The energy of the scattered photons in these types of scattering events is $h(\nu_0 \pm \nu_n)$. Because the energy levels of the molecule are discrete and well defined, energy can be lost or gained by the molecule only in quantized or discrete amounts. Therefore, two types of scattered radiation result from these inelastic scattering events.

Stokes radiation, the first type, is observed for molecules that gain a vibrational or rotational quantum of energy from the incident photon. When this occurs, the scattered photon is lower in energy than the incident photon by an amount $h\nu_n$ that equals the amount of energy required to excite a vibration or rotation in the molecule. The energy of the Stokes-scattered photon, $h\nu_S$, is $h(\nu_0 - \nu_n)$. Anti-Stokes radiation, the second type, is observed for molecules that lose a vibrational or rotational quantum of energy to the incident photon. The energy of the anti-Stokes scattered photon, $h\nu_{AS}$, is $h(\nu_0 + \nu_n)$. All these scattering events occur within 10^{-12} to 10^{-13} s.

Because anti-Stokes scattering can occur only for molecules that are in an excited vibrational or rotational state before scattering, the intensity of anti-Stokes radiation is significantly less than that of Stokes radia-

tion at room temperature. Therefore, Raman spectroscopy generally uses Stokes radiation. Overall, however, the total amount of inelastically scattered Stokes and anti-Stokes radiation is small compared to the elastically scattered Rayleigh radiation. This feature of molecular scattering makes the detection of Stokes radiation a serious problem.

When a molecule is in an electromagnetic field, it is distorted by the attraction of the electrons to the positive pole of the electric field and the attraction of the nuclei to the negative pole of the electric field. The extent to which this distortion occurs is a characteristic of the molecule known as its polarizability. The resulting separation of charge produces a momentary induced electric dipole moment that is usually expressed as the dipole moment per unit volume and is known as the polarization, P. Under these circumstances the molecule is considered to be polarized.

The magnitude of polarization of a molecule depends on the magnitude of the electric field, E, and on the characteristics of the molecule describing the ease with which the molecule can be distorted, its polarizability (α). Therefore:

$$P = \alpha E \qquad \text{(Eq 1)}$$

The oscillating electric field in an electromagnetic wave is:

$$E = E_0 \cos(2\pi\nu_0) \qquad \text{(Eq 2)}$$

The induced dipole also oscillates at frequency ν_0. Therefore:

$$P = \alpha E_0 \cos(2\pi\nu_0 t) \qquad \text{(Eq 3)}$$

According to classical electromagnetic theory, such an oscillating dipole moment can act as a source of radiation. Rayleigh scattering arises from radiation that the oscillating dipole emits at its own frequency, ν_0. If the molecule also undergoes some internal motion, such as vibration or rotation, that periodically changes the polarizability, the oscillating dipole will have superimposed on it the vibrational or rotational frequency. This effect is mathematically based on the equation describing the polarizability of the molecule. Polarizability, α, is:

$$\alpha = \alpha_0 + \sum_n \alpha_n \cos(2\pi\nu_n t) \qquad \text{(Eq 4)}$$

where α_0 is the static polarizability of the molecule, which in part produces Rayleigh scattering. The second term in the polarizability expression is a sum of terms having the periodic time dependence of the normal frequencies of the internal motions of the

molecule. Substituting this expression for the polarizability into Eq 3 yields:

$$P = E_0\alpha_0 \cos(2\pi\nu_0 t) + E_0 \sum_n \alpha_n$$
$$\cos(2\pi\nu_0 t)\cos(2\pi\nu_n t) \qquad \text{(Eq 5)}$$

This can be expanded to provide:

$$P = E_0\alpha_0 \cos(2\pi\nu_0 t) +$$
$$\tfrac{1}{2}E_0 \sum_n \alpha_n[\cos 2\pi(\nu_0 - \nu_n)t +$$
$$\cos 2\pi(\nu_0 + \nu_n)t] \qquad \text{(Eq 6)}$$

This equation predicts three components of the scattered radiation. The first term predicts scattering of radiation at the incident frequency, ν_0, or Rayleigh scattering. The second term predicts scattering at frequencies lower than the incident frequency by amounts corresponding to the normal frequencies of the molecule, $(\nu_0 - \nu_n)$. This is Stokes scattering. The third term predicts scattering at frequencies higher than that of the incident frequency by amounts corresponding to the normal frequencies of the molecule, $(\nu_0 + \nu_n)$. This is anti-Stokes scattering.

Polarizability is a tensor that leads to important consequences in the angular dependence and polarization of the scattered radiation. Therefore, the relationship between polarization and the electric field vector is more accurately written in matrix notation:

$$\begin{vmatrix} P_x \\ P_y \\ P_z \end{vmatrix} = \begin{vmatrix} \alpha_{xx} & \alpha_{xy} & \alpha_{xz} \\ \alpha_{yx} & \alpha_{yy} & \alpha_{yz} \\ \alpha_{zx} & \alpha_{zy} & \alpha_{zz} \end{vmatrix} \begin{vmatrix} E_x \\ E_y \\ E_z \end{vmatrix} \qquad \text{(Eq 7)}$$

This relationship also has consequences regarding selection rules in Raman spectroscopy. If a vibrational mode is to be Raman active, the vibration must alter the polarizability of the molecule; that is, α_n must not equal zero. This selection rule is best put into context by contrasting it with the selection rule of another vibrational spectroscopy, infrared spectroscopy (the article "Infrared Spectroscopy" in this Volume supplies additional information on this technique). Infrared active modes of a molecule produce a change in true electric dipole moment existing in the molecule. This fundamental difference between these two vibrational spectroscopies leads to the complementary and sometimes mutually exclusive nature of the vibrational modes measured by infrared and Raman spectroscopies.

In terms of the experimental utility of Raman spectroscopy, the Raman intensity of

Fig. 2 Conventional Raman spectrometer

M, mirror; A, polarization analyzer; C, collection optics; S, polarization scrambler

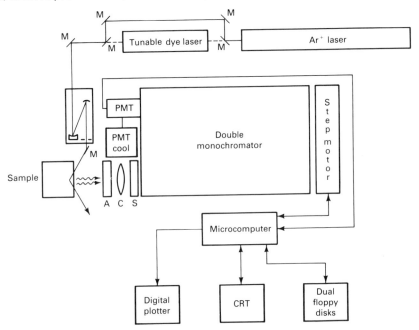

a particular vibrational mode is proportional to the intensity of the incident radiation and proportional to the fourth power of the scattered-light frequency:

$$I_n = \frac{2^3}{3^3 c^4} I_0 (v_0 - v_n)_{i,j}^4 (\alpha_{ij})_n^2 \qquad \text{(Eq 8)}$$

This relationship indicates that the sensitivity of a Raman analysis can be improved by using higher excitation powers or by increasing the energy (frequency) of the excitation. Additional information on Raman intensities is cited in Ref 2 and 3.

Experimental Considerations. The inherent weakness of Raman scattering that produces the poor sensitivity of the technique precluded the widespread use of Raman spectroscopy for materials characterization until recently. The advent of the laser as an intense, monochromatic light source revived interest in use of the Raman effect for the acquisition of molecularly specific information about materials.

Two types of Raman spectrometers are commonly used to analyze materials. A conventional scanning monochromator system is shown in Fig. 2. Figure 3 illustrates a Raman system developed around one of several multichannel detectors. The difference between these Raman spectrometers is the method of obtaining Raman intensity as a function of frequency information.

Lasers are used almost exclusively as excitation sources in Raman spectroscopy.

Laser radiation, possessing intensity, monochromaticity, and collimation, is well suited as a Raman excitation source. The most commonly used lasers for Raman spectroscopy are continuous-wave gas lasers. The most prevalent of these include the argon, krypton, and helium-neon lasers. Broadband tunable dye lasers are also commonly used to extend excitation capabilities further into the red region of the spectrum. Information on the fundamentals of lasers is cited in Ref 4.

Fig. 3 Raman spectrometer with multichannel detector

M, mirror; G, grating; A, polarization analyzer; C, collection optics; S, polarization scrambler

Pre-monochromater

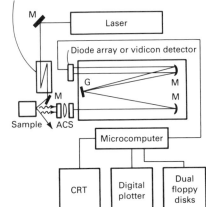

Typical laser powers used in Raman analyses range from several milliwatts to several watts. The laser beam is usually focused on the sample using a series of mirrors and lenses. Focusing of the beam results in luminous power densities of several watts to thousands of watts per square centimeter. For absorbing samples, these power densities can cause significant heating. One means of reducing the extent of heating is to focus the laser beam to a line on the sample using a cylindrical lens. This approach also produces scattered radiation in a lineshape such that the entrance slit of the monochromator can be completely filled with the slit-shaped image.

The output of either type of Raman system is a plot of scattered-light intensity as a function of frequency shift in which the shift is calculated relative to the laser line frequency that is assigned as zero. Presentation of the spectra in this way facilitates comparison with infrared spectra, because both spectra are on equivalent frequency scales.

Raman spectra can be plotted on a recording device in real time in the above-mentioned fashion. However, conventional recording devices are being replaced by microcomputer-based data systems that provide for data storage and subsequent manipulation. A data system is required when using multichannel detection systems.

The heart of any Raman system is the monochromator-detector assembly. Conventional scanning monochromators are usually based on the use of two dispersion stages (a double monochromator) or three dispersion stages (a triple monochromator). Multiple dispersion stages are essential in obtaining Raman spectra to reduce the amount of stray radiation reaching the detector. Figure 4 shows a plot of the intensity ratio of the grating scatter to the Rayleigh scattering as a function of the Raman shift. This plot demonstrates that without multiple dispersion stages, the intensity of stray radiation can overshadow the much less intense Stokes-scattered radiation. In these devices, the dispersion elements are ruled gratings. Commercial scanning systems generally incorporate gratings that are ruled holographically to reduce the effects of optical artifacts in the observed spectra.

Raman spectra are acquired using scanning monochromators by mechanical movement of the dispersion elements such that the single-element detector sequentially detects the frequencies of interest. High-sensitivity photomultiplier tubes (PMTs) cooled to -20 to $-40\,°C$ (-4 to $-40\,°F$) to reduce the dark current are typically used.

An alternative for the acquisition of Raman spectra is use of multichannel detectors in conjunction with a dispersion stage. Vidicon

Fig. 4 Stray light rejection for single, double, and triple monochromators

Source: Ref 5

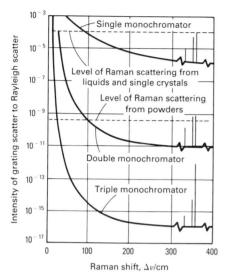

and diode array detectors may be used. To meet the requirements of Raman spectroscopy, these detectors usually incorporate image intensifiers that increase sensitivity. The benefit of the multichannel detector is known as Fellgett's advantage or the multiplex advantage. This signal-to-noise ratio advantage or time advantage relative to the performance

of a single-channel detector is realized, because many frequencies are detected simultaneously. Relative to a single-channel detector, a multichannel detector can increase the signal-to-noise ratio proportional to the square root of the number of individual spectral resolution elements simultaneously monitored by the multichannel detector.

Alternatively, Fellgett's advantage can be viewed as a time-saving benefit proportional to the square root of the number of spectral resolution elements. This is because a signal-to-noise ratio equivalent to that measured with a single-channel detector can be obtained in less time using a multichannel detector, assuming such factors as sensitivity and resolution equal those of a single-channel detector.

A single dispersion stage is the minimum requirement for use of a multichannel detector. Therefore, these detectors can be used with a single monochromator in many applications. However, problems can arise when using a single monochromator for Raman spectroscopy due to the poor stray light rejection capabilities of such a device. This problem has been addressed by the commercial availability of the Triplemate (Ref 5). This device incorporates a modified Czerny-Turner, zero-dispersion double spectrometer with a modified Czerny-Turner spectrograph. The double spectrometer acts as a wavelength-selectable interference filter, because the gratings disperse the radiation in opposite directions. Radiation is further dis-

persed in the final stage, and output at the exit is a line the width of the photosensitive area of the multichannel detector.

Multichannel systems may be used for investigation of kinetic phenomena and for Raman analysis of thermally labile species that would be decomposed by the laser beam in the time required to obtain the spectrum with a conventional system. Therefore, they may be useful in various materials characterization applications.

Sampling. Virtually any solid, liquid, or gas sample can be arranged to allow for acquisition of its Raman spectrum. Raman spectra of solid samples can be acquired in several ways. The solids can be in the form of pure powders in a glass capillary cell. Pure solids can be pressed into pellets or can first be mixed with an inert solid, such as potassium bromide (KBr), then pressed into pellets for characterization. Single crystals of organic or inorganic materials can be mounted on a goniometer head for Raman analysis. The presence of a fixed reference direction inside the crystal necessitates careful attention to the exact orientation of the direction of incidence of the exciting radiation and the direction of observation of the scattered radiation. Birefringence can be a problem in certain single crystals, depending on the symmetry of the species. Additional information on the optical properties of birefringent materials is cited in Ref 6.

A more recent development in the analysis of solid samples is the laser Raman molecular microprobe. This system is also termed the molecular optical laser examiner (MOLE) (Ref 7, 8). This innovative approach to the Raman characterization of materials allows molecular spectra to be obtained from samples on the microscopic level. Using this technique, the molecular components of a sample can be determined through their characteristic vibrational frequencies, and their distribution mapped across the sample. The instrument layout required for this technique is shown in Fig. 5.

The system is based on the single-channel detector/double monochromator arrangement or the multichannel detector/monochromator arrangement described above. A conventional optical microscope with bright- and dark-field illumination is the imaging system. The sample is placed on the microscope stage and can be analyzed in air, liquid, or a transparent medium. Two detectors are used in the system. The first is the PMT or multichannel detector for the acquisition of the actual spectra. The second is a TV detector that permits observation of the microstructure.

The MOLE can be operated in the punctual illumination or global illumination mode

Fig. 5 Laser Raman microprobe

Source: Ref 8

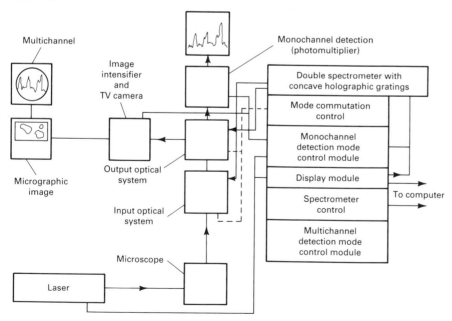

Fig. 6 Optical scheme of MOLE instrument

Source: Ref 8

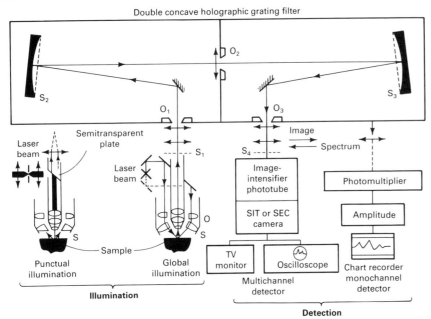

(Fig. 6). Punctual illumination allows recording of the Raman spectrum of one spot on the surface of the sample. This is also known as the spectral mode. Global illumination allows for obtaining the distribution or map of one component across the sample. Operation in this manner is also known as the imaging mode. The primary advantage of the laser Raman microprobe (MOLE) is that it provides molecular information on the microscale in a nondestructive analysis.

Raman spectroscopy may be used to analyze surface species, but its lack of sensitivity complicates these types of analyses. Several approaches are available to overcome the constraints imposed by the inherent weakness of the technique.

Raman spectra of surface species on high-surface-area solids, such as powders, are acquired easily in a glass capillary tube. Alternatively, powders can be pressed into pellets and analyzed. Careful analysis of species on metal surfaces also provides useful information. Raman analyses of these samples are usually performed by reflecting the laser beam off the metal surface and collecting the scattered radiation in the specular direction. Several mechanisms that enhance the intensity of the Raman-scattered radiation at metal surfaces under certain conditions may be used.

Several problems can arise in the Raman analysis of solids or surface species. Many solids frequently exhibit weak fluorescence, due to their inherent fluorescence or the presence of small amounts of fluorescent surface impurities. This fluorescence, even if weak, will be more intense than the scattered radiation and will have noise associated with it. The Raman bands, which are superimposed on the fluorescence background, are often difficult to locate in the noise associated with fluorescence. The background fluorescence for silicas is fairly weak, but that for the alumina and silica-aluminas is considerably more intense (Ref 9). Various fluorescent impurities on solid surfaces have been identified. Hydrocarbons are commonly found on metal oxide surfaces (Ref 10-12). Trace amounts of transition metals have also been identified as sources of background fluorescence on aluminas and zeolites (Ref 13).

Few options are available in the analysis of inherently fluorescent solids. Extensive signal averaging to minimize the effect of the fluorescence noise may allow obtainment of partial Raman spectra. Significantly lowering the excitation energy may reduce the overall intensity of the fluorescence.

Removal of fluorescing impurities from the surface of solids to be analyzed requires treatment of these solids under rigorously controlled conditions. The most common surface impurities encountered are hydrocarbons (Ref 10-12). These can usually be removed by holding the sample several hours at elevated temperature in an oxygen or air atmosphere. Once cleaned, extreme care must be taken to avoid recontamination of sample surfaces through exposure to the ambient environment. Another approach to eliminating or reducing background fluorescence from impurities is preactivation of the sample by exposure to the laser beam for several hours before acquisition of the Raman spectrum (Ref 9).

A second problem frequently encountered in the Raman characterization of solids and surfaces is decomposition of the sample in the laser beam. One method of minimizing or eliminating this problem is to alter the laser conditions under which the sample is analyzed. Decreasing the laser power or changing the excitation frequency to a more suitable energy can help to eliminate the decomposition problem. A second approach is to rotate the sample such that the laser beam does not remain on any one spot on the sample long enough to cause extensive local heating and decomposition.

Sample decomposition is further exacerbated when analyzing samples that are highly absorbing at the excitation frequency used. The most effective method for handling highly absorbing samples is sample rotation (Ref 14). This approach has been frequently used for absorbing solids, such as graphites.

Information Obtainable From Raman Analyses. The type of molecular vibrations that produce Raman scattering must alter the polarizability of the molecule. Therefore, those vibrations that originate in relatively nonpolar bonds with symmetrical charge distributions produce the greatest polarizability changes and thus yield the most intense Raman scattering. Organic functional groups that fit these criteria include such moieties as C=C, C≡C, C≡N, C–N, N=N, C–S, S–S, and S–H.

However, functional group information is not the only type of vibrational information present in a Raman spectrum. Raman spectra of solids and crystals also contain contributions from lattice vibrations at low frequencies. These vibrations are due to the vibration of the molecules around their centers of mass or the restricted translation of molecules relative to each other. Lattice vibrations can provide a wealth of information on crystal forces (Ref 2).

Analysis of Bulk Materials

Metal Oxide Systems. Raman spectroscopy has been used with considerable success in the analysis of metal oxide systems. Metal oxide glasses provide particularly illustrative examples. Raman spectroscopy was initially applied to the investigation of glasses to overcome the problems of infrared analysis of these materials. Metal oxides exhibit strong absorption in the infrared region, making analysis of bulk metal oxides virtually impossible. Therefore, alkali halide pellets, for example, KBr, of the metal oxides usually must be prepared.

One possible consequence of this type of preparation—ion exchange of the metal oxide with the alkali halide—is a serious limitation to the infrared analysis of these materials. The chemical interaction between the metal oxide and the matrix changes the composition of the metal oxide under investigation. However, Raman scattering from metal oxides is usually only of weak to medium intensity. Therefore, bulk metal oxides can be analyzed easily without the chemical complications of infrared analysis.

An early Raman study of the influence of various cations on the bonding in the phosphate skeleton in binary phosphate glasses has been reported (Ref 15). Binary phosphate glasses containing sodium oxide (Na_2O), beryllium oxide (BeO), magnesium oxide (MgO), calcium oxide (CaO), strontium oxide (SrO), barium oxide (BaO), zinc oxide (ZnO), cadmium oxide (CdO), aluminum oxide (Al_2O_3), gallium oxide (Ga_2O_3), lead oxide (PbO), and bismuth oxide (Bi_2O_3) were used at metaphosphate stoichiometry. Several important vibrational bands were observed in the spectra. A band at 700 cm^{-1} was assigned to the symmetrical vibration of the −P−O−P− group. Bands observed from 1155 to 1230 cm^{-1} represent the symmetric and antisymmetric vibrations of the −PO_2 group.

Effects on the frequency and the intensity of these bands were observed upon addition of the above-mentioned cations to these glasses. A quadratic increase in frequency of the −PO_2 feature occurred with an increase in the ionic potential (charge-to-radius ratio) of the cation. However, a linear decrease in intensity of this band was observed with an increase in ionic potential of the cation. These cationic dependencies were rationalized in terms of an increase in the ionic character of the oxygen-phosphorus bonds, P $\cdot\cdot$ O, as a result of the donor-acceptor interaction between oxygen and the metal, and oxygen and phosphorus.

Inclusions in glasses that contain gases associated with various chemical reactions and processing stages of glass formation have been studied (Ref 16). Because these inclusions generally degrade the appearance and mechanical strength of the glass, it is desirable to identify and eliminate their causes. Test samples were prepared for Raman analysis by bubbling carbon dioxide (CO_2) or sulfur dioxide (SO_2) through molten glass ($68SiO_2$-$14NaO_2$-$12BaO$-$6ZnO$). Raman bands associated with CO_2 and SO_2

were monitored, and their appearance correlated with the preparation conditions.

This approach was later expanded to the Raman analysis of glasses by using the Raman microprobe (MOLE) to characterize deposits and gaseous contents of bubbles in the glass (Ref 17). The MOLE technique enabled sampling of only the bubbles in the glass to the exclusion of the bulk glass matrix. In these studies, clear soda-lime-silica glass was prepared by the float glass process. Carbon dioxide and SO_2 gaseous inclusions were identified by their Raman bands at 1389 and 1286 cm^{-1} for CO_2 and 1151 cm^{-1} for SO_2. The ratio of the CO_2 to SO_2 concentrations was quantitatively determined by the relative band intensities to be 11:1. The Raman microprobe analysis further indicated that no nitrogen, oxygen, sulfite, or water vapor was present in the glass bubbles. However, solid deposits in the bubbles showed polymeric sulfur in the $S_\infty + S_8$ structure, as indicated by the Raman bands at 152, 216, and 470 cm^{-1}. Monitoring the 1151 cm^{-1} band of SO_2 revealed that the concentration of SO_2 in these bubbles can be decreased by heating to 450 °C (840 °F). The loss of SO_2 was attributed to the reaction:

$$2Na_2O + 3SO_2 \rightleftharpoons 2Na_2SO_4 + S$$

which also indicates the source of the sulfur deposits. Finally, the presence of sulfur or the absence of SO_2 in the bubbles was concluded to be a function of the cooling to which the glass is subjected during fabrication.

In a recent Raman characterization of SiO_2 glasses, the effect of alkali cations on the spectral response of SiO_2 glasses was monitored as a function of weight percent of lithium, sodium, potassium, rubidium, and cesium cations (Ref 18). High-frequency bands greater than 800 cm^{-1} have been assigned to the local distribution of silicon tetroxide (SiO_4) tetrahedra in these glasses. These features were found to be insensitive to large-scale clustering of alkali metal species. A Raman feature at 440 cm^{-1} is also characteristic of silica glass and indicates that regions of the three-dimensional SiO_4 network remain after introduction of the alkali metal cations. The intensity of the 440 cm^{-1} band was found to depend on the type of alkali metal cation introduced into the glass. This observation is thought to reflect a difference in the long-range distribution of the different cations. The conclusion was that the smaller cations, such as lithium, have a greater tendency to cluster than larger cations.

Another feature of the Raman characterization of glasses is that glasses have spectra

that are usually similar to those of the corresponding molten electrolyte. This led to use of molten salts as models for glass systems. Molten salts can be condensed at temperatures well below T_g, the glass transition temperature, to form glassy salts.

Polymers have traditionally been structurally analyzed using infrared vibrational techniques because of the lack of Raman sensitivity before development and widespread availability of laser excitation sources. Consequently, the identification schemes developed relied exclusively on the absence or presence of characteristic infrared active vibrational modes (Ref 19, 20). Nevertheless, because Raman analysis of polymer systems offers several advantages, many Raman investigations have appeared in the literature.

The weak Raman scattering of water makes the Raman analysis of polymers in aqueous media particularly attractive. Little sample preparation is required to obtain at least a survey spectrum of a polymer, and sample size and thickness present no problem as in infrared spectroscopy. One of the major advantages of Raman spectroscopy is the availability of the entire vibrational spectrum using one instrument. Vibrations that occur at frequencies lower than 50 cm^{-1} can be observed with little difficulty. The main problem that remains in handling polymeric samples involves sample fluorescence. The solution to this problem is similar to that used for other Raman samples and has been discussed above.

Infrared and Raman spectroscopy are complementary techniques. Neither can give all the information that a combination of the two techniques can provide because of differences in selection rules. However, depending on the type of information required, Raman spectroscopy can prove to be better suited for polymer characterization in terms of required sensitivity, simplicity of sampling methods, or vibrational region of interest.

One area of interest in the Raman characterization of polymers is the identification of components that may be present in only 5 to 10% concentrations. Studies of various types of degradation and polymerization have involved observing changes in vibrational features that affect only a small part of the polymer. In such cases, it is advantageous to monitor vibrational bands that are sensitive to the particular functional group that will reflect the change of interest. The dependence of Raman scattering intensity on changes in polarizability of a molecule makes it particularly sensitive to symmetrical vibrations and to vibrations involving larger atoms. In particular, Raman intensities are more sensitive than infrared for the detection of C=C, C≡C, phenyl, C–S, and S–S vibrations.

The structural identification of polymeric species is based on the presence or absence of characteristic vibrational modes. Many identification schemes are based exclusively on infrared active vibrational modes. Infrared bands at 1493, 1587, and 1605 cm^{-1} indicate the presence of phenyl functional groups. However, these are not particularly strong vibrations in the Raman spectrum. A useful feature of the Raman spectrum for polymers containing phenyl groups is the strong ring-breathing mode near 1000 cm^{-1}. In addition, the position of the band in this region indicates the type of ring substitution. A strong, sharp band near 1000 cm^{-1} is characteristic of mono-substituted, meta-disubstituted, and 1,3,5-trisubstituted rings. Substitution in the ortho position can be differentiated from the above by the shift of this band to 1050 cm^{-1}. However, a band in this region is absent for para-substituted compounds. The presence of phenyl groups can also be characterized by a strong aromatic C–H stretch from 3000 to 3100 cm^{-1}.

The strong Raman vibration associated with the C=C symmetric stretch facilitates identification of trans-substituted alkene polymers and investigation of several polymerization reactions. In particular, Raman spectroscopic studies have been used to follow the polymerization of butadiene (Ref 21) and styrene (Ref 22). Raman results indicate that polymerization of butadiene proceeds by several competing mechanisms (Ref 21). Because the polymer products all contain an unsaturated skeletal backbone, the Raman active C=C stretching mode can be conveniently monitored during polymerization due to its enhanced sensitivity. In this study, the trans-1,4-butadiene product was identified by its Raman spectrum.

The thermal polymerization of styrene has also been investigated using Raman spectroscopy (Ref 22). The decrease in the intensity of the C=C stretch at 1632 cm^{-1}, relative to that of an internal standard, was used to obtain kinetic information on the styrene polymerization reaction. Values obtained for the activation energy and percent styrene conversion were found to be in reasonable agreement with results from other methods.

The intensity of the asymmetric C–H stretching vibration has been used to determine quantitatively the percent vinyl chloride in the vinyl chloride/vinylidene chloride copolymer (Ref 23). Calibration curves showed a linear relationship between the ratio of the intensity of the C–H stretch at 2906 cm^{-1} to the scattering reference up to 100% vinyl chloride with an accuracy of

±2%. By comparison, an analysis based on a characteristic infrared absorption at 1205 cm^{-1} showed a correlation between vinyl chloride copolymer content and infrared intensity for concentrations only up to 25%.

Strong Raman vibrations of the S–S and C–S stretching modes in the regions from 400 to 500 cm^{-1} and 600 to 700 cm^{-1} are particularly useful for identification of polysulfides, because these modes are infrared inactive. These vibrational features have been used to investigate the structural changes accompanying vulcanization of cis-1,4-polybutadiene (Ref 24, 25). Several spectral features in these regions were assigned tentatively for vibrations corresponding to disulfide, polysulfide, and five- and six-membered thioalkane and thioalkene structures (Ref 24). The structures found after vulcanization varied with the length of time and temperature of the process (Ref 25). Corresponding information obtained from the C=C region provides information on skeletal chain modifications. The vibrational information from this spectral region suggests the formation of cis-1,4-trans-1,4, vinyl, and conjugated triene groups. The number of terminal mercapto groups in polythioethers has been quantitatively determined using the S–H stretching vibration at 2570 cm^{-1} (Ref 26). The method, based on a comparison of the peak area of the S–H band with that of an internal standard, has been shown to be effective to 0.5% mercapto group content with a precision of ±1%.

The Raman spectrum of aromatic silicones is characterized by a strong band near 500 cm^{-1} that is attributable to the symmetric Si–O–Si mode. The infrared-active asymmetric stretch is a strong, broad absorption from 1000 to 1100 cm^{-1} that overlaps characteristic bands due to vinyl and phenyl groups. Therefore, the determination of small amounts of vinyl and phenyl groups copolymerized in silicone systems is particularly well suited to Raman analysis. In addition, a Raman active C–Si stretch can be observed at 710 cm^{-1}. These Raman vibrational features have been used to investigate helix formation in polydimethylsiloxane (Ref 27). Depolarization measurements were obtained for the methyl C–H stretching mode at 2907 cm^{-1} and the Si–O–Si mode at 491 cm^{-1} as a function of temperature. Estimated values were obtained for the enthalpy of helix formation, the change in entropy, and the lower limit for the fraction of polymers existing in helix conformation.

A method has been devised to determine the percent conversion of polyacrylamide to poly(N-dimethylaminomethylacrylamide) using intensity ratios of the characteristic C=N stretching bands for the reactant at 1112

cm^{-1} and the product at 1212 cm^{-1} (Ref 28). The percent conversion results were in excellent agreement with results obtained using ^{13}C nuclear magnetic resonance (NMR).

Raman spectroscopic methods have been used to investigate formation of phenol-formaldehyde resins (Ref 29). The polymerization reaction is carried out in aqueous media that severely limit applicability of infrared analysis. The intensity of four characteristic Raman bands were measured as a function of time during the early stages of the condensation reaction. Raman results were consistent with results obtained by the analysis of the reaction mixture using paper chromatography. However, the Raman results provide more detailed information on structural changes occurring during the early stages of the reaction.

The extent of crystallinity of polyethylene has been monitored using Raman spectroscopy (Ref 30). Crystallization of polyethylene was found to produce a marked narrowing of the Raman band corresponding to the C=O stretch at 1096 cm^{-1}. This change in bandwidth was correlated with density changes in the polymer and found to be a reliable indicator of the degree of crystallinity.

Graphites. Raman spectroscopy has been used extensively to characterize the extent of surface structural disorder in graphites. More recently, Raman spectroscopy has been developed to investigate intercalated graphites. The analysis of graphites is experimentally complicated by strong absorption of laser radiation, which has been observed to damage the surface significantly. To avoid significant surface decomposition during analysis, low laser powers (20 to 40 mW) on a stationary graphite sample are used. An alternate, more prevalent technique is the use of a rotating sample cell (Ref 14, 31, 32) with which higher incident powers (300 to 400 mW) can be used.

The utility of Raman spectroscopy for graphite characterization derives from the various vibrational behaviors observed for different graphites. Group theory predicts two Raman active modes for smooth single-crystalline graphite. These vibrations are an in-plane mode at 1581 cm^{-1} and a low-frequency plane rigid shear mode at 42 cm^{-1}. Single-crystalline and highly oriented pyrolytic graphite (HOPG) exhibits a single sharp vibrational feature near 1580 cm^{-1} (Ref 33). Less highly ordered graphites, such as activated charcoal, vitreous carbon, and stress-annealed pyrolytic graphite, show additional vibrational modes. A vibrational feature near 1355 cm^{-1} is associated with surface structural defects in the graphite lattice. The relative intensity of the 1355 cm^{-1} band to that of the 1580 cm^{-1} band increases with the degree of surface disorder (Ref 34). The behavior of the 1355 cm^{-1} feature has been used extensively to characterize the effects of annealing (Ref 35), grinding (Ref 36), mechanical polishing (Ref 37), and ion implantation (Ref 38, 39) on the structural integrity of various graphites.

A similar increase in the intensity of the 1355 cm^{-1} band occurs after electrochemical oxidation and reduction of HOPG in 0.05 M sulfuric acid (H_2SO_4) solution (Ref 31). An additional vibrational feature at 1620 cm^{-1} appears after oxidation at 800 °C (1470 °F) (Ref 37), mechanical polishing (Ref 37), and grinding (Ref 36) of various graphites. This feature has been associated with a hexagonal ring stretching mode that has been modified by formation of carbon-oxygen complexes near the graphite surface or crystallite edges (Ref 37).

Raman microprobe analysis has been used with transmission electron microscopy (TEM) to characterize vapor deposition of carbon films on alkali halide cleavages (Ref 40). These results indicate that the graphite films graphitize in five distinct stages characterized by the release of a given structural defect at each stage.

Raman spectroscopy has also been a valuable tool for the analysis of intercalated graphite species. These studies have focused on the vibrational behavior of donor intercalates, such as K$^+$ (Ref 41), Li$^+$ (Ref 42), Rb$^+$ (Ref 43), and Cs$^+$ (Ref 44), and acceptor intercalates, such as ferric chloride ($FeCl_3$) (Ref 45), bromine (Br_2) (Ref 46-48), iodine chloride (ICl) (Ref 48), and iodine bromide (IBr) (Ref 48) of various stage numbers. The stage number refers to the number of carbon layers between any pair of intercalant layers. Therefore, the number of carbon layers between intercalant layers increases with the stage number. Although there is general agreement of the Raman data for stage two and greater species, some controversy remains regarding stage one compounds (Ref 49).

Several models have been proposed to explain the Raman vibrational behavior observed for various intercalated species (Ref 44, 50, 51). The nearest layer model (Ref 44) is based on a perturbation of the pristine graphite modes by the presence of intercalate nearest neighbor layers. This model predicts that pure stage one and stage two donor or acceptor compounds should exhibit a single Raman band in the vicinity of but displaced from that of HOPG, near 1580 cm^{-1}. For stage three and higher compounds, an additional vibration near 1580 cm^{-1} is anticipated due to the presence of graphite layers that do not have intercalates as nearest neigh-

bors. The intensity of the pristine graphite mode at 1580 cm^{-1} is expected to increase with the stage number relative to the displaced mode.

Several intercalate systems have been examined to test the nearest layer model. The Raman behavior of potassium (Ref 41) and rubidium (Ref 43) intercalated HOPG followed that predicted by the model. Further data analysis of the ratio of intensities of the 1581 cm^{-1} band to that of the displaced band as a function of stage number provides valuable information on charge transfer and charge localization in the various layers. The similarity in slope for potassium and rubidium cations indicates that both systems are electrically similar and that charge exchange to the carbon layers is not completely localized (Ref 49). Qualitative spectral agreement has been observed for intercalated $FeCl_3$ (Ref 45), an acceptor intercalate.

Raman spectroscopy has also provided evidence for the intercalation of Br_2, ICl, and IBr as molecular entities (Ref 48). The high-frequency bands were found to be insensitive to the intercalant species. The position of the low-frequency band was found to depend on the nature of the intercalant. These low-frequency bands were assigned to intramolecular modes of the intercalant species. The strong wavelength dependence of the Br_2 intramolecular mode has been interpreted as a resonance-enhancement effect due to an electronic Br_2 excitation (Ref 46).

Analysis of Surfaces

Use of the laser as an intense monochromatic light source exploits the advantages of Raman spectroscopy in the vibrational analysis of surfaces and surface species while surmounting the inherent sensitivity limitations of the technique that would preclude its applicability to surfaces. Moreover, Raman spectroscopy adequately overcomes several limitations of infrared spectroscopy, which has been used extensively over the past several decades to provide vibrational information on surfaces and surface species.

An advantage of Raman spectroscopy is its ready accessibility to the low-frequency region of the spectrum. Vibrational behavior can be characterized as close to the Rayleigh line as 10 cm^{-1} with conventional instrumentation. This frequency region, particularly below 200 cm^{-1}, is not accessible with infrared detectors. Such low-frequency data are important in the complete vibrational analysis of surface species, especially for investigations of the nature of the chemical interaction of a surface species with the underlying surface.

Raman spectroscopy is also valuable in probing surface processes in aqueous environments due to the extreme weakness of the Raman scattering of water. This advantage has made feasible the vibrational characterization of such materials problems in aqueous environments as corrosion. A third problem with infrared analysis of certain surface systems that Raman overcomes is interference from absorption of the radiation by the underlying bulk material. In particular, this advantage has been realized in the study of metal oxide systems. These species are strong infrared absorbers, but only weak to moderate Raman scatters.

Surface Structure of Materials. The study of metal oxide and supported metal oxide catalysts best illustrates application of Raman spectroscopy to analysis of the surface structure of materials. An example of the Raman analysis of metal oxide surface structure is a study on the effect of specific chemical treatments on the surface structure of molybdenum oxide catalysts used for coal hydrosulfurization (Ref 52). Raman surface spectra characteristic of molybdenum disulfide (MoS_2) after sulfidation of the catalyst by H_2/H_2S were observed. After these catalysts were used for coal hydrosulfurization, the Raman spectra were dominated by intense scattering characteristic of carbon. Furthermore, the Raman analysis of used catalysts subjected to regeneration showed that all the original features of the unused catalysts are not recovered in regeneration (Ref 52).

Raman spectroscopy has been used extensively to characterize the surface structure of supported metal oxides. The Raman investigation of chemical species formed during the calcination and activation of tungsten trioxide (WO_3) catalysts supported on silica (SiO_2) and alumina (Al_2O_3) has been documented (Ref 53). These Raman results indicate that crystalline and polymeric forms of WO_3 are present on SiO_2-supported surfaces. However, only polymeric forms of WO_3 are present on γ-Al_2O_3 supports.

Vanadium oxide catalysts supported on γ-Al_2O_3, cerium dioxide (CeO_2), chromium oxide (Cr_2O_3), SiO_2, titanium dioxide (TiO_2), and zirconium dioxide (ZrO_2) have been characterized using Raman spectroscopy (Ref 54). These catalysts are of industrial importance for the oxidation of SO_2, CO, and other hydrocarbons. In this study, the effects of catalyst preparation and catalyst surface coverage on the Raman vibrational behavior were investigated. For low surface coverages of vanadium oxide (1 to 40 wt%) on any support, the Raman spectra were found to be characteristic of a two-dimensional surface vanadate phase. This behavior was found to be independent of

Table 1   Model environments for pyridine vibrational behavior

Model compound	ν_1/cm	Nature of interaction	Ref
Pyr	991	Neat liquid	62
Pyr in $CHCl_3$	998	H-bond	12, 13, 63
Pyr in CH_2Cl_2	992	No interaction	12, 13, 63
Pyr in CCl_4	991	No interaction	12, 13, 63
Pyr in H_2O	1003	H-bond	12, 13, 63–65
$PyrH^+ BF_4^-$	1012	Pyridinium	64, 65
$Pyr{:}ZnCl_2$	1025	Coordinately bound	12, 64, 65
Pyr N-Oxide	1016	Coordinately bound	63
$Pyr{:}GaCl_3$ (benzene solution)	1021	Coordinately bound	12

catalyst preparation. For medium to high surface coverages of vanadium oxide on any support, the wet-impregnated preparation method resulted in a crystalline V_2O_5 surface phase.

Many Raman characterization studies have been performed on the effects of the nature of the support, the presence of other metals, impregnation order, molybdenum oxide loading, pH, and calcination and regeneration conditions on the resulting surface structure of molybdena catalysts (Ref 52, 55-61). Results indicate the presence of MoO_3 or MoO_4^{2-} surface species. An example of these studies is the Raman investigation of molybdena catalyst supported on γ-Al_2O_3 and n-Al_2O_3 (Ref 61). Various catalysts were prepared by impregnation from aqueous molybdate solutions of pH 6 and 11, and the development of the final catalytic moiety was followed using Raman spectroscopy and ultraviolet photoelectron spectroscopy (UPS). Vibrational modes of surface species were assigned on the basis of solution spectra of various isopolymolybdates. Results show that the initial species undergoes ion exchange with surface hydroxides to form MoO_4^{2-} regardless of the solution pH, and depending on the surface coverage of MoO_4^{2-}, the formation of Mo–O–Mo bridging species can occur during subsequent preparation to give a final polymeric surface species.

Surface Species on Nonmetals. One of the most prevalent chemical probes of the surface chemical environment in adsorption studies is pyridine. Its utility as a surface probe stems from the extreme sensitivity of the ring-breathing vibrational modes to chemical environment. Furthermore, its π-electron system, which is responsible for the large Raman scattering cross section for this molecule, makes pyridine useful for Raman studies in terms of detectability. Assignments of the ring-breathing vibrational modes of adsorbed pyridine species are usually made by comparison to a series of model environments of the pyridine molecule. Table 1 lists the accepted model environments for pyridine. The various interactions produce substantial shifts in the peak frequency, ν_1, of the symmetrical ring-breathing vibration of pyridine. In general, the more strongly interacting the lone pair of electrons on the pyridine nitrogen, the larger the shift in ν_1 to higher frequencies.

Similar behavior in the ν_1 ring-breathing mode of pyridine is observed when pyridine adsorbs to various metal oxide and related solid surfaces. Table 2 summarizes the Raman studies performed on pyridine adsorbed on diverse adsorbents. In general, for high coverages of pyridine on any solid adsorbent, the Raman spectrum closely resembles that of liquid pyridine. In these

cases, the interaction of the pyridine with the underlying adsorbent is thought to be weak. Therefore, the pyridine is considered physisorbed.

Two types of strong interaction of pyridine with the underlying adsorbent are possible for low coverages of pyridine on metal oxide and related surfaces. Hydrogen-bonded pyridinium surface species can be formed at Brönsted sites on the surface. These species give rise to the ν_1 pyridine band near 1010 cm^{-1}. Strong chemisorption of the pyridine species can also occur at Lewis acid sites, such as Al^{3+}, on these surfaces. This type of interaction produces the higher frequency ν_1 band near 1020 cm^{-1}.

In the Raman spectroscopy of pyridine on X and Y zeolites, the frequency of the ν_1 symmetric ring-breathing mode can be linearly correlated with the electrostatic potential (charge-to-radius ratio) of the balancing cation within the cation-exchange zeolite (Ref 13, 67, 69, 70). This correlation has been interpreted as indicating pyridine-cation interactions of varying strength in these systems. The strength of interaction of pyridine with the cation is thought to increase with the electrostatic potential of the cation, as indicated by the corresponding shift of ν_1 to higher frequencies.

Another feature of the pyridine surface studies that has important implications is the linear increase in pyridine band intensity with coverage (Ref 71). This observation suggests the utility of Raman spectroscopy as a probe of adsorption isotherms for surface species. Such studies may be significant in understanding catalytic systems that are important in industry.

Raman microprobe characterization of pyridine adsorbed on metal oxide surfaces has been reported. Pyridine adsorbed on Ni-Mo-γ-Al_2O_3 has been studied using the Raman microprobe (MOLE) (Ref 72). The catalyst used was 3 wt% nickel oxide (NiO) and 14 wt% molybdenum trioxide (MoO_3) with γ-Al_2O_3. The ν_1 feature of pyridine at 1014 cm^{-1} was attributed to pyridine chemisorbed at Lewis acid sites. It was determined that the physisorbed pyridine can be removed by heating to 100 °C (212 °F) as monitored by the disappearance of the bands at 991 and 1031 cm^{-1}. The chemisorbed pyridine remained on the surface even after heating to 200 °C (390 °F). The similarity between these results and those for pyridine on Co-Mo-γ-Al_2O_3 (Ref 73) was noted.

Corrosion on Metals. Raman spectroscopy is finding widespread use in the characterization of corrosion processes on metal surfaces. Corrosion can be easily monitored under gas phase or liquid conditions. The principal advantage of using Raman spectroscopy for corrosion is in corrosive aque-

Table 2   Vibrational behavior of adsorbed pyridine

Adsorption environment	ν_1/cm	Nature of interaction	Ref
Pyr	991	Neat liquid	62
Pyr/chromatographic grade silica	1010	Lewis acid site	12, 13, 63
Pyr/Cab-O-Sil HS5 (high coverage)	991	Physisorption	63
Pyr/Cab-O-Sil HS5 (low coverage)	1010	H-bonded	63
Pyr/aerosil	1006	H-bonded	63
Pyr/silica with excess Al^{3+}	1020	Lewis acid site	63
Pyr/porous vycor glass	1006	H-bonded	11
Pyr/γ-Al_2O_3	1019	Lewis acid site	13, 63, 66
Pyr/n-Al_2O_3	1019	Lewis acid site	63
Pyr/chlorided γ-Al_2O_3	1022	Lewis acid site	67, 68
Pyr/chlorided n-Al_2O_3	1022	Lewis acid site	63
Pyr/13% Al_2O_3-silica(a)	1007, 1020	Lewis acid site and H-bonded	66, 68
Pyr/13% Al_2O_3-silica(b)	999	Physisorption	66, 68
Pyr/TiO_2	1016	Lewis acid site	63
Pyr/NH_4^+-mordenite	1004	H-bonded	63
Pyr/magnesium oxide	991	Physisorption	63
Pyr/zeolites (X and Y)	998–1020	Physisorption and Lewis acid site	13, 69, 70

(a) Low-temperature pretreatment. (b) High-temperature pretreatment.

ous environments, such as acidic or alkaline solutions, in which the Raman scattering of the aqueous medium is weak and does not interfere with detection of the metal corrosion products. Most of the corrosion products of interest involve metal oxide species. Due to the relatively weak scattering of metal oxides, Raman spectroscopy was not successfully applied to the *in situ* characterization of corrosion until the use of lasers as excitation sources had become commonplace. However, advances in this materials characterization area since the late 1970s suggest that the Raman investigation of corrosive environments has the potential to provide much molecularly specific information about metal surface corrosion products, such as chemical composition, stoichiometry, and crystallographic phase.

In situ Raman spectroscopy has been used to study the surface oxides formed on common alloys during oxidation at elevated temperatures in air (Ref 74). By comparison of the surface spectra with those of mixed pure oxides, metal oxides, such as ferric oxide (Fe_2O_3), chromic oxide (Cr_2O_3), nickel oxide (NiO), and manganese chromite ($MnCr_2O_4$), were identified.

In a more recent gas-phase corrosion study, the chemical composition of iron oxide films formed on iron by air oxidation at 400 °C (750 °F) for 2 h were identified using Raman spectroscopy (Ref 75). The characteristic lattice vibrations of the different iron oxides enabled differentiation between Fe_2O_3 and iron oxide (Fe_3O_4) films. Further analysis using Ar^+ sputtering and Raman spectroscopy to depth-profile the oxide layer formed revealed the presence of two zones of different oxides. Raman spectra obtained after various sputtering times indicated that the composition of this two-zone layer was 200 nm Fe_2O_3 on 800 nm Fe_3O_4.

Electrochemically based corrosion systems in aqueous environments have been studied using Raman spectroscopy. The Raman characterization of the galvanostatic reduction of different crystallographic forms of FeOOH on weathering steel surfaces has been reported (Ref 76). Atmospheric corrosion of metals has been explained relative to the electrochemical response of the metal in which different regions of the metal act as anode and cathode of the electrochemical cell. This study was motivated by a previous claim that an inner layer of α-FeOOH is formed on weathering steels under atmospheric corrosion conditions. This layer of α-FeOOH presumably resists electrochemical reduction to Fe_3O_4 such that, upon formation of a layer of α-FeOOH of sufficient thickness, further corrosion is inhibited. The results of this study confirmed the previous claims. The Raman intensity of the 300 and 380 cm^{-1} bands of α-FeOOH were monitored in an electrochemical cell under reducing conditions. No change in intensity of these bands was observed, suggesting that no significant reduction of α-FeOOH occurs after 9 h.

Similar studies indicated that Fe$_3$ also is not reduced after 9 h under these conditions. In contrast, γ-FeOOH is reduced to Fe_3O_4, as shown by the disappearance of the band at 258 cm^{-1} and the appearance of the Fe_3O_4 band at 675 cm^{-1}. Furthermore, amorphous FeOOH can also be reduced to Fe_3O_4. Amorphous FeOOH is reduced more easily than γ-FeOOH. The overall conclusions of this study were that three of the four polymorphs of FeOOH present on weathering steels can be reduced to Fe_3O_4. The only form of FeOOH that resists reduction is γ-FeOOH.

Several reports of the Raman characterization of the corrosion of lead surfaces have appeared in the literature. Early research on lead in 0.1 M sulfate solutions showed the presence of surface films of compositions not in complete agreement with the predictions of the Pourbaix (potential-pH) diagram (Ref 77). The Pourbaix diagram does not predict the formation of lead oxide (PbO) under any conditions. However, the recorded spectra indicated the presence of PbO at certain potentials in acid and neutral solutions and at all potentials above the immunity region in basic solutions. Despite the lack of agreement of the Raman spectra with the Pourbaix diagrams, the Raman spectra were in agreement with the potentiodynamic polarization curves for these systems.

A later study of this system helped to resolve the above-mentioned anomalies (Ref 78). The objective of this study was to monitor the surface phases formed on lead during potentiodynamic cycling to obtain information on the cycle life and failure mechanisms in lead-acid batteries. The approach used was to anodize lead foils and acquire Raman spectra of the resulting lead surface films formed under potential control and after removal from the electrochemical cell. The surface spectra were then compared with spectra of the corresponding pure lead oxide for assignment. Lead surfaces anodized at −0.45 V versus a mercury/mercurous sulfate (Hg/Hg$_2$SO$_4$) reference electrode for 12 to 72 h were covered by a film of lead sulfate (PbSO$_4$), as indicated by bands at 436, 450, and 980 cm^{-1}. The surface expected to exist for lead anodized at +1.34 V versus Hg/Hg$_2$SO$_4$ is β-PbO$_2$, according to the Pourbaix diagram. This surface phase for *in situ* or *ex situ* analysis cannot be assigned unequivocally to this oxide in agreement with the previous study. Evidence for damage of the original phase due to laser irradiation was noted, however. Bands were observed that suggested that the β-PbO$_2$ film is converted to PbO during irradiation.

Raman spectroscopy has been used to study the oxidation of silver electrodes in alkaline environments (Ref 79). Earlier studies on this system suggested a two-step oxidation process of silver in which silver oxide (Ag_2O) is formed followed by further oxidation to AgO. It was also known that Ag_2O could be photoelectrochemically oxidized to AgO. However, the mechanism of this process was controversial. Therefore, this study was undertaken to monitor this process *in situ*.

Ex situ Raman analysis of silver electrodes anodized at +0.6 V versus a mercury/mercuric oxide (Hg/HgO) reference electrode showed no distinct vibrational features, although the Pourbaix diagram for this system predicts the formation of Ag_2O. Therefore, the Ag_2O was concluded to be a weak Raman scatterer or decomposed in the laser beam. However, *ex situ* Raman analysis of silver electrodes anodized at +0.8 V showed a strong peak at 430 cm^{-1}, with weaker features at 221 and 480 cm^{-1}. The surface phase formed at this potential was assigned to AgO by comparison with the Raman spectrum obtained on a sample of pure AgO.

When these analyses were performed *in situ* under potential control, the spectrum of AgO was always observed regardless of the applied potential. This observation was explained as evidence for the photoelectrochemical conversion of Ag_2O to AgO. The kinetics of this conversion were followed with Raman spectroscopy in potential step experiments in which the growth of the 430 cm^{-1} AgO band was monitored as a function of time.

Raman spectroscopy has been used to characterize the corrosion of nickel and cobalt in aqueous alkaline media (Ref 80). The metals were anodized in 0.05 M sodium hydroxide (NaOH), and the Raman spectra of the surface phases were acquired. Comparison of the surface phase formed on nickel with various pure oxides of nickel indicated the presence of $Ni_2O_{3.4} \cdot 2H_2O$, with vibrational bands at 477 and 555 cm^{-1}. The surface phase formed during anodization of cobalt was determined to be a mixture of cobaltous oxide (CoO), with Raman bands a 515 and 690 cm^{-1}, and cobalt oxide (Co_3O_4), with bands at 475 and 587 cm^{-1}. These assignments were also confirmed by comparison of the surface spectra with those of the pure cobalt oxides.

Surface-Enhanced Raman Scattering. The sensitivity constraints imposed by the normal Raman-scattering effect severely limits applicability of this technique to the study of species on smooth and low-surface-area surfaces. Therefore, Raman characterization of monolayer amounts of materials on metals was not feasible for some time. A significant advance in this field that prompted surface Raman spectroscopy was the 1973 Raman study of mercurous chloride (Hg_2Cl_2), mercurous bromide (Hg_2Br_2), and mercuric oxide (HgO) on a thin mercury film electrode in an operating electrochemical environment (Ref 81). Pyridine adsorbed at silver and copper electrodes was also studied (Ref 82, 83). Spectra of good quality were presented and attributed to a monolayer of adsorbed pyridine on high-surface-area silver and copper electrodes produced by anodization.

In 1977, it was recognized that the pyridine/silver spectra were anomalously intense (Ref 84, 85). The intensity enhancement of the pyridine surface species was estimated at approximately 10^5 to $10^6 \times$ that which would be expected for an equivalent amount of pyridine in solution. This began the extensive investigation of the phenomenon known appropriately as surface-enhanced Raman scattering (SERS). Since the early efforts in this field, a variety of adsorbates at metal surfaces have been studied. An extensive list has been compiled of atomic and molecular species whose surface vibrational behavior has been characterized using SERS (Ref 86). An in-depth review of the field through 1981 has also been published (Ref 87).

In addition, SERS can be observed in diverse materials environments. Along with the metal/solution studies performed as indicated above, SERS investigations have been readily performed at metal/gas and metal/vacuum interfaces (Ref 87-90) as well as metal/solid interfaces in tunnel junction structures (Ref 87, 91, 92).

The major limitation of SERS as a materials characterization tool is that surface enhancement is not supported by all surfaces. Only a limited number of metals can support surface enhancement. The list of metals for which SERS has been documented remains controversial. Although the three most prevalent SERS metals are silver, copper, and gold (Ref 87), other metals have also been previously demonstrated or claimed to exhibit SERS.

The alkali metals lithium and potassium exhibit SERS in a vacuum environment for adsorbed benzene (Ref 93). Several reports of surface enhancement at platinum in a vacuum, sol (a suspension of metal colloids), and electrochemical environments have appeared (Ref 94-96). A brief report of the SERS of pyridine adsorbed at a cadmium electrode appeared in 1981 (Ref 97). Palladium (Ref 98) and nickel (Ref 99, 100) have been claimed to support SERS in vacuum

environments. Beta-PdH electrodes are capable of surface enhancement of adsorbed pyridine and CO (Ref 101). Several recent reports of surface enhancement on semiconductor surfaces have also appeared. The SERS spectra of pyridine on NiO and TiO_2 surfaces in the gas phase have been reported (Ref 102, 103).

The general use of SERS as a surface characterization tool involves serious limitations. However, the potential for chemical modification of nonenhancing surfaces to allow for surface enhancement is under investigation. Surface-enhanced Raman scattering from pyridine adsorbed at a platinum electrode modified by small amounts of electrochemically deposited silver has been reported (Ref 104).

A similar approach has been used to investigate species adsorbed onto GaAs semiconductor surfaces (Ref 105, 106). Surface-enhanced resonant Raman scattering from $Ru(bipyridine)_3^{2+}$ has been observed on n-GaAs modified with small islands of electrochemically deposited silver (Ref 105). Normal SERS from $Ru(bipyridine)_3^{2+}$ has been documented on a silver-modified p-GaAs[100] electrode (Ref 106), and SERS has been reported from molecules adsorbed on thin gold overlayers on silver island films (Ref 107). These studies suggest that the potential exists in many systems for suitable modification of the surface to exploit the increase in sensitivity provided by SERS.

Relative to the restrictions imposed by the limited metals that can support SERS, it is necessary to determine the surface properties required for surface enhancement (Ref 87, 108). Proposed theoretical contributions to SERS can be classified as electromagnetic and chemical. The surface properties required to activate the chemical contributions fully are subtle and have eluded systematic investigation. The requisite surface properties necessary for electromagnetic effects are better understood and have begun to yield to systematic investigation. The latter include surface roughness and surface dielectric properties. These properties are related, because surface roughness dictates the resulting surface electronic structure.

Electromagnetic enhancement effects are based on the enhanced electric field found at roughness features on metal surfaces having the appropriate dielectric properties. The role of surface roughness has been recognized in electrochemical SERS (Ref 84). However, the anodization procedure used in these systems has not been completely investigated. Research is underway to understand systematically the chemistry, electrochemistry, and resulting surface morphology of the electrochemically generated surface roughness in SERS (Ref 109).

Systematic studies of the functional relationship between the extent of surface enhancement and surface dielectric properties are in their infancy. One approach in electrochemical systems is to alter the surface dielectric properties of an electrode by electrochemically depositing submonolayer and monolayer amounts of a foreign, that is, different metal (Ref 104, 110-113). The ability of that surface to support SERS for an adsorbate can then be correlated with some parameter describing electronic properties of the surface (Ref 113). This approach may yield a level of predictability about whether or not the surface of a new material can support SERS.

Despite the lack of general applicability of SERS, the wealth of information this technique can yield warrants further study. The ease of acquiring Raman spectral data from surface-enhancing systems is unsurpassed due to the remarkable intensities observed. Therefore, SERS should continue to receive consideration as a tool capable of providing molecular vibrational information about surfaces and interfaces. Although SERS will probably never gain acceptance as a general surface analytical tool, it can and should be used with other vibrational surface probes, such as infrared spectroscopy, to help provide a complete molecular picture of a given surface or interface.

Exploration of SERS for the study of relevant materials systems has only begun. Surface-enhanced Raman scattering has been used to study catalytic oxidation of nitric oxide (NO), nitrogen dioxide (NO_2), nitrogen peroxide (N_2O_4), and sulfur dioxide (SO_2) on silver powders. Surface SO_3^{2-} was detected on the surface of silver powder exposed to SO_2 gas in a helium atmosphere. Further, thermal desorption as SO_2 and oxidation to SO_4^{2-} were followed spectroscopically as the temperature was slowly raised to 108 °C (225 °F) in an oxygen-containing atmosphere (Ref 114). In a later study, brief exposure of oxygenated silver powder to NO and NO_2/N_2O_4 gases was found to result in SERS spectra of NO_2^- and NO_3^- (Ref 115).

The electropolymerization of phenol on silver electrodes in the presence and absence of amines has been studied using SERS (Ref 116). Results show the polymerization to be similar to that observed on iron. Surface-enhanced Raman scattering elucidation of the role of amines in polymerization indicates that amines displace phenoxide ions, which are adsorbed flat at the silver surface, and allow formation of thick protective films of the polymer (Ref 116). Further SERS studies on this system involving the role of the surfactant Triton in improving the adhesion characteristics of the polymer on the silver substrate have revealed that Triton is found at the silver/polymer interface and is dispersed throughout the polymer, chemically bonding to the polymer after curing in air (Ref 117).

The interest in SERS has signified the desirability of vibrational information about species at metal surfaces. This has led to the development of the technology for performing surface Raman measurements on metals without enhancement. The availability of sensitive multichannel detectors and appropriate optical components compatible with such systems has enabled obtainment of surface Raman spectra of molecules adsorbed on smooth metal surfaces. The first successful demonstration of surface Raman spectroscopy without enhancement was published in 1982 (Ref 118). High-quality Raman spectra from molecules adsorbed on well-characterized surfaces at low coverage were reported. The unenhanced Raman approach has since been used for the Raman spectroscopic investigation of molecules in tunnel junction structures (Ref 119) and metal/gas environments (Ref 120-122).

REFERENCES

1. C.V. Raman and K.S. Krishnan, *Nature*, Vol 122, 1928, p 501
2. D.A. Long, *Raman Spectroscopy*, McGraw-Hill, 1977
3. M.C. Tobin, *Laser Raman Spectroscopy*, John Wiley & Sons, 1971
4. D.C. O'Shea, W.R. Callen, and W.T. Rhodes, *Introduction to Lasers and Their Applications*, Addison-Wesley, 1977
5. Spex Industries, Metuchen, NJ, 1981
6. E.E. Wahlstrom, *Optical Crystallography*, 4th ed., John Wiley & Sons, 1969
7. M. Delhaye and P. Dhemalincourt, *J. Raman Spectrosc.*, Vol 3, 1975, p 33
8. P. Dhamelincourt, F. Wallart, M. Leclercq, A.T. N'Guyen, and D.O. Landon, *Anal. Chem.*, Vol 51, 1979, p 414A
9. P.J. Hendra and E.J. Loader, *Trans. Faraday Soc.*, Vol 67, 1971, p 828
10. E. Buechler and J. Turkevich, *J. Phys. Chem.*, Vol 76, 1977, p 2325
11. T.A. Egerton, A. Hardin, Y. Kozirovski, and N. Sheppard, *Chem. Commun.*, 1971, p 887
12. R.O. Kagel, *J. Phys. Chem.*, Vol 74, 1970, p 4518
13. T.A. Egerton, A.H. Hardin, Y. Kozirovski, and N. Sheppard, *J. Catal.*, Vol 32, 1974, p 343
14. W. Kiefer and H.J. Bernstein, *Appl. Spectrosc.*, Vol 25, 1971, p 609
15. Y.S. Bobovich, *Opt. Spectrosc.*, Vol 13, 1962, p 274
16. G.J. Rosasco and J.H. Simmons, *Am. Cer. Soc. Bull.*, Vol 53, 1974, p 626
17. G.J. Rosasco and J.H. Simmons, *Am. Cer. Soc. Bull.*, Vol 54, 1975, p 590
18. D.W. Matson and S.K. Sharma, *J. Non-cryst. Solids*, Vol 58, 1983, p 323
19. H.J. Sloane, in *Polymer Characterization: Interdisciplinary Approaches*, C. Craver, Ed., Plenum Press, 1971, p 15-36
20. R.E. Kagarise and L.A. Weinberger, "Infrared Spectra of Plastics and Resins," Report 4369, Naval Research Laboratory, Washington, DC, 26 May 1954
21. J.L. Koenig, *Chem. Technol.*, 1972, p 411
22. B. Chu and G. Fytas, *Macromolecules*, Vol 14, 1981, p 395
23. J.L. Koenig and M. Meeks, *J. Polymer Sci.*, Vol 9, 1971, p 717
24. J.L. Koenig, M.M. Coleman, J.R. Shelton, and P.H. Stramer, *Rubber Chem. Technol.*, Vol 44, 1971, p 71
25. J.R. Shelton, J.L. Koenig and M.M. Coleman, *Rubber Chem. Technol.*, Vol 44, 1971, p 904
26. S. K. Mukherjee, G.D. Guenther, and A.K. Battacharya, *Anal. Chem.*, Vol 50, 1978, p 1591
27. A.J. Hartley and I.W. Sheppard, *J. Polymer Sci.*, Vol 14, 1976, p 64B
28. B.R. Loy, R.W. Chrisman, R.A. Nyquist, and C.L. Putzig, *Appl. Spectrosc.*, Vol 33, 1979, p 174
29. S. Chow and Y.L. Chow, *J. Appl. Polymer Sci.*, Vol 18, 1974, p 735
30. A.J. Melveger, *J. Polymer Sci.*, A2, Vol 10, 1972, p 317
31. A.J. McQuillan and R.E. Hester, *J. Raman Spectrosc.*, Vol 15, 1984, p 17
32. T.P. Mernagh, R.P. Cooney, and R.A. Johnson, *Carbon*, Vol 22, 1984, p 1
33. F. Tunistra and J.L. Koenig, *J. Chem. Phys.*, Vol 53, 1970, p 1126
34. M. Nakamizo, R. Kammerzck, and P.L. Walker, *Carbon*, Vol 12, 1974, p 259
35. M. Nakamizo, *Carbon*, Vol 15, 1977, p 295
36. M. Nakamizo, *Carbon*, Vol 16, 1978, p 281
37. M. Nakamizo and K. Tami, *Carbon*, Vol 22, 1984, p 197
38. B.S. Elman, M.S. Dresselhaus, G. Dresselhaus, E.W. Maby, and H. Mazurek, *Phys. Rev. B.*, Vol 24, 1981, p 1027
39. B.S. Elman, M. Shayegan, M.S. Dresselhaus, H. Mazurek, and G. Dresselhaus, *Phys. Rev. B.*, Vol 25, 1982, p 4142
40. J.M. Rouzand, A. Oberlin, and C. Beny-Bassez, *Thin Solid Films*, Vol 105, 1983, p 75
41. N. Caswell and S.A. Solin, *Bull. Am. Phys. Soc.*, Vol 23, 1978, p 218
42. P.C. Eklund, G. Dresselhaus, M.S. Dresselhaus, and J.E. Fischer, *Phys. Rev. B.*, Vol 21, 1980, p 4705
43. S.A. Solin, *Mater. Sci. Eng.*, Vol 31, 1977, p 153
44. R.J. Nemanich, S.A. Solin, and D. Guerard, *Phys. Rev. B.*, Vol 16, 1977, p 2965
45. N. Caswell and S.A. Solin, *Solid State Commun.*, Vol 27, 1978, p 961
46. P.C. Eklund, N. Kambe, G. Dresselhaus, and M.S. Dresselhaus, *Phys. Rev. B.*, Vol 18, 1978, p 7068
47. A. Erbil, G. Dresselhaus, and M.S. Dresselhaus, *Phys. Rev. B.*, Vol 25, 1982, p 5451
48. J.J. Song, D.D.L. Chung, P.C. Eklund, and M.S. Dresselhaus, *Solid State Commun.*, Vol 20, 1976, p 1111
49. S.A. Solin, *Physica B & C*, Vol 99, 1980, p 443
50. S.Y. Leng, M.S. Dresselhaus, and G. Dresselhaus, *Physica B & C*, Vol 105, 1981, p 375
51. H. Miyazaki, T. Hatana, T. Kusunaki, T. Watanabe, and C. Horie, *Physica B & C*, Vol 105, 1981, p 381
52. J. Medema, C. van Stam, V.H.J. deBear, A.J.A. Konings, and D.C. Konigsberger, *J. Catal.*, Vol 53, 1978, p 385
53. R. Thomas, J.A. Moulijn, and F.R.J. Kerkof, *Recl. Trav. Chim. Pays-Bas.*, Vol 96, 1977, p m134
54. F. Roozeboom and M.C. Mettelmeijer-Hazeleger, *J. Phys. Chem.*, Vol 84, 1980, p 2783
55. B.A. Morrow, Vibrational Spectroscopies for Adsorbed Species, in *ACS Symposium Series No. 137*, A.T. Bell and M.L. Hair, Ed., American Chemical Society, Washington, 1980
56. F.R. Brown, L.E. Makovsky, and K.H. Ree, *J. Catal.*, Vol 50, 1977, p 385
57. C.P. Cheng and G.L. Schrader, *J. Catal.*, Vol 60, 1979, p 276
58. H. Knozinger and H. Jeziorowski, *J. Phys. Chem.*, Vol 82, 1978, p 2002
59. D.S. Znigg, L.E. Makovsky, R.E. Tischer, F.R. Brown, and D.M. Hercules, *J. Phys. Chem.*, Vol 84, 1980, p 2898
60. F.R. Brown, L.E. Makovsky, and K.H. Rhee, *J. Catal.*, Vol 50, 1977, p 162

61. H. Jeziorowski and H. Knozinger, *J. Phys. Chem.*, Vol 83, 1979, p 1166
62. J.K. Wilhurst and H.J. Bernstein, *Can. J. Chem.*, Vol 35, 1957, p 1183
63. P.J. Hendra, J.R. Horder, and E.J. Loader, *J. Chem. Soc. A*, 1971, p 1766
64. R.P. Cooney and T.T. Nguyen, *Aust. J. Chem.*, Vol 29, 1976, p 507
65. R.P. Cooney, T.T. Nguyen, and G.C. Curthoys, *Adv. Catal.*, Vol 24, 1975, p 293
66. P.J. Hendra, I.D.M. Turner, E.J. Loader, and M. Stacey, *J. Phys. Chem.*, Vol 78, 1974, p 300
67. T.A. Egerton and A.H. Hardin, *Catal. Rev. Sci. Eng.*, Vol 11, 1975, p 1
68. P.J. Hendra, A.J. McQuillan, and I.D.M. Turner, *Dechema*, Vol 78, 1975, p 271
69. T.A. Egerton, A.H. Hardin, and N. Sheppard, *Can. J. Chem.*, Vol 54, 1976, p 586
70. A.H. Hardin, M. Klemes, and B.A. Morrow, *J. Catal.*, Vol 62, 1980, p 316
71. R.P. Cooney and N.T. Tam, *Aust. J. Chem.*, Vol 29, 1976, p 507
72. E. Payen, M.C. Dhamelincourt, P. Dhamelincourt, J. Grimblot, and J.P. Bonnelle, *Appl. Spectrosc.*, Vol 36, 1982, p 30
73. C.P. Cheng, and G.L. Schrader, *Spectrosc. Lett.*, Vol 12, 1979, p 857
74. R.L. Farrow, R.E. Benner, A.S. Nagelberg, and P.L. Mattern, *Thin Solid Films*, Vol 73, 1980, p 353
75. J.C. Hamilton, B.E. Mills, and R.E. Benner, *Appl. Phys. Lett.*, Vol 40, 1982, p 499
76. J.T. Keiser, C.W. Brown, and R.H. Heidersbach, *J. Electrochem. Soc.*, Vol 129, 1982, p 2686
77. R. Thibeau, C.W. Brown, G. Goldfarb, and R.H. Heidersbach, *J. Electrochem. Soc.*, Vol 127, 1980, p 37
78. R. Varma, C.A. Melendres, and N.P. Yao, *J. Electrochem. Soc.*, Vol 127, 1980, p 1416
79. R. Kötz and E. Yeager, *J. Electroanal. Chem.*, Vol 111, 1980, p 105
80. C.A. Melendres and S. Xu, *J. Electrochem. Soc.*, Vol 131, 1984, p 2239
81. M. Fleischmann, P.J. Hendra, and A.J. McQuillan, *J. Chem. Soc. Chem. Comm.*, Vol 3, 1973, p 80
82. M. Fleischmann, P.J. Hendra, and A.J. McQuillan, *Chem. Phys. Lett.*, Vol 26, 1974, p 163
83. R.L. Paul, A.J. McQuillan, P.J. Hendra, and M. Fleischmann, *J. Electroanal. Chem.*, Vol 66, 1975, p 248
84. D.L. Jeanmaire and R.P. VanDuyne, *J. Electroanal. Chem.*, Vol 84, 1977, p 1
85. M.G. Albrecht and J.A. Creighton, *J. Am. Chem. Soc.*, Vol 99, 1977, p 5215
86. H. Seki, *J. Electron Spectrosc. Related Phenom.*, Vol 30, 1983, p 287
87. R.K. Chang and T.E. Furtak, Ed., *Surface Enhanced Raman Scattering*, Plenum Press, 1982
88. T.H. Wood and M.V. Klein, *J. Vac. Sci. Technol.*, Vol 16, 1979, p 459
89. J.E. Rowe, C.V. Shank, D.A. Zwemer, and C.A. Murray, *Phys. Rev. Lett.*, Vol 44, 1980, p 1770
90. H. Seki and M.R. Philpott, *J. Chem. Phys.*, Vol 73, 1980, p 5376
91. J.C. Tsang and J.R. Kirtley, Light Scattering in Solids, in *Proceedings of Second Joint USA-USSR Symposium*, J.L. Birman, H.Z. Cummins, and K.K. Rebane, Ed., Plenum Press, 1979, p 499
92. J.C. Tsang and J.R. Kirtley, *Solid State Commun.*, Vol 30, 1979, p 617
93. M. Moskovits and D.P. DiLella, in *Surface Enhanced Raman Scattering*, R.K. Chang and T.E. Furtak, Ed., Plenum Press, 1982, p 243
94. H. Yamada, Y. Yamamoto, and N. Tani, *Chem. Phys. Lett.*, Vol 86, 1982, p 397
95. R.E. Benner, K.U. van Raben, K.C. Lee, J.F. Owen, R.K. Chang, and B.L. Laube, *Chem. Phys. Lett.*, Vol 96, 1983, p 65
96. B.H. Loo, *J. Phys. Chem.*, Vol 87, 1983, p 3003
97. B.H. Loo, *J. Chem. Phys.*, Vol 75, 1981, p 5955
98. B.H. Loo, *J. Electron Spectrosc. Related Phenom.*, Vol 29, 1983, p 407
99. C.C. Chou, C.E. Reed, J.C. Hemminger, and S. Ushioda, *J. Electron Spectrosc. Related Phenom.*, Vol 29, 1983, p 401
100. H. Yamada, N. Tani, and Y. Yamamoto, *J. Electron Spectrosc. Related Phenom.*, Vol 30, 1983, p 13
101. M. Fleischmann, P.R. Graves, J.R. Hill, and J. Robinson, *Chem. Phys. Lett.*, Vol 95, 1983, p 322
102. H. Yamada, N. Tani, and Y. Yamamoto, *J. Electron Spectrosc. Related Phenom.*, Vol 30, 1983, p 13
103. H. Yamada and Y. Yamamoto, *Surf. Sci.*, Vol 134, 1983, p 71
104. J.E. Pemberton, *J. Electroanal. Chem.*, Vol 167, 1984, p 317
105. R.P. Van Duyne and J.P. Haushalter, *J. Phys. Chem.*, Vol 87, 1983, p 2999
106. Y. Mo, H. van Känel, and P. Wachter, *Solid State Commun.*, Vol 52, 1984, p 213
107. C.A. Murray, *J. Electron Spectrosc. Related Phenom.*, Vol 29, 1983, p 371
108. G.C. Schatz, *Acc. Chem. Res.*, Vol 17, 1984, p 370
109. D.D. Tuschel, J.E. Pemberton, and J.E. Cook, *Langmuir*, Vol 2, 1986
110. B. Pettinger and L. Moerl, *J. Electron Spectrosc. Related Phenom.*, Vol 29, 1983, p 383
111. L. Moerl and B. Pettinger, *Solid State Commun.*, Vol 43, 1982, p 315
112. T. Watanabe, N. Yanigaraha, K. Honda, B. Pettinger, and L. Moerl, *Chem. Phys. Lett.*, Vol 96, 1983, p 649
113. A.L. Guy, B. Bergami, and J.E. Pemberton, *Surf. Sci.*, Vol 150, 1985, p 226
114. P.B. Dorain, K.U. Von Raben, R.K. Chang, and B.L. Laube, *Chem. Phys. Lett.*, Vol 84, 1981, p 405
115. K.U. Von Raben, P.B. Dorain, T.T. Chen, and R.K. Chang, *Chem. Phys. Lett.*, Vol 95, 1983, p 269
116. M. Fleischmann, I.R. Hill, G. Mengoli, and M.M. Musiani, *Electrochim. Acta*, Vol 28, 1983, p 1545
117. G. Mengoli, M.M. Musiani, B. Pelli, M. Fleischmann, and I.R. Hill, *Electrochim. Acta*, Vol 28, 1983, p 1733
118. A. Campion, J.K. Brown, and V.M. Grizzle, *Surf. Sci.*, Vol 115, 1982, p L153
119. J.C. Tsang, Ph. Avouris, and J.R. Kirtley, *Chem. Phys. Lett.*, Vol 94, 1983, p 172
120. A. Campion and D.R. Mullins, *Chem. Phys. Lett.*, Vol 94, 1983, p 576
121. V.M. Hallmark and A. Campion, *Chem. Phys. Lett.*, Vol 110, 1984, p 561
122. D.R. Mullins and A. Campion, *Chem. Phys. Lett.*, Vol 110, 1984, p 565

Mass Spectroscopy

Spark Source Mass Spectrometry

D.L. Donohue and J.A. Carter, Oak Ridge National Laboratory

General Uses

- Qualitative and quantitative analysis of inorganic elements
- Measurements of trace impurities in materials

Examples of Applications

- Analysis of impurities in high-purity silicon for semiconductors
- Determination of precious metals in geological ores
- Measurement of toxic elements in natural water samples
- Verification of alloy compositions

Samples

- *Form*: Solid, solid residues from evaporation of liquids
- *Size*: Milligrams to micrograms, depending on impurity levels
- *Preparation*: If conductive, sawing or machining into electrodes. If nonconductive, grinding or mixing with high-purity conducting matrix, such as graphite or silver powder

Limitations

- Not generally used to measure gaseous elements
- Detection limits for most elements at parts per billion levels
- Chemical preparation can introduce significant contamination

Estimated Analysis Time

- Sample preparation requires 1 to 6 h
- Analysis requires 30 min to 1 h
- Data reduction requires 30 min to 1 h

Capabilities of Related Techniques

- *Laser ionization mass spectrometry*: Quicker; less sample preparation, but not as quantitative
- *Inductively coupled plasma atomic emission spectrometry*: Less expensive; can be easily automated for large number of samples per day. Requires dissolution of samples; does not measure all elements equally well

---

Introduction

Spark source mass spectrometry (SSMS) is a useful analytical technique that provides information on the concentration of elements in a sample. It offers nearly complete coverage of the periodic table with high sensitivity. Depending on the sample and the analysis method selected, quantitative measurements can be performed with precision of a few percent.

Spark source mass spectrometry has been successfully applied to a wide range of solid samples, including metals, semiconductors, ceramics, geological and biological materials, and air and water pollution samples. The sample must be conductive or capable of being intimately mixed with a conductive matrix. A high-voltage spark in a vacuum produces positive ions of the sample material that are extracted into a mass spectrometer and separated according to their mass. The spectrum is recorded on a photographic plate or measured using an electronic ion detector. The position of a particular mass spectral signal determines the element and isotope, and the intensity of the signal allows calculation of the concentration.

Basis of the Spark Source Technique

In a typical spark source mass spectrometer (Fig. 1), an ion beam of the substance under investigation is produced in a vacuum by striking a spark between two pieces of material using a pulsed high-frequency potential of 30 kV. During this process, the electrode substance is evaporated and ionized, and the positive ions formed in the spark plasma are accelerated through slits S1 and S2, which limit the ion beam to a small solid angle. Ions are formed in the source with widely varying energies, then transmitted to the electrostatic analyzer (ESA). The ESA is an energy filter of finite bandwidth. Thus, ions with wide energy ranges enter the ESA, and only those within the bandwidth of the analyzer traverse the ESA. At this point, the ion beam has a relatively narrow energy range (± 300 V) and is homogeneous relative to its mass-to-charge ratio. The aperture at S4 permits the narrow energy band of ions to enter the magnetic analyzer. The moving charged particles are deflected through curved paths by the magnetic field. They follow a circular path with radius r given by:

$$r = 144 \left(\frac{1}{B}\right)\left(\frac{m\mathrm{V}}{e}\right) \qquad \text{(Eq 1)}$$

Fig. 1 Typical spark source mass spectrometer

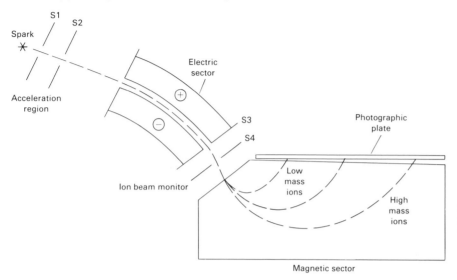

where r is in centimeters, B is the magnetic flux density in tesla, m is the mass of the ion in amu, V is the accelerating voltage in volts, and e is the charge state of the ion. Because the magnetic field and accelerating voltage are held constant, the radius of an individual ion beam depends on the mass-to-charge ratio of the ion. The net effect is that the individual ion images are brought to a focus along a plane, and a line spectrum results. The charged particles, usually as positive ions, impinge on an ion-sensitive photographic plate, which forms the mass spectrum. The masses of the positive ions can be determined from the relative positions of the lines, and the ion concentration as a function of the total ion beam can be obtained from the line blackening or intensity on the photographic plate. Knowledge of the total ion beam is obtained from an electronic monitor receiver that intercepts a fixed fraction of the ion beam just before the magnetic field.

Related Techniques

Laser Ionization Mass Spectrometry. Spark source mass spectrometry relies on the electrical conductivity of the sample electrodes. When the sample is an insulator, it must be dissolved or powdered and mixed with a conductive matrix. A more convenient technique for these sample types is the laser microprobe, which uses a focused high-power laser beam to evaporate a small amount of any material, regardless of its electrical conductivity. In this process, a certain number of ions are formed that can be accelerated into a mass spectrometer. The most common arrangement combines a neodymium-doped yttrium-aluminum-garnet (Nd:YAG) laser focused to a power density of 10^9 W/cm^2 on a location 1 μm in diameter coupled to a time-of-flight mass spectrometer with an electron multiplier detector. Each laser pulse produces a burst of ions that are separated in time according to their mass as they traverse the time-of-flight mass spectrometer. All ions are then detected sequentially to obtain a complete mass spectrum for each laser flash. The 1-μm spot size and limited depth of the laser craters enables elemental mapping and depth profiling.

A disadvantage is that relative sensitivities may vary by a factor of 1000 or more between elements. Because the amount of material ejected per laser shot is variable and unknown, absolute calibration of the signals obtained is difficult. Standards are necessary to obtain quantitative results, but few standards are homogeneous on the micron scale. Nevertheless, the technique is powerful and convenient for semiquantitative or qualitative analyses.

Glow Discharge Ion Source. Another technique uses a gas discharge between a cathode and anode to generate ions that can then be mass analyzed and detected. The sample may be dissolved and a small portion dried inside a cathode, or in the case of bulk analysis of metals, the sample may be appropriately machined to act as the cathode.

The mechanism for ion formation involves striking a discharge in a rare gas, such as argon, at approximately 133 Pa (1 torr) using 300 to 500 V. Ions of the gas are accelerated toward the cathode (negative electrode) and will sputter material from the surface into the discharge. Atoms from the cathode are efficiently ionized by collisions with electrons and Ar$^+$ ions. The atoms may then be extracted for mass analysis.

The ion signals produced by this type of source are extremely stable and long lasting. The absolute sensitivity for certain elements is less than 1 ng, and the mass spectrum is much cleaner than that produced by a radiofrequency (RF) spark. If sample handling problems can be overcome, that is, dissolution or fabrication into a cathode, this method provides higher precision than SSMS.

Laser-induced resonance ionization mass spectrometry uses tunable laser radiation to excite sample atoms resonantly, resulting in ionization. It is a selective technique, because the wavelength used will ionize only the atoms of one element. Thus, large amounts of interfering elements or isotopes may be present, but only the element of interest will be ionized and detected.

This technique has been applied to rare earth and actinide elements, which involve many cases of isotopic overlap between neighboring elements. The samples are usually in solution, and a small portion is dried onto a metal filament. When this filament is heated in a vacuum, atoms of the sample are boiled off and exposed to the laser beam, which is tuned to excite the element of interest. The ions thus formed are accelerated into a mass spectrometer for separation and detection.

Spark Source Mass Spectrometry Instrumentation

A typical SSMS instrument uses a cylindrical electrostatic sector with 31°50′ deflection and 38.1-cm (15-in.) central radius. This filters the ions produced in the spark, allowing only ions of a small band of energies to pass into the magnetic sector. The magnetic sector provides for normal entry of the ions, deflection through approximately 90°, and focusing onto a 25-cm (10-in.) long focal plane. Thus, ions of mass 6 to 240 amu can be detected using a single photographic plate.

Ion Source. Atomization and ion formation are accomplished using an RF high-voltage spark. An oscillator circuit produces RF voltage with a fixed frequency of 500 kHz, which is then pulsed at a repetition rate and duty cycle chosen by the operator. This waveform is applied to the primary of a high-voltage tesla coil transformer having a maximum output of 100 kV peak-to-peak. To this ac signal, a dc component is added (typically +20 to 25 kV) that serves as the ion-acceleration voltage.

This combination of voltages is applied to the two sample electrodes, various shields, and slit plate S1, which has a 2-mm (0.08-in.) hole for extraction of the ions formed by the spark. The ions are accelerated using a potential of +20 to 25 kV to ground between this slit and slit S2. They then pass through a field-free region and are collimated by the final object slit (typically 2 mm long by 0.1 mm wide, or 0.08 by 0.004 in.).

Electric Sector. Ions formed in the RF spark exhibit a wide distribution of kinetic energies. This would cause unacceptable line broadening of the spectrum in a single-stage mass spectrometer. Therefore, spark source instruments have an electrostatic analyzer to filter all ions except those having a narrow range of kinetic energies. This filter consists of two concentric cylindrical surfaces of 38.1-cm (15-in.) central radius and 31°50′ total deflection angle. Positive and negative voltages are applied to the upper and lower plates, respectively. The deflection voltage is usually a fixed fraction of the accelerating voltage, although some fine adjustment of this ratio is possible to maximize ion beam throughput. Exit slit S4 of the electric sector will determine the band pass and therefore the mass spectral resolution. The band pass in most instruments is 600 eV.

Magnetic Sector. The total ion beam monitor at the entrance to the magnetic sector consists of two slits (S4) arranged so that a fixed fraction (approximately ½) of the ion beam is intercepted while the remainder passes through. Such a measurement is necessary for integrating the total amount of ion current allowed to strike the photoplate during one exposure. It is also used in electrical detection to establish the instantaneous total ion beam signal, against which a particular mass peak is measured.

Fig. 2   Relationship between photoplate blackening and ion exposure for spark source mass spectrometry

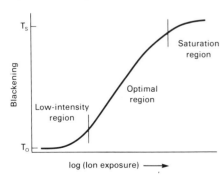

The magnetic sector consists of two coils in series, with a homogeneous field in a gap of 15 mm (0.2 in.) and a maximum field strength of 1.5 T (15 kG). The magnet power supply is regulated to a precision of ±0.001%, and the field strength is controlled with reference to a temperature-stabilized battery reference voltage. For scanning the magnetic field using electrical detection, the voltage on a discharging capacitor is used to provide this reference voltage, resulting in exponentially decreasing magnet current relative to time.

Ion Detection Methods

The photometric technique permits mass-resolved ions with high energy (20 to 25 kV) to strike an emulsion that contains silver halide "grains" similar to those of light-sensitive films. The subsequent release of kinetic energy in the emulsion causes a latent image to form that can be developed using reducing agents (p-methyl-amino phenol) and fixed using sodium thiosulfate. The response characteristics of such an ion detector can be plotted as the blackening or optical density of the developed image as a function of the integrated incident ion current (exposure). An idealized response curve is shown in Fig. 2.

The low-intensity background region, the relatively linear central portion, and the high-intensity or saturation region are of interest in this response curve. At the low end, the ion images become undetectable due to the background fog and granularity of the emulsion. The microscopic variations in this background limit to ±3 to 5% the precision of measurement for any mass spectral image. For lines approaching the detection limit (signal/noise = 2), precision degrades rapidly.

The central region of this response curve approximates linear behavior and provides the best opportunity for measurement. The slope of this linear portion is a measure of latitude of dynamic range. Emulsions exhibiting relatively steep slopes have smaller dynamic ranges and thus limited usefulness.

The high-intensity region of this curve represents saturation of the silver halide grains that, at even higher exposures, may result in solarization or reversal of the image. It is not possible to perform precise measurements in such a region, because small changes in measured optical density may be interpreted as large differences in ion exposure.

The measurement of mass spectral information from photoplates requires a calibration curve to convert the measured optical density into a value related to the ion exposure. The Churchill two-line method is most

often used to generate such a curve. It involves use of an element with two isotopes having a known isotope ratio from 1.2 to 1.5. A series of graduated exposures is made on a photoplate to produce pairs of spectral lines for this element with optical densities ranging from barely detectable to saturated. The lines are then read using a microdensitometer, and the transmittance is converted into optical density. An arbitrary point is selected in the center of the exposure range that enables construction of a calibration curve using the measured density ratios for the two isotopes, whose ion intensity ratio is known. Each ratio measurement represents the slope of the curve at the value of the average optical density.

Subsequent measurements with this emulsion can then be converted into ion intensities using the above calibration curve. It is usually sufficient to fit the curve to a second-order polynomial expression, which is then used for calibration. The reasons mentioned above and the errors this polynomial approximation introduces preclude obtaining precise ion-intensity data over a dynamic range exceeding 3 to 5 for a given exposure. Use of graduated exposures allows coverage of as wide a range as desired, but the error in measurement of the total ion beam exposure quickly predominates.

Other problems with the photoplate include variations in response from one region of the photoplate to another. This becomes important when comparing all spectral lines to a single internal standard line. In addition, variations in response between plates in one batch are a problem when only a few plates per batch are used for calibration. The best compromise is to check the calibration of each plate using few exposures. Furthermore, fogging of the plate near major (matrix) ion lines may be caused by secondary electrons and ions, scattered incident ions, or light quanta (visible, ultraviolet, or x-rays) produced when the ions strike the photoplate.

An advantage of the photoplate detector is its ability to detect simultaneously all mass spectral lines from mass 6 to 240 amu. This effectively covers the periodic table (except for hydrogen and helium) and can be used, by appropriate changes in accelerating voltage, for transuranic elements of mass 240 amu or higher. Another advantage is the high spectral resolution obtained. Electrical detection schemes do not have sufficient resolution to separate most analyte and interference lines that fall at the same nominal mass. Photoplates are capable of mass resolution approaching 10^4, although most SSMS instruments operate at a lower value due to throughput considerations. Finally, the photoplate, an integrating detector, is relatively insensitive to the rapid fluctuations in the ion current produced by the RF spark. Electrical detection methods must handle this rapidly varying signal by using electronic integration or signal averaging.

Electrical detection systems for SSMS instruments have been available for more than a decade. They have been based on use of discrete dynode electron multipliers. The use of imaging detectors based on channel electron multiplier arrays is a new area of research that promises to combine the best features of the photoplate and electron multiplier detectors. Imaging detectors for retrofitting spark source instruments are unavailable.

In standard electrical detection systems, the mass-resolved ions pass through an exit slit in the focal plane and strike the first dynode of the electron multiplier. Subsequent multiplication of the secondary electrons produces results in a current of approximately 10^6 electrons per incident ion. This current, when passed through a high resistance (10^8 to $10^9 \ \Omega$) provides a voltage that can be measured using an electrometer/amplifier. Linearity and dynamic range depend on the exact type of multiplier used, but three orders of magnitude of dynamic range with linearity exceeding 0.5% is typical.

A method for treating this ion current signal involves generating a ratio between it and the total ion beam current as detected by the monitor assembly. Both signals are typically sent through logarithmic amplifiers into a summing amplifier that forms the logarithmic ratio by:

$$\log \text{(ratio)} = \log \text{(individual ion current)}$$
$$- \log \text{(total monitor current)} \quad \text{(Eq 2)}$$

This ratio varies from $-\infty$ (no ion signal) to 0 (for sample matrix ion signals for which ion current approaches total monitor current) and represents an instantaneous measurement of the concentration of the selected species. It may be displayed on an oscillographic recorder while the magnetic field is scanned to produce a mass spectrum. In such a spectrum, however, only approximately 0.1 s is spent on each mass spectral line, and the microhomogeneity of the sample becomes important.

The precision and reproducibility of analysis by log ratio scanning is approximately ± 30 to 50%. It is useful primarily as a semiquantitative survey tool, because the spectrum can be obtained within 5 to 10 min. Precision of approximately ± 3 to 5% is possible when a number of spectra are averaged together using a dedicated computer or multichannel analyzer. Problems can arise,

however, due to poorer resolution and the possible brief extinguishment of the spark during one of the scans.

A second method for treatment of the ion current signal entails integrating the signal for a length of time determined by the integrated total ion beam monitor signal. Switching between a standard and analyte spectral line enables obtaining the highest accuracy and precision (± 2%) for SSMS analysis. This peak-switching technique is more static than the log ratio scanning method. Peak switching can be time consuming for multielement analyses and requires painstaking care in preparing the spectral lines for measurement.

The switching of mass spectral lines for a small range of masses (10 to 20 amu) is most conveniently accomplished by changing the accelerating voltage using a bank of potentiometers. Then, by switching the input for the reference voltage from one potentiometer to another, various spectral lines can be switched quickly and accurately onto the multiplier. This method is limited to small mass ranges, because changing the accelerating voltage introduces a bias into the extraction efficiency for all ions coming from the source. A large mass range would introduce unacceptable bias into the measurement.

A second switching method involves a similar change in the magnetic field setting. Potentiometers are used to set the reference voltage to the magnet power supply, or they can be used in a feedback circuit with a Hall-effect magnetic field probe. This is not as reproducible as electrostatic peak switching due to hysteresis and temperature changes in the magnet and Hall probe. Mass spectral lines can be positioned with an accuracy of ± 0.1 mass unit and must be centered manually on the exit slit before each measurement. However, magnetic switching introduces no bias and can be used over the entire mass range, facilitating multielement analyses.

Mass Spectra

A typical spark source spectrum contains:

- Singly charged ions of atomic species, M^+
- Multiply charged ions, M^{+b}, where $b = 2, 3, 4$, and so on; relative abundance decreases rapidly with the number b; these occur at mass positions m/b
- Molecular ions, for example, M_x^+, $M_xO_y^+$, and so on; these result primarily from the major constituents
- Residual gas species in the ion source, such as O^+, O_2^+, N^+, N_2^+, H_2O^+, and CO_2^+

- Hydrocarbon lines resulting from diffusion pump oil in the ion source; these occur in clusters, usually around $C_nH_m^+$, where $n = 1, 2, 3$, and $m = 2n$
- Photoplate fog associated with strong ion lines usually appears to the higher mass side (due to scattered or sputtered ions), although a halo may extend to 5 mm (0.2 in.) (several mass units) in both directions; this is affected by photoplate emulsion types and processing conditions

Photoplate and electron multiplier detectors will detect all the above constituents, except possibly photoplate fog. Some scattering of ions from the inner parts of the mass spectrometer can appear as noise near a strong ion line when using electrical detection. However, for most samples, the useful information from the first two types outweighs the interference from the last four species.

Interpretation and quantification of data in SSMS must consider the above factors. With the photoplate detector, the mass resolution is sufficiently high that many interference lines can be resolved from the lines of interest—usually not the case with electrical detection. Computer programs can predict the existence of possible interferents from an inspection of the major species in the spectrum (the sample matrix). These programs tend to be time consuming, depending on their degree of sophistication.

For samples that are not normally conductive, the elements to be analyzed affect the selection of a conductive matrix or substrate. Some matrices, such as graphite, can be obtained in highly purified form (99.9999%), but will produce many background lines (at masses $12n$ and $12n + 1$, where $n = 1, 2, 3$, and so on). Other matrices that have been used are high-purity silver, tantalum, copper, and gold as solid rods or compressed powders. These elements are selected for their spectral characteristics and availability in high purity. Multiply charged ions of these four elements rarely fall at integral masses, where they could interfere with other elements. In general, sample homogeneity can be a problem with these metal powder matrices, compared to graphite, due to the larger particle size and malleability.

General Elemental Surveys

In analysis by SSMS, sample preparation depends on the material and the form in which it is available. Cleaning procedures are essential, and chemical etching is used extensively. The purest reagents available are used, and the sample finally washed in deionized water. Porous or cracked samples may be contaminated by reagents not removed in the final washing. Cleaning methods that do not involve chemical reagents, such as turning with a diamond tool and argon-ion bombardment in a glow discharge, are sometimes preferred.

Whenever possible, a pair of electrodes approximately 13 mm (0.5 in.) long with 1.6 mm (0.0625 in.) square cross section are cut from the sample, cleaned, and inserted into the electrode holders in the source. This procedure is suitable for conductors and for semiconductors with resistivities to several megohms per cubic centimeter; special precautions may be required for low-melting-point materials, such as sodium, or for volatile materials, such as chlorine, gallium, bromine, and arsenic. Techniques for handling insulators, small fragments, and powders involve mixing the sample with ultra-pure graphite, silver, or bismuth and pressing the sample into suitable electrodes. Sample-enriched tips are often used.

The smallest samples and solution samples are most conveniently distributed over the tip of an ultra-pure support electrode. Amounts of certain elements as low as 10^{-11} g are detectable. Analysis of inclusions and other local defects may be accomplished using a finely pointed counter electrode. Using single sparks, a resolution of 25 μm has been obtained; multiple sparks would be used to observe a much larger area.

After the usual series of graded exposures of the mass spectrometer is recorded, the first stage in the interpretation is to identify the various masses of the spectrum. The mass scale may be established by identifying two lines in the spectrum, that is, the major constituent line and its doubly charged counterpart, or by reference to a previous plate taken under the same magnetic field conditions.

Microdensitometers used for qualitative and quantitative analysis often have split-screen viewing; therefore, a reference plate system can be devised by making exposures of an organic sample in a conductive matrix, such as silver. An exposure of 2×10^{-8} C results in a recorded mass spectrum that yields a line at nearly every mass from 9 to 298 amu. This reference photoplate exhibits lines of greatest intensity at 12, 16, 107, and 109 amu, which correspond to carbon, oxygen, and the two silver isotopes, respectively. Such a reference plate may be labeled and used to identify rapidly the mass spectra resulting from future samples.

Quantitative Elemental Measurements

Internal Standardization Techniques. The concentrations of elements in a sample are obtained most conveniently and reliably using an internal standard element. This may be an isotope of the matrix element if the concentration of that element is known in the sample, or it may be an element that is added to the sample in a known amount, against which all other elements are measured. The element chosen should ideally be rare to represent a low concentration in the original sample compared to the amount introduced. The internal standard must be readily available in a high degree of purity as the metal or in a compound with other elements not sought in the analyses. It should possess at least two isotopes with a ratio of approximately 100 to cover a large concentration range—important for trace analysis in solids. Erbium is suitable as an internal standard because its six isotopes possess a stepwise range of isotope ratios from 1.22 to 245.

Because all elements do not ionize with the same efficiency in the spark source, variations will arise in the relative ion signals for different elements at the same concentration in the sample. Relative sensitivity factors (RSFs) are used to compensate for this effect by comparing the relative sensitivity of all elements to a selected one, usually the internal standard element.

Relative sensitivity factors are most often obtained by measuring standards for which the concentrations of various elements are known. Use of a simple formula relating the known concentration for a given element to the observed intensity yields the RSF. Attempts to calculate RSFs based on physical properties, such as the melting points and ionization energies of the elements, generally have not been applicable. Spark source mass spectrometry is unique among analytical techniques in that most elements have RSFs approaching 1.0. The range is typically 0.3 to 3. Therefore, even in the absence of standards, use of an RSF of 1.0 will usually provide an adequate semiquantitative result.

Isotope dilution, a beneficial alternative to the internal standard method, is based on the use of separated isotopes of the elements to be determined. The enriched isotopic tracer or "spike" is added to the sample in known quantity, and isotopic equilibrium is established. It is then necessary only to measure the ratio of a sample isotope to the spike isotope to calculate the elemental concentration. This method is generally limited to these elements for which separated isotopes are available, that is, the polynuclidic elements. Mononuclidic elements can be analyzed using this technique only if a radioactive spike isotope is available, with attendant sample-handling problems.

Selection of the proper spike isotope is important for SSMS analysis, which usually involves samples of complex materials. For example, use of ^{87}Sr as the spike would be inadvisable in determining strontium if the sample contains much ^{87}Rb. This also holds for multiply charged species; for example, ^{138}Ba^{+2} interferes with ^{69}Ga. It is helpful to obtain the spectrum of a sample, unspiked, to determine what interferences would be present before the spike isotope can be chosen for a given element.

The optimum amount of spike to add depends on the natural isotopic composition of the sample and on certain instrument factors. The optimum ratio for measurement normally is 1:1, because this eliminates the effect of nonlinearity in the detection system. However, with certain elements, for which the natural isotopic ratio approximates 1, use of a measured spike to sample ratio of 2:3 is desirable. Use of a larger ratio is not recommended with the photoplate detector, but ratios as high as 100 may be precisely measured using the electron multiplier detector.

Isotope dilution is based on attaining isotopic equilibrium between the spike and sample—not always a simple matter, particularly with many solid materials analyzed by SSMS. The sample must be capable of complete dissolution, using only mineral acids, such as hydrofluoric (HF) or nitric (HNO$_3$). Such acids as sulfuric (H$_2$SO$_4$), perchloric (HClO$_4$), and hydrochloric (HCl) produce many mass spectral interferents due to molecular ion species. Free exchange of atoms or molecules must be ensured among the chemical forms of the spike and sample. A prevalent technique is to dry and redissolve the sample-spike mixture several times.

Multielement isotope dilution is suitable for determining more than one element using SSMS. A mixture of separated isotopes of the desired elements is prepared to match the expected concentration of elements in the sample. Multielement isotope dilution generally requires studied selection of the isotopes to be used to ensure chemical and mass spectral compatibility. A mixture of selected isotopes is prepared using high-purity acids, such as HNO$_3$ or HF, avoiding those reagents that produce numerous background interferences in the spectrum.

This mixed spike solution must be calibrated by analyzing it alone (for the blank level of each element present) and then mixed with known amounts of the analyte elements. This allows calculation, by reverse isotope dilution, of the amount of each spike isotope present. Once it has been well calibrated, this solution can be conveniently used by adding a single aliquot to the sample, followed by equilibration and SSMS analysis. The spike isotope concentrations should match the composition of the sample closely or problems will arise due to the limited dynamic range of some detectors, for which the optimum range of measured ratios is 0.3 to 3.

Dry Spike Isotope Dilution. Normal isotope dilution requires that the sample be in solution to achieve complete isotopic equilibrium. Because this is not always possible with refractory materials and certain metals and alloys, a method has been developed in which isotopic spikes are mixed with the sample in dry powder form, usually with a conductive binder, such as graphite or silver powder. Because this mixing will not achieve isotopic equilibrium, this technique is not true isotope dilution. However, the spark ion source produces a plasma in which atomization and homogenization can occur on a microscopic level. Therefore, if the sample and spikes (in powdered form) are intimately mixed, the resulting precision of analysis may approach that of true isotope dilution.

For those samples for which standards exist, dry mixing can achieve precision and accuracy of ±5 to 10%. Sample types to which this technique has been applied are coal, fly ash, precipitator and bottom ash, and geological materials.

Applications

Example 1: Stainless Steel. Spark source mass spectrometry can be used to determine the concentrations of chromium, nickel, and manganese in a stainless steel sample.

Sample Preparation. The as-received material is roughly cube shaped, 25 mm (1 in.) on a side. A 1.6-mm (0.0625-in.) slice is sectioned from one side using a high-speed silicon carbide saw. Further shaping using this saw produces two electrodes 13 mm (0.5 in.) long with 1.6 mm (0.0625 in.) square cross section. These are cleaned by immersion in hot dilute HNO_3 for 5 min, followed by profuse rinsing with distilled water. After a final rinse in ethanol, the electrodes are dried in a 100 °C (212 °F) oven.

The electrodes are mounted in tantalum holders, placed in the ion source compartment of the spark source mass spectrometer, and aligned visually so that two opposing flat surfaces will be sparked. This will reduce the amount of change in sparking geometry caused by erosion of the electrode surface. A 5-min prespark is used to clean the electrode surfaces.

Data Acquisition: Internal Standard. A series of graduated exposures is taken using a photographic plate detector. The longest exposure, 1.0 nC, is a measure of the total accumulated charge as detected by the ion

beam monitor collector. Successive exposures are taken side by side on the photographic plate in the sequence 0.3, 0.1, 0.03, 0.01, 0.003, 0.001, and 0.0003 nC. If available, an appropriate standard is prepared identically and sparked in the same sequence of exposures on the remainder of the photographic plate (each plate holds a maximum of 16 exposures). The plate is then removed from the mass spectrometer and developed normally.

Data Reduction. Calculation of the concentrations of chromium, manganese, and nickel in this sample requires:

- The relative intensity (blackening of the photographic plate) of the mass spectral lines for the three elements and that of iron, which is the matrix, or most abundant, element
- The natural isotopic composition of the four elements to correct the measured intensity of any given isotope to that of the total element; this information is tabulated in chemical handbooks
- An RSF for each element relative to iron. These are determined using standards of known composition. Laboratories performing SSMS would have a table of RSFs determined from many standards over a long period. Due to the unique nature of the spark source, these RSFs do not deviate far from unity and can generally be used regardless of the sample matrix
- A photographic plate calibration curve obtained using an element of known isotopic pattern; this is initially obtained for a given batch of photographic plates and is assumed to hold true for all plates in that batch if emulsion development conditions are held constant

The elements and isotopes of interest are shown in Table 1. Isotopes are unsuitable for measurement where they overlap between two elements. This occurs at masses 54 (iron and chromium) and 58 (iron and nickel). The

intensity of all other isotopes is then measured for all exposures using a previously obtained plate calibration curve. The raw data appear in Table 2. The previously measured RSFs for these three elements relative to iron are:

Element	RSF
Chromium	0.5
Manganese	1.5
Nickel	2.1

The concentrations of these elements can now be calculated relative to the internal standard, iron. Absolute concentrations can be obtained by assuming that iron, chromium, manganese, and nickel are the major elements present; that is, the sum of their concentrations equals 100%. This assumption is reasonable if no other elements are present at concentrations exceeding 1%, which can be verified by survey analyzing the photographic plate, obtaining estimates of the total concentration of all other elements.

Table 1 Natural isotopic composition of iron, chromium, nickel, and manganese for Example 1

Element	Isotope	Natural abundance, at.%
Iron	54	5.8
	56	91.7
	57	2.2
	58	0.3
Chromium	50	4.3
	52	83.8
	53	9.6
	54	2.3
Manganese	55	100
Nickel	58	67.8
	60	26.2
	61	1.2
	62	3.6
	64	1.2

Table 2 Measured intensity of iron, chromium, nickel, and manganese isotopes for Example 1

Isotope	Exposure, nC(a)							
	1	0.3	0.1	0.03	0.01	0.003	0.001	0.0003
^{56}Fe	S	S	S	S	S	S	61	18
^{57}Fe	S	S	142	45	14	4	ND	ND
^{50}Cr	S	129	43	13	ND	ND	ND	ND
^{52}Cr	S	S	S	S	85	24	8	ND
^{53}Cr	S	S	97	29	9	ND	ND	ND
^{55}Mn	S	S	S	S	72	21	8	ND
^{60}Ni	S	S	S	S	54	16	5	ND
^{61}Ni	S	75	24	9	ND	ND	ND	ND
^{62}Ni	S	S	75	23	8	ND	ND	ND
^{64}Ni	S	76	25	8	ND	ND	ND	ND

(a) S, saturated; ND, not detected

Concentration of an element for any isotope or exposure relative to the internal standard element (iron) is calculated using:

$$\text{Relative conc M} = \left(\frac{\text{Intensity } {}^{a}\text{M}}{\text{Intensity } {}^{b}\text{Fe}}\right)$$

$$\times \left(\frac{\text{Isotopic abundance } {}^{b}\text{Fe}}{\text{Isotopic abundance } {}^{a}\text{M}}\right)$$

$$\times \left(\frac{1}{\text{RSF(M)}}\right) \qquad \text{(Eq 3)}$$

where M is the element of interest, a is the particular isotope measured, b is the corresponding isotope of iron, and RSF(M) is the relative sensitivity of element M versus iron (assumed to be the same for all isotopes of M).

Using Eq 3, the data in Table 2 reduce as shown in Table 3. An example of this calculation for ^{50}Cr in the 0.1 nC exposure compared to ^{57}Fe is:

$$\text{Relative conc Cr} = \left(\frac{43}{142}\right)\left(\frac{0.022}{0.043}\right)\left(\frac{1}{0.5}\right)$$

$$= 0.310$$

The results of averaging the data in Table 3 and calculating absolute concentrations are summarized in Table 4. An easier, faster alternative to the above analysis involves use of electrical detection rather than a photographic plate and implements the external standard method. Instead of comparing all elements to an internal standard, such as iron, direct comparisons are made between a sample electrode pair and a suitable standard pair. The basis for comparison is the integrated ion intensity for a given isotope relative to the total ion beam as measured at the monitor collector. This method eliminates the need for RSFs, with their associated uncertainty.

Data Acquisition. A set of sample electrodes is prepared along with an identical set of electrodes made from a well-characterized standard, such as a National Bureau of Standards Standard Reference Material (NBS SRM). The two sets of electrodes may be mounted sequentially in the ion source, requiring a vacuum pump-out cycle each time, but a better method is to mount them simultaneously in the ion source, using a special dual electrode holder. This allows each set to be brought into sparking position within 1 min, permitting rapid sample and standard measurements and minimizing changes in spark, vacuum, or mass spectrometer conditions.

Table 3 Relative concentrations of chromium, nickel, and manganese compared to iron for Example 1

Isotope	Exposure, nC				
	0.1	0.03	0.01	0.003	0.001
^{50}Cr	0.310	0.296	...	...	...
^{52}Cr	...	...	0.319	0.315	0.287
^{53}Cr	0.313	0.295	0.295	...	...
^{55}Mn	...	...	0.075	0.077	0.080
^{60}Ni	...	...	0.154	0.160	0.137
^{61}Ni	0.148	0.175	...	...	...
^{62}Ni	0.154	0.149	0.166	...	...
^{64}Ni	0.154	0.155	...	...	...

Table 4 Summary of results for Example 1

Element	Concentration relative to iron	Absolute concentration, at.%
Iron	1.00	65.1
Chromium	0.304 ± 0.01	19.8
Manganese	0.077 ± 0.003	5.0
Nickel	0.155 ± 0.01	10.1

Data are acquired by setting the magnetic field and accelerating voltage of the mass spectrometer to focus one isotope of interest onto the detector, which is usually an electron multiplier operated at a gain of 10^3 to 10^4. The signal is then integrated during the time it takes the total ion beam monitor to register a fixed amount of charge. This is similar to taking one exposure on a photographic plate, but avoids the developing and reducing of data from a plate. The integrated ion signal for a sample isotope is measured several times using a digital voltmeter and recorded. The electrodes are then moved to bring the standard set into sparking position. A similar exposure is taken for the same isotope in the standard. Numerous sets of such data can be acquired quickly. The raw results are shown in Table 5 for the elements chromium, manganese, and nickel using a 0.01-nC exposure and an NBS SRM-442 stainless steel standard. Five integrations are taken for each isotope for the sample and standard. The total time required is 10 min.

Concentrations of the elements are calculated using:

$$\text{Conc M}_{\text{sam}} = \left(\frac{\text{Conc M}_{\text{std}}}{\text{Isotopic abundance } {}^{a}\text{M}}\right)$$

$$\times \left(\frac{\text{Intensity } {}^{a}\text{M}_{\text{sam}}}{\text{Intensity } {}^{a}\text{M}_{\text{std}}}\right) \qquad \text{(Eq 4)}$$

where M_{sam} is the concentration of the element in the sample, M_{std} is the standard, and a is the isotope measured. The data in Table 5 were reduced to those shown in Table 6 by

averaging the five integrations for each element in the sample and standard before applying Eq 4. An example of this calculation for ^{55}Mn is:

$$\text{Conc Mn} = \left(\frac{2.88\%}{1.00}\right)\left(\frac{0.240}{0.145}\right)$$

$$= 4.76\%$$

The final result is given in the same units as the known concentration in the standard.

Example 2: Coal Fly Ash. Spark source mass spectrometry can be used to determine the concentrations of copper and lead.

Sample Preparation. This analysis begins with the preparation of a spiked conductive matrix, which is a material that contains precisely known amounts of isotopically enriched elements. When intimately mixed with the fly ash powder and pressed into electrodes, it forms a conductive matrix that enables measurement of the elements present in the sample by comparison with the separated isotope standards. The method is similar to classical isotope dilution, but does not require dissolving the sample, which in this case is not feasible.

Table 5 Results for chromium, nickel, and manganese for Example 1

Isotope	Integrated signal, V	
	Sample	NBS SRM-442
^{52}Cr	0.237	0.228
	0.241	0.230
	0.230	0.222
	0.238	0.221
	0.245	0.232
Avg	0.238 ± 0.006	0.226 ± 0.005
^{55}Mn	0.241	0.147
	0.236	0.142
	0.238	0.142
	0.240	0.150
	0.245	0.145
Avg	0.240 ± 0.003	0.145 ± 0.003
^{60}Ni	0.047	0.182
	0.049	0.183
	0.050	0.187
	0.045	0.175
	0.047	0.182
Avg	0.048 ± 0.002	0.182 ± 0.004

Table 6 Calculated concentrations of chromium, manganese, and nickel for Example 1

Element	Concentration, wt%	
	NBS SRM-442	Sample
Chromium	16.1	20.2
Manganese	2.88	4.76
Nickel	9.9	9.89

Preparation of an isotopically spiked matrix material begins with super-pure silver powder, certified by the manufacturer to be 99.9999% pure. To this is added, from a solution, the separated isotope spikes. For copper and lead, the enrichments are:

Isotope	Enrichment, %
^{65}Cu	99.70
^{204}Pb	99.73

Determining the quantity of each isotope to add requires some knowledge of the sample composition. If fly ash has a copper concentration of 50 to 250 µg/g and a lead concentration of 50 to 150 µg/g, a reasonable level for spiking each element would be 100 µg/g in the silver powder, assuming the silver powder will be mixed 1:1 with the fly ash.

After the separated isotopes are dried onto the silver powder, the mixture is completely homogenized in a ball mill. This mixture must first be standardized to ensure that the concentrations of ^{65}Cu and ^{204}Pb are known. A weighed amount of NBS SRM-1633a (coal fly ash) containing 118 µg/g copper and 72.4 µg/g lead is mixed with the same weight of spiked silver powder. Following further homogenization, two spark source electrodes are formed by pressing the powder in a special die under hydraulic pressure. The resulting electrodes are sparked, and a photographic plate is exposed in a set of graduated exposures (1.0, 0.3, 0.1, 0.03, 0.01, 0.003, 0.001, and 0.0003 nC). The ^{65}Cu and ^{204}Pb concentrations in the spiked silver are calculated analogously to that described in the section "Data Reduction" in this article. Sufficient duplicate standardization analyses are performed until the concentrations of ^{65}Cu and ^{204}Pb in the spiked silver are well known and found to be:

$$^{65}\text{Cu} = 94 \pm 1 \ \mu\text{g/g}$$

$$^{204}\text{Pb} = 110 \pm 2 \ \mu\text{g/g}$$

Routine analyses can then be performed on unknown samples by mixing them 1:1 with fresh spiked silver, followed by taking a graduated set of exposures on a photographic plate.

Data reduction resembles isotope dilution in that the data consist of one isotope ratio for each element measured. The amount of spike isotope added is known, and the concentration of the unknown can be found by comparing the intensity of the spike isotope to a natural isotope of the element. Therefore, RSFs are not required. For example, using the data in Table 7, the intensity of ^{63}Cu represents the amount of normal copper present in the sample, but the ^{65}Cu

signal is the sum of sample and spike contributions. Element concentrations are calculated using:

$$\text{Conc } M_{sam} = \left(\frac{\text{Conc } ^bM_{spike}}{\text{Isotopic abundance } ^bM_{sam}} \right)$$
$$\times \left(\frac{R_{spike} - R_m}{R_m - R_{sam}} \right) \quad \text{(Eq 5)}$$

where M_{sam} is the element concentration in the sample, $^bM_{spike}$ is the concentration of the spike isotope b, $^bM_{sam}$ is the isotopic abundance of isotope b in the sample, R_{spike} and R_{sam} are the known isotope ratios for the spike and sample (defined as $^aM/^bM$), and R_m is the measured isotope ratio of the mixture (after spiking).

Using Eq 5 and data from Table 7, calculation of the copper concentration is:

$$\text{Conc Cu(sample)} = \left(\frac{94 \ \mu\text{g/g}}{0.309} \right)$$
$$\times \left(\frac{(0.0030/0.9970) - (141/250)}{(141/250) - (0.691/0.309)} \right)$$
$$= 102 \ \mu\text{g/g}$$

$$\text{Conc Pb(sample)} = \left(\frac{110 \ \mu\text{g/g}}{0.014} \right)$$
$$\times \left(\frac{(0.0015/0.9973) - (57/225)}{(57/225) - (0.517/0.014)} \right)$$
$$= 54 \ \mu\text{g/g}$$

Example 3: Ground Water. Spark source mass spectrometry can be used to detect and measure toxic trace elements in natural ground water.

Sample Preparation. The as-received sample is 100 mL of natural ground water with no trace of organic matter. After filtering to remove particulate matter, an internal standard element (erbium of normal isotopic composition) is added in a known amount to equal 1.0 µg/mL. The sample is then evaporated to near dryness in a teflon beaker, and the remaining few drops are dried onto the tips of two 3.2-mm (0.125-in.) diam high-purity graphite rods.

Data Acquisition. The graphite rods are mounted in the ion source chamber of the spark source mass spectrometer and sparked tip-to-tip to produce a set of graduated exposures on a photographic plate. The exposures taken are 10, 3, 1, 0.3, 0.1, 0.03, 0.01, and 0.003 nC. The plate is developed normally.

Data Reduction. A visual scan of the photographic plate at the longest exposure

Table 7 Raw intensities of copper and lead isotopes for Example 2

Isotope	Measured intensity	Natural abundance (atom fraction)	Spike abundance (atom fraction)
^{63}Cu	141	0.691	0.0030
^{65}Cu	250	0.309	0.9970
^{204}Pb	225	0.014	0.9973
^{208}Pb	57	0.517	0.0015

(10 nC) reveals the presence of the toxic elements chromium, arsenic, selenium, cadmium, and antimony. The intensities for selected isotopes of these elements and the erbium internal standard are then read out; results are shown in Table 8 with their natural isotopic abundances. The RSFs for these elements relative to erbium have been previously determined using known chemical standards:

Element	RSF
Chromium	0.5
Arsenic	2.0
Selenium	0.7
Cadmium	1.2
Antimony	0.9

Elemental concentrations may be calculated using:

$$\text{Conc } M = \text{Conc Er} \left(\frac{\text{Intensity } ^bM}{\text{Intensity } ^aEr} \right)$$
$$\times \left(\frac{\text{Isotopic abundance } ^aEr}{\text{Isotopic abundance } ^bM} \right)$$
$$\times \left(\frac{1}{\text{RSF}(M)} \right) \left(\frac{\text{Atomic wt (M)}}{\text{Atomic wt (Er)}} \right) \quad \text{(Eq 6)}$$

where ^bM is the measured isotope of the element, ^aEr is the measured isotope of the internal standard, erbium, and RSF(M) is the relative sensitivity factor for element M in relation to erbium; the final term corrects the concentration from atomic weight units. The commonly used isotopic abundance of the ^{166}Er isotope is 0.334.

For example, for ^{53}Cr using the 0.003-nC exposure, Eq 6 becomes:

$$\text{Conc Cr (µg/mL)} = 1.0 \ \mu\text{g/mL}$$
$$\times \left(\frac{130}{4} \right) \left(\frac{0.334}{0.838} \right) \left(\frac{1}{0.5} \right) \left(\frac{52}{167} \right)$$
$$= 8.1 \ \mu\text{g/mL}$$

Table 8 Measured intensities for isotopes of erbium, chromium, arsenic, selenium, cadmium, and antimony for Example 3

Isotope	Natural abundance (atom fraction)	Exposure, nC(a)							
		10	3	1	0.3	0.1	0.03	0.01	0.003
^{162}Er	0.001	52	17	6	ND	ND	ND	ND	ND
^{164}Er	0.016	S	S	80	25	8	ND	ND	ND
^{166}Er	0.334	S	S	S	S	155	50	17	4
^{52}Cr	0.838	S	S	S	S	S	S	S	130
^{75}As	1.00	S	S	195	62	17	ND	ND	ND
^{80}Se	0.498	S	S	S	S	S	62	23	5
^{114}Cd	0.288	84	26	8	ND	ND	ND	ND	ND
^{121}Sb	0.673	S	S	S	S	84	22	7	ND

(a) S, saturated; ND, not detected

Table 9 Calculated concentrations (μg/mL) of chromium, arsenic, selenium, cadmium, and antimony for Example 3

Element	Exposure, nC							
	10	3	1	0.3	0.1	0.03	0.01	0.003
Chromium	...	...	...	...	...	...	...	8.1
Arsenic	...	...	0.0073	0.0089	0.0076	...	...	...
	...	...	0.0088	...	0.0082	...	...	...
Selenium	...	...	...	...	...	0.56	0.61	0.57
Cadmium	0.0031	0.0030	0.0026	...	...	...	...	...
	...	...	0.0031	...	...	...	...	...
Antimony	...	...	...	...	0.24	0.21	0.20	...
	...	...	...	...	0.26	...	...	...

The remaining elements are calculated similarly to produce the results in Tables 9 and 10.

Example 4: Impurities in Uranium Dioxide. Spark source mass spectrometry can be used to determine concentrations of boron, iron, calcium, zirconium, and ^{239}plutonium impurities in a refractory oxide, UO_2.

Sample Preparation. The as-received sample is a sintered powder of $^{233}UO_2$ that is highly radioactive; all handling must take place in a radiation containment glovebox. One gram of $^{233}UO_2$ emits 3×10^8 α-particles per second, which can be effectively stopped by rubber gloves, plexiglass, or even paper. The greatest danger is from accidental ingestion or inhalation.

This sample requires two analyses. First, the iron will be determined by isotope dilution to obtain a precise value. The remaining trace elements in the sample can then be measured relative to the iron in a survey analysis. The isotope dilution measurement requires complete dissolution of the sample in high-purity acid. A 0.5-g portion of the $^{233}UO_2$ powder is accurately weighed, dissolved in 1 mL of 4 M HNO_3, and diluted to 10 mL total volume. A 0.1-mL aliquot containing the equivalent of 0.005 g of $^{233}UO_2$ is spike with 1 μg of highly enriched ^{57}Fe, and the mixture is dried on the tips of two high-purity graphite electrodes. A 0.1-g portion of the $^{233}UO_2$ powder is mixed with

high-purity silver powder, homogenized in a plastic ball mill, and pressed into electrodes.

Data Acquisition. The iron-spiked samples on graphite electrodes are sparked to produce a set of eight exposures on the photographic plate at the same total accumulated ion beam charge (1 nC) to determine the iron in the sample. The pressed silver powder electrodes are then placed in the ion source and sparked to produce a graduated set of exposures, including 10, 3, 1, 0.3, 0.1, 0.03, 0.01, and 0.003 nC, for measuring the other elements relative to iron.

Data Reduction. The photographic plate is read normally, converting plate darkening to ion intensity for the isotopic lines of interest. The data for the iron isotope dilution are shown in Table 11. Iron concentration is calculated using:

$$Conc\ Fe = \left(\frac{Weight\ Fe(spike)}{Weight\ UO_2(sample)}\right)$$
$$\times \left(\frac{Isotopic\ abundance\ ^{57}Fe(spike)}{Isotopic\ abundance\ ^{57}Fe(sample)}\right)$$
$$\times \left(\frac{R_{spike} - R_m}{R_m - R_{sample}}\right)$$
$$\times \left(\frac{Atomic\ weight\ Fe}{Atomic\ weight\ UO_2}\right) \quad (Eq\ 7)$$

where R_{spike} and R_{sample} are the ratios of ^{56}Fe/^{57}Fe in the spike and sample, and R_m is the ^{56}Fe/^{57}Fe ratio as measured for the mixture.

The calculation then becomes:

$$Conc\ Fe = \left(\frac{1\ μg}{0.005\ g}\right)\left(\frac{0.999}{0.022}\right)$$
$$\times \left(\frac{1 \times 10^{-3} - 0.845}{0.845 - 41.68}\right)\left(\frac{55.9}{265}\right)$$
$$= 39.6\ μg/g$$

The raw data for the powdered silver sample are shown in Table 12. The RSFs for these elements relative to iron are:

Element	RSF
Boron	0.8
Calcium	1.3
Zirconium	2.1
^{239}Pu	1.0

The concentrations of these elements are calculated using:

$$Conc\ M = Conc\ Fe \left(\frac{Intensity\ ^aM}{Intensity\ ^bFe}\right)$$
$$\times \left(\frac{Isotopic\ abundance\ ^bFe}{Isotopic\ abundance\ ^aM}\right)$$
$$\times \left(\frac{1}{RSF(M)}\right)\left(\frac{Atomic\ weight\ M}{Atomic\ weight\ Fe}\right)$$
$$(Eq\ 8)$$

where a is the measured isotope of the element M, b is the measured isotope of iron, and RSF(M) the relative sensitivity

Table 10 Summary of results for chromium, arsenic, selenium, cadmium, and antimony for Example 3

Element	Concentration, μg/mL
Chromium	8.1 ± 1(a)
Arsenic	0.0082 ± 0.0007
Selenium	0.58 ± 0.03
Cadmium	0.0030 ± 0.0002
Antimony	0.23 ± 0.03

(a) Estimated uncertainty

Table 11 Isotope dilution of iron for Example 4

Isotope	Intensity (average of 8)	Natural isotope abundance (atom fraction)	Spike isotope abundance (atom fraction)
^{56}Fe	98 ± 1	0.917	0.001
^{57}Fe	116 ± 3	0.022	0.999

factor for M relative to iron. For example, for ^{11}B in the 1 nC exposure:

$$\text{Conc B} = 39.6 \ \mu g/g \left(\frac{56}{19}\right)\left(\frac{0.022}{0.817}\right)$$

$$\times \left(\frac{1}{0.8}\right)\left(\frac{10.8}{55.9}\right) = 0.76 \ \mu g/g$$

The results for the remaining elements are shown in Table 13.

ACKNOWLEDGMENTS

Research sponsored by the U.S. Department of Energy, Office of Basic Energy Sciences, under Contract DE-AC05-84OR21400 with Martin Marietta Energy Systems, Inc.

SELECTED REFERENCES

- A.J. Ahearn, Ed., *Mass Spectrometric Analysis of Solids*, Elsevier, 1966

- J.A. Carter, "Quantitative Spark-Source Mass Spectrometric Techniques for the Simultaneous Determination of the Lanthanide Actinide Elements in Microgram Transuranium Samples," Ph.D. dissertation, University of Tennessee, 1970
- A. Cornu, R. Massot, and J. Ternier, *Analyse par Spectrometrie de Masse a Etincelles, Atlas de Raies*, Presses Universitaines de France, 1964
- A.J. Ahearn, Ed., *Trace Analysis by Mass Spectrometry*, Academic Press, 1972
- E.B. Owens and A.M. Sherman, "Mass Spectrographic Lines of the Elements," M.I.T. Lincoln Laboratory Technical Report 265, Boston, 1962

Table 12 Measured intensities for iron, boron, calcium, zirconium, and ^{239}Pu for Example 4

Isotope	Natural isotopic abundance (atom fraction)	Exposure, nC(a) 10	3	1	0.3	0.1	0.03	0.01	0.003
^{56}Fe	0.917	S	S	S	213	75	18	6	ND
^{57}Fe	0.022	158	51	19	5	ND	ND	ND	ND
^{11}B	0.817	S	165	56	16	5	ND	ND	ND
^{40}Ca	0.970	S	S	S	S	129	38	12	ND
^{90}Zr	0.515	38	10	ND	ND	ND	ND	ND	ND
^{239}Pu	1.00(b)	185	49	17	6	ND	ND	ND	ND

(a) S, saturated; ND, not detected. (b) Because only ^{239}Pu is specified, the abundance is assumed to be 1.00.

Table 13 Calculated concentrations of boron, calcium, zirconium, and ^{239}Pu for Example 4: UO_2

Element	Exposure, nC 10	3	1	0.3	0.1	0.03	0.01	Average concentration, μg/g
Boron	...	0.83	0.76	0.81	0.71	...	...	0.79 ± 0.05
	...	...	...	0.82	...	...	...	...
Calcium	...	...	...	...	35	44	41	40 ± 4
Zirconium	0.32	0.26	...	...	...	...	...	0.29 ± 0.04
^{239}Pu	4.4	3.6	3.3	4.4	...	...	...	4.0 ± 0.6
	...	...	...	4.5	...	...	...	...

Gas Analysis by Mass Spectrometry

Q.G. Grindstaff, J.C. Franklin, and J.L. Marshall, Oak Ridge Y-12 Plant*

General Uses

- Qualitative and quantitative analysis of inorganic and organic compounds and mixtures

Examples of Applications

- Analysis of internal atmospheres of sealed components
- Analysis of gas inclusions in ceramic or glass-to-metal seals
- Quantification of specific compounds in volatile liquids or gaseous mixtures
- Analysis of gases in inorganic or geologic materials
- Analysis of high-purity gases for contaminants
- Gas isotope ratios

Samples

- *Form*: Primarily gases
- *Size*: 1×10^{-4} mL (STP) or larger
- *Preparation*: Sample must be collected in a clean glass or steel bottle; air must not be allowed into the sample bottle

Limitations

- Low part per million detection limits for inorganic and organic gases
- Difficulty in identifying components in complex organic mixtures
- Components of interest must be volatile

Estimated Analysis Time

- 30 min to 1 h per analysis, not including sample preparation and calibration

Capabilities of Related Techniques

- *Gas chromatography/mass spectrometry*: Greater capability for compound identification in complex organic mixtures; not quantitative
- *Gas chromatography*: Quantitative, but requires larger sample size
- *Infrared/Raman spectroscopy*: Requires larger sample size; infrared spectroscopy does not detect some inorganic gases

---

Introduction

Gas analysis by mass spectrometry, or gas mass spectrometry, is a useful analytical tool for investigations performed in controlled atmospheres or in vacuum. A mass spectrometer may be defined as an analytical instrument that produces ions, then separates them according to their mass-to-charge (m/z) ratios. Therefore, gas mass spectrometry provides the capability of simultaneous identification of the components of the sample under analysis. With proper instrument calibration, the data obtained are such that a quantitative analysis of the components is available.

In a typical situation, a sample (a gas at room temperature or a low-boiling liquid) is introduced into the ion source of the mass spectrometer for ionization. The resulting ions are separated according to their m/z ratio by a mass analyzer and collected by a detector. The resulting mass spectrum contains all the information necessary to identify and quantify the components of that sample. This article will provide sufficient information to determine if gas mass spectrometry can produce the data required and to determine the type of instrument necessary for a particular application.

Gas Mass Spectrometer Components

The introduction system is the means by which the sample to be analyzed is introduced into the ion source of the mass spectrometer in a gaseous state and a con-trolled manner. The introduction system can be simple (Fig. 1) or complex (Fig. 2). In either system, the following steps are involved in the introduction of the sample.

First, the connecting pipework and the expansion volumes are evacuated using rotary and diffusion vacuum pumps. The gas from a sample or reference cylinder is then expanded into the introduction system. The resulting pressure is read by the sample pressure gage. The gaseous sample is then allowed to enter the mass spectrometer through the flow controller, which can be a molecular leak made from a gold foil with pin holes or a glass frit. The ion source of a mass spectrometer will operate only below 10^{-4} torr. Therefore, the amount of pressure in the introduction system must be controlled.

*Operated for the U.S. Department of Energy by Martin Marietta Energy Systems, Inc., under Contract No. DE-AC05-84OR21400.

Fig. 1 Schematic of a simple introduction system

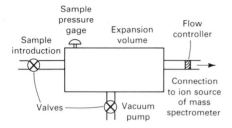

Fig. 2 Schematic of a computer-controlled multiple-expansion volume introduction system

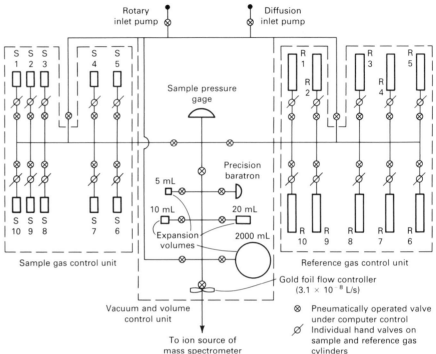

If all samples to be analyzed produce the same pressure when expanded into the system, the simple introduction system (Fig. 1) can be constructed with appropriate expansion volume and molecular leak to produce pressures suitable for analysis by the mass spectrometer. However, if all samples do not produce the same pressure when expanded into the system, an introduction system must be used that can control sample pressure. The system can be a modified Toepler pump or a manual or automatic multiple-expansion volume system. The Toepler pump is simply a mercury pump that can expand or compress the sample until the correct pressure is obtained in the expansion volume of the introduction system.

Figure 2 shows a multiple-expansion volume introduction system. In this system, samples can be expanded into small expansion volumes (5, 10, and 20 mL) before they are expanded into the final expansion volume. By using one or a combination of these expansion volumes, a desired pressure can be obtained in the final expansion volume. The desired pressure will be determined by the exact mass spectrometry system at some level below 10^{-4} torr and at a sufficient pressure so as not to change abruptly during analysis.

To introduce a gas sample into the mass spectrometer, molecular and viscous flows must be considered. Molecular flow occurs when the mean free path of the gas molecules is large compared to the diameter of the leak opening and the distance in which considerable change occurs in the density of the gas. The mean free path should be at least 20 times the diameter of the opening. Molecular flow describes the flow of the gas from the introduction system to the mass spectrometer ion source. Because the equation that describes molecular flow contains a $1/\sqrt{M}$ term (M represents the molecular weight of the gas), fractionation of the sample in the introduction system can occur. That is, the composition of the gas in the introduction system changes with time as the gas flows through the leak.

In noncomputerized gas mass spectrometry, an assumption used to deal with fractionation is that there is a canceling effect because the admission rate of gas molecules of molecular weight M in molecular flow conditions is proportional to $1/\sqrt{M}$, and the gas of molecular weight M is pumped from the ion source at a rate proportional to $1/\sqrt{M}$. Therefore, the composition of the sample in the ion source will be the same as that in the introduction system behind the leak. However, if the flow rates of the gases of different molecular weights are different, the composition of the sample in the introduction system preceding the leak to the ion source will change with time. That is, lower molecular weight gases will escape more rapidly than higher molecular weight gases.

Viscous flow occurs when the mean free path of the molecules is smaller than the diameter of the leak opening. This type of flow describes that which would occur when the sample is being expanded into the expansion volume of the introduction system. Because the equation that describes viscous flow does not contain a molecular weight term, fractionation does not occur when the sample is expanded into the introduction system.

Samples that can be introduced successfully by a batch inlet are gaseous at the temperature of the sample inlet. Traditionally, samples are gases at ambient temperature, but

liquids that boil at <150 °C (<300 °F) can be analyzed by appropriate sample handling. The samples should be 1×10^{-4} mL (STP) or larger in size. These samples require no preparation except collection in a glass or steel gas bottle in a manner that excludes contamination by air. The interior surfaces of the gas bottle must be clean and free of contamination. Samples such as ammonia, water, amines, and acid gases, which are polar, will almost certainly be absorbed by sample bottles and the introduction system; therefore, these types of compounds are difficult to analyze without extensive conditioning of the introduction system.

Ion Source. The molecular flow of gaseous molecules from the introduction system enters the ionization chamber of the ion source (Fig. 3). The ion source produces ions from the neutral gaseous molecules and forms a finely defined molecular ion beam that can be analyzed by the mass spectrometer. The ion beam is formed inside the ionization chamber at 10^{-6} to 10^{-4} torr and traverses the optics of the mass spectrometer in a vacuum envelope maintained at less than 10^{-7} torr.

Electron-impact ionization is the most common ionization technique for forming the ion beam for gas mass spectrometry. Electrons are emitted from a heated filament (Fig. 3) that is usually constructed of tung-

Fig. 3 Schematic of a gas mass spectrometer

Ion source components: A, trap; B, repeller; C, ionization chamber; D, filament; E, extractor; F, Y lens, G, earth plate; H, Z lens; I, source slit; J, Einzel lens; K, magnet

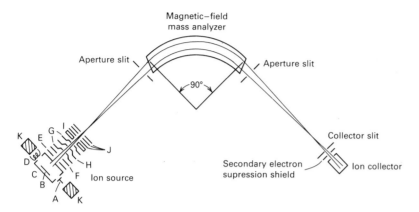

Fig. 4 Schematic of a quadrupole mass filter

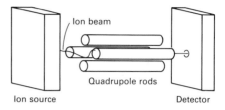

sten, tantalum, or rhenium. The emitted electrons are formed into a beam, passed through the ionization chamber, and collected by the trap. A weak magnetic field is used to align the electron beam between the filament and the trap. The magnet also causes the electrons to move in a spiral path, which increases the time the electrons spend in the ionization chamber. As shown in Fig. 3, the sample gas enters the ion source perpendicular to the electron beam.

The energy of the electrons can be varied typically from 5 to 100 eV. The conventional operating condition is 70 eV. When the electrons collide with an atom or molecule (M), the following situations can occur:

$$M + e^- \rightarrow M^+ + 2e^- \qquad \text{(Eq 1)}$$

$$M + e^- \rightarrow M^{2+} + 3e^- \qquad \text{(Eq 2)}$$

$$M + e^- \rightarrow M^{3+} + 4e^- \qquad \text{(Eq 3)}$$

$$M + e^- \rightarrow M^- \qquad \text{(Eq 4)}$$

$$M + e^- \rightarrow M^+ + 2e^-$$
$$\rightarrow F_1^+ + N_1 + 2e^-$$
$$\rightarrow F_2^+ + N_2 + 2e^- \ldots \qquad \text{(Eq 5)}$$

The situation described by Eq 1 occurs when the energy imparted is sufficient only to release an electron. This energy is termed the ionization potential. However, as the electron energy is increased above the ionization potential, enough energy can be transferred

to the molecule to release additional electrons (Eq 2 and 3) or to cause bonds to be broken (Eq 5). Bond breaking results in the formation of ions termed fragment (F) ions. Fragment ions can be defined as ions formed from a molecular ion (loss of only an electron) by a neutral (N) molecular loss. At the pressures in the ionization chamber, only approximately one molecule in a thousand is ionized. Of all the ions formed, only a small proportion (under 0.1%) are negatively charged (Eq 4).

After the positive ions are formed, they are repelled or drawn out of the ionization chamber by the weak electric field that exists between the repeller and the extractor plates (Fig. 3). The potential difference between the repeller and extraction plate is usually of the order of only a few volts per centimeter. If not for the combined field effects of the repeller and extractor, the positive ions would tend to accumulate around the negative space charge of the electron beam. These two fields draw out and accelerate the ions up to 10 keV.

After the ion beam has been extracted and accelerated, the beam passes through the Y lens. The Y lens is important in a gas mass spectrometer because any Nier-type ion source with a magnet (Fig. 3) to collimate the electron beam will, to a small extent, behave like a mass spectrometer. That is, there will be a small separation between ion beams of different masses, which causes some mass discrimination. The discrimination is greater for low masses than for higher masses. In modern computerized systems, the Y lens can be programmed to change as the masses are scanned to prevent mass discrimination.

The Z lens is used to center the beam through the source slit and the mass spectrometer. The source slit is used to define the

width of the beam, which in turn defines the peak shape and resolution (discussed below).

The Einzel lens is an ion optical converging lens consisting of three pairs of plates (Fig. 3). The two outer pairs are at earth potential, and the central pair is raised to several hundred volts. The lens controls resolution over the entire mass range. If the mass analyzer magnet (discussed below) is optimized for low mass ions, the magnet must be moved in or out to achieve first-order focusing for higher masses. This is especially critical at high resolution (600). Because typical gas mixtures for analysis contain high and low mass species, resolution is lost on some peaks because it is impractical to move the magnet during analysis. Consequently, some peaks are no longer flat topped, and the reproducibility of peak height measurements of these peaks is poor.

The alternative to moving the main magnet is to converge the ion beam with a lens before or after the magnet to simulate moving the magnet. Changing the voltage on the Einzel lens is equivalent to moving the magnet; therefore, each peak has an Einzel lens voltage to maintain flat-top peaks and reproducibility of measurement. This voltage change is programmable from the computer if the system is so equipped.

The ion source described above is for a modern gas mass spectrometer with a magnetic analyzer. However, because all sources have common parts, this discussion applies to most ion sources regardless of the type of mass analyzer used.

Mass Analyzer. After it has been formed and defined by the ion source, the ion beam passes through the mass analyzer section of the mass spectrometer. The quadrupole mass filter (Fig. 4) and the magnetic-field mass analyzers are the two types used almost exclusively for gas mass spectrometry.

The most economical analyzer is the ion quadrupole mass filter. This unit consists of a square array of four parallel rods arranged as shown in Fig. 4. Opposite rods are connected to radio frequency (RF) and direct current (dc) voltages, one pair of rods being

180° out of phase with the other. These potentials produce an electrostatic field that provides stable oscillations to ions with a specific m/z ratio and unstable oscillations to all others. Thus, with one set of potentials, only ions with a specific m/z ratio can pass through the mass filter; all others strike the rods and are neutralized. The potentials on the rods can be changed rapidly and precisely. Thus, the quadrupole is well suited for selected ion monitoring. The primary disadvantage of the quadrupole is its relatively low mass resolution and the extreme decrease in sensitivity with increasing mass of the ions.

The traditional analyzer of the ion beam after it is accelerated from the ion source is the permanent magnet or, in the most useful form, an electromagnet, with which the magnetic field can be scanned up or down. The magnetic sector can be arranged such that the ion source and the collector of ions are located in the field of the magnet or as shown in Fig. 3. In a magnetic-sector instrument, the ion beam exiting from the ion source enters the magnet perpendicular to the magnetic field and is deflected. The ions of different masses follow paths of different radii of curvature in the magnetic field, and analysis is effected.

A beam of ions of mass-to-charge ratio m/z is deflected upon passage through a magnetic field according to:

$$\frac{m}{z} = \frac{H^2 R^2}{2V} \qquad \text{(Eq 6)}$$

where H is the strength of the magnetic field, R is the radius of the circular path into which the ions are deflected, and V is the voltage used to accelerate the ions out of the ion source. Because the angle of deflection (radius, R) is usually fixed for a given analyzer tube (60°, 90°, 180°), H or V must be varied to focus ions of a given m/z value on the detector system. Three modes of scanning the mass spectrum are most often used in gas mass spectrometry: (1) hold V constant, scan H, (2) hold H constant, scan or step V, and (3) scan or step H and V. Scanning or stepping of V can be accomplished rapidly and precisely. However, as V is changed, the sensitivity (ratio of the number of molecules introduced to the number of ions collected) of the mass spectrometer changes. This change does not occur when the field (H) is scanned or stepped.

The mode of scanning or stepping H and V is used by state-of-the-art magnetic analyzer gas mass spectrometers. Using a field control, the magnet is stepped as close as possible to the value (H) that would cause the center of the ion beam for a given m/z value to be detected by the collector with the accelerating potential being held constant. Small changes are then made in the accelerating potential (V) to find the true center of the ion beam by first stepping to the 50% level of the ion beam on the low mass side, then stepping to the same level of the ion beam on the high mass side.

This method has two advantages. First, by stepping the magnetic field between m/z values instead of stepping the accelerating voltage, the sensitivity of the instrument remains unchanged. Because finding the ion beam center is comparatively slow when using the magnetic field alone, scanning the accelerating voltage to accomplish the centering hastens the process. Because the accelerating voltage is scanned only a few volts, the sensitivity of the mass spectrometer remains essentially unchanged.

Double-focusing mass spectrometers are also used in gas analysis. These instruments are used when mass resolutions exceeding 3000 are required. Single- and double-focusing instruments differ only in that a double-focusing instrument has an electrostatic field placed before or after the magnetic sector. The electrostatic field limits the range of kinetic energies for ions of equal m/z. The range of energies can be controlled by passing the ion beam through the radial electrostatic field, which acts as a direction and velocity (energy) focusing device. Directional focusing counteracts any angular divergence of the ion beam due to charge repulsion and the width of the ionizing electron beam. However, the sensitivity of a mass spectrometer is inversely proportional to the resolving power used. Therefore, the instrument should not be operated at resolving power higher than is necessary to resolve the different m/z values of interest.

Ion Detection. After the ion beam has been mass analyzed by the quadrupole array or the magnetic field, the beam passes through a defining slit (collector slit, as shown in Fig. 3) and is then collected by an ion detection device. Several ion detection devices are used in gas mass spectrometry. The most commonly used are the Faraday cup, the electron multiplier, and the Daly detector. Each has advantages and disadvantages. Of the three, the Faraday cup is the simplest.

The Faraday cup produces an electron current when bombarded with an ion beam. Statistical probability predicts that one electron is released for each ion that impinges on the cup. This one-to-one relationship is the reason Faraday cups are used for quantitative gas mass spectrometry. However, the Faraday cup arrangement must be designed well to maintain this relationship. This is why most spectrometers incorporate a guard slit and an electron suppressor slit (Fig. 3).

The guard slits are used to eliminate metastable ions or scattered ions. The electron suppressor slit is incorporated immediately ahead of the ion detector to return to the collector any secondary electrons emitted by the ion beam bombardment of the metal collector. The Faraday cup is useful as an ion detector when the ion beam current being detected exceeds 10^{-13} A. This lower limit is due to the fact that below this value the feedback resistor in the amplifier circuit becomes so large that the thermal (Johnson) noise begins to affect the accuracy and precision of the results. The dependence on the amplifier is the major disadvantage of using the Faraday cup.

The electron multiplier as an ion detector operates on a principle only slightly more complicated than the Faraday cup. Energetic ions impinge upon the metal surface of a cathode of the multiplier and cause the emission of a number of secondary electrons. These electrons are then accelerated and allowed to impinge upon another electrode (dynode), which causes additional electron emission. This process is typically repeated for 12 to 16 stages. The result is a large current collected on the anode of the multiplier for each ion that strikes the cathode.

The electron multiplier is a useful detector for ion beams ranging from a single ion to 10^{-9} A. The advantages of the electron multiplier are its high sensitivity and rapid response. The disadvantage of the electron multiplier is that the statistical probability of an electron being released when the multiplier is struck by an ion is less than one. In addition, there is a greater than zero probability that up to six ions impinging on the first dynode will release only one electron. This fact, coupled with the fact that the electron multiplier amplification or gain changes with time and sample, makes the electron multiplier less desirable than the Faraday cup for ion current and abundance measurements. That the gain of the electron multiplier is atomic-composition dependent compounds this problem.

The Daly collector is the most complex of the three detectors. It consists of a scintillator made of aluminum-coated steel. The potential of the scintillator is maintained at up to 25 000 V. Scintillation is produced by the ions impinging on the aluminum foil. Scintillation effects a response in a photomultiplier. Unlike the electron multiplier, the statistical probability of one ion producing one electron is very large. The probability of one ion producing 10 to 15 secondary electrons is large. This probability is also very constant when the scintillator is operated at 25 000 V. Therefore, in this sense, the Daly collector is better than the Faraday cup in that the range of ion current detectable (10^{-9} A to a single ion) is large and the reproducibility is as favorable.

As in the case of the electron multiplier, the statistical probability of the number of secondary electrons produced by the Daly detector depends on atomic composition. For example, N_2 and C_2H_4 have a molecular weight of 28; however, C_2H_4 will produce more secondary electrons than N_2. This is because C_2H_4 contains six atoms, and N_2 contains only two. This limitation is not a problem if the system can be calibrated with the gaseous species to be analyzed, and it can be avoided by the use of pulse counting techniques.

Resolution

The resolution of a gas mass spectrometer is a measure of its ability to separate ionic species. The resolution of a mass spectrometer is determined by the width of the source slit and the collector slit (Fig. 3). If the mass spectrometer is adjusted to produce a resolution of 500, mass peak 500 overlaps mass peak 501 no more than 10%. The term mass peak refers to the electronic representation of the ion beam that strikes the detector.

The resolution of the mass spectrometer is set to obtain a flat-top peak. The flat-top peak is obtained in a mixed slit mode; that is, the collector slit is set just wider than the source slit to allow the entire ion beam to pass through the collector slit. The flat-top peak enhances the precision and reproducibility of peak height measurements.

The resolution required can be calculated using:

$$R = \frac{M}{\Delta M}$$

where R is the resolution, M is the nominal mass or average mass of the gas under analysis, and ΔM is the difference in the masses of the components of the sample. An example is the calculation of the resolution necessary to separate N_2 completely from CO. The exact masses of N_2 and CO are 28.0061 and 27.9949, respectively. Therefore, the required resolution is 2500 for precise quantitative analysis:

$$R = \frac{28}{0.0112} = 2500 \qquad \text{(Eq 7)}$$

A lesser resolution of 1785 is necessary to separate Ne (19.9924) and the doubly charged argon ion Ar^{2+} (19.9812). Double-focusing gas mass spectrometers are used if resolutions of over 3000 are necessary. However, the resolution and the sensitivity of the mass spectrometer are inversely pro-

Fig. 5 Analog representation of a mass spectrum

The position of the D_2^+ line is displaced to apparent m/z 5 for operator convenience. Actual mass is 4.028 amu. Resolution of this scan is ~1200.

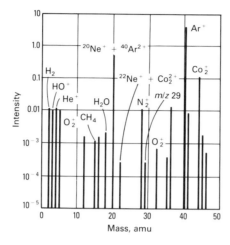

portional. Therefore, most routine analyses on gas samples are performed at resolutions of 500 to 1000.

Instrument Set-Up and Calibration

Set-up begins by tuning the ion source for maximum sensitivity and peak shape with minimum mass discrimination. The source tuning is usually performed on the N_2 peak. The tuning involves optimization of the Y and Z lens, beam centering plates, and ion repeller. Mass discrimination in the low-mass species is corrected using the Einzel lens system. The Einzel lens system is usually set for H_2 and D_2. To calibrate the response of the mass spectrometer and measure the linearity of the response, concentration standards are analyzed. These concentration standards contain known amounts of the gases to be analyzed, and the concentrations of these gases range from the lower detection limit (approximately 10 ppm) of the instrument to an upper limit determined by the operator.

The sample is constantly being depleted as it is analyzed. To conduct precise quantita-

tive analyses, the assumption stated in the section "The Introduction System" in this article must be used, or a depletion rate determined. Modern gas mass spectrometers with computerized data systems use depletion rates when performing quantitative calculations. Depletion rates allow quantitative calculations to be conducted for time zero, that is, the instant the sample is introduced into the mass spectrometer. The depletion rate is usually determined using H_2. This can then be used to calculate depletion rates for all other gases to be analyzed.

With a field-control magnet, the field setting required to focus each mass of interest on the detector is determined and entered into the computer file. Each time an analysis is carried out, this file is updated to correct for drift due to temperature or electronic changes.

After setup and calibration, the time required for the analysis of a given component is approximately 1 min. Therefore, if ten gases are to be determined in a sample, the total time of the analysis would be 10 min.

Results of Analysis

The signal from the detection device of the mass spectrometer can be output to a paper recorder or to a computerized data-acquisition system. In the case of a recorder, the mass spectrum is presented as a series of peaks on chart paper (Fig. 5). The heights of the peaks are proportional to the amount of each gas present in a Matheson standard gas sample. By measuring the heights of the peaks and knowing the response factor for each compound and the pressure of the introduction system with the sample loaded, the composition and the partial pressure for each gaseous species can be calculated.

The samples that were analyzed using gas mass spectrometry are primary standards (results are shown in Fig. 5 and Tables 1 and 2). The standards were chosen because they are representative of the gaseous components most often analyzed by gas mass spectrometry.

Table 1 presents typical output when the signal from the detection device is output to a computerized data-acquisition system. The system automatically measures the height (intensity) of each mass peak, subtracts the

Table 1 Summary of analysis

Compound	Composition	Intensity (corrected)	Background	Time, s	Partial pressure	Sensitivity, mV/μm
H_2	971.0 ppm	143.58	5.00	53.90	0.10	147.58
He	99.373%	62 675.56	0.00	74.86	99.57	62.95
	0.103%	311.98	0.00	105.26	0.10	301.64
N_2 + CO	0.218%	1 011.61	19.50	137.18	0.22	462.32
O_2	0.105%	401.06	1.12	155.97	0.11	381.20
CO_2	0.104%	603.69	8.00	197.09	0.10	580.03

background from the measured height, and calculates a corrected intensity. Background is the height of a given mass peak when the introduction system does not contain a sample. The computer system takes the corrected intensity, together with the depletion rate at the time of measurement and the response factor (sensitivity), and calculates the composition of the sample in the introduction system at time zero. The partial pressure of each gaseous component can also be calculated. A closure factor can be used to determine the accuracy of the measurement. The closure is calculated by subtracting the calculated pressure (sum of partial pressures) from the measured pressure. The smaller the closure the better the results are taken to be. In this case, the measured pressure is 101.9, and the calculated pressure is 100.2, giving a closure of 1.7%.

Table 2 demonstrates the accuracy and precision that can be expected routinely from a gas mass spectrometer. The resulting data from the analyses of a low-concentration sample (10 ppm) and a high-concentration sample (1000 ppm) are presented. The mean values are calculated from the results of 15 determinations. The accepted values are those supplied with the standards. Favorable accuracy and precision are shown for the high and low concentrations. These results are to be expected on a daily basis.

Applications*

Example 1: Relay Weld Integrity.
Conventional welding techniques, when used for the final hermetic seal on miniature (<0.1 mL internal free volume) relays have a history of inducing stress cracking in the glass-to-metal seals surrounding the electrical feedthroughs. With laser welding, however, temperature excursions and the resulting stresses can be confined to the weld area, minimizing the potential for stress cracking the seals.

In a recent study, a computer-controlled gas mass spectrometer was used to analyze the internal gas composition of a series of miniature relays (0.08 mL internal volume) that had been laser welded using different beam energies and techniques. The welding operations were performed within a controlled-atmosphere glovebox in which the gas composition in the glovebox and therefore in the relays was adjusted to contain approximately 10% helium, 86% nitrogen, and 4% oxygen. To determine the exact

*Example 1 was provided by Frank B. Burns, Sandia National Laboratories. Example 2 was supplied by Frank B. Burns and Phillip J. Rodacy, Sandia National Laboratories. This work was supported by the U.S. Department of Energy under Contract No. DE-AC04-76DP00789.

Table 2 Gas mass spectrometer capability

Compound	Mean ± standard deviation, ppm	Accepted value, ppm	Bias, ppm
Low concentration standard (10 ppm CO_2)			
H_2	12.8 ± 4.9	10.0 ± 0.1	2.8 ± 4.9
CH_4	10.8 ± 3.1	10.0 ± 0.1	0.8 ± 3.1
N_2 + CO	27.6 ± 7.6	20.0 ± 0.2	7.6 ± 7.6
O_2	13.1 ± 2.9	10.0 ± 0.1	3.1 ± 2.9
CO_2	10.5 ± 2.1	10.0 ± 0.1	0.5 ± 2.1
Ar	12.4 ± 2.0	10.0 ± 0.1	2.4 ± 2.0
High concentration standard (1000 ppm CO_2)			
H_2	970 ± 27.8	1014 ± 10	−44 ± 27.8
CH_4	1023 ± 15.9	1000 ± 10	23 ± 15.9
N_2 + CO	2169 ± 52.2	1999 ± 20	170 ± 52.2
O_2	1035 ± 31.5	1003 ± 10	32 ± 31.5
CO_2	1031 ± 28.8	1000 ± 10	31 ± 28.8

Table 3 Results of relay analysis

Sample	Gas, vol% (mole)					
	H_2	He	N_2	O_2	Ar	CO_2
1	0.02	9.49	86.85	3.55	0.02	0.06
2	0.01	0.00	78.02	21.01	0.92	0.04
3	0.00	0.00	77.87	21.16	0.93	0.03
4	0.02	9.77	86.15	3.98	0.02	0.05
5	0.02	9.54	86.26	4.13	0.02	0.04
6	0.02	9.29	86.83	3.75	0.01	0.10

compositional values for the glovebox atmosphere, gas samples were taken at the same time that the test relays were laser welded using cleaned and evacuated 75-mL stainless steel sample bottles. Quantitative compositional values for the glovebox atmosphere were ascertained using gas mass spectrometry.

To analyze its internal atmosphere, a relay was placed within a stainless steel puncturing fixture, which was then attached to the inlet system of a gas mass spectrometer and evacuated. The position of the relay within the fixture minimized puncturing damage to the weld area and the glass-to-metal seals, ensuring suitable samples for microscopic postmortems. After evacuation of the system, the relay was punctured by driving an externally controlled pin through the case. The released gases were expanded into the inlet system of the mass spectrometer and analyzed. Each relay was analyzed for the major gases in question: helium, nitrogen, and oxygen. Hydrogen, argon, and carbon dioxide were also measured, because they are often present as contaminants. Representative data for a few of the relays examined are shown in Table 3.

The hermeticity, or leak rate, of each relay could then be calculated with knowledge of the original glovebox helium concentration, the analyzed helium concentrations, and the dates of welding and analysis. Helium is

usually chosen as a tracer because of its rapid response to a leak-rate change. Assuming a constant storage temperature, the actual leak rates for the relays can be calculated:

$$P_{He}(t) = P'_{He} \exp \frac{-(F_{He})(t)}{V} \quad \text{(Eq 8)}$$

where $P_{He}(t)$ is the internal pressure of helium at time t, P'_{He} is the internal pressure of helium at time zero, F_{He} is the conductance of the leak, t is time in seconds, and V is the volume of the package. Results of these gas analyses facilitated optimization of the welding techniques with minimal expenditure of time and materials.

Example 2: Microcircuit Process Gas Analysis.
Contamination control is exceptionally important in facilities that produce integrated circuits and particularly in facilities that manufacture very large scale integration (VLSI) products. With circuit linewidths of micron or submicron dimensions, the presence of oxidants or oxidizable species in the process gases can seriously affect the complex chemical reactions in chemical vapor deposition, oxidation and annealing furnaces, and subsequent device performance.

The microcircuit fabrication process gases nitrogen, oxygen, and hydrogen are analyzed for trace-level (<10 ppm) contaminants on regular and on-demand bases. The gases are sampled at the input and output ports of the line purifiers as well as at the production furnace inlets. Occasionally, headspace gas samples will be taken directly from the cryogenic supply tanks. Because the fabrication facility is remote from the analytical laboratory, considerable care must be exercised to ensure that the sample analyzed is representative of the bulk gas and that it has not been contaminated during handling.

Gas samples are acquired by coupling a double-ended stainless steel bottle (~250-mL volume) that had previously been cleaned, leak checked, and evacuated to the appropriate port and purging it with the sample gas for approximately 4 h at 1 L/min or more flow rate. This will ensure that residual contaminants adsorbed on the interior walls of the sample bottle and other associated plumbing have been removed or reduced below analytical detection limits. Samples are normally analyzed the same day they are taken to minimize air contamination due to integral sample bottle leak rates. Moisture, an important contaminant in all three gas streams, cannot be determined accurately for gas samples obtained in this manner because of the wall sorption effects due to plumbing, sample bottles, and analytical inlet systems. Because of these wall effects, moisture is continuously measured using a solid-state monitor on-site.

The samples are analyzed primarily for oxygen and carbon dioxide impurities at the parts per million level using a computer-controlled gas mass spectrometer. Other suspected contaminants, such as hydrogen and methane, are also readily quantified during the analysis. The analytical results show 2 ppm of oxygen and 3 ppm of carbon dioxide.

SELECTED REFERENCES

- R.W. Kiser, *Introduction to Mass Spectrometry and Its Applications*, Prentice-Hall, 1965
- C.A. McDowell, *Mass Spectrometry*, McGraw-Hill, 1963
- B.J. Millard, *Quantitative Mass Spectrometry*, Heyden, 1979
- R.I. Reed, *Ion Production by Electron Impact*, Academic Press, 1962

Classical, Electrochemical, and Radiochemical Analysis

Classical Wet Analytical Chemistry

Thomas R. Dulski, Carpenter Technology Corporation

General Uses

- Quantitative elemental composition analysis
- Qualitative identification of material type
- Qualitative detection of component moieties
- "Umpire" check on quantitative instrumental methods
- Isolation and characterization of inclusions and phases
- Characterization of coatings and surfaces
- Determination of oxidation state

Examples of Applications

- Quantitative determination of alloy matrix elements for which instrumental methods are unavailable or unreliable
- Complete characterization of a homogeneous sample for use as an instrument calibration standard
- Quantitative determination of composition when sample is too small or of unsuitable shape for instrumental approaches
- Gross average composition determination of inhomogeneous samples
- Isolation of compounds and stoichiometric phases from metal alloy matrices for compositional analysis or examination by instrumental techniques
- Coating weight determination of plated metals, lubricant films, and other surface layers
- Partitioning of element oxidation states
- Sorting of mixed materials based on qualitative detection of one or more key matrix components

Samples

- *Form*: Crystalline or amorphous solids (metals, ceramics, glasses, ores, and so on) and liquids (pickling and plating baths, lubricants, and so on)
- *Size*: Depends on extent of required analyses—generally 1 to 2 g per element for solids and 20 mL total for process liquids, although requirements vary widely with technique
- *Preparation*: Solids are milled, drilled, crushed, or similarly dissociated into particles typically 2 mm (0.08 in.) in diameter or smaller. Machined alloys are solvent degreased. Materials lacking high order homogeneity require special care to ensure a representative laboratory sample

Limitations

- Slow compared to alternate instrumental techniques
- Except in rare cases, relatively large sample weights are required

Estimated Analysis Time

- 2 to 80 h per element (8 h per element is typical)

Capabilities of Related Techniques

- *X-ray spectrometry*: Rapid for major component elements with $Z > 9$
- *Optical emission spectroscopy*: Can be rapid for minor and trace components
- *Atomic absorption spectrophotometry*: Somewhat more rapid; better ultimate detection limits for trace components
- *Electrochemical analysis*: Better ultimate detection limits for trace components
- *Electron and ion microprobes*: In situ characterization of inclusions
- *Secondary ion mass spectroscopy, x-ray photoelectron spectroscopy, and Auger spectroscopy*: Much more sensitive studies of surface layers
- *Mössbauer spectroscopy*: Sensitive to certain oxidation states stable only in condensed solids

Introduction

Wet chemical analysis excludes all spectrographic techniques that measure the emission of electromagnetic energy from the sample. Similarly excluded from this article are all other fundamentally instrumental analytical techniques, although extensive chemical pretreatment may be required for their use. What primarily remains are those time-honored laboratory procedures often referred to as classical, many of which date back nearly five centuries to the beginnings of chemistry. In the area of quantitative elemental analysis, they include gravimetry, in which a chemical species is weighed; titrimetry, which involves volume measurement of a liquid reactant; and a host of separation techniques, which require diverse forms of laboratory manipulation. These latter include procedures necessary for isolating the analyte species before application of the former two techniques, although many of them find wider use in instrumental methods as well.

Also included in this article are procedures for isolating intact from the sample matrix some chemical compound that bears on the properties of the material, such as oxide inclusions in a steel alloy, and those that provide information on the oxidation state of the component, such as the FeO/Fe_2O_3 ratio in a slag. Finally, those applications in surface studies and in rapid material identification in which chemical techniques have proved useful will be briefly discussed.

The quantitative elemental analysis of industrial materials will be emphasized with virtual exclusion of functional group analysis of organic materials (described in the article "Elemental and Functional Group Analysis" in this Volume), physiochemical testing, environmental/industrial hygiene and forensic studies, and empirical or engineering tests peculiar to a specific product or industry. Background information is cited in Ref 1 to 4.

Appropriateness of Classical Wet Methods

Modern instrumental techniques for quantitative elemental analysis have advanced materials characterization. For example, a simultaneous x-ray fluorescence spectrometer can determine 30 elements in a high-temperature alloy to two decimal place accuracy in 40 s. Classical wet chemical techniques, which often require days or weeks, persist in industry because, first, sample size and form are important constraints on most rapid spectrographic methods. Most classical wet chemical methods can accommodate comparatively small amounts of sample in diverse shapes or

forms. Second, some spectrographic techniques are used to analyze small areas of a sample surface, and the validity of the results depends on a high degree of sample homogeneity. However, chemical methods may be applied to a laboratory sample devised to represent the gross chemistry of a moderately inhomogeneous material, for example, millings obtained at the mid-radius of a steel billet. Third, some spectrographic techniques are sensitive to the thermal and mechanical treatment the sample has received, or are affected seriously by sample surface preparation. Wet chemical methods are free of these problems. Fourth, and perhaps most significant, classical wet chemical methods provide the fundamental calibration for nearly all rapid spectrographic techniques.

Although alternatives exist, such as a fundamental parameters approach in x-ray fluorescence, a satisfactory substitute for the use of classical wet analysis to calibrate spectrographic methods is not available. Classical wet analysis often takes the form of establishing wet chemical values for several sizable lots of material known to be homogeneous and using these materials regularly to establish signal-to-concentration relationships on the high-speed spectrographs and to monitor the long- and short-term drift of those instruments.

Every small materials producer or consumer with a spectrograph need not provide this calibration support; various standardized materials are commercially available from diverse sources world-wide. These commercial standards have been analyzed using classical wet chemical techniques, among others, and include primary materials, with certified compositional values of high reliability, and secondary materials, with values traceable to primary standards. However, commercial standards do not provide the complete answer to spectrographic calibration. Some materials categories are not covered by a commercial standard. In addition, some industries require highly accurate analysis of a wide array of materials. Many spectrographic techniques require closely related standards for the most accurate analysis of unknowns. This situation often requires maintenance of a wet chemical laboratory to provide spectrographic calibration materials.

Finally, there remains a narrowing category of analytical requirements for which classical wet chemistry is the only applicable approach. High-accuracy analyses of major amounts of the halogens remain largely within wet chemistry, although ion chromatography handles halogens better in combination (see the Section "Chromatography" in this Volume). A similar situation prevails with multielement moieties, such as NH_4^+, CN^-, and SO_3^{2-}. For quantitatively distin-

guishing certain elemental oxidation states, for example, iron(II), (III), and (0), wet chemistry continues to be the primary approach.

Although instrumental approaches frequently produce precise data, and their detection limits may be extended to minute concentrations, a classical wet chemical "umpire" procedure still prevails in ultimate accuracy. Therefore, commercial agreements involving high-performance or critical commodities sometimes specify use of certain specific classical wet chemical procedures in the analysis. The time and cost intensity of such work is often reflected in the final value of the goods involved.

Basic Chemical Equilibria and Analytical Chemistry (Ref 5-7)

Fundamental to the rudimentary chemical principles upon which classical wet chemical analysis is founded is the concept of stoichiometry, which connotes the manner in which chemical species react. Although these reactions occur among discrete atoms, ions, and molecules, macroquantities of these substances must be studied, revealing useful relationships. A mole of a chemical compound is numerically equal to its molecular weight in grams. Similarly, a gram-atom of an element equals its atomic weight in grams. These units contain 6.023×10^{23} molecules or atoms, respectively—a quantity known as Avogadro's number. Reactions occur between integral numbers or fractions of moles or gram-atoms. The concept of equivalent weight simplifies calculations involving fractional quantities. An equivalent weight is numerically equal to the molecular or atomic weight in grams divided by the number of electrons transferred in the particular reaction under study.

Also useful is the preparation of solutions containing known, often integral numbers of these quantities. Thus, a one molar (1 M) solution contains 1 mole per liter and a one normal (1 N) solution contains one equivalent weight per liter. If these solutions are carefully prepared from pure substances (primary standards), their concentration is known accurately, and they may be used for subsequent analytical calculations. However, sufficiently pure starting materials are often unavailable, and the solution must be standardized by reacting a portion with a primary standard solution and calculating the exact molar or normal concentration. In volumetric work, the concept of molarity and normality is sometimes discarded for a titer, an exact relationship between a volume of the specific reactant solution and a weight of the substance sought in the determination. This relationship is established using primary standard materials, often with a certified material similar to the unknown sample.

Gravimetric analysis, or gravimetry, involves isolation of the analyte, that is, the element or other species sought, as a precipitate from a dissolved portion of the sample. This is usually accomplished by addition of a solution of a reagent that reacts rapidly with the analyte to form a compound of low solubility in the usually aqueous solvent mediums. The suitability of the reagent used may be predicted by examining the solubility products constant (K_{SP}) of the reaction product. This is a measure of its tendency to dissociate, that is, its solubility. Values of K_{SP} lower than 10^{-9} signify stable precipitates that generally form readily, although K_{SP} values to 10^{-5} have some analytical utility.

In practice, the slight solubility of precipitates in the reaction medium is reduced further by use of an excess of the precipitating reagent, exploiting the common ion effect. The presence of other diverse ions in the solution sometimes increases the solubility of the precipitate; to minimize this effect, precipitations are usually prepared in dilute solutions. An element may also be removed from solution as a neutral atomic form, as when selenium metal is precipitated by addition of a strong reducing agent or when copper metal is plated out by the application of an external electric current.

The goal of gravimetric analysis is the quantitative removal of the pure precipitate from the reaction medium for weighing. This is usually accomplished by filtration, followed by drying or ignition to a more stable form. For example, one common problem is coprecipitation, in which foreign ions from the sample solution contaminate the precipitate, usually by physical adsorption. Techniques for reducing this effect include aging the precipitate, dissolution and reprecipitation, reducing or oxidizing the potential contaminant ions, and the order in which the reactants are brought together. Other concerns include the growth of the precipitate particles to a size that may be filtered practically, possible loss of some filtered precipitate due to dissolution or colloid formation during washing, and possible reduction or volatilization of the residue during ignition.

The precipitation of a chemical compound is an example of chemical equilibrium that is shifted largely in one direction by the removal of a product species from solution. In chemical notation this is:

$$A + B \rightleftharpoons AB \downarrow$$

Similar equations apply to other reactions in which products are removed as a gas; for example, in the reaction of sodium borate with methanol, the methyl borate is distilled from the solution by application of heat. However, many other chemical reactions can be studied only by regarding the point at which an equilibrium state is reached:

$$A + B \rightleftharpoons C + D$$

At the equilibrium point, the rate at which A and B react equals the rate at which C and D react, and a constant may be defined based on the activity of the products and the reactants. Activity is derived thermodynamically from a consideration of the change in free energy of the system. However, in simple ionic reactions in which behavior is nearly ideal, the relationship may be reduced to:

$$K_{eq} = \frac{[C] \times [D]}{[A] \times [B]}$$

where the brackets signify molar concentrations. Any numerical coefficients in the reaction equation appear as exponents in the equilibrium expression. In the example given, they are all 1.

Such chemical systems at the equilibrium point are central to most types of volumetric analysis. In acid-base titrations, an acid and a base react to form a salt and water. The simplest example of this class of reactions involves the case in which both reactants are strong electrolytes; that is, both are completely ionized. For example, if portions of a 0.25 M sodium hydroxide solution are added to 25 mL of a 0.50 M nitric acid solution, equilibrium will be reached when 50 mL has been added:

$$0.25 \text{ mole/L} \times (0.05000 \text{ L}) =$$
$$0.50 \text{ mole/L} \times 0.02500 \text{ L}$$

At this equilibrium point, the solution is neutral; its hydrogen ion concentration is given by the dissociation of water:

$$2H_2O \rightleftharpoons H_3O^+ + OH^-$$

$$K_{eq} = 1.01 \times 10^{-14}$$

where H_3O^+ is the hydrated proton or hydronium ion, as the hydrogen ion is correctly known, and OH^- is the hydroxyl ion. At equilibrium, the concentration of each of

these species is 1.0×10^{-7} M. Such concentrations are expressed advantageously as pH, defined as $-\log [H_3O^+]$. In this case, the pH is 7. Acidic solutions have pH values below 7; basic solutions, above 7.

The situation is complicated when the acid or the base is a weak electrolyte, that is, incompletely ionized. The pH at the equilibrium point is not 7, because the salt product that forms establishes an equilibrium with water to produce hydronium or hydroxyl ions. When a weak acid is titrated using a strong base, the equilibrium pH is above 7 because the salt that forms produces hydroxyl ions. When a weak base is titrated using a strong acid, the equilibrium pH is below 7 because the salt that forms produces hydronium ions. In the laboratory, the equilibrium point (the titration endpoint) is detected by means of a pH meter or by the color change of a pH indicator, an organic dye that changes color within the appropriate pH interval.

Preparation of a solution that resists change in pH is sometimes desirable, exploiting the equilibria of weak electrolytes. For example, a mixture of a weak acid and its salt may constitute such a buffer solution. Such solutions are used to calibrate pH meters and are often added to solutions to maintain their pH while other chemical reactions proceed.

Oxidation-Reduction Reactions. A second major class of reaction used widely in volumetric analysis is the oxidation-reduction, or redox, reaction. A species that gains electrons is reduced, and one that loses electrons is oxidized. Half-cell reactions provide useful study:

Reduction	Oxidation
A . . $Fe^{3+} + e^- \rightarrow Fe^{2+}$	D . . $Fe^{2+} \rightarrow Fe^{3+} + e^-$
B . . $Cu^{2+} + 2e^- \rightarrow Cu^0$	E . . $2I^- \rightarrow I_2 + 2e^-$
C . . $Cr_2O_7^{2-} + 14H^+ + 6e^- \rightarrow 2Cr^{3+} + 7H_2O$	F . . $H_2SO_3 + H_2O \rightarrow SO_4^{2-} + 4H^+ + 2e^-$

In reaction A, the ferric ion (+III oxidation state) gains an electron, reducing it to ferrous ion (+II oxidation state). Similarly, in reaction D, iron(+II) loses an electron to form iron(+III). In reaction B, cupric ion (+II) gains two electrons and becomes copper metal (zero oxidation state). In reaction E, two iodide ions (both I^-) each lose an electron, and elemental iodine (oxidation state 0) is formed.

Reactions C and F illustrate that the aqueous medium participates. In reaction C, dichromate ions, in which chromium has the oxidation state of +VI, is reduced, gaining two electrons and forming two chromic ions, each of +III oxidation state. In reaction F, sulfurous acid, in which sulfur has a +IV oxidation state, loses two electrons and becomes sulfate ion, in which sulfur has a +VI oxidation state. In the absence of an applied electric current, these reactions must work in pairs, driving each other toward equilibrium, and only certain paired reactions are feasible for analytical purposes. Feasibility may be determined by considering the difference in the formal oxidation potential of the two half-cell reactions, which is a measure of the tendency to gain or lose electrons. For example, the reaction:

$$6Fe^{2+} + 14H^+ + Cr_2O_7^{2-} \rightleftharpoons 6Fe^{3+} + 2Cr^{3+} + 7H_2O$$

proceeds rapidly and is used analytically in the volumetric determinations of iron and chromium.

Half-cell potentials are deduced from first-principle thermodynamics, which take no account of other species in solution; formal potentials are derived by experimental measurement in analytically useful reactions. Only these latter potentials, applied within their qualifying conditions—for example, in the presence of a specific concentration of a specific strong acid—have predictive power in most analytical situations. Using formal half-cell potentials to calculate the equilibrium constant of a redox reaction can provide a measure of its analytical utility by predicting the net electrical potential change at the equivalence point and the degree of completeness of the reaction at the equivalence point. The potential change must be large enough to detect, and the completeness of the reaction must meet the tolerable error of the determination.

Redox endpoint detection may be accomplished visually or by monitoring the potential change electronically using an inert electrode, usually platinum. A color change due to one of the reactants sometimes occurs at the endpoint; for example, a tiny excess of permanganate ion colors a solution purple. An indicator is occasionally added that reacts with an excess of titrant at the equivalence point; for example, starch forms a blue color with a minute excess of iodine. An organic compound is sometimes added that undergoes a redox color change reaction at the endpoint potential.

The completeness of the redox reaction at the endpoint is sometimes cause for concern. In some instances, adding reagents alters the formal half-cell potentials, decreasing significantly the concentration of unreacted analyte at the endpoint. In other cases, a more practical method is the titer approach, in which a closely matching primary standard is titrated identically to the unknown sample; unreacted analyte and systematic manipulative errors are thus cancelled.

Precipitation titrations are a volumetric application of certain precipitation reactions that are rapid, complete, and for which suitable endpoint indicators are available. A frequent application is the titration of chloride using silver nitrate solution. As the titration proceeds, a white precipitate of silver chloride accumulates in the solution. Excess silver ion at the equivalence point is detected using various indicators, such as:

Mohr titration:

$$2Ag^+ \text{ (excess)} + CrO_4^{2-} \rightarrow Ag_2CrO_4$$
$$\quad\quad\quad\quad\quad\text{(chromate)}\quad\text{(red precipitate)}$$

Volhard titration:

$$Ag^+ \text{ (excess)} + 2SCN^- \rightarrow$$
$$\quad\quad\quad\quad\quad\text{(thiocyanate)}$$

$$AgSCN\downarrow + SCN^-\text{(excess)}$$
$$\text{(white precipitate)}$$

$$SCN^- \text{ (excess)} + Fe^{3+} \rightarrow FeSCN^{2+}$$
$$\quad\quad\quad\quad\quad\quad\quad\quad\quad\text{(red color)}$$

Indicators include a class of fluorescent organic compounds adsorbed on the silver chloride particles, forming a color. Bromide and iodide may be determined similarly, and related methods are useful for silver and mercury.

Complexometric titrations use reactions that result in the formation of stable, soluble molecular aggregates, usually without affecting the oxidation state of the analyte ion. Analytically useful reactions of this class occur in one step or have the last step as the rate-limiting step. The object is to achieve a readily detectable drop in the concentration of free (uncomplexed) analyte species at the equivalence point. An important category of these reactions are chelometric titrations, in which free metal ions form 1 to 1 complexes with those organic compounds, such as EDTA, known collectively as chelons.

In these reactions, multiple sites on the organic molecule simultaneously bond with a single metal ion—that is, the chelon coordinates with the metal ion—resulting in a large, soluble, often electrically charged metallorganic ion. Because the completeness of such reactions depends strongly on pH, an appropriate buffer solution is often added to maintain the pH in the optimal range. Endpoints are commonly detected using metallochromic indicators, which are chelons that exhibit different colors, depending on whether or not they have coordinated with a metal ion. In materials analysis, complexometric titrations are frequently used to determine the alkaline earth elements and certain transition metals.

Complexation reactions may also be used to mask interferences in any analytical measurement. Complexed ions, like precipitated species, are often blocked effectively from further reaction, allowing accurate measurement of the species of interest. However, elimination of interferences is often more complex. Certain measurements require complete or partial isolation of the analyte from matrix species. Such operations are grouped under the term "separation science" and find wide application.

Solvent Extraction. The interface between two immiscible liquids is permeable to some species and impermeable to others. When an aqueous solution and an organic solvent are agitated together, some amount of certain components passes from the aqueous to the organic phase, partitioning themselves between the two liquids. A distribution coefficient based on the ratio of the activity of a given species in both liquids is a measure of the effectiveness of the separation.

Ionic species ordinarily must be converted first to neutral compounds to pass in significant amounts from an aqueous solution into a nonpolar solvent, that is, a solvent, like chloroform, with no significant dipole moment. However, charged species may be isolated in a nonpolar solvent by passing over as an ion pair whose net charge is zero. By changing conditions, such as pH, or adding reagents, an analyte species extracted into an organic phase can sometimes be returned to fresh aqueous phase virtually free of its former matrix. In other cases, it may be necessary to evaporate and/or wet-ash the organic phase with oxidizing acids to return the analyte to aqueous solution. In some procedures, it is possible to finish the determination directly in the organic phase.

Ion exchange separation procedures use specially synthesized polymer resins containing ionizable functional groups. If the functional groups attached to the resin have a negative charge, the resin may be used to retain cations (positive ions) selectively. If the resin charge is positive, the resin retains anions (negative ions) selectively. The resin charge is always balanced by some counter-ion from the solution it contacts. The resin, in the form of a bed of beads, is usually contained in a column, and sample solutions

Table 1   Commonly used techniques for subdividing solids for wet chemical analysis

Technique	Remarks	Applications
Drilling	Use largest practical bit size; some hard materials may be annealed before sampling	Steel, pig iron, gray iron, malleable iron, and wrought or cast nonferrous metals and alloys
Crushing	Jaw crusher to reduce large pieces to marble-size; roll crusher, ring pulverizer, or ball mill to finish crushing process	Nodular iron, graphite iron, high-speed steel, ferroalloys, slags, limestone, fluorspar, ores, refractories, and rocks
Milling	Allows full cross section to be sampled	See Drilling
Punching, nibbling	Applicable to sheet forms	See Drilling

and various eluent solutions are passed over it.

The selectivity coefficient of a given system is a measure of the tendency for the resin to give up the counterion it has for an ion in the solution passing over it. The selectivity of a given ion-exchange system relates to the activity of the possible counterions, which pertains to such factors as charge and ionic radius. In general practice, the analyte is bound to the column while potential interferences from the sample matrix are washed out. The analyte is then stripped from the column using an appropriate eluent solution. Ion exchange is discussed in the Section "Chromatography" in this Volume.

Sample Dissolution

Although some liquid samples require classical wet chemical analysis, for example, acid pickling baths, plating solutions, or process water, most of the materials samples encountered in an industrial environment are solids. For classical techniques, these require some type of digestion to obtain an aqueous solution for analysis. Dissolution techniques are nearly as varied as sample types, but regardless of the approach, it is generally beneficial to work with the sample in a finely divided form. Drillings, millings, and powders dissolve more readily than large pieces, and the particulate sample, however it was obtained, must adequately represent the test material. Therefore, the solid sample must be carefully selected, prepared (for

example, alloy surfaces may be pickled with acid or solvent degreased), then subdivided in some manner (for example, ores may be crushed in a ball mill).

The particulate sample that results must be sieved, sized, riffled, and quartered, as with crushed slags, for example, or solvent cleaned, as with machined alloy chips. If samples are sieved, the fraction reserved for analysis must represent the desired analytical sample. Sometimes certain analytes are concentrated in fines and depleted in coarse fractions. Each part of this procedure is important, because subsequent analytical work is based on the assumption that the particulate sample is a microcosm of the material being tested, which is usually intended to be the gross composition of the material. Detailed procedures for sampling various materials for chemical analysis are cited in Ref 8 to 10. Table 1 summarizes commonly used techniques and the materials types to which they are frequently applied.

A weighed portion of the laboratory sample can often be dissolved using several approaches, but the medium used must be selected with consideration of the sample and the analysis. Many facile digestion techniques result in a sample solution whose ionic composition is incompatible with determination of a given analyte. In addition, because some samples are inherently heterogeneous, any one dissolution technique will likely leave an insoluble residue that occasionally may be ignored or removed and discarded, but often must be further treated to effect complete digestion (Ref 11-14).

Nonoxidizing Acids and Acid Mixtures. Treatment with mineral acids, the most widely used dissolution technique, is applicable to many metals, ores, and a multitude of other inorganic and organic industrial materials. Acid digestion may be broadly characterized as oxidizing or nonoxidizing.

Nonoxidizing acid attack is often associated with complex formation activity for some of the sample components. Hydrochloric acid is the most commonly used hydrohalic acid. In various dilutions with water, it attacks a wide spectrum of metals and alloys, except the precious and group VB metals. In commercial alloys, attack with hydrochloric acid often leaves insoluble compounds and phases. The attack of hydrochloric acid on oxides and other relatively stable compounds is considerably less comprehensive. Thus, for example, iron ore, limestone, and dolomite dissolve readily; fluorspar dissolves only when additional fluoride-complexing species, such as borate, are added; and glass, firebrick, and chromite ore are not attacked.

Important losses of sample components, as volatile hydrides or chlorides, can occur when hydrochloric acid is used alone; examples include boron, sulfur, phosphorus, arsenic, antimony, tin, mercury, and germanium. Use of an acid digestion bomb under high temperature and pressure greatly extends the range of materials that hydrochloric acid dissolves and can eliminate loss of volatiles. Inorganic constituents may sometimes be effectively leached from an organic sample using hydrochloric acid. Two other hydrohalic acids, hydrobromic and hydroiodic, are much less frequently used, especially alone.

Hydrofluoric acid, alone or mixed with hydrochloric, sulfuric, or phosphoric acid, is a useful nonoxidizing dissolution medium for siliceous samples, such as glasses, silicates, quartz, and high-silica minerals and refractories. Such operations must be conducted in special labware, usually of polytetrafluoroethylene (Teflon, Kel F, and so on) or platinum. Use of high pressure in an acid digestion bomb greatly facilitates some difficult dissolutions; for example, tantalum and niobium ores yield in this manner to a hydrofluoric acid/hydrochloric acid mixture. If a pressure vessel is not used, very stable materials, such as refractory nitrides, dissolve slowly, often requiring up to four days for completion. Loss of volatiles may be a problem, especially if the solutions are heated strongly in open vessels; arsenic, antimony, boron, and even certain earth acids (transition metals that precipitate as hydrated oxides from acid solution, such as niobium, tantalum, titanium, zirconium, hafnium, tungsten, and molybdenum) may be lost. Fluoboric acid, which selectively dissolves silicate minerals but not quartz, is applicable to certain determinations.

Sulfuric acid is a widely used nonoxidizing acid. Its dilute water solutions are often more aggressive toward iron-base alloys than the concentrated acid. The converse is true for other metals, which may involve the slight oxidizing power of the hot concentrated acid. Calcium, strontium, barium, and lead form insoluble sulfates, and volatile losses of mercury, selenium, and rhenium may occur during dissolution. The hot concentrated acid is often used to dissolve sulfide ores, mineral halides, and rare earth phosphates, such as monazite sand. With a pressure vessel, such difficult materials as alumina, boron nitride, and chromite ore dissolve.

Phosphoric acid is rarely used alone, but may be used to dissolve chromium and iron ores. With sulfuric acid, it will dissolve other oxide minerals as well, including many silicates and aluminates. The complexing properties of phosphate ion eliminate use of phosphoric acid for many analyses; for others, such as for the determination of iron in iron ore, it is advantageous.

Oxidizing Acids and Acid Mixtures. The most commonly used oxidizing acid is nitric acid. It dissolves most metals, except gold, the platinum group, and certain others, such as chromium, the group IIIA elements, and the earth acids, which form passive oxide coatings rapidly. It dissolves many sulfide ores and phosphate rocks. In the Carius method, small weights of organic material are destroyed in small volumes of nitric acid in sealed glass tubes in an armored furnace.

With hydrochloric acid, nitric acid forms a powerful oxidizing solvent that incorporates nitrosyl chloride and free chlorine. A 3:1 ratio of hydrochloric acid to nitric acid is aqua regia, although many other ratios are used. Gold and platinum dissolve in hot aqua regia, although such precious metals as iridium are resistant, and passive oxides generally do not form. Hydrochloric acid/nitric acid mixtures are used to dissolve stainless steels, high-temperature alloys, and many minerals and ores. Leforte aqua regia (1:3 hydrochloric acid to nitric acid) is frequently used to dissolve sulfide minerals for gravimetric sulfur determination, in which sulfides are oxidized to sulfates during dissolution. Addition of a third component, such as bromine or potassium iodide, often enhances the effectiveness of hydrochloric acid/nitric acid mixtures.

Many materials that resist other acids yield to a mixture of nitric acid and hydrofluoric acid. Refractory metals and their alloys dissolve, although the presence of high chromium requires addition of hydrochloric acid. Polytetrafluoroethylene vessels are necessary, but platinum vessels will serve if hydrochloric acid is excluded. Because these reactions are sometimes violent, it is often best to react the sample with hydrofluoric acid first at room temperature, followed by dropwise addition of nitric acid, applying heat only if necessary.

Excess nitric acid and its volatile reaction products often must be removed before analytical work may proceed. This is usually accomplished by adding sulfuric, phosphoric, and/or perchloric acid to the cooled solution and reheating to form strong fumes of the acid anhydride. Alternatively, these nonvolatile mineral acids may be added with nitric acid at the beginning of dissolution.

For special applications, particularly the dissolution of minerals, or to prevent sample hydrolysis, nitric acid may be used with other oxidizing or complexing substances. Sodium and potassium chlorate, hydrogen peroxide, tartaric, citric, and oxalic acids, and sodium oxalate are examples.

Perchloric acid, although weakly oxidizing at room temperature, is a powerful oxidant at high temperature. It is sometimes used, often with phosphoric acid, to dissolve metals and alloys; only gold and some of the platinum group metals are resistant. Avoidance of explosions necessitates the presence of nitric acid if organic material is present. An explosion is possible whenever hot perchloric acid contacts an easily oxidized substance. Fuming in perchloric acid requires a specially designed fume hood that may be washed periodically to eliminate potentially explosive condensates. Although such fuming is often valuable, it leads to losses of arsenic, boron, chromium, germanium, mercury, osmium, rhenium, and ruthenium, among others.

The liquid fire method of wet-ashing organic substances is based on a mixture of nitric and perchloric acids in which a large excess of HNO_3 is maintained. Mixtures of sulfuric and perchloric acid dissolve chromite ore and may be used in the presence of excess nitric acid to destroy organic matter.

Hydrogen peroxide, especially when used with hydrochloric acid, is a valuable dissolution medium for metals and alloys, particularly iron-, nickel-, and cobalt-base materials. Hydrogen peroxide also may be used with sulfuric acid, but this combination is generally less effective. Hydrobromic acid/bromine combinations are useful in dissolving lead and tin-base alloys, among others, when it is desirable to volatilize arsenic, selenium, antimony, and tin.

The list of oxidizing and nonoxidizing acid combinations used for special analytical applications is extensive. Additional information is cited in Ref 11 and 12. Table 2 lists common dissolution mediums and examples of their use.

Sinters and Fusions. When acid dissolution is ineffective, the next resort in attempting to digest a solid sample is usually a high-temperature reaction with a salt. For a sinter, the reaction between the salt and the sample occurs in the solid state below the melting point of an intimate mixture of the two. In the case of a fusion, the reaction occurs in the molten state. In both cases, the cooled reaction mass is dissolved in water or acids to achieve an aqueous solution of the sample. Sinters and fusions are sometimes applied to completing the dissolution of a sample that only partially dissolved in acid mediums. A small amount of acid-insoluble material often contains most of the analyte of interest. The insoluble materials are filtered, the filter medium is ashed, and the insoluble residue is sintered or fused, dissolved, and recombined with filtrate. The soluble and insoluble fractions may also be analyzed separately, providing additional information.

Table 2 Commonly used acid mediums for digesting solid samples

Medium	Remarks	Applications
HCl	Volatiles loss may be serious	Low-alloy steels and chromium metal
HCl/H_2O_2	Repeated H_2O_2 addition often required	Nickel- and cobalt-base alloys
HCl/HNO_3	Aqua regia and others— wide use	Stainless steels, gold, and platinum
HBr/Br_2	Tin, arsenic, antimony, and selenium lost as volatiles	Tin-lead solders and white bearing metal
HF	Teflon or platinum labware required; silicon lost	Glasses and quartz
HF/HNO_3	See above; reaction may be vigorous	Superalloys, niobium, and tantalum
HNO_3	Surface passivation of some metals	Nickel, mercury, and copper
H_2SO_4	Reaction rate sensitive to dilution	Low-alloy steels; sulfide ores
HNO_3/H_2SO_4	Excess HNO_3 must be present	Destruction of organic matter
HNO_3/$HClO_4$	See above; "the liquid fire method"	Destruction of organic matter

The reaction vessel for sinters and fusions is usually a crucible. Its material composition must be critically matched to the salt medium and the desired analyte. Muffle furnaces or gas burners generally provide the heat source. Sintering procedures specify an optimum temperature, which should not be exceeded to avoid incipient melting. Sodium peroxide, the most common sintering agent, may be applied to many minerals and ores, including feldspar, quartz, scheelite, beryl, and rutile. If the sample contains little sulfur, and the temperature remains below 500 °C (930 °F), a platinum crucible may be used. A 1:2 mixture of sodium carbonate and magnesium oxide is used to sinter coal and sulfide minerals for determination of sulfur. Silicates are decomposed for alkali metal determination by heating with a mixture of calcium carbonate and ammonium chloride.

Fusions, more widely used than sinters, may be categorized as acidic/basic or oxidative/nonoxidative (Fig. 1). Sodium peroxide fusions must be performed in iron, nickel, or zirconium crucibles (in increasing preference regarding durability and safety). As with all sinters and fusions, the sample should be finely divided and uniformly mixed in cor-

Fig. 1 Comparison of the properties of common fluxes

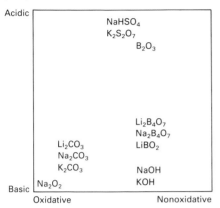

rect proportions with the reactant. Sinters and fusions with sodium peroxide should be conducted behind a shield for safety. Because heating of sodium peroxide with many materials may produce a violent or explosive reaction, extreme caution is necessary when working with materials of unknown reactivity. Organic and carbonaceous materials, among others, react violently and must be excluded. Other highly reactive materials include ferrosilicon and silicomanganese. Sodium peroxide fusion will solubilize many difficult materials, such as slags, ores, refractories, and ferroalloys. Moderation of the reaction may be accomplished by substituting a mixture of sodium carbonate and sodium peroxide for the pure reagent.

Sodium, potassium, and lithium carbonates are widely used fluxes. Potassium salt is the highest melting, sodium the intermediate, and lithium the lowest melting and the most corrosive to the platinum crucibles frequently used for carbonate fusions. Mixtures of two or three of these salts in various weight ratios are frequently used. Carbonate

fusions are generally applicable to silicate minerals and siliceous slags and refractories.

Frequently used fluxes include the anhydride of boric acid (boron trioxide), borax (sodium tetraborate), and lithium metaborate and tetraborate. Crucible materials are platinum or graphite. Various combinations with alkali metal carbonates have been proposed for specific sample materials and have been suggested as a "universal flux." Borate/carbonate combinations often succeed where carbonates alone fail to achieve complete solution, such as with high-alumina materials.

Fusion with sodium or potassium hydroxide is conducted in nickel, silver, or gold crucibles. The optimum approach is to melt the flux first, cool the crucible, add the sample, and reheat the crucible. This helps limit spattering from adsorbed water. Hydroxide fusions may be used for such materials as glass, quartz, sand, and bauxite.

The most important acidic fluxes are sodium bisulfate (anhydrous) and potassium pyrosulfate. The selection of crucibles includes platinum, quartz, and Vycor; for certain applications, small quartz or Vycor flasks are used. A small amount of concentrated sulfuric acid is sometimes added before heating, particularly with the use of anhydrous sodium bisulfate. During fusion, abundant fumes of sulfur trioxide evolve. These fluxes dissolve most forms of alumina (including corundum, ruby, and sapphire), commercial titanium ores, and most metals and alloys. Notably insoluble are quartz, the tin ore cassiterite, and zircon.

Another useful flux is potassium hydrogen difluoride, which decomposes beryl, zircon, cassiterite, and niobium and tantalum ores. Other fluoride fluxes are ammonium and potassium fluoride, as well as sodium or lithium fluoride with boric acid. All these fluxes require platinum vessels. Table 3 summarizes information on some commonly used fluxes.

Miscellaneous Techniques. Many specialized dissolution procedures are peculiar to a given sample matrix, analytical technique, or industry. For determination of inorganic materials in an organic matrix, the sample is often reacted with oxygen to remove carbon. In addition to techniques for simple ignition in air or a stream of oxygen, which result in the loss of some components, three widely used techniques minimize the loss of volatiles: Schöniger flask combustion, in which the sample is burned in atmospheric pressure oxygen in a closed glass vessel, and reaction products are absorbed in an aqueous solution; bomb calorimeter ignition, with the sample electrically ignited and burned in a high-pressure oxygen atmosphere in an armored cannister; and oxygen plasma dry ashing, which uses radio frequency (RF) generated oxygen plasma to remove carbon from the sample at low temperature. Organic materials are also frequently reacted with alkali metals or their salts before determination of inorganic constituents. Three common techniques are fusion with lithium, sodium, or potassium metal, reaction with sodium peroxide in an armored bomb, and reaction with sodium metal dissolved in liquid ammonia.

Some techniques for dissolving inorganic materials rely on producing a volatile product from the major component. Thus, tin ore is reacted with ammonium iodide to evolve tin tetraiodide. Reaction with steam at high temperature (pyrohydrolysis) may be used for borides and fluorides, often using a metal oxide catalyst.

A dissolution technique is sometimes designed to solubilize a distinct portion of the sample. For example, in the Freiberger decomposition, a lead alloy or other sample is heated in a porcelain crucible with sodium carbonate and sulfur. The soluble arsenic, antimony, tin, germanium, molybdenum, tungsten, and vanadium are extracted from the cooled melt, leaving the remainder of the sample as insoluble sulfides. The various techniques by which metal is dissolved, leaving behind various nonmetallic constituents for isolation and study, will be discussed in the section of this article on "Inclusion and Second-Phase Testing." Table 4 lists some miscellaneous mediums useful in dissolving specific materials.

Qualitative Methods

Classical wet chemistry primarily involves quantitative analysis of solutions obtained by one or more of the techniques described above. However, qualitative methods are sometimes used to identify materials by wet chemical reactions.

Table 3 Commonly used fluxes for fusing powder samples

Medium	Crucible material(s)	Remarks	Applications
Na_2O_2	Zirconium (preferred), nickel, and iron	Danger if carbonaceous matter present	Most minerals, slags, and refractories
Li_2CO_3, Na_2CO_3, and K_2CO_3	Platinum	Use lid; high temperature required	Silicate minerals and some organics
$NaHSO_4$ and $K_2S_2O_7$	Platinum, quartz, and Vycor	H_2SO_4 controls spattering; SO_3 evolved	Alumina minerals; metal alloys
B_2O_3, $Li_2B_4O_7$, $Na_2B_4O_7$, and $LiBO_2$	Platinum and graphite	Often used in combination with carbonates	Some minerals, slags, glasses, and so on
NaOH and KOH	Nickel, silver, and gold	Premelt flux to remove H_2O	Sand, glass, and quartz

Table 4 Miscellaneous dissolution mediums

Medium	Applications
Aqueous NaOH, KOH, or Na_2CO_3	Aluminum and aluminum alloys
NaOH + H_2O_2	Rhenium and uranium
NH_4OH + H_2O_2	Molybdenum and copper
CH_3COOH + H_2O_2	Lead and lead alloys
CH_3OH	Magnesium
Cl_2 + NaCl + heat	Platinum group metals

Table 5 Qualitative chemical tests used in materials identification

Test for:	Reagent	Positive result	Applications
Chromium	Diphenylcarbazide	Violet color	Identify chromium-free steel
Cobalt	Ammonium thiocyanate/acetone	Blue color	Identify cobalt-base alloys
Copper	Dithizone	Purple color	Sort copper-bearing stainless steels
Iron	Potassium ferricyanide	Blue precipitate	Sort low-iron high-temperature alloys
Lead	Sulfuric acid	White precipitate	Sort leaded bronze
Molybdenum	Potassium thiocyanate/stannous chloride	Pink color	Sort molybdenum-bearing stainless steels
Nickel	Dimethylglyoxime	Red precipitate	Sort 300 series from 400 series stainless steel

The most frequent applications of qualitative analysis relate to metals and alloys; identifying an alloy type in mixed stock situations is one example. Other situations include identification of a surface coating or surface contaminant and detecting the presence or absence of a major component in the sample matrix, for which such instruments as x-ray and optical emission spectrographs are effective (see the articles "X-Ray Spectrometry" and "Optical Emission Spectroscopy" in this Volume). Qualitative methods may be classified as those in which a portion of the solid sample is dissolved and the solution transferred to another medium (test tube, spot plate, or filter paper) and those in which all reactions take place on the sample surface. Acid attack, ionic displacement, or electrolysis initiate dissolution. Identification is generally based on a color reaction or a reaction yielding a precipitate.

Countless such tests are described in the literature. In addition, specialized tests include flame tests, in which sample components impart characteristic color to a flame; borax bead tests, which examine the color of a borax/sample fusion; and tests in which volatiles are collected and identified. Spot test kits for alloy identification and sorting are available. Finally, qualitative versions of separation techniques, such as paper chromatography and ion-exchange chromatography, have been designed. Table 5 lists qualitative methods, and applications are cited in Ref 15 to 18.

Separation Techniques (Ref 19-22)

In quantitative methods, partial or complete isolation of the analyte from its sample matrix is often necessary before the measurement step to eliminate interference from other sample components. Precipitation techniques are widely used with the element of interest in the precipitate or the filtrate. In the former case, the filtered residue may be dissolved off the filter medium, or the filter with its retained residue may be digested using nitric acid and sulfuric and/or perchloric acids.

Hydroxide precipitations are perhaps the most frequently used. Ammonium hydroxide precipitates the inaccurately termed R_2O_3 group (so called because the elements contained frequently occur as oxides of the form R_2O_3), which includes iron(III), chromium(III), aluminum, gallium, beryllium, tin, indium, niobium, tantalum, titanium, zirconium, hafnium, uranium, and the rare earths. Sodium hydroxide precipitates a slightly different array; manganese, nickel, copper, and cobalt must be added to the above list, and

Table 6 Widely applicable precipitation separations

Precipitant	Conditions	Elements precipitated	Remarks
NH_4OH	...	Fe(III), Cr(III), Al, Ga, Be, Sn, In, Nb, Ta, Ti, Zr, Hf, U, and rare earths	NH_4^+ in filtrate sometimes presents difficulties for its further use
NaOH	...	Mn, Ni, Cu, Co, Fe, Cr, Sn, In, Nb, Ta, Ti, Zr, Hf, U, and rare earths	+Na_2O_2 for Cr and V; +Na_2O_2 +Na_2CO_3 for U
H_2S	0.25–13 M HCl	Cu, Ag, Hg, Pb, Bi, Cd, Ru, Rh, Pd, Os, As, Au, Pt, Sn, Sb, Ir, Ge, Se, Te, and Mo	Tl, In, and Ga in presence of excess other precipitated species; tartaric acid prevents V and W from contaminating
H_2S	pH 2–3	Zn (also Tl, In, and Ga—incomplete)	Assumes removal of above H_2S groups
H_2S or $(NH_4)_2S$	pH > 7	Mn, Fe, Ni, and Co	Assumes removal of above H_2S groups; tartrate sometimes required to prevent interferences
Cupferron	Dilute H_2SO_4 or HCl (cold)	Fe, Ga, Sn, Nb, Ta, Ti, Zr, Hf, V, Mo, W, Pd, Sn, and Bi	Excess reagent in filtrate must be destroyed if filtrate is used
8-hydroxy-quinoline	Weak acid or base	Most metals except Re and Pt; in weak acid Pb, Be, and the alkaline earths are not precipitated	HCl will dissolve residue (sometimes used with volumetric finish)
Fluoride ion	Strong acid	Th, U(IV), Mg, Ca, Sr, Ba, and rare earths	Al precipitates from basic solution
Oxalate ion	Strong acid	Th, Mg, Ca, Sr, Ba, Al, rare earths, Co, Cu, Ni, Fe(II), Pb, Bi, Hg, Ag, and Zn	Rarely used without some preliminary separation

Table 7 Common narrow-range precipitants

Precipitant	Elements precipitated	Remarks
Dimethylglyoxime	Ni and Pd	Red Ni and yellow Pd precipitates are relatively clean; high Co requires reprecipitation
Chloride ion	Ag and Hg(I)	AgCl may be photoreduced if not protected from light; HgCl shows slight solubility
Mandelic acid	Zr and Hf	Best precipitated from hot solution; p-Bromo and p-chloro derivatives of mandelic acid also used
Sodium tetraphenylborate	K, Rb, Cs, and NH_4^+	Tl(I), Ag(I), and other monovalent ions; quaternary ammonium ions; and amines also precipitate
Sulfate ion	Ba, Sr, Ca, and Pb	At pH 4.0, only Ba precipitates
Alphabenzoinoxime	Mo	Nb, Si, Pd, W, Ta partially precipitate
Cinchonine	W	Mo, P, and As interfere; Si, Sn, Sb, Nb, and Ta contaminate

due to their amphoteric character, aluminum, gallium, and beryllium must be deleted. The quantitative completion of the sodium hydroxide precipitation of chromium, vanadium, and uranium may be ensured by first adding sodium peroxide; for uranium, sodium carbonate.

Precipitation using sulfide ion is a powerful technique, because its selectivity may be adjusted by altering the hydrogen ion concentration of the sample solution. Because hydrogen sulfide is a toxic gas, and thioacetamide, the principle means of *in situ* generation of hydrogen sulfide, is a known carcinogen, these separations are avoided; however, with proper precautions they remain useful techniques. Table 6 summarizes elements precipitated by sulfide ion under three conditions. Occasionally implemented is the principle that elements precipitated by sulfide from strong acid dissolve in basic sulfide solutions.

The next most important category is precipitation by cupferron, one of a class of broad-range organic precipitants. Cupferron precipitates the same elements as ammonium hydroxide with a few significant exceptions—aluminum, beryllium, indium, chromium, phosphorus, and uranium(VI). For example, a cupferron separation forms the basis of an important isolation step for aluminum determination of steels and allows separation of gallium from aluminum alloys.

Another broad-range precipitant is 8-hydroxyquinoline, or 8-quinolinol. It requires weakly acid or basic solutions and is rather nonspecific. Beryllium is not precipitated from weakly acid solution; this forms the basis of an important separation from aluminum. Other useful broad-range organics include phenylhydrazine, used as an or-

ganic base to precipitate various elements as hydrated oxides, and phenylthiohydantoic acid, used primarily in a separation of cobalt from most iron and nickel. Tannin is often useful with other precipitants, such as ammonium hydroxide, to facilitate precipitation and enhance the filtration characteristics of the residue. N-benzoyl-N-phenylhydroxylamine (BPA) and its derivatives precipitate a broad range of metals. Aluminum is not precipitated with 8-hydroxyquinaldine as it is with 8-hydroxyquinoline.

Examples of narrow-range, or specific, inorganic precipitants are few. Equilibrated suspensions of some oxides and carbonates in water produce pH conditions ideal for certain isolations. Thus, a saturated solution of zinc oxide (pH 5.5) is used to separate cobalt (filtrate) from nickel and iron (precipitate). Chloride ion is used to separate silver and mercury as precipitates. Sulfate ion is used primarily to separate barium, although it may be used under ideal conditions to isolate strontium, calcium, and lead. Fluoride may be used to precipitate scandium, yttrium, lanthanum, and the rare earths as well as calcium and thorium. Some of these are most frequently used in the final isolation step of a gravimetric method.

Narrow-range, or specific, organic precipitants include dimethylglyoxime for nickel and palladium, mandelic acid for zirconium and hafnium, and sodium tetraphenylborate for potassium, rubidium, cesium, and ammonium ion. Table 7 lists narrow-range organic and inorganic precipitants.

Some elements may be isolated by reduction to the elemental state or by hydrolysis to oxides. Reducing agents, such as stannous chloride, sulfurous acid, and hypophosphorous acid, reduce selenium, tellurium, gold,

and arsenic to the filterable element; niobium, tantalum, zirconium, hafnium, titanium, and tungsten are reduced to filterable hydrated oxides.

Certain species may be conveniently separated by distillation. Boron is routinely isolated by reaction with methanol and distillation of the methyl borate ester. Similarly, the volatility of arsenic(III) chloride (at approximately 110 °C, or 230 °F) from hydrochloric acid solution is frequently used to separate that element. Higher temperatures (approximately 160 °C, or 320 °F), reducing conditions, and hydrochloric acid are necessary to distill antimony(III) similarly; and tin(IV) chloride distillation requires extreme conditions (200 °C, or 390 °F) unless hydrobromic acid is added, in which case only approximately 140 °C (285 °F) is required to distill the tin. Under these conditions, germanium accompanies the arsenic quantitatively, and mercury may contaminate the distillate. In addition, molybdenum, rhenium, selenium, and possibly tellurium contaminate the antimony and tin fractions. Special conditions allow use of distillation to isolate germanium(IV) chloride. Selenium may also be separated by distillation from hydrobromic acid, although the technique is not prevalent. Fluorine is routinely distilled as fluosilicic acid. Osmium and ruthenium may be distilled as tetroxides from acid solutions of the platinum group.

Solvent extraction is an extremely important technique for the rapid isolation of many analyte species; the specific systems used are diverse, and few may be regarded as universally applied techniques. Extraction using ethyl ether, particularly from acid chloride mediums, was prevalent, especially for removing most of the iron(III) and molybdenum(VI) from the aqueous phase; the majority of the antimony(V), arsenic(III), gallium(III), gold(III), mercury(II), niobium(V), platinum(II), and thallium(III) is also removed. Inflammability and storage hazards for ethyl ether have diminished use of the technique in recent years. Extraction using methylisobutyl ketone (MIBK) from acid iodide mediums remains in common use, frequently for isolating trace amounts of lead(II), tin(II), antimony(III), and other species in the organic phase. Extraction using tri-N-butyl phosphate from acid nitrate mediums is important for concentrating uranium and the transuranic actinides in the organic phase.

Many other organic derivatives of phosphoric acid are useful extractants for metals, and some are in general use. For example, di-(2-ethylhexyl)phosphoric acid is a viscous liquid whose solution (in nonpolar solvents) extracts many metals from strong acid solu-

Table 8   Common solvent extraction separations

Reagent	Solvent	Remarks	Applications
Cupferron .... Chloroform		pH selective	"Clean up" aqueous phase, leaving analyte
Acetylacetone .... Acetylacetone		pH selective	Isolate analyte, then spectrophotometry, spectrofluorimetry, or gas chromatography on extract
N-phenylbenzo-hydroxamic acid .... Chloroform		Strong acid	Extract Nb, Ta, Ti, Zr, W, Sb, Sn, Zn, and V
Crown polyethers .... Chloroform		Add Li_4 EDTA	Isolate K from portland cement
8-hydroxyquinoline .... Chloroform		pH 9.0	Extract Al from traces of Fe
Dithizone .... Chloroform or carbon tetrachloride		pH selective	Zn, Pb, Bi, Sn(II), Tl(I), Ag, Cd, Se, Te, In, Hg, Cu, Ni, Co, Fe, Mn, Pd, Pt, Ag, and Au; selectivity enhanced by masking agents
Ammonium pyrrolidinedithio-carbamate (APDC) .... MIBK		pH 2.0	Concentration of trace metals
Tri-N-octylphosphine oxide .... Cyclohexane		Strong HNO_3	Extract Zr, Hf, U, Th, and Au

tion. Tri-N-octylphosphine oxide is a white solid that, dissolved in cyclohexane, is used to extract zirconium and tin (among others); dissolved in MIBK, it is used to ensure complete extraction of the iodides of lead, bismuth, thallium, antimony, and other metals. Another class of reagents is the alkyl amines. Tri-N-octylamine, a heavy liquid that dissolves in xylene, may be used to extract the lanthanides and actinides from strong nitric acid solution.

In all the solvent extraction systems discussed, the analyte forms an ion association with some species, resulting in an anion or a cation extracted as an ion pair with an electrically balancing species from the solution matrix (see the section "Basic Chemical Equilibria and Analytical Chemistry" in this article). However, coordinating or chelating reactions often result in electrically neutral species extracted as such into the organic phase. Examples of these latter systems are many. Among the most widely used are acetylacetone (2,4-pentanedione) and its various derivatives, known collectively as β-diketones. Some, like acetylacetone, are light liquids and act as chelating agent and solvent; others are heavy liquids or solids and require dissolution in chlorinated hydrocarbons.

Other examples of general-use reagents of this type are the crown polyethers (or cryptands; these compounds are useful for extraction of alkali and alkaline earth metals), cupferron, 8-hydroxyquinoline, and sodium diethyldithiocarbamate and their analogs. These may be used to extract select groups of cations into an organic phase, such as chloroform. In addition, many extractants—

some quite specific—produce a color reaction with a given analyte. Important use is made of this property for the contiguous isolation and spectrophotometric measurement of the analyte; Table 8 lists common solvent extraction techniques.

Other important separation techniques are treated in detail elsewhere in this Volume. The mercury cathode is commonly used to remove major amounts of matrix elements, leaving behind the earth acids (except molybdenum), aluminum, silicon, boron, the rare earths, the alkaline earths, and the alkali metals. Ion-exchange chromatography is a powerful separation tool used to isolate major sample components and groups of components and to concentrate trace components. Some of these separations are automated and combined with direct measurement of the eluting species in ion chromatography. Liquid chromatography of metal-organic complexes and gas chromatography of volatile metal-organic complexes are similar new technologies.

Gravimetry (Ref 9, 20, 23-25)

Classical gravimetric analysis remains the most accurate technique for determining many species. Because its application to an analytical problem is independent of the availability of and confidence in standard materials, it is often used in "umpire" situations. A primary disadvantage is the time and degree of manipulative skill required to secure the analyte in an isolated, weighable form. To a larger degree than for

most other techniques, the complexity of the analysis parallels that of the sample matrix.

Weighing as the Oxide. Over 40 elements are weighed as stable oxides, although this approach is the method of choice only in certain analytical situations. Hydrolysis of an earth acid, using sulfurous acid or precipitation of a member of the R_2O_3 group using ammonium hydroxide brings down the analyte as a hydrated oxide or hydroxide after scrupulous isolation by previous separations. These precipitates, washed free of solution matrix, may be readily ignited to the highest stable oxide for weighing. Instead, a broad- or narrow-range organic precipitant is often used to bring down the analyte as a complex, which is then ashed to the metal oxide. In either case, the temperature of the ignition requires careful attention to ensure complete conversion of the analyte to a stable oxide and removal of all traces of carbonaceous or other extraneous material and to prevent loss of the analyte due to volatility. This latter point is particularly important in the gravimetric determination of elements whose oxides sublime at relatively low temperatures; MoO_3, the best example, begins to sublime at 500 °C (930 °F).

Deciding whether optimum results will be obtained by merely drying an organic complex and weighing or by igniting it to the oxide and weighing is sometimes difficult. Some organic precipitates are nonstoichiometric or are contaminated with unreacted reagent, for example with the complex between molybdenum and alphabenzoinoxime; these are best ignited to the oxide. Other complexes melt, spatter, or volatilize long before the temperatures needed to produce stable oxide are reached. For example, the red precipitate nickel dimethylglyoxime volatilizes at 250 °C (480 °F); these must be dried at low temperature and weighed as the complex. Table 9 presents examples that illustrate the dilemma and the analytical routes it dictates. Either option is sometimes appropriate, such as when the isolated metal is precipitated using 8-hydroxyquinoline.

Weighing as the Metal. Few elements may be conveniently weighed in their elemental form. The precious metals (except gold) are determined in this way, usually by igniting a hydrated oxide in the presence of hydrogen gas. Gold is precipitated from solution as the metal. Fire assay methods, in which ores are reduced directly to metal and weighed, are also used for precious metals. Selenium is easily reduced to the filterable element, but tellurium requires stronger reducing conditions; advantage is taken of this property in separating and analyzing such combinations. Rhenium, mercury, and arsenic may also be chemically reduced to elemental species, but this approach for

Table 9 Common gravimetric finishes

Analyte	Precipitate as the:	Weigh as the:	Remarks
Calcium . . . . Oxalate		Oxide	Correction for occluded magnesium and strontium required
Copper . . . . Metal		Metal	Electrolytic deposition from dilute acid
Nickel . . . . Dimethylglyoxime complex		Dimethylglyoxime complex	Drying should not exceed 150 °C (300 °F)
Zinc . . . . Sulfide		Oxide	Ignite at 500 °C (930 °F) until filter carbon is gone, then higher
Selenium . . . . Metal		Metal	Use hydroxylamine·HCl if tellurium is present, otherwise H_2SO_3
Zirconium . . . . Pyrophosphate		Pyrophosphate	Ignite at low temperature until filter carbon is gone, then higher
Niobium . . . . Hydroxide		Oxide	Ion-exchange separation from tantalum, and so on, required
Molybdenum . . . . Alphabenzoinoxime complex		Oxide	Ignition should not exceed 500 °C (930 °F)
Ruthenium . . . . Hydrated oxide		Metal	Isolate by distillation of RuO_4
Rhodium . . . . Sulfide		Metal	Preliminary isolation as metal with TiCl
Palladium . . . . Dimethylglyoxime complex		Dimethylglyoxime complex	Dry at 110 °C (230 °F)
Silver . . . . Chloride		Chloride	Protect from light to avoid photoreduction
Cadmium . . . . Sulfate		Sulfate	Elimination of excess H_2SO_4 difficult
Tellurium . . . . Metal		Metal	Reduction with H_2SO_3 + hydrazine
Barium . . . . Sulfate		Sulfate	Fine precipitate; special precautions required
Tungsten . . . . Hydrated oxide		Oxide	Cinchonine aids hydrolysis
Osmium . . . . Hydrated oxide		Metal	Isolate by distillation of osmium
Iridium . . . . Hydrated oxide		Metal	As with others of platinum group: hydrogen-atmosphere furnace used to ignite to metal
Platinum . . . . Sulfide		Metal	Reprecipitate with formic acid for highest accuracy
Gold . . . . Metal		Metal	First reduction: H_2SO_3; for reprecipitation, use $NaNO_2$
Lead . . . . Sulfate		Sulfate	Recover soluble $PbSO_4$ from filtrate by electrolysis
Bismuth . . . . Carbonate		Oxide	If lead present, isolate bismuth as BiOCl and dissolve

these elements is not prevalent. Finally, several elements may be determined by their electrolytical plating as metals on a tared electrode. This technique is common for copper and is sometimes used for nickel, cobalt, cadmium, and silver.

Weighing as the Sulfate. Barium is best determined gravimetrically as the sulfate, and sulfate ion is similarly determined by reaction with barium chloride. Because the precipitate is finely divided, special precautions are required during filtration and ignition. The other alkaline earths and lead also react with sulfate, but the precipitates are somewhat soluble and tend toward contamination with undesired species.

Weighing as the Phosphate or Pyrophosphate. Zirconium and magnesium are the most important analytes in this

category. The precipitate is carefully treated to maintain its stoichiometric composition, then weighed as ZrP_2O_7 or $Mg_2P_2O_7$. Similar methods for aluminum, bismuth, cadmium, manganese, and zinc are less frequently used.

Weighing as the Sulfide. Arsenic may be weighed as As_2S_3 or As_2S_5, antimony as Sb_2S_3, and mercury and zinc as HgS and ZnS, respectively. Although these procedures may be routinely used, none is the method of choice for these elements.

Weighing as the Chloride. Gravimetric determination of silver as AgCl remains an important procedure, although it has been largely supplanted by volumetric methods. The principal difficulty is the light sensitivity of the compound, which causes reduction to metallic silver. Mercury may

also be weighed as HgCl, although better volumetric methods are available.

Weighing as the Chromate. When barium is to be determined in a sample containing calcium and/or strontium, precipitation of barium chromate avoids the positive errors associated with the sulfate precipitation. Thallium may also be effectively weighed as thallous chromate.

Weighing as the Dimethylglyoxime Complex. This is an important approach for nickel, which forms a bright red flocculent precipitate, and palladium, which forms a yellow crystalline precipitate. Both are dried at low temperature.

Miscellaneous Compounds. Innumerable other compounds are routinely weighed in gravimetric analysis. Calcium, thorium, scandium, yttrium, and the lanthanides may be effectively quantified as fluorides, lead as PbClF, bismuth as BiOCl, and palladium as the iodide. The alkali metals (except sodium) may be weighed as chloroplatinates or as tetraphenylborates. Sodium reacts with zinc uranyl acetate to yield a weighable compound. The halides (Cl^-, Br^-, and I^-), when present in isolation, are commonly weighed as silver salts, as are the pseudohalides CN^- and CNS^-. Ammonium ion (NH_4^+), a pseudo alkali metal, may be weighed as a tetraphenylborate. Table 10 illustrates some of the available diversity.

Other Analyte Moieties. Gravimetry is also useful in quantifying other compositional or empirical properties of a sample. Some of these are peculiar to an industry, process, or industrial commodity, often reflecting specific engineering needs.

Moisture and water of hydration are distinct properties measured by weight loss after treatment at different temperatures. However, loss on ignition and ash convey the same meaning, and the usage is largely industry specific. These measurements generally require the use of exact temperatures determined by the nature of the sample and sometimes by industry consensus. More empirical are gravimetric determinations of insoluble residue, filler, volatile matter, total solids, filterable solids, dissolved solids, or extractables. The analyst and the engineer must understand these terms to communicate effectively. Finally, the reporting of analytical results—often from gravimetry—using such prefixed terms as soluble aluminum, insoluble boron, free HF, or combined cyanide requires a similar understanding between the laboratory and its patrons.

Titrimetry (Ref 9, 20, 23-27)

Volumetric analysis is more versatile than gravimetry because, in addition to sample

Table 10 Additional species commonly weighed in gravimetry

Element	Species weighed
Lithium	Li_2SO_4
Beryllium	BeO
Fluorine	CaF_2, PbClF, and ThF_4
Sodium	Sodium zinc uranyl acetate hexahydrate
Magnesium	$Mg_2P_2O_7$ and magnesium 8-hydroxyquinolate
Aluminum	$AlPO_4$ and aluminum 8-hydroxyquinolate
Silicon	SiO_2
Phosphorus	$Mg_2P_2O_7$
Sulfur	$BaSO_4$
Chlorine	AgCl
Potassium	$K_2NaCo(NO_2)_6$, $KClO_4$, K_2PtCl_6, and potassium tetraphenylborate
Calcium	CaF_2 and $CaSO_4$
Titanium	TiO_2
Manganese	$Mn_2P_2O_7$
Iron	Fe_2O_3
Cobalt	Co, Co_3O_4, and $CoSO_4$
Copper	CuO
Zinc	Zn and $ZnNH_4PO_4$
Gallium	Ga_2O_3
Arsenic	As_2S_5
Bromine	AgBr
Rubidium	Rb_2PtCl_6 and rubidium tetraphenylborate
Strontium	$SrSO_4$ and SrO
Zirconium	ZrO_2
Molybdenum	$PbMoO_4$
Silver	Ag
Cadmium	Cd
Indium	In_2O_3
Tin	SnO_2
Antimony	Sb_2S_3 and Sb_2O_4
Iodine	AgI and PdI_2
Cesium	Cs_2PtCl_6 and cesium tetraphenylborate
Barium	$BaCrO_4$
Hafnium	HfP_2O_7 and HfO_2
Tantalum	Ta_2O_5
Rhenium	Re, nitron perrhenate, and tetraphenylarsonium perrhenate
Mercury	HgS, HgCl, and Hg
Thallium	Tl_2CrO_4, Tl_2O_3, and TlI
Lead	$PbMoO_4$ and PbO_2
Bismuth	BiOCl and $BiPO_4$
Scandium, yttrium, thorium, uranium, and the lanthanides	Oxides

Table 11 Common standardizations of titrants

Titrant	Primary standard	Remarks
Dilute strong base	Potassium hydrogen phthalate	Endpoint is pH 8.6 (phenolphthalein); CO_2 must be absent
Dilute strong acid	Standardized NaOH solution	See above
Potassium permanganate solution	Sodium oxalate	Dilute H_2SO_4 medium; heat before completing titration
Ferrous ammonium sulfate solution	$K_2Cr_2O_7$	Dilute H_2SO_4 medium, diphenylamine indicator
Iodine solution	As_2O_3	Starch indicator; protect from air
Sodium thiosulfate solution	Standardized iodine solution	See above

weight, titrant concentration may be adjusted to optimize accuracy for a given concentration range of analyte, the same reaction chemistry may be applied over broad ranges of concentration, and isolation of the analyte from its matrix is often unnecessary. Volumetric determinations are also typically much faster than gravimetric determinations and consequently more suitable for many process control applications. Disadvantages include a somewhat lower achievable ultimate accuracy compared with gravimetry, especially when "umpire" work at analyte concentrations below 1% is indicated. In volumetric "umpire" work, weight burets are sometimes used. These are glass burets with a sealable closure designed to be weighed before and after titration. Volumetric calculations are then based on a weight of titrant used. In addition, volumetric work, unlike gravimetry, requires the use of standard materials; thus, confidence in the results is based on the purity and accuracy of the standards.

As with any major analytical technique, numerous manipulative skills and laboratory practices must be mastered to achieve accurate volumetric results. The wetting of buret walls, room temperature variations, and such subjective apperceptions as reading the level of a meniscus or detecting a subtle color change are areas of concern.

When calculations are to be based on molarity or normality, a critical concern is

the standardization of the titrant; exceptions are when the titrant is a primary standard. Many titrant standardization procedures are well established (Table 11), although new approaches appear in the literature. The alternative to such procedures is to abandon the molarity/normality approach for the less scientifically pure but fast and effective titer technique. The basic concern is to obtain standard materials with accurate certified values for the analyte and with a matrix composition similar enough to that of the unknown sample to compensate for systematic errors. When such standards are available, the titer approach is often unsurpassed among wet chemical techniques for the rapid and accurate determination of certain analytes.

Acid-Base Titrations. Monitoring the hydrogen ion or the hydroxyl ion concentration of a process solution or a finished product is sometimes necessary. Acid pickling baths, plating baths, rinse waters, petroleum products, paper, and plastics are a few of the types of samples in which acidity or basicity are regularly measured. These tests resolve for the most part into simple acid-base titrations with selected appropriate conditions and indicators.

A more complex use of the acid-base titration relates to certain important elemental determinations in which the concentration of hydrogen ion is related to the concentration of analyte. Boron, especially in amounts above 0.1%, is determined by first isolating it by ion exchange or distillation, then reacting the borate anion with mannitol (sucrose or glycerine is sometimes used instead). The formation of the borate-mannitol complex releases hydrogen ions in stoichiometric amounts that are then titrated using standard base. One procedure of extremely wide applicability is the Kjeldahl determination of nitrogen. A concentrated sodium hydroxide solution is reacted with the nitrogen in a sulfuric acid solution of the sample. Before this step, use of catalysts, such as mercuric oxide, potassium sulfate, salicylic acid, formaldehyde, elemental zinc, or selenium, may be necessary to convert various nitrog-

Table 12 Frequently used acid-base indicators

Indicator	pH range	Application
Thymol blue	1.2–2.8 (red-yellow) 8.0–9.6 (yellow-blue)	Titrations of a mixture of one weak acid and one strong acid with NaOH
Methyl orange	3.1–4.4 (red-orange)	Titration of weak bases with strong acids
Bromcresol green	4.0–5.6 (yellow-blue)	First equivalence point of titration of H_3PO_4 with NaOH
Methyl red	4.4–6.2 (red-yellow)	Titration of weak bases with strong acids
Bromthymol blue	6.2–7.6 (yellow-blue)	Titration of weak acids with weak bases
Phenol red	6.4–8.0 (yellow-red)	Titration of weak acids with weak bases
Phenolphthalein	8.0–10.0 (colorless-red)	Titration of weak acids with strong bases
Thymolphthalein	9.4–10.6 (colorless-blue)	Second equivalence point of titration of H_3PO_4 with NaOH

enous compounds in the sample to ammonium sulfate. Steam distillation isolates the newly formed ammonia into water containing a known amount of standard acid that exceeds the amount necessary for reaction with all the ammonia. Back-titration of the excess acid using dilute standard sodium hydroxide solution determines the exact amount of nitrogen. Although alternatives for measuring the ammonia isolate are known, classical acid-base titration predominates.

Strongly acidic cation exchange resins in the hydrogen form are used frequently to exchange a sample component for hydrogen ions that are then titrated using standard base. The technique is applied for sodium and for potassium when they represent the major cation component of a sample and for the calcium content of gypsum. Wide application of the approach is limited by the requirement that the adsorbed cation reside neat in neutral solution.

In another class of determinations the analyte is isolated as a precipitate that is first washed free of all acids or bases, then dissolved in an excess of standard acid or standard base. For these selected precipitates, acid or base is consumed in direct proportion to the analyte concentration. Back-titration of the excess acid or base yields the amount consumed and thus the analyte concentration. The best example is the determination of phosphorus, in which the ammonium phosphomolybdate precipitate is dissolved in standard sodium hydroxide solution, and the excess base titrated using dilute hydrochloric acid. Another example is a method in which magnesium is first precipitated as the ternary phosphate $MgNH_4PO_4$. This precipitate is washed and dried, then dissolved in excess standard sulfuric acid solution; the excess is titrated using standard sodium hydroxide solution. Less useful is a similar method in which a precipitate of tungstic acid (H_2WO_4) is dissolved in excess sodium hydroxide solution.

Finally, the highest oxide of rhenium, Re_2O_7, may be dissolved in neutral water to form the strong acid $HReO_4$. This may be titrated directly using sodium hydroxide solution.

Although pH meters are more often used, few laboratories have abandoned the use of acid-base indicators for these determinations. Table 12 lists common indicators.

Precipitation Titrations. The Volhard titration of silver using ammonium or potassium thiocyanate in the presence of ferric sulfate is perhaps the best example in this category. As thiocyanate ion is added, it reacts to form the white AgSCN precipitate. At the equivalence point, a trace of excess titrant yields a pink color due to the strongly colored $FeSCN^{2+}$ cation. A similar method is used for mercury(II). In both cases, chloride ion must be absent. However, chlorides (or total halides) may be effectively determined by complete precipitation using a known excess of silver nitrate and determining the excess by application of the Volhard titration.

The Mohr titration may be used for chloride, using a silver nitrate titrant, or for silver, using an added excess of standard sodium chloride and silver nitrate as backtitrant. In both cases, potassium chromate is the indicator, and the pH should be 7 or slightly lower. At the equivalence point, the red precipitate Ag_2CrO_4 appears. In place of chromate ion, organic indicators, which adsorb on the surface of the AgCl particles, are often used; chief among these are fluorescein and 4′,5′-dichlorofluorescein, which yield a pink color at the endpoint.

None of these titrations provides any selectivity among the halides or the pseudohalide species CN^- and SCN^-. Application of these titrations to mixtures of these species often requires complex separation techniques.

Arsenic can be determined using an indirect version of the Volhard titration. Arsenic in the sample is reacted with excess silver nitrate to form the dark red precipitate Ag_3AsO_4. This is filtered, washed free of excess silver ion, then dissolved in nitric acid. The silver in the nitric acid solution is then titrated by the Volhard method, which tolerates acid conditions, and related to the concentration of arsenic in the sample.

Zinc can also be determined using an indirect Volhard titration. Zinc is first precipitated as $ZnHg(SCN)_4$, which is filtered, washed, then reacted with nitric acid and an excess of standard silver nitrate solution. The double salt is destroyed, and $Hg(SCN)_2$ and AgSCN precipitate the released thiocyanate ion. The excess silver ion present is determined using a Volhard titration.

Fluoride, after its isolation as fluosilicic acid by steam distillation, is most frequently titrated using a standard thorium (or lanthanum) solution, precipitating the insoluble metal fluoride. Sodium alizarin sulfate forms a pink color with excess titrant at the endpoint.

Complexation Titrations. An important class in this category is the chelometric titration, of which the principal titrant is ethylenediaminetetraacetic acid (EDTA). Other chelating titrants are generally applicable in one or two specific methods, and none shares the versatility of EDTA.

An analytical technique using an EDTA titration is available for virtually every element in the periodic chart. Calcium and magnesium are determined in limestone, dolomite, cement, slags, and refractories using elaborations of a basic procedure for water hardness determinations. The concentration of calcium + magnesium in a slightly ammoniacal sample aliquot is determined by titration using standard disodium EDTA solution to an Eriochrome Black T endpoint. A second aliquot is made slightly basic with NaOH and titrated using the same titrant to a Murexide endpoint, yielding a value for calcium alone. Magnesium is calculated as the difference between the two values.

The method relies on careful control of pH for both titrations and the low stability of the metallochromic complex between Murexide and magnesium ion. For higher accuracy work, the titration of calcium + magnesium is followed by precipitation of the calcium using oxalate in a second sample aliquot. Magnesium is then titrated to an Eriochrome Black T endpoint in the filtrate. Another approach is to separate calcium and magnesium by ion exchange and titrate each separately.

Zinc is frequently determined using EDTA titration, especially in nonferrous alloys in which it is a major alloying addition. Interference from cobalt, copper, and nickel can be handled by adding potassium cyanide, which complexes zinc and the interferences. Addition of formaldehyde selectively destroys the zinc complex and excess cyanide, freeing the zinc for titration using EDTA to an Eriochrome Black T endpoint. However, cadmium is a serious interference that, when present, must be removed by precipitation using sodium diethyldithiocarbamate. The precipitate may be filtered, dissolved, buffered appropriately, and the cadmium titrated, as for zinc. Alternatives for zinc involve isolating the element from its sample matrix by solvent extraction or by ion exchange.

Aluminum in amounts above 0.5% is often titrated using EDTA. In zinc alloys, sufficient excess EDTA is added to complex zinc and aluminum; the excess is titrated using standard zinc chloride solution and Xylenol Orange indicator. Sodium fluoride is then added, and the solution is boiled to precipitate AlF_3 and release that portion of the EDTA associated with aluminum. It is then titrated using the standard zinc solution. In copper alloys and iron ores, the same method, with preliminary separations to isolate the aluminum, may be applied.

Lead in large amounts in brasses and bronzes can be isolated from interferences by extraction of its diethyldithiocarbamate from a basic tartrate/cyanide medium into chloroform. The lead is returned to aqueous solution and titrated using EDTA in the presence

Table 13 Common metallochromic indicators

Indicator	Color change		Application/remarks
	Metal complex	Free dye	
Eriochrome Black T (Pontachrome Black TA)	Wine-red (pH 10)	Blue (pH 10)	Mg, Zn, Cd, Pb, Hg(II), total hardness
Murexide (ammonium purpureate)	Red or yellow (pH 11)	Blue (pH 11)	Ca, Cu, Co, and Ni
PAN (pyridylazonaphthaol)	Red/violet (pH 4–6)	Yellow (pH 4–6)	Many metals; solvent sharpens endpoint
Xylenol Orange and/or Methyl Thymol Blue	XO: red/violet MTB: blue XO + MTB: violet	Yellow Yellow Orange-yellow	Pb, Bi, Th, Zr, and rare earths
Pyrocatechol Violet	Blue	Yellow	Th and Bi in acid solution; many metals in basic solution
PAR (pyridylazoresorcinol)	Red/violet	Yellow	Similar to PAN
TAR (thiazolyazoresorcinol)	Red/violet	Yellow	Similar to PAN and PAR

of hexamethylenetetramine and cyanide to a Xylenol Orange endpoint.

Less useful are the methods for manganese in ferromanganese and manganese-copper alloys, both of which use separate arrays of masking agents for interferences, and a procedure for nickel and cobalt in high-temperature alloys, in which the two analytes are collected in separate eluents from an ion-exchange column, and nickel is further separated by dimethylglyoxime precipitation. The manganese and nickel titrations use Eriochrome Black T; the cobalt titration, Pyrocatechol Violet.

Table 13 lists common metallochromic indicators for chelometric titration. Several of these, as well as others, can also be used in a special mode often implemented to sharpen the detection of the endpoint. A metal (not the analyte) that forms an especially distinct metallochrome color is selected; copper is frequently used. The EDTA complex of this metal and the metallochromic indicator are added to the sample solution. The solution is titrated using EDTA, and when all the analyte has been chelated, the excess EDTA titrant reacts to release the added metal from its colored complex and produce a distinct endpoint.

Several important complexation titrations do not involve formation of a chelate. Manganese above 0.5% is readily determined by first forming the red complex between pyrophosphate and manganous ion in neutral or slightly acid solution. The complex is then titrated using potassium permanganate solution in a redox reaction in which the titrant manganese and the sample manganese become the +III manganic pyrophosphate complex. The endpoint is usually detected potentiometrically. A suitable method, which has fallen into disfavor due to the toxicity and disposal problems of cyanide, is

the titration of nickel in ammoniacal solution using potassium cyanide solution to form the nickel cyanide complex. A cloud of silver iodide is formed in the solution and used to signal the endpoint, because the solution clears distinctly when a slight excess of cyanide ion is present. Other methods of industrial importance involve cyanide ion as analyte or titrant. Silver or copper ion, which form soluble cyanide complexes, are typically involved.

Iodimetric Titrations. Iodimetry, a widely used and versatile class of redox titration, is based on the formation or destruction of iodine (the oxidizing species is actually triodide anion, I_3^-). Endpoints are invariably detected using a starch solution that becomes dark blue in the presence of the ground-state element.

Sulfur is frequently determined by combusting a solid sample in a stream of oxygen such that SO_2 is generated. Sulfur dioxide is absorbed in an acid solution containing iodide ion and starch. The solution is titrated using a standard iodate solution to the first appearance of the starch-iodine color. In this determination, the iodate and iodide ions generate *in situ* iodine that oxidizes the SO_2 to sulfate ion. The starch-iodine color signals excess iodine at the endpoint. Alternately, sulfur may be evolved as H_2S from an acid solution of the sample. Hydrogen sulfide is absorbed in an ammoniacal zinc sulfate solution. The absorbing solution is acidified to release free sulfide and ion titrated to a starch endpoint using iodine solution or (iodate solution if iodide has been added to the absorbing solution).

Tin in major amounts is most commonly determined using iodimetric titration. Tin is usually reduced to the +II state by reaction with a metal in acid solution; lead or nickel is most frequently used. The reduction is conducted under a CO_2 blanket, which is

maintained as the stannous ion is titrated using iodine (or iodate, if iodide was added) to prevent reoxidation by atmospheric oxygen.

Arsenic can be titrated iodimetrically following its isolation in the +III state by distillation from hydrochloric acid solution. The distillate is neutralized, made slightly acidic, and bicarbonate is added to neutralize the hydroiodic acid that forms during titration using iodine. Antimony may be determined similarly, although tartrate is added to prevent precipitation of the analyte.

Reduction of selenium to the elemental form with potassium iodide, followed by titration of the iodine that forms with standard sodium thiosulfate solution, may be used, but tellurium must be absent. The solution is titrated until the starch blue color disappears. Similar analytical techniques are used to determine chlorate (ClO_3^-), bromate (BrO_3^-), and iodate (IO_3^-) anions, the free halogens (Cl_2, Br_2, and I_2), ozone (O_3), and NO_x (in gases).

Numerous indirect iodimetric methods are also used. Lead is precipitated first as the sulfate; the filtered residue is dissolved, and the lead precipitated a second time as the chromate. The filtered residue is dissolved, and potassium iodide is added. Iodine is liberated in stoichiometric proportion to the lead content and is titrated using standard sodium thiosulfate solution. Similarly, mercury is precipitated as the periodate $Hg_5(IO_6)_2$, which is filtered, then dissolved in potassium iodide, which reacts to produce iodine. This is then titrated using sodium thiosulfate solution.

Copper can be determined by first separating it as the sulfide, dissolving the filtered residue, then reacting the bromine-oxidized slightly acid solution with potassium iodide. Copper(II) reacts to form copper(I) iodide, which precipitates; two iodide anions are oxidized to iodine. The iodine is titrated using sodium thiosulfate solution. Alternately, copper may be precipitated as copper(II) thiocyanate, then the filtered residue dissolved in hydrochloric acid and titrated using standard potassium iodate. The disappearance of iodine color (due to the formation of ICl) in a large drop of chloroform is used to detect the endpoint.

Miscellaneous Redox Titrations. Most volumetric methods in routine use fall under this general heading. Table 14 summarizes the most commonly used volumetric procedures. In most cases, endpoint detection can be accomplished potentiometrically or by use of an appropriate redox indicator.

Calcium is determined by precipitation as calcium oxalate, dissolution of the filtered and washed residue in dilute sulfuric acid,

Table 14 Commonly used volumetric procedures

Analyte	Titrant	Endpoint	Remarks
Boron . . . . NaOH		pH meter or visual-phenolphthalein	H^+ released by boratemannitol complex
Nitrogen . . . . NaOH		Back-titration—pH meter or visual	NH_3 collected in excess standard acid
Fluorine. . . . . Th$(NO_3)_4$		Sodium alizarin sulfate	Precipitation titration
Magnesium . . . . EDTA		Eriochrome Black T	Magnesium value by difference
Aluminum . . . . ZnCl$_2$		Xylenol Orange (back-titration)	F^- releases EDTA complexed with aluminum
Phosphorus . . . . HCl		Phenolphthalein (back-titration)	$(NH_4)_3PO_4 \cdot 12MoO_3$ dissolved in excess standard base
Sulfur . . . . KIO$_3$		Starch/potassium iodide	Absorb SO_2 in acid solution
Chlorine . . . . AgNO$_3$		Potassium chromate	Neutral or slightly acid solution
Calcium. . . . . EDTA		Murexide	Calcium value direct; magnesium does not interfere
Titanium . . . . KMnO$_4$		KMnO$_4$ pink (back-titration)	Ti(III) from Jones reductor reacted with excess standard ferric sulfate
Vanadium . . . . Fe$(NH_4)_2(SO_4)_2$		Potentiometric	HNO_3 oxidation
Chromium . . . . KMnO$_4$		KMnO$_4$ pink (back-titration)	Reduce with excess Fe$(NH_4)_2(SO_4)_2$; no vanadium correction required
Manganese. . . . . KMnO$_4$		Potentiometric	Pyrophosphate complex [Mn(+II) → Mn(+III)]
Iron. . . . . K$_2$Cr$_2$O$_7$		Diphenylamine	Iron reduced with SnCl$_2$; excess SnCl$_2$ destroyed with HgCl$_2$
Cobalt . . . . Co$(NO_3)_2$		Potentiometric (back-titration)	Oxidize to cobalt(+III) with excess standard K$_3$Fe(CN)$_6$
Nickel . . . . MnSO$_4$		Eriochrome Black T (back-titration)	Add excess standard EDTA
Copper . . . . Na$_2$S$_2$O$_3$		Starch/potassium iodide	Copper precipitates as CuI, and I$_2$ is formed stoichiometrically
Zinc . . . . EDTA		Eriochrome Black T	Cyanide/formaldehyde masking for interferences
Arsenic . . . . KBrO$_3$		Methyl Orange	Antimony must be absent
Molybdenum . . . . KMnO$_4$		KMnO$_4$ pink (back-titration)	Molybdenum(III) from Jones reductor reacted with excess standard ferric sulfate
Silver . . . . KSCN		Fe$_2$(SO$_4$)$_3$	Chloride must be absent
Cadmium. . . . . EDTA		Eriochrome Black T	Sodium diethyldithiocarbamate separation
Tin . . . . KIO$_3$		Starch/potassium iodide	Reduction with lead or nickel; solution kept under CO$_2$ blanket
Antimony . . . . KBrO$_3$		Methyl Orange	Arsenic must be absent
Mercury . . . . KSCN		Fe$_2$(SO$_4$)$_3$	All mercury must be in +II; Cl$^-$ must be absent
Lead . . . . Na$_2$S$_2$O$_3$		Starch/potassium iodide	PbCrO$_4$ dissolved with excess iodide and HCl to form I$_2$ stoichiometrically
Cerium . . . . KMnO$_4$		KMnO$_4$ pink (back-titration)	Reduce with excess Fe$(NH_4)_2(SO_4)_2$
Uranium . . . . KMnO$_4$		KMnO$_4$ pink	Uranium(IV) from air-oxidized Jones reductor effluent is titrated directly

and titration of the liberated oxalic acid using standard potassium permanganate solution to the first faint permanent pink.

Several important methods are suitable for chromium and vanadium. The permanganate titration approach involves oxidation with ammonium persulfate catalyzed by silver nitrate in a sample solution heated to boiling; chromium, vanadium, and manganese are oxidized. Chloride ion is added, and the boiling continued; manganese is selectively reduced. The cooled solution is reacted with excess standard ferrous ammonium sulfate solution, then titrated using standard potassium permanganate solution. This titration yields the chromium concentration.

Phosphoric acid and a measured excess of standard ferrous ammonium sulfate are then added to the solution, followed by ammonium persulfate solution, which destroys excess ferrous ion. The solution is again titrated using standard potassium permanganate, yielding the vanadium concentration. This approach for these two elements, exemplifying sophisticated analytical methodology, can yield accurate results. Figure 2 outlines the occurrences at each stage.

An alternate approach requires separate samples for chromium and for vanadium. The sample for chromium is oxidized with silver nitrate and ammonium persulfate, as described above, followed by a measured addition of excess ferrous ammonium sulfate, then by a measured excess of potassium dichromate, and finally by titration to the endpoint using ferrous ammonium sulfate. The reaction is followed potentiometrically, and the results represent chromium plus vanadium. It also is possible to titrate the excess ferrous ammonium sulfate using po-

tassium dichromate to a visual endpoint, such as that of diphenylamine indicator; in this case, vanadium correction is unnecessary. An accurate value for vanadium is used to correct the results of the potentiometric titration to the true chromium content. Such a vanadium value can be obtained by taking a separate sample, adding nitric acid, boiling 1 h to oxidize vanadium selectively, and potentiometrically titrating the cooled sample using ferrous ammonium sulfate and potassium dichromate, as for chromium.

Iron is most conveniently determined by reduction with excess stannous chloride, removal of excess stannous chloride by oxidation with mercuric chloride, and titration of the reduced iron using potassium dichromate to a diphenylamine visual endpoint in the presence of phosphoric acid. Preliminary separation to remove background color due to matrix cations is often required. Cobalt, once isolated from most matrix elements by ion exchange or other means, can be accurately determined by oxidation with potassium ferricyanide standard solution added in excess and back-titration using standard cobalt nitrate to a potentiometric endpoint.

Manganese was most often determined by oxidation with sodium bismuthate and titration of the resulting permanganate using ferrous sulfate. The current method of choice is the pyrophosphate procedure described in the section "Complexation Titrations" in this article, although some laboratories oxidize manganese with silver nitrate and ammonium persulfate, then titrate the cooled solution using standard sodium arsenite to a yellow endpoint. Arsenic and antimony in lead- and tin-base alloys can be determined by distilling the arsenic from a chloride medium, then titrating the distillate for arsenic and the solution remaining in the distillation vessel for antimony, both using standard potassium bromate to a methyl orange endpoint.

Selenium can be titrated using titanous sulfate even when tellurium is present, and tellurium can be determined by oxidation with potassium dichromate (ferrous ammonium sulfate back-titration) in the presence of selenium. Among the rare earths, only cerium and europium exhibit an analytically useful redox chemistry. Cerium(+IV) is often titrated using ferrous ammonium sulfate after oxidation with silver nitrate and ammonium persulfate or by other means.

The Jones reductor, essential in many redox volumetric methods, consists of a zinc/mercury amalgam contained in a glass tube having an outlet fitted with a stopcock. An acid solution of the sample is passed through the column, and the selected analyte is reduced by the amalgam. The column effluent is sometimes protected by an inert

Fig. 2 Permanganate titration for chromium and vanadium

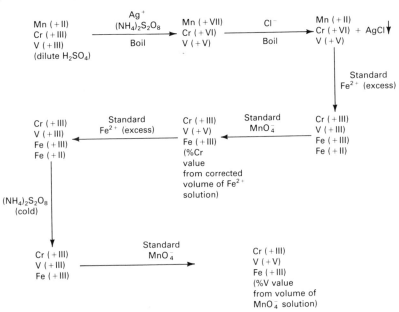

gas to prevent air oxidation; at other times, the effluent is collected under an excess of standard oxidant solution, and back-titration determines the amount of oxidant consumed. The method is suitable for titanium, molybdenum, uranium, and europium and is sometimes used for chromium, vanadium, and iron, for which more convenient methods have been discussed.

Inclusion and Second-Phase Testing

Metals and alloys, like most materials, are rarely encountered as pure perfectly homogeneous substances. Their complex elemental composition and the heat and mechanical work to which they are exposed engender a host of stoichiometric and nonstoichiometric compounds and alloy phases. Some of these influence critically the gross properties of the material, and many can be isolated for study using chemical techniques. This is prevalent in the basic steel industry and in certain industries that use its products. Therefore, plain carbon and low-alloy steels will be emphasized, although many of the techniques are adaptable to other alloys, including many nonferrous materials.

Inclusions are nonmetallic substances resulting from chemical reactions that occur within the alloy during its manufacture or from the physical entrapment of furnace refractories, slag, and so on. Examples include oxides, nitrides, carbides, sulfides, and carbonitrides; chemical reactivities vary widely in that some are stable in strong acid

and others ignite spontaneously in air. Phases are properly restricted in this context to metallic associations of elements, whether or not they can be assigned a precise formula.

Isolation of Residues. Digestion using dilute acid is the simplest and most common technique. Acids used include hydrochloric, nitric, sulfuric, and perchloric. The filtered residue represents only the most stable compounds, principally silica and alumina, and even their recovery is seldom complete. The acid digestion approach affords at best a useful estimate of the relative cleanliness of fully killed steels. The technique is ineffective for partially deoxidized or rim-grade products, because iron and manganese oxides dissolve. For highly alloyed, highly refined alloys, acid dissolution has some utility, but must be knowledgeably applied.

Ionic displacement techniques, in which the iron-alloy matrix is dissolved in a neutral solution of a copper or mercury salt, have been studied for years. Considered a milder attack than dilute acid, these procedures retain some compounds of intermediate stability.

Dissolution in bromine and absolute methanol is perhaps the most widely used means of isolating inclusions from steel. As with all inclusion isolation procedures, filed solid samples, rather than chips or millings, must be used to prevent loss of fines that may form during machining. In addition, the reaction rate may be difficult to control if the sample surface area is excessive. The most convenient apparatus allows dropwise addition of alcohol and dissolution of the metal

to be conducted under reflux. Bromine-methanol is well suited to the detailed study of aluminum-killed steels, from which over 30 compounds have been isolated by this means. However, rimming grades require even milder conditions to preserve low-stability iron and manganese oxides, carbides, and sulfides.

An older approach, iodine and absolute methanol, has the potential to be useful in this area if the temperature is maintained low. However, a slow reaction rate requires ultrasonic agitation to render the technique practical.

More widely used is dissolution in bromine and methyl acetate, which is most useful for semikilled and rimmed steel, because compounds of the form (Fe,Mn)O are retained. The technique was developed to isolate aluminum nitride and other nitrides for determination by Kjeldahl distillation, and it is still widely used for that purpose despite evidence that some aluminum nitride particles may be too small to filter.

Chlorination, or treatment with dry chlorine gas at 350 °C (660 °F), removes iron as an $FeCl_3$ sublimate and leaves behind oxides and graphite. Nitrides, carbides, and sulfides are supposed to be destroyed, although certain species may remain after treatment. Despite this and the difficulties and danger associated with the technique, it still finds use, especially in Germany.

Perhaps the ultimate approach to inclusion and phase isolation involves electrolytic techniques. Cell configuration, current density, and electrolyte composition are widely varied, based on the needs of different laboratories. A filed solid is typically coated with wax or plastic and a measured area of the coating is removed to expose the metal. The sample is suspended in a nitrogen-purged aqueous electrolyte that contains one or more iron-complexing moieties. For stainless steels, a nonaqueous medium, such as an alcohol, is sometimes used instead. Some provision for the introduction of fresh electrolyte and for the removal of electrolyte contaminated with complexed iron is usually necessary to allow a uniform current density throughout the dissolution, which takes several hours. At the same time, provision must be made that no particles are lost. At the end of the operation the metal sample is cleaned ultrasonically and mechanically, and the particulates combined. The difference in weight of the metal sample before and after the analysis is taken as the sample weight for quantitative work on the particulate residue.

Refinement of Residues. Removal of certain components of an isolated residue is sometimes desirable to facilitate its analysis or study. For example, the large amount of carbon that often accompanies residues from high-carbon steels is frequently a problem. Sink/float density separations using heavy liquids are one approach to the problem. The technique is potentially applicable to separating numerous residue components; unfortunately, highly toxic metallorganic compounds are frequently the only suitably dense liquids for use as the separation medium. Use of a low-temperature oxygen plasma dry-asher effectively removes carbon from isolated oxide residues. Unlike high-temperature ignition, the oxide state of iron and manganese oxides is not affected.

Chlorination can be used to remove iron and manganese carbides and sulfides from isolated residues; higher temperatures also remove chromium carbides but destroy some oxides. Finally, magnetic separation can be used to segregate magnetic and nonmagnetic compounds in the isolate. In one commercial unit, the magnetic particles, attracted to an oscillating field, adhered to the wall of a glass cylinder while nonmagnetic particles dropped to the bottom of the small vessel.

Study of Residues. Once a residue has been isolated and suitably refined, the following techniques may be implemented:

- *Chemical/spectrographic analysis*: For elemental composition. Carbon, sulfur, and nitrogen, as well as metallic elements, are frequently determined. Applying the same determination to residues isolated by different techniques allows the concentration of specific components, such as AlN and Al_2O_3, to be discerned. A frequent exercise that supplies a measure of the confidence attributable to the work is a comparison of total oxygen results on the metal with the oxygen summation calculated from a stoichiometrical treatment of the metallic composition of the isolated residue. Total oxygen results on metal are obtained using inert gas or vacuum fusion techniques (see the article "Inert Gas Fusion" in this Volume).
- *X-ray diffraction*: For compound identification. Residue refinement, especially carbon removal, is often necessary. See the Section "Diffraction Methods" in this Volume.
- *Infrared absorption spectrophotometry*: Useful for identification and even quantification of some compounds. See the article "Infrared Spectroscopy" in this Volume.
- *Microscopy/petrography*: For compound identification. See the articles "Optical Metallography," "Scanning Electron Microscopy," and "Analytical Transmission Electron Microscopy" in this Volume.
- *Particle size distribution analysis*: Using Coulter counter techniques or other

Table 15   Second-phase test methods

Technique	Remarks/example	Ref
Isolation		
Acid	Stable oxides (Al_2O_3 and SiO_2)	31, 32
Ionic displacement . .	Stable oxides + additional compounds	32, 33
Electrolysis.	Oxides, nitrides, carbides, sulfides, phases, and so on	34, 35
Iodine/methanol	Oxides + additional compounds	32, 36, 37
Bromine/methanol . .	Oxides + additional compounds; fully killed steel	32, 38
Bromine/methyl acetate	Oxides and nitrides + additional compounds; rim grade	32, 39, 40
Chlorination	Oxides	32, 35
Purification		
Dry ash (O_2 plasma)	Remove carbon	32
Chlorination	Remove carbides	32, 35
Magnetic separation	For example, Fe_3C and Fe_3P: magnetic; alloy carbides, Fe_2P: nonmagnetic	34
Analysis		
Particle size distribution	Coulter counter	32, 41
Thermal methods . . .	Differential thermal analysis/effluent gas analysis	32, 42

means. Such data are applied to the mechanical properties of the alloy. See the article "Image Analysis" in this Volume.
- *Thermal analysis/effluent gas analysis*: For compound identification and possible quantification. Differential thermal analysis (DTA) techniques are used extensively, other thermal methods to a lesser degree.

No comprehensive text on second-phase testing currently exists in English. Literature references are widely scattered, but are predominantly concentrated in foreign metallurgical journals. Table 15 highlights some significant published work, and significant review papers are cited in Ref 28 to 30.

Chemical Surface Studies

The primary means of studying surfaces is instrumental, but worthwhile wet chemical techniques remain in use and often prove to be the cheapest, fastest, or most practical approach.

Milling, or turning, followed by analysis seems crude compared with instrumental techniques that section and examine atomic layers from alloy surfaces, but some phenomena must be studied over a depth of several millimeters, rather than angstroms. Case-hardening phenomena and decarburization are studied in this way; the chips are carefully collected from as many as a hundred steps of precise machining and analyzed for carbon. Analogous work is performed to study surface nitriding and denitriding and deboronization. The results are cross-sectional profiles that provide valuable engineering data obtainable in no other practical way.

The precise weight per unit area of a coating deposited on a substrate surface often must be determined. X-ray gages, although suitable for thin metallic coatings, are ineffective for organic coatings. Ellipsometers and specular reflectance infrared instruments measure some organic coatings effectively, but have other restraints, such as coating transparency and substrate reflectivity. In each case, chemical techniques often are chosen by default. For example, metal coatings can be stripped from measured areas of samples, often without any attack of the substrate matrix, and the resultant solution analyzed using conventional techniques. Organic coatings, such as lubricants and lacquers, can be removed using solvent in the liquid or vapor phase. Evaporating the solvent and weighing the residue is often sufficient, although other techniques may be necessary, such as the conversion of tallow-base lubricant coatings to fatty acid methyl esters and their measurement by gas chromatography.

Surface oxides, such as rust, can be quantitatively assessed by dissolving the metal matrix in bromine and methyl acetate and filtering and analyzing the residue. Alternatively, the sample can be reacted with hydrogen at elevated temperature, and the effluent water vapor collected and measured gravimetrically or volumetrically. Gravimetric determination involves absorption of the water vapor in a weighed glass bulb of desiccant. Volumetric determination uses the Karl Fischer titration, in which water vapor is absorbed in absolute methanol and titrated to a visual or potentiometric endpoint using Karl Fischer reagent.

In addition, as an alternative to sensitive instrumental techniques, trace levels of contaminants, such as halide ions, that have adhered to surfaces may often be released by boiling with water or an appropriate dilute acid, the resultant solution being analyzed chemically. For large surfaces, such as large manufactured items, a simple wipe of a measured area with an absorbent material moistened with an appropriate agent may be suitable. The wipe pad receives special handling to avoid extraneous contamination, and the analyte ions must be released into solution for chemical determination.

Partitioning Oxidation States

Classical wet analysis is uniquely suited to the quantitative determination of the oxidation states of the sample component. This information is often valuable in providing data with which product properties can be predicted and process parameters can be fine tuned.

Iron. Three forms of iron are frequently determined in steelmaking slags: FeO, Fe_2O_3, and metallic iron, which occurs in the slag as particles of entrained steel. Total iron is determined on one portion of the sample using any of several standard procedures; the potassium dichromate redox titration described in the section "Titrimetry" in this article is the usual approach. A second portion of the sample is reacted with copper(II) sulfate, which selectively dissolves metallic iron (as ferrous ion) by ionic displacement, causing metallic copper to precipitate. When the reaction is complete, the solution is filtered, and residual color in the filtrate due to excess cupric ion is removed by adding metallic aluminum, which completes the precipitation of metallic copper. The solution is then quickly titrated to a diphenylamine endpoint using potassium dichromate solution. This result is recorded as metallic iron.

Finally, a third portion of the sample is dissolved in dilute hydrochloric acid under reflux and a carbon dioxide atmosphere. The CO_2 blanket is maintained as the dissolved sample is cooled and titrated using potassium dichromate solution to a diphenylamine endpoint. This result represents combined metallic iron and FeO; in the absence of metallic iron, it represents FeO. Ferric oxide is then calculated from the value for total iron by difference.

When the sample material resists nonoxidizing attack, it is sometimes feasible to quantify the ferrous state by dissolving the sample in the presence of a known excess of oxidant, such as ceric sulfate, under a blanket of inert gas, then back-titrating the excess using ferrous ammonium sulfate solution. This approach may be used with certain ferrites.

The $+IV$ oxidation state of iron does not occur in aqueous solution, but Mössbauer spectroscopy data support its presence in the solid state in certain ferrite materials. Iron($+IV$) can be quantified by using its oxidation of a measured excess of iron($+II$) during digestion of the sample under inert gas. However, the results are not unequivocal, and the results thus obtained are sometimes designated by the empirical term free oxygen.

Other Metallic and Semimetallic Elements. Chromium(II), chromium(VI), and chromium(0) may be quantified separately, and these distinctions are of interest for slags, especially those from the production of ferrochromium. Quantitative distinction between chromium(III) and chromium(IV) also is often necessary for chromium plating baths. One technique for ferrochromium slags implements brominemethanol to dissolve the free metal, acidic ferric chloride to dissolve CrO, and boiling sodium carbonate solution to dissolve CrO_3. The selected species are generally quantified volumetrically.

Metallic nickel in reduced NiO ores can be determined by dissolving the elemental form with bromine-alcohol or by ionic displacement using mercuric chloride solution after selective removal of soluble nickel sulfides. Methods have been documented for the determination of the metallic form of aluminum (in the presence of Al_2O_3, Al_4C_3, and AlN), magnesium (in the presence of MgO), titanium (in the presence of TiO_2, Ti_2O_3, and TiC), and boron (in the presence of B_2O_3, H_3BO_3, B_4C, BN, and borides), among others.

Silicon present in simple steels as iron silicide may be distinguished from silicon present as SiO_2. Total silicon is determined gravimetrically; a separate sample is then reacted with dry oxygen-free chlorine gas at 600 °C (1110 °F). As the iron matrix is removed as $FeCl_3$, iron silicide reacts to form $SiCl_4$, which similarly sublimes away. Gravimetric determination of silicon in the residue yields a value for SiO_2. Subtracting this silicon value from the total silicon value yields the iron silicide content. The presence of SiC and/or Si_3N_4 complicates the determination.

Nonmetallic Elements. Mobile, or interstitial, nitrogen, which is relatively free to move in the crystal lattice of a steel, may be determined in an apparatus in which hydrogen gas is passed over fine millings of the sample at 550 °C (1020 °F). The nitrogen reacts to form ammonia, which may be determined by any of several techniques. Subtracting the results from total nitrogen results, obtained by the Kjeldahl method (see the section "Titrimetry" in this article) or by any of several combustion techniques, yields a value for nitride nitrogen, or that portion of the sample nitrogen fixed in the lattice as a compound. Values for nitride or precipitated nitrogen, determined by difference in this way, correlate to results from direct determination of precipitated AlN in aluminum-killed steels, except where ultrafine (unfilterable) AlN particles are suspected. The difference values always correlate to the strain-aging behavior of the steel.

Mobile carbon is not so well defined as mobile nitrogen, but it is well known that methane is also produced with the hydrogen gas treatment described above. Graphitic carbon or graphite is commonly determined by dissolving steel or iron samples in dilute nitric acid and filtering directly into crucibles used for combustion analysis.

Applications

Example 1: "Umpire" Analysis of a Stainless Alloy. The x-ray fluorescence and optical emission spectrographs in the production control laboratory of a specialty alloy producer were not calibrated for a new grade of stainless alloy the melt shop planned to produce. Because the catalogs of primary and secondary standard suppliers showed nothing similar enough to be useful, the only practical alternative was to generate an in-house standard.

A 23-kg (50-lb) heat of the required composition was melted in a small vacuum induction furnace and cast into a 50-mm (2-in.) round ingot. After cropping pipe, the ingot was sliced into 19-mm (0.75-in.) thick disks. One was selected from the top, one from the bottom, and one from the middle of the ingot. They were pickled in hydrochloric and nitric acids, rinsed in water and dried, then milled across the full cross section. Three sets of chips were collected, degreased with solvent, and dried. Each set of chips was analyzed several times as a separate sample using the following techniques:

Estimated %	Technique
0.10 max	Carbon: Combustion in oxygen followed by infrared detection of CO_2
1.5–2.0	Manganese: Persulfate oxidation; arsenite titration to a visual endpoint
0.50–0.60	Silicon: Perchloric acid dehydration, gravimetric determination
0.025 max	Phosphorus: Phosphomolybdate precipitation, acid-base titration
0.025 max	Sulfur: Combustion in oxygen; infrared detection of SO_2
17.5–17.6	Chromium: Persulfate oxidation, ferrous reduction, $KMnO_4$ back-titration
0.5–0.6	Vanadium: Nitric acid oxidation, ferrous reduction, and potentiometric titration
12.75–13.0	Nickel: Dimethylglyoxime precipitation, gravimetric determination
4.0–4.5	Molybdenum: Alphabenzoinoxime, ignition to MoO_3, gravimetric analysis
2.5–3.0	Copper: Electrolytic deposition of Cu(O), gravimetric analysis

Comparison of the three sets of results indicated that the ingot was homogeneous. To avoid systematic errors, certain elements were analyzed using alternate techniques—manganese, vanadium, and phosphorus by spectrophotometric methods, nickel and copper by volumetric techniques. Operator bias was checked by repeating the same work with different analysts. Participation by different laboratories within or between organizations is sometimes feasible, but in this case was not undertaken. The results, after statistical checks for and elimination of outliers, were grand average values for each element—each with an associated estimate of variation. These values and the remaining slices of the ingot were then used routinely to calibrate the spectrographs for control of alloys of this type.

Example 2: Analysis of Solder. Four million parts had been manufactured and shipped before it was discovered that the solder used came from a supplier the customer had not approved. The solder used had to be proved to be equivalent to that from the list of approved suppliers. Unfortunately, only a 150-mm (6-in.) piece remained on the reel, which is not enough to melt a button sample for an x-ray fluorescence analysis.

The remaining strand weighed 4.5 g—just enough to characterize it by wet chemical analysis:

- *Tin* (1 g): Reduction with nickel under CO_2 iodimetric titration
- *Arsenic and antimony* (2 g): Distillation of arsenic; bromate titration of antimony in the reflux and arsenic in the distillate
- *Silver* (1.5 g): Volhard titration
- *Lead*: Approximate, determined by difference

No errors occurred, and none of the 4.5 g was lost. Based on the results, the customer was convinced that the solder used was suitable.

Example 3: Boron and Fluorine in Borosilicate Glass. A company that designs process chemical equipment received heat exchanger subassemblies that contain glass wool insulation in an area that may be exposed to chemical vapors during operation. The engineer in charge wanted to confirm that the material would not cause problems; therefore, a sample was submitted to an analytical laboratory. The lab melted some of the sample, cast a button, and checked it using x-ray fluorescence spectroscopy. Converting the elemental composition to oxides, they reported:

SiO_2	Al_2O_3	K_2O	Na_2O
81.2	1.8	0.5	~4.0

The engineer, upon receiving the results, questioned the missing 13%. If the material was borosilicate glass, most of that would be B_2O_3, so he requested a boron analysis. Because fluorine might be leached by the customer's caustic aerosol, he needed a determination of that element as well.

The lab had to rely on wet analysis for these determinations. Boron is at too high a level for accurate emission spectroscopy, and fluorine at too low a level for x-ray fluorescence.

Two samples were fused with sodium carbonate, leached, and the following work performed:

- *Boron*: Distillation as methyl borate/mannitol complex, followed by acid-base titration
- *Fluorine*: Distillation as fluosilicic acid, followed by thorium nitrate titration with alizarin indicator

Example 4: Chromium Depletion in a Weld Zone. A metallurgist was asked to specify a weld rod composition for welding a high-chromium alloy. He suspected that exact matching of the weld rod to the alloy would result in a weldment with lower than nominal chromium in the heat-affected zone. Some work with a nondispersive x-ray attachment to a scanning electron microscope supported this contention, but was not quantitative. To recommend a chromium-enriched composition for the weld rod, he needed to know how much chromium loss must be compensated for.

The weld was carefully cut out of a sample and milled. At the same time, a portion of the base metal, unaffected by the weld, was milled. Both samples were submitted for chromium determination:

- *Chromium*: Persulfate oxidation and ferrous reduction, followed by $KMnO_4$ back-titration

The weld was found to be almost 0.5% lower in chromium than the base metal. The engineer made experimental welds with a series of weld rods, each incrementally higher in chromium, and submitted the cutout and milled welds for determination of chromium. The weld rod composition that produced a weld whose chromium level is identical to the base metal level was selected.

Example 5: Free Lime in Portland Cement (Ref 43, 44). The presence of uncombined calcium oxide or free lime in commercial cements adversely affects the soundness of the set and hardened product. Although total calcium oxide is most accurately determined using a gravimetric or volumetric procedure, such alternatives as

x-ray fluorescence and atomic absorption spectrophotometry have been used where speed is important. No such option is available for free lime determination.

The quantitative estimation of free lime content is a critical test of product quality and has generated extensive literature. Several alternate procedures are recognized as standard techniques:

- *Franke method*: Boil with ethylacetoacetate and isobutyl alcohol under reflux, filter, and titrate using standard acid to methylene blue/thymol blue endpoint
- *Lerch and Bogue method*: Boil with glycerol and absolute ethanol (plus strontium nitrate catalyst) under reflux, filter, and titrate using standard ammonium acetate solution to phenolphthalein endpoint
- *Schlapfer and Bukowski method*: Shake with ethylene glycol (plus a small amount of clean quartz sand) in a water bath at 65 °C (120 °F); titrate using standard acid to phenolphthalein-α-naphtholphthalein endpoint

Alternate finishes for the extracts are sometimes used; for example, calcium can be determined gravimetrically as the oxalate or titrated using EDTA.

REFERENCES

1. *Official Methods of Analysis of the Association of Official Analytical Chemists*, 14th ed., Association of Official Analytical Chemists, Arlington, 1984
2. R.L. Shriner, R.C. Fuson, and D.Y. Curtin, *The Systematic Identification of Organic Compounds*, 5th ed., John Wiley & Sons, 1967
3. J. Rodier, *Analysis of Water*, John Wiley & Sons, 1975
4. *NIOSH Manual of Analytical Methods*, 2nd ed., Parts I to VII, U.S. Department of Health, Education and Welfare, Washington, DC, 1977
5. R.A. Day and A.L. Underwood, *Quantitative Analysis*, 2nd ed., Prentice-Hall, 1967
6. I.M. Kolthoff and E.B. Sandell, *Textbook of Quantitative Inorganic Analysis*, 3rd ed., MacMillan, 1952
7. D.A. Skoog and D.M. West, *Fundamentals of Analytical Chemistry*, 2nd ed., Holt, Reinhart, and Winston, 1969
8. "Sampling Ferroalloys for Determination of Chemical Composition," "Sampling Wrought Nonferrous Metals and Alloys for Determination of Chemical Composition," "Sampling Steel and Iron for Determination of Chemical Composition," "Sampling Nonferrous Metals and Alloys in Cast Form for Determination of Chemical Composi-

tion," "Sampling Copper and Copper Alloys for Determination of Chemical Composition," "Sampling and Sample Preparation of Iron Ores," E 32, E 55, E 59, E 88, E 255, and E 877, *Annual Book of ASTM Standards*, Vol 03.05, ASTM, Philadelphia, 1984

9. G.E.F. Lundell, J.I. Hoffman, and H.A. Bright, *Chemical Analysis of Iron and Steel*, John Wiley & Sons, 1931

10. "Collection and Preparation of Coke Samples for Laboratory Analysis," "Preparing Coal Samples for Analysis," D 346 and D 2013, *Annual Book of ASTM Standards*, Vol 05.05, ASTM, Philadelphia, 1984

11. J. Dolezal, P. Povondra, and Z. Sulcek, *Decomposition Techniques in Inorganic Analysis*, Elsevier, 1968

12. R. Bock, *A Handbook of Decomposition Methods in Analytical Chemistry*, John Wiley & Sons, 1979

13. T.T. Gorsuch, *The Destruction of Organic Matter*, Pergamon Press, 1970

14. A.A. Schilt, *Perchloric Acid and Perchlorates*, G. Frederick Smith, 1979

15. F. Feigl, *Spot Tests in Inorganic Analysis*, Elsevier, 1958

16. *Reagents and Reactions for Qualitative Inorganic Analysis* (IUPAC), Butterworths, 1964

17. *Symposium on Rapid Methods for the Identification of Metals*, STP 98, ASTM, Philadelphia, 1949

18. L.C. Pasztor, R.M. Raybeck, and T.R. Dulski, *Mater. Res. Stand.*, Vol 10, Nov 1970, p 9-34

19. G.E.F. Lundell and J.I. Hoffman, *Outlines of Methods of Chemical Analysis*, John Wiley & Sons, 1938

20. W.F. Hillebrand, G.E.F. Lundell, J.I. Hoffman, and H.A. Bright, *Applied Inorganic Analysis*, 2nd ed., John Wiley & Sons, 1953

21. K.L. Cheng, U. Keihei, T. Imamura, *CRC Handbook of Organic Analytical Reagents*, CRC Press, 1982

22. G.H. Morrison and H. Freiser, *Solvent Extraction in Analytical Chemistry*, John Wiley & Sons, 1957

23. N.H. Furman, Ed., *Standard Methods of Chemical Analysis*, Vol 1, 6th ed., D. Van Nostrand, 1966

24. F.J. Welcher, Ed., *Standard Methods of Chemical Analysis*, Vol 2, 6th ed., Parts A and B, D. Van Nostrand, 1963

25. L. Meites, Ed., *Handbook of Analytical Chemistry*, 1st ed., McGraw-Hill, 1963

26. J. Inczedy, *Analytical Applications of Ion Exchangers*, Pergamon Press, 1966

27. F.J. Welcher, *The Analytical Uses of Ethylenediaminetraacetic Acid*, D. Van Nostrand, 1958

28. R.G. Smerko and D.A. Flinchbaugh, *J. Met.*, Vol 20, July 1968, p 43-51

29. W. Koch and H. Sundermann, *J. Iron Steel Inst.*, Vol 190, Dec 1958, p 373-381

30. W.R. Bandi, *Science*, Vol 196, 8 April 1977, p 136-142

31. G.E.F. Lundell *et al.*, *Chemical Analysis of Iron and Steel*, John Wiley & Sons, 1931, p 421-423

32. R.G. Smerko and D.A. Flinchbaugh, *J. Met.*, Vol 20, 1968, p 43-51

33. L. Silverman, *Iron Age*, Vol 159, 1947, p 153

34. W. Koch and H. Sundermann, *J. Iron Steel Inst.*, Vol 190, 1958, p 373-381

35. H. Walz and R.A. Bloom, *J. Met.*, Vol 12, 1960, p 928-932

36. J.E. Garside and T.E. Rooney, *J. Iron Steel Inst.*, Vol 185, 1957, p 95-103

37. M. Ihida *et al.*, *Tetsu-to-Hagané*, Vol 51, 1965, p 1633-1645

38. Y. Okura, *Nippon Kinzoku*, Vol 24, 1960, p 237-300

39. R.M. Raybeck and L.C. Pasztor, *STP 393*, ASTM, Philadelphia, 1966, p 75-86

40. H.F. Beeghley, *Anal. Chem.*, Vol 24, 1952, p 1713-1721

41. R.M. Raybeck and L.C. Pasztor, Paper 63, presented at the Pittsburgh Conference on Analytical Chemistry and Applied Spectroscopy, 1967

42. W.R. Bandi *et al.*, *Anal. Chem.*, Vol 38, 1966, p 1336-1341

43. "Chemical Analysis of Limestone, Quicklime, and Hydrated Lime," "Chemical Analysis of Hydraulic Cement," "Chemical Analysis of Gypsum and Gypsum Products," C 25, C 114, and C 471, *Annual Book of ASTM Standards*, Vol 04.01, ASTM, Philadelphia, 1984

44. F.M. Lea, *The Chemistry of Cement and Concrete*, 3rd ed., Chemical Publishing, 1971

Potentiometric Membrane Electrodes

Mark A. Arnold, Department of Chemistry, University of Iowa

General Uses

- Quantification of cationic and anionic substances
- Quantification of gaseous species in aqueous solutions
- Detector for analytical titrations

Examples of Applications

- Activity or concentration determination of selected cationic, anionic, or gaseous species in a variety of materials, including supply waters, waste waters, plating baths, mineral ores, biological fluids, soils, food products, and sewage
- Elemental analysis of organic compounds, especially for nitrogen and halide content
- Titrimetric determination of major components in metal alloys
- Detector for chromatographic processes
- Detector to follow chemical reaction kinetics

Samples

- *Form*: The measurement must ultimately be made in a solution; aqueous solutions are generally used
- *Size*: Several milliliters of sample are typically needed, but samples of less than a microliter can be analyzed using a microelectrode. Samples as small as 0.5 mL can be measured using commercial gas sensors
- *Preparation*: Depending on the system, sample preparation can be extensive to remove interferents and to release the ion of interest from binding agents in the sample, but is sometimes unnecessary

Advantages

- Insensitive to sample turbidity
- Short analysis times
- Small sample volume requirement
- Simple to operate
- Inexpensive
- Portable
- Easy to automate
- Measures activity

Limitations

- Potential drift
- Interferences
- Often requires aqueous solutions

Estimated Analysis Time

- Several minutes per sample after dissolution or other sample preparation

Capabilities of Related Techniques

- *Amperometric gas sensors*: Quantification of oxygen and hydrogen peroxide
- *Ultraviolet/visible (UV/VIS) spectroscopy*: Direct or indirect determination of cation, anion, gaseous, and molecular species
- *Ion chromatography*: Determination of cation and anion species concentrations
- *Atomic spectroscopies*: Quantification of sample elemental components
- *Voltammetry*: Quantification of cations, anions, and certain organics

Introduction

Potentiometric membrane electrodes are electrochemical devices that can be used to quantify numerous ionic and nonionic species. This class of electrochemical sensors can be divided into ion-selective and gas-sensing membrane electrodes. In both cases, a selective membrane potential is related to the concentration or activity of the species of interest. This article will introduce potentiometric membrane electrodes; more detailed information is cited in the References.

Potentiometric membrane electrode measurements require an indicating electrode and a reference electrode. The potential of the indicating electrode depends on the activity of the ion of interest, and this potential is measured with respect to the constant potential of the reference electrode using a high-impedance potentiometer. The reference electrode is an important but frequently overlooked component of potentiometric membrane electrode measurement.

Ion-Selective Membrane Electrodes

Several types of ion-selective membrane electrodes have been developed in which different membrane compositions are used as the selective agent. Membranes composed of glass, solid crystalline, and polymer layers are commonly used in commercially available ion-selective membrane electrodes. Figure 1 illustrates these electrode systems.

Glass membrane electrodes are generally used to quantify monovalent cations, particularly protons (the pH electrode) and sodium ions. Figure 1(a) shows a glass membrane electrode. The ion-selective glass layer separates the sample or external solution from an internal reference solution. The composition of this internal solution remains constant throughout the operation of the electrode. In contact with this internal reference solution is a silver/silver chloride reference electrode. The several chemical potentials established throughout this system remain constant, except for the membrane potential, which is measured and related to the concentration or activity of the ion of interest. The response mechanism of glass membrane electrodes is thought to be based on selective exchange and mobility processes that occur between the glass matrix and solution ions (Ref 1). Composition of the glass membrane controls the selectivity of the electrode response (Ref 2).

Liquid or Polymer Membrane Electrodes. A similar electrode system uses a liquid or polymer membrane as the selective component (Ref 3-6). Figure 1(b) shows such an electrode system, in which a polymer membrane separates the internal and external solutions. In this case, electrode selectivity is achieved by incorporating into the polymer membrane an agent that will selectively complex with the ion of interest. During the electrode response, the complexing agent in the membrane complexes the ion of interest, creating a charge separation at the membrane/solution interface. This charge separation results in the measured membrane potential. Numerous reports are available concerning models for this type of electrode response (Ref 3, 7).

Solid Crystalline Membrane Electrodes. A third ion-selective membrane electrode uses a solid crystalline membrane (Ref 8-10). Figure 1(c) shows a common arrangement for this type of electrode system. Membranes in the form of a single crystal or a pressed pellet composed of highly insoluble inorganic salts are used. For many solid crystalline membrane electrodes, the internal reference solution may be eliminated by connecting the internal reference electrode to the internal side of the solid membrane, due to the conductivity of the crystalline membrane. For the most part, the response of solid crystalline membrane electrodes is based on the solubility of the ionic species comprising the membrane (Ref 7).

Fig. 1 Types of ion-selective membrane electrodes

(a) Glass membrane electrode. (b) Polymer membrane electrode. (c) Solid crystalline (pressed pellet or single crystal) membrane electrode

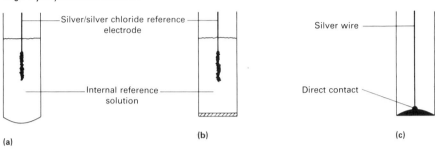

The membrane potential of an ion-selective electrode is described by Eq 1, which relates the measured potential to the ionic activity of the species of interest:

$$E_{cell} = E_{const} + \frac{RT}{nF} \ln \left(\frac{a_i}{a_i'} \right) \qquad (Eq\ 1)$$

where E_{cell} is the measured cell potential, E_{const} is a potential term that includes all cell potentials remaining constant throughout the measurement, R is the universal gas constant (8.31441 V · C/K/mol), T is the temperature of the cell in degrees Kelvin, n is the number of electrons transferred in the appropriate half reaction, F is the Faraday constant (estimated at 96 486.332 C/mol), and a_i' and a_i are the activities of the principal ion in the internal reference and sample solutions, respectively. Because the activity of the ion of interest is constant in the internal reference solution, Eq 1 can be simplified:

$$E_{cell} = constant + 0.05916 \log a_i \quad (Eq\ 2)$$

Therefore, the measured cell potential is related to the logarithm of the ion activity. Electrode calibration curves are typically prepared as a plot of potential versus logarithm of standard ion activity, and sample ion activities are obtained by extrapolation from this standard curve using a measured potential value.

Realization of the difference between ion activity and concentration is important in ion-selective electrode measurements. The measured membrane potential is related to the ion activity as opposed to its actual concentration. The ion activity can be thought of as the effective or free ion concentration in solution and can be related to its concentration by:

$$a_i = \gamma_i C_i \qquad (Eq\ 3)$$

where γ_i is the activity coefficient for species

i, and C_i is the concentration. In dilute solutions, the activity coefficient goes to unity, and the activity and concentration are equivalent. At high concentrations or in solutions of high ionic strength, the activity coefficient falls below unity. The activity coefficient of an ion in a solution of known ionic strength is typically estimated using:

$$\log \gamma_i = -A z_i I^{1/2} \qquad (Eq\ 4)$$

where A is a solvent coefficient, z_i is the ionic charge of species i, and I is the solution ionic strength (Ref 11). Substituting Eq 3 into Eq 1 creates a relationship between ion concentration and measured potential. If the activity coefficient of interest remains constant between the measure of the standards and the sample, the ratio of activity coefficients will remain constant, and concentration of the free ion in solution can be determined. Therefore, concentrations can be measured by estimating the activity coefficients or by preparing the electrode calibration curve in a suitable matrix.

Determining Electrode Selectivity. Selectivity of an ion-selective membrane electrode is extremely important and must be considered before applying such an electrode to a system. Selectivity limitations of certain ion-selective electrodes are often overlooked, leading to major problems for the operator. No ion-selective electrode is specific for a particular ionic species. The commonly used pH electrode, which displays one of the highest degrees of selectivity, will respond to sodium ions under certain circumstances (Ref 1). Equation 5 may be used to account for interferences:

$$E_{cell} = constant + 0.05916 \log$$
$$(a_i + K_{i,j}\, a_j^{(z_i/z_j)}) \qquad (Eq\ 5)$$

where z_i is the ionic charge on the species of interest, and $K_{i,j}$ is the selectivity coefficient for species i relative to species j. Analysis of

Eq 5 reveals that smaller values for the selectivity coefficient correspond to higher degrees of selectivity. For example, a typical selectivity coefficient for the sodium-selective glass electrode for sodium over potassium is approximately 1×10^{-5}; therefore, the electrode is approximately 10^5 times more selective for sodium than potassium. That is, such a selectivity coefficient indicates that potassium ion activity must be five orders of magnitude greater than sodium ion activity to produce the same electrode response.

The fixed interference and the separate solution methods may be used to measure electrode selectivity coefficients (Ref 6). It is important to know which method has been used to obtain a particular value, because the two techniques often will not agree exactly. The fixed interference method is preferred, because it characterizes electrode response under conditions that are similar to actual use. Table 1 lists selectivity coefficients for various commercially available ion-selective electrodes (Ref 12, 13).

Selectivity coefficients can change during the life of an ion-selective membrane electrode, especially for solid crystalline and polymer membrane electrodes. These changes are primarily caused by alterations in membrane composition during extended electrode use. This problem is not as severe with glass membrane electrodes. Selectivity coefficients must be considered before applying ion-selective membrane electrodes to an analysis.

Methods of Analysis

Calibration Curves. Perhaps the simplest method for ion-selective membrane electrodes is use of a calibration curve. Standards are prepared from suitable salts with a background matrix that approximates the background of the sample. Steady-state potential values are read from the electrode system in the various standards, and a calibration plot of potential versus the logarithm of the standard activity is prepared. If the system is performing as expected, a Nernstian slope should be obtained as defined by Eq 1. For a system that senses a monovalent cation at 25 °C (75 °F), a slope of 59.16 mV per activity decade should be observed, but values of 54 to 60 are not uncommon. A slope lower than 54 generally indicates a problem in the system. Slopes of 29.58 and 19.72 are anticipated for divalent and trivalent species, respectively.

After the slope and y-intercept are established, potential readings from a particular sample can be obtained, and the species activity can be extrapolated from this standard calibration curve. Linear least squares

estimates must be used for analyses that involve electrode calibration curves. Linear least squares methods can be used only in a simple fashion when the linear region of the electrode response is being used.

Most ion-selective electrodes have a linear range that extends over at least two orders of magnitude, and many display a linear response over several orders of magnitude. The linearity is sometimes extreme, as for the pressed pellet silver sulfide electrode, for which the range of linearity exceeds 25 orders of magnitude (Ref 14). Similarly, the limit of detection for ion-selective electrodes can vary considerably, but generally is from 10 to 1 μM. Extreme cases are known, such as the pH and cupric selective electrodes that have detection limits of 10^{-14} and 10^{-18} molar, respectively. Metal ion buffers are required for measurements at these low concentrations to prepare suitable standards accurately (Ref 15). Various electrode detection limits have been summarized (Ref 16).

Typical electrode response times are on the order of minutes, and most are within 1 mV of the final steady-state potential in under 2 min. Some electrodes possess response times of 10 to 30 s. The frequency at which the electrode system must be recalibrated to maintain accurate results depends on the electrode system being used. Certain electrode systems require hourly recalibration; others maintain calibration for several days (Ref 4).

Addition techniques are commonly used with ion-selective membrane electrodes. Analytical techniques such as standard addition, multiple standard addition, and unknown (analyte) addition are included in this category. Standard addition analysis eliminates the need to recalibrate the electrode system continually if the electrode slope remains constant during the measuring period. In this technique, the electrode system is immersed in the sample, and a steady-state potential is attained. After this value is noted, a known volume of a standard solution is added to the sample, and a modified steady-state potential is measured. These potential values are used to calculate the species concentration using:

$$C_o = C_s \left(\frac{V_s}{V_o} \right) (10^{\Delta E/S} - 1)^{-1} \quad \text{(Eq 6)}$$

where C_o is the concentration of the species of interest in the sample, C_s is the standard concentration, V_s is the volume of the standard added, V_o is the initial sample volume of the sample solution, ΔE is the change in cell potential, and S is the electrode slope. Equation 6 assumes that the volume of the stan-

dard addition is negligible with respect to the volume of the sample. Conditions under which this assumption is invalid require:

$$C_o = C_s \left(\frac{V_s}{V_s + V_o} \right)$$

$$\left[10^{\Delta E/S} - \left(\frac{V_o + V_s}{V_o} \right) \right]^{-1} \quad \text{(Eq 7)}$$

Under typical assay conditions, standard addition is the most appropriate method of analysis, because it encompasses fluctuations in the constant potential portion of the electrode response (see Eq 2). Other addition techniques for ion-selective membrane electrode techniques are variations of this standard addition method (Ref 17).

Various subtraction techniques involve adding a known amount of a chelating agent to the sample following determination of sample potential. A second potential is obtained from the modified solution, and these two potentials are used to calculate the unknown concentration (Ref 12). This latter method is appropriate when the analyte is unstable in its free state and when complexation helps to stabilize the analyte.

Titration Methods. Numerous analytical procedures entail use of an ion-selective membrane electrode to determine the endpoint of a particular titration. The intrinsic selectivity of a titration method has resulted in the application of ion-selective membrane electrodes for various analytical assays. Additional information is available in the article "Electrometric Titration" in this Volume.

Potentiometric Gas-Sensing Electrodes

Gas-sensing membrane electrode systems are potentiometric devices in which a second membrane barrier is included with an ion-selective electrode system to alter the selectivity properties of the sensor. Gas-sensing electrodes are available for ammonia, carbon dioxide, nitrogen oxide, and hydrogen disulfide (an amperometric gas sensor is available for oxygen).

Figure 2 shows a typical configuration for the ammonia gas sensor, which is a pH ion-selective electrode housed in a plastic body. Also included in this plastic body is the reference electrode, which is required to complete the electrochemical circuit. At the pH-sensing surface of the glass electrode is an electrolyte solution composed mainly of ammonium chloride. A thin gas-permeable membrane separates this thin layer of electrolyte from the external or sample solution. This membrane is generally made of a homogeneous gas-permeable polymer, such as silicon rubber, or a microporous polymer, such as microporous teflon.

In either case, ammonia gas in the sample will diffuse across the gas-permeable membrane until the partial pressure of ammonia is equal on both sides. The influx of ammonia will shift the electrolyte equilibria to the right, altering the solution pH. The pH electrode senses this change in pH, and the resulting steady-state potential can be related to the sample ammonia concentration using Eq 1. Sensors for carbon dioxide, nitrogen oxide, and hydrogen disulfide operate similarly, but the internal electrolyte is composed of a different salt.

The response of a gas sensor depends on the pH of the sample solution. For example, the ammonia sensor will not respond to ammonium ions, because only gaseous species can pass through the membrane. Therefore, the ammonia gas sensor can be used in only basic solutions. Optimal pH for this sensor is 10.5 to 12.0.

Steady-state response characteristics of gas sensors are generally favorable, with limits of detection approaching the micromolar concentration range for the ammonia sensor. A slope of 54 to 60 mV per concentration decade can be expected over a region of linearity that should extend over two orders of magnitude. The dynamic behavior of these electrodes can sometimes cause problems, because obtaining potentials to within 1 mV of the final steady-state potential may require up to 10 min at low analyte concentrations or as little as 30 s at the higher concentration region. In addition, 40

Fig. 2 Configuration of an ammonia gas-sensing membrane electrode

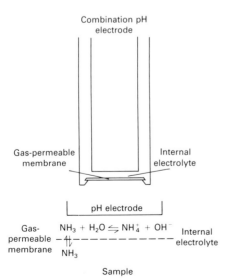

Table 1 Selectivity constants for some commercially available electrodes

Electrode	Type and model	State	Selectivity constant
Boron tetrafluoride	Orion 92-05	Liquid	F^- 10^{-3}, Cl^- 10^{-3}, Br^- 0.04, I^- 20, NO_3^- 0.1, $SO_4^=$ 10^{-3}, HCO_3^- 4×10^{-3}, CH_3COO^- 4×10^{-3}, OH^- 10^{-3}
Boron tetrafluoride	Beckman 39620	Liquid	F^- 2×10^{-4}, Cl^- 5×10^{-4}, Br^- 0.02, I^- 0.13, NO_3^- 0.02, $SO_4^=$ $< 10^{-6}$, $S^=$ 10^{-4}, $CO_3^=$ 6×10^{-6}, CH_3COO^- 1.5×10^{-4}, ClO_3^- 0.03, CN^- 6×10^{-4}, PO_4^{3-} 2×10^{-4}, $[Fe(CN)_6]^{3-}$ $< 10^{-6}$
Bromide	Beckman 39602	Solid	Cl^- 3×10^2, I^- 1.8×10^{-4}, OH^- 4.4×10^4, CN^- 4.1×10^{-4}, SCN^- 1.8
Bromide	Coleman 3-801	Solid	Cl^- 400, I^- 2×10^{-4}, OH^- 3×10^{-4}
Bromide	Orion 94-53	Solid	Cl^- 400, I^- 2×10^{-4}, OH^- 3×10^{-4}, CN^- 8×10^{-5}
Bromide	Radelkis OP-I-711	Solid	Cl^- 200, I^- 7.7×10^{-3}
Bromide	Philips IS-550	Solid	Cl^- 6×10^{-3}, I^- 20, OH^- 10^{-3} CN^- 25, $CO_3^=$ 2.3×10^{-3}, $S_2O_3^=$ 1.5, CrO_4^{-2} 1.6×10^{-3}
Calcium	Beckman 39608	Liquid	Mg^{++} 0.11, Ba^{++} 0.08, Sr^{++} 0.09, Na^+ 0.015, H^+ 70, K^+ 0.034, Cd^{++} 3, Mn^{++} 4, Cu^{++} 3, Fe^{++} 0.2
Calcium	Orion 92-20	Liquid	Zn^{++} 3.2, Fe^{++} 0.8, Pb^{++} 63, Mg^{++} 0.01, Ba^{++} 0.01, Sr^{++} 0.017, Ni^{++} 0.08, Cu^{++} 0.27, Na^+ 1.6×10^{-3}, K^+ 10^{-4}, NH_4^+ 10^{-4}, H^+ 10^5
Calcium	Corning 476041	Liquid	Mg^{++} 0.01, Ba^{++} 0.01, Sr^{++} 0.01, Ni^{++} 0.01, Na^+ 10^{-3}, K^+ 10^{-3}
Calcium/magnesium (water hardness)	Orion 92-32	Liquid	Zn^{++} 3.5, Fe^{++} 3.5, Ba^{++} 0.94, Sr^{++} 0.54, Ni^{++} 1.35, Cu^{++} 3.1, Na^+ 0.01, K^+ < 0.015
Calcium/magnesium (water hardness)	Beckman 39614	Liquid	Zn^{++} < 0.1, Mg^{++} 0.95, Ba^{++} 0.8, Na^+ 0.013, K^+ 0.013
Chloride	Beckman 39604	Solid	Br^- 3×10^{-3}, I^- 5×10^{-7}, OH^- 80, CN^- 2×10^{-7}
Chloride	Coleman 3-802	Solid	Br^- 4.9×10^{-3}, I^- 10^{-6}, OH^- 100, $S_2O_3^=$ 0.01
Chloride	Orion 94-17	Solid	Br^- 3×10^{-3}, I^- 5×10^{-7}, OH^- 80, CN^- 2×10^{-7}
Chloride	Philips IS-550	Solid	Br^- 1.2, I^- 86.5, OH^- 0.024, CN^- 400, $CO_3^=$ 3×10^{-3}, $S_2O_3^=$ 0.01, $CrO_4^=$ 1.8×10^{-3}
Chloride	Radelkis OP-Cl	Solid	Br^- 4.95×10^{-3}, I^- 2.8×10^{-3}, $SO_4^=$ 4.95×10^5
Chloride	Corning 476131	Liquid	Br^- 2.5, I^- 15, NO_3^- 2.5, CH_3COO^- 0.21, ClO_4^- 5, OH^- 0.4
Chloride	Orion 92-17	Liquid	F^- 0.1, Br^- 1.6, I^- 17, NO_3^- 4.2, $SO_4^=$ 0.14, HCO_3^- 0.19, CH_3COO^- 0.32, ClO_4^- 32, OH^- 1.0
Copper	Orion 92-29	Solid	Zn^{++} 10^{-3}, Fe^{++} 1.0, Mg^{++} 10^{-4}, Ba^{++} 10^{-4}, Sr^{++} 10^{-4}, Ni^{++} 5×10^{-3}, Ca^{++} 5×10^{-4}, Na^+ $< 10^{-5}$, K^+ $< 10^{-3}$, H^+ 10

(continued)

Table 1 (continued)

Electrode	Type and model	State	Selectivity constant
Cyanide	Philips IS550-CN	Solid	Cl^{-2} 2×10^{-4}, Br^- 2×10^{-5}, I^- 3, $CO_3^=$ 3.6×10^{-4}, $S_2O_3^=$ 2.2×10^{-3}, $CrO_4^=$ 1.4×10^{-2}
Cyanide	Orion 94-06	Solid	Cl^- 10^6, Br^- 5×10^{-3}, I^- 0.1
Cyanide	Radelkis OP-CN	Solid	Cl^- 1.7×10^5, Br^- 210, $SO_4^=$ 3.2×10^7, $PO_4^{\equiv}$ 4.8×10^5, ClO_4^- 1.6×10^6
Iodide	Beckman 39606	Solid	Cl^- 1.6×10^6, Br^- 5.6×10^{-3}, CN^- 0.4, $S_2O_3^=$ 10^5, SCN^- 10^4
Iodide	Orion 94-53	Solid	Cl^- 10^6, Br^- 5×10^3, CN^- 0.4, $S_2O_3^=$ 10^5
Iodide	Radelkis OP-I	Solid	Cl^- 1.7×10^5, Br^- 210, $SO_4^=$ 3.2×10^7, $PO_4^{\equiv}$ 4.8×10^5, ClO_4^- 1.6×10^6
Iodide	Philips IS-550-I	Solid	Cl^- 6.6×10^{-6}, Br^- 6.5×10^{-5}, CN^- 0.34, $CO_3^=$ 1.2×10^{-4}, $S_2O_3^=$ 7.1×10^{-4}, $CrO_4^=$ 3.7×10^{-3}
Lead	Orion 92-82	Solid	Zn^{++} 3×10^{-3}, Fe^{++} 0.08, Mg^{++} 8×10^{-3}, Ni^{++} 7×10^{-3}, Cu^{++} 2.6
Nitrate	Corning 476134	Liquid	Cl^- 4×10^{-3}, Br^- 0.011, I^- 25, $SO_4^=$ 10^{-3}, HCO_3^- 10^{-3}, CH_3COO^- 10^{-3}, ClO_4^- 10^3
Nitrate	Orion 92-07	Liquid	F^- 6×10^{-5}, Cl^- 6×10^{-3}, Br^- 0.9, I^- 20, NO_2^- 0.06, $SO_3^=$ 6×10^{-3}, $SO_4^=$ 6×10^{-3}, $S_2O_3^=$ 6×10^{-3}, $S^=$ 0.57, HS^- 0.04, $CO_3^=$ 6×10^{-3}, HCO_3^- 0.02, CH_3COO^- 6×10^{-3}, ClO_3^- 2, ClO_4^- 10^3, CN^- 0.02, $PO_4^{\equiv}$ 3×10^{-4}, $H_2PO_4^-$ 3×10^{-4}, $HPO_4^=$ 8×10^{-5}
Nitrate	Beckman 39618	Liquid	F^- 6.6×10^{-3}, Cl^- 0.02, Br^- 0.28, I^- 5.6, NO_2^- 0.066, $SO_4^=$ 10^{-5}, $S^=$ 3.5×10^{-3}, $CO_3^=$ 1.9×10^{-4}, CH_3COO^- 5×10^{-3}, ClO_3^- 1.1, ClO_4^- 95.5, CN^- 0.02, $PO_4^{\equiv}$ 7.4×10^{-3}
Perchlorate	Orion 92-81	Liquid	F^- 2.5×10^{-4}, Cl^- 2.2×10^{-4}, Br^- 5.6×10^{-4}, I^- 0.012, NO_3^- 1.5×10^{-3}, $SO_4^=$ 1.6×10^{-4}, HCO_3^- 3.5×10^{-4}, CH_3COO^- 5.1×10^{-4}, OH^- 1.0
Perchlorate	Beckman 39616	Liquid	F^- 10^{-4}, Cl^- 10^{-4}, Br^- 3×10^{-3}, I^- 0.04, NO_3^- 6.6×10^{-3}, $SO_4^=$ $< 10^{-6}$, $S^=$ 5×10^{-5}, $CO_3^=$ 2×10^{-6}, CH_3COO^- 5×10^{-5}, ClO_3^- 0.01, CN^- 2×10^{-4}, $PO_4^{\equiv}$ 10^{-4}
Sulfide	Orion 94-16	Solid	CN^-, $CO_3^=$ HCO_3^-, $SO_4^=$, $SO_3^=$, $S_2O_3^=$, F^-, Cl^-, Br^-, I^- $< 10^{-3}$

Source: Ref 12, 13

to 60 min may be required for the electrode to return to baseline conditions.

Gas sensors generally display a high degree of selectivity because of the gas permeability of the outer membrane. Ionic and other nonvolatile constituents in the sample, being unable to penetrate the membrane, cannot alter the inner solution, the pH of which is being monitored. In addition, the volatile substances that can pass through the polymer barrier will change the internal electrolyte pH before their presence can be sensed. The interferences of ammonia (Ref 18, 19) and carbon dioxide (Ref 20) gas-sensing electrodes have been documented.

General Considerations

Several items must be considered in addition to the potentiometric membrane electrode to ensure proper electrode response. Most important are the reference electrode, temperature control, recording of the potential with respect to time, electrode storage, and sample pretreatment.

The reference electrode is extremely important for ion-selective electrode measurements. A poor choice of reference electrode can lead to severe interferences and electrode drift. For gas-sensing electrodes, less consideration is necessary concerning the reference electrode, because the indicator and reference elements are supplied as a single package. Figure 3 shows two typical reference electrodes that are frequently applied to ion-selective electrode measurements.

Figure 3(a) illustrates a single-junction reference electrode that consists of a silver/silver chloride electrode immersed in a concentrated solution of potassium chloride. Saturated potassium chloride or 4 M potassium chloride is generally used. This internal solution contacts the sample solution through a junction that allows ions to pass from one solution to the next without permitting complete mixing of the solutions. Many types of junctions are available, but porous ceramic frits are prevalent (Ref 21). Ion transport across this junction provides the ion conductivity necessary to complete the electrochemical circuit. Due to ion movement, chloride and potassium ions can contaminate the sample solution. For many assays, this contamination is not important; however, when detecting potassium or chloride or when either of these ions interfere with the analyte of interest, a double-junction reference electrode must be used.

Figure 3(b) shows a double-junction reference electrode that is similar to the single-junction electrode, except an additional solution is between the sample and the internal reference solution. The composition of this middle solution is such that ions flowing into the sample will not interfere with the assay procedure. For example, potassium nitrate is generally used for chloride analyses.

Perhaps the most common reason for inaccurate results from ion-selective electrode measurements stems from improper use of the reference electrode. The junction of the electrode must be open to allow free flowing of ions. These junctions often become plugged, halting ion movement and resulting in a noisy electrode system that produces inaccurate data. Therefore, suitable care and maintenance are necessary. Proper procedures for care, storage, and rejuvenation of reference electrodes have been summarized (Ref 22).

Temperature Control. Equation 1 indicates that the response of an ion-selective electrode depends on temperature. Many

Fig. 3 Schematic of reference electrodes

(a) Single junction. (b) Double junction

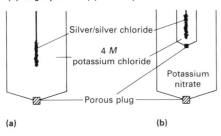

analytical applications of ion-selective electrodes require temperature control. Without proper temperature control, electrode potentials drift continuously, which can complicate establishing the correct steady-state potential. Temperature changes are more problematic for gas-sensing electrodes. A temperature change of only 3 °C (5 °F) will require approximately 2 h before the electrode system can reestablish a steady-state potential. Although various factors contribute to this lengthy time period for reequilibration, osmotic effects have been suggested as the primary cause (Ref 5). The most convenient way to control the temperature of the potentiometric membrane electrode system is to use jacketed thermostatted cells for all measurements.

Potential Versus Time. Accurate measurements necessitate use of a strip chart recorder to follow the potential with time. Drifting potentials are often difficult to detect without a recorder. Moreover, use of a recorder enhances measurement reproducibility between operators. Figure 4 shows a typical potentiometric membrane electrode arrangement that includes the electrodes, a stir motor in conjunction with a stir bar in the sample solution, a potentiometer, a strip chart recorder, and a circulating temperature bath connected to a jacketed glass cell.

Electrode storage requirements vary for different types of electrodes. For example, glass membrane electrodes require a hydrated layer for proper performance and must be conditioned in an aqueous solution before use. Therefore, electrodes should be stored in an aqueous solution for short-term situations. However, dry storage is more suitable for long-term storage. All electrode systems should be stored according to manufacturer's recommendations.

Sample pretreatment is necessary for many analyses to remove possible interferents. Such procedures are common with all analytical techniques and must be applied before accurate measurements can be obtained. Several reference sources provide appropriate procedures for numerous substances (Ref 23-25).

Applications

Example 1 involves the determination of copper in archaeological samples (Ref 25). Similar experimental procedures would be used to quantify numerous elements in various sample materials using ion-selective electrodes.

In this example, a standard addition procedure is used. Alternatively, direct potentiometry or complexometric titration methods could be used. From 10 to 20 mg of the sample is usually digested in a suitable solvent; a strong acid, such as 12 M nitric acid, is generally used. The resulting solution is diluted with an ionic strength adjustment buffer. For this analysis, a 5 M sodium nitrate solution is used. Electrode calibration curves are obtained in this 5 M sodium nitrate solution using an appropriate copper standard. Calibration curves are necessary to establish the slope of the electrode system.

The reference electrode for these studies is a single-junction saturated calomel electrode, and the ion-selective electrode is a pressed pellet electrode. Following determination of the slope using a least squares analysis of the data, a set volume of the sample is placed into a cell that is maintained at 30 °C (85 °F), and the electrodes are immersed in this solution. After a steady-state potential is attained, a known volume of a copper standard is added to the solution, and a second potential is measured. The concentration of copper in the sample is calculated using Eq 6 or 7. Iron is a positive interferent in this system, but the iron can be easily removed by adding ammonium hydroxide, which precipitates the iron as the hydroxide. This precipitate is simply removed by centrifugation before analytical measurement.

The ion-selective electrode method compares well to an atomic absorption technique (Ref 25) and is sometimes preferred because the sample solution is not destroyed; therefore, a second analysis can be performed on the sample if necessary. Applications for the atomic absorption technique are discussed in the article "Atomic Absorption Spectrometry" in this Volume.

Extensive studies have discussed the development of microanalytical procedures for the elemental analysis of organic substances. One of the most common procedures for determining nitrogen content in a sample involves digesting the sample and measuring the resulting ammonia production using an ammonia gas-sensing membrane electrode (Ref 13). This is the Kjeldahl determination.

The Kjeldahl method involves digesting the sample in sulfuric acid in the presence of a catalyst; ammonium sulfate is formed from the sample ammonia. Conventional procedures dictate increasing the pH of the resulting digest to release ammonia gas. This gas is distilled into a second solution, and the ammonium ion concentration in the second solution is quantified. Application of the ammonia gas-sensing electrode to this problem makes distillation unnecessary. Ammonia, which is liberated after the digested sample is made alkaline, can be determined directly because of the selectivity of the gas sensor.

One assay procedure requires digestion of the sample in sulfuric acid with a mixture of potassium sulfate (K_2SO_4), hydrated copper sulfate ($CuSO_4 \cdot 5H_2O$), and selenium (10:1:0.1) added as the catalyst. After complete digestion, the sample is made alkaline using sodium hydroxide, and the ammonia gas sensor is positioned in the solution. The electrode potential is obtained, and the nitrogen concentration is calculated from a standard calibration curve. Alternatively, a standard addition technique can be used. The ammonia gas-sensing electrode technique is faster than distillation, while maintaining the necessary accuracy and precision (Ref 13).

Numerous examples of ion-selective membrane electrodes in organic analysis have been summarized (Ref 12, 13), and general electrode applications in industrial situations have been reviewed (Ref 26). Finally, application of potentiometric membrane electrodes of all types have been tabulated in recent biannual reviews (Ref 27-29).

Fig. 4 General experimental arrangement for potentiometric membrane electrodes

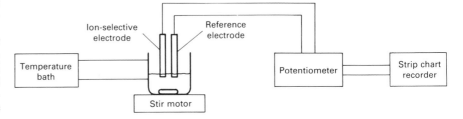

REFERENCES

1. G. Eisenman, R. Bates, G. Mattock, and S.M. Friedman, *The Glass Electrode*, Interscience, 1964
2. R.A. Durst, *Ion-Selective Electrodes*, Special Publication 314, National Bureau of Standards, 1969
3. D. Ammann, W.E. Morf, P. Anker, P.C. Meier, E. Pretsch, and W. Simon, Neutral Carrier Based Ion-Selective Electrodes, *Ion-Sel. Electrode Rev.*, Vol 5, 1983, p 3-92
4. H. Freiser, *Ion-Selective Electrodes in Analytical Chemistry*, Vol I and II, Plenum Press, 1978
5. P.L. Bailey, *Analysis with Ion-Selective Electrodes*, Heyden Press, 1980
6. A.K. Covington, *Ion-Selective Electrode Methodology*, Vol I and II, CRC Press, 1979
7. W.E. Morf, *The Principles of Ion-Selective Electrodes and of Membrane Transport*, American Elsevier, 1981
8. J. Gulens, Surface Effects in Relation to the Response of Solid-State Ion-Selective Electrodes, *Ion-Sel. Electrode Rev.*, Vol 2, 1980, p 117-157
9. E. Pungor, *Ion-Selective Electrodes*, American Elsevier, 1978
10. J. Koryta, *Ion-Selective Electrodes*, Cambridge University Press, 1975
11. F. Daniels and R.A. Alberty, *Physical Chemistry*, John Wiley & Sons, 1975
12. T.S. Ma and S.S.M. Hassan, *Organic Analysis Using Ion-Selective Electrodes*, Vol I, *Methods*, Academic Press, 1982
13. T.S. Ma and S.S.M. Hassan, *Organic Analysis Using Ion-Selective Electrodes*, Vol II, *Applications and Experimental Procedures*, Academic Press, 1982
14. J. Vesely, O.J. Jensen and B. Nicolaisen, Ion-Selective Electrodes Based on Silver Sulphide, *Anal. Chim. Acta*, Vol 62, 1972, p 1-13
15. D.D. Perrin and B. Dempsey, *Buffers for pH and Metal Ion Control*, Chapman and Hall Press, 1974
16. D. Midgley, Detection Limits of Ion-Selective Electrodes, *Ion-Sel. Electrode Rev.*, Vol 3, 1981, p 43-104
17. M. Mascini, Uses of Known Addition, Gran's Plots and the Related Methods with Ion-Selective Electrodes, *Ion-Sel. Electrode Rev.*, Vol 2, 1980, p 17-71
18. M.E. Lopez and G.A. Rechnitz, Selectivity of the Potentiometric Ammonia Gas Sensing Electrode, *Anal. Chem.*, Vol 54, 1982, p 2085-2089
19. Y.M. Fraticelli and M.E. Meyerhoff, Selectivity Characteristics of Ammonia-Gas Sensors Based on a Polymer Membrane Electrode, *Anal. Chem.*, Vol 53, 1981, p 1857-1861
20. R.K. Kobos, S.J. Parks, and M.E. Meyerhoff, Selectivity Characteristics of Potentiometric Carbon Dioxide Sensors with Various Gas Membrane Materials, *Anal. Chem.*, Vol 54, 1982, p 1976-1980
21. A.K. Covington and M.J.F. Rebelo, Reference Electrodes and Liquid Junction Effects in Ion-Selective Electrode Potentiometry, *Ion-Sel. Electrode Rev.*, Vol 5, 1983, p 93-128
22. J.E. Fisher, Measurement of pH, *Am. Lab.*, Vol 16, 1984, p 54-60
23. L. Meites, *Handbook of Analytical Chemistry*, McGraw-Hill, 1963
24. W.J. Williams, *Handbook of Anion Determination*, Butterworths, 1979
25. A. Varma, Determination of Copper in Archaeological and Corrosion Samples with an Ion-Selective Electrode, *Talanta*, Vol 28, 1981, p 785-787
26. P.L. Bailey, Industrial Applications for Ion-Selective Electrodes, *Ion-Sel. Electrode Rev.*, Vol 1, 1979, p 81-137
27. M.A. Arnold and M.E. Meyerhoff, Ion-Selective Electrodes, *Anal. Chem.*, Vol 56, 1984, p 20R-48R
28. M.E. Meyerhoff and Y.M. Fraticelli, Ion-Selective Electrodes, *Anal. Chem.*, Vol 54, 1982, p 27R-44R
29. G.H. Fricke, Ion-Selective Electrodes, *Anal. Chem.*, Vol 52, 1980, p 259R-275R

Voltammetry

By D.R. Crow, Department of Chemistry, The Polytechnic, Wolverhampton, England

General Uses

- Qualitative and quantitative analysis of metals and nonmetals in solutions of concentration 10^{-2} to 10^{-9} mol/L
- Multicomponent, effectively nondestructive repeatable analysis
- Elucidation of solute-solute and solute-solvent equilibria
- Kinetic investigations
- Structure determination in solution

Examples of Applications

- Analysis and characterization of metals in commercial chemicals, pharmaceuticals, high-purity metals, and alloys
- Monitoring of pollutant metals and nonmetals in foodstuffs, water, effluents, herbage, biological/medical systems, and petroleum
- Detection of herbicide and pesticide residues in plant and animal tissue
- Continuous monitoring of major and minor metallic and nonmetallic compounds in commercial electroplating baths

Samples

- *Form*: Solution, mostly aqueous
- *Size*: Cell capacities from 10 to 100 mL are common, but cells less than 1 mL have been devised for special purposes
- *Preparation*: Bulk samples (solids or liquids) must be pretreated to obtain required species in an acceptable and manageable concentration range together with an excess concentration of electroinactive background electrolyte

Limitations

- Sample preparation may sometimes be time consuming relative to the usually short probe time
- Interference from electrochemical signals of species other than those whose analysis is required
- Restricted anodic or cathodic ranges of some electrode materials
- Perfect renewal of electrode surface between analyses is not always feasible
- Complexities in electrochemical or chemical behavior of required species in solution may prevent straightforward detection

Estimated Analysis Time

- 15 min to 3 h per sample, depending on sample preparation time. In batch analysis, the probing of individual solutions for several components may require only minutes

Capabilities of Related Techniques

- *Electrogravimetry*: Extremely accurate but more time consuming; more skill required to eliminate interferences from codeposition; deposition reaction allowed to continue to completion
- *Coulometry*: Small amounts of reagents may be electrogenerated without the need for standardization and storage of dilute solutions. Analysis possible in same lower regions as voltammetry but without the same versatility of multielement analysis
- *Potentiometry*: The exceptional sensitivity of many ion-sensitive systems makes them widely and often simply used as direct probes and in titration methods. Some redox couples may be slow in establishing equilibrium at indicator electrodes
- *Amperometry*: Offers more flexibility in selection of convenient solid electrode materials, because electrode history is less significant in titration techniques. May be used at low concentrations at which other titration methods are inaccurate ($\sim 10^{-4}$ mol/L), but cannot reach the low levels attained by voltammetry for direct analysis
- *Conductometry*: May not be used in the presence of high concentrations of electrolyte species other than that required
- *Classical wet chemistry*: Generally more accurate, but electrochemical methods offer better detection limits for trace analyses

Introduction

Voltammetry is the study of the current-voltage relationships observed when electroactive species in solution are subject to oxidation or reduction at electrodes under carefully controlled conditions. It involves probing a small region of a solution containing, for example, metal ions, by performing small-scale electrolysis between an indicator microelectrode and a reference electrode. A reference electrode, such as the saturated calomel electrode (SCE), is by definition nonpolarizable. That is, its potential remains the same regardless of the potential difference imposed between it and the indicator electrode. The latter is described as polarizable, because it faithfully adopts any potential imposed on it relative to the reference.

If the potential difference between indicator and reference electrode can be controlled accurately and varied uniformly, criteria which modern potentiostatic devices ensure, the corresponding currents that flow reflect the nature and concentration of oxidizable or reducible solutes in solution. Currents flow because of the exchange of electrons between the indicator electrode and electroactive solutes. The latter are frequently metal ions, and the electrode processes monitored are reductions. The indicator electrode then acts as a cathode.

Considerable care is necessary to ensure that electroreducible material reaches the indicator electrode only by natural diffusion. The other important mass transfer processes, electrical migration and convection, are controlled rigorously; the former, an electric field effect, is related to the transport number of the metal ions and may be eliminated effectively by the presence of a large excess of a supporting, or base, electrolyte. The ionic components of this electrolyte (frequently potassium chloride) do not react with the indicator electrode at potentials at which the required species does, but the presence of the base electrolyte ensures that the transport number of the species whose analysis is required is reduced virtually to zero.

Convection effects may arise from stray vibrations and shock or even from temperature gradients within the solution. Thermostatic control and protection from any form of inadvertent stirring ensures that this interference is minimal. Under less common circumstances, controlled convection, particularly as rapidly rotated electrodes, is used to enhance current signals. For most circumstances, the current-voltage curves for metal ions in solution may be interpreted in terms of the interplay of the diffusion process, by which they arrive at the surface of the indicator electrode, and their reduction there

when the applied potential has reached characteristic values.

The selection of indicator electrode material presents some problems. Prolonged accumulation of the products of reduction processes tends to alter the physical and electrochemical characteristics of solid microelectrodes. Mechanical or electrochemical removal of these depositions is not always satisfactory. That is, many solid electrodes develop an irreversible history if suitable precautions are not taken.

The most satisfactory microelectrode at applied potentials more negative than 0.0 V relative to the saturated calomel electrode is that based on mercury in the form of exactly reproducible drops issuing from the end of a capillary attached to a constant head reservoir. Voltammetry performed using the dropping mercury electrode (DME) is known as polarography.

Principles of Voltammetry

Figure 1 shows the essential circuit and cell arrangement for classical direct current (dc) polarography. Values of applied potential derive from the potential divider circuit, and resultant currents are recorded on the microammeter (G). Observed currents oscillate between maximum and minimum values with the growth and detachment of the mercury drops. Modern instruments use the classical dc mode of the technique, but the drop time is often controllable. Electromechanical detachment enables selection of drop times from 0.5 to approximately 5 s.

Apart from the reproducibility of the shape and size of the electrode material, the exceptionally high overvoltage that mercury exhibits toward hydrogen is a principal advantage. Virtually all the common metal ions are reduced at potentials that are more positive than those at which hydrogen is discharged. The final current rise, which sets the practical limit to the potential range available, is due to the reduction of the cation of the supporting electrolyte.

Figure 2 illustrates current-voltage curves shown by a solution containing the species Cd^{2+}, Zn^{2+}, and Mn^{2+}. These curves were obtained using a recording polarograph operating on a mechanically controlled drop time of 1 s, with potassium chloride as supporting electrolyte. Because dissolved oxygen is reduced in an elongated two-stage process whose effects influence the entire cathodic range available for analysis, this interference must be removed before measurement by purging the solution for several minutes using an oxygen-free nonreacting gas, such as nitrogen. Further, maintaining gentle flow of the gas over the surface of the

Fig. 1 Polarographic circuit

G, microammeter

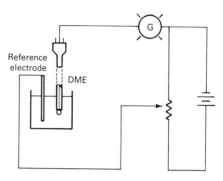

working solution during measurements is usually a wise precaution. If this is not carried out, the presence of oxygen will soon become apparent again, particularly if the measurement period must be prolonged. Although a mild nuisance in probing for metals, the sensitivity of the DME to traces of oxygen is useful in determining the element.

Figure 2 shows the curve due to the supporting electrolyte alone and those due to the clearly separated reduction signals of the three cationic species; the latter are superimposed on the supporting electrolyte line. The gently sloping region between the anodic dissolution of mercury and the potassium ion reduction signals represents the available range of normal working potentials. Alkali and alkaline earth metals exhibit reduction at approximately -1.7 V versus SCE and beyond. Viewing the reduction signals of such species necessitates use of an alkyl ammonium salt as base electrolyte. These methods enable extending the cathodic potential range to approximately -2.3 V versus SCE. To suppress electrical migration efficiently to insignificant levels, the concentration of the base electrolyte must be 50 to 100 times that of any electroactive species under determination.

The gently sloping baseline is the residual current. This is non-Faradaic and capacitative, being associated with charging of the electrical double layer formed at each new mercury drop as it presents itself to the working solution. Faradaic signals, such as those produced during reduction of the metal ions, display the characteristic sigmoid form shown. Figure 2 shows that as the increasingly negative potential is applied, a point is reached at which this reaction occurs:

$$Cd^{2+} + 2e^- \rightarrow Cd(Hg)$$

As this begins to take place, the region of solution near the electrode surface becomes depleted of cadmium ions, and a concentra-

Fig. 2 Direct-current polarograms of 10^{-4} mol/L Cd^{2+}, Zn^{2+}, and Mn^{2+} in 0.1 mol/L KNO_3 as supporting electrolyte

The baseline curve is that obtained with supporting electrolyte alone.

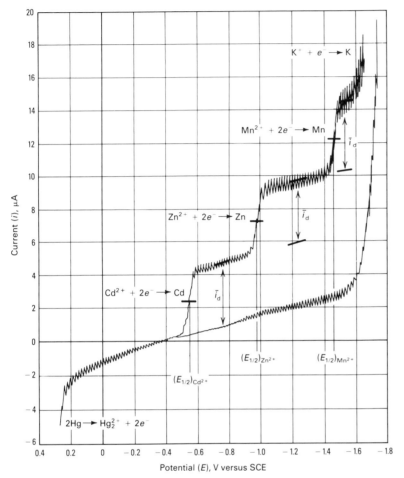

tion gradient is established. Additional increase of potential accelerates the reduction process above, depletes the surface concentration still further, steepens the concentration gradient, and results in an enhanced current.

A stage is reached at which the bulk concentration of Cd^{2+} can supply this species at no faster (diffusion) rate, and the concentration gradient is at its steepest, with the surface concentration effectively zero. In this condition, cadmium ions are reduced as rapidly as they arrive by natural diffusion at the electrode surface. The current can rise no further, and a plateau region is shown. No significant further current rise occurs until the reduction potential of the zinc ions is reached, and a "polarographic wave" for this species is observed that arises in the same way as that of Cd^{2+}. This is followed by the reduction wave for manganese and finally by a steeply rising current corresponding to the reduction of the potassium ion.

Polarography is based on a type of steady-state process in which the solution in the immediate vicinity of the drop that detaches itself from the capillary is stirred. With drop frequencies usually adopted, this stirring ensures development of subsequent drops in almost identical environments. This is shown clearly by the limiting current regions in Fig. 2; the depletion of metal ions caused by the electrochemical process taking place at one drop is replenished in time for an identical interaction with the next drop. Only the first drop, acting as an electrode in a given solution, is in an environment different from others.

The important parameters associated with a polarographic wave are the diffusion current (i_d) and the half-wave potential ($E_{1/2}$). The former, directly proportional to the concentration of the species reacting at the electrode, is the foundation for quantitative analysis. The latter, characteristic of that species regardless of its concentration, pro-

vides qualitative analysis and corresponds to the value of the applied potential at which the observed current is exactly one half the limiting diffusion current. However, half-wave potentials must be used with some caution as a means of "fingerprinting," because their values are particularly sensitive to complexation reactions. Under appropriate circumstances, the effects of complexing may be exploited in the separation of interfering waves. This effect is discussed in the section "Applications" in this article.

The direct proportionality between diffusion current and concentration expressed in terms of the mean diffusion current is:

$$i_d = 607nD^{1/2} m^{2/3} t^{1/6} C \qquad \text{(Eq 1)}$$

where n is the number of electrons transferred, D is the diffusion coefficient of electroactive species (cm^2/s), m is the rate of flow of mercury through capillary (mg/s), t is the drop time in seconds, and C is the concentration of electroactive species (mmol/L).

With the units for the various parameters shown and the numerical constant of 607, the mean diffusion current is given in microamps. Equation 1 in this form provides immediate indication of the small size of the currents observed and emphasizes the minute extent of the electrochemical decomposition that takes place. This is small enough that repeated analysis does not impair the observed magnitude of limiting currents. For practical purposes, the technique is nondestructive.

Equation 1 also shows that the values of diffusion currents produced by metal ions are approximately proportional to the number of electrons exchanged in the electrode process. Thus, the wave heights for Tl^+, Cd^{2+}, and In^{3+} are, for equal concentrations, in the approximate ratio 1:2:3. The slight departure from exactness reflects relatively small variations in the diffusion coefficients.

Diffusion-controlled limiting currents are directly proportional to concentration, which may not be true of currents on the rising portion of polarographic waves. For reversible electrode reactions, diffusion is rate determining at all points on the wave; that is, the electron transfer process is rapid. The rate constants for such rapid reactions characteristically are $\geq 2 \times 10^{-2}$ cm/s. Under such circumstances, the shape and position of the polarographic wave are:

$$E = E_{1/2} + \frac{RT}{nF} \ln \frac{\bar{i}_d - \bar{i}}{\bar{i}} \qquad \text{(Eq 2)}$$

where E and $\bar{i}$ are corresponding values of applied potential and resultant mean current

Fig. 3 Polarograms for equal concentrations of two species whose reduction involves the same number of electrons

A, reversible; B, irreversible

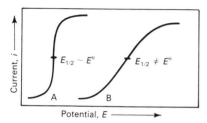

on the rising portion of the wave, R is the universal gas constant, T is absolute temperature, and F is the Faraday constant.

For irreversible electrode processes, electron transfer is slower than the rate of diffusion at potentials corresponding to the rising portion of the wave. As increase in applied potential accelerates electron exchange, diffusion finally becomes rate determining. Therefore, for processes that are less than reversible, the shapes of waves are elongated, and their positions are removed from the vicinity of their reversible redox potentials. Both of these factors may have important analytical implications for signal clarity and its accessibility on the potential scale. Electron transfer rate constants less than 2×10^{-2} cm/s exhibit increasing degrees of irreversibility; values less than 3×10^{-5} cm/s are characteristic of totally irreversible electrode processes. Figure 3 shows a comparison of the two extremes of behavior.

If unambiguous measurement of a diffusion current is possible, Eq 1 is equally valid for reversible and irreversible reductions. Unknown concentrations can be conveniently assessed using a calibration graph or standard addition methods, which are particularly appropriate to polarographic analysis.

A serious limitation of the classical dc technique arises at a lower concentration level in the region of 5×10^{-5} mol/L, at which the analytically significant Faradaic current decreases to and finally becomes less than the constant background capacitance current. The developments in the technique over the last 25 years have focused on improving this unsatisfactory relationship between the two types of current at low concentrations.

One advantage of polarography as an analytical tool is the possibility of multiple analyses on a single solution sample. However, signals for different species may interfere seriously with one another in the more usual supporting electrolytes, and instrumental or chemical resolution of overlapping

waves is required. The former means depend on modern electronic developments; the latter require selection of a working medium that contains appropriate complexing agents showing a selective affinity for species whose waves interfere. Both methods of resolution are often used in combination. Complexation of metal ions shifts their half-wave potentials, usually to more cathodic values. For reversible reductions, the shift is a function of the thermodynamic stability of complexes formed, but for irreversible reductions it depends on the kinetics of the electrode processes.

The classical dc circuit applies the potentials across the polarographic cell rather than across the indicator/solution interface. This demands the use of low-resistance mediums so that the iR (potential) drop through the cell is negligible. The presence of fairly high concentrations of supporting electrolyte maintains low resistance in aqueous mediums, although components of the cell, such as the reference electrode, may have a high resistance and distort voltammetric signals. When organic solvents or mixed aqueous/nonaqueous solvents must be used, high resistances will be encountered. Modern instruments incorporate three-electrode systems to control the potential potentiostatically at the indicator electrode/solution interface. The reference electrode, which may under these circumstances be a high-resistance type, is positioned as closely as possible to the indicator electrode and connected to the instrumentation such that no current flows through it. Even if the resistance of the solution is high to allow a significant voltage drop, an operational amplifier control loop maintains the reference

Fig. 4 The shape of a polarogram distorted by a maximum

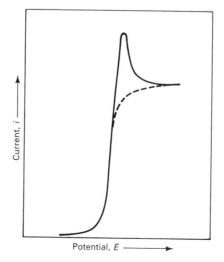

electrode potential at its proper value by supplying compensating potential to a counterelectrode, usually a large platinum coil or carbon rod.

The sigmoid shape expected and observed during the polarographic reduction of many metal ions is sometimes obscured by the presence of maxima. Such phenomena (Fig. 4) derive from unusually high mass-transfer rates in some regions of the potential range in which the wave occurs. They are associated with the unstable interfacial effects that cause electroactive material to stream tangentially around the surface of the mercury drop rather than radially, as in the ideal situation. Addition of a small concentration of surface-active material eliminates such interferences. Triton-X-100 is used virtually universally as the maximum suppressor. The concentration of such additives should always be kept to a minimum; too much can distort and suppress current signals. Calibration curves should be constructed using standard solutions bearing the same concentration of suppressor as the working solutions.

Voltammetry With Other Electrodes

The major limitation of using mercury as an electrode material is its restricted anodic range, which at best extends to $+0.4$ V versus SCE. This is not a disadvantage for metal analysis, although silver in many supporting electrolytes exhibits simply a diffusion current at 0.0 V versus SCE, the wave due to reduction of silver ion being obscured by the dissolution curve. Similar, though less serious, problems are encountered with Cu^{2+} ions in noncomplexing mediums.

Many electrode systems based on carbon have been devised that offer a much extended anodic range and the simplification of a stationary indicator electrode without the complications of the DME, with its continuously varying area and resultant signal. However, such electrodes do not always have the same reproducibility as those based on mercury. The hanging mercury drop electrode (HMDE) is based on a syringe device that combines the advantages of mercury as an electrode material with the stability of a stationary surface. After brief usage, the drop is replaced by an exactly reproduced one.

In linear sweep voltammetry, a rapidly and linearly varying potential is applied to the indicator electrode. Modern instrumentation provides sweep rates to 500 mV/s. Because of the rapid removal of electroactive material from the vicinity of the electrode, forced convection is sometimes used to maintain surface concentration. The result-

Fig. 5 Single-sweep voltammogram obtained at a carbon-wax electrode for 10^{-3} mol/L Ag^+ ion in 0.1 mol/L KNO_3 as supporting electrolyte

The reversal of the potential scan direction after the cathodic signal is fully developed produces an anodic signal whose size is enhanced relative to the first, because its origin is in material deposited and accumulated in the forward sweep. The principle, used for longer cathodic deposition times at constant potential, is the basis for stripping analysis.

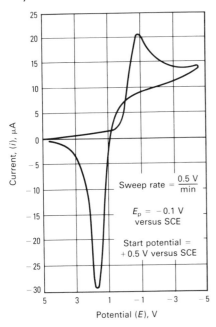

where k is a numerical constant, A is the electrode area, D is the diffusion coefficient, v is the potential sweep rate, and C is the concentration. As in Eq 1, n represents the number of electrons transferred; although $n^{3/2}$ applies to reversible processes, it must be modified to the form $n(\alpha n)^{1/2}$ for irreversible cases. Alpha is the transfer coefficient.

The advantages of peaked wave forms are offset somewhat by the reduced sensitivity to irreversible reductions. Further, the position of the peak potential (E_p) is independent of sweep rate for reversible but not for irreversible systems. A considerable advantage of carbon-base electrodes is the negligible residual current obtained.

In cyclic voltammetry, the applied potential is varied with time in a symmetrical saw-tooth wave form (Fig. 6), and the resultant current is measured over the entire pattern of forward and reverse sweeps. Solid electrodes are used frequently, especially carbon-paste, glassy carbon, or pyrolytic carbon. Material reduced and deposited in the forward part of each cycle is reoxidized in the reverse scan. The technique finds application in investigations of mechanisms, particularly identification of intermediate compounds. Short-lived species can be identified at high sweep rates. With the comparatively slow sweep rates normally used, such intermediate compounds have decomposed before their presence and response can be detected.

Stripping voltammetry is based on the principle that a concentration of reduced metal may accumulate at an electrode by prolonged electrolysis at an appropriate potential in a solution containing such a low concentration of reducible species that its presence would be virtually undetectable

using direct voltammetry. The extent of deposition must be compatible with the production of a measurable anodic current when the deposited material is reoxidized. Application of a potential more cathodic than the half-wave potential of the metal required causes continuous reduction and accumulation as an amalgam in a hanging drop. A mercury-base electrode, which ensures occurrence of the extended reduction at a surface of constant nature and area, should be used. With solid microelectrodes, the nature of the surface changes continuously as products accumulate in the surface. Amalgam formation requires considerable time to affect seriously the surface characteristics of a drop; further, the formation of intermetallic species resulting from simultaneous deposition of two metals is decreased in significance.

In principle, determination of low concentrations—to approximately 10^{-11} mol/L—should be possible using such techniques. In practice, a concentration limit of the order of 10^{-9} mol/L is more realistic. Excessive deposition times may result in instrumental instabilities; more importantly, the last remnants of a wanted species may be removed from a solution by adsorption on the walls of the cell or its components, not by deposition. Even using modern syringe-base systems for producing stationary mercury drops, the effective life for deposition purposes is limited because such drops cannot be maintained in a stable condition longer than 30 min. Extended deposition also encourages the undesirable diffusion of metals into the interior of the electrode. The rapid anodic polarization that follows to achieve maximum sensitivity (via the peaked anodic wave form) does not cause reoxidation, during the sweep time, of

ant current-voltage curve is then little different from that obtained using polarography, except for the lack of current oscillations. However, different signals are observed in unstirred solutions. Peaked voltammograms are produced; the rapid change in applied potential accelerates the electrode reaction so drastically that the diffusion layer thickness increases as the mass-transfer process attempts to replenish the depletion of material near the surface of the electrode. The peak potential corresponds to the situation in which the electron exchange and depletion rate are equal. Beyond the peak, the current drops sharply as the layer of solution near the surface is deprived of reducible material. Figure 5 shows a single sweep peaked voltammogram obtained for silver using a carbon-wax electrode.

Direct proportionality between the magnitude of the peak current (i_p) and concentration is expressed in the following equation applicable to reversible reactions:

$$i_p = kn^{3/2} AD^{1/2} v^{1/2} C \qquad \text{(Eq 3)}$$

Fig. 6 Fundamentals of cyclic voltammetry

(a) Symmetrical saw-tooth potential-time variation used in cyclic voltammetry. (b) Corresponding cyclic voltammogram expected for a near-reversible system. The greater the separation between the peaks for forward and reverse scans, the more irreversible the electrode reactions. Letters a through g show the stages of the cyclic variation and the corresponding positions adopted by the resultant signal.

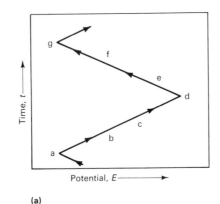

(a)

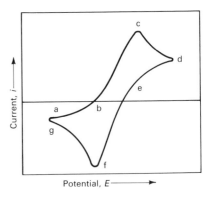

(b)

Fig. 7 Relative rates of decay of Faradaic (i_f) and capacitance (i_c) currents after imposition of voltage change in the potential square-wave profile

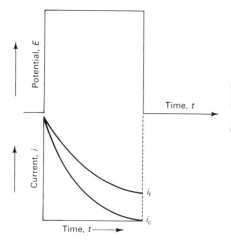

Fig. 7 Relative rates of decay of Faradaic (i_f) and capacitance (i_c) currents after imposition of voltage change in the potential square-wave profile

Fig. 8 Relationship between drop time, pulse duration, and current measurement period used in normal pulse polarography

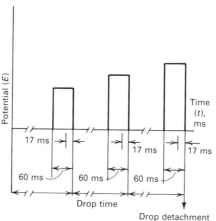

Fig. 8 Relationship between drop time, pulse duration, and current measurement period used in normal pulse polarography

material that has penetrated significantly into the mercury.

Improvements and Developments

Application of dc polarography is limited at low concentrations by the large current oscillations that obscure small voltammetric signals and by the poor ratio of Faradaic to capacitance components of those signals. Modern instrumentation enables complete use of several electrochemical characteristics. The development of fast sweep rates, rapid response recorders, and the electronic sophistication to sample currents resulting from unusual potential wave forms at stable parts of a drop life have resulted in various well-defined techniques.

Current-sampled polarography offers small improvements in analytical sensitivity. The current is probed once at the end of the life of each drop to obtain a stepped polarogram uncomplicated by large current oscillations.

Pulse Polarography. The various techniques of pulse polarography derive from the principle of using a square potential waveform synchronized with the dropping electrode. After imposition of each potential change, Faradaic and capacitance currents result, but they decay over the period of constant potential that takes place before the next reversal of potential in the square wave cycle. Although both current components decay during this period, that due to capacitance effects is reduced almost to zero so that by the end of each cycle a net Faradaic

current remains. Figure 7 shows the relationship between the two currents.

In normal pulse polarography, the initial potential applied to the dropping mercury electrode is held constant until near the end of the drop life, then stepped to a new value for the remaining 60 ms of that drop (Fig. 8). Current is measured only during the last 17 ms of the pulse, that is, at the most stable part of the drop life when its area is virtually constant. Precise synchronization of voltage pulses, drop time, and current detection are crucial and may be achieved only by synchronizing the electronic parameters with mechanical detachment of drops at accurately determined intervals. Potential pulses of increasing magnitude are applied to successive drops, and the resultant plot of current flowing against applied potential constitutes the pulse polarogram. These measures improve detection limits by an order of magnitude.

Differential pulse polarography provides significant increase in detection limits; the range of trace analysis extends to 10^{-7} to 10^{-8} mol/L. A linearly increasing voltage with superimposed voltage pulses of equal magnitude is applied to the working electrode. Modern instrumentation provides considerable flexibility in the selection of the size of pulses, and those from 5 to 100 mV are not unusual. As with the previous technique, synchronization of applied potential and drop time is such that each pulse is imposed once during the last stages of the life of each drop. The duration of the pulse and the period during which current is measured are of the same order as those used in the normal pulse technique. However, in this

case, the difference in current flowing just before application of the pulse and that flowing during the last few milliseconds of the pulse is measured. This current difference is measured instrumentally and is plotted as a function of the applied potential. Figure 9 shows the potential wave form.

The heights of the peaked polarograms obtained are directly proportional to concentration and provide improved resolution between adjacent signals compared with the dc and normal pulse methods. The modulation amplitude may be varied to improve sensitivity. Figure 10 illustrates the normal pulse and differential pulse polarograms obtained for the same mixture of ions shown in Fig. 2, except the concentration of each species is 10^{-5} mol/L.

The principle of differential pulse stripping voltammetry differs little from that of dc stripping. However, shorter deposition times—often only a few minutes—are possible because of the considerable increases in sensitivity. The differential pulse mode detects the much smaller quantities of material that must be deposited, and problems arising from diffusion into the interior of an electrode are much less significant. The development over recent years of various mercury film electrodes offers mechanical stability to prevent such unwanted diffusion.

Other Information Obtainable Using Voltammetric Methods

If a metallic species exhibits reversible polarographic reduction in the absence and presence of a complexing agent, the shifts in half-wave potential that occur with increasing ligand concentration can be used to obtain values of the formation, or stability, constants of complexes formed. When several complexes are formed between which the chemical equilibria are established rapidly, the shift $\Delta E_{1/2}$ is:

$$\text{antilog}_{10} \left[\frac{0.4343nF}{RT} \cdot \Delta E_{1/2} \right] \simeq 1$$
$$+ \ \beta_1 \ [X] \ + \ \beta_2 \ [X]^2 \ + \ ... \ + \ \beta_N \ [X]^N$$

$$(\text{Eq 4})$$

where β_1, β_2, . . . β_N are the overall formation constants of the complex ions MX, MX_2, . . . MX_N, and $[X]$ is the free ligand concentration. For complexing systems of significance in analytical polarography, for example, for overlapping wave separation, the stability must be such that one stable species exists in solution for most values of

Fig. 9 Relationship between drop time, pulse duration, and current signal in differential pulse polarography

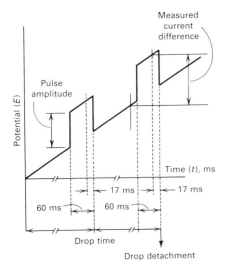

Fig. 10 Polarograms of 10^{-5} mol/L Cd^{2+}, Zn^{2+} and Mn^{2+}

A, normal pulse mode; B, differential pulse mode. Supporting electrolyte 0.1 mol/L KNO_3. Curves A and B indicate the presence of some impurity showing a signal at approximately -0.85 V. This may originate in the supporting electrolyte and emphasizes the importance of extreme purity of such salts required in analysis at these levels. In this case, the interference does not prevent the measurement of the peak heights in curve B.

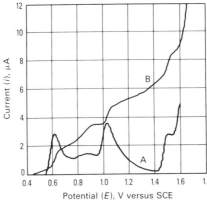

ious systems have been analyzed successfully for the diverse rate constants involved, and many complex mechanisms have been verified. Such investigations serve as a guide to the mediums and conditions under which determination of metallic species in diverse environments may be feasible. Kinetic investigations of homogeneous processes taking place in solution may sometimes be carried out using diffusion currents as indicators of reactant or product concentrations.

Applications

Determination of Trace Amounts of Nickel in Cobalt Compounds. Nickel and cobalt react similarly toward many reagents, and determination of one element in the presence of large amounts of the other is challenging. The similarity extends to the overlap of their polarographic signals in many common supporting electrolytes. However, successful separation of these signals is conducted in a medium consisting of pyridine and pyridinium chloride, the nickel step preceding that due to cobalt. Although dc polarography is adequate for determining commercial-grade cobalt salts, which may contain 0.5% Ni, the low nickel content of analytical grade salts, often under 0.01%, demands the additional sensitivity of the differential pulse mode.

The following details applied to the analysis of the two grades of samples of cobalt nitrate. Samples of the salts weighing 1 g were dissolved in 50 mL distilled water in 100-mL volumetric flasks. To each solution

ligand concentration. Equation 4 then takes the limiting form:

$$\frac{0.4343nF}{RT} \cdot \Delta E_{1/2} \simeq \log_{10} \beta_N$$

$$+ N \log_{10} [X] \qquad \text{(Eq 5)}$$

A plot of $\Delta E_{1/2}$ against $\log_{10} [X]$ allows determination of the coordination number N from the slope and overall stability constant, β_N, from the intercept.

For the effects of complexation to be suitable for the separation of overlapping waves, the stability constants of the complexes formed between the metal ions whose signals interfere and the added complexing agent must differ considerably. The use of such competitive complexation for analytical purposes is particularly significant in the analysis of copper-base alloys for other metals, such as lead, cadmium, zinc, and nickel. Reduction of Cu^{2+} occurs at approximately 0.0 V versus SCE in many supporting electrolytes—well to the positive side of signals for the other species that would be entirely engulfed by currents resulting from Cu^{2+}. However, in cyanide-base supporting electrolytes, although all species required have their half-wave potentials shifted in the direction of negative potential, the shift of copper exceeds the rest, owing to the considerable difficulty in reducing the cyanocuprate$^+$ ion. The required species can then be determined easily.

When redox behavior at working electrodes takes place irreversibly, electrochem-

ical (as opposed to mass-transfer) processes occur slowly. Such slowness should usually be regarded as the slow formation of a structure of reducible or oxidizable species capable of exchanging electrons rapidly with the electrode, not as slow electron transfer as such. Complex situations may arise in which slow chemical and electrochemical processes are involved in multistage mechanisms. Var-

Fig. 11 Direct-current and differential pulse polarograms of nickel in general-purpose cobalt nitrate

A, sample solution; B, after addition of 2 mL of 0.01 mol/L standard; C, after addition of 4 mL of standard; D, after addition of 6 mL of standard. All traces begin at -0.5 V versus SCE.

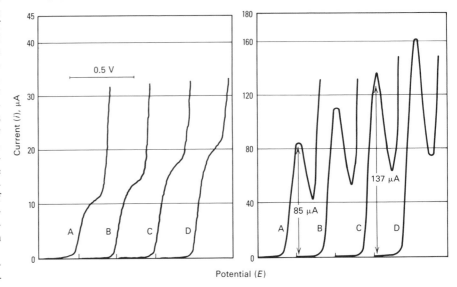

Fig. 12 Direct-current and differential pulse polarograms of nickel in analytical-grade cobalt nitrate

A, sample solution; B, after addition of 0.1 mL of 0.01 mol/L standard; C, after addition of 0.2 mL of standard. All traces begin at −0.5 V versus SCE.

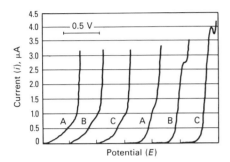

were added 2.0 mL 12 M hydrochloric acid, 5.0 mL pyridine, and 5.0 mL 0.2% gelatin solution. The solutions were then diluted to the mark and transferred to a clean, dry polarographic cell, then deoxygenated 5 min. They were then polarographed using dc and differential pulse modes. Voltage scans began at −0.5 V versus SCE and were halted soon after −1.0 V versus SCE due to the onset of the cobalt step, whose magnitude would have driven the pen off the chart.

Quantification of the nickel content was accomplished by standard additions. For the higher concentrations, successive additions of 2.0 mL 0.01 M standard nickel solution were added to the solutions in the cell, which were then repolarographed after a few seconds of additional deoxygenation. For the much lower nickel concentrations present in solutions of the analytical grade material, additions of 0.1 mL standard solution were found to be more appropriate. Figures 11 and 12 illustrate experimental traces obtained for samples of both grades of the salt. Figure 11 shows that although the dc technique clearly identifies the presence of nickel, its reduction is followed so closely by that of cobalt that the limiting currents of the required metal are less clear than desirable. Consequently, use of the differential pulse mode is advantageous because of the enhanced resolution provided by a peaked signal with consequent unambiguous measurement of its height, not the increased current sensitivity. Figure 12 illustrates that the dc technique cannot analyze the low level of nickel present in the high-purity salt.

The nickel concentration was assessed in each case using:

$$C_{\text{test}} = \frac{ivC_{\text{std}}}{\Delta i(V + v) + iv} \qquad \text{(Eq 6)}$$

where i is the original signal height, Δi is the change in signal height after standard addition, V is the original volume (100 mL), C_{test} is the concentration of test solution, and C_{std} is the concentration of standard solution.

Thus, use of Eq 6 and the peak current data for curves A and C shown in Fig. 11 yields:

$$C_{\text{test}} = \frac{85 \times 4 \times 0.01}{(52 \times 104) + (85 \times 4)}$$

$$= 5.92 \times 10^{-4} \text{ mol/L} \qquad \text{(Eq 7)}$$

Because the relative atomic mass of nickel is 58.71, this figure corresponds to a mass of nickel of 3.48×10^{-2} g/L, or 3.48×10^{-3} g/100 mL. This corresponds to the mass of nickel in 1.0263 g of cobalt salt; therefore, the proportion of nickel in the original sample is 0.34%. Similar calculations based on curves A and C of Figure 12 produce $C_{\text{test}} = 9.04 \times 10^{-6}$ mol/L, that is, 5.31×10^{-5} g Ni/100 mL solution containing 1.0037 g of analytical-grade cobalt nitrate, or 0.0053% Ni.

Multielement Fingerprinting and Approximate Quantification in Effluent Samples.

A fingerprinting method was necessary for the simultaneous detection of the presence and level of several metals in various effluent systems. This was to form the basis of a continuous monitoring setup to produce a method that could effect rapid preliminary qualitative and quantitative analysis by relatively unskilled operators. Where the presence of certain species is clear, refined subsequent analysis may be necessary—perhaps using a method other than voltammetry, such as atomic absorption (see the article "Atomic Absorption Spectrometry" in this Volume).

The most appropriate supporting electrolyte was found to be a mixture of ammonium hydroxide and ammonium chloride; as a stock solution, this was prepared to a concentration of 1 M and used to prepare pretreated samples to a selected volume before analysis. To maintain the simplicity of the method, the reference electrode used was a mercury pool on the bottom of the cell. Major interference from iron was removed, because it was precipitated as Fe^{3+} from the medium used. The method was found to be effective for effluent samples where there was concern over the possible presence of specific metal ions. In a particular case, it was necessary to monitor for the presence of copper, lead, cadmium, nickel, and zinc.

Some pretreatment was required to destroy organic material present in the samples

Fig. 13 Differential pulse polarogram obtained in analysis of effluents

A, standard solution; 10 mL supporting electrolyte + 1 mL solution containing 10 mg/L copper, lead, cadmium, nickel, and zinc (copper/lead appear under the same peak in the medium used); B, effluent sample I; C, effluent sample I + standard solution A—presence of copper/lead, nickel, and zinc indicated; D, effluent sample II; E, effluent sample II + standard solution A—presence of cadmium and possibly small amounts of copper/lead and zinc indicated

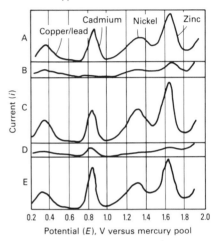

and to ensure that the metals were present only as uncomplexed ions before addition of the supporting electrolyte. A 100-mL sample was evaporated with 1 mL concentrate nitric acid to approximately half the initial volume. Hydrogen peroxide (6%) was added dropwise as necessary until the sample cleared. The sample was then evaporated to approximately 20 mL to ensure decomposition of excess peroxide; 1 mL 5% citric acid solution was added, and supporting electrolyte added to a total volume of 100 mL.

Following the pretreatment to remove organic matter and iron, 10 mL working solution was deoxygenated 3 min in a cell with a mercury pool reference electrode and polarographed from −0.2 to −2.0 V relative to this. A 1-mL quantity of standard solution containing 10 mg/L of the above metals and the same supporting electrolyte was added, and the measurement repeated. Enhancement of the appropriate peaks from the first run confirmed the presence and identity of various species and approximate estimation of their concentrations by application of the standard addition formula. Appearance of a peak where there was none in the first run confirmed the absence of that species in the original sample. Figure 13 shows results obtained for two samples.

SELECTED REFERENCES

- R.N. Adams, *Electrochemistry at Solid Electrodes*, Marcel Dekker, 1969
- A.M. Bond, *Modern Polarographic Techniques in Analytical Chemistry*, Marcel Dekker, 1980

- D.R. Crow, *Polarography of Metal Complexes*, Academic Press, 1969

- Z. Galus, *Fundamentals of Electrochemical Analysis*, Ellis Horwood Series in Analytical Chemistry, Halsted Press, 1976

- M. Heyrovsky and J. Kuta, *Polarography*, Academic Press, 1968

- L. Meites, *Polarographic Techniques*, Interscience, 1955

- J. Wang, *Stripping Analysis*, VCH Publishers, 1985

Electrogravimetry

D.R. Browning, Consultant

General Uses

- Removal of easily reduced ions before analysis by another method
- Quantitative determination of ions after removal of interfering ions
- Quantitative determination of metal ions in the presence of other metal ions
- Quantitative determination of metal ions using electrogravimetry in conjunction with other techniques

Examples of Applications

- Quantitative analysis of metals in alloys
- Precision analysis of metallurgical products and samples
- Quantitative measurement of microgram amounts of metals
- Quantitative determination of metals in the presence of other ions, such as chloride

Samples

- *Form*: Solution

- *Size*: Down to decigram amounts of solid
- *Preparation*: Solutions of analyte

Limitations

- Limited to the analysis of ionizable species; complete deposition (99.5%) is essential for precise results

Estimated Analysis Time

- After sample preparation, electrolysis requires 15 min to well over an hour, depending on conditions

Capabilities of Related Techniques

- *Controlled-potential coulometry*: Quantitative determination of metal ions
- *Coulometric titrations*: Applicable for all volumetric reactions
- *Atomic absorption spectrophotometry*: Quantitative and qualitative determination of metal ions in the presence of other ions
- *X-ray fluorescence*: Qualitative and quantitative determination of elements

Introduction

Electrogravimetry is the oldest electroanalytical technique. The element of interest must be deposited electrolytically onto an electrode and weighed. Unlike most electrochemical techniques, the reaction often must be allowed to go to completion efficiently, prolonging analysis times. However, the technique is more accurate (0.1%) than controlled-potential coulometry (0.2 to 5%) or polarography (2%). Use of efficient stirring lessens analysis time. Overall analysis time depends on the technique used.

Determining the voltage of the cell necessary to achieve the required separation requires knowing the reactions that occur at each electrode. The potential of each electrode (*E*) may then be calculated using the Nernst equation:

$$E = E^0 - \frac{RT}{nF} \log \frac{[\text{oxid}]}{[\text{red}]} \qquad \text{(Eq 1)}$$

The applied electromotive force (emf), E_{app}, may be determined from this result coupled with knowledge of the *iR* drop and the overpotentials of the cathode and anode ($\omega_{cathode}$ and ω_{anode}, respectively):

$$E_{app} = E_{cal} + iR + \omega_{cathode} + \omega_{anode} \qquad \text{(Eq 2)}$$

Application of an emf to the cell initiates current flow and thus the desired reaction. The overpotential developed at an electrode usually results from the difference in concentration of the ions in the bulk solution and at the electrode surface and provides one source of resistance to current flow. For an anodic process exhibiting an overpotential

effect, the applied emf must be more positive than the calculated potential; for a cathodic process with associated overpotential, it must be more negative than the calculated value.

In a dilute solution, depletion in concentration near the electrode increases resistance *R*, yielding a change *iR* in potential. This *iR* drop may lead to serious disadvantages in instrumental conditions, because it is not always constant and is sometimes unknown.

Electrogravimetry Principles

Determination of emf Conditions for Separation. Such factors as the applied voltage, the electrode potential at the electrodes of interest, the current flowing, the amount of electricity used, and the nature of the deposit at the electrodes affect electrolysis of a solution. The deposition of copper on a platinum cathode best exemplifies the principles of electrogravimetry. The cell may be represented as:

$$Pt, Cu | Cu^{2+} (0.100 \ M),$$

$$H^+ (1.000 \ M) | O_2 \ (0.2 \ atm), Pt$$

Using Eq 1 for the electrode reactions (at 25 °C, or 75 °F):

$$Cu \rightarrow Cu^{2+} + 2e^-$$

$$E_{Cu} = 0.337 + \frac{0.0591}{2} \log [Cu]^{2+}$$

$$= 0.337 + 0.0296 \log$$

$$(0.100) = 0.307 \ V \qquad (Eq \ 3)$$

$$O_2 + 4H^+ + 4e^- \rightarrow 2H_2O$$

$$E_{O_2} = 1.229 + \frac{0.0591}{4}$$

$$\log \frac{[O_2] \ [H^+]^4}{[H_2O]^2} \qquad (Eq \ 4)$$

Because $[H_2O] \approx$ constant and $[O_2] \approx 0.20$ atm (partial pressure):

$$E_{O_2} = 1.229 + 0.0148 \log [H^+]^4 \ p_{O_2}$$

$$= 1.229 + 0.0148 \log (1.00)^4 (0.20)$$

$$= 1.219 \ V$$

Therefore, the cell potential for the reaction $2Cu + O_2 + 4H^+ \rightarrow 2Cu^{2+} + 2H_2O$ is $E_{cell} = E_{O_2} - E_{Cu} = 1.219 \ V - 0.307 \ V = 0.912 \ V$.

To deposit copper metal, the reaction must be reversed by applying an external voltage at least equal to the cell potential together with the overpotentials and any iR drop. This value of voltage is the decomposition potential. The anodic overvoltage of oxygen in this cell may be taken as 0.40 V. The decomposition potentials vary with concentration, as does the iR drop; this must be considered. Current will flow only when:

$$E_{app} = 0.912 \ V + 0.40 \ V + iR \ drop$$

Therefore, E must be increased until it exceeds this sum to sustain electrolysis. The limiting current, proportional to concentration, decreases with concentration. In this case, the decomposition potential increases, and iR decreases.

A major problem is that voltages frequently must be maintained within close limits to ensure efficient separation of metals. Other factors affect separation. For example, the smoother the deposited metal, the higher the overpotential. In addition, increases in temperature affect the result. As temperature is raised, overpotential is decreased. In some cases, particularly in strong acid solution, overpotential may become pH dependent. Determination of a working potential may be difficult, and often a rough value is obtained from Eq 1 and modified by experiment.

Various parameters are occasionally advantageous in determination of the voltage conditions required by two metals to enable deposition of one in the presence of the other. The use of complexing agents may provide solutions with decomposition potentials very different from those in the uncomplexed state. This sometimes allows reversal of the order of deposition.

Conditions for Complete Deposition. According to Eq 1 for the cell reaction at 25 °C (75 °F):

$$M^{n+} + ne^- \rightarrow M$$

$$E = E° + \frac{0.0591}{n} \log [M^+] \qquad (Eq \ 5)$$

Therefore, the voltage becomes more negative by 0.0591/n V or 59/n mV for each ten-fold decrease in concentration. Electrogravimetry normally requires complete or nearly complete deposition. The electrode must be totally covered by the metal to ensure formation of a monolayer. If not, the activity of the solid metal cannot be considered to be unity, and Eq 5 will not hold. This presents problems in the deposition of small amounts of metal.

Physical Properties of Deposits. To ensure purity of the metal and quantitative deposition, electrolysis must exhibit the following characteristics.

The ability of metals to adhere to the cathode is most important because any loss from the cathode causes an error in the weight of the metal that cannot be accommodated. Smoother deposits generally adhere more favorably to the electrode. Therefore, effects that cause the metal deposit to be flaky or spongelike must be reduced or eliminated. The most common cause of this failing—the evolution of a gas coincident with metal deposition on the same electrode—must be prevented if possible by arranging electrolysis conditions.

The chemical nature of the medium may affect the smoothness of the deposit. For example, copper is deposited readily from a solution in nitric acid, but silver yields a

better deposit when precipitated from the silver cyanide complex. In samples of cobalt, nickel, or copper containing chloride ions, the chloride ions must be removed to deposit the metals quantitatively (Ref 1).

Temperature increases hasten the rate of diffusion and thus the current density, which decreases deposition time. Hydrogen overpotential is also decreased; this may affect the degree of separation, particularly when metal complexes are involved.

The rate of flow of ions to an electrode is hastened by increasing their rate of movement in the solution. This is achieved by efficient stirring using a stirrer or a rotating or vibrating electrode (Ref 2). Again, the increased rate of diffusion decreases deposition time, but lessens the concentration potential. This increases current density, which further decreases deposition time, as outlined above.

Use of Incomplete Deposition. Small mass changes arising from electrolytic deposition may be monitored using the piezoelectric effect. For example, in the determination of cadmium, metallic electrodes of a piezoelectric crystal are used as cathodes. The weight of cadmium deposited is related linearly to the fundamental frequency of the crystal; this is used to determine incomplete deposition of cadmium from a solution of 0.1 M $NaClO_4$ (Ref 3). Analysis takes 15 min.

Selection of Method

Separation is normally carried out under conditions of constant current or constant or controlled voltage.

Constant current methods are the oldest in electrogravimetry. Continual increases in voltage maintain constancy of current. Two problems arise in the separation of two ions in aqueous solution. First, the overpotential of hydrogen, if reached, causes deterioration in the smoothness of the deposit, with the effects considered earlier. Second, any second metal to be deposited must have a decomposition potential more negative than that of the hydrogen overpotential or the first deposited metal.

Considerable increases in voltage maintain analysis speed and ensure complete deposition. For example, when separating copper from other metals, such as zinc, copper is reduced to approximately 1/100 of its concentration at 1.43 V. The current may be increased to give a final voltage of 2.2 V before hydrogen is evolved. For example, using 0.5 M sulfuric acid as the electrolyte, the hydrogen ion remains effectively constant while hydrogen is evolved. Codeposition will not occur if the metal from which copper is to be separated has a more negative potential than that for hydrogen.

Fig. 1 Typical internal electrolysis cell

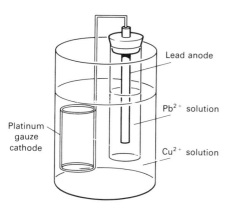

Fig. 2 Typical dual anode cell

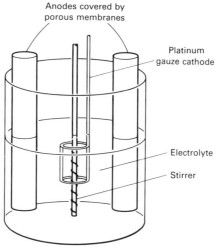

Constant Voltage Electrogravimetry. In the above example, hydrogen is not evolved below 2.2 V. Therefore, if electrolysis is conducted at a constant voltage from 1.43 to 2.2 V, copper may be deposited without hydrogen. However, the method, involving small currents and long separation times, is rarely used.

Controlled-potential electrolysis (controlled cathode potential technique), by far the most significant technique, is discussed in the article "Controlled-Potential Coulometry" in this Volume.

Internal Electrolysis. In this method, current is obtained from a secondary reaction usually consisting of attack of the anode by the electrolyte. The anode and cathode are connected directly to one another, creating a short-circuited galvanic cell (Fig. 1). Analysis of copper in the presence of lead necessitates use of the cell:

$$-Pb\,|\,Pb^{2+}\,|\,|\,Cu^{2+}\,|\,Cu+$$

where lead is the attackable anode. Energy is lost only by ohmic resistance, which controls the maximum current flowing through the cell:

$$iR = 0.22 + 0.0296 \log [Cu^{2+}]$$

for a 1 M Pb^{2+} solution at 25 °C (75 °F). Metal ions with decomposition potentials below −0.12 V, for example, silver and copper but not cadmium, may be deposited using this technique. To make i as large as possible, R must be kept as low as possible by using a high electrolyte concentration.

Electrolysis will take too long if large quantities of deposit are handled. In addition, the deposit becomes spongy, and metal ions may diffuse to the anode during pro-

longed electrolysis. Deposits are usually restricted to approximately 25 mg.

Considerations of High Precision and Automation. Advances in instrumentation and computer techniques have furthered high-precision analysis, automated techniques of analysis, and process on-line control. Electroanalytical probes are gaining acceptance in process control.

Metals may be separated using automated techniques (Ref 4). One such device consists of a stabilized operational amplifier that acts

as a power potentiostat/galvanostat with voltages ≤10 V and a current ≤2 A. At the beginning of electrolysis, the apparatus maintains constant current until the working electrode reaches a preselected value of potential. This value is then constant throughout electrolysis. The apparatus was used to separate 0.1 g of Ag$^+$ from 0.3 g Cu^{2+} using platinum-rhodium working and auxiliary electrodes and a 1.0 M Hg$_2$SO$_4$ solution as the reference electrode. The instrument may be used as a potentiostat for polarography as well as a voltage amplifier and current/voltage converter.

The anode may be selected not to affect the potential of the cell. In addition, dual anodes may be used to enlarge surface area (Fig. 2) and may be protected from the electrolyte by a porous membrane. A platinum gauze electrode is placed between the cathode and anode, and the circuit is completed.

Instrumentation

Cells and Electrodes. The cell is fundamental to electrogravimetry equipment. Two primary classical types of cells are used in the major techniques, which are conducted at constant current and controlled potential. The difference between the techniques is the addition of a reference electrode for controlled-potential analysis. These two cells contain large platinum gauze electrodes (Fig. 3a) or a mercury cathode and a flat spiral wire anode (Fig. 3b). The mercury

Fig. 3 Classical cell types

(a) Constant current (top) and controlled potential (bottom) cells. (b) Cell for constant current electrolysis with mercury cathode. Source: Ref 10

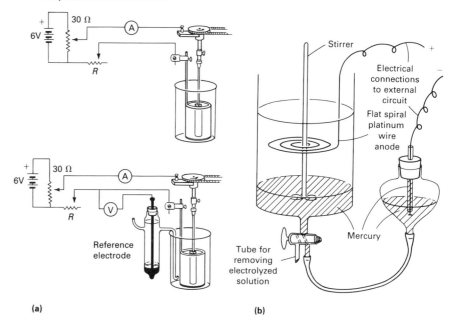

Table 1 Electrogravimetric determination of some metals using vibrating electrodes

Metal	Mass, g	Relative error, %	Analysis time, min(a)
Copper	0.1994	0.06	10
Lead	0.0972-0.6635	0.20	12
Bismuth	0.2013	0.05	15
Antimony	0.1022	0.11	14

(a) Note reduction in analysis time compared to that shown in Table 2. Source: Ref 6

cathode has the advantages of a high hydrogen overpotential and the ability to form an amalgam with most metals. In both cases, efficient stirring is used to prevent concentration polarization.

In the case of the mercury cathode, solution may be removed without interfering with the electrolysis current. Thus, there is no oxidation of the elements deposited at the solution-amalgam interface. In the simple cell shown in Fig. 3(b), this may be accomplished using the stop cock and siphon. The cell constant and specific resistance of the solution are low, allowing flow of a current of several amperes—normally sufficient to reduce all the solution components. This can be prevented by efficient stirring and by the heating effects of the current. New and modified cells and electrodes are available to improve precision or to be used at the microgram level.

Microelectrogravimetry is conducted easily in the following simply constructed cell using controlled potential (Ref 5). The cell contains a rapidly rotating helical platinum wire, 10 to 15 cm (4 to 6 in.) long and 0.05 cm (0.02 in.) in diameter. From 3 to 10 mg copper in copper foil have been recovered (99.5%) in 90 min using this cell. Recovery from brass was lower (97.4 ± 0.8%). Lead and tin have also been deposited from brass. Cadmium was analyzed in micromolar concentration using a piezoelectric electrode as described earlier.

An electrolytic cell fitted with a mechanically homogenized system for decreasing concentration polarization yields dense, adhering, smooth brilliant deposits that provide high precision analysis of metallurgical samples and that may be used in quality control of metallurgical products. Use of vibrating

Table 2 Determination of copper using internal electrolysis

Mass, g	Relative error, %	Analysis time, min
0.02019	0.23	20
0.05029	0.90	35
0.10056	1.62	45

Source: Ref 6

Fig. 4 Automatic potentiostat for controlled-potential analysis

The cell emf may be varied automatically using this type of device. Source: Ref 11

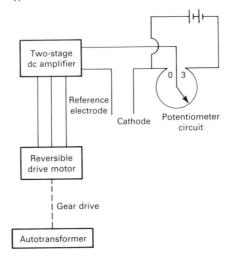

electrodes improves the structure of the deposit and reduces the analysis time of electrogravimetry (Ref 6). Table 1 shows typical results. Table 2 lists results obtained using internal electrolysis to deposit copper.

Power Supplies and Circuit Requirements. The circuit requirements for electrogravimetry are a direct current (dc) source, a variable resistance, an ammeter for measuring current, and a voltmeter for voltage measurement. Direct current may be provided by batteries or a power supply that converts alternating current (ac) to direct current.

Controlled-potential analysis requires a reference electrode against which to measure the potential of the working electrode, cell potential being measured using a potentiometer. The cell emf may be varied automatically using an automatic potentiostat (Fig. 4).

Types of Analysis

The separation and quantitative determination of metal ions from combinations of metals in alloys may be performed using constant current electrolysis if there is sufficient difference between the decomposition potentials of the metals and other elements, such as hydrogen, being deposited on the cathode. Many elements are determined using this method, such as Cu^{2+}, Cd^{2+}, Fe^{3+}, Sn^{2+}, Zn^{2+}. Controlled-potential electrogravimetry may be used to determine many elements in the presence of others. Examples are copper in the presence of bismuth, cadmium, nickel,

antimony, tin, or zinc and nickel in the presence of iron and zinc.

Removal of Interfering Ions. The mercury cathode is useful for removing ions that interfere with the metal of interest. Typical elements separated from those that interfere are aluminum, magnesium, titanium, and vanadium. These metals are high in the electromotive series of elements. Those much lower amalgamate with mercury and are separated before determination of those higher.

Effects of Complexation. When attempting to separate ions whose decomposition potentials are close, it is often appropriate to convert them to complexes having different potentials. A typical separation is that of bismuth and copper. When these are electrolyzed in sulfuric acid, the difference in potential is only 0.024 V. If the ions are then treated with a cyanide, the copper is reduced and complexes with cyanide:

$$Cu^+ + 3(CN)^- \rightleftharpoons Cu(CN)_3^{2-}$$

The potential of this complex is much lower than before, providing a greater difference between the potentials than previously. In this case, copper is deposited quantitatively before the bismuth separates.

Internal Electrolysis. In this technique, analysis is restricted to small samples for which separation time is brief. A typical example is the deposition of silver using $Cu/CuSO_4$ as an anode. This may be accomplished in the presence of such elements as copper, iron, nickel, and zinc, which have higher deposition potentials. Another example is the selective deposition of traces of silver, cadmium, copper, and lead using several techniques. For example, an anode of $Cu/CuSO_4$ precipitates silver; an anode of $Pb/PbSO_4$ precipitates copper and silver; an anode of $Cd/CdSO_4$ precipitates lead, copper, and silver; and an anode of $Zn/ZnSO_4$ precipitates all four metals, which can then be analyzed by difference.

Use of Potential Buffers. If chlorocuprous ions are in solution, two competing reactions exist:

$$Cu^+ + e^- \rightarrow Cu \text{ (cathode)}$$

$$Cu^+ \rightarrow Cu^{2+} + e^- \text{ (anode)}$$

In the presence of sufficient hydrazine:

$$N_2H_5^+ \rightarrow N_2 + 5H^+ + 4e^- (0.17 \text{ V})$$

$$CuCl_3^{2-} \rightarrow Cu^{2+} + 3Cl^- + e^- (0.15 \text{ V})$$

Oxidation of hydrazine is preferred, and oxidation of Cu^+ at the anode is suppressed, allowing only reduction at the cathode to occur. The action of hydrazine, termed a potential buffer, resembles that of a buffer when stabilizing pH.

Analysis of oxidizable species is carried out at the anode by increasing oxidation potential in a manner similar to the method of increasing reduction potential at the cathode. The effect of using attackable anodes in internal electrolysis has been noted. The discharge of ions is usually restricted to halide, hydroxyl, and sulfide ions. In the case of other ions, the hydroxyl ion from aqueous solutions is discharged as oxygen in preference. Decomposition potential in such cases depends mainly on the metal ions present.

Oxides of a metal may be deposited on the anode. In this case, the anode, of platinum gauze, has a larger surface area than the cathode. The situation is complicated by the tendency of the oxides to form hydrates. Suitable correction factors must be applied.

Applications

Estimation of Copper in a Copper-Manganese Alloy (Ref 7, 8). Approximately 1 g of the alloy, which should contain 0 to 0.5 g copper and 0.5 to 1.0 g manganese, was weighed accurately to 0.1 mg and dissolved in 25 mL of a solution of 5 parts sulfuric acid, and 3 parts nitric acid, and 7 parts water. This mixture was heated until all the oxides of nitrogen had evolved, and the reddish color of nitrogen dioxide had disappeared. The solution was cooled, diluted to 150 mL with water, and placed in a tall form beaker with platinum gauze electrodes. The electrolysis circuit was arranged as shown in Fig. 3(a). The cathode was weighed accurately before use.

Manganese interferes with deposition of copper unless it is reduced from the Mn_{7+} state. This can be accomplished by using a solution of ascorbic acid or of the disodium salt of ethylene diamine tetracetic acid (EDTA). Convenient strengths are 10 g in 10 mL water for ascorbic acid and 25 g in 50 mL water for the disodium salt of EDTA. In both cases, electrolysis takes approximately 1 h, but the currents applied should be different: 3 to 4 A in the presence of disodium EDTA and 4 to 6 A in the presence of ascorbic acid. These solutions must be added dropwise from a burette to remove the color of the Mn^{7+} salt as it forms.

The cathode was then removed from the cell, washed carefully with water, dried in an oven for approximately 30 min, and weighed. It was then returned to the oven for a further short period and reweighed. This procedure was repeated until a constant weight was achieved. The experiment was repeated a sufficient number of times to provide a suitable degree of precision.

Determination of Nickel in Samples Containing Chloride Ion (Ref 1). A sample containing approximately 0.3 g nickel was weighed to 0.1 mg in a 250-mL beaker; 4.1 mL concentrated sulfuric acid was added. A yellow precipitate formed with the evolution of hydrochloric acid fumes. The mixture was heated to near boiling on a hot plate until the solid precipitate changed through white to pale green. At this stage, all the chloride ions had been removed. The sides of the beaker were flamed continuously with a bunsen burner or other means. The mixture was heated for another 5 min.

Next, 65 mL distilled water and 35 mL concentrated ammonia were added, and the solution heated to approximately 70 °C (160 °F). Using a weighed net cathode and a platinum spiral anode, electrolysis was conducted at 70 to 80 °C (160 to 175 °F) with a current of approximately 2 A. Analysis required approximately 90 min. Dimethylglyoxime was added to a drop of the solution as a check that all the nickel had been removed from the solution. The electrodes were removed while the potential was applied, and the cathode was washed with water, then ethanol. It was dried in a current of air, then weighed. Table 3 shows typical results. Cobalt may be determined similarly.

Separation of Cadmium and Lead by Internal Electrolysis (Ref 9). Standard solutions of cadmium and lead were prepared as the nitrates. To a solution of each nitrate, a few drops nitric acid were added to prevent hydrolysis, and the solution was diluted to 500 mL. The cadmium and lead were standardized by complexometric titration using EDTA. A solution containing approximately 1 to 3 mg of each of the lead

and cadmium ions was prepared and placed in a tall form beaker. A solution of EDTA (the volume to contain approximately 500 mg EDTA) was added. The solution was diluted to 250 mL with distilled water, and the pH adjusted to 2.5.

The combined electrode, previously weighed to 0.1 mg and consisting of a platinum gauze cathode and a bent zinc plate attached securely to it with copper wire, was added to the solution. Deposition of lead was complete in approximately 6 h. The electrode was removed from the bath and washed over the bath with a jet of distilled water. It was washed with ethanol, dried at 70 to 80 °C (160 to 175 °F), and weighed. The procedure was repeated for the deposition of cadmium, with the pH adjusted to 4.0. Electrolysis required approximately 12 h.

Table 3 Determination of Ni^{2+} in $NiCl_2$ solution

Solution, g	Nickel, g	mmol of nickel per gram of solution
2.3625	0.2657	1.9159
2.6052	0.2929	1.9153
2.6204	0.2983	1.9133
2.8191	0.3168	1.9144
2.4832	0.2792	1.9154
2.7186	0.3056	1.9150
2.3413	0.2632	1.9151
2.4821	0.2791	1.9156
2.4626	0.2767	1.9142
2.6911	0.3024	1.9143

Source: Ref 1

REFERENCES

1. J.F. Owen, C.S. Patterson, and G.S. Rice, *Anal. Chem.*, Vol 55 (No. 6), 1983, p 990-992
2. G. Facsko, *Galvanotechnik*, Vol 66 (No. 5), 1975, p 391-395
3. J.P. Mieura and J.L. Jones, *Talanta*, Vol 16 (No. 1), 1969, p 149-150
4. M. Stastny, R. Volf, and Z. Orbal, Sb. Vys. Sk. Chem. Technol. Praze, *Anal. Chem.*, Vol H11, 1976, p 123-134
5. D.D. Olm and J.T. Stock, *Mikrochim. Acta*, Vol 2 (No. 5-6), 1977, p 575-582
6. K. Kuchta, *G.I.T. Fachz Lab.*, Vol 17 (No. 4), 1973, p 355-358
7. B.L. Rai, *J. Inst. Chem. Calcutta*, Vol 48 (No. 3), 1976, p 141-143
8. V.B. Khanna, B.L. Rai, and B.B. Banerjee, *Res. India*, Vol 19 (No. 3), 1974, p 120-121
9. A.K. Majumdar and S.G. Browal, *Anal. Chim. Acta*, Vol 35 (No. 2), 1966, p 206-211
10. D.R. Browning, Ed., *Electrometric Methods*, McGraw-Hill, London, 1969, p 123, 124
11. H.H. Willard, L.L. Merritt, Jr., J.A. Dean, and F.A. Settle, Jr., Ed., *Instrumental Methods of Analysis*, 6th ed., D. Van Nostrand, 1981, p 736

SELECTED REFERENCES

- J.J. Lingane, *Electroanalytical Chemistry*, 2nd ed., Wiley-Interscience, 1958
- N. Tanaka, in *Treatise on Analytical Chemistry, Part I: Theory and Practice*, Vol 4, Kolthoff, Elving, and Sandell, Ed., Wiley-Interscience, 1963, p 2417-2473

Electrometric Titration

John T. Stock, Department of Chemistry, University of Connecticut

General Uses

- Widely applicable as a branch of volumetric analysis
- Automated determinations
- High-precision determinations
- Potentiometric continuous monitoring and process control

Examples of Applications

- Determinations in colored, turbid, or very dilute solutions that preclude use of chemical indication
- By electrogeneration, use of titrants that are unstable if stored or have no real lifetime
- Assay of primary standards
- Analyses that must be controlled remotely, for example, of radioactive samples
- Maintenance of constant conditions, for example, of pH or component concentrations, during fermentation, sludge treatment, and so on

Samples

- *Form*: Any
- *Size*: Small, unless lacking homogeneity or of very low analyte concentration
- *Preparation*: If a solution, frequently none. Solids must be made into a suitable solution without loss of analyte; interfering substances must be masked or removed

Advantages

- Submicrogram amounts of analyte can be determined, because a single drop of solution can be titrated
- Electrical quantities need not be measured absolutely, except in coulometric titration. Because results are determined from changes in these quantities, instrumental requirements and conditions are usually less rigid than indirect-measurement determinations

Limitations

- Precision and accuracy are usually better when the titration determines a single analyte, although the successive titration of several analytes may be possible
- Concentration and reaction speed must be high enough to permit rapid equilibration and to yield reproducible end points. Approximately $10^{-5}M$ may be taken as the lowest practical limit, although titration at lower concentrations is sometimes possible

Estimated Analysis Time

- At least several minutes after sample preparation

Capabilities of Related Techniques

- *Controlled-potential coulometry*: Determination of major constituents, metals, and certain organics; study of electrochemical reactions. Suitable for determinations requiring greater selectivity than obtainable by constant-current techniques. Small-scale preparations
- *Catalytic techniques*: Determinations by effect of a substance upon the speed of a normally slow reaction. The effect can be monitored electrochemically, or electrochemical titration can be used to maintain constancy of the reacting system
- *Voltammetry and polarography*: Provides direct electrochemical measurement of metals and nonmetals and is the basis of amperometric titration
- *Stripping analysis*: Quantitative determination of analytes, usually metals in very dilute solutions
- *Electrographic analysis*: Qualitative or at best semiquantitative analysis of metallic samples

Introduction

Methods such as electrolytic conductivity and electrophoresis depend primarily on the rate of movement of charged species (ions) in an electric field. Electron transfer, or its tendency to occur, is the basis of a larger group of methods. Electrogravimetry, though little used, is an example of this group. At the other extreme is pH determination by use of a glass electrode. The extremely high electrical resistance of the glass electrode necessitates performing measurements at low (ideally, zero) current so that essentially no electrochemical change occurs during the process.

Faraday's laws of electrolysis are involved in several electroanalytical techniques. These laws may be combined in the formulation $Q = nFx$, where F is the faraday constant (96 495 C/g eqvt), and Q is the minimum number of coulombs required to alter the charge of x moles of a given species by n units. If the reaction proceeds with 100% current efficiency, Q is also the amount of electricity required. The reaction may involve deposition (of silver, for example) on an electrode; dissolution from an attackable anode, such as of silver or tin; or alteration of the charge of a species in the solution, for example, $Fe^{3+} + e \rightarrow Fe^{2+}$.

If the current is constant at i amperes and flows for t seconds, $Q = it$, or the relationship $Q = \int_{0}^{t} i \cdot dt$ must be used. The integration is rarely performed mathematically, but usually by a coulometer placed in series with the system under investigation. Electronic coulometers may be arranged to read in units, such as microcoulombs, microequivalents, or micrograms, of a given analyte.

Conductometric Titration

A liquid must contain ions to be an electrolytic conductor. The purest water has a small but definite conductance due to slight (approximately one molecule in 10 million) self-ionization: $2H_2O \rightleftharpoons H_3O^+ + OH^-$. Traces of electrolytes greatly increase the conductance of water. In aqueous solution, most salts, common acids such as hydrochloric (HCl), nitric (HNO_3), and perchloric ($HClO_4$), and bases such as sodium hydroxide (NaOH) and potassium hydroxide (KOH), are strong electrolytes; that is, they exist virtually completely as ions. Weak electrolytes, such as ammonia (NH_3), carbonic acid (H_2CO_3), most organic acids, and few salts, are only partially dissociated. The nature, charge, and concentration of all the ions in a solution govern its conductance. The hydrogen or hydronium ion, H_3O^+

(written as H^+ for convenience), and the hydroxyl ion, OH^- are better conductors than the other ions. Measurements are made using alternating current. If the solutions are at ambient temperature, routine conductometric titration does not require thermostatic control.

The titrant is added in small increments; titrant volume and conductance readings are performed after each addition. Eight to ten additions are usually made before and approximately the same number after the expected end point. The conductances, in absolute or arbitrary units, are then plotted against the corresponding total volumes of titrant. The end point is determined by extrapolating the linear portions of the branches of the titration curve to intersect. To minimize its diluting effect, the titrant is usually more concentrated than the titrand solution.

Conductometric titration is most widely used in dilute acid/base reactions. In the titration of 10^{-4} to 10^{-3} M HCl using NaOH ($H^+ + Cl^- + Na^+ + OH^- \rightarrow H_2O + Cl^- + Na^+$), the overall effect is the progressive replacement of highly conducting H^+ by the less conducting Na^+ ion. At the equivalence point, the solution consists of NaCl. Because continued titration again increases conductance, the resulting titration curve is V-shaped. An L-type curve is obtained if a weak base, such as NH_3, replaces NaOH as the titrant. The conductance remains essentially unchanged as titration continues past the end point.

In the titration of the typical weak electrolyte acetic acid using NaOH, conductance decreases slightly before increasing as the strong electrolyte sodium acetate (AcONa) forms. Because the slope of the titration

curve increases as excess NaOH accumulates in the solution, the titration curve is the reversed-L type. If NH_3 is used as the titrant, the conductance remains essentially constant beyond the end point. This weak acid/weak base titration is easily performed using conductometry, but not potentiometry or chemical indication.

In the precipitation titration of NaCl using silver nitrate ($AgNO_3$), the Cl^- ion is progressively replaced by NO_3^-, which has similar mobility. Thus, the titration curve is the reversed-L type. The pre-end point branch of the complexometric titration curve of buffered solutions of Cu^{2+}, Ni^{2+}, and some other metal ions with ethylene diaminetetraacetic acid (EDTA) has a considerable upward slope.

Conductometric oxidation-reduction (redox) titrations are rare. They are usually carried out in strongly acid or other high-ionic-strength mediums. The titration reaction then produces only a small change in the massive total conductance. This limitation applies to any conductometric titration. Although low concentrations of HCl can be easily titrated using NaOH, an almost flat curve would be obtained if the acid solution also contained a larger concentration of NaCl, potassium nitrate (KNO_3), and so on.

Oscillometric (High-Frequency) Titration

If alternating current of radio frequency (RF) is used (typically several MHz), the electrical system need not contact the titrand. The titration vessel may be placed within a coil that constitutes part of the titrator. The titration vessel and its contents more often form the dielectric of a capacitor system.

Fig. 1 Potentiometric titration curves

(a) Direct. (b) First derivative. (c) Second derivative

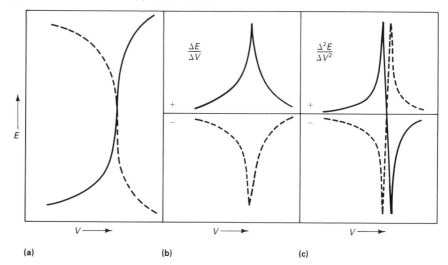

One vessel configuration has two parallel metal rings mounted on the outside that are connected to the titrator. Although many conductometric titrations can also be performed oscillometrically, nonlinear or inverted titration curves may result unless conditions are carefully selected.

Potentiometric Titration

Potentiometric titration is highly developed and is applicable to all the general reactions in aqueous and nonaqueous mediums. The potential developed by the titration system changes rapidly in the region of the end point (Fig. 1a), because the potential of the indicator electrode is logarithmically related to the concentration (strictly, the activity) of a given ion. The development of ion-selective electrodes (ISEs) has greatly widened the scope of direct and titrimetric potentiometry.

If the change in potential around the end point of the titration is large, the end point may be located by observing the meter response as the remaining drops of titrant are added. This is analogous to and as precise as use of a color-change indicator. If greater precision is required, or the change in potential is small, the end point may be located (1) by a method involving transformation of potential (E) into a suitable function, P, such that a plot of P versus V, the volume of titrant, is linear (Ref 1, 2), (2) by finding the point of steepest slope, that is, $\Delta E/\Delta V_{max}$, of the curve, or (3) by halting titration when the potential reaches a predetermined value. The manual operation of method 2 is tedious. However, titrators can record the peaked first derivative curve (Fig. 1b) and in some cases the second derivative curve (Fig. 1c).

The response shown in Fig. 1(c) is ideal for arresting the flow of titrant, that is, for automatic titration. This form of arrest is useful with titrations that can be executed rapidly and is universal, that is, independent of the value of the potential at the end point. However, the titration rate must not be high enough to cause significant end-point overshoot. The adjustment of the titration stop value of the potential to suit a particular titration required in method 3 is no disadvantage in routine titrimetry. An automatic titrator based on this method can handle reactions that are slow or do not produce abrupt changes in potential near the end point. High precision can be achieved in minimum time by diminishing the rate of titration as the end point is approached.

Amperometric Titration

Amperometric titration (with one indicator electrode), biamperometric titration, and bipotentiometric titration (both with two identical electrodes) are based on voltammetric principles (see the article "Voltammetry" in this Volume). The potential of the indicator electrode is fixed in amperometric titrimetry to enable the titrant, titrand, or both to provide a limiting current proportional to the concentration of the particular species. Amperometry and conductometry are similar only in that both yield linear titration curves. Foreign electrolytes, deleterious to conductometric titration, are necessary in amperometry to suppress migration currents. Nonelectrolytes, "invisible" in conductometry, can produce amperometric current. Dissolved oxygen, which readily undergoes electroreduction, is normally removed from the titrand by sparging unless conditions are such that oxygen interference does not occur. Dimethylglyoxime (DMG), at best a weak electrolyte, can provide a limiting current as large as that of a similar concentration of a typical metal ion and can thus act as an active amperometric titrant.

When Ni^{2+} ion in an ammoniacal medium is titrated using DMG at a dropping mercury electrode (DME) potential of -1.85 V (all potentials are relative to the saturated calomel electrode, SCE), titrant and titrand are fully electroactive. The current decreases to a small value as precipitation proceeds, then increases to produce a V-type titration curve. If the DME potential is changed to -1.4 V, DMG provides little current, and an L-type curve results (Ref 3).

Various other titration curves are possible. For practical purposes, Ca^{2+} and oxalate (salts of oxalic acid) ions lack electroactivity, yet the titration of Ca^{2+} using oxalate is possible if a known amount of a suitable amperometric indicator, such as Zn^{2+} ion, is added to the titrand. The current (due to the reduction of Zn^{2+}) decreases to a small constant value when the precipitation of both cations is complete. The end point represents the sum of Ca^{2+} and known Zn^{2+}.

Mercury readily undergoes anodic attack, especially in the presence of such ions as Cl^-. The rotating platinum microelectrode (RPE) often replaces the DME in amperometric titrimetry, particularly when redox reactions are involved. Although normally conducted with simple apparatus under direct-current conditions, amperometric titration can also be performed using alternating-current and pulse techniques. Amperometric titration and associated techniques are applicable to all the usual titrations, but are not used extensively for acid/base reactions.

Biamperometric Titration

In biamperometric titration, a small constant voltage is applied to identical electrodes, usually of platinum, and the current is measured. Significant current flow is possible only if both electrodes are depolarized, such as in a solution that contains iodine and iodide ions. If iodine is destroyed, for example, by titration using $S_2O_3^{2-}$, the current flow ceases abruptly at the end point (hence the obsolete term dead-stop end-point titration).

The technique is widely applicable; if the titrand and titrant systems are effectively reversible, the decrease of current is followed by an increase after the end point. Nonhorizontal branches of the titration curves are hyperbolic, but approximate linearity may be assumed when near the end point. Because no liquid-liquid junctions are involved, biamperometric systems are valued for their simplicity and their use in nonaqueous systems. An example is the determination of traces of water by titration using Karl Fischer reagent, consisting of pyridine, liquid SO_2 (sulfur dioxide), iodine, and methanol.

Bipotentiometric Titration

The electrode system used for biamperometry can also be used for bipotentiometry. A small constant current is forced through the system, and the voltage developed across the electrodes observed. The natures of the titrant and titrand control the shape of the titration curve. If both species exhibit electrolytic reversibility, the curve has a peak at the end point similar to that shown in Fig. 1(b).

Bipotentiometric titration possesses many of the advantages of biamperometry and its applications are increasing. Biamperometry or bipotentiometry, rather than amperometry with one indicator electrode, is commonly used in automated titrators.

Coulometric Titration

The passage of electricity through the solution of an electrolyte will cause equivalent amounts of chemical reaction at each electrode. If the mutual interference of the reaction products at the two electrodes can be prevented, electrolysis may be used as a preparative method. When one of the products can be produced with or near 100% current efficiency, quantitative production of a titrant species at a generator electrode becomes possible. The actual titrant is universal—a stream of electrons. The products at the second, or auxiliary, electrode are usually prevented from interfering by isolating this electrode in a suitable solution contained in a glass tube closed at the bottom by a porous glass disk. Figure 2 shows a beaker-type cell with a platinum generator electrode. A mercury pool is a useful alternative for generation of certain reducing titrants. The marking XX represents a suitable detector for indicating the end point of a titration. Electrochemical indication is common, but spectrophotometric or visual indication can be used.

Interferences due to the nature of the sample sometimes prevent generation of titrant within the cell. External generation provides a method of overcoming this difficulty. With titrant flowing into the cell, this technique is similar to classical titrimetry.

Coulometry with constant current is widely used as coulometric titration. Apparatus and manipulation are simple; favorable selectivity may be achieved by suitable selection of electrolyte. The technique is a direct analog of classical, or buret, titrimetry. If known and constant, the current, i, is the analog of titrant concentration; the time, t, of current flow is the analog of the volume of titrant needed to reach the end point. Therefore, the observed variable is time.

Because the titrant is generated as required, it need not be previously made, stored, and standardized. Accordingly, "difficult" titrants, such as Cr^{2+}, BrO^-, or Ag^{2+}, can be used with comparative ease.

Fig. 2 Coulometric titration cell

A, sparge gas inlet tube (sometimes not needed); B, generator electrode; C, isolation tube; D, auxiliary electrode, E, gas escape groove; F, stirrer bar; G, magnetic stirrer; XX, suitable indicating system

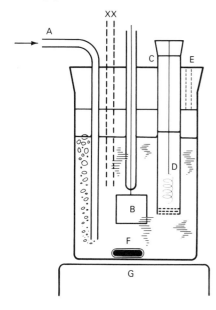

Except for measurement of the sample, volumetric apparatus is unnecessary. Small quantities of titrant can be accurately generated, facilitating microchemical determinations. Manual or automated remote operation is relatively simple.

In the constant-current anodic electrolysis of a dilute solution of Fe^{2+} ion, the potential of the anode becomes increasingly positive as the reaction $Fe^{2+} \rightarrow Fe^{3+} + e$ proceeds. An unwanted reaction, the oxidation of water, will eventually begin before the last trace of Fe^{2+} has reacted. An excess of Ce^{3+} may be added to surmount this difficulty by providing redox buffering. As the potential rises, the reaction $Ce^{3+} \rightarrow Ce^{4+} + e$ begins before the oxidation potential of water is reached. The Ce^{4+} thus generated reacts chemically: $Ce^{4+} + Fe^{2+} \rightarrow Ce^{3+} + Fe^{3+}$. Although the analytical process is described as coulometric titration of Fe^{2+} with Ce^{4+}, the result is achieved partly by direct electrolysis and partly by the intermediacy of Ce^{4+} ion. Overall titration efficiency should be 100%.

In buret titrations, the end point is approached using dropwise additions to prevent or minimize overshoot. In coulometric titration, the constant current is arrested when the end point is judged to be near. Current flow is then resumed for successive periods of 1 or 2 s until titration is complete. The timer must function only when the current is flowing.

This sequence can be automated. Amperometric or biamperometric indication provides an essentially linear signal in the all-important region just before the end point. This signal is particularly suitable for initiating the change from continuous to intermittent titration or for the current reversal required for dual-intermediate titration, a back-titration process that has been automated (Ref 4). The nonlinear potentiometric or bipotentiometric signals are more complex to use in automatic coulometric titration, but approaches similar to those used in automatic buret titration are possible. One such approach, implemented in some modern instruments, uses a controlled, diminishing current rather than a constant current and requires a coulometer instead of a timer.

Applications

Potentiometric indication is used in the acid/base determination of boron in seawater (Ref 5) and of phenols and organic acids in isopropanolic medium (Ref 6). Portable monitors for sulfur dioxide (SO_2) (measured as sulfuric acid, H_2SO_4) and carbon monoxide (CO) (after conversion to CO_2) in factory atmospheres use photometric indication (Ref 7).

The determination of total chlorine in coals, catalysts, and so on, by combustion in moist oxygen and titration of HCl using Ag^+ (Ref 8) and of microequivalent levels of lead by titration using CrO_4^{2-} (Ref 9) are examples of coulometric precipitation titration (titrants will be written as simple ions, although they may exist as complexes). Addition of Hg^{2+}-EDTA complex to the titrand and the use of a mercury-generating electrode permits coulometric titrations using EDTA or Hg^{2+}. Examples are the bipotentiometric determination of microgram amounts of Ni^{2+}, Cu^{2+}, and other metal ions (Ref 10) and the determination of Ga^{3+} by addition of EDTA and amperometric back titration of the excess (Ref 11). A similar approach may be used for titrations involving cycloaminotetraacetic acid (CDTA) or other analogs of EDTA.

Common halogen coulometric titrants are bromine, BrO^-, and iodine. Titration with bromine generated in 1,2-propanediol cyclic carbonate (propylene carbonate) medium can be used to determine olefinic unsaturation in vegetable oils (Ref 12). A coulometric procedure for the determination of nitrogen in high-purity metals involves the biamperometric titration of NH_3 using BrO^- (Ref 13). Potentiometric indication is used in the coulometric iodometric titration of SO_2 produced in the combustion determination of lower levels of sulfur in organic substances (Ref 14). An important iodine-related determination is of traces of water by coulometric titration using Karl Fischer reagent (Ref 15). The determination of galactose ($C_6H_{12}O_6$) in serum exemplifies indirect iodometry. The action of galactose oxidase produces hydrogen peroxide (H_2O_2), which liberates iodine from potassium iodide (KI). Excess sodium thiosulfate ($Na_2S_2O_3$) is added, then coulometrically back-titrated to a biamperometric end point (Ref 16).

The coulometric titration of antihistamines using Ce^{4+} (Ref 17) and of microgram amounts of Fe^{2+}, Sn^{2+}, or Sb^{3+} using $Cr_2O_7^{2-}$ (Ref 18) are examples of the use of these oxidizing titrants. The coulometric replacement for permanganate is Mn^{3+}, which has been used to titrate submilligram amounts of rhenium biamperometrically (Ref 19). Other coulometric oxidizing agents are Ag^{2+}, Tl^{3+}, and Pb^{4+}.

Ferrous ion, usually generated from acidified iron ammonium sulfate (Fe-NH$_4$(SO$_4$)$_2$), can be used for titration of such oxidants as Ce^{4+}, $Cr_2O_7^{2-}$, and MnO_4^- and thus for indirect determinations as a back-titrant of the excess of one of these ions. An example is the coulometric, potentiometric, or biamperometric titration of excess potassium permanganate (KMnO$_4$) involved in determination of selenium and tellurium in semiconductor alloys (Ref 20).

A common medium for the generation of Ti^{3+} at a platinum cathode is 6 to 8 M H_2SO_4 with 0.3 to 0.6 M $Ti(SO_4)_2$. A wax-impregnated carbon electrode is used to titrate submilligram amounts of Mo^{6+} to a spectrophotometric end point (Ref 21). A lower acidity can be used with a mercury-generating electrode. In the coulometric amperometric titration of ClO_3^- by this approach, 2 M HCl is used (Ref 22).

The powerful reducing titrant Cr^{2+} can be generated at a mercury electrode from chromium bromide, the effective generant species being $CrBr(H_2O)_5^{2+}$. This generating solution is best made fresh in 1.5 M HCl. A typical titration is of submillimolar amounts of aromatic nitro compounds (Ref 23).

Other useful reducing titrants are Sn^{2+} and Cu^+. Generation at a gold cathode in 3 M NaBr, 0.3 M HCl, and 0.2 M $SnCl_4$ has been used to titrate milligram amounts of Au^{3+} or VO_3^- (Ref 24). Generation at a tin or a wax-impregnated carbon cathode (Ref 25) and external generation from tin amalgam (Ref 26) have been reported.

An example of coulometric titration using Cu^+ is the determination of vanadium in such compounds as V_3Si (Ref 27). The 200-mg sample is dissolved in a mixture of hydrofluoric and nitric acids (HF-HNO$_3$), heated to fuming after addition of H_2SO_4, diluted, alkalinized using NaOH, boiled, stored overnight, and prepared to 200 mL. A 20-mL aliquot is acidified using H_2SO_4. Urea and $KMnO_4$ are then added, and the excess $KMnO_4$ is destroyed by dropwise addition of sodium nitrite (NaNO$_2$) solution. After addition of 12.5 mL of 0.32 M copper sulfate (CuSO$_4$) and 35 mL of 6 M HCl, the solution is diluted to 100 mL. Dissolved oxygen is removed, and Cu^+ is generated at a platinum gauze cathode to a potentiometric end point. By suitable change of medium, Fe^{2+} can be used as an alternate titrant.

REFERENCES

1. G. Gran, *Analyst*, Vol 77, 1952, p 661
2. D. Midgley and K. Torrance, *Potentiometric Water Analysis*, John Wiley & Sons, 1978
3. I.M. Kolthoff and A. Langer, *J. Am. Chem. Soc.*, Vol 62, 1940, p 211
4. J.T. Stock, *Anal. Chim. Acta*, Vol 124, 1981, p 85
5. T.P. Tsaikov, E.S. Boichinova, and E.D. Brynzova, *Zh. Anal. Khim.*, Vol 37, 1982, p 1329
6. B.G. Cooksey, B. Metters, J.M. Ottaway, and D.W. Whymark, *Talanta*, Vol 20, 1973, p 371
7. H.J. Boniface and R.H. Jenkins, *Analyst*, Vol 103, 1978, p 1185
8. M.C. Van Grondelle and P.J. Zeen, *Anal. Chim. Acta*, Vol 116, 1980, p 397
9. G.S. Kelsey and H.W. Safford, *Anal. Chim. Acta*, Vol 84, 1976, p 53
10. R.G. Monk and K.C. Steed, *Anal. Chim. Acta*, Vol 26, 1962, p 305
11. P. Gruendler and P.K. Agasyan, *Anal. Chim. Acta*, Vol 90, 1977, p 253
12. M.C. Cheney and K.S. Fletcher, *Anal. Chem.*, Vol 51, 1979, p 807
13. W. Werner and G. Toelg, *Fresenius Z. Anal. Chem.*, Vol 276, 1975, p 103
14. M.C. Van Grondelle, P.J. Zeen, and F. Van de Craats, *Anal. Chim. Acta*, Vol 100, 1978, p 439
15. J. Mitchell and D.M. Smith, *Aquametry*, 2nd ed., Part III, John Wiley & Sons, 1980
16. C.D. McGlothin and W.C. Purdy, *Anal. Chim. Acta*, Vol 88, 1977, p 33
17. G.J. Patriarche, *Mikrochim. Acta*, 1970, p 950
18. A.I. Kostromin and A.A. Akhmetov, *Zh. Anal. Khim.*, Vol 24, 1969, p 503
19. R. Chavdarova, E.R. Nikolaeva, and P.K. Agasyan, *Zh. Anal. Khim.*, Vol 33, 1978, p 111
20. P.K. Agasyan, A.N. Denisova, L.B. Agasyan, and E.R. Nikolaeva, *Zavod. Lab.*, Vol 34, 1968, p 129
21. P.K. Agasyan, E.R. Nikolaeva, and R.D. Chavdarova, *Zh. Anal. Khim.*, Vol 33, 1978, p 730
22. P. Gruendler and H. Holzapfel, *Talanta*, Vol 17, 1970, p 246
23. D.A. Aikens, and M. Carlita, *Anal. Chem.*, Vol 37, 1965, p 459
24. A.J. Bard and J.J. Lingane, *Anal. Chim. Acta*, Vol 20, 1959, p 581
25. P.K. Agasyan, E.R. Nikolaeva, and K.Kh. Tarenova, *Zavod. Lab.*, Vol 35, 1969, p 1034
26. V.N. Basov, P.K. Agasyan, and B.G. Vikharev, *Zh. Anal. Khim.*, Vol 28, 1973, p 2344
27. A. Drescher and R. Kucharkowski, *Fresenius Z. Anal. Chem.*, Vol 298, 1979, p 144

SELECTED REFERENCES

- A.J. Bard and L.R. Faulkner, *Electrochemical Methods: Fundamentals and Applications*, John Wiley & Sons, 1980
- J.K. Foreman and P.B. Stockwell, *Automatic Chemical Analysis*, John Wiley & Sons, 1975
- H. Freiser, Ed., *Ion-Selective Electrodes in Analytical Chemistry*, Plenum Press, 1978, 1980
- J.S. Fritz, *Acid-Base Titrations in Nonaqueous Solvents*, Allyn & Bacon, 1973
- B. Kratochvil, Titrations in Nonaqueous Solvents, *Anal. Chem.*, Biennial reviews, Vol 48, 1976, p 355R through Vol 54, 1982, p 105R
- J.J. Lingane, *Electroanalytical Chemistry*, 2nd ed., John Wiley & Sons, 1958
- G.W.C. Milner and G. Phillips, *Coulometry in Analytical Chemistry*, Pergamon Press, 1967
- E. Pungor, *Oscillometry and Conductometry*, Pergamon Press, 1965
- J.W. Ross, Conductometric Titrations, in *Standard Methods of Chemical Analysis*, Vol 3, Part A, F.J. Welcher, Ed., Van Nostrand, 1966
- E.P. Serjeant, *Potentiometry and Potentiometric Titrations*, John Wiley & Sons, 1984
- J.T. Stock, *Amperometric Titrations*, Interscience, 1965
- J.T. Stock, Automatic Coulometric Titrators, *Trends Anal. Chem.*, Vol 1, 1981, p 59; 1982, p 117
- J.T. Stock, Amperometric Titration (later Amperometric, Bipotentiometric, and Coulometric Titration), *Anal. Chem.*, Biennial reviews, Vol 36, 1964, p 355R through Vol 56, 1984, p 1R

Controlled-Potential Coulometry

Jackson E. Harrar, Chemistry and Materials Science Department, Lawrence Livermore National Laboratory

General Uses

- Quantitative chemical analysis; major constituent assay of solutions, alloys, nonmetallic materials, and compounds
- Accuracy and precision are typically 0.1%
- Primarily applicable to the transition and heavier elements
- Studies of electrochemical reaction pathways and mechanisms

Examples of Applications

- High-accuracy assays of nuclear fuels for uranium and plutonium
- Assays of electroplating solutions and alloys for gold, silver, palladium, or iridium
- Measurement of Fe^{3+}/Fe^{2+} ratios in ceramics
- Verification of standards for other analytical techniques, for example, titanium in titanium dioxide
- Determination of molybdenum in molybdenum-tungsten alloys
- Assays of organic compounds containing nitro groups

Samples

- *Form*: Samples must be dissolved in a solvent suitable for electrolysis—usually aqueous solutions
- *Size*: Quantity sufficient for 1- to 10-mg analyte per determination

Limitations

- Not recommended for trace or minor impurity analysis
- Requires dissolution of samples—destructive analysis technique
- Not useful for determination of alkali and alkaline earth metals
- Qualitative knowledge of sample composition is required
- For inorganic constituent analysis, organic constituents must be completely destroyed
- Requires good electrolysis cell design and potential control
- May require elimination of oxygen from sample solutions

Estimated Analysis Time

- 5 to 30 min per measurement, after solution preparation

Capabilities of Related Techniques

- *Controlled-potential electrolysis*: Can be used as a separation technique before other measurement techniques
- *Polarography and solid-electrode voltammetry*: These techniques measure electrolysis current-potential characteristics of solution samples, provide more global qualitative information on sample composition, and are more suitable for minor constituent and trace analysis but not as accurate or precise

Introduction

Substances determined by controlled-potential coulometry are electrolyzed in a portion of the sample solution using the methodology of controlled-potential electrolysis. A specially designed electrolysis cell and feedback controller called a potentiostat is used. The conditions for analytical coulometry are designed to electrolyze only the desired substance (among possibly several in a mixture) and to convert the substance rapidly and completely to a desired product. For example, electrolysis of a metal ion species may result in its transformation to a soluble species of another oxidation state or reduction to a metal deposit on the electrode, as in electroplating.

As the analyte is consumed during electrolysis, the current decays more or less exponentially toward zero, and the electrolysis is terminated when the current reaches suitably low value, indicating complete electrolysis. The electrolysis current is integrated by an electronic integrator (coulometer), and the measured quantity of electricity is related to the amount of the analyte electrolyzed.

Controlled-potential coulometry is similar in applicability to the classical solution techniques of gravimetry and titrimetry. Like the classical methods, it is used primarily for major constituent analysis and is characterized by high precision and accuracy (typically 0.1%). Coulometry routinely requires only approximately 1 to 10 mg of analyte substance. This relatively small sample size is advantageous when the quantity of material available for analysis is small or must be limited because of its value, toxicity, or radioactivity. Controlled-potential coulometry is especially applicable to assays of alloys, compounds, and nonmetallic materials for the transition and heavier elements. Organic compounds and nonmetals—for example, halides and nitrogen-oxygen compounds—are also suitable for determination. Detailed information on the techniques and applications of controlled-potential coulometry is available in Ref 1 and 2.

Controlled-Potential Electrolysis

Figure 1 illustrates the apparatus for controlled-potential coulometry, showing the three major components of the system. The working electrode, where the desired reaction occurs, is usually a mercury pool or a platinum screen, although other inert materials have been used. The area of the working electrode is as large as possible, and the solution is vigorously stirred to maximize the rate of electrolysis. The counterelectrode is also an inert material, usually platinum.

As shown in Fig. 1, the electrolysis cell is divided into two compartments by a porous glass, ceramic, or teflon semipermeable separator or by an ion-exchange membrane. The separator is designed to minimize intermixing of the solutions in the working-electrode and counterelectrode compartments while allowing passage of the current-carrying ions. This ensures that analyte will not be lost from the working-electrode compartment and that the electrochemical reactions at the two electrodes will be isolated from one another. Examples of cells and instrumentation used in controlled-potential coulometry are available in the References at the end of this article.

In operation of the cell, the electrolysis current flows between the working electrode

Fig. 1 Apparatus for controlled-potential coulometry

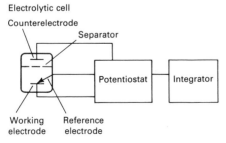

Electrolytic cell

Counterelectrode

Separator

Potentiostat

Integrator

Working electrode

Reference electrode

Table 1 Types of reactions in controlled-potential electrolysis and applicable Nernst equations

Type of reaction(a)	Nernst equation(b)	
I. Oxidized and reduced species soluble in solution $M(m) + ne^- \rightarrow M(m-n)$ Example: $Fe^{3+} + e^- \rightarrow Fe^{2+}$	$E = E^{\circ\prime} + \dfrac{RT}{nF} \cdot \log \dfrac{[M(m)]}{[M(m-n)]}$	(Eq 1)
II. Solid metal electrodeposition $M(m) + me^- \rightarrow M(s)$ Example: $Ag^+ + e^- \rightarrow Ag(s)$	$E = E^{\circ\prime} + \dfrac{RT}{nF} \cdot \log [M(m)]$	(Eq 2)
III. Amalgam formation $M(m) + me^- \rightarrow M(Hg)$ Example: $Cu^{2+} + 2e^- \rightarrow Cu(Hg)$	$E = E^{\circ\prime} + \dfrac{RT}{nF} \cdot \log \dfrac{[M(m)]}{[M(Hg)]}$	(Eq 3)

(a) m and n represent the number of electrons in the reaction or, in M(m), the oxidation state of the metal. (b) In the equations, E is the working electrode potential, $E^{\circ\prime}$ is the formal potential of the reaction, R is the gas constant, T is the absolute temperature, and F is the faraday constant. Brackets indicate concentrations of the oxidized and reduced species of the metal at equilibrium.

and counterelectrode. A stable reference electrode of known potential (versus the standard hydrogen electrode) acts as a sensor of the working-electrode potential. Typical reference electrodes are the types used for measuring pH, such as $Hg-Hg_2Cl_2$, KCl(sat'd) (the saturated calomel electrode, SCE); Ag-AgCl(s), KCl(sat'd); or Hg-Hg_2SO_4(s), K_2SO_4(sat'd). During electrolysis, the potentiostat compares the potential (voltage) between the working and reference electrodes with the desired control potential and minimizes this difference by controlling the voltage applied to the counterelectrode.

Selectivity in an analysis by controlled-potential coulometry is achieved by maintaining the working-electrode potential constant and by using the differences in the potentials at which different substances react. In aqueous acidic solutions, the available potential range (versus SCE) extends from approximately +1.2 to −0.1 V at platinum and from +0.1 to −1.0 V at mercury. The positive limit is established at platinum by the evolution of oxygen and at mercury by its dissolution; the negative limits are established by the evolution of hydrogen. In chloride media, the positive limit at platinum is lowered by the evolution of chlorine and at mercury by the formation of Hg_2Cl_2.

The standard potential of the reaction considered or, more specifically, the formal potential in the particular medium of the electrolysis determines the potential at which a substance is electroactive. Metal ion species having reactions that have positive formal reduction potentials, for example, Fe^{3+}, Ce^{4+}, and Au^{3+} in certain media, and which are therefore considered oxidizing agents, are electrolytically reduced at positive control potentials, usually at a platinum

electrode. The ions of metals with negative or slightly positive formal potentials, for example, Cu^{2+}, Pb^{2+}, Ti^{4+}, and Zn^{2+}, are reduced at negative control potentials, usually at a mercury electrode.

When the rate of charge transfer in an electrolysis reaction is large compared to the rate of mass transport and there are no complicating side reactions, the extent of the electrolysis reaction as a function of potential can be expressed by a form of the Nernst equation. Such processes are generally known in electrochemistry as "reversible." The exact form of the equation depends on the type of reaction considered. Table 1 summarizes the three most common types of reactions encountered in controlled-potential electrolysis, together with the relevant Nernst equations. Equation 1 (for a Type I reaction) shows the logarithmic relationship between the working-electrode potential and the ratios of the concentrations of the oxidized and reduced species at equilibrium, that is, when the current is zero in the electrolysis.

Figure 2 presents a graph of the extent of reaction versus potential for a Type I electrolysis. This graph is similar to the current-potential curve for reversible processes in voltammetry and polarography (see the article "Voltammetry" in this Volume). At 25 °C (75 °F), the value of RT/nF is 59.2/n mV; thus, for the reduction of 99.9% of the M(m) in the solution, that is, for $[M(m)]/[M(m-n)]$ to be 0.001 at equilibrium, the control potential E must be $3 \times (59.2/n)$, or $177/n$ mV more negative than $E^{\circ\prime}$. Quantitative oxidations require E to be more positive than $E^{\circ\prime}$ by the same voltage.

In reversible electrolytic processes, the electrolysis can be reversed by appropriate

Fig. 2 Completeness of reaction as a function of potential for the reversible reduction of a metal ion species to another soluble species

E is the control potential required for 99.9% conversion of M(m) to M(m−n).

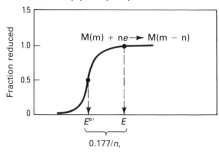

Table 2 Metals determined by controlled-potential coulometry

Metal	Working electrode	Overall reaction	Supporting electrolyte	Ref
Antimony	Hg	$Sb^{3+} \rightarrow Sb(Hg)$	0.4 M tartaric acid, 1 M HCl	5
Arsenic	Pt	$As^{3+} \rightarrow As^{5+}$	1 M H_2SO_4	6
Bismuth	Hg	$Bi^{3+} \rightarrow Bi(Hg)$	0.5 M tartrate, 0.2 M HCl	7
Cadmium	Hg	$Cd^{2+} \rightarrow Cd(Hg)$	1 M HCl	8
Chromium	Hg	$Cr^{3+} \rightleftarrows Cr^{2+}$	6 M HCl	9
	Au	$Cr^{6+} \rightarrow Cr^{3+}$	1 M H_2SO_4	10
Cobalt	Pt	$Co^{2+} \rightarrow Co^{3+}$	1,10-phenanthroline, acetic acid	11
Copper	Hg	$Cu^{2+} \rightarrow Cu(Hg)$	1 M H_2SO_4	12
Europium	Hg	$Eu^{3+} \rightleftarrows Eu^{2+}$	0.1 M HCl or $HClO_4$	13
Gold	Pt	$Au^{3+} \rightarrow Au(s)$	0.5 M HCl	14
Indium	Hg	$In^{3+} \rightarrow In(Hg)$	1 M KCl, 0.25 M HCl	15
Iridium	Pt	$Ir^{4+} \rightleftarrows Ir^{3+}$	0.5 M HCl	16
Iron	Pt	$Fe^{3+} \rightleftarrows Fe^{2+}$	0.5 M H_2SO_4	17
Lead	Hg	$Pb^{2+} \rightarrow Pb(Hg)$	1 M $HClO_4$	8
Manganese	Pt	$Mn^{2+} \rightarrow Mn^{3+}$	0.25 M $Na_4P_2O_7$	18
Mercury	Hg	$Hg^{2+} \rightarrow Hg(liq)$	1.5 M $HClO_4$	19
Molybdenum	Hg	$Mo^{6+} \rightarrow Mo^{5+}$	0.2 M $(NH_4)_2C_2O_4$, 1.3 M H_2SO_4	20
Neptunium	Pt	$Np^{6+} \rightleftarrows Np^{5+}$	1 M H_2SO_4	21
Nickel	Hg	$Ni^{2+} \rightarrow Ni(Hg)$	1 M pyridine, 0.5 M HCl	22
Palladium	Pt	$Pd^{2+} \rightleftarrows Pd^{4+}$	0.2 M NaN_3, 0.2 M Na_2HPO_4	23
Plutonium	Pt	$Pu^{4+} \rightleftarrows Pu^{3+}$	1 M $HClO_4$ or, to avoid iron interference, 5.5 M HCl, 0.015 M sulfamic acid, NaH_2PO_4	24 25
Rhodium	Hg	$Rh^{3+} \rightarrow Rh(Hg)$	0.2 M HCl	26
Ruthenium	Pt	$Ru^{4+} \rightarrow Ru^{3+}$	5 M HCl	27
Silver	Pt	$Ag^{+} \rightarrow Ag(s)$	0.1 M H_2SO_4	14, 28
Technetium............	Hg	$Tc^{7+} \rightarrow Tc^{3+}$	Acetate-tripolyphosphate	29
Thallium..............	Pt	$Tl^{+} \rightarrow Tl^{3+}$	1 M HCl	30
Tin	Hg	$Sn^{4+} \rightleftarrows Sn(Hg)$	3 M KBr, 0.2 M HBr	31
Titanium..............	Hg	$Ti^{4+} \rightarrow Ti^{3+}$	6-9 M H_2SO_4	32
Uranium	Hg	$U^{6+} \rightarrow U^{4+}$	0.5 M H_2SO_4	33
Vanadium	Pt	$V^{5+} \rightarrow V^{4+}$ $V^{4+} \rightarrow V^{5+}$	1.5 M H_3PO_4	34
Zinc	Hg	$Zn^{2+} \rightleftarrows Zn(Hg)$	1 M NH_4H citrate, 3 M NH_4OH	8, 35

adjustment of the control potential. This technique is used in several procedures in coulometry (see Table 2). The first control potential is used to transform all the substance determined in the sample to one oxidation state. The potential is then changed to reverse the electrolysis. The current is integrated during the second electrolysis to measure the quantity of the substance present.

The Nernst equation may also be used to calculate the difference in formal potentials required for the complete separation of two species in the same sample solution or to calculate their mutual interference. For example, for two Type I reactions, equal molar concentrations of the two species, and less than 0.1% interference, the minimum difference in formal potentials at 25 °C (75 °F) in millivolts must be:

$$E_1^{\circ\prime} - E_2^{\circ\prime} = \frac{177}{n_1} + \frac{177}{n_2} \qquad \text{(Eq 4)}$$

For a Type II reaction—the electrodeposition of metal on a substrate of the same metal—the metal film is assumed (for greater than monolayer deposits) to have an activity of 1; thus, only the concentration of the solution species appears in Eq 2 (Table 1). Therefore, unlike Type I reactions, the fraction of metal deposited is not independent of potential. A decreasing initial concentration of the metal requires an increasingly negative control potential to deposit a given fraction. Very low concentrations of metals and depositions on foreign substrates exhibit different characteristics.

Type III processes, in which the metal ion is reduced at a mercury electrode to form an amalgam, are generally reversible if the metal is soluble in mercury to the extent required by electrolysis. Otherwise, a metal film will form on the electrode, and the process will be similar to a Type II reaction. Equation 3 (Table 1) for amalgam formation is similar to that for Type I, except that the concentrations of M(m) and M in the logarithmic term are their concentrations in the solution and mercury, respectively. Because of their solubility in mercury, metals that participate in electrolytic amalgam formation, for example, copper, lead, indium, and thallium, have formal potentials for the reactions that are significantly more positive than those for the formation of the corresponding solid metal.

Many other electrolytic processes exhibit lower rates of charge transfer (termed irreversible or nonnernstian) or involve chemical reactions, such as a follow-up reaction, coupled to the electron transfer. Many of the analytical methods of controlled-potential coulometry are based on such reactions; examples are the procedures for vanadium and uranium. Irreversible processes require a greater difference between the control potential and the $E^{\circ\prime}$ to effect rapid electrolysis, and, depending on the degree of irreversibility, a reverse electrolysis may not be feasible. In addition, separation factors for systems involving irreversible couples must be determined empirically.

Controlled-Potential Coulometry

When a single substance is quantitatively electrolyzed, and all the electrolysis current is consumed in transforming that substance to another species, that is, the current efficiency is 100%, the number of moles, N, of the substance electrolyzed can be calculated using Faraday's Law:

$$N = \frac{1}{nF} \int_0^t i \, dt \qquad \text{(Eq 5)}$$

where i is the electrolysis current, t is the time of the electrolysis, and F (the value of the faraday constant) is 96 486 C/mole (Ref 3). Because of this fundamental relationship, instrumental calibrations in coulometry are usually based on standards of electricity (voltage and resistance) and time (a clock) rather than on chemical standards, making the technique and its results more fundamentally accurate.

Accurate coulometry requires that electrolysis be performed as rapidly as possible by controlling the potential at a point where the rate of electrolysis is limited only by mass transport of the reacting species. For reversible processes, E is not far from the value shown in Fig. 2, which will also

ensure complete electrolysis. When E is set at this value, the electrolysis current as a function of time is:

$$i = i_0 \exp(-pt) \qquad \text{(Eq 6)}$$

where i_0 is a constant (a theoretical initial current) and p is an overall rate constant of the electrolysis. These constants incorporate parameters that are determined by the mass transport characteristics of the cell and the diffusion coefficient of the species electrolyzed.

Figure 3 shows the current-time curves observed in the coulometric determinations of gold and silver. Because the current scale is logarithmic, the curves should theoretically be straight lines. These curves deviate slightly from Eq 6 at the beginning of electrolysis due to imperfect compensation of the solution resistance by the potentiostat and at the end of electrolysis because the current tends to level off at the background current.

Technique

Because of the absolute nature and inherent linearity of controlled-potential coulometry, specific analytical determinations, when possible, should be based on the electrical calibration of the integrator, which is usually stable for long periods of time. This method of calibration requires correcting the total integrated current (charge) for the contribution of the background current before calculating the quantity of substance electrolyzed from Eq 5.

The various sources of background current can be corrected for in several ways (Ref 1). The simplest and most satisfactory procedure is to base the correction on a blank determination, that is, an electrolysis of the supporting electrolyte, without the substance determined present, for the same length of time required for the principal electrolysis. The blank charge is then subtracted from the total charge. For analyses of most metals at the 5- to 10-mg level, background correction does not exceed 0.5% of the total; for the electrolyses depicted in Fig. 3, in which background current is several orders of magnitude below the initial current, background corrections are less than 0.1%.

For determinations of metals by coulometry, solid samples are usually dissolved in acid or fusion mixtures. The dissolution mixture selected must be compatible with the electrolysis medium. Because the formal potentials of most metal ion reactions are sensitive to the exact species present, care must be taken that the procedure yields the proper species in solution. The details of

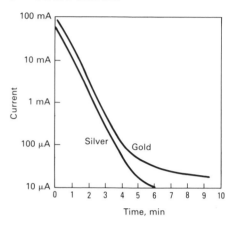

Fig. 3 Current-time curves for the reduction of Ag⁺ to Ag(s) and Au³⁺ to Au(s) on a platinum electrode

Electrolysis conditions: silver, 0.1 M H_2SO_4, $E = +0.16$ V versus SCE; gold, 0.5 M HCl, $E = +0.48$ V versus SCE

sample pretreatment and electrolytic procedure can usually be modified to minimize the effects of interferences.

Applications

Table 2 lists the metals for which accurate methods have been developed and the basic electrochemistry of the procedures. A double arrow in the reaction indicates that the method involves a multistep or reverse electrolysis. Several published procedures are available for the coulometric determinations of mixtures of metallic elements in industrial materials. For example, lead, cadmium, and tin have been determined in a glass (Ref 4), and numerous coulometric methods exist for determining uranium and plutonium in mixed-oxide reactor fuels (Ref 1, 24, 25).

Determination of Gold. Because the quantities of metal available for analysis are usually small and high accuracy (0.1%) is frequently desired, the assay for gold in various materials is a useful example of the application of coulometry. The current-time curve for this electrolysis was discussed and shown above in Fig. 3. If the sample contains none of the few interfering elements, such as iridium or ruthenium, the gold can usually be determined immediately after dissolution without further pretreatment. Each determination requires approximately 10 min. Aqua regia—3 parts hydrochloric acid (HCl) and 1 part nitric acid (HNO_3)—typically is used for the dissolution, and sulfamic acid (NH_2SO_3H) is included in the supporting electrolyte to remove the interfering nitrogen oxides and nitrite ion produced during the dissolution. If large quantities of iron are present in the sample, phosphoric acid (H_3PO_4) can also be added to remove its interference.

Gold electroplating solutions that contain cyanide or sulfite ions and scrap materials containing organic compounds must be subjected to a more severe pretreatment before measurement of the gold (Ref 14). This typically involves a sulfuric acid-nitric acid (H_2SO_4-HNO_3) boildown or fuming with perchloric acid ($HClO_4$), which removes or destroys the complexing species and organics. This treatment precipitates most of the gold as the metal; it is then redissolved in aqua regia for coulometric measurement. After several determinations, the gold metal that has been deposited on the platinum electrode is stripped electrolytically by controlling the potential at $+1.00$ V in 2 M HCl.

Uranium is another element that has been determined frequently in various sample types by controlled-potential coulometry (Ref 1, 33). The adaptability of coulometry to automated and remote operation makes it useful for nuclear materials that contain uranium, plutonium, or both. Highly radioactive samples can be handled if there are no chemical interferences. Methods have been developed for separating the uranium from fission products in nuclear-reactor and waste samples before coulometric determination. A procedure is also available for coulometrically measuring the ratio of uranium oxidation states in uranium oxide fuels.

As indicated in Table 2, coulometric determination involves conversion of U^{6+} to U^{4+}. However, electrolysis proceeds in two steps. First, the U^{6+} is reduced directly at the electrode by the reaction:

$$U^{6+} + e^- \rightarrow U^{5+}$$

The U^{5+} then disproportionates:

$$2U^{5+} \rightarrow U^{6+} + U^{4+}$$

Thus, an exhaustive electrolysis results in the reduction of U^{6+} to U^{4+} and an overall 2-electron change in valence.

The reduction is carried out at a mercury-pool electrode, usually in H_2SO_4 (also containing sulfamic acid if HNO_3 was used to dissolve the sample), at a control potential of -0.325 V versus SCE. A preliminary electrolysis performed at $+0.075$ V pre-reduces any oxides of mercury and substances such as Fe^{3+}, Cr^{6+}, and Pu^{4+} that would interfere in the subsequent uranium electrolysis. Copper, if present in the sample, can also be determined, because the reduction of uranium is irreversible at the mercury electrode. The Cu^{2+} and U^{6+} are reduced together at -0.325 V. The Cu(Hg) is then oxidized back to Cu^{2+} at $+0.100$ V (Ref 12). Integration of the current during the second electrolysis yields the amount of copper, and subtraction of this quantity of electricity from the total in the first electrolysis provides the amount of uranium.

Coulometric measurement requires approximately 30 min, including removal of oxygen from the solution (which also would be reduced at -0.325 V), pre-electrolysis, and uranium electrolysis. Because of the homogeneous disproportionation reaction, the uranium electrolysis is somewhat slower than most, and its electrolysis current-time curve differs slightly from that predicted by Eq 6 for simple reactions.

ACKNOWLEDGMENTS

This work performed under the auspices of the U.S. Department of Energy by the Lawrence Livermore National Laboratory under Contract W-7405-ENG-48.

REFERENCES

1. J.E. Harrar, Techniques, Apparatus, and Analytical Applications of Controlled-Potential Coulometry, in *Electroanalytical Chemistry*, Vol 8, A.J. Bard, Ed., Marcel Dekker, 1975
2. L. Meites, Controlled-Potential Electrolysis and Coulometry, in *Techniques of Chemistry*, Part IIA, A. Weissberger and B.W. Rossiter, Ed., Wiley-Interscience, 1971
3. V.E. Bower, R.S. Davis, T.J. Murphy, P.J. Paulsen, J.W. Gramlich, and L.J. Powell, *J. Res. Natl. Bur. Stand.*, Vol 87, 1982, p 21
4. W.M. Wise and D.E. Campbell, *Anal. Chem.*, Vol 38, 1966, p 1079
5. L.B. Dunlap and W.D. Shults, *Anal. Chem.*, Vol 34, 1962, p 499
6. W.M. MacNevin and B.B. Baker, *Anal. Chem.*, Vol 24, 1952, p 986
7. J.J. Lingane, *J. Am. Chem. Soc.*, Vol 67, 1945, p 1916
8. P.R. Segatto, *J. Am. Ceram. Soc.*, Vol 45, 1962, p 102
9. L. Meites, *Anal. Chim. Acta*, Vol 18, 1958, p 364
10. D.E. Harrington, R.C. Propst, and R.D. Britt, *Anal. Chem.*, Vol 34, 1962, p 1663
11. M. Cakrt, J. Bercik, and Z. Hladky, *Chem. Zvesti*, Vol 27, 1973, p 446
12. W.D. Shults and P.F. Thomason, *Anal. Chem.*, Vol 31, 1959, p 492
13. W.D. Shults, *Anal. Chem.*, Vol 31, 1959, p 1095
14. J.E. Harrar and M.C. Waggoner, *Plat. Surf. Finish.*, Vol 68 (No. 1), 1981, p 41
15. W.R. Mountcastle, W.D. Shults, and P.F. Thomason, *Anal. Chem.*, Vol 35, 1963, p 871
16. J.A. Page, *Talanta*, Vol 9, 1962, p 365
17. H.J. Boniface and R.H. Jenkins, *Analyst*, Vol 105, 1980, p 705
18. J.E. Harrar and L.P. Rigdon, *Anal. Chem.*, Vol 41, 1969, p 758
19. H. Muntau and R. Cenci, Comm. Eur. Commun. (Ispra) Rept. EUR-5125e, 1974
20. L.P. Rigdon and J.E. Harrar, *Anal. Chem.*, Vol 40, 1968, p 1641
21. R.W. Stromatt, *Anal. Chem.*, Vol 32, 1960, p 134
22. J.J. Lingane and J.A. Page, *Anal. Chim. Acta*, Vol 13, 1955, p 281
23. L.P. Rigdon and J.E. Harrar, *Anal. Chem.*, Vol 46, 1974, p 696
24. "Chemical, Mass Spectrometric, and Spectrochemical Analysis of Nuclear-Grade Plutonium Dioxide Powders and Pellets," E 697; "Chemical, Mass Spectrometric, and Spectrochemical Analysis of Nuclear-Grade Mixed Oxides [(U,Pu)O$_2$]," C 698; "Chemical, Mass Spectrometric, Spectrochemical, Nuclear, and Radiochemical Analysis of Nuclear-Grade Plutonium Nitrate Solutions," C 759, *Annual Book of ASTM Standards*, Vol 12.01, ASTM, Philadelphia, 1984
25. D.D. Jackson, R.M. Hollen, F.R. Roensch, and J.E. Rein, *Anal. Chim. Acta*, Vol 117, 1980, p 205
26. G.W. Van Loon and J.A. Page, *Anal. Chem.*, Vol 43, 1971, p 602
27. G. Weldrick, G. Phillips, and G.W.C. Milner, *Analyst*, Vol 94, 1969, p 840
28. L.L. Merritt, Jr., E.L. Martin, Jr., and R.D. Bedi, *Anal. Chem.*, Vol 30, 1958, p 487
29. A.A. Terry and H.E. Zittel, *Anal. Chem.*, Vol 35, 1963, p 614
30. R.W. Ramette and D.A. Palmer, *J. Solu. Chem.*, Vol 13, 1984, p 637
31. W.M. Wise and J.P. Williams, *Anal. Chem.*, Vol 37, 1965, p 1292
32. L.P. Rigdon and J.E. Harrar, *Anal. Chem.*, Vol 43, 1971, p 747
33. "Uranium by Controlled-Potential Coulometry," E 217, *Annual Book of ASTM Standards*, Vol 12.02, ASTM, Philadelphia, 1984
34. L.P. Rigdon and J.E. Harrar, *Anal. Chem.*, Vol 41, 1969, p 1673
35. L. Meites, *Anal. Chim. Acta*, Vol 20, 1959, p 456

Elemental and Functional Group Analysis

Walter T. Smith, Jr., Department of Chemistry, University of Kentucky

General Uses
- Identification of organic compounds
- Determination of the empirical formula of organic compounds
- Determination of the composition of a mixture
- Determination of purity

Examples of Applications
- Identification of the product of a reaction or process
- Identification (or determination of the composition) of plastics, fibers, fuels, or other organic materials
- Determination of the approximate composition of a mixture of organic substances or of a mixture of organic and inorganic substances
- Determination of water in a sample
- Determination of unsaturation in polymers

Samples
- *Form*: Solid or liquid. For solutions, some form of chromatography (gas chromatography or high performance liquid chromatography) is usually preferable
- *Size*: From a few milligrams for carbon, hydrogen, and nitrogen to a few tenths of a gram for most functional groups
- *Preparation*: Careful purification and drying of the sample is essential if the purpose of the analysis is identification or determination of an empirical formula

Limitations
- See the individual methods discussed in this article

Estimated Analysis Time
- If the proper apparatus or equipment and a trained operator are available, the time required can be less than 1 h for carbon and hydrogen or several hours for some functional group determinations. Results can be obtained from a commercial laboratory in a few days. Purification of the sample may add hours to the times given above

Capabilities of Related Techniques
- *Mass spectroscopy*: High-resolution methods may provide elemental composition
- *X-ray spectroscopy*: May provide complete structure of a crystalline compound
- *Infrared spectroscopy, nuclear magnetic resonance*: May provide supplemental information about the sample
- *Gas chromatography*: Mixtures of acids can be separated and quantitatively determined using this method, although the acids are usually converted to their esters before the chromatographic separation

Introduction

Elemental analysis, the determination of the percentage composition of the various elements present in an organic compound, is one of the oldest quantitative techniques. It remains one of the first steps taken to investigate a new or unknown substance. The determination of the elemental composition of a sample usually enables the writing of an empirical formula for the substance under investigation, that is, writing a formula expressing the relative number of the different atoms present. Some examples of empirical formulas are CH_4 (methane, natural gas), $HC_2H_3O_2$ (acetic acid), and C_2H_6O (ethyl alcohol).

However, when even slightly complex organic compounds are encountered, it becomes obvious that empirical formulas are not sufficient. The last example given, C_2H_6O, is the empirical formula for ethyl alcohol and for methyl ether. Thus, additional information is needed to enable the writing of a more detailed or structural formula that distinguishes between these two possibilities. This information can be obtained using several methods or, most likely, their combination. One of these methods is functional group analysis.

Functional group analysis attempts to examine the kinds of reactive (or functional) groups present in the molecule and to determine the amount of those groups. With this type of information, it is usually possible to write a more descriptive formula for the compound under study. If the material under study is not a compound but a mixture of substances, the elemental analysis and functional group analysis results will provide useful information about the composition and chemical properties of the material. This article will discuss methods for determining the more common elements and functional groups.

Elemental Analysis

Identification of Organic Compounds. Within limits, it may be possible to identify a compound from its elemental composition. If a reaction or series of reactions is expected to produce a new compound having a certain composition, the elemental analysis will indicate (within the limits of experimental error) if a compound of the expected composition has been obtained. Thus, a compound having the empirical formula $C_8H_9N_5O_2$ would have the following calculated percentage composition: carbon, 46.38%; hydrogen, 4.35%; nitrogen, 33.82%; oxygen, 15.45%.

If the results found for a pure sample of this compound were within the experimental error limits, the results would be presumptive evidence that the desired compound had been obtained. In general, the results should be within ±0.3% of the calculated value. Thus, for the carbon determination above, results between 46.08 and 46.68% C would be acceptable.

The ±0.3% is arbitrary, and exceptions are possible in the experimental portions of published articles. However, journals are generally strict on this point, and some may have more stringent standards. For work that is not to be published, individual standards can be set, but the more lax these standards, the less certain is the identity of the sample under examination. Adherence to the above standard is advisable for reasonable certainty. The acceptable range does not necessarily reflect the uncertainty or lack of precision of the analytical method used. The purity of the sample is an important factor and can influence results.

In the above example, the calculated values were given for all the elements present. The determined values are usually given only for carbon, hydrogen, and nitrogen or in some cases only for carbon and hydrogen or only for nitrogen. Direct determination of oxygen is often troublesome and is determined by difference if all the other elements present are determined directly. The error in the oxygen value will likely be large because

it reflects all the errors in each of the other determinations.

Elemental analysis for identification of an organic compound is not usually used to identify compounds that have already been reported in the chemical literature. Such compounds can be identified from their melting points and/or from various spectral methods. In the case of new compounds, additional information, mainly spectral, would be used to confirm identity.

Determination of the Empirical Formula. From the complete elemental analysis, it is a simple matter to calculate an empirical formula for the compound under study. For example:

%C ÷ at. wt of C	= relative number of C atoms
%H ÷ at. wt of H	= relative number of H atoms
%N ÷ at. wt of N	= relative number of N atoms

The relative number of each atom is then reduced to whole numbers by dividing each value by the lowest relative number. If this does not yield whole numbers (or nearly whole numbers), the relative number must be multiplied by two, three, or whatever number is required to make each of the numbers a whole number (within some reasonable margin of error). The value thus obtained is the simplest or empirical formula. A molecular weight determination would be necessary to determine the molecular formula. The molecular formula will be some whole number multiple of the empirical formula. Thus, CH_2O is the empirical formula of glucose, but the molecular formula is $6(CH_2O)$, or $C_6H_{12}O_6$.

Determination of the Composition of a Mixture. The composition of a mixture can often be determined from the elemental analysis results. An example is the analysis of a mixture of benzoic acid and benzamide. Because the benzamide contains nitrogen and the benzoic acid does not, a nitrogen determination provides a direct measure of the benzamide present. Pure benzamide contains 11.56% N; therefore, a mixture of benzamide and benzoic acid that has 7.8% N would contain (7.8/11.56) × 100 or 67% benzamide. A polymer consisting of styrene ($C_6H_5CH=CH_2$) and acrylonitrile ($CH_2=CH-CN$) could be analyzed similarly. If the polymer were 100% acrylonitrile, the percentage of nitrogen would be 26.4%. A sample containing 8.3% N would contain (8.3/26.4) × 100 or 31.4% acrylonitrile. The uncertainty in the percentage of nitrogen is transferred and magnified into uncertainty in the composition of the polymer or mixture. The limit on the composition is (8.3 ± 0.3/26.4) × 100 or 31.4 ± 1.1%.

Sample Preparation. To identify organic compounds and to determine empirical formulas, the sample must be pure before elements or functional groups can be determined. For solids, the sample should be recrystallized repeatedly until the melting point remains unchanged after the last two recrystallizations.

When this constant melting point has been obtained, the sample is pure or is as pure as can be obtained from the solvent system being used. The sample should then be recrystallized from another solvent system. If the melting point remains the same, there is a high probability that the sample is pure. In practice, this recrystallization from a second solvent system is sometimes omitted. If additional evidence of purity is desired, the homogeneity of the sample can be checked using thin-layer chromatography.

In removing the purified sample from the filter, care should be taken to ensure that no tiny fragments of filter paper are scraped up with the sample. Any filter paper (or other extraneous material) included in the sample can greatly affect the analytical results. The problem with filter paper can be avoided by using sintered glass funnels of coarse or medium porosity. Water or other solvents can be a serious impurity if the sample is not dried thoroughly.

Drying is best accomplished using an Abderhalden pistol or dryer, which is described in many laboratory supply catalogs. The liquid used to heat the sample in the Abderhalden apparatus should have a boiling point below the melting point of the sample and, if possible, above the boiling point of the solvent used for recrystallization of the sample. The drying agent used in the apparatus is usually phosphorus pentoxide. Less reliable methods of drying the sample include use of desiccators and drying ovens. A commercial laboratory can also dry the samples it receives for analysis.

For liquid samples, the material should be distilled through a distillation column, and a small middle fraction should be collected for the analytical sample. Alternatively, the sample can be analyzed in a gas chromatograph, and a portion of the major fraction can be collected. If the column in the gas chromatograph is appropriate for the sample, gas chromatography will yield a pure sample and is the optimum method. Gas chromatography is discussed in the Section "Chromatography" in this Volume.

The purified sample, solid or liquid, should be stored or shipped to a commercial analytical laboratory in a clean, dry vial. The final cleaning should be accomplished by rinsing the vial with acetone. While still wet with acetone, the vial should then be held with tongs in a Bunsen flame until dry.

Combustion Method for Carbon, Hydrogen, and Nitrogen

Methods for determining carbon and hydrogen are based on combustion of the sample in oxygen to convert the carbon to carbon dioxide and the hydrogen to water:

$$\underset{\text{(sample)}}{CHx} + O_2 \xrightarrow[1290\ °F]{700\ °C} CO_2$$

$$+ H_2O + \underset{\text{other elements } (x)}{\text{Other products from}}$$

The sample is heated, and the volatile material passes through a tube packed with a solid oxidant, usually copper oxide. Other oxidants and empty tubes are sometimes used. In the classical procedures, carbon dioxide and water are absorbed separately in suitable absorbents, then weighed. Ascarite is used to absorb the carbon dioxide, and anhydrone is used to absorb the water.

In procedures using very small samples, the amount of carbon dioxide and water formed is too small to measure gravimetrically in an atmosphere that normally contains some carbon dioxide and water. Alternatives to gravimetric measurements include gas chromatographic, infrared spectrometric, manometric, and thermal conductometric methods. Automated equipment is available that uses gas chromatography or thermal conductivity to measure the carbon dioxide and water.

Nitrogen, if present in the compound, is converted to oxides of nitrogen. Because these oxides would interfere in the measurement of the carbon dioxide and water, they must be removed by transferring the gases through a packing of manganese dioxide or lead peroxide pellets. The method can be modified to enable simultaneous determination of nitrogen as well as carbon and hydrogen.

Many reliable commercial laboratories can provide reasonably priced elemental analyses for carbon, hydrogen, and nitrogen. In view of the elaborate and expensive configurations necessary for conducting these analyses in a personal laboratory, samples should be sent to a commercial laboratory if only a few analyses or occasional analyses are required. The determination should be requested with an understanding of the method to be used in order to avoid or clarify problems that may arise because of the nature of the sample. This article will discuss only one method of analysis, although other methods may be referred to briefly.

Limitations. Any of the following sample types present special problems that, if not limiting, will at least require special modifications or precautions: hygroscopic samples (high hydrogen values), samples of steroids with angular methyl groups (low carbon values), carbohydrates (low values due to charring), samples containing alkali metal salts (low carbon value due to formation of stable carbonates), and samples of organometallic substances (low carbon and hydrogen values due to incomplete oxidation). The presence of elements other than carbon, hydrogen, and oxygen usually necessitates modifying the packings to remove interfering substances formed by oxidation of these other elements. Detailed information on ways to overcome the limitations associated with these types of samples is provided in Ref 1.

Kjeldahl Method for Nitrogen (Ref 1)

Using the Kjeldahl method, the nitrogen in the sample is converted to ammonia; the ammonia is separated from the reaction mixture by steam distillation and is usually determined by a titration:

$$\underset{\text{(sample)}}{CHNx} \xrightarrow[\substack{\text{Heat}\\\text{catalysts}}]{\text{Conc } H_2SO_4} NH_3$$

The method was originally developed for determining the nitrogen content of proteins. The nitrogen in these substances is readily converted to the ammonia stage by digestion with concentrated sulfuric acid. In samples in which the nitrogen is in some other form or oxidation state, the problem of quantitative conversion to the ammonia stage must be solved by modifying the sample digestion procedure.

The breakdown of the organic compound is promoted by the addition of mercury or selenium to the digestion mixture. Selenium is effective for samples consisting of proteins, α-amino acids, amides, and amines. Mercury is required for samples containing heterocyclic compounds, such as pyridine and pyrrole.

pyridine   pyrrole

Some types of heterocyclic compounds consistently produce low results and are best determined using the Dumas method for nitrogen (Ref 1). Compounds in this category include pyrazolones, diazines, and triazoles.

a pyrazolone   pyridazine   a triazole
                (a 1,2-diazinine) (1,2,4-triazole)

If the nitrogen in the sample is in some other combination or at some higher oxidation state, such as hydrazo, azo, azoxy, nitroso, or nitro, the success of the method depends on the complete reduction of these groups to the ammonia stage.

Although the sulfur dioxide and carbon formed during the digestion may serve as reducing agents, a reducing step is usually advisable before the digestion step.

If the sample contains nitrites or nitrates, special reduction techniques are required.

RONO   RONO_2
nitrite   nitrate

Nitrates can be reduced with chromium metal and acid. Nitrites are oxidized to the nitrate stage before reduction.

Applications. In its simplest form, the method is applied to feeds, fertilizers, proteins, amines, and amino acids and is particularly useful when a large number of samples must be determined. The method can be modified for application to nitriles, hydrazines, azo compounds, nitro compounds, nitrates, and metallurgical samples containing metal nitrides. Some heterocyclic nitrogen compounds will probably present difficulties.

Limitations. This method is suitable for many types of nitrogen compounds if the procedure is modified appropriately. Certain heterocyclic compounds, such as pyrazolones, diazines, and triazoles, yield low results.

The estimated analysis time for the Kjeldahl method is approximately 3 to 4 h.

Schöniger Flask Method for Other Common Elements

This method, also termed the oxygen flask combustion or closed-flask combustion method, is most commonly used for halogens and sulfur, and this discussion is limited to their determination. However, the technique can be used with appropriate modifications to determine phosphorus, arsenic, boron, mercury, zinc, cadmium, magnesium, calcium, cobalt, barium, copper, manganese, and nickel (Ref 2).

The sample is wrapped in paper and placed in a platinum basket inside the combustion flask. It is then burned in an atmosphere of oxygen in the closed flask. The platinum catalyzes the decomposition of the sample, particularly the cleavage of the bonds between carbon and the elements to be determined.

Combustion can be initiated by lighting the paper in which the sample is wrapped, quickly inserting the sample, and closing the flask. The platinum basket is attached permanently to the stopper to facilitate this maneuver. An alternate method of ignition involves infrared heating of the sample after it has been placed in the closed flask. Whatever method of ignition is used, precautions should be taken to protect the operator in case the flask explodes during the rapid high-temperature oxidation of the sample. The special flask and infrared ignition equipment are available commercially.

As in most determinations of elements other than carbon, hydrogen, and nitrogen in organic compounds, a major problem is the liberation of the organically bound elements. In this method, the problem is solved by rapid high-temperature oxidation of the compound. The halogens are usually converted to soluble halides and are absorbed in a sodium hydroxide solution. The halide in the solution can be determined using several standard halide determination methods. A typical technique is potentiometric titration of the solution with silver nitrate, after first having acidified the solution with nitric acid.

Sulfur is oxidized to oxides of sulfur. The absorbing solution in the flask contains hydrogen peroxide, which converts all the oxides to sulfate. The sulfate thus formed can be determined by titration with barium perchlorate in an aqueous acetone solution after adjustment of the pH to three. If the sample contains only carbon, hydrogen, and oxygen in addition to the sulfur, the product of the oxidation by the oxygen and the peroxide is sulfuric acid, and this can be titrated directly with standardized sodium hydroxide solution.

Limitations. Sulfones and sulfonamides may not be completely oxidized, resulting in low results. Sulfate must be titrated carefully to obtain favorable results. It may be necessary to remove metal ions, nitrate, and chloride anions by passage through appropriate chromatographic columns. Perfluoro compounds and polymeric materials containing fluorine also may not produce reliable results (Ref 3).

The problem is related to the stability of the carbon-fluorine bond and the formation of volatile silicon tetrafluoride and bromine trifluoride by reaction with the glass used for the flask. Bromine compounds may not provide complete combustion. Polyhalogen compounds may be difficult to decompose, and an additional oxidizing agent, such as potassium nitrate or potassium chlorate, may be required.

Estimated Analysis Time. Combustion takes only a few minutes. The time-consuming portion is the determination of the inorganic halide liberated by the combustion. The time required will vary with the type of halogen to be determined and with the type of procedure selected for the halide determination, but will generally range from one-half to a full day.

Functional Group Analysis

Purity Determination. Determination of the percent composition of a given functional group can be used in much the same way as the percent composition of a given element is used to determine purity of a sample. If there is some doubt as to the significance of the elemental analysis (although the elemental results are correct), a determination of the amount of one or more functional groups thought to be present may be useful.

For example, if the sample is thought to be an alcohol of the formula R_2CHOH, the elemental analysis results could fit satisfactorily, within the limits of experimental error, for the expected formula, yet the sample could be contaminated with an appreciable amount of the ketone $R_2C=O$. Because R_2CHOH and $R_2C=O$ differ by only 2H, either one or a mixture of the two would yield similar results from an elemental analysis. If the sample did not behave as expected, the presence of some other functional group is a possibility. The possible presence of significant amounts of carbonyl compound (ketone) in the alcohol (suggested perhaps by an infrared spectrum of the sample) could be ascertained by obtaining a quantitative determination of the amount of carbonyl group present. Alternatively, a determination of the amount of hydroxyl group

present could establish whether the sample fit the appropriate formula for R_2CHOH.

The above example illustrates that one technique should not be relied upon too heavily or entirely and that all the information available or readily obtainable should be used. Thus, if the sample discussed above were a mixture of R_2CHOH and $R_2C=O$, the melting point of the sample would probably not be sharp.

The lack of a sharp melting point usually indicates that the sample is not pure; such an indication signals a potential problem. If an infrared spectrum were available for the sample, it would show the presence or absence of the carbonyl group as well as the hydroxyl group. In most laboratories, obtaining an infrared spectrum is relatively simple, and its proper interpretation can be useful.

Composition of a Mixture. In the above discussion, if the sample is not pure, it is obviously a mixture, and by having determined the amount of the hydroxyl group or carbonyl group, something about the composition of the mixture has been determined. Some of the same points discussed in the section "Determination of the Composition of a Mixture" in this article also apply to functional group analysis.

Characterization of an Unknown. To investigate an unknown, the various types of spectral evidence would presumably be obtained at an early stage of the investigation. These results, perhaps along with some simple chemical tests, would indicate the types of functional groups that may be present in the sample. The quantitative determination of these groups can provide much useful information, leading to complete characterization of the sample.

Acids*

In the context of organic chemistry, the term acids generally denotes carboxylic acids, RCO_2H, but the method described below can be used to titrate other organic acids, for example, sulfonic acids, or to determine the total acidity of a sample, which would include other substances, such as the inorganic acid sulfuric acid.

This is often one of the simplest determinations, yet it can be quite informative. Fundamentally, the procedure is simply the titration of the sample (suitably dissolved) with a standardized solution of a base, such as sodium hydroxide. A few acids are soluble in water (formic, acetic, propionic in the carboxylic acid category and benzenesulfonic and toluenesulfonic acid) and can be

*In each of the discussions on individual functional groups, sample preparation will not be covered unless information is necessary other than that provided in the section "Sample Preparation" in this article.

dissolved in water and titrated directly with a sodium hydroxide solution of known normality. Acids having a limited solubility in water can usually be dissolved in an alcohol, then titrated. An effective general-purpose procedure uses isopropyl alcohol to dissolve the sample, with an alcoholic solution of sodium hydroxide as the titrant. This sodium hydroxide solution can be 0.1 N or 0.5 N, depending on the acid content of the sample. Phenolphthalein is used as the indicator (Ref 4). The reaction is:

$$RCO_2H + NaOH \rightarrow RCO_2^- + Na^+ + H_2O$$

Equivalent Weight of an Unknown Acid. If the sample is pure, its titration can provide the equivalent weight of the acid. The equivalent weight equals the molecular weight if the acid is a monobasic acid. That is, the equivalent weight is the molecular weight per carboxyl group. For a dibasic acid, the equivalent weight is one-half the molecular weight; for a tribasic acid, one-third, and so on. From this information, the possible formulas that would fit the equivalent weight can be written within experimental error, and the acid can often be identified on this basis. It is helpful to have available other information about the sample. Thus, if the acid contains chlorine or is aromatic, this knowledge considerably limits the choices as to the identity (see the section "Identification of an Acid" in this article).

Purity of an Acid. If the sample is represented to be a certain acid, determination of acidity can be used as a measure of the purity of the sample. This method is effective only if the impurities are not acidic.

If the impurities in a sample are known to be neutral substances, the sample can be titrated to determine its acid content and thus the purity of the acid. The history of the sample will often indicate the nature of the impurities.

Identification of an Acid. Titration of the sample provides data from which the neutralization equivalent is calculated to be 121 ± 1 (assuming a calculated 1% experimental error). If aliphatic, the acid would consist of several CH_2 (methylene) units plus the carboxyl group, $-CO_2H$. The $-CO_2H$ accounts for 45 units of the 120 of the equivalent weight (C = 12, O_2 = 32, H = 1). Subtracting 45 from 120 yields 75, and 75 ÷ 14 (CH_2) = 5.36. Because it is not possible to have 5.36 methylene units (5 methylene units would add up to 70, and 70 + 45 = 115, which is outside of the allowable experimental error), it must be concluded that the acid is not comprised of methylene units; that is, it is not aliphatic. At

this point, it would be helpful to know that the acid does not contain elements other than carbon, hydrogen, and oxygen. If it is assumed (or perhaps known) that these are the only elements present, the possibility that the acid is aromatic must be considered. The simplest aromatic acid (shown below) would have one phenyl group, C_6H_5; $(6 \times 12) + (5 \times 1) = 77$, and 77 + 45 (for the carboxyl group) = 122, which equals the neutralization equivalent within the allowed experimental error.

benzoic acid

If an unknown acid had a neutralization equivalent of 83 ± 1, it would be found that 83 − 45 = 38 and that 38 ÷ 14 = 2.7, not sufficiently close to a whole number of methylene units to provide an acceptable answer. There cannot be one phenyl group (77) and one carboxyl group (75) in the acid whose equivalent weight is only 83, but if the possibility of two carboxyl groups is considered, then the molecular weight of such an acid would be 76 (phenyl less one H) + (2 × 45) or 166. The equivalent weight will be 166/2 or 83, as found experimentally. This indicates that the formula is one of the following.

terephthalic

isophthalic   orthophthalic

This illustrates a limitation on the usefulness of the determination of acidity as a means of identification. Once the choices have been narrowed to the three phthalic acids shown above, it is relatively simple to determine the melting point of the unknown and compare with the melting points reported in the literature for the three isomers shown.

Alcohols

The characteristic functional group of alcohols is the hydroxyl group, but alcohols

can vary in the nature of the alkyl group to which the hydroxyl is attached. This is reflected in the classification of alcohols as primary, secondary, and tertiary (1°, 2°, and 3°):

$$RCH_2OH \quad R_2CHOH \quad R_3CHOH$$
$$1° \qquad\qquad 2° \qquad\qquad 3°$$

These classes of alcohols differ in their reactivities, and some methods of determination are not equally suited to all classes of alcohols. For example, one of the commonly used and more convenient methods is not suitable for tertiary alcohols. In this method, the sample is acetylated with acetic anhydride (or sometimes acetyl chloride) in the presence of pyridine. Under these conditions, the reaction is quantitative for the primary and secondary alcohols, but the hydroxyl group of tertiary alcohols is acetylated only slightly (Ref 5).

After the above reaction is complete, the excess of unreacted acetic anhydride is decomposed by adding water to the reaction mixture.

The reaction mixture is then titrated with standardized 1 N sodium hydroxide solution. A reaction blank (the reaction mixture with no sample added) is also titrated with the standardized sodium hydroxide solution. In the blank, all the acetic anhydride will have been converted to acetic acid. In the reaction containing the sample, part of the acetic anhydride will have been consumed by reaction with the alcohol and will not produce acetic acid to be titrated with the sodium hydroxide. The difference in the amount of base consumed by the blank and by the reaction containing the sample is a measure of the amount of primary and secondary alcohol in the sample.

The above method is simple and does not require highly specialized or unusual equipment, but it is useful only with primary and secondary alcohols. An alternative requires some specialized equipment, but has the advantage of suitability for tertiary alcohols and for primary and secondary alcohols. The chemistry of this method is simple (Ref 6):

$$4ROH + LiAlH_4 \rightarrow 4H_2 + LiAl(OR)_4$$

The hydrogen gas liberated in the reaction is collected and measured. It is a direct measure of the amount of hydroxyl group in the sample. Despite the simplicity of the chemistry, conducting the determination involves specialized equipment to hold the reactants and to collect and measure the hydrogen evolved. In addition, the lithium aluminum hydride solution requires special preparation and handling.

Aldehydes and Ketones

These compounds are often referred to as carbonyl compounds.

$$RC\overset{\displaystyle O}{\underset{\displaystyle H}{\diagdown}} \quad \text{and} \quad R-\overset{\overset{\textstyle O}{\|}}{C}-R \quad (R \text{ may be Ar})$$

They should not be confused with other compounds that contain the C=O (carbonyl) group, but are not aldehydes or ketones. Such compounds as acids, esters, amides, and acid halides are not considered carbonyl compounds in the same sense as aldehydes and ketones, and they are not susceptible to analysis by the same methods used to determine aldehydes and ketones.

$$RC\overset{O}{\diagup}OH \quad RC\overset{O}{\diagup}OR \quad RC\overset{O}{\diagup}NH_2 \quad RC\overset{O}{\diagup}Cl$$

acid   ester   amide   acid chloride

The most common methods for determining aldehydes and ketones are based on the reaction of the carbonyl compound with hydroxylamine hydrochloride to form an oxime.

$$RC\overset{\displaystyle O}{\underset{\displaystyle R(H)}{\diagdown}} + H_2NOH \cdot HCl \rightleftharpoons$$

aldehyde
or ketone

$$R-\underset{\displaystyle R(H)}{\overset{\displaystyle |}{C}}=NOH + HCl + H_2O$$

oxime

Because the oxime is less basic than the hydroxylamine from which it is prepared, an

equivalent of hydrochloric acid is liberated for every equivalent of carbonyl compound that reacts. This liberated hydrochloric acid can be titrated directly, but the end point is difficult to determine and requires careful matching of indicator colors.

Another difficulty is that the reaction is an equilibrium reaction and does not proceed to 100% completion. Thus, the values for such common carbonyl compounds as acetone and methyl-ethyl ketone will be only slightly better than 98% of the theoretical value. Nevertheless, the values are reproducible, and the method is useful. The difficulty caused by the incompleteness of the reaction can be avoided by adding pyridine to the system and carrying out the reaction in a mixed water-alcohol solvent. The addition of pyridine makes the end point even more difficult to discern.

In the other useful modification of this reaction, the second by-product of the reaction, water, is measured. The amount of water formed can be determined using the Karl Fischer method (see the section "Karl Fischer Method for Water Determination" in this article) if the reaction is conducted in nonaqueous mediums. The reaction is usually conducted in pyridine, sometimes with an additional inert solvent. The simple acidimetric procedure is limited to aldehydes or ketones that are reasonably soluble in water; therefore, the procedure in which anhydrous solvents are used has the additional advantage of efficient determination of the higher molecular weight aldehydes and ketones that are insoluble in water.

Limitations. The acidimetric method may not provide suitable results if organic acids are present. Epoxides, if present, will react with the hydrogen chloride liberated, yielding low results.

Amines

Amines are classified, according to the degree of substitution on the nitrogen, as primary, secondary, or tertiary:

RNH_2	R_2NH	R_3NS
Primary	Secondary	Tertiary

Regardless of the classification, most common amines are sufficiently basic that they can be determined by a simple titration with acid. Strong bases, such as simple alkyl amines, can be titrated in aqueous solution using 0.1 to 1.5 N sulfuric acid as the titrant and methyl red as the indicator. For weaker bases, such as aniline, pyridine and its alkyl derivatives, and quinoline and its alkyl derivatives, it is necessary to titrate in an acetic acid solution using perchloric acid as the titrant and crystal violet as the indicator (Ref 7).

Under these conditions, the stronger bases that are titratable in water can be determined as well as the weaker bases mentioned above, but the method has limitations and is not suitable for weaker amines, such as 2-haloanilines, diphenylamine, pyrrole, and indole.

The above methods are simple and effective for amines of the type described. If the sample consists of a single amine, that amine can be determined readily. If the sample consists of a mixture of amines, titration will provide a measure of the total basicity of the samples but it will not provide information regarding which individual amines are present in the sample. If this information is required, use of a chromatographic method that will separate and quantify the individual components of the mixture is advisable (see the Section "Chromatography" in this Volume).

Methods other than chromatography can be used to determine the amounts of primary, secondary, and tertiary amines. For example, primary aliphatic amines can be determined by treatment with nitrous acid (generated *in situ* from sodium nitrite and acetic acid) to form nitrogen gas. A special glass inverted burette (azotometer) is required for separating and measuring the nitrogen. The reactions that take place are simplified as:

$$RNH_2 + HONO \rightarrow ROH + N_2 + H_2O$$

One mole of nitrogen gas is liberated per mole of primary amine. During the reaction, the nitrous acid decomposes to provide oxides of nitrogen. These oxides must be separated from the nitrogen gas by absorption in an alkaline permanganate solution. This method has been used extensively to determine the amino acids produced by the hydrolysis of protein (Ref 8-10).

A method for determining combined secondary and tertiary amines is based on the titration of the secondary and tertiary amines after conversion of the primary amines to imines by reaction with salicyl aldehyde (Ref 11).

imine

The basis of the method is that the imine formed by the primary amine is only weakly basic and is not titrated when the other amines present are titrated with alcoholic hydrochloric acid.

A similar principle is used to determine tertiary amines in the presence of primary and secondary amines. In this case, the sample is treated with acetic anhydride to convert the primary and secondary amines to their neutral amides, leaving the tertiary amines unreacted and still basic so that they can be titrated with perchloric acid in glacial acetic acid.

$$
\left.\begin{array}{c} RNH_2 \\ R_2NH \\ R_3N \end{array}\right\} + CH_3C\!\!\stackrel{O}{\underset{}{{\diagup}}}\!\!)_2O \longrightarrow \begin{array}{c} CH_3C\!\!\stackrel{O}{\underset{}{{\diagup}}}\!\!NHR \\ CH_3C\!\!\stackrel{O}{\underset{}{{\diagup}}}\!\!NR_2 \\ R_3N \end{array}
$$

The difference between the total basic nitrogen and the tertiary amine can be taken as a measure of the combined primary and secondary amines present in the sample (Ref 12). Methods based on the fluorescence of the products formed by the reagent fluorescamine when it reacts with primary amines (Ref 13) and secondary amines (Ref 14) appear to be promising and useful if a suitable spectrofluorimeter is available.

Aromatic Hydrocarbons

The chemical reactivities of aromatic hydrocarbons are variable, depending on the structure of the compound. Methods based on chemical reactivity are not likely to provide quantitative results. The methods of analysis are, therefore, usually based on spectroscopic methods. Perhaps the most useful analytical property of aromatic compounds is their characteristic absorption in the ultraviolet. Most of the simpler monocyclic compounds absorb between 250 and 280 nm. Measuring the absorption at the appropriate wavelength can be a relatively simple and useful technique. It is helpful to know exactly which compounds are being determined so that the extinction coefficient and wavelength of maximum absorption are known. Fluorescence measurements can be even more sensitive (Ref 15, 16).

Some of the newer developments in spectroscopic techniques for aromatic hydrocarbons include Shpol'skii spectrometry (Ref 17) and Fourier transform/NMR spectroscopy (Ref 18). A suitable alternative to spectroscopic methods is gas chromatography (for the more volatile hydrocarbons) or high-performance liquid chromatography (HPLC) (for the polynuclear aromatic hydrocarbons). Gas chromatography is also useful for aliphatic hydrocarbons (see the Section "Chromatography" in this Volume).

Esters

Esters are derivatives of acids, and their most useful analytical reaction is their hydrolysis or saponification to the acid:

$$RCO_2R + NaOH \rightarrow RCO_2Na + ROH$$

If a measured excess of NaOH is used, it is relatively simple to titrate the NaOH remaining after saponification is complete. Each ester group consumes one equivalent of the base, permitting calculation of the amount of ester group present in the sample. If the sample is a pure compound, it is possible to calculate the saponification equivalent. This value is useful because it equals the molecular weight of the compound if the compound has only one ester group per molecule; that is, the compound is a monoester. For diesters, the saponification equivalent will equal one-half the molecular weight, and so on for tri- and polyesters. The situation is analogous to the neutralization equivalent of acids (see the section "Acids" in this article).

A problem that arises in this determination is due to the difficulty of saponifying all but the simplest esters. If the esters are not soluble in aqueous NaOH, or if the R groups of the above formula are large or bulky, it becomes virtually impossible to effect complete saponification in a reasonable period of time. This difficulty can usually be surmounted by carrying out the saponification reaction in a high-boiling medium containing diethylene glycol or a similar solvent (Ref 19).

Peroxides

In general, peroxides are compounds that have an oxygen-oxygen bond. The simplest case is hydrogen peroxide, and all other peroxides may be conceptualized as derivatives of hydrogen peroxide in which one or both of the hydrogens have been replaced by some organic group. Some of these are illustrated below.

$$RC\!\!\stackrel{O}{\underset{}{{\diagup}}}\!\!O-O-H \qquad R-O-O-H$$
peracid   hydroperoxide

$$R-O-O-R \qquad RC\!\!\stackrel{O}{\underset{}{{\diagup}}}\!\!O-O\!\!\stackrel{O}{\underset{}{{\diagdown}}}\!\!CR$$
dialkyl peroxide   diacyl peroxide

$$\begin{array}{c} O-O-H \\ | \\ ROCHR \end{array}$$
ether peroxide

Diacyl peroxides and dialkyl peroxides are used primarily as initiators (sometimes termed catalysts) for the polymerization of vinyl-type monomers. Perhaps the most important uses of a peroxide analytical determination are inspecting the purity of these initiators and checking for residual amounts of initiators that may remain after polymerization is complete. In addition, it sometimes becomes important to determine the peroxide content of carbonyl compounds, hydrocarbons, and especially ethers that have been stored for a considerable length of time. These compounds slowly form peroxides in the presence of air, and the accumulation in an old sample can become dangerous (samples containing peroxides represent a possible explosion hazard, and solutions containing peroxides should never be evaporated to dryness).

Peroxides are usually determined using a reduction procedure. A common method uses iodide as the reducing agent. The resulting iodine is then titrated with thiosulfate:

$$ROOH + 2I^- + 2H^+ \rightarrow ROH + I_2 + H_2O$$

Acetic acid is a commonly used solvent, but depending on the sample, it may be necessary to add an additional solvent, such as isopropyl alcohol or chloroform. When the sample consists of a dialkyl peroxide, for example, di-*tertiary*-butyl peroxide, that is less reactive than an alkyl hydroperoxide or a diacyl peroxide, more strenuous conditions are necessary for the reduction. This can be accomplished by heating the reaction mixture to 60 °C (140 °F) with constant boiling hydrogen iodide and acetic acid (Ref 20).

Phenols

The hydroxyl group of phenols is in many respects similar to the hydroxyl group of alcohols in terms of analytical methods (see the section "Alcohols" in this article). In general, methods for alcohols that involve a reaction of the hydroxyl group are usually suitable for phenols. Any method that is specific for phenols must depend on some other characteristic of a phenol rather than on the hydroxyl group alone.

One of the most widely used techniques for phenols is based on the color formed by the oxidative coupling of 4-aminoantipyrine with phenol.

It is apparent that phenols with a substituent in the para position should not condense with the 4-aminoantipyrine. This is the case if the substituent in the para position is an alkyl group (as in *p*-cresol).

p-cresol

The method is, nevertheless, very useful. If the substituent in the para position is a halogen of methoxyl, the substituent is lost in the condensation process, and the colored product is formed (Ref 21, 22).

Coupling occurs in an alkaline solution, with potassium ferricyanide as the usual oxidizing agent. The red product is extracted using a suitable solvent and measured in a colorimeter. In the older literature, chloroform is used as the solvent, but a less hazardous solvent, methylene chloride, is now recommended.

The method is particularly useful for determining trace amounts of phenols in, for example, waste waters and plant effluents. Substituents on the phenol ring affect the response to the reagent. A list of 35 phenols and their responses to the 4-aminoantipyrine reagent is provided in Ref 23. A procedure that combines the development of a color using the antipyrine reagent with HPLC is applicable to the determination of phenols at part per million and part per billion levels in water (Ref 24).

Karl Fischer Method for Water Determination

A general and simple method of determining water in a sample is to heat a weighed sample to constant weight, then assume that the loss in weight was due to loss of water.

Some of the obvious sources of error in this technique include the possibilities that the sample contains other volatile solvents in addition to water, that whatever temperature was selected for the heating may not have been sufficiently high to effect the loss of all the water present, or that the heating temperature was so high that a weight loss occurred because of some reaction or decomposition in the sample. A technique for avoiding these problems is the Karl Fischer method for the determination of water. The advantage of the method is that the reagent used is specific for water and does not detect other volatile solvents that may be present.

Examples of applications for this method include determination of water in solvents, chemicals, petroleum, plastics, pharmaceuticals, cosmetics, foods, tobacco, and textiles. The samples are solids, liquids, or gases. Sample size depends on water content. The amount of water that can be detected can be as low as a few micrograms. Caution should be exercised in handling samples to prevent contamination with additional moisture.

The chemistry of the process is:

$$I_2 + SO_2 + 3R_3N + ROH + H_2O \rightarrow$$
$$R_3NH^+ + ROSO_3^- + 2R_3NH^+ + 2I^-$$

In the classical procedure, the tertiary amine used is pyridine, and the alcohol was methanol (Ref 25). In later versions, other alcohols, such as methyl Cellosolve ($CH_3OCH_2CH_2OH$), have been used (Ref 26, 27). The odor and toxicity of pyridine has led to the development of a commercial reagent that does not use pyridine (Ref 28).

Various other commercial modifications have been devised, including one in which the iodine used is generated electrolytically, permitting a coulometric determination of water. An alternative to the Karl Fischer method is a gas chromatographic determination of water, which permits detection limits as low as 1 to 10 ppm (Ref 29).

Unsaturation (Alkenes)

Because addition and vinyl-type polymers involve unsaturated monomers, determination of unsaturation may be important in studies of these types of polymers. Unsaturated and polyunsaturated fats and oils are another area in which this determination is important.

The common chemical methods for determination of alkenes or olefinic unsaturation involve an addition reaction typical of the carbon-carbon double bond:

$$R_2C=CR_2 + Br_2 \rightarrow R_2CBr-CBrR_2$$

Bromine and iodine monochloride (ICl) are frequently used reagents, although the results are sometimes expressed as the "iodine number," as if the reagent added to the unsaturation were iodine. The iodine number has been widely used to indicate the degree of unsaturation in unsaturated fats and oil. A problem with the determination of unsaturation by halogen addition is that some of the halogen may be consumed by substitution reactions rather than by the expected addition. The addition reaction is not rapid, and to ensure complete reaction, a known excess of the halogen reagent is used. After a suitable period of time, the excess is determined, often by titration with thiosulfate. Several procedures based on halogen addition are discussed in Ref 30. Pseudohalogens, such as thiocyanogen, have also been used in the determination of unsaturation in fatty acids (Ref 31). In branched-chain alkenes, the problem of substitution reactions becomes important, and methods based on the addition of hydrogen to the unsaturation are more useful (Ref 32):

$$R_2C=CR_2 + H_2 \xrightarrow[\text{Catalyst}]{} R_2CH-CHR_2$$

REFERENCES

1. T.S. Ma and R.C. Rittner, *Modern Organic Elemental Analysis*, Marcel Dekker, 1979
2. A.M.G. Macdonald, in *Advances in Analytical Chemistry and Instrumentation*, Vol 4, C.N. Reilly, Ed., John Wiley & Sons, 1965, p 75
3. R.C. Rittner and T.S. Ma, *Mikrochim. Acta*, Issue 3, 1972, p 404
4. F.T. Weiss, *Determination of Organic Compounds: Methods and Procedures*, Wiley-Interscience, 1970, p 66
5. F.T. Weiss, *Determination of Organic Compounds: Methods and Procedures*, Wiley-Interscience, 1970
6. G.A. Stenmark and F.T. Weiss, *Anal. Chem.*, Vol 28, 1956, p 1784
7. F.T. Weiss, *Determination of Organic Compounds: Methods and Procedures*, Wiley-Interscience, 1970, p 237, 241
8. D.D. Van Slyke, *J. Biol. Chem.*, Vol 9, 1911, p 185
9. D.D. Van Slyke, *J. Biol. Chem.*, Vol 23, 1915, p 407
10. G. Kainz, H. Huber, and F. Kasler, *Mikrochim. Acta*, Issue 5, 1957, p 744
11. C.D. Wagner, R.D. Brown, and E.D. Peters, *J. Am. Chem. Soc.*, Vol 69, 1947, p 2611
12. C.D. Wagner, R.D. Brown, and E.D.

Peters, *J. Am. Chem. Soc.*, Vol 69, 1947, p 2609
13. B.A. Tomkins V.H. Ostrum, and C.H. Ho, *Anal. Lett.*, Vol 13, 1980, p 589
14. H. Nakumura and Z. Tamura, *Anal. Chem.*, Vol 52, 1980, p 2087
15. B.L. Van Duuren, *Chem. Rev.*, Vol 63, 1963, p 325
16. M.L. Lee, M.V. Novotny, and K.D. Bartle, *Analytical Chemistry of Polycyclic Aromatic Hydrocarbons*, Academic Press, 1981
17. Y. Yang, A.P. D'Silva, and V.A. Fassel, *Anal. Chem.*, Vol 53, 1981, p 2107
18. J.T. Joseph and J.L. Wong, *Fuel*, Vol 59, 1980, p 777
19. R.L. Shriner, R.C. Fuson, D.Y. Curtin, and T.C. Morrill, *The Systematic Identification of Organic Compounds*, 6th ed., John Wiley & Sons, 1980, p 293-298
20. F.H. Dickey, J.H. Raley, F.F. Rust, R.S. Treseder, and W.E. Vaughan, *Ind. Eng. Chem., Anal. Ed.*, Vol 41, 1949, p 1673

21. E. Emerson, *J. Org. Chem.*, Vol 8, 1943, p 417, 433
22. E. Emerson and K. Kelley, *J. Org. Chem.*, Vol 13, 1948, p 532
23. J. Farino, G. Norwitz, W.J. Boyko, and P.N. Kelliher, *Talanta*, Vol 28, 1981, p 705
24. G. Blo, F. Dondi, A. Betti, and C. Bighi, *J. Chromatography*, Vol 257, 1983, p 69
25. K. Fischer, *Z. Angew. Chem.*, Vol 48, 1938, p 395
26. J. Mitchell, Jr. and D.M. Smith, *Aquametry*, Interscience, 1948
27. E.D. Peters and J.L. Jungnickel, *Anal. Chem.*, Vol 27, 1950, p 450
28. E. Scholz, *Fresenius Z. Anal. Chem.*, Vol 303, 1980, p 203
29. J. Hogan, R. Engel, and H. Stevenson, *Anal. Chem.*, Vol 42, 1970, p 249
30. F.T. Weiss, *Determination of Organic Compounds: Methods and Procedures*, Wiley-Interscience, 1970, p 29-55
31. L.S. Silbert and R.J. Maxwell, *Fatty Acids*, E.H. Pyrde, Ed., American Oil

Chemists' Society, Champaign, IL, 1979, p 403-425
32. C.A. Brown, S.C. Sethi, and H.C. Brown, *Anal. Chem.*, Vol 39, 1967, p 823

SELECTED REFERENCES

• I.M. Kolthoff and P.J. Elving, *Treatise on Analytical Chemistry*, Vol 11, Part 2, *Analytical Chemistry of Inorganic and Organic Compounds*, Interscience, 1965
• S. Siggia, Ed., *Instrumental Methods of Organic Functional Group Analysis*, Wiley-Interscience, 1972
• C.A. Streuli and P.R. Averell, *Analytical Chemistry of Nitrogen and its Compounds*, Vol 28, *Chemical Analysis*, P.J. Elving and I.M. Kolthoff, Ed., Wiley-Interscience, 1970
• F.T. Weiss, *Determination of Organic Compounds: Methods and Procedures*, Vol 32, *Chemical Analysis*, P.J. Elving and I.M. Kolthoff, Ed., Wiley-Interscience, 1970

High-Temperature Combustion

R.B. Fricioni and Loren Essig, Leco Corporation

<table>
<tr><td>

General Use

- Determination of carbon and sulfur in metals and organics

Samples

- *Form*: Solids, chips, or powders
- *Size*: 1 g or less, depending on type of material
- *Preparation*: Bulk samples must be cut to prescribed size required for determination. Specimen should not be contaminated with carbon or sulfur before analysis

Limitations

- Specimen must be homogeneous

</td><td>

- Graphite-bearing specimens require special handling
- Method is destructive

Estimated Analysis Time

- *Sample preparation*: 2 to 3 min
- *Analysis time*: 40 s to 2 min

Capabilities of Related Techniques

- *Optical emission*: Determination of total carbon and sulfur in metals
- *X-ray fluorescence*: Determination of sulfur in most metals

</td></tr>
</table>

Introduction

High-temperature combustion is primarily used to determine carbon and sulfur contained in a variety of materials. Carbon and sulfur are found to some extent in virtually all materials and are often present in association with other elements in a variety of compounds. The exact formation of the molecules gives each compound distinctive characteristics. The carbon and sulfur content of a material must be closely monitored and controlled during processing to provide a good-quality material. These elements are controlled by oxygen injection, which causes excess carbon and sulfur to leave as a carbon dioxide (CO_2) and sulfur dioxide (SO_2) gas. High-temperature combustion uses this principle to determine the total content of these elements in a material.

A high-temperature furnace capable of attaining 1370 to 1425 °C (2500 to 2600 °F) is used. In the combustion furnace, oxygen is used to flood the chamber. The combination of a heated environment and abundant oxygen causes the sample to combust. The released gases pass through a series of traps, absorbers, and converters to remove interfering elements and ensure that the gases have the proper structure for detection. Detection of the resulting gases is most commonly provided by thermal conductivity or infrared absorption. Each detection method provides a specific and consistent measurable signal as the concentration of gases applied to the detector changes. This signal is processed electronically to provide a percentage of carbon or sulfur by specimen weight.

Combustion Principles

In high-temperature combustion, a weighed sample and required accelerators are placed into a ceramic crucible or combustion boat, which is then introduced into a high-temperature furnace. High-frequency induction or resistance furnaces are used. The central part of a high-frequency furnace is the load or work coil section (Fig. 1). A quartz or vycor glass tube is positioned through the center of the work coil to provide a sealed chamber while the sample is combusting. A high-frequency furnace requires some portion of the crucible load to be inductive; if the sample is not, inductive accelerators are required. Application of high-frequency power to the work coil establishes a high-frequency field around the sample. The inductive material contained in the crucible couples with this field and heats the specimen.

In a resistance high-temperature furnace, carbide or molydisilicide elements are used to heat the furnace to a constant 1370 to 1425 °C (2500 to 2600 °F). In this type of furnace, coupling is unimportant, but the combustion point of the sample is significant; the accelerators used with these furnaces will normally combust more readily than the specimen.

Oxygen applied to the high-temperature furnaces provides the key ingredient to high-temperature combustion. Oxygen will cause the heated sample to combust and be oxidized. The carbon and sulfur released form CO, CO_2, and SO_2. Oxidation changes the specimen material to an oxide slag.

Accelerators for combustion are also referred to as combustion aids. Adding an accelerator to the sample load provides a material that is more susceptible to oxidation. Sample combustion characteristics are basically the same with either furnace system, as is the nominal sample size of 1 g. However, different sample forms have different combustion characteristics. Solid specimens, which require more energy to reduce than chips or powders, may require

Fig. 1 Typical high-frequency combustion configuration

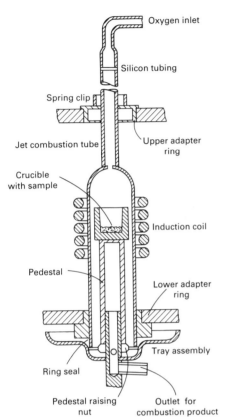

Oxygen inlet

Silicon tubing

Spring clip

Jet combustion tube

Upper adapter ring

Crucible with sample

Induction coil

Pedestal

Lower adapter ring

Tray assembly

Ring seal

Pedestal raising nut

Outlet for combustion product

Table 1 Combustion accelerators

Accelerator	Characteristics
Copper chip	Good combustion aid for steel, iron, and nonferrous metals and alloys in a high-frequency furnace for determination of percent carbon; may be combined with iron chips for nonferrous alloys; may be combined with tin chips on some systems for sulfur determination
Copper strip	Same guidelines as copper chips, but used with resistance furnace systems
Iron chip	Good accelerator for combusting steel, iron, or nonferrous metals and alloys for determination of carbon or sulfur; when analyzing for concentrations below 0.05% C and 0.002% S, high-grade iron chips should be used to provide consistent results; iron chips must be used when combusting nonferrous materials in a high-frequency furnace system
Tin chip	Good additive accelerator for combustion of steel, iron, and nonferrous materials; tin chips have relatively low combustion point and assist in the initial stages of combustion by generating a higher temperature at an earlier stage
Tungsten	Good accelerator for most steels, irons, and nonferrous materials; provides excellent combustion when combined with tin chips; used primarily where very low carbon and sulfur concentrations are being determined

slightly longer combustion periods or additional accelerators.

Accelerators are also used to bring the sample combustion point into the temperature capability of the furnace. Using the proper accelerators, even high melting point materials can be analyzed. The types of accelerators required vary according to the detection system and the element to be determined. The basic characteristics of various accelerators are listed in Table 1. In addition to efficiency, other factors include the contribution of carbon or sulfur from the accelerator to the analysis, its reaction with the element being determined, and its reaction with the material being combusted.

Blank is defined as carbon or sulfur obtained from sources other than the sample. Additional carbon or sulfur can be obtained from the oxygen supply, crucibles or combustion boats, and the accelerators. Normal blank concentrations are consistent and range from 0.010 to 0.0005%, depending on the detection system and particular grades of crucibles, combustion boats, and accelerators used. Automatic determinator systems can compensate for the additional carbon and sulfur determined as blank. Manual or semi-automatic determinators require subtraction of the determined blank from the final result.

Copper accelerators cannot be used alone for determination of sulfur. The high concentration of copper present during combustion will cause much of the sulfur being removed to combine and form copper sulfate ($CuSO_4$). If the copper is combined with tin chips, this reaction usually does not occur. Iron or tin chip accelerators can cause an adverse reaction with some alloys. The reaction is indicated by a large amount of spattering to the combustion tube walls. Poor reproducibility of results will be observed on these materials due to the loss of specimen material before complete reduction. In these cases, a reduced sample weight to accelerator ratio should be applied, or varied accelerator combinations should be used.

Separation of Interfering Elements

In addition to CO and CO_2 relative to carbon content of the material and SO_2 relative to sulfur content, oxides are formed by other elements in the material during combustion. The oxide compounds formed in the combustion zone of the furnace must be separated to ensure detection of only the desired elements. Separation begins with the removal of metal oxides; this is normally accomplished using a porous trap that will stop the metal oxide particles while allowing gases to pass through. Hydrogen in the sample will form water vapor; this must be removed from the stream of gases. Moisture is normally removed by use of a desiccant, such as magnesium perchlorate ($Mg(ClO_4)_2$).

When analyzing for sulfur using infrared absorption detection, remaining gases will not cause interference because of the selectivity of the detection systems. In carbon analysis using a thermal-conductive detection system, the released SO_2 must be removed once the metal oxides are removed. The thermal conductivity of SO_2 is similar to that of CO_2 and will cause interference. Sulfur dioxide usually is removed by manganese dioxide (MnO_2). In most systems for carbon determination, a heated catalyst material maintained at approximately 400 °C (750 °F) is used to convert any CO to CO_2 before it reaches the detection system. The catalyst material used for this conversion is rare earth copper oxide or platinized silica. In infrared detection systems, the detectors are highly discriminate, and there is no need to remove SO_2 from the flow stream.

Sulfur dioxide, however, as it passes through the catalyst material, may form sulfur trioxide (SO_3). Sulfur trioxide as a residue can contaminate the system and must be removed. Cellulose placed directly after the catalyst will absorb any SO_3 coming out of the catalyst. Some thermal conductive detection systems for carbon use a 5-Å molecular sieve trap to collect all the CO_2 during the combustion stage. A separate carrier is then used to carry the CO_2 from the collection trap as it is resistively heated.

A collection-type thermal-conductive carbon system is useful in determining carbon contents of 0.1 to 1000 ppm. In this application, helium can be used as the carrier to the thermal-conductivity cell, providing higher sensitivity in the detection system. When using thermal-conductive detection to determine low carbon contents, remaining oxygen from the collection system must be separated from the CO_2 and helium. A silica chromatographic column delays the oxygen until all the CO_2 has been detected.

Detection of Combustion Products

High-frequency and resistance furnace combustion systems deliver the extracted carbon and sulfur to the detection system as CO_2 and SO_2. Determinators detect these gases and provide results as direct percentages of carbon and sulfur. The primary methods of detection are thermal conductivity or infrared absorption. The determinator systems provide a stabilized environment of temperature and flow for the detection systems.

Infrared detection can be applied to carbon or sulfur determination. A high-frequency or resistance furnace may be used. Infrared detection is applied on the basis that various gases can absorb energy within a specific wavelength of the infrared spectrum. The amount of energy absorbed by combustion gases within the CO_2 or SO_2 absorption wavelengths determines the carbon and/or sulfur content of the material. A solid-state infrared detection system is constructed with an energy source at one end of a chamber and a bandpass filter and detector at the other. The interior of the chamber is sealed on either end to allow transmission of energy through the chamber. The energy source transmits a broad spectrum of energy wavelengths through the measure chamber. The only energy wavelength allowed to reach the detector is the wavelength at which the gas under determination is absorbed.

The infrared detector is a pyroelectric device that is highly sensitive to direct changes in heat. As combustion gases are carried to the measure chamber, the energy that the gas under determination absorbs reduces the output of the detector. This reduction in detector output is proportional to the amount of gas in the measure chamber. Due to the high selectivity of detection, interference from other combustion gases is eliminated.

Thermal-conductive detection systems respond to changes in heat conduction. The detector is a basic Wheatstone bridge balanced under a helium or oxygen flow. The system is based on the principle that each gas has a distinct capability of carrying heat from a body. Table 2 lists the thermal conductivity of various gases. Separation in a high-temperature combustion system removes any gas that may cause a thermal-conductive offset similar to CO_2. As the CO_2 extracted from the sample enters the detection system, the environment in the cell becomes hotter, because CO_2 has a lower thermal conductivity than oxygen or helium. The offset generated by CO_2 is proportional to the amount of carbon extracted from the sample. Measurement systems are automated to provide the required processing of the detected signal to enable displaying a final direct percentage of carbon and/or sulfur as a percentage of sample weight.

Total and Selective Combustion

The quantitative determination of carbon and sulfur by high-temperature combustion can be performed on various materials. This method is used primarily for all grades of steels and irons. Other materials that can be analyzed using this method include such hydrocarbons as oils, coals, and shales; such inorganic compounds as sand, glass, carbonates, sulfates, and ores; and such metals as gold, cobalt, zirconium, uranium, and magnesium.

High-temperature combustion systems require a nominal 1-g sample. Normal maximum carbon content that can be determined at the 1-g weight ranges from 2.5 to 3.5% C. Lower sensitivity limits range from 0.1 to 10 ppm C. Maximum sulfur contents may range from 0.2 to 2.5% S with a 1-g sample. Lower sensitivity limits for sulfur will range from 0.1 to 50 ppm. Higher concentrations of carbon or sulfur may be determined by decreasing the specimen weight to an actual concentration within the capabilities of the measurement system.

For example, if the maximum detection capability of a system is 3% at 1 g, and a material containing 30% is to be analyzed, a specimen weight of less than 0.1 g will provide an observed content of less than 3%. The actual determined value at 1 g can be calculated automatically, or manually using the equation:

$$\%C \text{ or } S \text{ at } 1 \text{ g} = v \times \frac{1}{w}$$

where v is the value as determined and w is the actual sample weight.

Total combustion of a sample requires high temperature and sufficient oxygen to the combustion area to sustain oxidation. Proper and sufficient accelerators are required to provide thorough reduction of the sample. In high-frequency furnace systems, inductive capabilities of the material must be considered. A noninductive material—for example, one with low or no iron or copper content—requires addition of either of these materials as accelerators to provide the needed inductance. Materials having high melting points require addition of tin to increase temperature rapidly to begin combustion of the sample.

During sample preparation, any contamination added to the surface of the material will affect the analysis. Solid samples can be taken in the form of a pin from molten metal. Before taking a pin sample, surface slag should be cleared; this will provide a clean sample. A solid sample can be sectioned using a saw, abrasive wheel, or shears. The cut surface should not be overheated to the point of oxidation. An oxidized cut surface may indicate a loss of carbon during sectioning. After sectioning, the sample should be cleaned to remove any accumulated surface contamination. Samples are normally cleaned in acetone or freon, then air dried.

Optimum homogeneity of graphite-bearing metals is found in solid specimens. Chip specimens are bored or milled from solid materials. During the process, graphite may segregate from the material as graphite powder, creating a carbon loss. When a chip sample of a graphitic material must be used, the chips should be thoroughly combined with any segregated graphite powder. Materials with high melting points are best combusted as chips or powders. Chip or powder samples provide a greater surface area for oxidation reduction than solid samples.

Because the hydrocarbons contained in body oils will add extraneous carbon, a properly prepared sample, once cleaned of surface contaminants, should not be handled. Scoops, tweezers, or spatulas should be used for weighing and loading the sample. Samples that are allowed to corrode before analysis will generally provide varying results, depending on the amount of surface corrosion.

Selective combustion for determining surface carbon on a material is performed using a standard high-temperature combustion system. A controlled-acid washing of the material will remove hydrocarbons from oils and solvents introduced to the material during processing as well as any graphitic carbon inherent on the surface of the material. Solid materials are cleaned with a steel wool pad saturated with a dilute hydrochloric acid (HCl) solution. One square foot of material is generally cleaned to provide a consistent area for analysis and to facilitate conversion in values from weight percent carbon to milligrams of carbon per square foot. Blank compensation for the analysis is established by first combusting specimens of the clean steel wool material at the prescribed pad size with the crucible and accelerators.

Surface hydrocarbons and graphitic carbons will leach to the acid-saturated pad as

Table 2 Thermal conductivity of gases

Gas	Thermal conductivity, cal/cm · s · C × 10⁵
Water vapor	150
Hydrogen	39
Helium	33
Neon	10.4
Oxygen	5.7
Nitrogen	5.6
Air (dry)	5.4
Carbon monoxide	5.4
Argon	3.8
Carbon dioxide	3.3
Sulfur dioxide	1.6

the material is washed. After washing, the pad is placed in a drying oven at 75 to 105 °C (165 to 220 °F). After drying, the pad is combusted with the proper accelerators, then analyzed.

The procedure is modified for performing surface carbon determinations on granular materials. A weighed sample is placed in a filter medium, such as filter paper or a special filtering crucible, then washed with the dilute HCl solution. The surface carbon leaches to the filter medium while the acid solution washes through. Once washed, the specimen is removed from the filter. The filter medium is dried and analyzed as described above for the steel wool pad. To prepare the combustion system for such a procedure, the background carbon content of the filtering medium must be determined, and a blank compensation must be applied to correct for carbon attributable to the filter.

Before determining for surface carbon contents using these procedures, a halogen trap must be installed in the separation path. The trap is generally placed directly after the oxide-removal section to remove the halogens as soon as possible. The halogens generated are the result of the acid solution and can be highly corrosive to the system. The most common halogen trap material is antimony metal, which has a high affinity for fluorides and chlorides.

Because different types of carbon form at different temperatures, and a resistance furnace can maintain preset temperatures, hydrocarbons and amorphous carbon can be determined separately from graphitic carbon. Hydrocarbons and amorphous carbon will oxidize at approximately 400 °C (750 °F). Graphitic carbon will oxidize at 600 °C (1110 °F). Surface carbon can be determined with a resistance furnace system by sectioning solid samples to the recommended dimensions of the combustion system and inserting the sample directly into the combustion zone. Granular specimens can be weighed into a clean boat and inserted into the furnace. Because the furnace temperatures used are not high enough to change the structure of the material, the specimen will appear the same before and after analysis, with only the surface being oxidized.

The determination of only graphitic carbon by this procedure requires heating of the specimen to 400 °C (750 °F) to remove hydrocarbons and amorphous carbon before analysis for graphitic carbon at 600 °C (1110 °F). Specimens under determination for only total surface carbon content can be analyzed at 600 °C (1110 °F). Systems that have been developed for surface carbon analysis generally allow expression of the determined content as milligrams of carbon per square foot or as weight percent for granular materials. Because acids are not used in resistance furnace systems for surface carbon analysis, a halogen trap is not necessary, and corrosion within the system is not a concern.

Applications

Example 1. Surface carbon on a material can generate many finishing problems in a product. An appliance manufacturer was experiencing a problem with paint adherence on cabinetry. An investigation indicated that paint adherence varied with batches of sheet steel used for the cabinets. The cabinet cleaning process used before painting was examined. Even though all the cabinets were exposed to exactly the same cleaning process, some cabinets exhibited good paint adherence, but others did not. Environmental studies were performed on the cabinets through all the manufacturing stages. It was concluded that effects due to variation in the manufacturing environment were eliminated during cleaning.

To determine the differences in the cabinets, 25- by 100-mm (1- by 4-in.) samples were cut from the sheet steel supply. Surface carbon analyses of the raw stock material were performed by high-temperature combustion. Each sample was heated to 400 °C (750 °F) to determine the amorphous carbon content, then to 600 °C (1110 °F) to determine the graphitic carbon content. Once these values were established, duplicate specimens were exposed to the entire manufacturing process. After cleaning, the duplicate specimens were analyzed under the same conditions as the original specimens.

It was determined that the total surface carbon initially found on the sheet steel ranged from 0.9 to 2.1 mg/ft^2. The analysis of the duplicate sheets ranged from 0.5 to 1.5 mg/ft^2. The reduction in the total surface carbon content was attributable primarily to the amorphous carbon that cleaning removed. The samples that contained less than 1 mg/ft^2 surface carbon exhibited good paint adherence, but samples with higher surface carbon contents did not. Removing the remaining graphitic carbon with an additional caustic bath to control the surface carbon content solved the problem.

Example 2. A transformer under design was to operate with a 75% duty cycle and a specified secondary voltage. Testing of the designs revealed that some of the prototypes did not attain the desired output. These same transformers could not withstand the duty cycle requirements. The design basics were confirmed, then the materials being used were examined.

The transformer core material in this case was a high alloy and extremely low carbon material. The carbon determination was performed using high-frequency combustion with infrared detection. According to the specifications of the material, the carbon content was to be controlled between 20 and 30 ppm. To provide the best accuracy for this low concentration, the system was set up with ultrahigh-purity oxygen. The crucibles were preheated to 1350 °C (2460 °F) for a minimum of 20 min. The normal accelerator used in the combustion system was tungsten. Due to the high nickel, manganese, and chromium content and relatively low iron content of the sample, 500 mg of a low-carbon iron chip standard was added to the crucible load for coupling. The determined carbon content of the core material ranged from 50 to 100 ppm. Analysis indicated improper designation of the core material.

Example 3. The composition of a material determines the precise method to be used in combusting a specimen. A material that can be readily combusted and contains carbon or sulfur well within the limits of the detection system could be of such a density that reduced specimen weights must be used to contain the specimen in the crucible. Organic and synthetic materials will most commonly present this problem. As an example, a state department of natural resources was interested in establishing the overall health of the state's deer herds. At the same time, the department wanted to determine the quality of food the deer were finding in their grazing areas. Because the protein contained in the deer's food supply forms a sulfate in the hair follicles, a determination of the sulfur content in the deer's hair follicles would indicate the quality of food the deer were finding and their general well-being.

Collection stations were established throughout the state during hunting season. Hair samples were taken from deer brought in by the hunters; the samples were labeled according to area, then sent for sulfur analysis by high-temperature combustion. An inductive high-temperature furnace and infrared detection determinator were used for the analysis. Due to the low density of hair, it was necessary to weigh the samples to 250 mg for analysis. The combustion accelerators used were a combination of tungsten and tin chips weighted to 1 g, and 500 mg of iron powder. Because the samples combusted readily, and a total reduction of the sample was possible without generation of interfering elements, the assigned operational parameters of the system were used.

SELECTED REFERENCES

- P.G. Ashmore, *Catalysis and Inhibition of Chemical Reactions*, Butterworths, 1963

- D.O. Hayward and B.M.W. Trapnel, *Chemisorption*, Butterworths, 1964

- C.L. Mantell, *Adsorption*, McGraw-Hill, 1951

- Rapid High Temperature Combustion for Determining Total Sulfur by Microprocessor Controlled Infrared Absorption, in *Coal Testing Conference Proceedings*, Vol 3, 1983, p 16-18

Inert Gas Fusion

R.B. Fricioni and Loren Essig, Leco Corporation

General Use

- Quantitative determination of oxygen, nitrogen, and hydrogen in ferrous and nonferrous materials

Samples

- *Form*: Solids, chips, or powders
- *Size*: Usually 2 g or less, depending on material type and the expected amount of gases present
- *Preparation*: Bulk materials must be cut to prescribed size. Care must be taken not to contaminate specimens with nitrides, oxides, or hydrides. Materials for oxygen and hydrogen must be kept cool during sectioning to prevent hydrogen diffusion and surface oxidation

Limitations

- Metals with low boiling points require special precautions

- Materials with stable nitrides or oxides require addition of fluxes
- Method is destructive to the material

Estimated Analysis Time

- 1 to 10 min after sample preparation

Capabilities of Related Techniques

- *Vacuum fusion*: Total nitrogen, oxygen, and hydrogen in some metals without fusing the specimen
- *Hot extraction*: Total nitrogen, oxygen, and hydrogen in some metals without fusing the specimen
- *Optical and mass spectroscopy*: Nitrogen, oxygen, and hydrogen by x-ray bombardment on some metals

---

Introduction

Inert gas fusion is used to determine the quantitative content of gases in ferrous and nonferrous materials. These gases, such as hydrogen, nitrogen, and oxygen, are introduced to a material by physical and chemical adsorption. Surface metals deposited on base materials physically adsorb atmospheric gases to form metal-bearing compounds. The type of metal atom available and its compatibility with the types and concentrations of atmospheric gases available under the temperatures and pressures to which the material is exposed determines the types of metallic compounds formed. Although the bond at low temperatures is unstable, the metallic compounds formed become more stable as temperature increases and the physical adsorption bond becomes a chemical adsorption bond.

As base materials are smelted, the adsorbed gases are chemically absorbed into the melt. The less stable compounds are reduced in the melt of the material, allowing each to recombine and form a more complex stable compound. The metallic elements will absorb atmospheric gases based on the affinity of the metal for each gas at various temperatures during the melt.

Processed materials are again subject to gas adsorption as the material is initially cooled and worked. Stages of drawing, rolling, heat treating, or annealing provide favorable conditions for physical and chemical adsorption of atmospheric gases. Strict control of hydrogen, nitrogen, and oxygen levels minimizes their adverse effects on material strength.

Hydrogen causes internal cracks that generally appear during cooling in such processes as drawing, rolling, or forging of the material. Materials with large cross sections can break under high or continuous stress due to internal cracks. Hydrogen is adsorbed and diffused often during working of the material. Hydrogen that is adsorbed will generally diffuse during cooling or aging. Materials used under high temperatures and pressures and exposed to high-hydrogen en-

vironments can develop structural problems due to hydrogen embrittlement.

Nitrogen in some materials can provide strength. For example, nitrogen is added to austenitic manganese steels to increase yield strength. A material may be subjected to nitriding to increase hardenability. Nitrogen may decrease ductility.

The effects of oxygen on a material are similar to those of hydrogen in that inclusions and blowholes can appear in the material. Oxygen, when combined with the carbon and nitrogen in a material, will also cause increased hardness with age. Oxygen is often the hardest to control because it is available from various sources and reactive with many metals. Smelting and processing regulate the levels of gases introduced into materials by controlling temperature, pressure, and environment, which create adsorption and absorption of gases.

Gases introduced into the material are commonly quantitatively determined using inert gas fusion. Inert gas fusion reverses the physical and chemical bonding between the gases and the metals to dissociate the gases and sweep them from the fusion area with an inert carrier gas. Resistance or induction heating of a sample in a pure graphite crucible dissociates the gas/metal bonds. Because they are formed over a wide range of temperatures, bonds can be broken only by heating the specimen above the highest temperature at which the gas/metal bonding occurred.

Principles of Operation

A pure graphite crucible used as a sample container in an impulse fusion furnace acts as a carbon resistor, completing a high-current circuit. When activated, the circuit applies an impulse current of 600 to 1300 A through the graphite crucible, heating the crucible to 3000 °C (5430 °F).

Inert gas fusion by induction heating uses the pure graphite crucible as an inductor centered in the load or work coil portion of a high-frequency induction furnace. When the furnace is activated, the crucible inductively couples with the high-frequency field (nominally 4-kW power), heating the crucible to 2500 °C (4530 °F). The graphite crucible also is a source of highly heated carbon in these furnaces. Oxygen, being highly reactive, immediately bonds to carbon upon its release. The carbon/oxygen bond isolates the oxygen from further reactions in the fusion melt.

Graphite crucibles, like other materials, contain gases that have been introduced through adsorption and absorption during processing. These gases must be removed before a sample can be fused in the crucible. Cleaning of the crucible during preanalysis is known as degassing or outgassing. In the degas stage, the crucible is heated above the temperature to be used for analysis. For example, an impulse heating method requires 600 A to fuse a sample. Therefore, the crucible would be degassed at 650 A. Currents required for impulse fusion are a function of crucible and electrode style. Figure 1 shows typical configurations of crucibles. Inductive heating furnaces incorporate single-use crucibles.

With inductive heating, crucible degas and fusion temperatures are set by coupling the graphite crucible to the high-frequency field, which is measured by the amount of current the high-frequency oscillator draws. For example, a high-frequency furnace operating at 4 MHz with a power output of 4 kW requires 750 mA through the plate current portion of the oscillator section to attain a crucible degas at 2400 °C (4350 °F). Fusion can then take place at 2300 °C (4170 °F) and a plate current of 700 mA.

The properly prepared, weighed sample for inert gas fusion is commonly held in a chamber above the fusion area. The analysis being performed is relative to common gases found in the atmosphere. Atmosphere surrounding the specimen can be removed during degassing by placing the specimen in this holding chamber. After interfering gases have been removed from the fusion area, the sample can be transferred to the cleaned crucible for fusion.

In an impulse fusion system (Fig. 2), the crucible completes a high-current circuit. The copper alloy electrodes are water cooled to prevent their decomposition. The heat of the graphite crucible is directly transferred to the sample. The sample fuses to a molten state, causing the gases that had been absorbed into more stable metal/gas compounds in the sample to desorb. As they dissociate from the material, hydrogen and nitrogen are carried from the fusion chamber as H_2 and N_2; oxygen is removed as carbon monoxide (CO). The same gas extraction process occurs in an induction fusion system. Figure 3 shows a simplified version of an inductive inert gas fusion system.

An inert carrier gas sweeps the evolved gases of the specimen from the fusion chamber. Carrier gases are selected for their effect on the gases to be determined and the ability of the detection system to differentiate be-

Fig. 1 Graphite crucibles used in inert gas fusion analysis

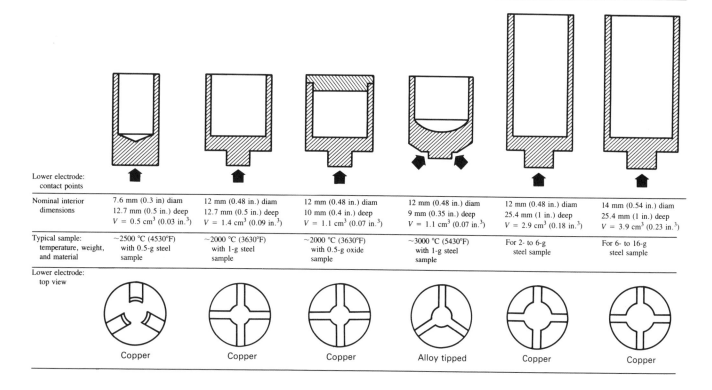

Fig. 2 Simplified impulse inert gas fusion furnace

The graphite crucible acts as a resistor, completing a high-current circuit and reaching 3000 °C (5430 °F).

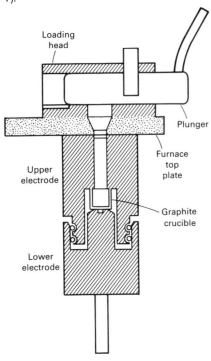

Fig. 3 Simplified inductive inert gas fusion furnace

The graphite crucible acts as an inductor in a high-frequency induction furnace, reaching 2500 °C (4530 °F).

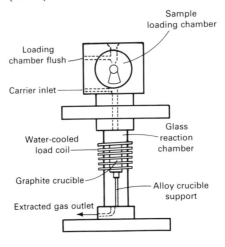

Separation of Fusion Gases

Gases evolving from the inert gas fusion chamber must be treated to ensure that the inert carrier and the gas under determination are the only gases being presented to the detection system. To perform these functions, inert gas fusion analysis uses particle traps, catalytic converters, gas chemical ab-

sorbers, and chromatographic columns in the flow stream between the fusion and detection areas. Figures 4 and 5 show two methods of gas separation used in inert gas fusion.

The separation system first removes the graphite dust generated in the fusion chamber. Heating of the graphite crucible drives particles of graphite off its surface. Glass wool placed directly after the fusion chamber will remove these particles. For some applications, systems using nitrogen as the inert carrier will contain clay impregnated with sodium hydroxide (NaOH) at this position. When carbon and nitrogen are combined above 2300 °C (4170 °F), some of the nitrogen will form cyanogens, which may cause interferences in the detection system. Because the affinity of heated carbon for nitrogen is not high at elevated pressures, cyanogen formation, although slight, is detectable and must be removed.

Oxygen can be detected as CO or as carbon dioxide (CO_2), depending on system design. Oxygen as CO is generally detected using an infrared system that is highly discriminate and requires no further gas separation after graphite dust or cyanogen removal. Oxygen as CO_2 is detected by thermal conductivity or infrared detection systems. The main criterion in deciding which gas form to use to detect oxygen involves the detection system and whether the inert gas fusion system is determining single or multiple elements.

tween the carrier and the gases being determined. Inert gas fusion systems are generally single or dual gas determination systems. Helium is the most common inert carrier gas used in determining nitrogen or nitrogen and oxygen. Nitrogen or argon is often used as the carrier for the single determination of oxygen or hydrogen. The inert carrier gas is a reference gas for the detection system, a carrier for the contaminants during degas, and the carrier for the evolved gas from the sample.

Because the gas to be determined is part of the gases found in the atmosphere, the system must be isolated from interfering gases. The inert carrier functioning as referenced carrier to the detection system sweeps the flow system clear of atmospheric gases from the fusion section through the detection section. During degas and preanalysis, a separate flow line sweeps the flow line from the fusion section to the atmosphere as the referenced flow line maintains flow to the detection section. Figure 3 illustrates a typical inert gas fusion system. During fusion of the sample, the referenced flow line is directed through the furnace; the flow line used during preanalysis is stopped until the next degas stage. Constant pressures and flows are used in inert gas fusion to desorb gases properly relative to sample temperature.

Fig. 4 Inert gas fusion system for detecting nitrogen and oxygen

1, Helium supply; 2, pressure regulator; 3, heated copper; 4, NaOH-impregnated clay; 5, $Mg(ClO_4)_2$ desiccant; 6, flow control; 7, flow manifold; 8, gas doser (optional); 9, sample holding chamber; 10, electrode (impulse) furnace; 11, dust filter; 12, heated rare earth copper oxide; 13, $Mg(ClO_4)_2$ desiccant; 14, silica gel column; 15, thermal conductive detector/readout; 16, flow rotameter

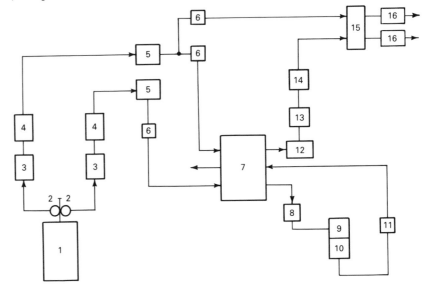

Fig. 5 Insert gas fusion system for detecting nitrogen and oxygen

1, Helium supply; 2, two-stage pressure regulator; 3, NaOH-impregnated clay; 4, Mg(ClO₄)₂ desiccant; 5, flow restrictor; 6, flow meter; 7, pressure regulator; 8, needle valve; 9, gas doser (optional); 10, flow manifold; 11, sample holding chamber; 12, electrode (impulse) furnace; 13, dust filter; 14, heated rare earth copper oxide; 15, flow control; 16, infrared detector/readout; 17, thermal-conductive detector/readout

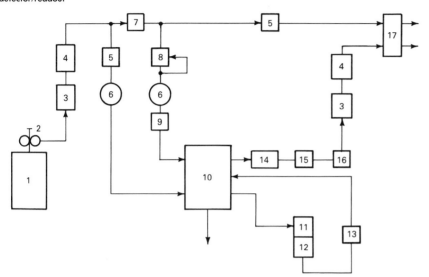

When determined with nitrogen, oxygen must be converted to CO_2 to allow isolation of the gases flowing through the detection systems. Figure 4, which illustrates a nitrogen/oxygen detection system, shows heated rare earth copper oxide in the flow stream to the detection system. Oxygen to be detected as CO_2 enters the copper oxide section as CO. The heated, highly oxidized copper contains an excess of oxygen molecules. When CO is presented to this area, excess oxygen molecules in the copper will be attracted to the next higher oxide level, CO_2. The catalyst material is 350 to 400 °C (660 to 750 °F). The oxygen molecules in the copper are also cohesive to hydrogen gases at this temperature, causing water vapor to form.

Water vapor is removed with desiccants, such as magnesium perchlorate (Mg $(ClO_4)_2$), that absorb moisture efficiently without releasing byproduct gases. With the hydrogen from the fusion chamber converted to moisture and absorbed by Mg $(ClO_4)_2$, the remaining gases in the flow stream are CO_2 (relative to the amount of oxygen in the sample), nitrogen, and the inert carrier. For oxygen determination alone, the inert carrier can be nitrogen. This enables referencing the detection system to nitrogen; any nitrogen extracted from the specimen will be of the same characteristic as the carrier. Oxygen combined with nitrogen determination requires further isolation of the gases.

Figure 4 shows a silica gel column between the Mg$(ClO_4)_2$ section and the detec-

tion section. Inert gas fusion often involves use of gas chromatography in separation of gases. The molecular density of gases as they are transferred through a chromatographic column causes gases with lower density to pass more rapidly through the columns than the higher density gases. The time required for gases to transfer through a column varies with the temperature of the column.

In Fig. 4, the silica gel column is held at a stable temperature to permit reproducible separation and detection of nitrogen and CO_2. Fusion gases can also be combined and determined using separate detection systems without a chromatographic column. In these systems, oxygen, after conversion to CO_2 and removal of water vapor, is directed through a selective infrared detection system.

After oxygen detection, the flow stream enters NaOH-impregnated clay. Sodium hydroxide will absorb CO_2 to form sodium carbonate (Na_2CO_3) and water vapor. A desiccant, such as Mg$(ClO_4)_2$, placed directly after the NaOH will absorb the released moisture, leaving only nitrogen and the inert carrier in the flow stream to enter the nitrogen detection system. An inert gas fusion system that determines only nitrogen will use the same separation process of CO to CO_2 conversion, CO_2 removal, and moisture removal to isolate oxygen and hydrogen from the detection system.

The separation method for hydrogen by inert gas fusion follows the same principles

as separation of oxygen and nitrogen. Nitrogen can be used as the carrier gas, and oxygen as CO can be absorbed using a molecular sieve; or argon can be used as the inert carrier, and oxygen as CO_2 can be removed using NaOH. Hydrogen and nitrogen are then separated by a chromatographic column that allows nitrogen to elute after detection of hydrogen.

Separation of CO by a molecular sieve requires more time than the other separation method. Conversion of CO to CO_2 must be performed in this case without converting hydrogen to moisture. Conversion of CO to CO_2 for determining hydrogen is carried out by using untreated iodine pentoxide (I_2O_5) impregnated into an inert base material in the flow stream after graphite dust removal. The I_2O_5 provides abundant active oxygen molecules for the formation of CO_2. The nonelevated temperature of the material prevents moisture formation.

Gas separation ensures that only the gas being determined and the inert carrier enter the detection section at the time of measurement. Selection of the separation system is based on the gas to be determined, the inert carrier gas used, and the sensitivity of the detection system to other gases.

Detection of Fusion Gases

The inert carrier gas maintains a constant inert environment from the fusion chamber through the detection system. The gases under determination flow from the separation system into the detection system at a rate established by the flow of the carrier gas. The voltage output of the detection system changes proportionally with the concentration of gas being determined as the gas flows through the detection system.

The evolved gases are detected by a thermal-conductive system or an infrared absorption system. Thermal-conductive detection systems are suitable for any of the gases discussed. Infrared absorption is generally used to detect oxygen as CO or CO_2.

Thermal-conductive detection uses the ability of each specific gas to draw heat away from a body. Figure 6 shows a typical thermal-conductive detection cell, and Table 1 lists thermal conductivity rates for a number of gases. The thermal-conductive rates of the inert carriers helium, argon, and nitrogen are used to establish the baseline output of the detection system. Maintaining a constant flow of these gases through the detection system establishes a stable rate of heat transfer. A thermal-conductive detector, being temperature sensitive, is held in a temperature-

Fig. 6 Typical thermal-conductive detection cell

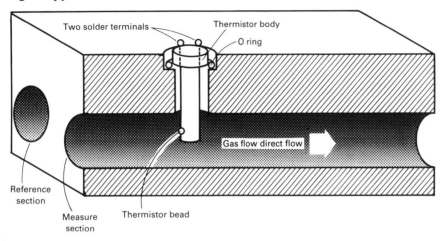

stabilized compartment. Because carrier flow and the environment of the detection system are constant, any change in heat transfer will result from a gas other than the carrier.

Fine filament wires called thermistors sense the change in heat transfer. The thermistors are mounted in a cell body having porting for two flow streams, one for carrier gas only and the other for carrier gas and the gases from the separation section. One dual-filament to two single-filament thermistors are mounted in each port. The thermistors are matched sets selected on the basis of equal resistance and gain capability. A constant current is applied equally to the reference-ported thermistor and the measure-ported thermistor, heating the filament wire and lessening its resistance. The reduction in resistance increases the voltage at the output of the thermistor.

With carrier gas flowing and the output of the measure and reference thermistors stable, the detection system is electronically nulled to a set level. Fusion gases from the separation section alter the heat transfer rate in the measure port. The thermistor mounted in that port senses this change, then responds with a variation in voltage corresponding to the fusion gas content present.

Infrared Detection. In contrast to hydrogen and nitrogen, oxygen as CO or CO_2 is best detected by infrared absorption. Infrared absorption of CO and CO_2 takes place in highly selective regions of the absorbance spectrum. The ability to consider the absorbance of energy that takes place at a specific wavelength may reduce or eliminate the need to remove or separate the other fusion gases.

An infrared absorption detection system consists of four main components, as shown in Fig. 7. An infrared source transmits a broad spectrum of energy through a measure chamber. At the opposite end of the measure chamber, a bandpass filter selected for the absorption wavelength of CO or CO_2 allows only energy of that wavelength to pass

through an energy-condensing chamber. The chamber directs the energy to the energy-detection material, which is highly responsive to direct changes in heat. The detection material responds to changes in energy with proportional changes in current and voltage.

The voltage response of an infrared detector at maximum emissivity for a given wavelength is in the low millivolt region. To achieve sensitivity to minute changes in energy, a blade is placed in front of the infrared source and attached to a synchronous motor. As the motor rotates the blade through the energy beam, the energy is blocked from the detector, presenting the energy to the detection material in pulses. Due to the pulsed energy, the detection output is an alternating millivoltage that increases the sensitivity to changes within the selected wavelength.

Gases in the carrier stream being introduced to the measure chamber will absorb infrared energy at given wavelengths. The detection system senses absorption in the wavelength of the bandpass filter, which results in an offset relative to the CO or CO_2 content in the carrier stream. Inert gas fusion uses the offset voltage of the detection system to process the output electronically into the quantitative content of the gas according to specimen weight.

Determination of Gases

Graphite crucibles, even after degassing, will contain a small amount of the element to be determined. The carrier mediums will also contain trace amounts of the element. Performing initial analyses using only crucibles and any required flux material will establish the background content for the analysis. The determined background content is then subtracted from the determined sample value.

The determined sample content must be referenced to a sample of known gas content. The reference, which sets a slope relationship between the detected content and the actual sample content, is established through analyses of known specimens or of a known volume of the gas to be determined. A correction for the difference between the detected content and the actual content is applied to all subsequent analyses.

Nitrogen Determination. Analysis of a sample for nitrogen requires total decomposition of all nitrogen compounds in the material. Because the compounds were formed at various temperatures during processing of the material, the sample must be heated above the highest point at which the nitrogen compounds were formed. Samples can be solids, chips, or powders sized to a nominal

Table 1 Thermal conductivity of gases

Gas	Molecular weight	Thermal conductivity, cal/cm · s · °C × 10⁵
Water vapor	18	150
Hydrogen	2	39
Helium	4	33
Neon	20	10.4
Oxygen	32	5.7
Nitrogen	28	5.6
Air (dry)	29	5.4
Carbon monoxide	28	5.4
Argon	40	3.8
Carbon dioxide	44	3.3
Sulfur dioxide	64	1.6

Fig. 7 Typical infrared detection system

weight of 1 g. Mass reduction in relation to the temperature being applied is more efficient with lower mass chip or powder specimens. Materials with a high content of high-temperature nitrogen compounds will exhibit better recovery with a lower specimen weight. A nickel or platinum flux is sometimes required as well.

Oxygen analysis follows the same parameters as those described for nitrogen. Samples to be analyzed for oxygen content are susceptible to contamination; any oxidation of the surface will increase the oxygen content of the sample. Chip and powder samples require extended flushing after the material is added to the crucible to remove atmosphere from between the granules. Materials with high oxygen contents sometimes require addition of carbon black to the crucible to increase the amount of free carbon available and ensure that all oxygen in the sample is converted to CO.

Hydrogen analysis normally uses a solid 2-g sample. Because hydrogen will continue to diffuse from the material at ambient temperatures, the sample must never be overheated and should be handled at reduced temperatures. Hydrogen in some materials, such as titanium, is compounded into many hydride forms. These materials may require addition of a tin flux to help reduce the hydride compounds.

Samples

The accuracy of inert gas fusion analysis begins with sampling and sample preparation. Samples can be obtained from molten metal using a pin sampling device; finished product materials can be sectioned to the desired weight. Regardless of the element being determined, samples should be rinsed in acetone or freon to remove surface contaminants.

Solid samples for oxygen determination should be abraded before analysis to remove surface oxidation. Chip samples for oxygen analysis are prepared by boring into the material while keeping it cool and free of oxidation. Before its analysis, a powder sample must be dried in an inert environment to remove moisture introduced by ambient humidity. Powder materials are normally weighed into tin capsules for analysis. Once the weight is established, the capsule is degassed and crimped closed.

Following preparation and cleaning, the sample should be handled only with tweezers to prevent contamination. The cleaned sample is dried to remove solvent moisture, then analyzed immediately.

Samples for hydrogen analysis, when taken from molten metals, will have a higher hydrogen content in the molten state than at ambient temperature. After the sampling device is removed from the molten metal, a hydrogen sample will most often be quenched in liquid nitrogen to halt hydrogen diffusion. Hydrogen samples taken from molten metal are kept cold until preparation and analysis. Sample preparation for hydrogen involves a solvent rinse and an air dry to remove surface hydrides.

Hydrogen samples taken from finished product materials are sized to a nominal 2-g solid sample. The sample must not be heated during sectioning. Overheating of the material will cause hydrogen to evolve from the material before analysis. The larger sample weight provides a more representative sample for lower hydrogen contents. Some finished product materials will have a hydrogen content from 0.1 to 2 ppm. Materials such as titanium may contain 30 to several hundred ppm. These materials can be analyzed at reduced sample weights to maintain the total content within the detection limits of the system.

Selective Fusion

Nitrogen and oxygen compounds form at specific temperatures in the processing of metals. If the fusion furnace is controlled to heat the sample gradually, nitrogen and oxygen compound contents can be determined. A compound will decompose when the sample reaches the temperature at which the compound was formed; therefore, correlating the temperature of the sample with the nitrogen or oxygen content at that temperature will establish the content of that particular compound.

Nitrogen and oxygen compounds evolve in a regimented order. Evolution of nitrogen compounds begins with molybdenum, followed by tungsten, chromium, vanadium, boron, silicon, and aluminum. High-temperature nitrides, such as tantalum, niobium, zirconium, and titanium, evolve above 2700 °C (4890 °F). Oxide evolution begins with iron, followed by silicon, calcium, and aluminum. Tantalum and zirconium oxides evolve above 2700 °C (4890 °F).

Analysis for nitride and oxide contents requires strict monitoring of sample temperature versus detector output. Sample temperature is determined by optically monitoring the crucible temperature or referencing the crucible current to the resulting temperature. Although it allows constant measurement, optical temperature determination is subject to interferences due to graphite buildup on the optical window. The current monitor is more dependable.

To establish a temperature for a given current, the temperature of a specific crucible type must be monitored under the various crucible currents. Once the correlation between crucible current and temperature is known, succeeding crucibles will provide the same temperatures within a small deviation. Selective nitride and oxide analysis requires knowledge of the possible compounds contained in the sample to provide a correlation among detector offset, crucible temperature, and the nitrogen or oxygen compound that falls within the specific evolution order.

Examples

Tensile and yield strength problems in aluminum-killed steel prompted metallographic studies, which indicated a high aluminum oxide (Al_2O_3) content. Oxygen analysis by inert gas fusion indicated the total oxygen content to be correct, and a spectrographic analysis showed the aluminum content to be correct. A solid specimen of the material was prepared and analyzed by a controlled heating of the crucible.

The cleaned crucible and specimen were heated to 1500 °C (2730 °F) and increased 50 to 75 °C (90 to 135 °F) every 3 s. An offset attributable to iron oxide occurred at 1650 °C (3000 °F), an offset due to silicon dioxide (SiO_2) at 1950 °C (3540 °F), and an offset resulting from Al_2O_3 at 2150 °C (3900 °F). The Al_2O_3 content exceeded considerably the expected limits for the material. During killing, the temperature of the steel permitted an inordinate amount of aluminum to bond with the available oxygen.

Structural problems in titanium were solved using inert gas fusion after metallographic studies pointed to oxygen content. Oxygen in titanium is generally between 1000 to 2000 ppm. Titanium also consists of tightly bonded compounds. Therefore, the titanium sample was sectioned to a 100-mg weight. Total analysis for a given gas requires a sample weight that provides a gas concentration within the measurement capabilities of the system.

The sample was cleaned, pressed into a pellet with nickel chip flux, then fused in an impulse furnace with 1000 A applied through the crucible. The material contained 2500 ppm oxygen, indicating insufficient degassing during processing.

Cracking in finished copper was thought to be due to oxygen, which causes most of the structural problems in copper processing. An inert gas fusion analysis indicated the oxygen level to be within limits. Excessive hydrogen in metals generally causes embrittlement or work stress problems. To establish acceptability, several known, good batches of copper were analyzed.

A nominal hydrogen value on the known samples was established at less than 2 ppm. Samples from the suspected material were sectioned to 3-g weights. Surface hydrides were removed by lightly abrading the specimen. The preparation procedure from the known specimens was duplicated. Analyses of the suspected material indicated hydrogen content of 6 to 8 ppm. The analysis indicated the copper was retaining an inordinate amount of hydrogen from working or processing.

SELECTED REFERENCES

- P.G. Ashmore, *Catalysis and Inhibition of Chemical Reactions*, Butterworths, 1963
- D.O. Hayward and B.M.W. Trapnel, *Chemisorption*, Butterworths, 1964
- C.L. Mantell, *Adsorption*, McGraw-Hill, 1951
- L.M. Melnic, L.L. Lewis, and B.D. Holt, *Determination of Gaseous Elements in Metals*, Wiley Interscience, 1974
- M. Smailowski, *Hydrogen in Steel*, Pergamon Press, 1962
- A. Mead, "The Determination of Oxygen and Nitrogen in Some Nitrides and Carbides by Inert Gas Fusion Using an Impulse Heating Furnace," United Kingdom Atomic Energy Authority Research Group Report, 1970
- D.H. Bollman, Platinum, Vanadium and Nickel Baths for Oxygen Inert Gas Fusion Determination, *Analytical Chemistry*, Vol 46 (No. 9), 1974, p 1191-1194

Neutron Activation Analysis

M.E. Bunker, M.M. Minor, and S.R. Garcia, Los Alamos National Laboratory

General Uses

- Nondestructive trace-element assay of essentially any material
- Ultrasensitive (as low as 10^{-12} g/g) destructive quantitative analysis
- Measurement of isotope ratios in favorable cases

Examples of Applications

- Quality control for purity or composition of materials
- Element-abundance measurements in geochemical and cosmochemical research
- *Resource evaluations*: Assay of surface materials, drill cores, ore samples, and so on
- *Pollution studies*: Assay of air, water, fossil fuels, and chemical wastes for toxic elements
- *Biological studies*: Determination of the retention of toxic elements in humans and laboratory animals, in some cases by *in vivo* measurements
- *Forensic investigations*: Trace-element assay of automobile paint, human hair, and so on

Samples

- *Form*: Virtually any solid or liquid
- *Size*: Typically 0.1 to a few grams, but the full range extends from a microgram to at least 100 kg (220 lb)
- *Preparation*: None required in many cases

Limitations

- Several elements are unobservable except through sample irradiation with high-energy neutrons or use of radiochemical (destructive) techniques
- Access to a nuclear reactor or some other high-intensity neutron source is required
- Turnaround time can be long (up to 3 weeks)
- The samples usually become somewhat radioactive—objectionable in some cases
- Intense radioactivity induced in one or more of the major elements in a sample may mask the presence of some or all of the trace elements

Estimated Analysis Time

- Counting times can range from under 1 min (for short half-life radioisotopes) to many hours (for low-intensity long-lived radioisotopes)

Capabilities of Related Techniques

- *X-ray fluorescence*: Useful for determining major and minor elements (concentrations >0.1%), but several elements with $Z \geq 11$ can be observed at 5 to 20 ppm
- *Atomic absorption*: Can determine most elements individually. Requires dissolution of the sample. Some elements observed at levels of 10^{-9} g/mL, which usually corresponds to $\geq 10^{-7}$ g/g of the original solid sample
- *Inductively coupled plasma emission spectroscopy*: Requires dissolution of the sample. Typical detection limits are a few parts per million
- *Inductively coupled plasma mass spectroscopy*: Can determine trace elements in the presence of high levels of major and minor elements in the sample matrix, such as in alloy and metal analysis. Requires dissolution of the sample. Detection limits for most elements are from 0.05 to 0.1 ng/mL of solution
- *Isotope dilution mass spectrometry*: Can quantitatively measure as few as 10^6 atoms of most elements individually. Isotope ratios are used. Analysis time is at least one day per element
- *Spark source mass spectrometry*: Simultaneous detection of most elements at levels down to approximately 1 ppm. Data are recorded on a photoplate, limiting accuracy. Sample preparation may take several hours
- *Particle-induced x-ray emission spectroscopy*: Measures element concentrations near the surface of a sample. Several elements can be measured at a few parts per million. Access to a proton accelerator is required.

Introduction

Neutron activation analysis (NAA) is a highly sensitive and accurate method of assaying bulk materials for trace levels of many elements. Neutron activation analysis has recently found broad application in materials science and in geological, biological, archaeological, health, forensic, and environmental studies (Ref 1). Much of what is known about the composition of the lunar surface was learned using NAA. The technique has become an increasingly important assay method because of its many advantages, which include:

* Simultaneous observation of large blocks of elements, minimizing analysis time and increasing the reliability of element ratio values
* Nondestructive analysis of virtually any material regardless of chemical form, resulting in the possibility of conducting repeated measurements on the same sample, the elimination of reagent addition (greatly reduces the possibility of sample contamination), and ease of automation of analysis
* Detection limits under 1 μg for several trace elements, assuming only minor interference from the radioactivity induced in the major elements of the sample (see the section "Nondestructive TNAA" in this article). In destructive (radiochemical) NAA, the detection limits for some elements are below 1 ppt

The NAA method most commonly used involves irradiation of the sample using slow neutrons in a reactor, followed by observation of the γ-rays emitted from the sample by radioactive isotopes formed through capture of neutrons by the sample elements. Individual γ-rays can be identified with specific elements, and the intensity of each γ-ray provides a direct measure of the element abundance.

Basic Principles

Neutron Reactions. Neutron activation analysis is a powerful assay technique primarily because neutrons, which have no electric charge can penetrate deeply into most bulk materials, enabling activation of elements throughout the sample volume. In addition, the γ-rays emitted by the neutron-induced radioisotopes are also very penetrative and for most materials suffer little attenuation in escaping from the interiors of samples weighing several grams.

Slow, or thermal, neutron capture is the nuclear reaction most often used in NAA to produce radioisotopes. "Slow" denotes an energy of a few hundredths of an electron volt. The capture of a slow neutron by an isotope of mass A leads (except for fission) to a residual isotope of mass A + 1, which may or may not be radioactive. In either case, immediately after its formation, the A + 1 isotope is in a highly excited state, several million electron volts above the ground state (corresponding to the neutron binding energy). De-excitation to the ground state or to a low-lying isomeric state occurs almost instantaneously by γ-ray emission; therefore, this reaction is referred to as an (n,γ) reaction. The γ-rays emitted are referred to as prompt neutron-capture γ-rays, and in one variation of NAA, they can be used for element assay (see the section "Prompt Gamma Activation Analysis" in this article).

The probability of a slow neutron being captured by an atomic nucleus varies dramatically throughout the periodic table, ranging from a cross section* of a fraction of a millibarn for many light-element isotopes to 61 000 b for ^{155}Gd. Some elements, such as zirconium, are not easily detectable using thermal neutron activation analysis (TNAA), because their neutron-capture cross sections are so low. In addition, several other elements are overlooked in nondestructive TNAA assays because the induced radioactive species have very long half-lives or because no γ-rays (or only very weak γ-rays) are emitted. Detailed information on the approximate amount of activity (decays/second per microgram) induced in each isotope of every element through irradiation for various times using slow and fast reactor neutrons and 14-MeV neutrons is cited in Ref 2. Such activity values must be used only as estimates because of uncertainty in the effective reaction cross section, which depends on the neutron energy spectrum in which the sample is irradiated. Accurate assay measurements necessitate calibrating the detection system using standard target materials of known composition (see the section "Nondestructive TNAA" in this article).

Neutrons with energies above approximately 0.5 eV are referred to as epithermal. At a nuclear reactor, samples can be irradiated with epithermal neutrons by shielding the sample with cadmium or boron. For example, 1 mm of cadmium will absorb most of the incident neutrons of energy less than 0.5 eV. For energies above 0.5 eV, the neutron cross section for most atomic nuclei is far less than for thermal neutrons; how-

---

*Cross-section values are normally expressed in barns, where 1 b = 10^{-24} cm^2. The production rate, R, of a particular isotope is given by $R = N\Phi\sigma_{eff}$, where N is the number of target nuclei; Φ is the neutron flux in n/cm^2 · s, where n is the number of neutrons; and σ$_{eff}$ is the effective reaction cross section in barns.

ever, for many isotopes, the curve of cross section versus energy exhibits large resonance peaks, resulting in much greater relative strength of certain induced activities after epithermal irradiation of a sample than would exist after thermal neutron irradiation (Ref 3).

If a material is irradiated with high-energy (several mega electron volts) neutrons, reactions other than (n,γ) can occur, such as (n,p), (n,α), or (n,2n) reactions, that is, emission of a proton α particle, or two neutrons. A typical example is the ^{27}Al(n,α)^{24}Na reaction, which has a neutron-energy threshold at approximately 5 MeV. In general, use of these reactions for assay measurements has been limited to irradiations with 14-MeV neutrons produced at accelerators through the bombardment of tritium with deuterium (Ref 4, 5). The primary advantage of using 14-MeV neutrons is that the radioisotopes produced are different from those produced by the (n,γ) reaction, enabling detection of several elements normally difficult to observe in TNAA, such as oxygen, silicon, phosphorus, zirconium, and lead. The disadvantage is that several competing reactions may produce the same final radionuclide, making it difficult to determine the concentration of the element of interest.

Neutron Sources

The most common source of low-energy neutrons for TNAA is the research reactor, where thermal and epithermal fluxes exceeding 10^{12} n/cm^2 · s are typically available. Other neutron sources that have been used in NAA are spontaneous fission sources, such as ^{252}Cf (Ref 6, 7), and sources based on the (α,n) reaction, such as ^{238}Pu-Be (Ref 8). The ^{252}Cf and (α,n) sources have the advantage of semiportability, making them useful for certain medical and industrial applications. However, the low fluxes available from these sources limit their value for multielement analysis. An exception is the ^{252}Cf neutron multiplier (Ref 9). This nonportable device is a subcritical assembly containing 1.5 kg (3.3 lb) of ^{235}U, which can produce a thermal neutron flux of approximately 3×10^8 n/cm^2 · s by 100-fold multiplication of the neutrons emitted from a 3-mg source of ^{252}Cf. With this facility, as many as 30 trace elements can be detected in complex materials without performing postirradiation chemical separations.

Nondestructive TNAA

Thermal neutron activation analysis is the most common NAA technique primarily because of the relatively high activation cross sections that many elements have for thermal neutrons. Through the nondestructive ver-

Fig. 1 γ-ray spectrum of a neutron-irradiated ore sample from the Jemez mountains, New Mexico, recorded using a Ge(Li) detector five days after irradiation

The lower figure is an expanded view of Detail A in the upper figure. The necessity of high resolution is evident from the proximity of the peaks at 1115.5 keV (^{65}Zn) and 1120.5 keV (^{46}Sc).

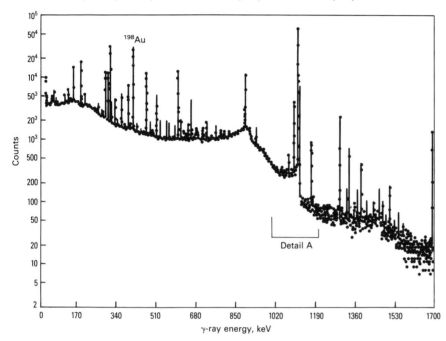

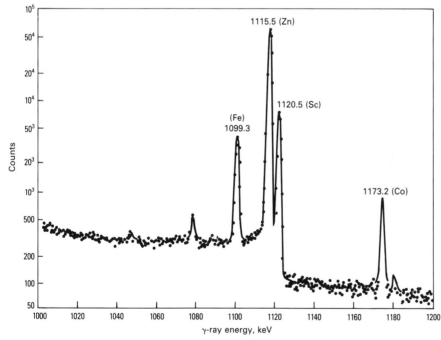

short lived. For example, ^{28}Al, $T_{1/2} = 2.24$ min, where $T_{1/2}$ represents half-life, the length of time required for the number of radioactive nuclei to be reduced through decay by a factor of two.

The full power of nondestructive TNAA can be realized only through use of a high-resolution solid-state γ-ray detector, usually lithium-doped germanium, Ge(Li), or intrinsic germanium, because of the numerous γ-rays typically emitted from neutron-irradiated materials (Fig. 1). However, when the γ-ray spectra are relatively simple, tellurium-doped sodium iodide, NaI(Tl), detectors can be used successfully. These units exhibit higher efficiency, are far less costly, have simpler associated electronics, and need not be operated at liquid-nitrogen temperatures. The NaI(Tl) detectors typically have only approximately 6% resolution at 1000 keV; large Ge(Li) detectors, approximately 0.2% resolution at this energy. Additional information on the various γ-ray detectors is cited in Ref 10.

Optimization of detection for a particular element depends strongly on the half-life of its associated radioisotope as well as complex considerations related to interfering background produced by other radioisotopes that may be present in the irradiated sample. One consideration is that during irradiation the number of atoms, N_r, of a given radioisotope increases almost linearly at first, but eventually saturates after a few half-lives, that is, the rate of decay equals the rate of production. This is confirmed by time-dependent Eq 1 for N_r:

$$N_r(t) = N_t \sigma \Phi \tau [1 - e^{-t/\tau}] \qquad \text{(Eq 1)}$$

where N_t is the number of target nuclei, σ is the activation cross section, Φ is the neutron flux, τ is the mean life ($\tau = 1.44\, T_{1/2}$) of the radioactive nuclei, and t is the length of the irradiation. Equation 1 reveals that after an irradiation time of only two half-lives, N_r has already reached three-quarters of its saturation value. However, more important in NAA is that the decay rate of a radioisotope is inversely proportional to its half-life, which means that at early times after bombardment of a multielement sample, the short-lived activities dominate the γ spectrum. Thus, in nondestructive assays of complex samples, the γ-ray spectrum must be recorded at several decay times to detect the full set of observable elements. In addition, more than one irradiation may be necessary.

For example, to observe fluorine using ^{20}F (11 s), the sample should be irradiated approximately 20 s, and data recording begun within 20 s of the irradiation. Because of the rapid decay of ^{20}F, acquiring data for more

sion of this technique, that is, no post-irradiation chemistry, as many as 40 elements can often be observed in complex materials, such as geologic samples, assuming the neutron flux available is at least 10^{12} n/cm$^2 \cdot$ s. However, when the principal element or elements become radioactive—true for several metals—the nondestructive version of NAA has only limited application unless the main-element radioactivity is

Fig. 2 γ-ray spectra of a neutron-irradiated NBS fly ash sample showing the change that occurs as a function of time

The upper spectrum was recorded in the time interval 18 to 27 min after irradiation; the lower spectrum is a 2-h count recorded after 20 days of decay. None of the peaks in the lower spectrum is visible in the upper spectrum. Peaks denoted by (b) represent background lines.

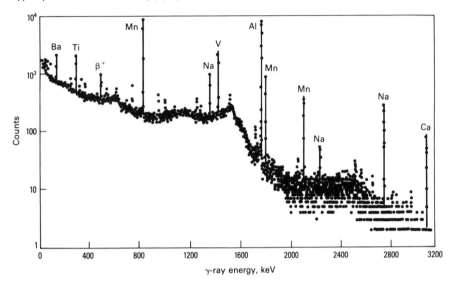

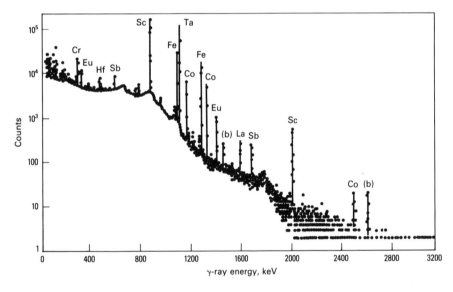

clean container before recording the γ spectrum. However, such a transfer is impractical in many cases, for example, in cyclic measurements. An alternative is to use an irradiation container made of a material that becomes negligibly radioactive upon neutron bombardment and to use a very clean irradiation system that transfers a negligible amount of activity to the exterior surface of the container. An excellent material for the irradiation vial is high-density polyethylene (ethylene-butylene copolymer), which is virtually free of troublesome trace elements.

Another sample-handling technique involves use of double containment, that is, placing the sample in a separate vial inside the irradiation container. After irradiation, the vial is removed from the container for counting. This procedure eliminates all problems associated with radioactivity of the outer container.

Calibration. Except when nuclear isomers complicate the γ-emission rate, the number of counts observed in a particular γ-ray line in a given time can be related to the fractional concentration, Z (parts per million), of the element responsible for the γ-ray using:

$$Z = \frac{IC_{\gamma_i} \times 10^6}{W\epsilon_{\gamma_i} B_{\gamma_i} \Phi \left[1 - e^{-\lambda t_{ir}}\right] \left[1 - e^{-\lambda t_c}\right] e^{-\lambda t_d}}$$

(Eq 2)

where W is the weight of the sample in grams; ϵ_{γ_i} is the probability that γ_i will contribute a count to the full-energy peak at E_{γ_i}; B_{γ_i} is the intensity (per β decay) of γ_i; Φ is the number of neutrons/cm$^2 \cdot$ s during irradiation; C_{γ_i} is the integrated number of counts in the full-energy peak at E_{γ_i}; t_{ir} is the length of irradiation in seconds; t_c is the length of count in seconds; t_d is the time delay between the end of irradiation and the beginning of count in seconds; λ equals $0.693/T_{1/2}$, the decay constant of an isotope; and I is the isotope factor:

$$\frac{\lambda A}{0.6024 f_A \sigma_{eff}}$$

where σ_{eff} is the neutron cross section (barns) for producing radioisotope A + 1 from stable isotope A, A is the atomic weight of a stable isotope, and f_A is the fractional abundance of isotope A in element Z.

In practice, the detection system is usually calibrated using standards containing known weights of the elements to be measured, then σ_{eff} adjusted for each element to obtain the known concentration value. Equation 2 can then be used for any combination of t_{ir}, t_d,

than 30 s yields a diminishing return. Observing iron in the same sample, which is detected using ^{59}Fe ($T_{1/2} = 44.6$ d), necessitates much longer irradiation and counting times. In addition, it is highly advantageous to wait at least two weeks before scanning the γ-ray spectrum to allow the shorter-lived radioisotopes to decay, which reduces the general background upon which the ^{59}Fe γ-ray lines must sit.

Figure 2 shows examples of the changes that can occur in the γ-ray spectrum of a sample as a function of time. Spectral measurements conducted using decay times after

bombardment of 10 s, 20 min, 4 d, and 3 wk permit detection of a large fraction of the elements observable using nondestructive TNAA.

Sample Handling. A primary concern in NAA measurements is avoidance of radioactive contamination. Before irradiation, the sample should not be touched with bare hands; such handling would transfer trace levels of sodium, chlorine, and possibly other elements to the sample. Following irradiation, the optimum procedure in a nondestructive measurement is to transfer the sample from the irradiation container to a

Table 1 Typical nondestructive TNAA detection limits for elements in rock or soil samples 20 min after irradiation

Element	Radioisotope detected, $T_{1/2}$	Principal γ-rays used, keV	Detection limit(a), µg/g
Sodium	^{24}Na (15 h)	1368.6, 2753.85	1000
Magnesium	^{27}Mg (9.5 min)	843.76, 1014.24	2700
Aluminum	^{28}Al (2.24 min)	1779.0	3200
Chlorine	^{38}Cl (37 min)	1642.68, 2167.5	120
Potassium	^{42}K (12.4 h)	1524.66	4500
Calcium	^{49}Ca (8.7 min)	3084.15	1500
Titanium	^{51}Ti (5.8 min)	320.08	750
Vanadium	^{52}V (3.8 min)	1434.05	8.0
Manganese	^{56}Mn (2.6 h)	846.75, 1810.66	60
Copper	^{66}Cu (5.1 min)	1039.0	350
Strontium	^{87}Sr (2.8 h)	388.52	400
Indium	^{116m}In (54.1 min)	416.9, 1097.3	0.2
Iodine	^{128}I (25 min)	442.87	40
Barium	^{139}Ba (83 min)	165.85	200
Dysprosium	^{156}Dy (2.35 h)	94.68, 361.66	0.9

Note: The superscript m, as in ^{116m}In, represents the metastable state.
(a) Based on a nominal 4-g sample, a 20-s irradiation in a 6×10^{12} n/cm^2 · s flux, and an 8-min γ-ray count beginning 20 min after irradiation. Spectral measurements were conducted using a 50 cm^3 Ge(Li) detector.

Table 2 Typical nondestructive TNAA detection limits for elements in rock or soil samples five days after irradiation

Element	Radioisotope detected, $T_{1/2}$	Principal γ-rays used, keV	Detection limit(a), µg/g
Sodium	^{24}Na (15 h)	1368.6, 2753.85	300
Potassium	^{42}K (12.4 h)	1524.66	4500
Gallium	^{72}Ga (14.1 h)	834.07, 629.9	45
Arsenic	^{76}As (26.5 h)	559.09	3.0
Bromine	^{82}Br (35.4 h)	776.5, 619.09, 554.3	4.0
Molybdenum	^{99}Mo (2.76 d)	140.5	50
Antimony	^{122}Sb (2.70 d)	564.09	1.0
Barium	^{131}Ba (11.7 d)	496.2, 373.3, 216.1	800
Lanthanum	^{140}La (40.3 h)	1596.2, 487.01	7.0
Samarium	^{153}Sm (47 h)	103.18	4.0
Ytterbium	^{175}Yb (4.2 d)	396.32	1.0
Lutetium	^{177}Lu (6.7 d)	208.40	0.2
Tungsten	^{187}W (23.8 h)	685.72	5.0
Gold	^{198}Au (2.70 d)	411.79	0.04
Uranium	^{239}Np (2.35 d)(b)	106.13, 228.2, 227.6	10(c)

(a) Based on a nominal 4-g sample, a 4-min irradiation in a 6×10^{12} n/cm^2 · s flux, and a 30-min γ-ray count taken five days after irradiation. Spectral measurements were conducted using a 50 cm^3 Ge(Li) detector. (b) ^{239}Np is the daughter of ^{239}U (23.5 min). (c) Natural uranium can be observed with heightened sensitivity by delayed neutron counting (see the section "Uranium Assay by Delayed Neutron Counting" in this article).

and t_c. A common calibration standard is NBS Fly Ash (Standard Reference Material 1633a), which contains known trace amounts of many elements (Ref 11, 12). Figure 2 shows portions of the γ-ray spectra emitted at two different times by irradiated NBS Fly Ash.

A simple method of calibration that avoids use of Eq 2 involves the same irradiation and counting times for the calibration standards and the samples under assay. The quantity of a given element in the sample is then obtained by multiplying the element mass in the standard by the ratio of the respective areas of the element-associated γ-ray lines observed in the two measurements. A common variant of this approach is to irradiate the sample and a standard simultaneously (in the same irradiation vial, if possible) and to count the two samples later at different times using the same detector and counting geometry. Each of the observed activities is then corrected to activity at the end of bombardment by the decay factor, $e^{-\lambda t_d}$, before the ratio is taken. Whatever calibration method is used, a calibration sample should be used that has approximately the same size and density as the sample to be analyzed. Thus, geometrical correction can be avoided, and possible corrections for γ-ray self-absorption by the sample can be minimized.

Some of the radioisotopes observable in NAA emit many different γ-rays, each of which could in principle be used to determine the concentration of the associated element. However, only one or two of the major γ-ray lines are typically used, selecting those having clean full-energy peaks, that is, minimal overlap with other lines in the spectrum. Tables 1 to 3 list γ-rays typically used in TNAA. When more than one line from a given isotope is used, the deduced values for the element concentration can be combined into a single value by appropriate statistical procedures.

The total number of counts in a given photopeak, C_{γ_i}, can be determined using numerous methods, many of which involve digital computers. Comparisons of various integration techniques are cited in Ref 13 to 15. Most methods display favorable agreement for intensities extracted for intense peaks, but methods applied to weak peaks or overlapping peaks vary considerably.

In studying spectra of complex samples, there may be a few elements for which it is impossible to find an isolated clean γ-ray. Extracting concentrations for these elements necessitates identifying all the lines in the spectrum and apportioning the area of multiplet lines to the various contributing γ-rays using a self-consistent least squares calculation. Several computer codes have been written that accomplish this task (Ref 16).

Detection Limits. The element-detection limits achievable in nondestructive TNAA depend on many factors, several of which have been discussed above, such as half-life, sample size, neutron flux, σ_{eff}, and irradiation and counting times. Table 4 shows calculated order of magnitude detection sensitivities for essentially all the elements observable using TNAA, assuming that only one element in the sample has become radioactive. The footnote to Table 4 explains the timing assumed in arriving at these data. The background under a specific γ-ray peak is a limiting factor in determining if that peak can be considered to have been detected. In Table 4, it has been assumed that any peak with an integrated area of 100 or more counts will be observed. A criterion commonly used in computer analysis of γ-ray spectra to define detectable is that the integrated area must exceed the square root of the integrated number of background counts under the base of the peak by a factor of 2.5 to 3.0.

The calculated detection limits can often be approximated experimentally, especially for elements for which the induced radioactivity is long-lived ($T_{1/2} > 5$ d). However, the γ radioactivity induced in other elements, particularly the major constituents, can increase the detection limits for the trace elements severely, sometimes by several orders of magnitude.

For example, Tables 1 to 3 list typical detection limits for many of the trace elements often observed in rock or soil samples. The table footnotes provide the parameters of the measurements. The detection limits are in general not as favorable as those indicated in Table 1, primarily because the

Table 3 Typical nondestructive TNAA detection limits for elements in rock or soil samples three weeks after irradiation

Element	Radioisotope detected, $T_{1/2}$	Principal γ-rays used, keV	Detection limit(a), μg/g
Scandium	^{46}Sc (83.8 d)	889.26	0.04
Chromium	^{51}Cr (27.7 d)	320.08	2.5
Iron	^{59}Fe (45.1 d)	1099.22, 1291.56	300
Cobalt	^{60}Co (5.20 yr)	1173.21, 1332.46	0.20
Zinc	^{65}Zn (244 d)	1115.52	15
Selenium	^{75}Se (120 d)	279.5, 264.5	5.0
Rubidium	^{86}Rb (18.7 d)	1076.77	20
Silver	^{110m}Ag (250 d)	657.8	5.0
Antimony	^{124}Sb (60.2 d)	602.7, 1691.0	0.50
Cesium	^{134}Cs (2.05 yr)	604.73, 795.84	0.60
Barium	^{131}Ba (11.7 d)	496.2, 373.0, 216.1	300
Cerium	^{141}Ce (32.5 d)	145.44	4.0
Neodymium	^{147}Nd (11.1 d)	531.0	45
Europium	^{152}Eu (13.4 yr)	1408.02, 778.87	0.09
Terbium	^{160}Tb (72 d)	879.36, 966.2	0.15
Ytterbium	^{169}Yb (30.7 d)	197.99, 307.68	0.50
Lutetium	^{177}Lu (6.7 d)	208.40	0.06
Hafnium.............	^{181}Hf (42 d)	482.18	0.35
Tantalum	^{182}Ta (115 d)	1221.38, 1189.02	0.45
Mercury	^{203}Hg (46.6 d)	279.2	0.90
Thorium	^{233}Th (27.4 d)	311.9	0.35

Note: The superscript m, as in ^{110m}Ag, represents the metastable state.
(a) Based on a nominal 4-g sample, a 4-min irradiation in a 6×10^{12} n/cm$^2 \cdot$ s flux, and a 2-h γ-ray count taken three weeks after irradiation. Spectral measurements were conducted using a 50 cm^3 Ge(Li) detector.

Table 4 Single-element interference-free detection limits for TNAA

Sensitivity(a), 10^{-12} g	Elements
1–10	Mn, Rh, In, Eu, Dy
10–100	Ar, V, Co, I, Cs, Yb, Ir, Sm, Ho, Lu, Au
100–1000	F, Na, Mg, Al, Sc, Ti, Ga, Br, Ge, As, Sr, Pd, Ag, Sb, Te, Ba, La, Nd, Er, W, Re
10^3–10^4	Cl, Cr, Ni, Cu, Zn, Se, Ru, Cd, Sn, Ce, Pr, Gd, Tb, Tm, Hf, Pt, Th, U
10^4–10^5	K, Ca, Co, Rb, Y, Mo, Ta, Os, Hg
10^5–10^6	Zr, Nb
10^6–10^7	Si, S, Fe

(a) Assumptions: Sample irradiated 1 h in a neutron flux of 10^{13} n/cm$^3 \cdot$s and γ counted using a 50-cm^3 Ge(Li) detector for 2 h (or one half-life if 15 min $< T_{1/2} < 1$ h). If $T_{1/2} < 15$ min, cycle measurements conducted over a 2-h period, with timing of each cycle being (irradiation time) = (count time) = $T_{1/2}$. Detection is defined as 100 counts recorded in the full-energy peak, with the source placed 2 cm (0.8 in.) from the detector container.

numerous radioisotopes in the irradiated sample provide a background that limits the ability to discern individual peaks. Significant improvement (as much as a factor of ten) in the indicated detection limits for the longer-lived ($T_{1/2} > 1$ d) radioisotopes could be obtained by increasing the irradiation and counting times.

However, the detection limits would be considerably worse except the main constituent of most rock and soil samples is SiO$_2$, which becomes only slightly γ radioactive upon irradiation with thermal neutrons. For example, if equal masses of silicon and manganese were neutron irradiated for a few minutes, the induced activities, ^{31}Si (2.6 h) and ^{56}Mn (2.6 h), would differ in γ-emission rate by a factor of approximately 5.5×10^6 (in favor of ^{56}Mn). Thus, TNAA can easily reveal a few parts per million manganese in SiO$_2$, but would not be able to detect trace levels of silicon in a manganese compound.

Automated Systems. When many similar samples are to be assayed, use of an automated pneumatic system offers considerable savings in time. In addition, a computer-controlled system provides highly accurate timing of the irradiation, delay, and counting times. Such a facility typically proceeds thus: (1) loading of the sample into the pneumatic system, (2) transfer to the reactor, (3) irradiation, (4) transfer to the counter, (5) spectrum measurement, and (6) transfer to a storage location. A new sample is then loaded into the system automatically. Because counting times typically exceed irradiation times, the sample throughput rate can be increased by using more than one

detector, with the first sample diverted to detector No. 1, the second to detector No. 2, and so on. A four-detector system can analyze 200 samples per day for approximately 30 elements (Ref 17).

Some automated systems are designed for cyclic measurement on the same sample. This technique increases the number of counts and thus the statistical accuracy in measurements conducted on short-lived activities, such as ^{207}Pb (0.8 s) and ^{20}F (11 s). One such system is discussed in Ref 18.

Uranium Assay by Delayed-Neutron Counting (DNC)

Delayed-neutron counting is a highly sensitive, nondestructive TNAA method of analyzing for uranium. The basis of the technique is that some of the short-lived radioisotopes formed in thermal-neutron fission of ^{235}U are able to β decay to states lying sufficiently far above ground state such that neutrons are emitted (referred to as delayed neutrons). The principal delayed-neutron emitters have half-lives ranging from a few seconds to approximately 1 min. Because no other naturally occurring element except uranium (which contains 0.72% ^{235}U) gives rise to delayed-neutron emission after bombardment with thermal neutrons, the post-irradiation delayed-neutron emission rate from a sample yields a direct measure of its uranium content. The neutrons can be counted with up to 40% efficiency using counters described in Ref 19. Calibration is accomplished by mea-

surements on reference materials containing known amounts of uranium. Delayed neutrons can also be observed from ^{17}N ($T_{1/2} = 4.2$ s), produced using the ^{17}O(n,p)^{17}N reaction, if the bombarding neutrons are not well thermalized. The energy threshold of this (n,p) reaction is 8.4 MeV.

A typical timing sequence used in DNC is a 10-s thermal neutron irradiation, followed by a 10-s delay, and finally a 30-s neutron counting period. For complex solid materials containing many trace elements, a uranium detection limit of 0.05 μg/g is usually attainable in a single measurement, assuming a sample weight of at least 1 g and a neutron flux of at least 5×10^{12} n/cm$^2 \cdot$ s. Because the neutron counters are slightly γ sensitive, the uranium detection limit may be somewhat higher when the γ radioactivity of the sample is extremely high during counting (Ref 20). In DNC analyses of water and organic materials, sensitivities of 1 ppb are easily achieved (Ref 21).

Radiochemical (Destructive) TNAA

Some element assay problems are not solvable using nondestructive TNAA. Some elements, for example, phosphorus and tellurium, upon irradiation with thermal neutrons, yield radioisotopes that are pure β emitters or emit virtually no γ-rays. Selective observation of such a radioisotope necessitates chemical isolation of the element using as little carrier as possible. The β-ray emission rate of the active isotope can then be measured, preferably using a 4π proportional counter. This counting rate can be converted to element mass using a calibration factor obtained by subjecting a material standard (containing a known weight of the element in question) to the same procedure, which determines the product of σ_{eff}, the chemical yield, and the counting efficiency.

Destructive TNAA is also useful when the fractional amount of an element is so small that the neutron-induced γ-ray activity associated with that element cannot be detected (or is marginally detectable) above the background produced by other activities. This situation is encountered frequently in studies of lunar material, in which many of the elements of interest are present at levels of only a few parts per billion. Another example, involving observation of iridium in terrestrial rocks at the few parts per trillion level, is discussed in Example 2 in the section ''Applications'' in this article. Radiochemical procedures for isolating various elements (or references to such procedures) are provided in Ref 22 to 24.

Epithermal Neutron Activation Analysis (ENAA)

Epithermal neutron irradiation of a sample results in radioisotope activities having different relative strengths than those observed after a thermal neutron bombardment (see the section ''Neutron Reactions'' in this article. The activity ratios often change substantially. For example, an epithermal irradiation conducted by surrounding the sample with cadmium increases the $^{99}Mo/^{24}Na$ activity ratio by a factor of approximately 40 compared with that obtained using thermal neutrons (Ref 3). If boron is used as the thermal neutron shield instead of cadmium, the relative enhancement of the $^{99}Mo/^{24}Na$ ratio is approximately 390 because boron stops more energetic neutrons than cadmium (Ref 25).

Thus, to observe molybdenum in a substance containing significant sodium, use of epithermal neutron to activate the sample would be highly beneficial, although the epithermal neutron flux available may be much lower than the available thermal flux. Lists of advantage factors for ENAA versus TNAA are available for many elements (Ref 3, 22, 26). Epithermal neutron activation analysis is advantageous for at least 20 elements, including nickel, gallium, arsenic, selenium, bromine, rubidium, strontium, zirconium, molybdenum, indium, antimony, cesium, barium, samarium, holmium, tantalum, tungsten, thorium, and uranium (Ref 26). The irradiation and counting techniques used in ENAA are essentially the same as in TNAA.

14-MeV Fast Neutron Activation Analysis (FNAA)

Neutrons of several million electron volt energy can produce various nuclear reactions in the target element, the most likely being (n,p), (n,α), and (n,2n). These reactions lead to different final nuclei than those produced in the (n,γ) reaction, enabling the nondestructive assay of several elements usually overlooked in TNAA, including oxygen, phosphorus, silicon, tellurium, and lead. This is FNAA.

The most common method of producing high-energy neutrons is to bombard tritium with deuterium at an accelerator, which yields approximately 14-MeV neutrons. Because the reaction cross sections at 14 MeV are relatively low (in many cases less than 0.1 b), a high flux of neutrons (at least 10^{10} n/cm$^2 \cdot$ s) is required to produce enough activity for useful trace-element measurements. Table 5 shows an example of the quality of analytical data obtainable using a flux of approximately 2×10^{11} n/cm$^2 \cdot$ s. Irradiations as long as 4 h and counting times as long as five days were used to obtain these data.

A problem encountered in 14-MeV FNAA is that there may be more than one method of producing the radioisotope to use to detect a given element. For example, the best tracer for phosphorus is ^{28}Al (2.24 m), produced by the $^{31}P(n,\alpha)$ reaction. However, ^{28}Al is also produced by the $^{28}Si(n,p)$ reaction as well as by the $^{27}Al(n,\gamma)$ reaction. Therefore, obtaining accurate phosphorus analysis necessitates preparing methods of estimating the contribution to the total ^{28}Al activity of these interfering reactions. Additional information is cited in Ref 4 and 5. The γ-ray detection system, the timing sequence, and the calibration methods used in FNAA are essentially the same as in TNAA and ENAA.

Prompt Gamma Activation Analysis (PGAA)

Neutron-capture prompt gamma ray activation analysis is another nondestructive nuclear technique that can be used for elemental assay. It involves observation of the prompt γ-rays emitted by a substance during thermal neutron bombardment rather than detection of the delayed γ-rays emitted in radioactive decay. Thus, PGAA is essentially an on-line method of analysis and does not involve the 2- to 3-week turnaround time

Table 5 Elemental concentrations in NBS fly ash (Standard Reference Material 1633) determined using 14-MeV FNAA

Element sought	Radioisotope(s) detected(a), $T_{1/2}$	Measured element concentration(a), µg/g unless % indicated	NBS value(b), µg/g unless % indicated
Sodium	^{20}F (11 s), ^{22}Na (2.6 yr)	3330 ± 170	3100 ± 200
Magnesium	^{24}Na (15 h)	(2.1 ± 0.5)%	(1.6 ± 0.25)%
Aluminum	^{27}Mg (9.5 min)	(12.2 ± 0.5)%	(12.6 ± 0.5)%
Silicon	^{28}Al (2.2 min), ^{29}Al (6.5 min)	(22.4 ± 1.6)%	(22.1 ± 1.1)%
Potassium	^{38}Cl (37 min)	(1.8 ± 0.3)%	(1.69 ± 0.09)%
Calcium	^{47}Ca (4.5 d)	(4.40 ± 0.18)%	(4.6 ± 0.3)%
Scandium	^{44m}Sc (58 h)	29 ± 3	26.6 ± 1.7
Titanium	^{46}Sc (84 d), ^{48}Sc (44 h)	7600 ± 200	7300 ± 300
Chromium	^{51}Cr (28 d)	<150	128 ± 8
Iron	^{56}Mn (2.6 h)	(6.40 ± 0.15)%	(6.14 ± 0.24)%
Cobalt	^{59}Fe (44 d)	45 ± 16	40 ± 2
Nickel	^{57}Co (272 d)	106 ± 12	98 ± 6
Zinc	^{69}Zn (57 min)	<300	210 ± 9
Arsenic	^{74}As (18 d)	68 ± 12	61 ± 4
Selenium	^{75}Se (120 d)	35 ± 13	9.6 ± 0.6
Rubidium	^{84}Rb (33 d)	102 ± 5	115 ± 8
Strontium	^{87m}Sr (2.8 h)	1310 ± 60	1380 ± 100
Yttrium	^{88}Y (107 d)	150 ± 15	63 ± 7
Zirconium	^{89}Zr (78 h)	380 ± 20	300 ± 60
Molybdenum	^{99}Mo (66 h)	22.3 ± 1.6	28 ± 6
Antimony	^{120}Sb (16 min), ^{122}Sb (2.7 d)	8.3 ± 1.8	6.8 ± 0.5
Cesium	^{132}Cs (6.5 d)	10 ± 1	8.6 ± 0.7
Barium	^{135}Ba (29 h)	2250 ± 110	2650 ± 150
Cerium	^{139}Ce (138 d), ^{141}Ce (32 d)	136 ± 8	149 ± 7
Tellurium	^{202}Tl (12 d)	18 ± 6	3.4 ± 0.6
Lead	^{203}Pb (52 h)	100 ± 25	72 ± 6

Note: the superscript m as in ^{44m}Sc, ^{87m}Sr, and ^{135m}Ba, represents the metastable state.
(a) Source: Ref 5. (b) Source: Ref 12

Table 6 Concentrations of elements observed in NBS standard coal (Standard Reference Material 1632a) using PGAA

Element	Concentration, µg/g unless % is indicated	Minimum detection limit, µg/g unless % is indicated(a)
Hydrogen	(3.7 ± 0.1)%	12
Boron	52.7 ± 1.8	0.05
Carbon	(71 ± 4)%	1.6%
Nitrogen	(1.27 ± 0.08)%	920
Aluminum	(3.01 ± 0.13)%	450
Silicon	(5.8 ± 0.01)%	610
Sulfur	(1.59 ± 0.02)%	180
Chlorine	784 ± 17	7.2
Potassium	(0.42 ± 0.02)%	69
Calcium	(0.24 ± 0.02)%	490
Titanium	1550 ± 40	27
Manganese	29 ± 5	49
Iron	(1.11 ± 0.06)%	16
Cadmium	0.21 ± 0.03	0.06
Neodymium	11.8 ± 0.4	7.4
Samarium	2.10 ± 0.07	0.03
Gadolinium	1.95 ± 0.03	0.05

(a) Estimate based on a 20-h count of a 1-g sample. Source: Ref 28

Fig. 3 γ-ray spectrum of a neutron-irradiated high-purity nickel sample

The spectrum, recorded in the time interval 3 to 8 min after a 20-s irradiation, shows the presence of titanium, manganese, and vanadium in the sample.

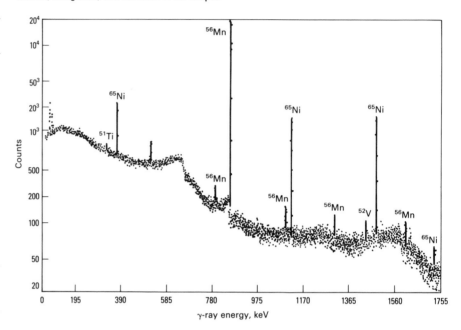

of TNAA and ENAA. The elements most easily detected are those having large thermal (n,γ) cross sections, such as boron or cadmium. The γ-ray energies may range as high as 10 or 11 MeV, necessitating use of a detector having reasonably good efficiency at such energies.

In PGAA at a reactor the counting arrangement can be such that the sample is placed in the reactor thermal column, with the emitted γ-rays being observed through a collimator by a detector located outside the reactor shield (Ref 27), or a neutron beam can be extracted from the reactor and allowed to impinge on the sample, with the emergent prompt γ-rays being observed by a detector located a short distance from the sample (Ref 28). The overall detection efficiency is similar for the two methods, but the external neutron beam configuration has several advantages, including simplified sample changing; no heating of samples, little radiation damage, and slight radioactivity; and assay of samples too fragile, too large, or too dangerous to be placed in the reactor. Table 6 shows PGAA results obtained using an external neutron beam setup at the National Bureau of Standards reactor.

The number of elements that can be observed in PGAA is more limited than in TNAA or ENAA; no more than 20 elements are observable in typical complex materials. However, PGAA can detect eight or nine elements nondestructively, including hydrogen, boron, carbon, nitrogen, silicon, and gadolinium, that are virtually unobservable in TNAA and ENAA, making it a valuable complementary technique. Prompt gamma ray activation analysis is particularly useful

in analyzing many metals, alloys, and catalysts because the interfering radioactivity induced in the major matrix elements is much less than in TNAA (Ref 29-33).

Capture γ-rays induced by neutrons from semiportable neutron generators, such as ^{252}Cf or ^{238}Pu-Be, have proven useful in monitoring element concentrations in various industrial process streams and slurries (Ref 34). Applications to copper mining and copper mill analyses and to on-line coal analysis are discussed in Ref 35 and 36. Californium-252 neutron sources are also frequently used in borehole logging; many of the elements in the material surrounding the borehole are revealed through prompt or delayed γ-rays produced through neutron capture (Ref 37).

Applications

Example 1: Impurities in Nickel Metal. Certain experiments at Los Alamos National Laboratory require knowledge of the trace-element concentrations in high-purity nickel. Because nickel, unlike some of its impurities, becomes only slightly radioactive through neutron irradiation, NAA is an obvious choice for acquiring the assay data. The principal activity induced in nickel by slow neutrons is ^{65}Ni (2.5 h), produced though n-capture by the rare isotope ^{64}Ni (0.9% abundance, thermal neutron cross section, $\sigma_{n,th} = 1.49$ b).

Figure 3 shows the γ-ray spectrum of a typical nickel sample. Although the titanium, manganese, and vanadium impurities are present at only a few parts per million, the associated γ-ray lines are easily observed in the presence of the ^{65}Ni activity. After a few days of decay, other metallic elements were detected in this sample, including cobalt (13 ppm), chromium (51 ppm), antimony (0.1 ppm), and tungsten (2.7 ppm).

Example 2: The Iridium Anomaly at the Cretaceous-Tertiary Boundary. Large iridium abundance anomalies were discovered recently at the Cretaceous-Tertiary boundary in marine sedimentary rocks from several world locations (Ref 38). It was proposed that such anomalies could have been produced by the impact of a large extraterrestrial body, which caused the great extinction of plant and animal life that occurred 65 million years ago at the end of the Cretaceous Period.

Further searches for iridium anomalies at the Cretaceous-Tertiary boundary in favorable areas of the United States have been carried out using radiochemical NAA as the assay technique (Ref 39-41). Figure 4 shows one such anomaly, found at a depth of 256 m (840 ft) in the Raton Basin of New Mexico (Ref 39).

To obtain these data, 3- to 5-g samples of drill core were irradiated 24 h in a thermal neutron flux of 1.4×10^{12} n/cm$^2 \cdot$ s to increase the activity level of ^{192}Ir (74 d). After

Fig. 4 Iridium concentration found as a function of depth in strata

The peak at approximately 256 m (840 ft) corresponds to the Cretaceous-Tertiary boundary.
Source: Ref 39

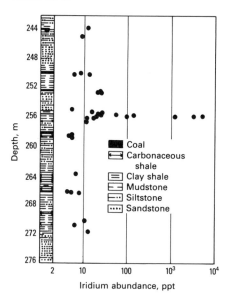

Fig. 5 Comparison of γ-ray spectrums

Upper spectrum shows a neutron-irradiated rock sample that contains 3 ppb iridium (26 days decay). Lower spectrum shows the chemically isolated iridium fraction (pure 74.2-d ^{192}Ir).

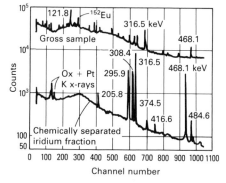

nearly a month of decay, the platinum-group metals, including iridium, were isolated radiochemically, and the γ-ray spectrum of each residual sample was examined using a large Ge(Li) detector. The lower spectrum in Fig. 5 was recorded from the chemically separated fraction of a core sample that contained 3 ppb iridium (near the maximum of the anomaly). All the labeled γ-rays belong to ^{192}Ir. The upper spectrum is that emitted from the gross sample, in which the strong 316.5-keV γ-ray of ^{192}Ir is barely visible. Thus, to detect a few parts per trillion of iridium in such samples, radiochemical separation is essential. The detection limit for iridium using this technique is estimated at approximately 0.5 ppt.

REFERENCES

1. S. Amiel, Ed., *Nondestructive Activation Analysis*, Elsevier, 1981
2. G. Erdtmann, *Neutron Activation Tables*, Weinheim/Verlag Chemie, 1976
3. E. Steinnes, in *Activation Analysis in Geochemistry and Cosmochemistry*, Universitets Forlaget, Oslo, Norway, 1971, p 113-128
4. S.S. Nargolwalla and E.P. Przybylowicz, *Activation Analysis with Neutron Generators*, John Wiley & Sons, 1973
5. R.E. Williams, P.K. Hopke, and R.A. Meyer, *J. Radioanal. Chem.*, Vol 63, 1981, p 187
6. W.C. Reinig and A.G. Evans, in *Modern Trends in Activation Analysis*, Vol 2, NBS 312, National Bureau of Standards, Washington, 1969, p 953-957
7. P.E. Cummins, J. Dutton, C.J. Evans, W.D. Morgan, and A. Sivyer, in *6th Conference on Modern Trends in Activation Analysis (Abstracts)*, University of Toronto Press, 1981, p 242-243
8. D. Vartsky, K.J. Ellis, N.S. Chen, and S.H. Cohn, *Phys. Med. Biol.*, Vol 22, 1977, p 1085
9. J.T. Gerard and J.L. Pietruszewski, *Anal. Chem.*, Vol 50, 1978, p 906
10. Gamma and X-Ray Detection, in General Catalog, 6th ed., Canberra Industries, Inc., Meriden, CT, 1984, p 2-9
11. R.H. Filby, Son Nguyen, C.A. Grimm, G.R. Markowski, V. Ekambaran, T. Tanaka, and L. Grossman, *Anal. Chem.*, Vol 57, 1985, p 551
12. E.S. Gladney, C.E. Burns, D.R. Perrin, I. Roelands, and T.E. Gills, "1982 Compilation of Elemental Concentration Data for NBS Biological, Geological, and Environmental Standard Reference Materials," NBS 260-88, National Bureau of Standards, Washington, 1984
13. J. Hertogen, J. De Donder, and R. Gijbels, *Nucl. Instrum. Meth.*, Vol 115, 1974, p 197
14. P.A. Baedecker, *J. Radioanal. Chem.*, Vol 39, 1977, p 239
15. H. Petri, *J. Radioanal. Chem.*, Vol 39, 1977, p 213
16. R. Gunnink and J.B. Niday, University of California Radiation Laboratory report UCRL-51061, Vol I, Lawrence Livermore Laboratory, Livermore, CA, March 1972
17. M.M. Minor, W.K. Hensley, M.M. Denton, and S.R. Garcia, *J. Radioanal. Chem.*, Vol 70, 1981, p 459
18. M. Wiernik and S. Amiel, *J. Radioanal. Chem.*, Vol 3, 1969, p 393
19. S.J. Balestrini, J.P. Balagna, and H.O. Menlove, *Nucl. Instrum. Meth.*, Vol 136, 1976, p 521
20. E.S. Gladney, D.B. Curtis, D.R. Perrin, J.W. Owens, and W.E. Goode, "Nuclear Techniques for the Chemical Analysis of Environmental Materials," report LA-8192-MS, Los Alamos National Laboratory, Los Alamos, NM, 1980
21. H.M. Ide, W.D. Moss, M.M. Minor, and E.E. Campbell, *Health Phys.*, Vol 37, 1979, p 405
22. F. Girardi, in *Modern Trends in Activation Analysis*, Vol 1, NBS 312, National Bureau of Standards, Washington, 1969, p 577-616
23. A.A. Levinson, Ed., *Proceedings of the Apollo 11 Lunar Science Conference*, Vol 2, *Chemical and Isotopic Analyses*, Pergamon Press, 1970
24. G.J. Lutz, R.J. Boreni, R.S. Maddock, and J. Wing, *Activation Analysis: A Bibliography Through 1971*, NBS 467, National Bureau of Standards, Washington, 1972
25. E.S. Gladney, D.R. Perrin, J.P. Balagna, and C.L. Warner, *Anal. Chem.*, Vol 52, 1980, p 2128
26. J.J. Rowe and E. Steinnes, *J. Radioanal. Chem.*, Vol 37, 1977, p 849
27. E.T. Jurney, H.T. Motz, and S.H. Vegors, *Nucl. Phys.*, Vol A94, 1967, p 351
28. M.P. Failey, D.L. Anderson, W.H. Zoller, G.E. Gordon, and R.M. Lindstrom, *Anal. Chem.*, Vol 51, 1979, p 2209
29. M. Heurtebise and J.A. Lubkowitz, *J. Radioanal. Chem.*, Vol 31, 1976, p 503
30. M. Heurtebise, H. Buenafama, and J.A. Lubkowitz, *Anal. Chem.*, Vol 48, 1976, p 1969
31. H. Zwittlinger, *J. Radioanal. Chem.*, Vol 14, 1973, p 147
32. M.R. Najam, M. Anwar-Ul-Islan, A.F.M. Ishaq, J.A. Mirza, A.M. Khan, and I.H. Qureshi, *J. Radioanal. Chem.*, Vol 27, 1975, p 115
33. M. Heurtebise and J.A. Lubkowitz, *J. Radioanal. Chem.*, Vol 38, 1977, p 115
34. D. Duffey, P.F. Wiggins, and F.E. Senftle, in *Proceedings of the American Nuclear Topical Meeting on Neutron Source Applications*, Vol 4, Savannah River, Aiken, SC, 1971, p 18-29
35. D. Duffey, J.P. Balagna, P.F. Wiggins,

and A.A. El-Kady, *Anal. Chim. Acta*, Vol 79, 1975, p 149

36. H.R. Wilde and W. Herzog, in *6th Conference on Modern Trends in Activation Analysis (Abstracts)*, University of Toronto Press, 1981, p 324

37. R.M. Moxham, F.E. Senftle, and R.G. Boynton, *Econ. Geol.*, Vol 67, 1972, p 579

38. L.W. Alvarez, W. Alvarez, F. Asaro, and H.V. Michel, *Science*, Vol 208, 1980, p 1095

39. C.J. Orth, J.S. Gilmore, J.D. Knight, C.L. Pillmore, R.H. Tschudy, and J.E. Fassett, *Science*, Vol 214, 1981, p 1341

40. J.S. Gilmore, J.D. Knight, C.J. Orth, C.L. Pillmore, and R.H. Tschudy, *Nature*, Vol 307, 1984, p 224

41. C.J. Orth, J.D. Knight, L.R. Quintana, J.S. Gilmore, and A.R. Palmer, *Science*, Vol 223, 1984, p 163

Radioanalysis

George M. Matlack, Los Alamos National Laboratory

General Uses

- Quantitative determination of radioactive isotopes
- Measurement of efficiency in separations for chemical analysis
- Tracer for diffusion measurements or for chemical reactions
- Dating of prehistoric materials
- Measurement of natural radioactive elements in geological materials
- Quantitative measurement of chemical elements by activation analysis

Examples of Applications

- Measurement of the diffusion of nickel into iron
- Measurement of chemical reaction rates under various conditions of temperature and concentration
- Measurement of trace impurity concentrations in nonradioactive materials
- Identification and measurement of radioactive pollutants in environmental materials
- Measurement of the efficiency of chemical separation procedures, such as precipitations, extractions, and distillations
- Determination of radioactive elements in chemical recovery processes for nuclear materials
- Measurement of segregation of uranium isotopes and their daughters in geologic processes

Samples

- *Form*: Solid, liquid, or gas
- *Size*: Limited by minimum and maximum count rates that can be handled by the radioactivity detector, which ordinarily has a range of 100 to 100 000 cpm (counts per minute)
- *Preparation*: None when the radioactive species is the only one in the sample and has penetrating radiation. In other cases, chemical separations are required

Limitations

- Half-life of the radioactive element should be greater than several hours and less than approximately 1 000 000 years
- Accuracy and precision are usually not less than 5%, although in some cases 1 to 2% can be achieved
- Radioactive elements that are pure α-particle or β-particle emitters (no γ-ray emission) generally require chemical separations before measurement

Estimated Analysis Time

- 1 h to several days, depending on whether chemical separations are needed
- Chemical separations may require additional procedures to ensure chemical equivalence of the radioactive isotope tracer with its stable element

Capabilities of Related Techniques

- *Isotope dilution—mass spectrometry*: Accuracy and precision are generally better—less than 1%. Sample preparation is required, and suitable stable or long-lived radioactive isotopes must be available
- *X-ray spectrometry*: Useful for trace analysis of stable elements or of radioactive elements with half-lives greater than 10 000 000 years. May be an alternative for neutron activation analysis

Introduction

Radioanalysis is an analytical chemistry technique that uses the radiation properties of a radioactive isotope of an element for its detection and quantitative determination. It can be applied to the detection and measurement of natural and artificial radioactive isotopes. It differs from other analytical techniques only in its method of detecting the element.

All elements determined by radioanalytical methods are measured by their radioactivity, which consists primarily of charged particles or photons. In the case of natural radioactive elements, the charged particles are α-particles (helium nuclei) or β-particles (electrons), usually accompanied by γ-rays (photons). The radioactivity from artificial radioactive elements useful in radioanalysis includes these three types in addition to positrons, neutrons, and x-rays. The term radiation usually applies to the emission of particles and photons. The radiation that is measured is present in direct proportion to the quantity of the nuclide producing it. The characteristic advantage of radioanalysis is its capability for the quantitative determination of submicrogram amounts of many elements.

Principles of Radioactive Decay. Radioactive isotopes are unstable; that is, they change or decay to isotopes of a different atomic number (Z), which may also be unstable. The change in Z is a decrease by 2 for α-particle decay or an increase by 1 for β-particle decay. The degree of instability is characterized by the decay constant λ, which denotes the fraction of the atoms of the isotope that will decay during a short period of time. Another more useful method of describing the instability is to use the term half-life, $t_{1/2}$, which is related to λ by:

$$t_{1/2} = \frac{\ln 2}{\lambda} = \frac{0.693}{\lambda} \qquad \text{(Eq 1)}$$

The half-life of a radioactive isotope describes the time it takes for one half of the unstable atoms to decay to the atoms of its daughter element such that only one half of the original or parent atoms remains. The half-life is a constant that is unique for a given radioactive isotope, and its measurement can be used to identify the nuclide in the absence of more sophisticated methods.

That the half-life is a constant for a given radioactive isotope leads directly to the simple basis for radioanalysis. The disintegration rate D of a given isotope in a sample is directly proportional to the number of atoms N of that isotope that are present in a sample:

$$D = \frac{dN}{dt} = \lambda N = \frac{0.693N}{t_{1/2}} \qquad \text{(Eq 2)}$$

In practice, it is difficult to measure the disintegration rate, because ordinary circumstances, such as the detector efficiency, may prevent detection of all the disintegration events. The number of observed events or counts is some fraction (< 1) of the number of true disintegration events. Therefore, a count rate is actually measured:

$$R = KD = K\left(\frac{0.693N}{t_{1/2}}\right) \qquad \text{(Eq 3)}$$

where K is the detection coefficient, defined as the ratio of observed count rate to the true disintegration rate of the sample.

The specific activity of a radioactive isotope is the ratio of its disintegration rate to the total number of radioactive atoms, or to their mass, in the sample. It is commonly expressed as disintegrations per second per gram of the isotope. Expressing the specific activity as disintegrations per minute per microgram is sometimes more convenient. The specific activity S in disintegrations per gram per second is calculated using:

$$S = \frac{0.693 \times (6.02 \times 10^{23})}{At_{1/2}} \qquad \text{(Eq 4)}$$

where S is the specific activity, A is the atomic weight of the radioactive nuclide, 6.02×10^{23} is Avogadro's number, and $t_{1/2}$ is the half-life in seconds.

Decay Corrections. The radioactive decay of an isotope causes a continuous decrease in the number of atoms of that isotope. The change N in the number of atoms as a function of time is obtained by integrating Eq 2:

$$N = N^o \exp(-\lambda t) \qquad \text{(Eq 5)}$$

where N is the number of atoms at time t, N^o is the original number of atoms, and t is the elapsed time. If the corresponding disintegration rate is required, both sides of Eq 5 must be multiplied by λ:

$$\lambda N = N^o \lambda \exp(-\lambda t) \qquad \text{(Eq 6)}$$

Parent-Daughter Relationship. The decay of a radioactive isotope results in the formation of another isotope known as the daughter, which may also be radioactive. An example is the decay of ^{241}Pu, whose half-life is 13 years, into ^{241}Am, also radioactive, with a half-life of 435 years. In such cases, it may be necessary to know the number of daughter atoms in an initially pure sample of the parent after a given decay time.

This problem is solved by realizing that the decay rate of the parent equals the formation rate of the daughter. Because the daughter in this case is also decaying, its net growth rate equals the difference between the decay rate of the parent and the decay rate of the daughter. The formation rate of the daughter atoms is:

$$\frac{dN_2}{dt} = \lambda_1 N_1 - \lambda_2 N_2 \qquad \text{(Eq 7)}$$

where N_1 is the number of atoms of the parent isotope, and N_2 is the number of atoms of the daughter isotope. Integrating Eq 7, with the assumption that $N_2 = 0$ at $t = 0$, yields the number of daughter atoms at any time t:

$$N_2 = \left(\frac{\lambda_1}{\lambda_2 - \lambda_1}\right) N_1^o [\exp(-\lambda_1 t)$$
$$- \exp(-\lambda_2 t)] \qquad \text{(Eq 8)}$$

where N_1^o represents the number of parent atoms present at $t = 0$.

Radioactive Decay Modes

Alpha-Particle Emission. Alpha-particle decay of a radioactive isotope is the emission of an α-particle (or helium nucleus) from the nucleus of the decaying atom. The nucleus thus loses 4 atomic weight units and decreases in atomic number by 2. This decay mode is common among the elements with a nuclear charge (Z) exceeding 82 (lead), all of which are radioactive. The naturally occurring thorium and uranium isotopes all decay by α-particle emission, producing daughters that are also radioactive and decay by α-particle emission or β-particle emission. This process continues until the decaying chain reaches an atomic number of 82 and produces a stable isotope of lead. A few of the naturally occurring rare-earth isotopes also exhibit α-particle decay, but their prolonged half-lives preclude practical use in radioanalysis.

The range of energies released in the α-decay of most of these elements is between approximately 4 and 10 MeV. Although this energy release is large and 98% of it is carried by the α-particle, penetration of matter by the α-particle is shallow. In air, this range is approximately 3 to 5 cm (1.2 to 2 in.); in most solid materials, the range is of the order of tens of micrometers.

The α-particle energy spectrum of each α-particle emitter is unique for that isotope. For example, nearly all ^{235}U atoms decay with an α-particle energy of 4.40 MeV, and nearly all ^{238}U atoms decay with an α-particle energy of 4.20 MeV. This property of α-particle emitters is used to distinguish them in mixtures by α-particle energy spectrometry.

Beta-Particle Emission. In the naturally occurring radioactive isotopes, β-particle decay is characterized by the emission of an electron from the nucleus. The atomic number Z is increased by 1, but the mass number A is unchanged.

Beta-particle energies can range from 5 to 10 MeV. Generally, the shorter the half-life of a β-particle emitter, the larger the maximum β-particle energy. Unlike an α-particle emitter, which exhibits discrete α-particle energies, a β-particle emitter produces a continuous energy spectrum up to the maximum energy allowed for that particular isotope. Therefore, in a mixture of β-particle emitters, use of the observed particle energies is difficult as an analytical tool for identifying the various radioactive isotopes present.

Beta-particles are much more penetrating in their passage through matter than α-particles of equivalent energies, because β-particles are much smaller, with a mass that is approximately $\frac{1}{8000}$ that of an α-particle. This makes them easier to detect in situations in which an absorbing material may be present between the radioactive source and a detector. Use of β-particle emitters in radioanalysis may require chemical separations before the radioactivity can be measured, similar to the situation with α-particle emitters, because of absorption of the radiation in the sample matrix.

Positron Emission and Electron Capture. Some artificial radioactive isotopes decay by the emission of a positron, a particle equal in mass to the electron with a positive charge equal in magnitude to the negative charge of the electron. This process can occur when the unstable nucleus contains an excess of protons relative to the proton/neutron ratio in stable isotopes of the same mass region; the available decay energy must exceed 1.022 MeV (twice the rest mass of an electron). This decay mode produces a daughter nucleus whose atomic number Z is 1 less than its parent, but whose mass number A is unchanged.

Orbital electron capture is an alternative decay process to positron emission. In this decay mode, an orbital electron is captured by the unstable nucleus, whose atomic number is thus reduced by 1. The vacancy in the orbital shell must be filled by an outer electron, resulting in the emission of an x-ray.

Gamma-Ray Emission. When a radioactive isotope decays by charged-particle emission, the decay transition often proceeds first to an excited state of the daughter nucleus. The daughter nucleus then emits one or more γ-rays as it decays to its lowest energy level, or ground state. The emission of these γ-rays usually occurs in a fraction of a microsecond, although in a few cases it may be delayed much longer, up to several years. When the delay exceeds the order of 1 s, the daughter nucleus in its excited state is termed a metastable isomer, and its decay to the ground state is termed an isomeric transition.

Gamma-rays from radioactive decay have energies ranging to 5 MeV or more; the very energetic γ-rays are usually seen in isotopes with brief half-lives. A few β-particle emitters, for example, Sr-90, with a half-life of 28 years, emit no γ-rays.

Gamma-rays originate in the nucleus of the atom; x-rays originate in processes that involve the orbital electrons of the atom. X-ray energies can overlap with those of γ-rays up to approximately 120 keV for the naturally occurring heavy elements.

Internal Conversion. An alternative decay process for γ-ray emission is termed internal conversion. It involves the direct transfer of energy from the excited daughter nucleus to an orbital electron. This results in the emission of an x-ray due to the vacancy in the electron shell being filled by an outer orbital electron. The probability for internal conversion increases as the energy of the γ-ray transition decreases.

X-Ray Emission. In addition to internal conversion and orbital electron capture, x-rays are produced by the interaction of emitted charged particles or γ-rays with the atoms in the radioactive source matrix and other nearby materials. The photon spectrum may contain x-rays characteristic of the radioactive isotope and its daughter as well as the mounting materials of the source and detector shielding materials. For example, tantalum and lead x-rays will be observed from an intense α- or β-particle source encapsulated in a tantalum container, and measured with a γ-counter shielded by lead.

Detection and Measurement of Radioactivity

Charged-Particle Detectors. Alpha- and β-particles create tracks of ion pairs when they are absorbed in any material. When produced in an easily ionized gas, an ion-pair track creates an electrical pulse that can be detected when the gas is contained in a chamber fitted with an electrode with a positive direct-current (dc) voltage applied to it. Electrons from the track are accelerated to the charged electrode, creating more ion pairs, so that an amplified burst finally reaches the electrode and creates an easily detectable pulse that can be further amplified and shaped by suitable instruments for a particular purpose. Several types of detection chambers are available, such as Geiger counters, ionization chambers, and proportional chambers.

Proportional chambers are widely used in radioanalysis. They are operated under conditions that produce an electrical pulse proportional to the energy deposited by the charged particle from the radioactive isotope. The counting gas is usually methane or methane mixed with a small amount of carbon dioxide, a mixture known as P-10. The dc voltage applied to the collecting electrode is a function of the size and shape of the wire that forms the electrode and whether the detector is being used for α- or β-particle detection. Voltages can range from 500 to 3000 V. Each chamber and type of use has a characteristic region where a significant voltage change produces very little change in the observed count rate of a radioactive source. This is termed the plateau, which may extend for 200 to 500 V. The plateau is the operating region of the chamber.

The end-window and internal-sample proportional chambers are the two types available. The end-window chamber can be used for α- and β-particles, although its efficiency may be low for α-particles. The radioactive source is placed outside the chamber, and the radiation enters the chamber through a very thin window of aluminum foil, typically 15 μm or less. This allows the entrance of nearly all β-particles and α-particles with energies exceeding 5 MeV. The internal-sample proportional chamber has a provision for placing the radioactive source directly within the chamber. This is the chamber of choice for α-particle emitters because there are no window absorption losses; thus, the chamber has a constant efficiency approximating 50% for detecting the α-particles.

The silicon diode detector, also known as a surface-barrier detector, is much simpler in construction than a proportional gas chamber and is useful for α-particle spectrometry and gross α-counting. It can also be used for β-particle measurements. The sensitive region in this detector is very near the surface of an ultrapure silicon wafer coated with a layer of gold 100 nm thick. When 50 to 100 V dc is placed between the back of the wafer and the gold layer, a region 50 to 200 μm thick is created adjacent to the gold layer. This region is depleted in electrons and electron holes. The depleted region behaves the same way as the methane gas in a proportional chamber. Any charged particle that passes through it leaves a track of electron pairs, creating an electrical pulse at the electrode at the back of the wafer.

For a given energy deposited in the wafer, the electrical pulse is approximately ten times as large as that produced in a proportional chamber. This results in a much higher signal-to-noise ratio, making the silicon diode detector the instrument of choice for high-resolution α-particle energy spectrometry. The detector is simple to use and requires only a small chamber that can be evacuated of air after the radioactive sample is placed in it. The vacuum is required to prevent the α- or β-particle from losing energy before it enters the detector.

Liquid scintillation counting is another widely used technique for counting α- and β-particles. It is perhaps the most convenient method because the detector, data-recording system, and data-processing instrumentation reside in a single unit.

The method is based on the production of photons in the ultraviolet and visible wavelengths when a charged particle passes through a solution of certain organic compounds. The extremely faint flashes of light are detected by photomultiplier tubes that amplify the signal into a recordable electrical pulse. The sample containing the radioactive element, dissolved in an aqueous or organic solvent, is mixed in a glass vial with the scintillator solution, known as a cocktail. The vial is then placed in the liquid scintillation counter.

Such an instrument can detect very low energy β-particles, such as those from T_2 (tritium) or ^{14}C, and is effective for the measurement of low concentrations of β- and α-emitters in samples that would otherwise require tedious chemical separation for counting by the detection methods described above. The technique is not suitable for α-particle energy spectrometry, because energy resolution is poor. The disposition of the contaminated counting solutions can be a problem, because many samples will accumulate a large volume of organic solution that contains toluene. These instruments are relatively expensive, but can handle many samples without constant attendance and probably require the least amount of experience and training in their use.

Photon detectors are used for counting γ-rays and x-rays and are used in many procedures that formerly depended on α-particle or β-particle counting. This is the case because many charged-particle emitters also are γ-ray and x-ray emitters, and these radiations are usually easier to measure than α- or β-particles. The primary disadvantage is a decrease in sensitivity of measurement

because the detector may not be as efficient or because the decay scheme of the nuclide involves very few photons.

Nearly all photon detectors used in radioanalysis depend on the conversion of the photon to an electrical pulse in a specially prepared solid material. The two most common detector materials are sodium iodide and germanium. The sodium iodide detector produces a flash of light when a γ-ray or x-ray is absorbed in it, and the intensity of this flash, which is proportional to the photon energy, is measured by a photomultiplier tube, which transmits the resulting electrical pulse to the recording instruments. The germanium detector, which must be operated at liquid nitrogen temperatures, converts the energy of the photon directly into the electrical pulse.

The germanium detector provides much higher resolution for γ-ray spectrometry than the sodium iodide detector, but is considerably more expensive. However, sodium iodide detectors usually provide a greater detection efficiency. The germanium detector is nevertheless the detector of choice for most applications that require the measurement of γ-rays. Use of these solid-state detectors is discussed more fully in Ref 1.

The detection efficiency of these photon detectors, unlike charged-particle detectors, depends on the energy of the photon and the thickness of the detector. The absorption of a photon in any material is described by the exponential absorption law:

$$\frac{I}{I_o} = \exp\left(-kx\right) \qquad \text{(Eq 9)}$$

where k is a constant characteristic of the absorbing material for the particular energy of the photon, and x is the thickness of the material. In general, large-volume detectors are required for high-efficiency detection of high-energy photons; relatively small volume detectors can be used for low-energy photons. Large-volume detectors are more expensive than small detectors. The material, its thickness, and the energy of the photon determine the detection efficiency of a detector material for γ-rays and x-rays.

Counting and Recording Instruments. The measurement of radioactivity requires a high-voltage power supply for the detector and other components for amplifying and shaping the electrical pulses from the detector and for recording the number of pulses over a certain time period. The necessary components are the detector, the high-voltage power supply, an amplifier, a scaler for recording the pulses, and a timer. For measurements that require alpha, beta, or gamma spectrometry, a multichannel analyzer is also required for sorting the pulses

according to their energies. Together with the detector, this system constitutes a counter, a commonly used term for this collection of instruments. The components are commercially available as separate units or may be obtained as a single system.

Most counting systems have other controls that allow adaptation of the counter to the various situations encountered when working with various radioactive nuclides. The amplifier can be equipped with gain controls that permit adjusting the voltage level of the output pulse to match the desired attributes for the scaler to operate; switches may be available to match the polarity of the incoming detector pulse or to shape the wave form of the output pulse.

Time-constant selections may be available to control the time width of the output pulse; therefore, narrow pulse widths can be selected for high count rates, or wider pulse widths with better stability can be used for radiation spectrometry. The scaler may have discriminator controls for rejecting very weak pulses from the amplifier that may represent unwanted noise pulses and for rejecting pulses that exceed a certain voltage level. Use of such lower- and upper-level discriminators enables creation of a window that accepts only pulses within a defined energy range. Some scalers also permit display of the accumulated count or elapsed time at any time during the counting period. Scalers are also available with a built-in timer and controls for interrupting preset counting periods. Many combinations are available.

Radioactive Decay Spectrometry. Detection of radioactive events using the techniques described above are usually referred to as gross counting procedures, because they measure the detected radioactive events with no discrimination regarding their energies. More sophisticated instruments are available that will measure the number of radioactive events that occur during a time interval and sort them according to the energy from each event deposited in the detector. Such systems are grouped as α-particle energy spectrometers, β-particle energy spectrometers, and γ-ray energy spectrometers. These are used to identify individual radioactive nuclides in samples that contain mixtures of different nuclides.

Sensitivity, Accuracy, and Precision

Detection Limits. In terms of the smallest amount of a radionuclide that can be measured, the detection limit depends on the specific activity of the nuclide, its branching ratio, the efficiency of the detector, and the background (blank determination level) of the measuring system. The last two factors are common to all analytical chemistry methods.

Regarding the specific activity factor, nuclides with high specific activities clearly provide greater sensitivity for detection than those with lower specific activities. The efficiency of the detector, however, must also be considered. If the detector will measure only 10% of the radioactive events, it will decrease the measurement sensitivity by a factor of five compared with a detector having an efficiency of 50%.

The background factor contains two contributions to the sensitivity. The first is the count rate measured in the counting system in the absence of a sample in the detector, and the second is the amount of radioactive material introduced into the sample during its preparation for counting. Detector backgrounds are lowest for α-particle counting, usually being 1 cpm or lower. Beta-particle backgrounds in ordinary detectors range from 20 to 100 cpm, and γ-ray backgrounds are several hundred counts per minute.

Accuracy depends primarily on the use of a reliable calibration standard that can be processed through the entire measurement procedure. Most radioactive standards can be supplied with known specific activities having a relative accuracy of 2 to 5%. In some cases, standards can be obtained with an accuracy of 1%.

The precision of radioactive measurements, relative to the counting procedure alone, is simple to estimate. It is proportional to the square root of the total number of counts observed (minus the background counts), irrespective of the duration of the counting period. A total count of 10 000 will have a standard deviation (σ) of 100 counts or a relative standard deviation (RSD) of 1%; a total count of 100 will have a standard deviation of 10 counts or a RSD of 10%. If significant deviations from the predicted standard deviation are observed, some instrumental defect in the counting system should be suspected.

Chemical Preparations

Radioactive spectrometry techniques have eliminated the need for many chemical procedures that were used to eliminate interferences in the counting measurement of the radioactive nuclide. When required, chemical separations are carried out by standard methods used for stable elements, except for one modification. An additional step is required near the beginning of the chemical separation to ensure that valence equivalence is achieved between the radioactive species and its stable isotopes present in the sample. This is often accomplished by reducing or

oxidizing all isotopes of the species of interest to their lowest or highest valence state. For monovalent elements this may not be necessary, but for multivalent elements it is vital to ensure this equivalence so that chemical separations affect the radioactive species in the same manner as they affect the stable element. If this precaution is not observed, there is a high probability that the radioactive species and the stable element will follow different paths in the chemical separation steps.

Analytical Procedure

Radioactive Material Requirements. A license that permits the use of radioactive materials must be obtained from state and federal agencies. In many institutions, this license is already present for radioactive materials handling; therefore, it becomes a matter of ensuring that the projected experiment can be conducted under the terms of the license.

The selection of the radioactive isotope to be used in the experiment is a matter of deciding which one to choose of the several that are available for the particular chemical element that is the target of the experiment. Several considerations are important in this selection. A high specific activity is desirable because it provides a suitable analytical sensitivity for a minimum mass of the radioactive nuclide. The isotope should decay to a stable nuclide to avoid corrections caused by interference from the radioactivity of the daughter nuclide as it grows into the sample. Isotopes with short half-lives (several days or weeks) make disposal of residues less complicated than with long-lived isotopes.

The type of radiation from the radioactive nuclide affects its ease of measurement. For most radioactive nuclides whose Z is less than 82 (lead), the radioactive mode is β-decay, with or without significant γ-ray emission. If possible, a nuclide should be selected with γ-rays whose energy exceeds 50 keV and where the γ-ray emission rate is greater than 10% of the β-particle emission rate. Gamma-rays are easier to detect without absorption interferences than β-particles, unless the β-particles have maximum energies of 500 keV or more. Furthermore, γ-rays permit the use of spectrometric measurements in mixtures of radioactive nuclides, which may eliminate the need for chemical separations.

For experiments with elements having $Z > 82$, β- and α-particle emitters are usually available. These very heavy nuclides typically emit γ-rays; therefore, two types of radioactive emission can be measured. Alpha-particle counting yields relatively high measurement precision if suitable

Fig. 1 Schematic of apparatus for radioanalysis

All components except the detector obtain their power from a common supply that furnishes ±6 V dc and ±12 V dc.

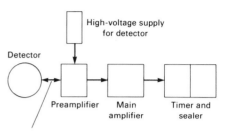

This cable provides both the high voltage to the detector, and the detector signal to the preamplifier

chemical separations are used to prepare the final counting form of the nuclide in a very thin deposit (<10 μg/cm^2). It also provides a high counting efficiency of 50% in an internal sample counting chamber, significantly better than the 35% or less efficiency that can be achieved using β-counting techniques. When the utmost in detection sensitivity is not an important requirement, however, γ-ray measurement will provide greater flexibility if γ-ray spectrometry capabilities are available.

Radiation Protection Needs. It is universally recognized that radioactive substances can present a health hazard, although the environment contains small amounts of naturally occurring radioactive nuclides. It is the responsibility of the experimenter to ensure that the experiment does not present a hazard to the environment and to individuals who may be exposed to the experimental activities. The use of short-lived radioactive nuclides will minimize environmental health hazards.

Laboratory Equipment. Most of the equipment that will be useful can be found in any well-equipped chemistry laboratory. This includes glassware, hot plates, heating lamps, and a selection of micropipettes with capacities from 10 to 1000 μL. The experimental apparatus for radioanalysis is shown schematically in Fig. 1.

Of special use is a setup for mounting and drying the final sample aliquot that is to be counted. The mounting medium should be some material that has a polished surface and is inert to the solution containing the radioactive material. Stainless steel, tantalum, and platinum planchets are commonly recommended. One of the least expensive mounting substrates, however, is a 25-cm (1-in.) square or circular micro cover glass that is 0.13 to 0.25 mm (0.005 to 0.01 in.)

Fig. 2 Thermal control plate

Approximately 0.1 mL of liquid is being evaporated on a glass plate.

thick. This has the advantage of a very high polish and low heat conductivity, which enables a small quantity of liquid to remain in the center of the glass while being heated on a thermal control plate (Fig. 2). The small glass plates are easily manipulated with forceps.

Sample Preparation. The procedures required for preparing a sample counting plate for α- or β-particle counting depend on the nature of the original sample, assuming it is liquid and contains the radioactive element to be measured. The goal is to make a source plate that has between 1000 and 100 000 cpm of the radioactive isotope. Higher count rates can be used if coincident counting losses are not severe. It may be possible to use counting rates as low as 100 cpm if the detector background is sufficiently low.

The concentration of dissolved salts in the sample solution affects what fraction of the sample can be used on the counting plate. Alpha-particles are easily stopped by small amounts of any dried material on the plate; therefore, any inert residue on the plate should be limited to less than 100 $\mu g/cm^2$. These absorption effects can be minimized by planning the quantity of radioactive material to use in the experiment and the types of dilutions that will be practicable.

Absorption effects may become excessive when it is impossible to limit the concentration of dissolved materials in the sample. In such cases, γ-ray counting may be an alternative if the isotope emits γ-rays with energies greater than 50 keV. Such γ-rays are affected minimally by absorbing materials. Gamma-ray detectors into which holes have been drilled are available so that a test tube containing the liquid sample can be inserted and counted without using evaporation techniques. These are known as well counters.

If chemical separations are unavoidable, one that uses a liquid-liquid extraction procedure for its final step should be selected; this may help to isolate the radioactive element in a pure solvent containing only volatile solutes or may permit the counting of a liquid aliquot in a well counter. Ion-exchange procedures may also allow the isolation of the radioactive material in pure form without interfering salts. So-called carrier techniques require exacting laboratory procedures that are frequently time consuming and should be avoided if possible. Use of a γ-ray spectrometer will eliminate many chemical preparations.

Radioactive Measurement Techniques. The final step after the sample preparation is the measurement of the radioactivity in the sample aliquot that was dried or placed in a test tube. The manner in which this is accomplished depends on the type of radioactivity to be measured: α- or β-particles or γ-rays.

Nearly all α-active samples are measured in internal-sample proportional chambers. That is, the sample is placed within the sensitive volume of the detector, which, in the absence of absorbing materials in the prepared sample, will detect almost 51% of the α-particles. Theoretically, 50% are emitted downward into the counting plate, but some of those emitted at a very shallow angle toward the plate will be scattered into the chamber. The sample plate should be placed at the center of the chamber shelf. The counting gas for the chamber should be flushed through the chamber to remove air that was introduced while placing the plate in the chamber; this may take 30 s to 1 min. The gas flow can then be reduced so that only a very slight positive pressure exists within the chamber, which will prevent the admittance of air. The counting period is then started.

Beta-active samples are counted similarly in β-chambers, except in most cases the sample is placed on a shelf that is external to the sensitive volume of the chamber, which is separated from the sample by a gastight thin metal foil. In many β-chambers, several shelves are available at various distances from the metal foil window. This allows the use of a wider variation in sample activities. Each shelf must be calibrated for its detection efficiency. Empty shelves between the sample and the window can be used to hold calibrated metal foil absorbers to eliminate, if necessary, any weaker interfering β-particles from the detector. A thin absorber should be used when α-particle contamination is present; in most cases, it will remove all of the α-particles and only a small fraction of the β-particles. The detector is ordinarily shielded with lead

to reduce the detector background caused by natural radioactivity in the environment.

Solid sample preparations for γ counting are often measured with sodium iodide detectors, in which the physical arrangement is similar to that of β-counters in that the sample is external to the detector and may be placed on one of the series of shelves to control the count rate entering the detector. Again, each shelf used must be calibrated for the detection efficiency for the particular radioactive nuclide to be measured. An absorber may be necessary to prevent the entrance of energetic β-particles into the detector. Although sodium iodide detectors can be used for γ-ray spectrometry, their resolution is inferior to that of solid-state γ-ray detectors.

Silicon diode detectors can be used for α and β counting. They require a small chamber that holds the sample plate and the detector and that can be evacuated to a suitable vacuum. Each setup must be calibrated for the particular radioactive nuclide to be measured. These detectors are particularly useful in α-particle spectrometry.

Background and Coincidence Corrections. Background counts are caused by a source other than the radioactivity of the sample. They are primarily caused by radioactive isotopes present at very low concentrations in the construction materials of the counting system, by the natural environmental radioactivity, and by any radioactivity introduced during preparation of the sample. Background rates can fluctuate and should be measured frequently by operating the counting system in the absence of the prepared sample source. Background counts introduced by sample preparation procedures should be ascertained by processing a blank sample in which the radioactive sample material is absent. These two background corrections must be subtracted from the observed count rate.

Coincidence corrections refer to the fact that the counting system will record two detector pulses as only one pulse if they occur very close together in time. The magnitude of the correction depends on the time resolution of the detector system (of the order of several microseconds) and the count rate of the radioactive sample. This coincidence loss causes the observed count rate to be lower than the true count rate. As a first-order approximation, the coincident count loss is proportional to the square of the count rate; if the coincidence loss is 1% at 100 000 cpm, it will be 4% at 200 000 cpm and 16% at 400 000 cpm. In general, coincidence losses can be held to 1% or less by maintaining count rates under 100 000 cpm.

Applications

Example 1: Diffusion of Plutonium Into Thorium.
There was a need to measure the diffusion rate of plutonium metal into thorium metal as a function of temperature between 20 and 500 °C (70 and 930 °F). The initial part of the experiment was carried out by preparing a number of sets of the two metals, each clamped tightly together so that a highly polished plutonium metal face was in contact with a highly polished thorium metal face. Each set was held at a controlled temperature for a predetermined time.

Sample preparation consisted of separating the thorium block from the plutonium block of each set and carefully removing successive 0.02-mm (0.001-in.) layers from the thorium face. Each thorium layer was then dissolved in 6 M hydrochloric acid (HCl) and adjusted to a concentration of 1 mg/mL in approximately 1 M HCl.

The counting plates were prepared by transferring 100 μL of the thorium solutions to a 2.5-cm (1-in.) square micro cover glass and evaporating it to dryness. The assembly shown in Fig. 2 was used for this step.

The α-activity on each counting plate was measured in an internal-sample proportional α-counting chamber for 10 min. The chamber background count rate was previously determined, using a clean counting plate, to be 1 cpm. The background count rate caused by 100 μg of thorium was determined experimentally to be 0.2 cpm (the expected rate calculated from its half-life of 1.39×10^{10} years, and for a counting efficiency of 50%, was 0.12 cpm). Thus, the only significant background correction was that of the chamber itself.

The correction for absorption of the plutonium α-particles emitted from the plates was estimated as follows. A solution was made that contained 100 mg of thorium in 100 mL of 1 M HCl. To this was added 1 mL of 1 M HCl containing 100 μg of plutonium. By comparing the count rates from 100 μL of the thorium-plutonium solution with the count rates from a 1:100 dilution of the plutonium solution, the absorption correction was determined for the thorium matrix on the sample counting plates. These measurements showed that the count rate on the thorium-plutonium plates was 4% lower than on the plates containing only plutonium.

Plutonium count rates for plates made from a few of the thorium metal layers closest to the plutonium metal block were significantly higher than 100 000 cpm, which would have required a coincidence counting correction. To avoid the experiments needed to measure these corrections, the solutions from these layers were simply

Fig. 3 Results of ion-exchange separation of praseodymium and neodymium

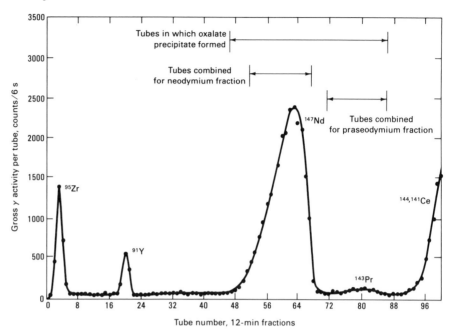

diluted by a factor of 10 or 100 prior to preparation of the counting plates.

This experiment produced the data required to estimate the diffusion rate of plutonium metal into thorium metal at various temperatures. The diffusion rates were calculated from the mole fraction of plutonium in thorium as a function of distance from the plutonium/thorium interface for each of the various temperatures.

Example 2: Separation of Praseodymium and Neodymium.
This example illustrates the usefulness of radioanalytical methods for the evaluation of a procedure that requires a large number of measurements.

A procedure was needed to evaluate the effectiveness of a proposed analytical method to separate praseodymium and neodymium from other rare earths by an ion-exchange technique. The procedure devised used the following radioactive isotopes as tracers: ^{141}Ce, a β-particle emitter with a half-life of 335 days; ^{143}Pr, a β-particle emitter with a half-life of 14 days; and ^{147}Nd, a β-particle emitter with a half-life of 11 days.

The starting solution contained approximately 500 000 cpm of each of the radioactive isotopes and 10 mg of each of the rare earths cerium, praseodymium, and neodymium. The separation procedure was based on the sequential elution of lactic acid complexes of the rare earth elements, which had been absorbed on a cation resin. The exper-

iment was set up on an automatic fraction collector, which allowed the collection of approximately 100 fractions of the 1 M lactic acid eluate into individual 13- × 100-mm (0.5- × 4-in.) test tubes for each experimental run. The elution rate of the lactic acid through the column was adjusted to 0.5 mL/min, and each fraction contained 5 mL.

At the conclusion of each experimental run, 0.5 mL of saturated oxalic acid was added to each test tube. This allowed visual estimation of which tubes contained significant amounts of the three rare earths, based on the quantity of rare-earth oxalate precipitate that formed. The color of the precipitates also aided in the identification of the particular rare earth.

Measurement of the radioactivity in each test tube provided detailed information on the efficiency of the separation procedure. Each of the 100 test tubes was placed in a well-type γ-ray counter and counted for 6 s. When the counts were plotted as a function of tube number, the shapes of the peaks corresponding to the concentrations of the rare earths was clearly apparent. Figure 3 shows a typical plot of this kind. In this particular experiment, ^{95}Zr and ^{91}Y radioactivities were also present; these two isotopes eluted well ahead of the three rare earths. The peak for ^{143}Pr is small, because ^{143}Pr is a pure β-particle emitter, with no γ-ray emission. The small peak observed was caused by x-rays excited in the samples by the β-particles.

The information provided by the plot of the experimental data was used to determine which fractions could be combined for each of the two rare earths without contamination by the other. The combined fractions for the praseodymium and for the neodymium were filtered, dried, and weighed to determine the yield from the original 10 mg in the starting solution. By measuring the β-particle activity of each of the two oxalate precipitates, it was possible to establish a correlation between the precipitate weight and the β activity. Because the ^{147}Nd emits an abundant 92-keV x-ray, its radioactivity could also be determined by γ counting.

REFERENCE

1. Gamma and X-Ray Detection, in *General Catalog*, 6th ed., Canberra Industries, Inc., Meriden, CT, 1984, p 2-9

SELECTED REFERENCES

- G. Friedlander, J.W. Kennedy, E.S. Macias, and J.M. Miller, *Nuclear and Radiochemistry*, John Wiley & Sons, 1981
- D.L. Horrocks, *Applications of Scintillation Counting*, Academic Press, 1974
- Y. Kusaka and W.W. Meinke, *Rapid Radiochemical Separations*, National Academy of Sciences/National Research Council, 1961 (available from the Office of Technical Services, Department of Commerce, Washington, DC)
- C.M. Lederer and V.S. Shirley, Ed., *Table of Isotopes*, 7th ed., John Wiley & Sons, 1978
- W.H. Tait, *Radiation Detection*, Butterworths, 1980

Resonance
Methods

Electron Spin Resonance

Charles P. Poole, Jr. and Horatio A. Farach, Department of Physics and Astronomy, University of South Carolina

General Uses

- Identification of elements of the various transition series in solids and solutions
- Identification of the valence states of transition-element ions
- Detection of color centers and defects in crystalline solids
- Characterization of local crystal environments around transition ions in solids
- Identification of magnetic states of materials, such as ferromagnetic, antiferromagnetic, ferrimagnetic, and spin glass
- Detection of defect centers and radiation damage

Examples of Applications

- Determination of the main and trace-level transition-ion content and of the crystallinity of minerals
- Study of catalyst surfaces and their free-radical reactions
- Characterization of the paramagnetic properties and the kinetic reactions of inorganic and organic free radicals
- Determination of the transition-ion and free-radical content and of the crystallinity and viscosity of fossil fuels

Samples

- *Form:* Crystalline, semicrystalline, or amorphous solids in the form of crystals, powders, or films; also liquid crystals, liquids, and occasionally gases
- *Size:* Crystals—typically $2 \times 1 \times 1$ mm ($0.08 \times 0.04 \times 0.04$ in.) to 0.1% of this volume. Powders—typically 1 mg to 1 g. Solutions—1 mL, aqueous samples with high dielectric losses require use of a special flat sample cell
- *Preparation:* Generally none; large crystals must be cut to size; some solutions require deoxygenation; some samples require cryogenic temperatures

Limitations

- Sample must be paramagnetic; that is, it must contain transition ions, free radicals, defect centers, and so on
- Paramagnetic centers must be sufficiently high in concentration; typical amounts are 0.1 nmole

Estimated Analysis Time

- 10 min to several hours per sample, depending on circumstances

Capabilities of Related Techniques

- *Nuclear magnetic resonance:* Identifies molecular structure, mainly of organic molecules in solution; less sensitive than electron spin resonance by two or three orders of magnitude
- *Mössbauer resonance:* Similar information gained, but less versatile than electron spin resonance because in most applications iron or perhaps tin must be present
- *Quadrupole resonance:* Related to nuclear magnetic resonance, but much less versatile; rarely used routinely
- *Microwave spectroscopy:* Identification of relatively small molecules in the gas phase

Introduction

Electron spin resonance (ESR), also known as electron paramagnetic resonance (EPR) and paramagnetic resonance, is an instrumental technique that can provide a great deal of information on any material containing unpaired electrons. Such materials are ordinarily paramagnetic, although they can sometimes be ordered magnetic solids, such as ferromagnets. If placed in a microwave-resonant cavity between the pole pieces of a strong electromagnet, such a sample absorbs microwave energy at particular values of the magnetic field that are characteristic of the positions and the crystalline environments of the unpaired electrons. Plotting the microwave absorption intensity against the magnetic-field strength yields a line spectrum. The number, positions, intensities, and shapes of the component lines provide information used to identify and specify such components and properties of the sample as the degree of crystallinity, valence states of ions, local crystalline environments, defects and trace transition ions, radiation products, and free radicals.

Principles of Magnetic Resonance

The field of ESR was founded almost 40 years ago and has since become a standard instrumental technique of the physical sciences. An extensive literature has accumulated on the various aspects of this instrumentation. Application of ESR to problems in solids is broad and diverse. It is effective in cases involving unpaired electrons, such as free radicals, odd electron molecules, triplet states, transition-metal ions, color centers, and irradiated materials. Modern ESR techniques can detect the presence of unpaired electrons down to low levels and characterize them precisely regarding their location and energy states.

Electron spin resonance is based on the principle that an electron is a charged particle that spins constantly about its axis with a certain angular momentum. Associated with the intrinsic spin is a magnetic moment whose value is termed the Bohr magneton (β). If an external magnetic field is impressed on the system, the electron aligns itself with the direction of this field and precesses about this axis. This behavior is analogous to that of a spinning top in the gravitational field of the earth. Increasing the applied magnetic field accelerates precession of the electron. In practice, the magnetic field splits the electrons into two groups. In one group, the magnetic moments of the electrons are aligned with the magnetic field; in the other, the magnetic moments are aligned opposite or antiparallel to this external field.

In terms of quantum mechanics, the spin quantum number S of an electron equals $\pm \frac{1}{2}$. Quantum conditions dictate that resolved components of quantum numbers along an axis of quantization must differ by one. The two possible orientations of these electrons in the applied field correspond to the projections $M_s = \pm \frac{1}{2}$ along the magnetic-field direction. Each orientation is associated with a different energy; the one with the spins antiparallel to the external field ($M_s = -\frac{1}{2}$) is in the lower energy state. These two levels, at which the quantum number M_s is $+\frac{1}{2}$ or $-\frac{1}{2}$, are often referred to as the $+\frac{1}{2}$ and the $-\frac{1}{2}$ states.

For example, if a second weaker alternating magnetic field is now applied at right angles to the main field using a high-frequency microwave-resonant cavity, an electron can be "tipped over" when the precession frequency equals the incident microwave frequency. Electron spin resonance

can also be described in terms of quantum mechanics by noting that the quanta of the incident microwaves may induce transitions between the two states of the unpaired electron. When the energy $h\nu$ of these quanta coincides with the energy-level separation $E_{1/2} - E_{-1/2}$ between the two states, resonance absorption takes place.

In practice, the applied radio frequency (RF) is maintained at a certain value, and the magnetic-field strength is varied to locate the values at which resonance occurs. The incoming radiation quanta $h\nu$ absorbed by the electrons in the lower energy level induces these electrons to jump into the higher energy state. However, the incoming radiation is also absorbed by the electrons in the higher energy level. The absorbed energy results in stimulated emissions by these electrons. Because the coefficients of absorption and stimulated emission are equal, no net value would be observed if the spin population were distributed equally between these two levels. In general, n_1, the population of the ground state, exceeds n_2, the population of the excited state, and a net absorption of microwave radiation takes place. This signal is proportional to the population difference $n_1 - n_2$.

The population ratio of these two states can in most cases be described using:

$$\frac{n_1}{n_2} = e^{-h\nu/kT} \qquad \text{(Eq 1)}$$

where h is Planck's constant, ν is frequency, k is the Boltzmann constant, and T is temperature. Therefore, use of a high applied frequency improves the sensitivity of this technique. In practice, the frequencies in the well-developed radar wavebands, such as 10 GHz (or a wavelength of 3 cm, or 1.2 in.), are the most common in ESR. Low operating temperatures also benefit signal enhancement.

The resonance condition can be described in another way. In a typical ESR experiment, the sample is placed in a high quality factor (Q) resonant cavity at the microwave frequency ω_0, and the magnetic field is varied until resonance occurs at the value H_0 given by:

$$\omega_0 = \gamma H_0 = \frac{g\beta}{\hbar} H_0 \qquad \text{(Eq 2)}$$

where γ is the gyromagnetic ratio, a distinct and fixed ratio of the magnetic moment of the electron to its angular momentum; g is the g-factor, a dimensionless constant and a physical property of the electron; $\hbar$ is Planck's constant h divided by 2π; and β is

the unit magnetic moment of the spinning electron (the Bohr magneton):

$$\beta = \frac{e\hbar}{2mc} = 0.92731$$

$$\times 10^{-20} \text{ erg/G} \qquad \text{(Eq 3)}$$

where e is the charge of the electron, m is the mass of the electron, and c is the velocity of light. The first part of Eq 2, $\omega_0 = \gamma H_0$, is ordinarily used in nuclear magnetic resonance (NMR), in which gyromagnetic ratios are tabulated. In ESR, it is customary to measure the g-factor. In liquids and solids, the orbital motion is usually "quenched," and only the spin motion is observed; therefore, most values of g are fairly close to $g = 2.0023$, which characterizes a free electron. The conversion $\gamma = g\beta/\hbar$ is facile.

In most substances, chemical bonding results in the pairing of electrons because they are transferred from one atom to another to form an ionic bond or shared between different atoms to form covalent bonds. The spins and magnetic moments of paired electrons point in opposing directions, and there is no external spin paramagnetism. However, in a paramagnetic substance in which unpaired electrons are present, the resonance occurs at definite values of the applied magnetic field and incident microwave radiation.

Although the resonance spectrum of an unpaired electron may appear always to be the same, the magnetic behavior of the electron is ordinarily modified by the magnetic and electric fields in its surroundings. This deviation from the standard behavior provides information on the structure of the substances under examination.

In conducting an ESR measurement, the sample is placed in a microwave-resonant cavity between the pole pieces of an electromagnet. The microwave source frequency is adjusted to the cavity resonant value. The magnetic field is then varied through the resonant values, and the amount of microwave energy the sample absorbs is plotted on a recorder. The resulting spectrum is analyzed to determine the mechanisms associated with the interaction of the unpaired electron with the external magnetic field and its environment.

Instrumentation

For ESR measurements, the spectrometer is generally operated at a constant frequency, but the magnetic field is varied through the region of interest. The magnetic-field sweep should be linear and calibrated to provide a satisfactory spectrum. A sensitive detection system, with its preamplifier and lock-in

Fig. 1 Typical ESR spectrometer

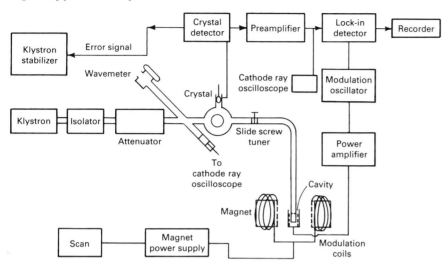

detector, is used to eliminate noise and to obtain high-quality spectra.

A typical ESR spectrometer (Fig. 1) consists of a microwave bridge housing a klystron that generates microwaves; a waveguide (attached to the bridge) at the end of which is a waveguide cavity suspended between the magnet polepieces; a large electromagnet and its power supply; and electronic circuitry that detects and amplifies the microwave signal, eliminates noise, and displays the results on a chart recorder.

The microwave power is generated in a klystron suspended in an oil (or water) bath for greater stability and provided with automatic frequency control (AFC). The isolator impedance matches the klystron to the waveguide system. The frequency meter (wavemeter) measures the microwave frequency. A directional coupler side arm monitors klystron output. The circulator impresses the incident microwave power on the microwave-resonant cavity and directs the reflected signal to the crystal detector. The detector demodulates the microwaves by extracting the information in the sidebands.

After detection, the signal is split: one portion conveys the error signal to the AFC, and the other goes to the preamplifier. The latter signal carries the information on the microwave absorption line. It traverses a lock-in detector that eliminates noise, then is plotted on a recorder. An oscilloscope can be used as an alternative mode of presentation for rapid checks on a sample and for tuning.

Microwave Frequency. For routine studies, use of an X-band frequency (8.5 to 10 GHz) is convenient. If more information is desired, additional measurements can be conducted at other frequencies, such as Q-

band (approximately 35 GHz) or S-band (2 to 4 GHz).

The frequency is changed primarily to sort out the frequency-dependent and the frequency-independent terms in the Hamiltonian. Hyperfine component spacings are independent of frequency, and anisotropic g-factors produce separations that vary linearly with frequency.

Another reason for changing the microwave frequency is to ascertain the principal line-broadening mechanisms. If the linewidth is due to dipole-dipole broadening, exchange narrowing, or unresolved hyperfine structure, this parameter will not change with frequency; if it is due to unresolved g-factor anisotropy, it will increase with increasing frequency. Therefore, it is easier to interpret an ESR spectrum that has been measured at two or more microwave frequencies than at one.

The magnet contains a field-dial Hall-effect device that provides a sweep that is linear in magnetic-field strength. This device removes the nonlinearities associated with magnet saturation. The sweep permits variation of the magnetic field over a desired range—for example, 5000 G, 1000 G, 100 G, 5 G—with a preselected center field, such as 3400 G. Thus, broad and narrow lines can be recorded conveniently.

The magnetic field can be modulated at a low frequency (20 or 400 Hz) or at a medium frequency (100 kHz). Use of field modulation permits detection and amplification at the modulation frequency, providing greater sensitivity than a direct current (dc) detection technique. The modulation coils are usually mounted on the sides of the microwave-resonant cavity.

Modulation. A modulation frequency, f_m, that is much less than the linewidth ΔH_{pp} expressed in frequency units Δf_{pp} should be used:

$$f_m \ll \Delta f_{pp} = \frac{\gamma}{2\pi} \Delta H_{pp} = \frac{g\beta}{h} \Delta H_{pp} \text{ (Eq 4)}$$

A modulation frequency of 100 kHz may be used for linewidths as narrow as 0.01 G, but will appreciably distort lines less than this width.

As the modulation amplitude H_m is gradually increased, the observed linewidth remains unchanged as long as H_m is much less than the linewidth ΔH_{pp}. When H_m nears ΔH_{pp}, the observed line begins to broaden and distort. When $H_m \ll \Delta H_{pp}$, the amplitude of the ESR signal increases linearly with the modulation amplitude; after H_m exceeds ΔH_{pp}, the amplitude begins to decrease with increasing H_m. The ESR signal reaches a maximum near the highest sensitivity point $H_m \sim 3\Delta H_{pp}$. To determine ESR spin concentrations and lineshapes, it is best to have $H_m \ll \Delta H_{pp}$, and a practical criterion is to keep $H_m \leq \Delta H_{pp}/5$. Detecting weak signals requires setting $H_m \sim 3\Delta H_{pp}$ for maximum sensitivity.

Scan. An ESR spectrum can be spread over several thousand gauss or confined to a fraction of a gauss, and searching for unknown resonances necessitates estimating the linewidth and setting the scan accordingly. Conducting several scans covering different ranges of gauss and perhaps centered at different field values is sometimes advantageous. If a narrow scan is used to record a broad line, the resonance will manifest itself as a sloping baseline, and if a broad scan is used to record narrow resonance, absorption will be unusually weak and distorted. Use of too broad a scan with a weak sharp resonance may render it undetectable.

Once the overall appearance of a complex resonance is known, use of specially selected narrow scans may be necessary to resolve particular features. Even when a narrow resonance is recorded properly, a broad scan, for example, over a range of 1000 G, is useful to ensure that an additional broad background resonance has not been overlooked.

Increasing the response time decreases the amplitude of the noise on the recorder. However, if the time constant τ is too long, the observed lineshape will be distorted. In general, the strongest undistorted line is obtained when the peak-to-peak scanning time is ten times τ, but the optimum signal-to-noise ratio occurs when the peak-to-peak scanning time equals τ. The former should be used routinely for most applications; the latter may be resorted to for signals near the limit of detectability, at which a distorted lineshape is acceptable. Computer-averaging procedures can be used for signal-to-noise enhancement if sensitivity is a problem. Examination of a complex spectrum containing broad and narrow absorption lines may benefit from use of several scans with different time constants to resolve all the component resonances properly.

Sample Cavity. The cylindrical TE_{011} and the rectangular TE_{102} cavities are the two primary types in current use. Both are transverse electric (TE) modes; therefore, the electric-field lines are confined to the plane perpendicular to the longitudinal axis. No such restriction exists for the magnetic-field lines. For a general cylindrical TE_{mnp} mode, the subscripts m, n, and p indicate the number of half-cycle variations along the angular, radial, and longitudinal directions, respectively; in the rectangular case they represent the number of half-cycle variations along the x, y, and z (Cartesian) axes. The cylindrical TE_{012} mode, which has axial symmetry, and the rectangular TE_{102} mode are shown in Fig. 2, which illustrates the orientations of the electric and magnetic fields. The common cylindrical TE_{011} cavity is half as long as its TE_{012} counterpart.

Locating the sample at a point of maximum RF magnetic-field strength is best. For sample tubes, the optimum position in the cylindrical TE_{011} cavity is along the axis centered in the middle; for the rectangular case, it is in the position shown in Fig. 2c. Because the best position is also at a minimum of the RF electric field, dielectric losses are minimized. These losses become appreciable if the sample tube diameter is too large. Excessive losses are evident as a lowering of the cavity Q and a decrease in sensitivity.

Most ESR investigations use a standard 3-mm (0.12-in.) inner diameter, 4-mm (0.16-in.) outer diameter pure quartz sample tube. High-purity quartz is necessary because glass usually contains traces of interfering Fe^{3+}. For maximum sensitivity, this tube can be filled to a height of 2.5 cm (1 in.) for a rectangular cavity and 5 cm (2 in.) for a cylindrical cavity. This is convenient for investigation of a powder or a low dielectric loss solution.

Liquids with high dielectric losses, such as water and strong acids, would load down a microwave-resonant cavity excessively by reducing the quality factor Q if they were placed in a standard 4-mm OD quartz tube, because the sample extends too far into the region of appreciable microwave electric-field strength. A thin quartz cell (flat cell) is used to obviate this difficulty by reducing

Fig. 2 Microwave-resonant cavity modes

(a) Cylindrical TE_{012} cavity. (b) Rectangular TE_{102} cavity. (c) Position of sample in rectangular TE_{102} cavity. RF magnetic field lines (dashed) and electric field orientation (dots and Xs) are shown. The dots denote vectors directed up from within the cavity; Xs denote vectors aimed down into the cavity.

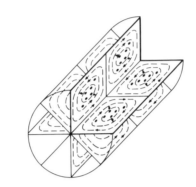

(a)

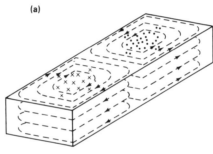

(b)

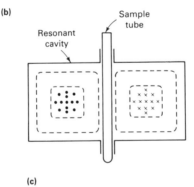

(c)

considerably the amount of sample in the region of appreciable electric-field strength. Instead, it spreads the sample in the transverse plane of a rectangular TE_{102} cavity at which the microwave magnetic-field strength remains a maximum. Consequently, a high sensitivity can be obtained with highly polar (lossy) samples.

A liquid mixing cell in which two liquids flow together, then enter the microwave-resonant cavity is available. This permits examination of chemical reactions as they occur in a cavity. To study photolytic and

Fig. 3 Power reflected from a microwave-resonant cavity as a function of frequency

The resonant frequency is ω_0 the full width at half amplitude is $\Delta\omega$.

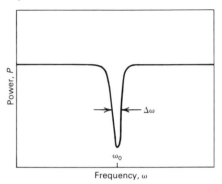

photochemical systems, a cavity end plate is provided with slots to admit light.

Single crystals measuring $1 \times 1 \times 2$ mm ($0.04 \times 0.04 \times 0.08$ in.) are convenient for ESR studies; larger crystals can be used if they do not have high dielectric losses. Anisotropic effects can be investigated by mounting the crystal on a goniometer and rotating it within the cavity or by rotating the magnet about the cavity. Conducting a rotation about three mutually perpendicular crystal planes is usually desirable to enable calculation of the Hamiltonian parameters.

To compare measurements performed with different cavities, the quality factor Q is used:

$$Q = \frac{2\pi \text{ (stored energy)}}{\text{Energy dissipated per cycle}} = \frac{\omega_0}{\Delta\omega}$$

(Eq 5)

where the width $\Delta\omega$ is defined in Fig. 3. Equation 5 allows Q to be estimated from the width of the cavity dip. Typical values are 4000 for the rectangular and 12 000 for the cylindrical cavities discussed above. In addition, the filling factor, η, a measure of the efficiency with which the RF magnetic field is concentrated in the sample, should be considered. The filling factor depends strongly on the sample position because RF field varies throughout the cavity. The positions described above correspond to maximum filling factors.

Detection. The last electronic system to be discussed is the crystal detector/preamplifier/lock-in detector combination. Electron spin resonance entails absorption of microwave energy in a magnetic field adjusted to satisfy Eq 2. Any absorption occurring in the sample will be detected as a change in the output of the crystal detector and can be displayed on an oscilloscope. In practice, a more sophisticated approach is used to measure this signal quantitatively.

Because the magnetic field is modulated at the frequency ω_{mod}, absorption of microwave energy also occurs at this frequency. The crystal detector demodulates the microwaves by extracting the ESR signal oscillating at the frequency ω_{mod} and directs it to the preamplifier, which amplifies it without introducing much additional noise.

The signal then enters the lock-in detector, sometimes referred to as a coherent detector or a phase-sensitive detector. The ESR signal is compared with a reference signal at the frequency ω_{mod} derived from the same oscillator driving the modulation coils. Only that small portion of the noise at the same frequency and in phase with the reference signal is allowed to traverse the lock-in detector; most other noise is eliminated. This enhances sensitivity considerably. In addition, a long-time constant filter averages the noise at frequencies greater than the reciprocal of its time constant, τ_0. This detection procedure converts the ESR signal that entered at the modulation frequency to a dc signal for display on the recorder.

A more sophisticated method of noise elimination entails use of a computer for the electronic addition of many repeatedly scanned superimposed spectra. This removes low- and high-frequency noise efficiently. In comparison, the long-time constant filter does not remove low-frequency noise. Signal enhancement, although expensive, is helpful with weak signals.

Variable Temperatures. Because many chemical and physical phenomena of interest occur only in a definite temperature range, temperature control of the sample is advisable in any spectrometer system. In addition, the population distribution of the different spin states is a function of temperature (Eq 1). Low-temperature operation may be necessary in many systems to increase sensitivity to detectable levels. In general, the g-factor, hyperfine interaction constants, and other terms in the Hamiltonian are independent of temperature. The lineshape, linewidth, and relaxation times T_1 and T_2 are the principal quantities that are sensitive to temperature.

The standard method for obtaining variable temperatures from 100 to 500 K is to pass a controlled stream of cooled or heated nitrogen gas past the sample. A thermocouple is placed in the nitrogen stream before it impinges on the sample container to monitor the temperature. For subambient operation, an overpressure of dry nitrogen is maintained within the microwave-resonant cavity

to prevent moisture condensation. The output of the thermocouple can also be connected to an automatic temperature controller that regulates the temperature of the gas blowing past the sample. Another method for obtaining high temperatures consists of placing the microwave-resonant cavity in an oven.

Cryogenic temperatures near 4 K are generally obtained by immersing the microwave-resonant cavity in a liquid-helium bath. This requires use of a double dewar with liquid nitrogen in the outer chamber and liquid helium in the inner chamber. If stainless steel dewars are used, a radiation shield maintaining contact with the liquid-nitrogen bath can substitute for the outer chamber. Variable-temperature investigations from 4 to 100 K can be conducted by inserting a small heater between the cavity and the liquid helium. An alternative uses the Joule-Thompson effect to cool helium gas near the microwave-resonant cavity and sample.

Many relaxation-time experiments have been performed in this low-temperature region. Low-temperature operation is also important because sensitivity of the ESR signal increases with decreasing temperature. Some spin systems, such as Co^{2+}, are often difficult to observe at higher temperatures.

Most investigations at cryogenic temperatures require the use of a low-power microwave bridge because the relaxation times are so long that saturation occurs in the milliwatt range. Microwatt power levels are produced by stabilizing the klystron off a reference cavity instead of the sample cavity. Superheterodyne detection is often used in this temperature range.

Most of the terms in the Hamiltonian are independent of temperature, but the linewidth and relaxation times are often strongly dependent. For a rigid lattice, the dipole-dipole broadening, exchange interaction, and g-factor anisotropy mechanisms do not change appreciably with temperature. If any of the electron spins or nuclei responsible for line-broadening undergo changes in their translational, rotational, or vibrational motion, such changes will produce strongly temperature-dependent linewidths and relaxation times.

In general, rapid motion can average the other line-broadening mechanisms and narrow an ESR resonance-absorption line. Consequently, solids usually have much broader lines than fluids, and highly viscous liquids and glasses are intermediate between these two. Variable-temperature investigations can sometimes sort out the range at which certain groups, such as methyl, stop rotating. Variable-temperature studies supply detailed information on crystallographic phase transitions and such magnetic phenomena as the

onset of paramagnetism, ferromagnetism, and antiferromagnetism.

Low-temperature relaxation-time measurements often reveal a strong dependence of the spin lattice relaxation time T_1 on the temperature, that is, $T_1 \propto 1/T$ or $T_1 \propto T^{-7}$. Such information enables the principal relaxation process—for example, the direct process or the Raman scattering process—to be deduced. Some spin systems are detectable only at very low temperatures. The intensity of an ordinary ESR spectrum depends inversely on the temperature when $g\beta H \ll kT$ and otherwise exponentially on $1/T$ in accordance with Eq 1. At X-band frequencies, $h\nu \cong kT$ when $T \sim 0.5$ K.

Supplementary Experimental Techniques

Relaxation. The population distribution between the spin states is a strong function of the energy density of the incident radiation. The rate at which transitions are induced increases with radiation intensity. The signal from a typical paramagnetic spin system will at first increase in amplitude, reach a maximum, then decrease at greater power levels. The latter phenomenon is termed saturation. The onset of saturation is accompanied by a gradual broadening and distortion of the resonance line.

Switching off the incident microwave power allows the spin system to return to equilibrium. This is relaxation, a process by which the spin populations return to their thermal equilibrium values, satisfying Eq 1. Its rapidity is influenced strongly by the environment of the electron. Accordingly, relaxation data can provide information on the environment. This decay occurs with a time constant, T_1, referred to as the spin lattice relaxation time because the spin system equilibrates with its lattice or environment.

Another process that systems of electron spins undergo is spin-spin relaxation, commonly denoted by the characteristic time constant T_2. The individual spins lose phase coherence with each other as they precess around the magnetic-field direction. The resulting variation of the local magnetic field at each spin site broadens the ESR line.

The saturation method and the pulse method are the two general means of measuring relaxation times. The former is convenient for use with all commercial spectrometers; the latter requires specialized instrumentation. The saturation method, although suitable for some spin systems, provides information that is not as detailed or complete as that obtained using the more sophisticated pulse methods.

Saturation Method of Measuring Relaxation Times. The magnitude of saturation is measured by the saturation factor s:

$$s = \frac{1}{1 + \gamma^2 H_1^2 T_1 T_2} \qquad \text{(Eq 6)}$$

where the RF field equals $H_1 \cos \omega_0 t$. Above saturation, s becomes small; at low power levels, s is close to unity because $H_1^2 \gamma^2 T_1 T_2 \ll 1$. The relaxation times T_1 and T_2 can be evaluated by plotting $1/s$ versus H_1^2 using measurements of the linewidth or the amplitude as a function of power, where the power, P, is proportional to H_1^2. The slope of the straight line in each case is $\gamma^2 T_1 T_2$, and $1/s = 1$ when $H_1 = 0$. Thus, this plot determines the product $T_1 \cdot T_2$. To separate these two factors, the spin-spin relaxation time, T_2, is assumed to be proportional to the linewidth below saturation:

$$T_2 = \frac{2}{\gamma \Delta H_{pp}^0 \sqrt{3}} = \frac{1.3131 \times 10^{-7}}{g \Delta H_{pp}^0} \qquad \text{(Eq 7)}$$

where ΔH_{pp}^0 is the limiting linewidth below saturation. The term ΔH_{pp}^0 is the distance in gauss measured between the two peaks of the absorption-derivative line. Both T_1 and T_2 are expressed in seconds.

Pulse Method of Measuring Relaxation Times. This method consists of exposing the sample to a brief high-power pulse of microwave energy and measuring the strength and decay rate of the induced magnetization. This method measures T_1 or T_2 directly, without use of Eq 7.

To perform a typical pulse measurement, a high-power pulse of known intensity and duration is generated and applied to the sample. After completion of the pulse, a low-power klystron is used to perform a regular ESR experiment that monitors the saturation factor of the strongly saturated resonance. The magnitude of the ESR signal at this low power depends on the population difference between the energy levels, and the rate at which these population differences return to their Boltzmann thermal equilibrium values (Eq 1) is reflected in the measured magnitude of the detected signal as a function of time.

Another pulse experiment uses the spin-echo technique, in which two or three pulses of microwave energy are applied to the spin system, and an echo is detected at a fixed interval between the pulses. In addition, "holes" of simple form and controllable width can be "burned" in the line, and the rate at which these holes are filled in observed.

Double Resonance. In double-resonance experiments, the sample, already at resonance in a magnetic field at a particular microwave frequency, is subjected to an additional resonance frequency from a supplementary circuit. Most ESR spectrometers do not permit routine use of double-resonance techniques, although in NMR this technique is applied often by using spin decouplers. Accessories are available for ESR double-resonance investigations.

The principle double-resonance experiments that have been carried out using ESR spectrometers irradiate the unpaired spins with a microwave frequency (approximately 10^{10} Hz) and a RF (approximately 10^7 Hz). Many of these are nuclear-polarization techniques; therefore, the nuclear spin levels become populated with a Boltzmann factor characteristic of electron spins. This can produce a hundred or thousand fold increase in the NMR resonance amplitude.

Electron Nuclear Double Resonance (ENDOR). This technique, also termed the fast-passage effect, places no requirements on the relaxation processes. ENDOR measures the decrease in the ESR signal when saturation is relieved by inducing nuclear transitions. It was first described in a system consisting of an unpaired electron with quantum number $S = \frac{1}{2}$ interacting with a nucleus with spin $I = \frac{1}{2}$ to produce a hyperfine ESR doublet. To conduct the experiment, an adiabatic fast passage is carried out on one hyperfine component to invert the populations. A net nuclear polarization is established by performing an NMR adiabatic fast passage on the upper or lower NMR transition. The term adiabatic fast passage denotes a sweep-through resonance slow enough to avoid disturbing alignment of the spins along the RF field and fast enough to prevent relaxation of the spins.

Electron-electron double resonance (ELDOR) occurs when the two frequencies are in the microwave region. It uses a double-frequency microwave-resonant cavity. High microwave power at one frequency saturates one transition while low power at another frequency monitors its effect on another hyperfine component or another part of the same resonant line. This technique should prove useful in sorting out cross relaxation and other phenomena.

Acoustic Electron Spin Resonance. This technique measures the influence of applied ultrasonics on the ESR signal. In an ordinary ESR experiment, the spins absorb microwave energy, then relax by passing this energy to the certain lattice vibrations (those "on speaking terms" with the spins). The inverse process is also possible, by which the sample is irradiated with ultrasonic energy at the resonant frequency. The effect on the ESR absorption may be observed due to the simultaneous irradiation with ultrasonics. Pulsed and continuous wave (CW) spectrometers have been used for these investigations.

Optical double magnetic resonance (ODMR) is another less commonly used type of double resonance that measures ESR signals in optical excited states. Visible light is used to raise atoms of the sample to an optically excited state for performing the ESR experiment. The measurement is easiest to conduct with fluorescent materials having relatively long-lived excited states. Optical detection of ESR can be quite sensitive if the optical excited state can be populated appreciably. Optical double magnetic resonance is not ordinarily used for routine testing and is usually performed at cryogenic temperatures.

A related technique, known as spin-dependent recombination, is the measurement of the change in photo-induced conductivity produced by simultaneously scanning through an electron spin resonance-absorption line. This technique has been applied to the study of silicon crystals. It can be 100 times as sensitive as ordinary ESR.

Sensitivity

The amplitude, Y_m', is related to the number of spins, N, in a sample by:

$$Y_m' = \frac{N}{N_{min}} \qquad \text{(Eq 8)}$$

where N_{min} is the minimum detectable number of spins, that is, the number of spins that produces a signal-to-noise ratio of one. This number depends on such factors as linewidth, lineshape, number of hyperfine components, sample volume, spectrometer characteristics, cavity Q, temperature, microwave power, and noise.

The reduction in sensitivity because of hyperfine splitting, for example, is given by the multiplicity factor, D, which accounts for the spreading of the intensity in a hyperfine multiplet over several lines such that even the strongest line is lower in amplitude. For example, the standard free-radical DPPH (α,α'-diphenyl-β-picryl hydrazyl) in benzene solution has a 5-line hyperfine pattern with intensity ratios 1:2:3:2:1. Because the three center lines of a multiplet overlap and thus yield misleading relative intensities, calibrated spin measurements should be conducted on the outer lines of a multiplet. In this case, each outer line contains $\frac{1}{9}$ of the total integrated area; there-

Fig. 4 ESR spectrum of DPPH

Y_1 is the amplitude of the first peak of the spectrum; the amplitude of the peak in the hypothetical spectrum in the absence of hyperfine structure is Y_1 multiplied by the multiplicity factor D. In this case, $D = 9$.

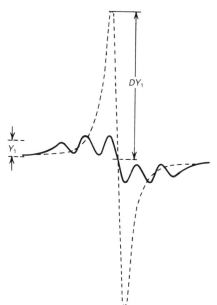

Fig. 5 Lorentzian and Gaussian absorption curves

(a) Curves with the same half amplitude line width. (b) First-derivative curves with the same peak-to-peak linewidth. (c) Second-derivative curves with the same peak-to-peak linewidth

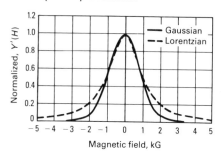

(a)

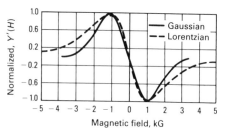

(b)

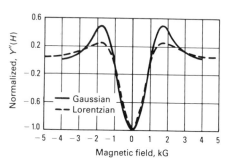

(c)

$$N_{min} = K \frac{V_s T_s D \Lambda' (\Delta H_{pp})^2}{Q \eta g^2 S(S + 1)\omega_0^2 H_{mod}}$$

$$\left(\frac{T_d \Delta f}{P}\right)^{1/2} [F_k - 1 + (t + F_{amp} - 1)L]^{1/2}$$

(Eq 11)

where V_s is the volume of the sample, K is the constant characteristic of the spectrometer, Q is the quality factor of the cavity, D is the multiplicity factor, η is the filling factor, g is the g-factor, S is spin, ω_0 is the microwave angular frequency, ΔH_{pp} is the peak-to-peak full linewidth, H_{mod} is the peak-to-peak modulation amplitude, Λ' is the

lineshape factor ($\Lambda' = 3.63$ for a Lorentzian line, 1.03 for Gaussian line), T_d is the detector temperature in K (usually 300 K), T_s is the sample temperature, P is the microwave power incident on the resonant cavity, Δf is the effective receiver-detector bandwidth, F_k is the klystron noise figure, t is the detector noise temperature, F_{amp} is the pre-amplifier noise value, and L is the detector insertion loss (reciprocal of detector conversion gain). This formula assumes that the microwave-resonant cavity is well matched to the waveguide, that the power level is below saturation, that the line is not over-modulated, and that the temperature is sufficiently high so that the population difference in equilibrium is proportional to $h\nu/kT$.

ESR Spectra

The resonance-absorption line has a finite width $\Delta\omega$ that varies from approximately 0.01 G for radical ions to approximately 3 G for exchange-narrowed free radicals to over 1000 G for some transition-metal compounds. The reason for the finite linewidth is that electrons interact with the externally applied magnetic field and interact more or less randomly with the magnetic fields in their environment. Observing this linewidth and line intensity provides information on the spin environment. Electron spin exchange between identical and nonidentical molecules, chemical exchange between the paramagnetic species and its neighbors, tumbling rates in solution, and the interactions with neighboring molecules having spin are some examples of environmental effects that can influence linewidth.

An observed spectrum frequently contains several lines because it exhibits hyperfine structure due to interactions with nuclear spins. The electronic spin of a transition-metal ion usually interacts with its own nuclear spin; however, in some systems, such as aromatic molecules, the unpaired electron is delocalized over several atoms, and the resultant hyperfine structure is the outcome of the interaction of this electronic spin with several nuclear spins. Figure 6 illustrates the energy levels of an unpaired electron interacting with two nuclear spins.

The simplest case is the absence of hyperfine interaction. Placing the unpaired electron in a magnetic field increases the number of energy levels from one ($E = E_0$) to two ($E = E_0 \pm \frac{1}{2} g\beta H$) (Fig. 6a). Figure 6(b) shows the two nuclear spins interacting with the electron. A measure for the strength of the interaction is given by the hyperfine coupling constant, A_i.

Each nuclear spin splits half of each original level into two levels. Therefore, for

fore, the multiplicity factor D is nine for each of these lines. Figure 4 shows the spectrum of DPPH together with the hypothetical singlet that would result if all the lines collapsed to a single one of the same width.

The minimum detectable number of spins is proportional to the inverse square root of the microwave power, $P^{-1/2}$. This dependence assumes that the power level is sufficiently low to prevent saturation of the sample.

The number of spins in a sample is proportional to the area under the absorption curve. For the two singlet lineshapes shown in Fig. 5:

$$\text{Area} = 3.63 Y'_m (\Delta H_{pp})^2$$

(Lorentzian shape)   (Eq 9)

$$\text{Area} = 1.03 Y'_m (\Delta H_{pp})^2$$

(Gaussian shape)   (Eq 10)

Other lineshapes have constants that can be determined by direct integration.

A general expression for the minimum detectable number of spins N_{min} in an unsaturated undermodulated line is:

Fig. 6 Energy-level diagrams for an unpaired electron

(a) In the absence of hyperfine structure.
(b) With two unequal hyperfine coupling constants A_1 and A_2. (c) With two equal coupling constants. Corresponding ESR spectra are shown in Fig. 7 and 8

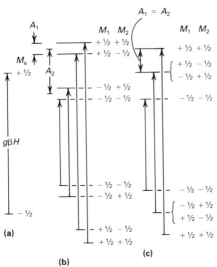

(a)

(b)

(c)

Fig. 7 ESR absorption spectra

(a) A singlet as shown in Fig. 6(a). (b) A quartet due to hyperfine structure with two protons ($A_2 > A_1$) (Fig. 6b). (c) $A_1 = A_2$ (Fig. 6c). Intensity ratios are given below the lines.

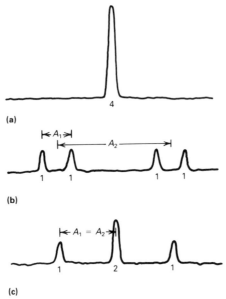

(a)

(b)

(c)

Fig. 8 First-derivative spectra arising from the energy levels shown in Fig. 6

(a) $A_1 = A_2 = 0$. (b) $A_2 \gg A_1$. (c) $A_2 = A_1$

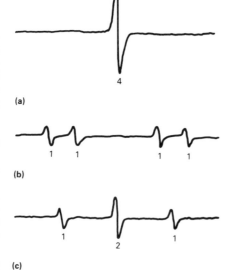

(a)

(b)

(c)

Fig. 9 Hyperfine structure patterns

Three equally coupled nuclei with nuclear spin $I = \frac{1}{2}$ and coupling constant A_p plus two equally coupled $I = 1$ nuclei with coupling constant.
(a) $A_N \ll A_p$. (b) $A_N \gg A_p$. (c) $A_N = A_p$

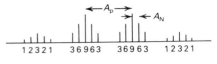

(a)

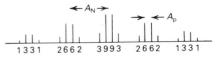

(b)

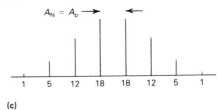

(c)

$A_1 \ne A_2$, the original two levels are split into eight levels. Although there are eight levels, only four transitions are possible because of the selection rules:

$$\Delta M_S = \pm 1 \qquad \text{(Eq 12)}$$

$$\Delta M_I = 0 \qquad \text{(Eq 13)}$$

where M_S is the electron spin quantum number, and M_I represents the values of the possible orientations of the angular momenta of the nuclei. Figure 6 illustrates the allowed transitions. Figure 6(c) shows the collapse to three transitions for A_1 equal to A_2 because in that case the energy levels for $M_1 = +\frac{1}{2}$, $M_2 = -\frac{1}{2}$ and $M_1 = -\frac{1}{2}$, $M_2 = +\frac{1}{2}$ are superimposed. Figure 7 depicts the spectra for these cases.

The absorption peaks shown are analogous to those observed in ultraviolet (UV), infrared (IR), and high-resolution NMR spectroscopy and to those seen in chromatography. However, in practice, modulation of the magnetic field produces first-derivative spectra (Fig. 8).

The hyperfine coupling constant A varies with the nuclear species. It is a measure of the strength of the interaction between the nuclear and electronic spins. When studying transition-group metals in which the electron interacts almost exclusively with a single atom, hyperfine splitting of the order of 100 G or more can be observed. In organic compounds, in which the electron may inter-

act with several nuclei, the hyperfine splitting between the individual lines may be as low as a few milligauss, with a total splitting between the terminal lines of approximately 25 G. To resolve these small differences,

large demands are placed on the applied magnetic field because it must have a homogeneity exceeding the linewidth.

When several $I = \frac{1}{2}$ nuclei are coupled equally, that is, have the same A_i, the resultant absorption peaks exhibit an intensity ratio that follows the binomial coefficient distribution. The intensity ratio of 1:3:3:1 is obtained with the methyl radical $\cdot CH_3$ ($I = \frac{1}{2}$); the ratio of 1:2:3:2:1 arises from two equally coupled nitrogen nuclei ($I = 1$), such as those found in DPPH (Tables 1 and 2). A system containing three equally coupled protons (A_p) and two equally coupled nitrogens (A_N) with $A_p \gg A_N$ (Fig. 9a) will consist of four widely separated groups of lines with the relative intensity ratio 1:3:3:1, each of which is split into a 1:2:3:2:1 quintet (Fig. 9). When $A_p \ll A_N$ (Fig. 9b), the main split is into a widely spaced 1:2:3:2:1 quintet, with each of these components further split into a 1:3:3:1 quartet. When $A_p = A_N$, the resulting spectrum has eight lines with the intensity ratio 1:5:12:18:18:12:5:1 (Fig. 9c).

If n nuclei with $I = \frac{1}{2}$ contribute to the hyperfine structure, there will be 2^n different hyperfine components if all the coupling constants differ, and no degeneracy occurs. If there are n nuclei with the nuclear spin I, there will be $(2I + 1)^n$ hyperfine components. For several nuclei with the individual values I_i and n_i, the total number of hyperfine components, N_{hfs}, will be:

$$N_{hfs} = \Pi_i (2I_i + 1)^{n_i} \qquad \text{(Eq 14)}$$

where Π_i denotes the formation of a product. For example, the system depicted in Fig. 9 has:

$$I_p = \tfrac{1}{2} \qquad n_p = 3 \qquad \text{(Eq 15)}$$

$$I_N = 1 \qquad n_N = 2 \qquad \text{(Eq 16)}$$

with the result that:

$$N_{hfs} = [2(\tfrac{1}{2}) + 1]^3$$

$$(2 + 1)^2 = 72 \qquad \text{(Eq 17)}$$

This may be confirmed by adding the intensities shown in Fig. 9(c): $1 + 5 + 12 + 18 + 18 + 12 + 5 + 1 = 72$.

When some nuclei are equivalent to others, the resulting degeneracy decreases the number and increases the amplitude of the components in the hyperfine pattern without affecting the overall integrated intensity. All the lines in the hyperfine pattern usually have the same linewidth and lineshape, but relaxation mechanisms sometimes cause deviations.

Many ESR spectra are more complicated than those shown in Fig. 7 and 8 due to the presence of zero-field splittings, anisotropic hyperfine coupling constants, additional hyperfine splittings, saturation effects, and so on.

Lineshapes

Gaussian and Lorentzian lineshapes are the most common. The former is typical of solids with relatively low concentrations of paramagnetic species in which the magnetic fields from the surrounding electronic and nuclear spins constitute the dominant broadening mechanism. The Lorentzian shape is found in solids with high concentrations of paramagnetic species in which exchange interactions between nearby electronic spins narrow the line. It is also common in solutions in which Brownian motion is primarily responsible for the width.

Absorption lines are observed in most spectroscopies. In ESR, the magnetic field modulation-phase-sensitive detection technique produces first-derivative lines that provide better resolved spectra. In the following equations, the direct-absorption $Y(H)$ and first-derivative $Y'(H)$ forms for the Gaussian lineshape are:

$$G_{Y(H)} = Y_m \exp\left[-\left(\frac{H - H_0}{\tfrac{1}{2}\Delta H_{1/2}}\right)^2 \ln 2\right]$$

$$\text{(Eq 18)}$$

Table 1   Determination of hyperfine structure intensity ratios for three equally coupled $I = \tfrac{1}{2}$ nuclei, for example, protons

Spin configuration			m_1	m_2	m_3	$M = m_1 + m_2 + m_3$	Intensity ratio
↑	↑	↑	½	½	½	3⁄2	1
↑	↑	↓	½	½	−½		
↑	↓	↑	½	−½	½	½	3
↓	↑	↑	−½	½	½		
↑	↓	↓	½	−½	−½		
↓	↑	↓	−½	½	−½	−½	3
↓	↓	↑	−½	−½	½		
↓	↓	↓	−½	−½	−½	−3⁄2	1

Table 2   Determination of hyperfine structure intensity ratios for two equally coupled $I = 1$ nuclei, for example, nitrogen, such as those found in DPPH

Spin configuration		m_1	m_2	$M = M_1 + M_2$	Intensity ratio
↑	↑	1	1	2	1
↑	→	1	0	1	2
→	↑	0	1		
↑	↓	1	−1		
→	→	0	0	0	3
↓	↑	−1	1		
→	↓	0	−1	−1	2
↓	→	−1	0		
↓	↓	−1	−1	−2	1

$$G_{Y'(H)} = Y_m' \left(\frac{H - H_0}{\tfrac{1}{2}\Delta H_{pp}}\right) \exp$$

$$\left\{-\tfrac{1}{2}\left[\left(\frac{H - H_0}{\tfrac{1}{2}\Delta H_{pp}}\right)^2 - 1\right]\right\} \qquad \text{(Eq 19)}$$

and for the Lorentzian lineshape:

$$L_{Y(H)} = \frac{Y_m}{1 + [(H - H_0)/\tfrac{1}{2}\Delta H_{1/2}]^2}$$

$$\text{(Eq 20)}$$

$$L_{Y'(H)} = \frac{16 Y_m'[(H - H_0)/\tfrac{1}{2}\Delta H_{pp}]}{\{3 + [(H - H_0)/\tfrac{1}{2}\Delta H_{pp}]^2\}^2}$$

$$\text{(Eq 21)}$$

In these expressions, Y_m and Y_m' are the amplitudes of the direct-absorption and first-derivative lineshapes, respectively. The linewidth $\Delta H_{1/2}$ of the absorption line is measured between the two half-amplitude points

of the line, and ΔH_{pp} is the peak-to-peak linewidth of the first derivative (Fig. 5). Computer programs are available that simulate complex spectra using these lineshape expressions. Observed spectra can have shapes between the Gaussian and Lorentzian types; other shapes are sometimes encountered.

An observed ESR line will sometimes consist of a Gaussian distribution of individual Lorentzian spin packets that can be expressed mathematically in terms of a convolution integral. This can arise with unresolved superhyperfine structure.

Study of conduction electrons yields asymmetric lineshapes termed Dysonian shapes that depend on the time T_D required for an electron to diffuse through the skin depth of the sample. The lineshape in the normal region in which the electron mean free path is small compared to the skin depth differs from that in the anomalous case in which the mean free path exceeds this depth.

Anisotropies

The observed spectrum sometimes depends on the orientation of the sample in the magnetic field, and this ordinarily arises from angular dependencies termed anisotropies of the Hamiltonian parameters. When this is the case, the information obtainable from the ESR measurements is maximized by rotating a single crystal systematically about three mutually perpendicular axes and recording spectra every few degrees. When single crystals are not available, powder samples must be examined in which the various microcrystallites have random orientations and the observed spectrum will be a composite of many individual spectra. Such a spectrum is termed a powder pattern, and its characteristic shape depends on such Hamiltonian parameters as the values of the g-factor along the three principal directions in a microcrystallite. Figure 10 shows an example of a powder-pattern spectrum in which two of the principal g-factors have the same value ($g_x = g_y = g_\perp$), and the third ($g_z = g_\parallel$) is different. Example 3 in the section "Applications" in this article discusses a completely anisotropic case. The principal values of the g-factor can be estimated from the powder spectrum.

In another type of material, such as a glassy or amorphous substance, the paramagnetic species is oriented randomly and exhibits a range of Hamiltonian parameters. The spectrum of such a material is then an average over angle and Hamiltonian parameters. Other cases occur, such as a semirandom distribution, in which the spins have a characteristic probability distribution relative to a given axis, but are randomly oriented in planes perpendicular to this axis. Electron spin resonance is often the primary method of providing quantitative information on such cases.

Information Gained Using ESR

A typical ESR spectrum is characterized by the position, intensity, and shape of each component line. The position of the main line or the center of gravity of a hyperfine pattern:

$$E = \hbar\omega = g\beta H M_s + A M_s M_I \qquad \text{(Eq 22)}$$

provides the g-factor of Eq 2, and the spacing A between the lines of a hyperfine multiplet provides the hyperfine coupling constant A. This is illustrated in Fig. 7 and 8 for the more complicated case with two separate hyperfine coupling constants A_1 and A_2. A proton magnetometer can be used to calibrate the magnet scan to provide accurate line positions and spacings for determining these quantities.

If symmetric, the curve will usually be Lorentzian or Gaussian in shape (Fig. 5). An

Fig. 10 The effect of increasing the component linewidth on the calculated spectrum for an axially symmetric powder pattern

Lorentzian linewidths: A, 1 G; B, 10 G; C, 50 G; D, 100 G

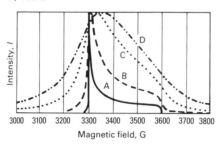

unsymmetric shape is characteristic of an anisotropic g-factor. The Lorentzian lineshape is usually observed in low-viscosity liquids in which the Bloch equations are satisfied; dipole-dipole broadening in typical solids produces a Gaussian shape. In solids having high spin concentrations, such as solid DPPH, exchange narrowing occurs, and the shape appears Lorentzian in the center, with a more Gaussian contour in the wings.

The number of spins in the sample is proportional to the intensity of the resonant line. For a singlet, the intensity is the integrated area under the absorption curve, and for first-derivative presentation, this area can be obtained using a double integration:

$$\text{Intensity} = \int_{-\infty}^{+\infty} dH \int_{-\infty}^{H}$$

$$Y'(H' - H_0)\, dH' \qquad \text{(Eq 23)}$$

or a mathematically equivalent single integration:

$$\text{Intensity} = \int_{-\infty}^{+\infty} (H_0 - H)$$

$$Y'(H - H_0)\, dH \qquad \text{(Eq 24)}$$

Performing the integration yields Eq 9 and 10, with the area factors 3.63 for a Lorentzian and 1.03 for a Gaussian shape. The presence of structure can be taken into account using the multiplicity factor D mentioned above.

The number of spins can be determined by measuring a known and unknown sample and evaluating the ratio: $\text{area}_{known}/\text{area}_{known}$. This procedure is valid only if the unknown and known samples are similar types of spin systems—for example, if both

are free radicals; otherwise, corrections from Eq 11 must be used.

Electron spin resonance measurement is often used to determine the identity of a paramagnetic species. This can be best accomplished by comparing the unidentified spectrum with those obtained from various sources. The g-factor, the hyperfine structure, the linewidth and line intensity, and shape anisotropy are frequently characteristic of particular species.

Systems Favorable for ESR Analysis

Transition Elements. A large percentage of ESR studies have been conducted using transition-element compounds, particularly with the first transition series. The second and third series, the rare earths, and the transuranic elements have also been investigated. Among the most favorable and widely studied valence states are $V^{4+}(3d^1)$, $Cr^{3+}(3d^3)$, $Mn^{2+}(3d^5)$, $Fe^{3+}(3d^5)$, $Co^{2+}(3d^7)$ at low temperature, $Cu^{2+}(3d^9)$, $Eu^{3+}(4f^7)$, and $Gd^{2+}(4f^7)$. The spectra in doped single crystals exhibit such effects as hyperfine structure (V^{4+}, Mn^{2+}), zero-field splitting, (Cr^{3+}, Mn^{2+}, Fe^{3+}, Co^{2+}), and an anisotropic g-factor (Co^{2+}, Cu^{2+}). Typical systems that have been studied include single crystals (1% doping), relaxation-time studies (mostly liquid helium temperature, low power), chelates and sandwich compounds, and alloys.

Table 3 lists the principal valence states of the first transition series. Most of the common valence states can be observed at room temperature or below. Some, such as Co^{2+}, ordinarily require low temperatures for detection. Ions having an even number of electrons are observable only under special conditions. The zero-field splittings and hyperfine coupling constants are given in the units of reciprocal centimeters. The conversion factor:

$$1\ \text{cm}^{-1} = 29.98\ \text{GHz} = (21.42/g)\ \text{kG}$$

$$\text{(Eq 25)}$$

is useful for transforming to the units of gauss measured directly in an experiment.

Table 3 shows the wide variation in nuclear spins and g-factors that occurs for various ions. These are useful for identification. Several tabulations of data for specific host lattices and compounds have been compiled.

Conduction electrons have been detected using conventional ESR methods and the related cyclotron-resonance technique.

Table 3 Summary of typical ESR data on the first transition series

Values are given for the g-factor, the zero-field term D, and the hyperfine interaction A.

Number of electrons	Ions	Spectroscopic state(a)	g-factor	$|D|$, cm^{-1}	$|A|$, cm^{-1}
1	Ti^{3+}, Mn^{6+}, V^{4+}, Cr^{5+}	^{2}D	1.1–2.0	0	0.015 (^{55}Mn, ^{51}V)
2	V^{3+}, Ti^{2+}, Cr^{4+}	^{3}F	1.9	5–10	0.02 (^{51}V)
3	V^{2+}, Cr^{3+}, Mn^{4+}	^{4}F	2.0	10^{-3}–1.0	0.001 (^{53}Cr)
					0.008 (^{51}V, ^{55}Mn)
4	Cr^{2+}, Mn^{3+}	^{5}D	2.0	2	
5	Mn^{2+}, Fe^{3+}	^{6}S	2.0	10^{-3}–0.2	0.006–0.01 (^{55}Mn)
6	Fe^{2+}, Co^{3+}	^{5}D	0–9	0.2	
7	Co^{2+}	^{4}F	1.4–7	4.5	0.01–0.03
8	Ni^{2+}	^{3}F	2.2–2.3	0.1–4	
9	Cu^{2+}	^{2}D	2–2.5	0	0.002–0.02

(a) The superscript number is based on the spin quantum number S and is equal to $2S + 1$. The letter is based on the orbital quantum number L. S demotes $L = 0$, D denotes $L = 2$, and F denotes $L = 3$.

Fig. 11 High-resolution ESR spectrum of DPPH in tetrahydrofuran after removal of dissolved oxygen

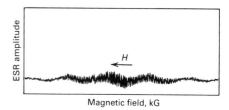

The latter uses an ESR spectrometer, and the sample is located in a region of strong microwave electric-field strength. By contrast, in the usual ESR arrangement, the sample is placed at a position of strong microwave magnetic-field strength. Conduction electrons have been detected in solutions of alkali metals in liquid ammonia, alkaline earth metals (fine powders), alloys (for example, small amounts of paramagnetic metal alloyed with another metal), graphite, and through nonresonant absorption of microwaves by superconductors.

Semiconductors. Commercially useful semiconductors, being naturally or intentionally doped with impurities, lend themselves to ESR studies. Examples are germanium, silicon, and InSb; doped semiconductors, for example, silicon with arsenic, antimony, or lead; irradiated semiconductors; and graphite.

Chemical Systems. Several chemical substances contain free radicals that depend on the method of synthesis and on the history of the substance. Recent refinements in instrumentation have permitted detection of free-radical intermediates in chemical reactions. Typical chemical systems that have been studied using ESR are polymers, catalysts, rubber, free-radical intermediates, charred carbon, and chemical complexes, especially with transition metals.

A free radical is a compound that contains an unpaired spin, such as the methyl radical ·CH$_3$ produced through the breakup of methane:

$$CH_4 \rightarrow \cdot CH_3 + H^- \qquad (Eq\ 26)$$

where the hydrogen atom and the methyl radical are electrically neutral. Free radicals have been observed in gaseous, liquid, and solid systems. Although sometimes stable, they are usually short-lived intermediates in chemical reactions.

Free radicals and radical ions usually have g-factors close to the free-electron value of 2.0023, for example, for DPPH $g = 2.0036$. In low-viscosity solutions, they exhibit hyperfine patterns with a typical overall spread of approximately 25 G. The scrupulous removal of oxygen often reveals as yet unresolved structure. In high-concentration solids, a single exchange narrowed resonance appears ($\Delta H_{pp} \sim 2.7$ G for DPPH precipitated from benzene solution). In irradiated single crystals, the free radicals may have strongly anisotropic hyperfine interactions and slightly anisotropic g-factors.

Experimentally, the following have been detected using ESR: stable solid free radicals (a single exchange-narrowed resonance), stable free radicals in solution (hyperfine structure obtained), free radicals produced by irradiation (often at low temperature, sometimes single crystals), condensed discharges (free radicals produced in a gas condensed on a solid at low temperature), biological systems, biradicals, electrochemical generation of radical ions (polarography), triplet states, paramagnetic molecules (for example, NO, NO$_2$, and ClO$_2$, and intermediates in chemical reactions.

Radical ions of many organic compounds can be produced in an electrolytic cell, usually a flat quartz cell with a mercury-pool cathode and a platinum anode. This electrolytic cell can be connected to a flat measuring cell located in the microwave-resonant cavity. When the applied voltage in the electrolytic system is increased, the current first increases but soon levels off to a plateau at which radical ions are formed. Radical formation can sometimes be observed because of color changes in the solution. To conduct the experiments, the magnetic field is scanned for resonance over a 50-G region near the free electron value of $g = 2.0023$. Radical ions can also be formed in flow-through cells.

Because oxygen is also paramagnetic, dissolved air must be scrupulously removed before experiment. The best method is the freeze-pump-thaw technique, in which the sample is frozen, then connected to a high-vacuum source. After closing off the vacuum pump, the sample is melted and refrozen. The cycle is repeated until no air is released during the solid to liquid transformation. Comparison of Fig. 4 and 11, which show DPPH in solution, demonstrates the difference in spectra when dissolved oxygen is present and absent. For this type of experiment, low power levels and low modulation amplitudes are necessary because linewidths are typically from 50 to 100 mG.

Irradiated Materials. Free radicals and color centers produced by irradiation have been investigated extensively. Most irradiations are carried out using x-rays, γ-rays, or electrons whose energies far exceed chemical-bond energies. Paramagnetic spins can also be produced photolytically by less-energetic ultraviolet light and by neutrons.

Most ESR spectra are obtained after the sample is irradiated. Many paramagnetic centers are sufficiently long lived to warrant such a procedure. More sophisticated experimental techniques entail simultaneous irradiation and ESR detection. This is especially prevalent when the irradiation source is an ultraviolet lamp. Low-temperature irradiation and detection can reveal the presence of new centers that can be studied at gradually increasing temperatures to elucidate the kinetics of their recombination. Routine spectrometers are satisfactory for most radiation-damage investigations.

Some typical systems that have been studied are ionic crystals, for example, alkali halides, color centers, and other centers; solid organic compounds; liquid organic compounds; organic single crystals; polymers; semiconductors, such as germanium and silicon; and photoconductors, for example, dyes.

Naturally Occurring Substances. Although most of the systems studied using ESR are synthetic, various naturally occurring substances have been investigated since the inception of the field. These include minerals with transition elements, for ex-

Table 4 Various categories of spectroscopy

Category	Frequency, Hz	Wavelength	Typical energy unit		Phenomenon	Typical radiation generator	Typical detector
			Name	Value			
Static	0–60	...	Joule	1	...	Battery	Ammeter, voltmeter
			Calorie	4.186			
Low or audio frequency	10^3–10^5	3–300 km	Kilohertz	6.626×10^{-31}	Dielectric absorption	Mechanical	Ammeter, voltmeter
RF	10^6–10^8	3–300 m	Joule	1	Nuclear quadrupole resonance (NQR), NMR, Dielectric absorption	Tuner circuit, crystal	Antenna
			Inverse centimeter	1.986×10^{-23}			
Microwave	10^9–10^{11}	30 cm to 3 mm	Megahertz	6.626×10^{-28}	Molecular rotation, ESR	Klystron, magneton, Gunn diode	Antenna, crystal, bolometer
IR	10^{12}–3×10^{14}	300–1 μm	Inverse centimeter	1.986×10^{-23}	Molecular vibrations	Heat source	Bolometer, PbS cell
			Kilocalories/mole	4.186×10^3			
			Joule	1			
Visible, UV	4×10^{14}– 3×10^{15}	0.8–0.1 μm	Erg	1×10^{-7}	Electronic transitions	Incandescent lamp	Photocell, photographic film
			Electron volt	1.602×10^{-19}			
X-ray	10^{16}–10^{19}	30–0.03 μm	Electron volt	1.602×10^{-19}	Electronic transitions		
			Kilo electron volt	1.602×10^{-16}			
γ-ray	10^{19}–10^{22}	3×10^{-9}– 3×10^{-12} cm	Mega electron volt	1.602×10^{-13}		Discharge tube	Photocell
Low energy, nuclear	10^{19}–10^{23}	3×10^{-9}– 3×10^{-13} cm	Mega electron volt	1.602×10^{-13}	Inner-shell electronic transitions	Heavy-element bombardment	Geiger counter, photomultiplier
High energy, nuclear	10^{23}–10^{26}	3×10^{-13}– 3×10^{-17} cm	Giga electron volt	1.602×10^{-10}	Nuclear energy level transitions	Naturally radioactive nuclei	Scintillation detector
			Tera electron volt	1.602×10^{-7}			
High-energy cosmic ray	$>10^{25}$	...	Giga electron volt	1.602×10^{-10}	Elementary particle creation	Accelerator (synchrotron)	Bubble chamber, spark chamber
			Tera electron volt	1.602×10^{-7}	Extraterrestrial	Star, magnetic field in galaxy	Extensive shower detector

ample, ruby (Cr/Al_2O_3) and dolomite [$(Ca,Mg)CO_3$] containing manganese; minerals with defects, such as quartz; hemoglobin (iron); petroleum; coal; rubber; and various biological systems.

Biological Systems. Electron spin resonance has been applied extensively to biological systems. The variations that occur under changing environmental conditions can be followed by monitoring the intensity of a free-radical signal. For example, the presence of free radicals has been studied in healthy and in diseased tissue. If a transition-metal ion is present, as in hemoglobin (iron), its valence-state changes may be studied using ESR. Early concrete evidence that free-radical activity is linked to photosynthesis was provided using ESR. Irradiating cells that contain chloroplasts with light in the same wavelength range that produces photosynthesis results in a sharp ESR line. When the incident light is turned off, the resonance soon weakens or disappears completely.

An inconvenience when biological samples are analyzed is the presence of water in the sample. This results in high dielectric losses, which necessitate use of a flat quartz sample cell. Some typical systems that have been studied using ESR are hemoglobin, nucleic acids, enzymes, chloroplasts when irradiated, riboflavin (before and after ultraviolet irradiation), and carcinogens.

Magnetic Samples. In addition to paramagnetic samples in which the spins are randomly oriented along the magnetic-field direction, several other types of spin ordering occur. For example, in a ferromagnetic sample, the spins are oriented parallel to a particular direction, and a very broad strong absorption signal is observed. By contrast, antiferromagnetic samples generally produce broad weak signals. Other types of spin ordering, such as that in ferrites and spin glasses, also produce characteristic absorption spectra. Significant aspects of the ESR spectra of ordered spin systems are the temperature dependence and that the sample reverts to a paramagnetic form above a transition temperature.

Comparison with Other Techniques

Spectroscopy is categorized variously, depending on the energy involved in a typical quantum jump (Table 4). Historically, these categories developed as separate fields of research. Each used particular experimental techniques, and these instrumentation differences coincided with different physical phenomena, such as the progressively increasing energies associated with rotational, vibrational, and electronic spectra.

Electron spin resonance is frequently considered to be in the microwave category of spectroscopy, and NMR is usually classified as RF spectroscopy; however, these are merely instrumental characterizations based, for example, on the last two columns of Table 4. Regarding the observed phenomena, ESR studies the interaction between electronic magnetic moments and magnetic fields. Electron spin resonance studies are occasionally carried out with NMR instrumentation using magnetic fields of several gauss rather than several thousand gauss. The splitting of energy levels by a magnetic field is termed the Zeeman effect. Therefore, ESR is the study of direct transitions between electronic Zeeman levels, and NMR is the study of direct transitions between nuclear Zeeman levels. That is, ESR and NMR study the energy required to reorient electronic and nuclear magnetic moments, respectively, in a magnetic field.

Straight microwave spectroscopy uses apparatus similar to that implemented in ESR, but measures molecular rotational transitions directly and rarely uses a magnetic field. In this category of spectroscopy, it is much more customary to produce Stark-effect splittings using an applied electric field. By contrast, in ESR, a strong magnetic field is an integral part of the experimental arrangement. Nuclear magnetic resonance, ESR, IR, and UV spectroscopy share certain similarities (Table 5).

Table 5 Comparison of NMR, ESR, IR, and UV spectroscopies showing typical values of several parameters

Spectroscopy	Energy difference between upper and lower levels, cal/mol	Wavelength of observed and emitted quanta, cm	Population in excited state, %	Typical lifetime of excited state, s	Relative shift of energy levels by magnetic field
NMR	10^{-3}	3×10^3	49.9999	10	Large
ESR	1	3	49.9	10^{-3}	Large
IR	300	10^{-2}	20	10^{-5}	Small
UV	10^5	3×10^{-5}	Negligible	10^{-8}	Negligible

Applications

Example 1: The Stable Free Radical Hydrazyl. Figure 4 shows the 5-line hyperfine pattern obtained from α,α'-diphenyl-β-picryl hydrazyl (DPPH) in benzene solution. This pattern arises from the unpaired electron spending most of its time approximately equally divided between the two central nitrogen atoms of the radical structural formula shown in Fig. 11. The two nitrogen nuclei each have spin $I = 1$ to give the orientations of the total spin quantum number M (Table 2):

$$M = M_1 + M_2 \qquad \text{(Eq 27)}$$

The number of ways of forming the $M = 2, 1, 0, -1, -2$ states are 1, 2, 3, 2, 1, respectively; therefore, the observed hyperfine pattern has the intensity ratios 1:2:3:2:1. If oxygen is scrupulously removed from the sample using the freeze-pump-thaw technique, the much smaller splitting constants can be resolved from the ring protons (Fig. 11). This occurs because the relaxation effect of the paramagnetic oxygen molecules is removed.

The spectra illustrated in Fig. 4 and 11 were obtained in solution. Solid DPPH exhibits an exchange-narrowed singlet similar to the dotted line curve shown in Fig. 4, but somewhat narrower ($\Delta H_{pp} \sim 2.7$ G). The strong exchange interaction between adjacent radicals in the solid state averages the hyperfine structure to produce the singlet.

Example 2: Chromia Alumina Catalysts. Figure 12 shows a spectrum of a chromia alumina catalyst that extends from zero to beyond 6000 G. It results from the superposition of spectra from three phases: a broad line centered at $g = 2$ rising from clumped or clustered Cr^{3+} ions, a low-field line peaking at 1600 G due to isolated Cr^{3+} ions, and a sharp singlet near $g = 2$ attributed to Cr^{5+} ions. This spectrum illustrates the possibilities of studying catalysts and distinguishing valence states using ESR. The catalytic activity for ethylene polymerization was found to correlate well with the amplitude of the Cr^{5+} ESR line. Chromium in the valence state Cr^{6+} was distributed over the surface of the catalyst, and catalytic activity appeared to be associated with ionization of this species to Cr^{5+}.

Example 3: Turquoise and Metatorbernite. Turquoise $[CuAl_6(PO_4)_4(OH)_8 \cdot 5H_2O]$ is triclinic, and the cupric ions (Cu^{2+}) are easily detected using ESR. The spectrum shown in Fig. 13 is a typical powder pattern arising from a completely anisotropic g-factor. The arrows show the magnetic-field positions corresponding to the three principal g-factors g_1, g_2, and g_3. Some turquoise samples exhibit an additional isotropic line arising from Fe^{3+} that decreased in intensity as the temperature was lowered below ambient, suggesting the onset of antiferromagnetic ordering.

The mineral metatorbernite $[Cu(UO_2)_2(PO_4)_2 \cdot 8H_2O]$ also contains divalent copper, and its ESR spectrum was a single line whose position and width depend on the orientation of the crystal in the magnetic field. The linewidth anisotropy was explained in terms of the layered structure associated with the cupric ions.

Example 4: Electrolytically Generated Radical Ions. When the voltage is varied across a polarographic cell containing polycyclic hydrocarbons, the compounds become ionized, and a plot of the current through the cell versus the applied voltage exhibits flat regions termed plateaus arising from the presence of particular ionic species. Measuring the ESR spectrum of a polycyclic hydrocarbon, such as anthracene or benzpyrene, in the plateau region yields a spectrum containing many narrow lines, each perhaps 50 mG wide. Obtaining such a spectrum necessitates scrupulous removal of oxygen by alternately freezing the sample, pumping on it to remove the oxygen, then melting it. The number, spacings, and intensity ratios of the various lines in the spectrum permit deduction of the amount of time the unpaired electron spends at each carbon atom in the molecule.

Example 5: Kinetics of Radical Production and Subsequent Decay. Free radicals are produced when an organic sam-

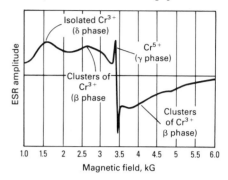

Fig. 12 Observed ESR spectrum of chromia alumina catalyst

The sample contained 5.3 mol% Cr_2O_3.

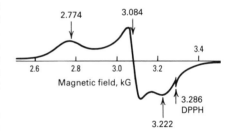

Fig. 13 ESR spectrum of turquoise

Left to right: locations in gauss of the three principal g-values of Cu^{2+} ions and that of the free-radical marker DPPH

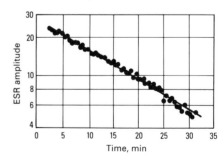

Fig. 14 Kinetics of the free-radical decay in irradiated α-alanine at 162 K showing the linear decrease in the logarithm of the ESR amplitude with time

The slope of the line gives the rate constant k in accordance with Eq 30.

ple is irradiated. If irradiation is continued for a period of time, the concentration of radicals gradually increases until a dynamic steady state is reached at which the rate of radical generation is balanced by the rate of radical recombination.

Fig. 15 Arrhenius plot of the logarithm of the rate constant k for free-radical decay in irradiated glycine versus reciprocal temperature

The slope of the straight line gives the activation energy ΔE for the radical-decay process in accordance with Eq 31.

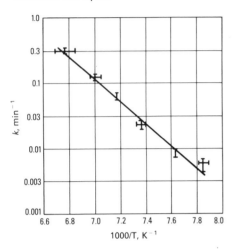

Electron spin resonance is useful for studying the reaction kinetics involved in the formation and decay of free radicals. For first-order kinetics, the concentration of free radicals decays exponentially with time. Thus, if the sample contains N_0 atoms at the termination of the irradiation, the number that remains after a time T is:

$$N = N_0 e^{-kT} \qquad \text{(Eq 28)}$$

where k is a measure of the decay rate. In typical cases, the rate constant k decreases with increasing temperature according to:

$$k = k_0 \exp\left(\frac{-\Delta E}{k_B T}\right) \qquad \text{(Eq 29)}$$

where ΔE is the activation energy for recombination or decay. A two-step procedure is followed to determine activation energy. First, $k(T)$ is determined for various temperatures by plotting the logarithm of the relative ESR signal amplitude Y/Y_0 versus the time (Fig. 14):

$$\log \frac{Y}{Y_0} = -kT \qquad \text{(Eq 30)}$$

because Y/Y_0 is proportional to N/N_0 in Eq 28. The slope of each straight line yields the rate constant k at a particular temperature. The logarithms of k are then plotted versus $1/T$ (Fig. 15):

$$\log k = \log k_0 - \frac{\Delta E}{k_B T} \qquad \text{(Eq 31)}$$

to determine the frequency factor k_0 and the activation energy ΔE from the intercept and slope, respectively, of the resultant straight line.

The results obtained here for irradiated amino acids are typical of free-radical decay kinetics. When irradiation is conducted at low temperatures (77 or 4 K), the initial radicals formed can sometimes be detected. These radicals are often unstable, and at higher temperatures, secondary or perhaps tertiary radicals are usually detected that result from reactions subsequent to the initial or primary radiation-damage event. The kinetic events leading to production of a final radical stable at room temperature can sometimes be followed by monitoring the growth and decay of intermediate paramagnetic species.

SELECTED REFERENCES

- F.M. Bukanaeva, Yu.I. Pecherskaya, V.B. Kazanskii, and V.A. Dzis'ko, *Kinet. Catal.*, Vol 3, 1962, p 315
- C.O. Clark, C.P. Poole, and H.A. Farach. *Am. Mineralog.*, Vol 64, 1979, p 449
- Y. Deguchi, *J. Chem. Phys.*, Vol 32, 1960, p 1584
- J. Diaz, H.A. Farach, and C.P. Poole, Jr., *Am. Mineralog.*, Vol 56, 1971, p 773
- G. Feher, *Phys. Rev.*, Vol 103, 1956, p 500
- J.A. Ibers and J.D. Swalen, *Phys. Rev.*, Vol 127, 1962, p 1914
- R.C. Nicklin, H.A. Farach, and C.P. Poole, Jr., *J. Chem. Phys.*, Vol 65, 1976, p 2998
- F.J. Owens, C.P. Poole, Jr., and H.A. Farach, Ed., *Magnetic Resonance of Phase Transitions*, Academic Press, 1979
- C.P. Poole, Jr., *Electron Spin Resonance*, 2nd ed., Wiley-Interscience, 1984
- C.P. Poole, Jr., and H.A. Farach, *Appl. Spectrosc. Rev.*, Vol 19, 1983, p 157
- C.P. Poole, Jr., H.A. Farach, and T.P. Bishop, *Magn. Resonance Rev.*, Vol 4, 1978, p 137, 225
- C.P. Poole, Jr., and H.A. Farach, *Relaxation in Magnetic Resonance*, Academic Press, 1972
- C.P. Poole, Jr., and H.A. Farach, *Theory of Magnetic Resonance*, Wiley-Interscience, 1971
- C.P. Poole, Jr., W.L. Kehl, and D.S. MacIver, *J. Catal.*, Vol 1, 1962, p 407
- C.P. Poole, Jr., and D.S. MacIver, *Adv. Catal.*, Vol 17, 1967, p 223
- C. Smith, C.P. Poole, Jr., and H.A. Farach, *J. Chem. Phys.*, Vol 74, 1981, p 993

Ferromagnetic Resonance

S.M. Bhagat, Department of Physics and Astronomy, University of Maryland

General Uses

- Identification of magnetic state
- Quantitative determination of static magnetic parameters
- Determination of microwave losses

Examples of Applications

- Measurement of magnetization
- Study of magnetocrystalline anisotropy
- Investigation of exchange stiffness

Samples

- *Form*: Crystalline or amorphous solids—metals and alloys
- *Size and shape*: Thin films, needles, ribbons, disks with thickness small in comparison to lateral dimensions

Limitations

- Data from other techniques should be available for unequivocal conclusions

Estimated Analysis Time

- A few hours per specimen

Capabilities of Related Techniques

- *Mössbauer spectroscopy*: Magnetic structure analysis, phase analysis, and surface analysis; limited to relatively few isotopes
- *Electron spin resonance*: Identification of magnetic states of materials; identification of valence states of transition element ions. Samples must be paramagnetic

Introduction

Ferromagnetic resonance (FMR) describes resonant absorption of electromagnetic (usually microwave) radiation in a magnetic material containing strongly exchange coupled electrons; absorption is measured as a function of an applied magnetic field. In this sense, FMR encompasses any system containing a high concentration of paramagnetic ions with predominantly ferromagnetic exchange coupling. Materials that exhibit ferromagnetism in at least some temperature regime and metallic ferromagnetic materials will be considered in this article.

Among the materials of interest are the classical ferromagnetic metals iron, nickel, and cobalt and their alloys in single crystal and polycrystalline form. The rare earths (except gadolinium) are difficult to study using FMR because of their enormous anisotropy fields. However, remarkable developments have taken place over the past ten years in the fabrication and study of amorphous or glassy ferromagnets (Ref 1). The advent of these new classes of complexes

(and other disordered alloys) has revealed the existence of conventional ferromagnetism, which prevails at all temperatures between 0 and the Curie temperature T_c, and reentrant magnetism, in which the ferromagnetic state collapses when $T > T_c$ or when T drops below a "freezing" temperature T_f. These are best described using magnetic phase diagrams (Ref 2). Two typical examples are shown in Fig. 1(a) and (b).

In such diagrams, the zero field characteristic temperatures T_c, which marks the transition from paramagnet (PM) to ferromagnet (FM); T_f, the transition from FM to spin glass (SG); and T_{SG}, the transition from PM to SG are plotted as functions of the concentration (x) of the magnetic species. At high x, the material is more or less a conventional FM; at low x, PM goes over to SG. This article will emphasize the high x, or conventional FM, region and the intermediate x, or reentrant (REE), regime in which the system becomes FM on cooling but collapses from the FM state on further lowering of temperature.

For a prototypical alloy series, $Fe_x N_{80-x} P_{14} B_6$ (Fig. 2), whose phase diagram is shown in Fig. 1(b), FMR provides a direct signature for identifying the FM and REE phases (Ref 3). In the simple FM alloys, exemplified by $x = 40$, the linewidth for FMR is independent of temperature over wide ranges of temperature below T_c. In the REE regime, $9 \leq x \leq 19$, the linewidth exhibits a characteristic increase at low T. Historically, the first indication of the complexity of the phase diagram came from FMR data, although FMR alone cannot be used to determine the phase transition lines shown in Fig. 1, because it is always performed in a sizable applied field.

As for any other resonant phenomenon, FMR is characterized by two parameters, the resonance field (H_R) and the linewidth (Γ). Careful measurement of H_R at several frequencies and in different geometries can be used to establish several material parameters, such as magnetization and magnetic anisotropy. In contrast, linewidths yield invaluable information on high-frequency

Fig. 1 Magnetic phase diagrams

(a) Zero field phase diagram for an amorphous alloy series $(Fe_xNi_{1-x})_{75}P_{16}B_6Al_3$. Note the intermediate x (reentrant) region in which the material loses its ferromagnetism when $T > T_c$ or $T < T_f$. This contrasts sharply with high x alloys in which ferromagnetism prevails from T_c to 0 K. (b) Phase diagram for amorphous $Fe_xNi_{80-x}P_{14}B_6$ ribbons. See comments for Fig. 1(a).

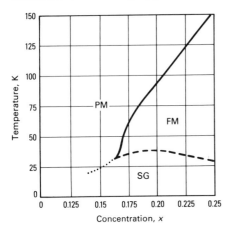

(a)

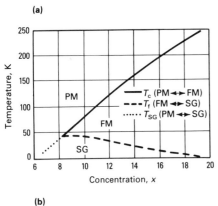

(b)

Fig. 2 Temperature dependence of FMR linewidths in $Fe_xNi_{80-x}P_{14}B_6$ alloys at 11 GHz

Note the characteristic difference between a ferromagnetic alloy (Fe40), which has Γ independent of T, and the REE alloys, which exhibit a large rise at low T. This experiment provides a quick criterion for deciding between a ferromagnet and a reentrant magnet.

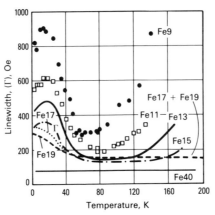

Fig. 3 Recommended sample shapes and sizes for FMR studies

(a) Cylinder. (b) Parallelepiped. (c) Circular disk. See also Eq 1(a), (b), and (c).

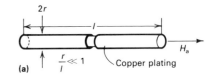

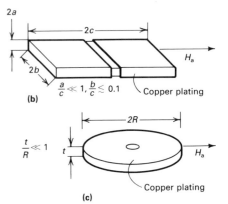

losses. However, FMR is also useful in revealing subtler features, such as surface contamination, frozen-in strains, and magnetic inhomogeneities. Ferromagnetic resonance uncovers inhomogeneous effects often missed by other means of examination. The surface sensitivity arises from the fact that in materials having a conductivity of approximately 10^{-2} to 1 μΩ · m, the microwaves penetrate only the first few microns of the sample surface.

For routine measurements of magnetic parameters, FMR is one of the least demanding techniques. Because signals are usually large, sample size is never of much concern; a few microns of thickness and a few square millimeters of surface area are sufficient. High-precision measurements on pure metals require single crystals, and considerable effort must be expended to produce the narrowest lines. The methods for growing highly defect-free single crystals and subsequent preparation of sample surfaces are reviewed in detail in Ref 4. Glassy ribbons can also be prepared variously (Ref 5). Thin films are usually prepared using evaporation in a vacuum or diverse sputtering techniques. Thin films of iron and body-centered cubic (bcc) cobalt have also been grown using molecular beam evaporation (Ref 6, 7). However, the full apparatus of FMR has not yet been used for this last class of samples.

Although reasonable values for the parameters can be achieved by measuring at several frequencies and in different geometries, other measurements are useful for facilitating and corroborating FMR. For example, availability of independent data on magnetization (from vibrating sample or Faraday balance magnetometry) facilitates obtaining the anisotropy constants using FMR. Although the exchange stiffness parameters can be measured by studying volume modes of FMR in thin films (also termed spin wave resonances, or SWR), it is helpful to find equivalent data obtained from inelastic neutron scattering, even if the latter are invariably confined to somewhat larger wave vectors than are available to SWR. Finally, in working with single-crystal samples, use of x-ray techniques for identifying the relevant high symmetry directions is invaluable to the analysis of FMR data.

Theory

Because the microwaves penetrate only a few microns into the sample, most macro-scopic samples can be regarded as flat plates, except when calculating the static demagnetizing fields. Powder samples should be avoided, because interpretation of results requires several systematic corrections. The problem is considerably simplified if the sample takes one of the forms shown in Fig. 3 and if the dimensions satisfy the conditions $r/l \ll 1$, $a/c \ll 1$, and $t/R \ll 1$, as defined in Fig. 3. The sample surface should be covered, for example, by electroplating, with a few microns of copper, leaving only a small central region exposed (Fig. 3). This enables reliable estimation of the static demagnetizing field (H_d) near the center and avoids deleterious effects arising from the spatial variation of H_d near the extremities. For thin films, many of the problems associated with demagnetizing effects do not occur. Background information on the theory of FMR in metals is cited in Ref 4.

For the geometries shown in Fig. 3, the resonance fields satisfy the following equations. For a cylinder (Fig. 3a):

$$\left(\frac{\omega}{\gamma}\right)^2 = \left[H_a + H_k - \pi M\left(\frac{r}{l}\right)^2\right] \times$$

$$\left[H_a + H_k - \pi M\left(\frac{r}{l}\right)^2 + 4\pi M\right] \text{(Eq 1a)}$$

where H_a is the applied magnetic field parallel to the axis; H_k represents any anisotropy fields arising from magnetocrystalline anisotropy or induced by the combined effects

Fig. 4 Geometry of applied field H_a and magnetization M for use with Eq 2

(a) Parallelepiped. (b) Circular disk

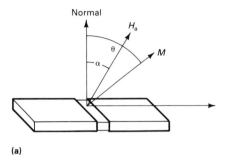

(a)

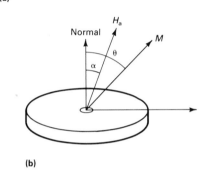

(b)

of strain and magnetostriction; γ is the gyromagnetic ratio, $g\mu_B/\hbar$, where g is the spectroscopic splitting factor, μ_B is the Bohr magneton, and $\hbar = h/2\pi$, where h is Planck's constant; $\omega = 2\pi \times f$ (the microwave frequency); and M is the magnetization (assumed uniform). For a parallelepiped (Fig. 3b) with H_a parallel to the c-axis:

$$\left(\frac{\omega}{\gamma}\right)^2 = (H_a + H_k - H_d)$$

$$\times (H_a + H_k - H_d + 4\pi M) \quad \text{(Eq 1b)}$$

with

$$H_d = 8M\cot^{-1}\frac{(a^2 + b^2 + c^2)c}{ab}$$

where H_k is as defined in Eq 1(a). For a circular disk (Fig. 3c) with H_a parallel to the disk surface:

$$\left(\frac{\omega}{\gamma}\right)^2 = \left[H_a\cos(\alpha - \theta) + H_k(\theta) - \frac{\pi M t}{R}\right]$$

$$\times \left[H_a\cos(\alpha - \theta) + H'_k(\theta)\right.$$

$$\left. + 4\pi M - \pi M\frac{t}{R}\right] \quad \text{(Eq 1c)}$$

where α and θ represent the inclinations of H_a and M relative to the symmetry axis and

H_k, H'_k, the concomitant anisotropy fields. Table 1 lists a few special cases.

In principle, terms arising from the exchange conductivity effect should be included in Eq 1(a), (b), and (c), which would be roughly equivalent to introducing an internal field that augments the effects of H_a. However, this contribution can be neglected, except where high precision is desired. For amorphous ferromagnets, it is negligible.

Another important case arises when the in-plane anisotropy is small, and the magnetic field is rotated in a plane perpendicular to the plane of the sample, as shown in Fig. 4(a) and (b). The resonance equation is:

$$\left(\frac{\omega}{\gamma}\right)^2 = [H_a\cos\alpha - 4\pi M\cos\theta]^2 +$$

$$H_a\sin\alpha\,[H_a\sin\alpha + 4\pi M\sin\theta]^2$$

$$\text{(Eq 2)}$$

with

$$\frac{\sin(\theta - \alpha)}{\sin\theta\cos\theta} = \frac{4\pi M}{H_a} \quad \text{(Eq 3)}$$

In Eq 2 and 3, the in-plane static demagnetizing field has been assumed to be negligible. Two cases are significant. For perpendicular geometry, $\alpha = 0$:

$$\frac{\omega}{\gamma} = H_a - 4\pi M \quad \text{(Eq 4)}$$

For parallel geometry, $\alpha = \pi/2$:

$$\left(\frac{\omega}{\gamma}\right)^2 = H_a(H_a + 4\pi M) \quad \text{(Eq 5)}$$

In some cases, the material has a uniaxial anisotropy K_u, with the symmetry axis along the normal to the sample (film) plane. This can be taken into account by replacing $4\pi M$ in Eq 4 and 5 with:

$$4\pi M_{eff} = 4\pi M + \frac{2K_u}{M} \quad \text{(Eq 6)}$$

where M_{eff} is the effective magnetization. Further, isotropic planar stress in the sample and isotropic magnetostriction produce torques that mimic an anisotropy torque with symmetry axis along the normal:

$$4\pi M_{eff} = 4\pi M + \frac{3\lambda_m\sigma}{M} \quad \text{(Eq 7)}$$

Table 1   Resonance equations for single crystals

Cubic crystal: (anisotropy energy: $F_a = K_0 + K_1(\alpha_1^2\alpha_2^2 + \alpha_2^2\alpha_3^2 + \alpha_1^2) + K_2\alpha_1^2\alpha_2^2\alpha_3^2$ where K is the anisotropy constant

Sample plane [011]

$$H_a \parallel (100) \quad \left(\frac{\omega}{\gamma}\right)^2 = \left(H_a + \frac{2K_1}{M} - H_d\right)\left(H_a + \frac{2K_1}{M} - H_d + 4\pi M\right)$$

$$H_a \parallel (111) \quad \left(\frac{\omega}{\gamma}\right)^2 = \left[H_a - \frac{4}{3}\frac{K_1}{M} - \frac{4}{9}\frac{K_2}{M} - H_d\right]\left[H_a - \frac{4K_1}{3M} - \frac{4}{9}\frac{K_2}{M} - H_d + 4\pi M\right]$$

$$H_a \parallel (110) \quad \left(\frac{\omega}{\gamma}\right)^2 = \left[H_a - \frac{2K_1}{M} - H_d + 4\pi M\right]\left[H_a + \frac{K_1}{M} + \frac{K_2}{2M} - H_d\right]$$

Sample plane [001]

$$H \parallel (100) \quad \left(\frac{\omega}{\gamma}\right)^2 = \left(H_a + \frac{2K_1}{M} - H_d\right)\left(H_a + \frac{2K_1}{M} - H_d + 4\pi M\right)$$

$$H \parallel (110) \quad \left(\frac{\omega}{\gamma}\right)^2 = \left[H_a + \frac{K_1}{M} + \frac{K_2}{M} + 4\pi M - H_d\right]\left[H_a - \frac{2K_1}{M} - H_d\right]$$

Uniaxial crystal: $[F_a = K_0 + K_1\sin^2\theta + K_2\sin^4\theta]$

Sample plane contains symmetry axis, $H_a \parallel (0001)$: $\left(\frac{\omega}{\gamma}\right)^2 = \left[\frac{2K_1}{M} + H_a + 4\pi M - H_d\right]$

Note: In general, for $\alpha = \theta$:

$$\left(\frac{\omega}{\gamma}\right)^2 = \left[\frac{K_1}{M}(2\cos 2\theta) + \frac{4K_2}{M}\sin^2\theta(1 + \cos 2\theta) + H_a\cos\theta - H_d\right]$$

$$\times \left[\frac{K_1}{M}(2\cos^2\theta) + \frac{4K_2}{M}\sin^2\theta\cos^2\theta) + H_a\cos\theta - H_d + 4\pi M\right]$$

Fig. 5 Typical reflection spectrometer for measuring FMR

See Fig. 6 for expanded view of section C.

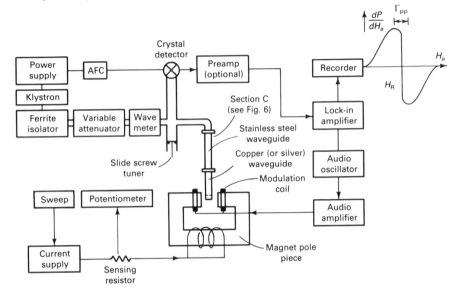

Fig. 7 Probe used for FMR study at high temperatures

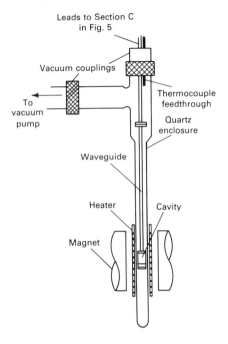

where λ_m is the magnetostriction constant, and σ is the planar stress. In the same way, a tensile stress can contribute to H_k in Eq 1(a) and (b).

Inspection of Eq 1 through 5 reveals that by making measurements at several frequencies and combining them with data taken in

Fig. 6 Probe for FMR measurement at low *T*

This probe attaches to the system shown in Fig. 5 at section C.

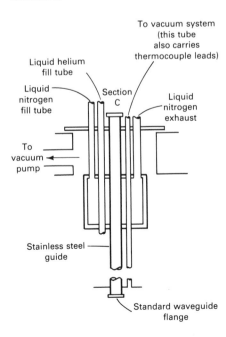

parallel and perpendicular geometries, reasonably precise determinations of the various material parameters can be obtained. Alternatively, combining FMR with vibrating sample magnetometer (VSM) studies enables confident charting of the magnetic behavior of a ferromagnetic or REE alloy.

Estimation of microwave losses requires analysis of FMR linewidths. In a conductor at room temperature, the linewidth (defined as the field separation between the points of maximum slope) is:

$$\Gamma_{PP} = \frac{1.45\omega\lambda}{\gamma^2 M} + C(A\omega\sigma_0)^{1/2} \qquad \text{(Eq 8)}$$

where σ_0 is direct-current conductivity, A is the exchange stiffness parameter, and C is a numerical factor.

Additional complications arise at low temperatures (Ref 4). The material parameter of major interest is the relaxation rate λ. For most amorphous ferromagnets, the second term on the right of Eq 8 is negligible. For most ferromagnets based on one or more of the transition metals (iron, nickel, and cobalt), λ values lie in the range of 0.2 to 2×10^8 Hz. Larger apparent values of λ would be symptomatic of rare-earth impurities or other inhomogeneities. For various soft FM alloys, λ/M is relatively independent of temperature (refer to $x = 40$ alloy in Fig. 2). Lambda is independent of frequency for fairly wide ranges of ω; thus, when the λ term dominates, a linear increase in Γ_{PP} with ω should be expected. Additional information is cited in Ref 4.

Ferromagnetic resonance measurements can be performed on magnetic films whose thickness is only a fraction of a micron. For the perpendicular geometry—for example, $\alpha = 0$ in Fig. 4—the situation becomes particularly simple. With appropriate boundary conditions for the surface spins, a film of thickness t can support several standing wave modes, satisfying:

$$\frac{\omega}{\gamma} = H_a - 4\pi M_{\text{eff}} + \frac{2A}{M}\left(\frac{p\pi}{t}\right)^2 \qquad \text{(Eq 9)}$$

where p takes on odd integer values. Again, A is the exchange stiffness parameter and is fundamental because it appears in the spin wave dispersion relation:

$$\epsilon = Dq^2 \qquad \text{(Eq 10)}$$

where $D = 2(\gamma A\hbar/M)$. Application of Eq 9 provides a direct measure of A (or D) for immediate comparison with data obtained by inelastic neutron scattering. The latter has the advantage of being conducted in zero applied field, but requires access to a high-flux reactor.

Microwave Spectrometers

Because FMR signals tend to be rather large, detection and measurement of FMR is relatively straightforward. Simple homodyne detection techniques are common, and Fig. 5

Fig. 8 Insert used in a standard varian 9-GHz cavity for FMR studies at high temperatures

la and b, copper plates with O-ring in between; 2, stainless steel tube; 3, copper rod; 4 and 5, heater and leads; 6, thermocouple; 7, sample; 8, quartz tube. Source: Ref 8

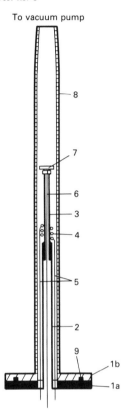

To vacuum pump

shows a typical reflection spectrometer. The microwave components are mounted on a horizontal bench, and the cavity system is attached to a vertical section of a stainless steel waveguide.

To avoid overloading, the filling factor (the ratio of sample volume to cavity volume) should be maintained small. An automatic frequency control system (AFC) is used to keep the klystron locked to the sample cavity, yielding absorption data without sizable interference from dispersion effects. The sample should be mounted in as strain-free a manner as possible. A thin solution of GE 7031 cement is usually adequate. Thin films on substrates can be held in place with vacuum grease used sparingly. The magnetic field is modulated at an audio frequency. Thus, the derivative of the absorption, dP/dH_a (Fig. 5), is measured instead of the absorption itself. The field separation between the peaks in dP/dH_a yields Γ_{pp}; for narrow lines, H_R can be marked directly at the zero crossing. Wide lines require more careful analysis (Ref 3). For investigations at 9 GHz and above, the cavity can be formed from a length of standard waveguide. The sample is mounted on the bottom face to study in-plane angular dependence, as in Eq 1, or the side wall to measure out-of-plane effects, as in Fig. 4 and Eq 2.

For low-temperature investigations, the stainless steel waveguide forms the central portion of the probe (Fig. 6). This probe can be enclosed in a double Dewar system. In addition, the cavity and bottom few inches of the stainless steel waveguide are enclosed in a thin-wall stainless steel can (not shown) that can be evacuated. This prevents the cryogenic fluid from contacting the sample and enables control of the sample temperature by judicious adjustment of the level of cryogen in the Dewar combined with a small amount of heat from a wire heater wrapped around the waveguide. A simple copper-constantan thermocouple suffices for temperature measurement, although more sophisticated devices can be used if necessary.

The system can be adapted for high-temperature investigation by using a probe of the type shown in Fig. 7. The enclosure is made of quartz, and the vacuum should be better than 10^{-5} torr. Using a spectrometer that is otherwise operational (stabilization of klystrons requires approximately 30 min), room-temperature FMR data can be obtained within 1 h so that several samples can be studied in a morning. A low-temperature experiment down to 4 K may take the better part of a day.

Standard varian spectrometers operating at approximately 9 GHz are available in many laboratories. These systems usually incorporate a low-temperature acccessory introduced into the cavity through a port at its base. A probe is available for high-temperature experiments with the varian system (Fig. 8). The sample is glued to one end of a copper rod that is thermally insulated from the bottom plate by the stainless steel tube. Because only the rod and sample are heated, the heater requires little power. An advantage is that the cavity remains at room temperature throughout the experiment. However, the frequency of operation is restricted to 9 GHz. Availability of several frequencies is beneficial. Meaningful analysis of linewidth data is extremely hazardous without an adequate range of frequency variation.

Ferromagnetic Antiresonance Spectrometers. Closely allied to FMR is ferromagnetic antiresonance (FMAR). In FMAR, at a certain applied field, the sample becomes relatively transparent to microwaves. Study of FMAR usually yields information complementary to that obtained using FMR. The experiments must be conducted in transmission, with consequent difficulties. The spectrometer shown in Fig. 9 has been developed and used successfully for FMAR investigations. Approximately ⅓ W of microwave power is fed into a critically coupled transmitter cavity and is incident on the sample through a hole cut in the narrow side of the cavity. The small amount of transmitted energy (typical transmission ratio ≤100 dB) is collected in a receiver cavity, chopped at 30 MHz by an electronic switch, and fed into a balanced mixer and preamplifier. The reference signal is tapped directly from the klystron. The 30-MHz signal is directly proportional to the amplitude of transmitted microwave power and the cosine of its phase angle relative to the reference.

With suitable further amplification and detection, the amplitude and the relative phase of the transmitted signal can be measured. Because leakage is a problem, extreme care is necessary when performing these experiments. Conducting measurements at two phase angles enables construction of FMAR signals for comparison with lines obtained from theory and thus provides independent determination of the material parameters. The length scales involved in FMAR are much longer than those in FMR; therefore, FMAR is less susceptible to surface effects. The requirements on sample surfaces are thus less stringent, and, in principle, information pertaining to the interior of the sample can be obtained. However, the technique is intrinsically more difficult. Additional information on the use of FMAR is cited in Ref 10.

Applications

Example 1: Magnetization. All the ferromagnetic parameters can be obtained (Eq 1a) by using needle-shaped samples (Fig. 3a) and by conducting measurements at several frequencies. This procedure was implemented to investigate a series of amorphous $(Fe_{1-x}Ni_x)_{80}P_{10}B_{10}$ alloys at room temperature (Ref 11). Because the samples were under tension, H_k values ranging from 0 to 0.04 T were included. Figure 10 shows the $4\pi M$ values deduced from FMR. The values for $x > 0.7$ were obtained from VSM, and the data corroborate well.

In another study, measurements were performed using strain-free samples in perpendicular and parallel geometries (see Fig. 3b and Eq 4 and 5) at several frequencies (Ref 3). In this investigation, $4\pi M$ was derived as a function of T in a series of $Fe_xNi_{80-x}P_{14}B_6$ alloys (Fig. 11). Use of data in the parallel and perpendicular geometries at a fixed frequency enables accurate (within a few percent) determination of mag-

Fig. 9 Microwave spectrometer used for FMAR measurements in transmission
Source: Ref 9

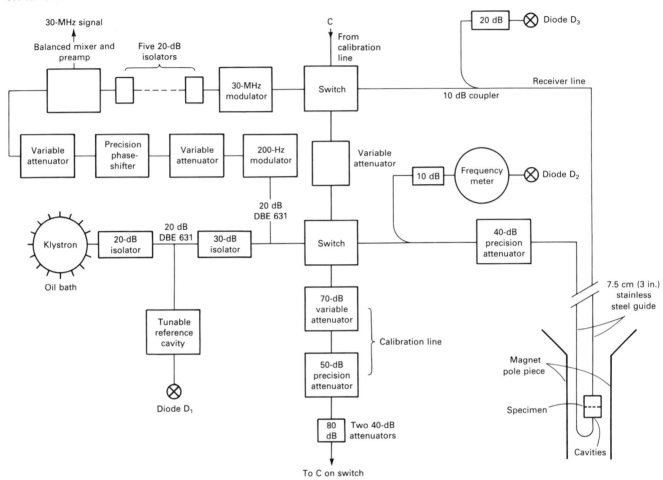

netization without involving such complicating factors as unidirectional anisotropy fields. As shown in Fig. 11, the data have been plotted versus $T^{3/2}$ to demonstrate that the reduction in M with increasing T can be attributed to spin wave excitations. The stiffness parameter D (Eq 10) can be deduced from the slope, and the manner in which it vanishes (Fig. 12) can be studied as x is reduced toward the value at which ferromagnetism cannot be maintained at any temperature (see the magnetic phase diagram in Fig. 1b). Thus, FMR helps to delineate the FM and REE phases and indicates the way in which the FM state collapses with reduction of the concentration of the magnetic species.

Example 2: Magnetic Anisotropy. Figures 13(a) and (b) show the use of FMR for obtaining anisotropy constants in hexagonal close-packed (hcp) cobalt and fcc nickel. In the former case (Ref 12), measurements were conducted on single crystal whiskers, with the whisker axis along (001). Magnetization was taken from VSM data, and $2K_1/M$ deduced from FMR using the equation in Table 1. The figure also compares $2K_1/M$ derived from FMR and that obtained using torque magnetometry. The nickel data were obtained using disk samples cut in the [110] plane, and the FMR results are compared with torque data (Ref 4). The crystallographic symmetry is well illustrated by the angular dependence of the resonance field (Fig. 14) (see also Eq 1c).

When first examined, amorphous magnetic materials were generally believed to exhibit no anisotropy. Ferromagnetic resonance data on amorphous $GdCo_2$ were the first indications of the presence of a K_u term (see Eq 4 to 6). An important case arises when there is a uniaxial anisotropy, but the symmetry axis is not in the sample plane or along the normal to it. Figure 15 shows a typical example. Careful analysis of the data

Fig. 10 Saturation magnetization at 300 K as a function of concentration x in amorphous $(F_{1-x}Ni_x)_{80}P_{10}B_{10}$ alloys
Source: Ref 11

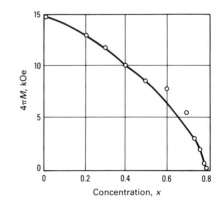

Fig. 11 Temperature dependence of magnetization deduced from FMR data on $Fe_xNi_{80-x}P_{14}B_6$ alloys

Note the linearity at low T, which indicates that the reduction in magnetization occurs due to excitation of spin waves. The slope can be used to calculate the spin wave stiffness D in Eq 10. An exceptionally small ($\sim$100 meV/Å^2) value of D is characteristic of glassy ferromagnets. Source: Ref 3

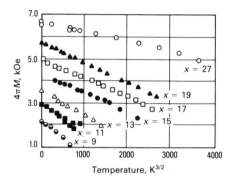

Fig. 12 Spin wave stiffness, D (see Eq 10), as a function of iron concentration in $Fe_xNi_{80-x}P_{14}B_6$

The arrow marks the concentration at which the FM phase disappears (see Fig. 1b).

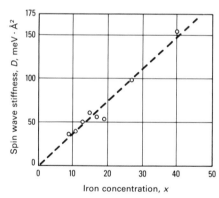

Fig. 14 Resonance center versus field angle in [110] plane of nickel at 25 GHz

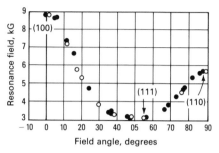

revealed that the anisotropy axis was inclined 28° to the normal for the amorphous GdFe$_2$ results shown in Fig. 15 (Ref 13, 14).

Example 3: Surface Effects. The most significant example of the importance of FMR to delineate surface effects is the case of amorphous YFe$_2$. Magnetization and susceptibility measurements suggested that amorphous YFe$_2$ is paramagnetic at room temperature, showing a PM-SG transition at approximately 60 K. However, FMR data indicate unequivocally that the material has a layer of ferromagnetic material on its surface (Ref 15). Figure 16 shows the observed spectrum in the parallel and perpendicular geometries. Use of Eq 4 and 5 enables derivation of the value of $4\pi M_{eff}$ required to characterize the behavior of S$_1$. Use of Eq 2 allows prediction of the angular dependence exactly as observed (Fig. 17).

Ferromagnetic resonance can also reveal some of the changes that accompany oxidation (Ref 16), as seen in studies of single-crystal iron whiskers (Fig. 18). The unoxidized surface shows a single line (see line A), but an extra line (presumably due to an oxide) appears as oxidation proceeds and

Fig. 15 FMR fields for a 0.85-μm amorphous GdFe$_2$ film measured at 9.2 GHz

The applied magnetic field H_a was rotated in the film plane, and anisotropy arose because the symmetry axis was tilted approximately 28° away from the normal to the film plane. Source: Ref 13

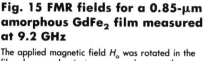

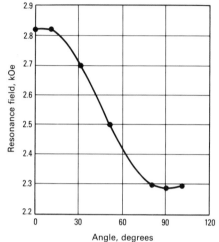

Fig. 16 Field derivative of absorption in amorphous YFe$_2$ measured at 300 K and 10.8 GHz

Note the shift in S$_1$ as the field is rotated from the parallel (a) to the perpendicular (b) geometry, indicating the presence of a thin layer of ferromagnetic material. Bulk amorphous YFe$_2$ is paramagnetic at 300 K and produces the weak signal centered at 3.5 kOe.

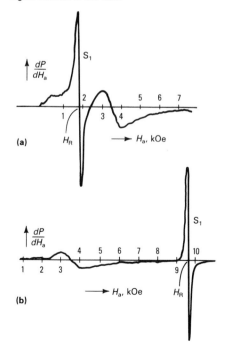

Fig. 13 Effect of temperature on the first anisotropy constant, K

(a) hcp cobalt. (b) fcc nickel. Results obtained from FMR are compared with measured values from torque magnetometry. See Table 1 for resonance equations for cubic and uniaxial crystals.

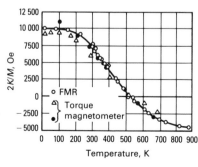

(a)

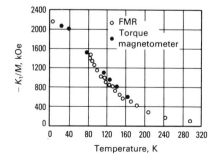

(b)

Fig. 17 Angular dependence of resonance field for S₁ in amorphous YFe₂

As noted in Fig. 16 (bulk amorphous YFe_2 being paramagnetic), these data indicate the presence of a ferromagnetic layer at the surface. Field measured at 300 K and 24 GHz, with $4\pi M = 6.2$ kOe

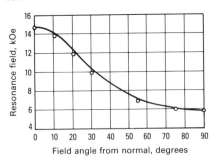

Fig. 18 Effect of oxidation on FMR in single-crystal iron whisker

A, unoxidized; B, C, D, E, and F were oxidized for 1.5, 3, 10, 45, and 240 min, respectively. The numbers describe the relative sensitivities of the spectrometer.

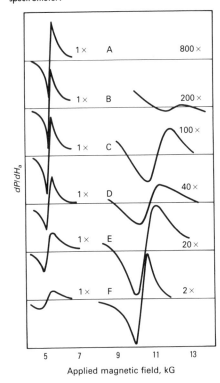

Fig. 19 FMR study of abraded ribbons

A, both surfaces; B, shiny surface; C, rough surface, abraded. Source: Ref 17

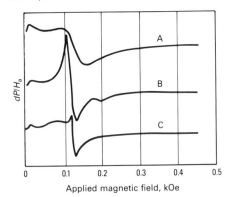

Fig. 20 Field derivative of power absorbed in 2250-Å-thick film of amorphous Zr₃₈Co₆₂ measured at 300 K and 10.71 GHz

S_1, S_2, and S_4 correspond to $4\pi M_{eff}$ values with a spread of 5 kOe. (a) Parallel sample geometry. (b) Perpendicular sample geometry

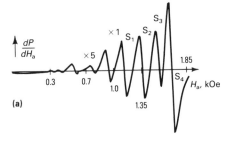

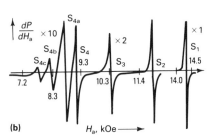

ultimately becomes stronger than the line due to the iron itself.

Abrasion of glassy ribbons also leaves signatures on the FMR lines (Ref 17). Because the two surfaces of a ribbon are not identical (one is much rougher than the other), differences between the effects of abrading either surface can be determined (Fig. 19). A far subtler surface effect is contained in the surface anisotropy parameter that affects FMR linewidths in high-quality single-crystal metal samples. Additional information is cited in Ref 4.

Example 4: Inhomogeneity. With the advent of magnetic glasses as important materials for research and industry, the question of magnetic inhomogeneity acquires utmost importance. Ferromagnetic resonance is the most sensitive technique for observing gross and subtle magnetic inhomogeneities.

Figures 20 and 21 are clear examples of gross inhomogeneities. In Fig. 20, a thin film of amorphous $Zr_{68}Co_{32}$ was examined

using FMR. Magnetization, electron microprobe, and other tests indicated high uniformity in this sample. However, the FMR spectra suggest the presence of at least four independent magnetic networks with $4\pi M_{eff}$ values spread over 5 kOe. Figures 21(a) and (b) show the difference between two amorphous FeB films prepared by sputtering.

Secondary ion mass spectroscopy investigations failed to reveal the inhomogeneities clearly discovered by an FMR study in the film of Fig. 21(b).

In the case of subtler inhomogeneities, local variations of exchange and anisotropy in a glassy magnetic material and, to a lesser extent, in crystalline magnetic materials prevent the spins from becoming collinear even in the saturated state. The existence of this subtle effect was clear in the first systematic examination of FMR in amorphous fer-

Fig. 21 FMR in amorphous FeB showing the difference between (a) a homogeneous sample and (b) an inhomogeneous sample

Secondary ion mass spectroscopy suggested that both samples were identical.

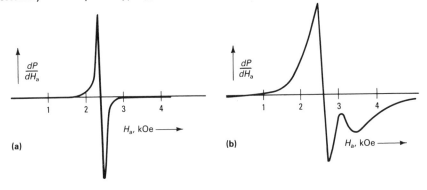

Fig. 22 Frequency dependence of FMR linewidths in amorphous $(Fe_xNi_{100-x})_{0.75}Gd_{0.25}$ samples at ≥ 10 GHz

Note the linear increase (determined by λ) and a nonzero intercept, which indicate a subtle inhomogeneity in amorphous ferromagnets.

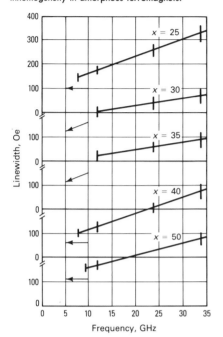

Fig. 23 Frequency dependence of FMR linewidths over a wide range of frequencies

The lines were derived from a model (Ref 3) that takes into account the inhomogeneity suggested by earlier data at high frequency. See also Fig. 22.

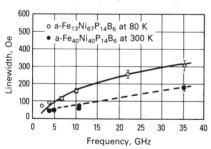

Fig. 24 Spin wave resonance spectrum in a 3800-Å-thick amorphous $Y_{20}Co_{80}$ film at 22 GHz and 300 K

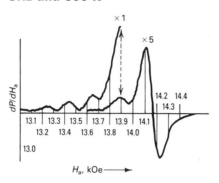

Fig. 25 Resonance field in amorphous $Fe_{49}B_{51}$ samples (parallel geometry) as a function of temperature at 35 GHz

Data for $T \geq 100$ K are unique and represent ordinary FMR. For $4 < T < 100$ K, the system appears to have many possible paths. Different symbols represent different cooling cyles: for ▲, ●, and △, resonance was measured while cooling slowly to 4 K, ▲ being the slowest. For ○, data were taken after cooling to 4 K.

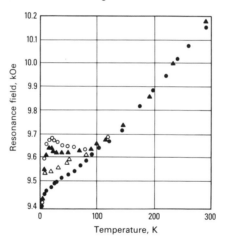

Table 2 Effective magnetization in stressed nickel films

Film thickness, Å	$4\pi M_{eff}$, Oe
500	492
800	1700
1000	1170
1300	559
1800	1700
Bulk	6100

Source: Ref 20

Table 3 Spin wave resonance values for ferromagnetic materials

Material	D, 10^{-29} erg/cm^2
Iron	5.5 ± 0.03
Nickel	6.6 ± 0.7
hcp Cobalt	5.6 ± 0.3
$Fe_{25}Ni_{75}$ (Permalloy)	6.0
Ni-22Cu	1.9
Ni-34.6Pd	2.5
$Fe_{19}Ni_{81}$	4.7
a-$Y_{29}Co_{71}$(a)	4.9
a-$Y_{20}Co_{80}$(a)	2.4

(a) a stands for amorphous

may become so large that interpretation of perpendicular resonance in terms of Eq 4 will yield $4\pi M_{eff}$ values much less than the $4\pi M$ obtained from VSM. Table 2 lists effective magnetization values for stressed nickel films (Ref 20). The dramatic variation relative to the bulk value of $4\pi M$ is evident.

More complicated effects appear if the magnetostriction constants $(\lambda_m)_{100}$ and $(\lambda_m)_{111}$ are disparate. The resonance fields and the linewidths are altered, and more than one resonance may be observed due to values of H_R that are stationary relative to grain orientation in the film. Ferromagnetic resonance is sensitive to strains because of the effects of magnetostriction; thus, FMR has been used to measure magnetostriction constants by observing shifts in FMR lines in response to an applied stress.

Example 6: Spin Wave Resonances (Exchange Stiffness). Since its discovery, SWR has been used to measure exchange stiffness coefficients in magnetic films with the aid of Eq 9. All elemental ferromagnetics have been studied and considerable effort expended on various permalloys because they allow fabrication of materials with vanishing anisotropy and magnetostriction, making the observation of well-defined SWR modes particularly useful. Table 3 lists some of the results obtained. Figure 24 shows a typical SWR spectrum.

Example 7: Relaxation Parameter. Ferromagnetic resonance and FMAR are the only techniques for determining spin relax-

romagnets (Ref 18). At high frequencies (≥ 10 GHz), a linear increase in Γ_{pp} (first term on the right-hand side of Eq 8) is evident, but upon extrapolation there is invariably an intercept at frequency = 0 (Fig. 22). A down turn in FMR linewidths at low frequencies (Fig. 23) has recently been discovered. At the macroscopic level, the entire frequency dependence can be understood in terms of a distribution of magnetization (or

its projection along H_a) and a concomitant distribution of demagnetizing fields (Ref 3). Microscopically, a two-magnon term has been invoked to account for the data (Ref 19).

Example 5: Strains. During deposition of thin films, considerable strains are frozen into the material. If the material has sizable magnetostriction, the presence of the strains makes itself apparent through a profound effect in the resonance field for FMR. For example, an isotropic planar stress in a nickel film, assuming $(\lambda_m)_{100} = (\lambda_m)_{111}$, will appear as an effective uniaxial anisotropy field of value $3\lambda_m\sigma/M$. Strain effects

Table 4   Relaxation parameter for ferromagnetic materials

Material	$4\pi M$, Oe	$\lambda/10^8$ Hz	$\gamma/(10^7$ Hz/Oe)	$\alpha = \lambda/\gamma M$
Iron	21 000	0.4–0.7	1.84	0.002
Nickel	6 000	2.3	1.95	0.025
Cobalt	17 900	1.0	1.92	0.004
Ni-25Fe	11 600	0.88	1.85	0.005
Ni-5.4Cu	5 350	2.1	1.93	0.026
a-Y-Co(a)	5 700	1.3	1.87	0.015
a-GdFe$_2$(a)	3 900	1.0	1.55	0.021
Metglass 2826A	4 600	1.7	1.90	0.24
Metglass 2826B	4 800	0.8	1.85	0.011
Iron	21 000	0.4	1.82	0.0013
Nickel	6 000	2.4	1.97	0.026
Fe-3% Si	20 240	0.4	1.85	0.001
Fe-58% Ni	15 600	0.4	1.86	0.002
$(Fe_{0.40}Ni_{0.60})_{75}P_{16}B_6Al_3$	3 340	0.88	1.86	0.018
a-Gd-Co(a)	10 200	1.7	1.93	0.011
	7 900	1.1	1.93	0.009
	4 900	1.4	2.10	0.017
	2 400	0.8	2.15	0.019
	460	0.4	2.15	0.051
a-TbFe$_2$(a)	4 600	7.4	1.80	0.112
Moly-Permalloy (79Ni-4Mo-17Fe)	. . .	1.8	. . .	0.015
$Fe_{40}Ni_{40}P_{14}B_6$	8 800	1.00	1.86	0.006
$Fe_{11}Ni_{69}P_{14}B_6$	3 000	0.67	1.84	0.020
$Co_{75}P_{16}B_6Al_3$	8 900	3.1	1.84	0.024

(a) a stands for amorphous

ation rates at long wavelengths (Ref 4, 9, 11). In many cases, the exchange term (second term on the right-hand side of Eq 8) is small, linewidth varies linearly with frequency, and a value for λ may be extracted. Table 4 lists some of the values of λ. For all transition metal-base ferromagnets (crystalline or amorphous), the relaxation parameter $\lambda/\gamma M$ lies between the extremes represented by pure iron and pure nickel.

Example 8: Exotic Effects. In disordered magnetic materials, in which a considerable variation of exchange leading to the REE and SG phases is likely, the ground-state free energy, as a function of the spin configuration, cannot have a single minimum, but presents a corrugated profile, with the minima separated by fairly high barriers. Thus, the spin system may become trapped in a configuration without being able to "visit" all the microscopic states consistent

with the macroscopic parameters, that is, broken ergodicity. Ferromagnetic resonance is a powerful tool for exploring this phenomenon, as seen in an amorphous Fe$_{49}$B$_{51}$ film (Fig. 25), in which the resonance field follows different paths, depending on the particular configuration acquired by the spins as the sample is warmed from 4 K (Ref 21).

REFERENCES

1. K. Moorjani and J.M.D. Coey, *Magnetic Glasses*, Elsevier, 1984
2. J.A. Goehegan and S.M. Bhagat, *J. Magn. Magn. Mater.*, Vol 25, 1981, p 17
3. D.J. Webb and S.M. Bhagat, *J. Magn. Magn. Mater.*, Vol 42, 1984, p 109; M.L. Spano and S.M. Bhagat, Vol 24, 1981, p 143
4. S.M. Bhagat, *Technology in Metals Research*, Vol VI, John Wiley & Sons, 1983
5. H.S. Chen, *Rep. Prog. Phys.*, Vol 43, 1980, p 353
6. G.A. Prinz and J.J. Krebs, *Appl. Phys. Lett.*, Vol 39, 1981, p 397
7. C. Vittoria, G.A. Prinz, J.J. Krebs, and K. Hathaway, *J. Appl. Phys.*, April 1985
8. S. Haraldson and L. Patterson, *J. Phys. Chem. Solids*, Vol 42, 1981, p 681
9. J.F. Cochran, B. Heinrich, and G. Dewar, *Can. J. Phys.*, Vol 55, 1977, p 834
10. L. Pust and Z. Frait, *Solid State Commun.*, Vol 45, 1983, p 103
11. L. Kraus, Z. Frait, and J. Schneider, *Phys. Status Solidi*, Vol 64a, 1981, p 449
12. S.M. Bhagat and P. Lubitz, *Phys. Rev.*, Vol B10, 1974, p 179
13. C. Vittoria, P. Lubitz, and V. Ritz, *J. Appl. Phys.*, Vol 49, 1978, p 4908
14. D.C. Cronemeyer, *AIP Conference Proceedings*, Vol 18, American Institute of Physics, New York, 1974, p 85
15. S.M. Bhagat, J.N. Lloyd, and D.K. Paul, *J. Magn. Magn. Mater.*, Vol 10, 1979, p 65
16. Z. Frait, D. Fraitova, and R. Gemperle, *Czech. J. Phys.*, Vol B25, 1975, p 906
17. I.C. Baianu, J. Patterson, and A. Rubinson, *Mater. Sci. Eng.*, Vol 40, 1979, p 273
18. S.M. Bhagat, S. Haraldson, and O. Beckman, *J. Phys. Chem. Solids*, Vol 38, 1977, p 593
19. J.F. Cochran, K. Myrtle, and B. Heinrich, *J. Appl. Phys.*, Vol 53, 1982, p 2261
20. G.R. Mather, Jr., *Phys. Lett.*, Vol 38A, 1972, p 37; A. Stankoff and G. Suran, Vol 42A, 1973, p 391
21. D.J. Webb, S.M. Bhagat, K. Morjani, T.O. Poehler, F.G. Satkiewicz, and M.A. Manheimer, *J. Magn. Magn. Mater.*, Vol 44, 1984, p 158

Nuclear Magnetic Resonance

L.H. Bennett and L.J. Swartzendruber, National Bureau of Standards

General Uses

- Phase analysis
- Electronic structure of metals
- Near-neighbor environment of atoms in solids
- Measures rate of kinetic processes, for example molecular reorientation or diffusion
- Magnetic structural studies
- Defect and annealing studies
- Molecular structure of organic compounds
- Quantitative analysis of specific components and functional groups

Examples of Applications

- Detection of phase changes
- Study of hydrogen diffusion in metals
- Studies of long-range order in intermetallic compounds
- Spin wave studies in ferromagnetic materials
- Effect of pressure on electronic structure
- Isomer identification and quantification
- Determination of copolymer ratios

Samples

- *Form*: Inorganic powders, thin wires, or thin foils, with one dimension small compared with the radio frequency skin depth, generally 10 μm or less. Special shapes and single crystals are used in some cases. Organic solids are usually dissolved in an appropriate solvent; organic liquids can be run directly or diluted. For conventional nuclear magnetic resonance, samples must generally be nonmagnetic. For ferromagnetic nuclear resonance, samples must generally be strongly magnetic
- *Size*: Several grams (inorganic) to 0.1 g (organic)

Estimated Analysis Time

- 30 min to 48 h

Capabilities of Related Techniques

- *Optical metallography*: Shows morphology and number of phases present
- *X-ray diffraction*: Gives related crystal structure information
- *Mössbauer effect*: Provides a detectable effect in the presence of many defects
- *Infrared/Fourier transform infrared spectroscopy*: More sensitive for compound identification; applicable to gases; easier data interpretation
- *Gas chromatography/mass spectrometry*: Useful for identification of complex mixtures; more sensitive

Introduction

Nuclear magnetic resonance (NMR) is a radio frequency (RF) spectroscopy involving the interaction of the nuclear magnetic dipole or electric quadrupole moments with external or internal magnetic fields or electric-field gradients. These interactions provide detailed information on the atomic (chemical) environment. Most NMR spectra are obtained using radio transmitters, pulse generators, sensitive radio receivers, and a large laboratory electromagnet. The frequency or the magnetic field is swept to obtain a resonance. The information in such a resonant spectrum includes line position, often related to the chemical shift or the metallic (Knight) shift; quadrupole splitting; and linewidths. This information can then be interpreted to give insight into the local atomic environment of those atoms responsible for the resonance.

Fundamental Principles

Properties of Nuclei. Although small ($\sim 10^{-14}$ m) when compared to atomic dimensions ($\sim 10^{-10}$ m), nuclei have finite sizes and shapes as well as resultant distinct distributions of charge and magnetization. Nuclei may thus be invested with such physical properties as electric and magnetic multipole moments. In using nuclear resonances to study materials, these nuclear properties can be considered fixed intrinsic parameters.

All nuclei are constructed of Z protons and N neutrons. The mass number A is given by $A = N + Z$. The charge Z of the nucleus determines its position in the periodic table and its chemical name. Nuclei with common Z but different A are termed isotopes. Certain properties associated with the nucleus influence the observation of NMR.

The spin angular momentum is denoted by

Table 1　Nuclear properties of the elements

Charge, Z	Mass number, A	Element	Gyromagnetic ratio/2π	Nuclear spin, I	Natural isotopic abundance, %	Quadrupole moment Q, barns	Sensitivity relative to hydrogen	
							Constant field	Constant frequency
1	1	Hydrogen	42.5774	1/2	99.985	0	1	1
1	2	Deuterium	6.5359	1	<0.02	0.0028	$<2 \times 10^{-6}$	$<8 \times 10^{-5}$
2	3	Helium	32.435	1/2	<0.004	0	$<2 \times 10^{-5}$	$<3 \times 10^{-5}$
3	6	Lithium	6.2655	1	7.5	−0.0008	6.4×10^{-4}	0.03
3	7	Lithium	16.5466	3/2	92.5	−0.04	0.27	1.8
4	9	Beryllium	5.9833	3/2	100	0.05	0.014	0.72
5	10	Boron	4.5742	3	19.8	0.08	0.039	0.35
5	11	Boron	13.660	3/2	80.2	0.04	0.13	1.3
6	13	Carbon	10.7054	1/2	1.11	0	1.8×10^{-4}	0.0028
7	14	Nitrogen	3.0752	1	99.63	0.01	0.001	0.2
7	15	Nitrogen	4.313	1/2	0.366	0	3.8×10^{-6}	3.8×10^{-4}
8	17	Oxygen	5.7719	5/2	0.038	−0.026	1.1×10^{-5}	6.1×10^{-4}
9	19	Fluorine	40.059	1/2	100	0	0.83	0.96
10	21	Neon	3.361	3/2	0.27	0.1	6.6×10^{-6}	0.0011
11	23	Sodium	11.262	3/2	100	0.14	0.093	1.3
12	25	Magnesium	2.6055	5/2	10	0.22	2.7×10^{-4}	0.073
13	27	Aluminum	11.094	5/2	100	0.15	0.21	3.1
14	29	Silicon	8.4577	1/2	4.7	0	3.7×10^{-4}	0.0095
15	31	Phosphorus	17.237	1/2	100	0	0.066	0.41
16	33	Sulfur	3.2655	3/2	0.75	−0.055	1.7×10^{-5}	0.0029
17	35	Chlorine	4.172	3/2	75.77	−0.0797	0.0036	0.38
17	37	Chlorine	3.473	3/2	24.23	−0.0621	6.3×10^{-4}	0.1
19	39	Potassium	1.9867	3/2	93.3	0.055	4.7×10^{-4}	0.22
19	41	Potassium	1.0905	3/2	6.7	0.067	5.6×10^{-6}	0.0088
20	43	Calcium	2.8646	7/2	0.14	?	9×10^{-6}	0.002
21	45	Scandium	10.343	7/2	100	−0.022	0.3	5.2
22	47	Titanium	2.400	5/2	7.5	0.29	1.6×10^{-4}	0.05
22	49	Titanium	2.401	7/2	5.5	0.24	2.1×10^{-4}	0.066
23	50	Vanadium	4.243	6	0.25	±0.06	1.4×10^{-4}	0.014
23	51	Vanadium	11.193	7/2	99.75	−0.05	0.38	5.6
24	53	Chromium	2.406	3/2	9.5	±0.03	8.6×10^{-5}	0.027
25	55	Manganese	10.500	7/2	100	0.4	0.32	5.3
26	57	Iron	1.3757	1/2	2.14	0	7.2×10^{-7}	7.1×10^{-4}
27	59	Cobalt	10.03	7/2	100	0.4	0.27	5
28	61	Nickel	3.79	3/2	1.1	0.16	3.9×10^{-5}	0.005
29	63	Copper	11.285	3/2	69.1	−0.211	0.064	0.93
29	65	Copper	12.089	3/2	30.9	−0.195	0.035	0.45
30	67	Zinc	2.663	5/2	4.1	0.17	1.2×10^{-4}	0.031
31	69	Gallium	10.209	3/2	60	0 19	0.041	0.73
31	71	Gallium	12.984	3/2	40	0.12	0.057	0.62
32	73	Germanium	1.4852	9/2	7.7	−0.28	1.1×10^{-4}	0.09
33	75	Arsenic	7.2919	3/2	100	0.29	0.025	0.87
34	77	Selenium	8.13	1/2	7.5	0	5.3×10^{-4}	0.015
35	79	Bromine	10.67	3/2	50.69	?	0.04	0.65
35	81	Bromine	11.50	3/2	49.3	0.27	0.049	0.68
36	83	Krypton	1.64	9/2	11.5	0.27	2.2×10^{-4}	0.15
37	85	Rubidium	4.1099	5/2	72.15	0.26	0.0076	0.83
37	87	Rubidium	13.928	3/2	27.83	0.12	0.049	0.46
38	87	Strontium	1.8450	9/2	7.0	0.3	1.9×10^{-4}	0.1
39	89	Yttrium	2.086	1/2	100	0	1.2×10^{-4}	0.05
40	91	Zirconium	3.958	5/2	11.2	?	0.001	0.12
41	93	Niobium	10.405	9/2	100	−0.22	0.48	8.2
42	95	Molybdenum	2.774	5/2	15.9	±0.12	5.1×10^{-4}	1.2
42	97	Molybdenum	2.932	5/2	9.5	±1.1	3.6×10^{-4}	0.078
44	99	Rubidium	1.9	5/2	12.7	0.076	1.3×10^{-4}	0.067
44	101	Rubidium	2.1	5/2	17.1	0.44	2.4×10^{-4}	0.1
45	103	Rhodium	1.340	1/2	100	0	3.1×10^{-5}	0.032
46	105	Palladium	1.95	5/2	22.2	0.8	2.5×10^{-4}	0.12
47	107	Silver	1.723	1/2	51.83	0	3.4×10^{-5}	0.021
47	109	Silver	1.9808	1/2	48.17	0	4.9×10^{-5}	0.023
48	111	Cadmium	9.028	1/2	12.8	0	0.0012	0.028
48	113	Cadmium	9.445	1/2	12.3	0	0.0013	0.028
49	113	Indium	9.3092	9/2	4.3	0.85	0.015	0.32
49	115	Indium	9.3295	9/2	95.7	0.86	0.33	7.1
50	115	Tin	13.922	1/2	0.35	0	1.2×10^{-4}	0.0012
50	117	Tin	15.168	1/2	7.6	0	0.0034	0.028
50	119	Tin	15.867	1/2	8.6	0	0.0045	0.033
51	121	Antimony	10.189	5/2	57.3	−0.2	0.092	1.6
51	123	Antimony	5.5175	7/2	42.7	−0.5	0.02	1.2
52	123	Tellurium	11.160	1/2	0.87	0	1.6×10^{-4}	0.0023
52	125	Tellurium	13.454	1/2	7	0	0.0022	0.023
53	127	Iodine	8.557	5/2	100	−0.79	0.095	2.4

(continued)

Table 1 (continued)

Charge, Z	Mass number, A	Element	Nuclear gamma, $\gamma/2\pi$	Nuclear spin, I	Natural isotopic abundance, %	Quadrupole moment Q, barns	Sensitivity relative to hydrogen	
							Constant field	Constant frequency
54	131	Xenon	3.491	3/2	21.2	−0.12	5.8×10^{-4}	0.089
55	133	Cesium	5.5844	7/2	100	−0.003	0.047	2.8
56	135	Barium	4.2295	3/2	6.5	0.18	3.2×10^{-4}	0.033
56	137	Barium	4.7315	3/2	11.2	0.28	7.7×10^{-4}	0.063
57	138	Lanthanum	5.618	5	0.09	0.51	8.3×10^{-5}	0.0048
57	139	Lanthanum	6.0146	7/2	99.91	0.22	0.059	3.02
59	141	Praseodymium	1.3	5/2	100	−0.07	3.3×10^{-4}	0.36
60	143	Neodymium	2.33	7/2	12.2	−0.5	4.2×10^{-4}	0.14
60	145	Neodymium	1.4	7/2	8.3	−0.3	6.2×10^{-5}	0.058
62	147	Samarium	1.76	7/2	15	−0.18	2.2×10^{-4}	0.13
62	149	Samarium	1.45	7/2	13.8	0.05	1.1×10^{-4}	0.10
63	151	Europium	10.49	5/2	47.8	1.1	0.083	1.4
63	153	Europium	4.632	5/2	52.2	2.9	0.0078	0.68
64	155	Gadolinium	12.8	3/2	14.9	1.1	0.02	0.23
64	157	Gadolinium	17.1	3/2	15.7	2.0	0.05	0.32
65	159	Terbium	10.1	3/2	100	1.3	0.067	1.2
66	161	Dysprosium	1.4	5/2	18.9	2.4	7.8×10^{-5}	0.07
66	163	Dysprosium	2.0	5/2	24.9	2.6	3×10^{-4}	0.14
67	165	Holmium	8.91	7/2	100	3.5	0.19	4.5
68	167	Erbium	1.22	7/2	22.9	2.8	1.1×10^{-4}	0.14
69	169	Thulium	3.51	1/2	100	0	5.6×10^{-4}	0.084
70	171	Ytterbium	7.44	1/2	14.3	0	7.6×10^{-4}	0.025
70	173	Ytterbium	2.050	5/2	16.2	2.8	2.1×10^{-4}	0.093
71	175	Lutetium	4.8	7/2	97.4	3.5	0.029	2.4
71	176	Lutetium	3.43	7	2.6	8.0	0.001	0.16
72	177	Hafnium	1.3	7/2	18.5	4.5	1.1×10^{-4}	0.12
72	179	Hafnium	0.8	9/2	13.8	5.1	3×10^{-5}	0.087
73	181	Tantalum	5.096	7/2	99.99	3.9	0.036	2.6
74	183	Tungsten	1.7716	1/2	14.3	0	1×10^{-5}	0.0061
75	185	Rhenium	9.5854	5/2	37.5	2.3	0.05	1.0
75	187	Rhenium	9.6839	5/2	62.5	2.2	0.086	1.7
76	187	Osmium	0.9717	1/2	1.6	0	1.9×10^{-5}	3.7×10^{-4}
76	189	Osmium	3.306	3/2	16.1	0.8	3.8×10^{-4}	0.064
77	191	Iridium	0.7318	3/2	37.4	0.86	9.5×10^{-6}	0.033
77	193	Iridium	0.7968	3/2	62.6	0.78	2.1×10^{-5}	0.060
78	195	Platinum	9.094	1/2	33.8	0	0.0033	0.074
79	197	Gold	0.7292	3/2	100	0.55	2.5×10^{-5}	0.087
80	199	Mercury	7.5901	1/2	16.9	0	9.6×10^{-4}	0.031
80	201	Mercury	2.802	3/2	13.2	0.4	1.9×10^{-4}	0.044
81	203	Thallium	24.327	1/2	29.5	0	0.055	0.17
81	205	Thallium	24.567	1/2	70.5	0	0.14	0.42
82	207	Lead	8.874	1/2	22.1	0	0.002	0.047
83	209	Bismuth	6.8418	9/2	100	−0.4	0.14	5.4
92	235	Uranium	0.76	7/2	0.72	4.5	8.6×10^{-7}	0.028

$\hbar\mathbf{I}$. The spin I is always integral or half-integral. Experimentation shows that for an even-A nucleus $I = 0, 1, 2, \ldots$, and for an odd-A nucleus $I = \frac{1}{2}, \frac{3}{2}, \frac{5}{2}, \ldots$. An even-A nucleus having N and Z even has $I = 0$. No exceptions to these rules have been found.

The magnetic dipole moment μ is related to the angular momentum by:

$$\mu = \gamma\hbar\mathbf{I} = g\mu_N\mathbf{I} \qquad \text{(Eq 1)}$$

where γ is the gyromagnetic ratio, g is the nuclear g-factor, and μ_N is the nuclear magneton. The magnetic dipole moment interacts with the magnetic fields at the nuclear site.

The quadrupole moment arises from an asymmetric charge distribution $\rho(r)$ in the nucleus. The quadrupole moment interacts with the electric field gradient at the nuclear site arising from external charges. All nuclei with $I \geq 1$ have nonvanishing quadrupole moments. Although multipole moments higher than those of the magnetic dipole and electric quadrupole undoubtedly exist, their interaction energies are orders of magnitude smaller and can be neglected. Values for the nuclear spin I, gyromagnetic ratio γ, and quadrupole moment Q for various nuclei are given in Table 1. Also given are the naturally occurring relative abundances of each nuclear isotope.

Basic Equation of Nuclear Magnetic Resonance. Nuclear magnetic resonance is observed by using a sensitive detector to determine the change in response of a nuclear spin system to an applied RF field (often pulsed) as either the applied RF frequency or an applied magnetic field is changed. This change is observable only near the resonance frequency of the nuclear spins. For free nuclei, the resonance frequency ν_0 in an applied magnetic field H_0 is:

$$\nu_0 = \left(\frac{\gamma}{2\pi}\right) H_0 \qquad \text{(Eq 2)}$$

The frequency ν_0 is often referred to as the Larmor frequency.

In a metal, the magnetic field at the nucleus may differ from the applied field H_0. This can be expressed by replacing H_0 with:

$$H_0 \rightarrow H_0 + \Delta H = H_m \qquad \text{(Eq 3)}$$

where H_m is the field for resonance in the metal. In this case, ΔH is known as the internal magnetic field, and $-\Delta H/H_m$ as the Knight shift. In many metals, the Knight shift arises primarily from the conduction electron paramagnetism. Relaxation times are also determined by the electrons at the Fermi level, which induce nuclear spin flips.

Fig. 1 In the presence of a magnetic field H_0, the net nuclear magnetization M precesses around the z axis with angular frequency ω_0

The time period for one revolution is termed the Larmor period.

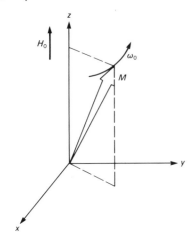

In magnetically ordered materials, an internal magnetic field can be measured in the absence of a steady external field. The NMR maps these internal, or hyperfine, fields and can thus supplement magnetization measurements.

The shape of a nuclear resonance depends on interactions among nuclei and between nuclei and their immediate environment (Ref 1-7). A comparison between theoretical and experimental lineshapes frequently enables (1) placing the location of a particular atom in the unit cell, (2) making quantitative statements about the atomic motion, that is, self-diffusion, (3) studying short- and long-range order, and (4) discovering the presence of second phases. Nuclear magnetic resonances in metals have also been used to measure ultralow temperatures.

Precessing Nuclear Magnetization. The classical theory describing the nuclear magnetization in a magnetic field is useful in visualizing the NMR process. A classical magnetic moment μ in a field H experiences a torque, $\mu \times H$, that equals the rate of change of angular momentum. It is expressed in terms of the nuclear gyromagnetic ratio:

$$\frac{d\mu}{dt} = \gamma\mu \times H \qquad (Eq~4)$$

The total nuclear magnetization M (that is, the number of nuclei per unit volume multiplied by the average value of μ for all the nuclei) in a homogeneous field obeys Eq 5:

$$\frac{d\mathbf{M}}{dt} = \gamma\mathbf{M} \times \mathbf{H} \qquad (Eq~5)$$

Equation 5 assumes free magnetic moments, that is, that the only interaction is between the nuclear moments and the magnetic field. The steady-state solution of this differential equation for a constant field, $\mathbf{H} = \mathbf{H}_0$, is simply that the magnetization $\mathbf{M}$ makes a constant angle with $\mathbf{H}_0$ and precesses about $\mathbf{H}_0$ at an angular frequency ω_0:

$$\omega_0 = \gamma H_0 \qquad (Eq~6)$$

This precession is illustrated in Fig. 1. The resonance frequency $\nu_0 = \omega_0/2\pi$ depends only on the gyromagnetic ratio of the nucleus and the magnetic field at the nuclear site. This internal magnetic field is often measurably different from the field applied externally. This difference, which limits attempts to measure nuclear magnetic moments, is one reason for the usefulness of NMR in the study of materials.

The Bloch Equations (T_1 and T_2). For a system of free spins in a homogeneous magnetic field, the net nuclear magnetization obeys Eq 5. Accordingly, once a magnetization $\mathbf{M}$ is established, it does not change in magnitude as a function of time. In reality, the nuclear moments exchange energy with each other (spin-spin interactions) and with the lattice in which they are embedded (spin-lattice interactions). In a static magnetic field, the magnetization tends toward an equilibrium value parallel to the field H_0 (assumed to be in the z-direction). Therefore:

$$M_z = \chi_0 H_0$$

and

$$M_x = M_y = 0 \qquad (Eq~7)$$

where χ_0 is the static nuclear susceptibility, and M_x, M_y, and M_z are the x, y, and z components of the net nuclear magnetization.

If the magnetization is disturbed from equilibrium, each component will tend to relax toward these values. This relaxation can often be described by two relaxation times, T_1 and T_2. Representing the characteristic time with which M_z approaches equilibrium, T_1 is termed the longitudinal (or spin-lattice) relaxation time; T_2, representing the characteristic time with which M_x and M_y approach zero, is termed the transverse (or spin-spin) relaxation time. Bloch (Ref 8) first modified the classical torque equation (Eq 5) to include these relaxation times. The resulting "Bloch" equations are phenome-

nological, but for certain conditions (Ref 9) can be derived from first principles:

$$\frac{dM_z}{dt} = \gamma(\mathbf{M} \times \mathbf{H})_z - \frac{M_z - M_0}{T_1} \qquad (Eq~8a)$$

$$\frac{dM_x}{dt} = \gamma(\mathbf{M} \times \mathbf{H})_x - \frac{M_x}{T_2} \qquad (Eq~8b)$$

$$\frac{dM_y}{dt} = \gamma(\mathbf{M} \times \mathbf{H})_y - \frac{M_y}{T_2} \qquad (Eq~8c)$$

It is convenient to express the solution of Eq 8(a) in terms of the complex susceptibility $\chi = \chi' - i\chi''$ (the minus sign is the usual convention). The real part χ' is known as the dispersion, and the imaginary part χ'' as the absorption. The power absorbed, p, is (Ref 10):

$$p = 2H_1^2\omega\chi'' \qquad (Eq~9)$$

where ω is the angular frequency of the applied RF field, and H_1 is half the maximum value of the RF magnetic field. The components of the transverse magnetization are given in complex form by:

$$M_x + iM_y = \chi(2H_1)e^{i\omega t} \qquad (Eq~10)$$

The steady-state solutions (Ref 3) of the Bloch equations, that is, $dM_z/dt = d\chi'/dt = d\chi''/dt = 0$, can then be expressed as:

$$M_z = \chi_0 H_0 \times$$
$$\frac{1 + (\omega_0 - \omega)^2 T_2^2}{1 + (\omega_0 - \omega)^2 T_2^2 + \gamma^2 H_1^2 T_1 T_2} \qquad (Eq~11a)$$

$$\chi' = \frac{1}{2}\chi_0\omega_0 T_2 \times$$
$$\frac{(\omega_0 - \omega)T_2}{1 + (\omega_0 - \omega)^2 T_2^2 + \gamma^2 H_1^2 T_1 T_2} \qquad (Eq~11b)$$

$$\chi'' = \frac{1}{2}\chi_0\omega_0 T_2 \times$$
$$\frac{1}{1 + (\omega_0 - \omega)^2 T_2^2 + \gamma^2 H_1^2 T_1 T_2} \qquad (Eq~11c)$$

Absorption and Dispersion Lineshapes. In continuous-wave experiments, either the applied RF field is kept constant as the applied magnetic field H_0 is slowly swept, or the opposite occurs. If the detection system output is proportional to the power absorbed by the nuclear spin system,

Fig. 2 Lorentzian absorption lineshape (a) and corresponding dispersion lineshape (b)

These shapes derive from the unsaturated ($\gamma^2 H_1^2 T_1 T_2 \rightarrow 0$) Bloch equations (Eq 11). x is in units of $(\omega_0 - \omega)T_2$; χ'' and χ' are in units of $\frac{1}{2}\chi_0\omega_0 T_2$.

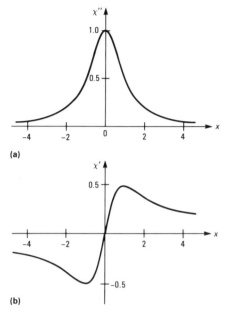

(a)

(b)

the resonance signal observed will be proportional to χ'', as given by Eq 11(c). This is termed an absorption lineshape, and if $\gamma^2 H_1^2 T_1 T_2 \quad 1$, it will have a Lorentzian shape. It is also possible to make the detection system sensitive to χ', and in this case a dispersion lineshape is observed. These shapes are illustrated in Fig. 2. More sensitive detection systems add a small audio-frequency modulation to the applied field H_0 and produce an output proportional to the slope of the lineshapes shown in Fig. 2. These are then termed derivative absorption and derivative dispersion lineshapes.

Line Broadening. Although only phenomenological, Eq 11 provides at least qualitative predictions for the behavior of the absorption (χ'') and dispersion (χ') signals. For small values of the applied RF field (H_1 small, so that $\gamma^2 H_1^2 T_1 T_2 \ll 1$), the intrinsic linewidth is determined by the spin-spin relaxation time T_2. This is the basic line-broadening mechanism in liquids, in which the broadening is homogeneous. Additional broadening mechanisms, such as random variations in the nuclear environment, are more important in solids than in liquids. The spin-lattice relaxation time, T_1, becomes important when $\gamma^2 H_1^2 T_1 T_2$ is no longer much less than unity. When $\gamma^2 H_1^2 T_1 T_2$ becomes significant, the lineshape begins to change,

and the resonance approaches saturation. In most solids, it is necessary to use large values of H_1 for sufficient sensitivity to observe the resonance, and the meaning of lineshape must be considered carefully.

Measurement Sensitivity. Because the nuclear magnetic resonance of protons is readily observed, it is convenient to reference the sensitivity of other isotopes to that of hydrogen. In an experiment in which the field is held constant, and where the relaxation and the spin relaxation times are comparable, the relative sensitivity is proportional to $\gamma^3 I(I + 1)$ times the nuclear abundance. If the frequency is held constant and the field is varied, the relative sensitivity will be proportional to $\gamma I(I + 1)$ times the nuclear abundance. These values are compared in Table 1; they have been normalized so that hydrogen is unity. At constant field, hydrogen always has the greatest sensitivity, and it also has the highest resonance frequency. At constant frequency, some metallic isotopes, such as ^{95}Mo, have a higher sensitivity than hydrogen, but a higher applied magnetic field must be used.

The Pulse-Echo Method. Experiments involving observation of a resonance line, such as that shown in Fig. 2, by holding either the magnetic field or RF frequency constant and slowly varying the other are referred to as continuous-wave experiments. Another useful technique for observing NMR is the pulse-echo method.

In the pulse-echo method, RF at the resonant frequency is applied in a series of pulses. The sequence of events is shown schematically in Fig. 3. The first pulse, the so-called $\pi/2$ pulse, is applied until the nuclear magnetization is rotated into the x-y plane (perpendicular to the direction of the applied magnetic field H_0). When inhomogeneities in the applied field or from other sources cause the spins to spread out and become incoherent, then a free-induction tail signal is produced. After a time τ, another pulse is applied, the so-called π pulse, which rotates all the nuclear spins through an angle of 180°, effectively reversing their direction. After a time τ, the nuclear spins come back together and are coherent for a brief period of time, causing the spin-echo signal.

The spin-echo method, in addition to measuring the resonant frequency, can be used to measure T_1 and T_2. For example, if the echo amplitude is determined as a function of the first pulse to echo separation time 2τ, it decays with a time constant T_2. The shape and width of the echo reflect the distribution of magnetic-field inhomogeneities. If inhomogeneous broadening due to quadrupole interactions is the primary cause of the linewidth, echoes other than the echo at 2τ can appear. To measure T_1, two $\pi/2$

pulses are applied with a time interval τ. If some of the spins have returned to the z direction during the interval τ due to spin-lattice relaxation, a free-induction decay will also be observed after the second pulse. If the free-induction decay amplitude is determined as a function of τ, it recovers with a characteristic time T_1 (Fig. 4). Many other pulse sequences can be used to measure T_1, T_2, and other characteristics of the nuclear resonance (Ref 1-7).

Ferromagnetic Nuclear Resonance (FNR). In a conventional NMR apparatus using a magnet with a large, homogeneous magnetic field (Fig. 5), even a small amount of ferromagnetic precipitate or impurity would severely distort and weaken the resonance. Nonetheless, strong resonances are observed in such ferromagnetic materials as iron, cobalt, nickel, Ni_3Fe, Mn_4N, Fe_2B, $GdAl_2$, and Heusler alloys due to the enhancement factor produced by the magnetic domain wall. Nuclear magnetic resonance in ferromagnetic materials is traditionally termed ferromagnetic nuclear resonance, which should not be confused with ferromagnetic resonance that arises from electrons rather than from nuclei. Generally, the experimental apparatus used to observe ferromagnetic resonance is different from the conventional NMR equipment. No large magnet is needed; the Zeeman splitting of the nuclear states is accomplished by the large effective internal magnetic field at the nuclear site. Ferromagnetic resonance has been used to measure order-disorder, sublattice magnetization, stacking faults, domain wall dynamics, and precipitation phenomena in magnetic materials. In disordered alloys, satellite lines due to neighboring solute atoms have been observed and interpreted on the basis of local environments.

Nuclear Quadrupole Resonance (NQR). In materials in which the atomic environment has less than cubic or tetrahedral symmetry, an electric-field gradient at the nuclear site is possible. The interaction of the nuclear quadrupole moment Q with this electric-field gradient leads to well-defined energy levels. The excitation and detection of transitions among these levels in zero or small constant magnetic fields is usually termed nuclear quadrupole resonance. Other terms for NQR include pure quadrupole resonance, pure nuclear quadrupole resonance, and electric quadrupole resonance.

Experimental Arrangement

A block diagram illustrating a continuous-wave NMR spectrometer is shown in Fig. 5.

Fig. 3 Schematic representation of a spin echo in the frame rotating about the direct current field at the resonant frequency

The RF field H_1 is applied at time a. M_0, the equilibrium magnetization, is rotated by $\pi/2$ from its direction along the z axis into the xy plane during the time period t_w (a to b). The RF field is turned off suddenly at b. The spins begin to spread out as the result of an assumed magnetic-field inhomogeneity. Some spins precess faster than the rotating frame; others precess slower. A decaying nuclear signal is seen during bb'. The spins have no net magnetization in the xy plane during cc'. At c', the RF field is again turned on. The spins are rotated through an angle of π during $c'd$ (follow V, for example). All the spins resume their previous precessional motion at d. Neglecting spin-spin relaxation, the spins gradually become coherent and add up again to M_0 at e. Past e, the dephasing process is repeated, and the echo signal decays just as it built up before e. Source: Ref 11

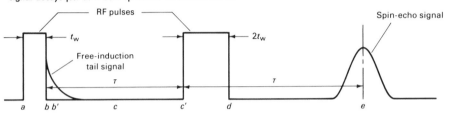

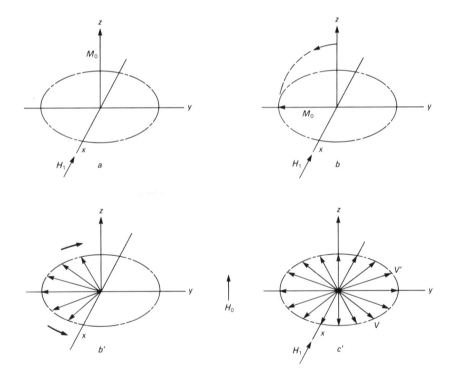

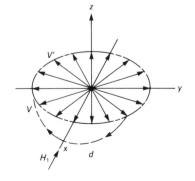

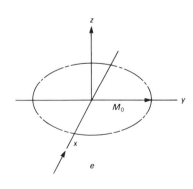

Fig. 4 $\pi/2$-$\pi/2$ pulse sequence for measuring T_1

The RF pulses are represented by the shaded rectangles. The free-induction decay that follows immediately after the second pulse has an amplitude $M(\tau)$ that is proportional to the recovered nuclear magnetization.

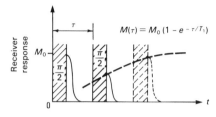

$$M(\tau) = M_0 (1 - e^{-\tau/T_1})$$

Most studies on metals have been performed by detecting changes at fixed frequency as the field is swept. Most resonance signals require the signal-to-noise enhancement provided by audio-frequency modulation of the magnetic field coupled with phase-sensitive detection. Further enhancement is provided by the use of digital averaging over a large number of repetitive magnetic-field sweeps.

Figure 6 shows a block diagram illustrating a pulse NMR spectrometer. The sample under study is placed in the transmitter coil in a magnetic field. Considerable RF power is generally necessary, requiring a high-power amplifier and careful matching to the transmitter coil. The tuned preamplifier must have moderate gain and low noise, the ability to withstand high RF voltages induced while the transmitter is on, and quick recovery from saturation. The spectrometer illustrated in Fig. 6 provides for phase control between two pulses in a pulse train.

Inorganic Applications

Example 1: Detection of Phase Changes. An important application of NMR in metals is the determination and understanding of alloy phase diagrams (Ref 4, 5). Nuclear magnetic resonance can be used in two different ways to determine phase boundaries and phase transitions in alloys. First, the NMR parameters, for example, linewidth and Knight shift, may change in a measurable way when the alloy changes phase. The NMR parameter then provides a signature by which to identify each phase. Second, in a two-phase mixture, two NMR signals may be observed. In such a case, quantitative information on the integrated intensity of the two signals can be used to provide quantitative information on the positions of the phase boundaries. The second method will be discussed.

Use of a technique such as NMR, which depends on sensing atomic nuclei, can pro-

Fig. 5 Block diagram of a continuous-wave NMR spectrometer using a field sweep and crossed-coil detector system

1, magnet and associated power supply; 2, continuous-wave RF transmitter and receiver; 3, sample placed in the transmitter coil and a receiver coil; 4, provision for audio modulation of the magnetic field; 5, phase-sensitive detector and data acquisition, processing, and display

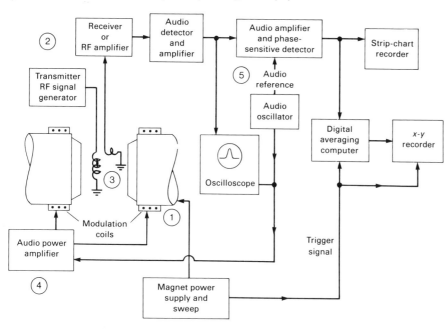

Fig. 6 Block diagram illustrating a pulse NMR spectrometer

A single oscillator and two modulator channels allow pulse trains that are phase coherent. 1, magnet and associated power supply; 2, RF pulse generating and timing equipment; 3, transmitter and receiver coil, with the sample placed within the transmitter coil; 4, amplifiers and phase-sensitive detection apparatus; 5, data acquisition, processing, and display equipment

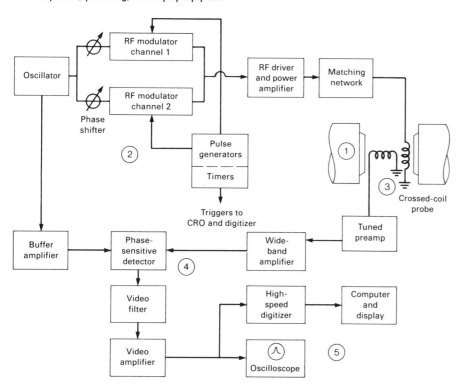

Fig. 7 Room-temperature ^{115}In NMR absorption derivative spectrum for the two-phase alloy $(AuAl_2)_{95}(AuIn_2)_5$

A distinct resonance for the indium nuclei in each of the two phases is visible. Also shown is the weaker ^{113}In line. Source: Ref 12

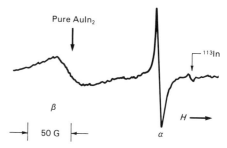

vide an advantage over the usual lever rule of metallurgy. In the lever rule, concentrations at phase boundaries are calculated from the ratio of the phase concentrations in the two-phase region. Nuclear magnetic resonance measures the proportion of resonant nuclei present in the two phases. This preferential sense leads to an enhanced lever rule (Ref 12), which can be expressed for an $\alpha + \beta$ two-phase region in an *A-B* alloy as:

$$R = \frac{C_\alpha f_\alpha}{C_\beta f_\beta} \qquad \text{(Eq 12)}$$

where R is the ratio of the intensity of the NMR signal from the B atoms in the α phase to the intensity from those in the β phase; C_α and C_β are the concentrations of the B atoms in the α and β phases, respectively; and f_α and f_β are the fractions of α phase and β phase present, as given by the usual lever rule.

When close to the α-phase boundary, the enhancement of the signal from the minority β phase arises from the high concentration of B atoms in the β phase. Figure 7 shows the NMR signals obtained in the two-phase region of the pseudobinary system $AuAl_2$-$AuIn_2$. From this single measurement, the solubility of $AuIn_2$ in $AuAl_2$ at the homogenization temperature can be obtained accurately. The ability of the enhanced lever rule to be used for high-precision phase-boundary determinations is greatest when the two-phase region is widest.

Example 2: Sublattice Ordering in Intermetallic Compounds. Nuclear magnetic resonance is especially useful in investigating details of atomic order in intermetallic compounds. An example of vacancy ordering in an intermediate phase is vanadium monocarbide, which does not exist at 50

Fig. 8 Atomic structure of LaNi₅-LaPt₅

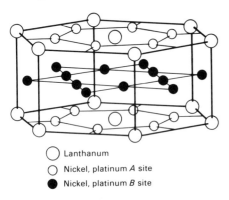

○ Lanthanum
◎ Nickel, platinum *A* site
● Nickel, platinum *B* site

Fig. 9 Fraction of *A* and *B* sites (see Fig. 8) occupied by platinum in LaNi₅-LaPt₅ pseudobinary alloys as determined by NMR

Source: Ref 14

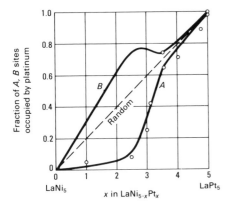

Fig. 10 NMR Knight shifts in liquid cesium-gold alloys at 600 °C (1110 °F)

Source: Ref 16

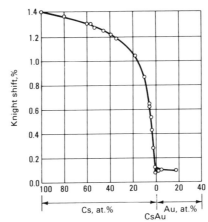

Fig. 11 ³¹P NMR Knight shifts in amorphous nickel-phosphorus alloys prepared using different techniques

Also shown are Knight shifts for three crystalline alloys. Source: Ref 18

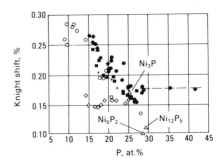

at.% C, but is stable only from 39 to 47 at.% C. Knight shift and quadrupole measurements (Ref 13) revealed that this phase is actually a series of line compounds, such as V₈C₇ and V₆C₅.

An example involving sublattice ordering is provided by the rare-earth/Ni₅ compounds, which have the hexagonal structure shown in Fig. 8. Compounds of this structure have attracted considerable attention for technological and scientific reasons, with applications to hard magnets (for example, SmCo₅) and to hydrogen storage. The LaNi₅-LaPt₅ pseudobinary alloy system, which has this structure, was studied using NMR relaxation time and Knight shift measurements and using x-ray diffraction (Ref 14).

There are two crystallographically inequivalent transition metal sites (Fig. 8).

The *A* sites, holding two of the five transition metal atoms per molecular unit, lie in the basal plane with the lanthanum atoms. The *B* sites, holding the remaining three, lie between. Two distinct ¹⁹⁵Pt shifts are visible for platinum atoms on the *A* and *B* sites in LaPt₅. Monitoring the relative intensities in the two resonance lines provides a measure of the relative populations of platinum at *A* and *B* sites in LaNi₅₋ₓPtₓ. It was thus found to be possible to measure quantitatively the sublattice ordering of the pseudobinary alloy. The nuclear magnetic resonance demonstrated that there is a high degree of ordering of nickel on the *A* sites and of platinum on the *B* sites. The ordering at LaNi₂Pt₃ is more than two thirds complete (Fig. 9). Although the occurrence of ordering at this composition could also be inferred from the *c/a* ratio measured by x-ray diffraction, the NMR method was more sensitive to changes in *A*-site occupation than conventional x-ray methods.

Example 3: Electronic Structure of Liquid Metals and Alloys. Nuclear magnetic resonance is easy to measure in liquids if the apparatus has a high-temperature probe, because the linewidths are generally narrow and the resonance intense. One application is investigation of the electronic structure.

The electronic structure of such metals as sodium or aluminum in the crystalline solid is not very different from the liquid. Thus, for such metals the Knight shift does not change appreciably upon melting. However, the melting of a semiconductor can involve appreciable change in the electronic struc-

ture. For example, the ¹¹⁵In resonance frequency in the semiconductor InSb changes abruptly from zero to a substantial Knight shift upon melting (Ref 15). From the behavior of the Knight shift and of the electrical resistivity and magnetic susceptibility, it was concluded that there is a change to the metallic state in the liquid.

In contrast to liquid InSb, which is metallic, liquid CsAu has been shown to be ionic. Using NMR Knight shift (Fig. 10) and relaxation time measurements, liquid cesium-gold alloys have been shown to change abruptly with increasing gold concentration from metallic for cesium-rich alloys to ionic alloys near the CsAu stoichiometry (Ref 16). Electrical transport properties and magnetic susceptibility measurements also suggest that the electrons introduced by small excess metal concentrations in CsAu are localized. Similarly, NMR measurements have confirmed (Ref 17) the assumption of a partially saltlike mixture around the composition Li₄Pb in liquid lithium-lead alloys and Li₄Sn in liquid lithium-tin alloys.

Example 4: Knight Shift Measurements on Metallic Glasses. Knight shift measurements (Fig. 11) on nickel-phosphorus glassy alloys (Ref 18) have established the existence of two distinct glassy states; that is, this metallic glass is polymorphic. For compositions between 14 and 25 at.% P, a constant Knight shift was measured for glasses made by one processing method. Over a similar composition range, samples prepared by other methods showed an increasing Knight shift with decreasing phosphorus concentration. Of particular significance is the bimodal nature of the results; that is, as Fig. 11 shows, no Knight shifts were recorded in the region

Fig. 12 Room-temperature zero-field NMR spin-echo spectra of Ni₃

A, ordered; B, disordered, Source: Ref 19

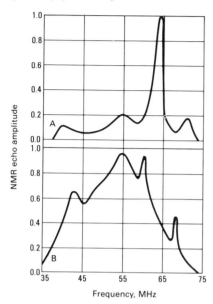

Fig. 13 NMR analysis of a polyimide resin

(a) The chemical structure of the resin. (b) to (d) ^{13}C NMR spectra of the resin, the cured polyimide polymer, and the post-cured polyimide polymer, respectively. Source: Ref 24

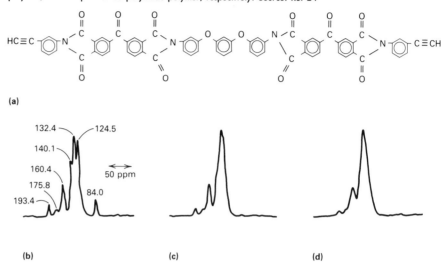

(a)

(b)   (c)   (d)

between the two types. The absence of data in this region is in contrast to what would be expected if these materials were not structurally distinct, but were related by a relaxation process. The occurrence of polymorphism in nickel-phosphorus metallic glasses has also been detected in density measurements, annealing studies, and extended x-ray absorption fine structure (EXAFS) results (Ref 18).

Example 5: Order-Disorder in Ferromagnetic Alloys. At high temperatures, the iron-nickel alloy system shows complete solid solubility in the face-centered cubic (fcc) (austenite) crystal structure. At lower temperatures, near a composition of 75 at.% Ni, there is a tendency to long-range order to an AuCu₃ structure. Using NMR in the ferromagnetic alloy (Ref 19), that is, ferromagnetic nuclear resonance, the difference between the ordered and disordered states is evident (Fig. 12). This is a situation in which the ordering is very difficult to detect using x-ray diffraction and even neutron diffraction because of the similarities of the nickel and iron form factors.

In addition to long-range order, it may be possible to use the structure shown in the resonance lines in Fig. 12 to investigate the details of the remaining disorder in the ordered Ni₃Fe. This will depend on the development of a model (Ref 20) for the origin of the magnetic hyperfine fields in the alloy.

Organic Applications*

Nuclear magnetic resonance spectroscopy has long been a primary characterization technique for liquid samples (Ref 21). The chemical shift and spin-spin couplings of such nuclei as ^{1}H and ^{13}C are used routinely to analyze the chemical composition of organic compounds. The recent development of combined cross-polarization (CP), high-power proton decoupling, and magic angle spinning (MAS) has extended these capabilities to solid materials (Ref 22).

Cross-polarization involves transferring the spin polarization to an abundant nucleus, ^{1}H, to a dilute spin system, such as ^{13}C, ^{15}N, or ^{29}Si. During the observation period, the strong magnetic dipole interactions of the ^{1}H spin system are eliminated with high-power decoupling. The chemical shift anisotropies of the dilute spin are averaged by spinning the sample at several kilohertz about its magic angle. The result is a high-resolution spectrum of the dilute spin. Two examples are presented: a ^{13}C NMR study used to elucidate the curing mechanism of a polyimide resin and a ^{29}Si NMR study used to examine the structure and degradation of a plasma-polymerized organosiloxane. These examples are representative of the many NMR studies being directed toward understanding the structure, reaction kinetics, degradation, and chain dynamics of organic and inorganic materials.

*Examples in this section were provided by Roger A. Assink, Sandia National Laboratories. Work performed at Sandia National Laboratories supported by the U.S. Department of Energy under Contract No. DE-AC04-76DP00789.

Fig. 14 The ^{29}Si NMR spectra of PP-HMDSO

(a) Before heat treatment. (b) After 24 h at 100 °C (212 °F). (c) After 24 h at 200 °C (390 °F). (d) After 24 h at 300 °C (570 °F). Source: Ref 25

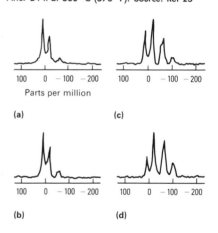

(a)   (c)

(b)   (d)

Example 1: Curing Mechanism of a Polyimide Resin. Polyimide materials are used for such high-temperature applications as coatings, adhesives, and thermosetting laminates (Ref 23). Acetylene-terminated polyimide resins (Fig. 13a) are homopolymerized at elevated temperatures. The acetylenic end groups are believed to form aromatic units during the cure. The ^{13}C NMR spectra of this material have been observed to establish the cure mechanism (Ref 24).

Figure 13(b) shows the spectra of the polyimide resin, the cured polyimide polymer, and the postcured polyimide polymer.

The spectra have sufficient resolution to identify the peaks corresponding to acetylenic carbons (84 ppm), aromatic carbons (125 to 140 ppm), the amide carbonyl and aryl carbons with oxygen substituents (160 ppm), and the benzophenone carbonyls (193 ppm). The disappearance of the acetylenic carbons for the cured and postcured polymers demonstrates that the primary mechanism for cross-linking involves loss of the acetylenic end-capping groups. Careful examination of the intensity of the aromatic carbon resonances using difference spectra reveals that no more than 30% of the acetylene groups trimerize to form benzene. Several specific addition reactions, consistent with the observed spectra, can be formulated.

Example 2: Structure and Degradation of Plasma-Polymerized Hexamethyldisiloxane.

Plasma-polymerized organosiloxanes have been the subject of considerable interest for use as corrosion- and abrasion-resistant coatings, encapsulants, and surface modifiers. The very properties that make these films useful, such as high cross-link density and high molecular weight, often make it difficult to obtain information concerning their structure. The structure of plasma-polymerized hexamethyldisiloxane (PP-HMDSO) was studied using ^{29}Si (Ref 25). Substantial changes were observed when the material was heat-aged in air.

Figure 14 shows the ^{29}Si NMR spectra of PP-HMDSO as prepared and after successive heat treatments at 100, 200, and 300 °C (212, 390, and 570 °F) in air. The major peaks could be assigned to silicon bonded to 1 (11 ppm), 2 (-18 ppm), 3 (-55, -64 ppm), and 4 (-99, -106 ppm) oxygens, with the remaining bonds linking silicon to a methyl group. The evidence for only minor amounts of hydroxy, methoxy, and hydride moieties indicates that rearrangement, although it occurs, is not pervasive. Heat treatment leads to additional siloxane cross-linking. Spectral simulation was used to determine the functional group composition of the initial material and the changes occurring during heat aging. Comparison of the silicon and oxygen weight percents calculated from the spectra simulations with the weight percents measured by neutron activation analysis demonstrated that the ^{29}Si NMR spectra were quantitative.

REFERENCES

1. C.P. Slichter, *Principles of Magnetic Resonance*, Harper and Row, 1963
2. C. Carrington and A.D. McLachlan, *Introduction to Magnetic Resonance*, Harper and Row, 1967
3. E.R. Andrew, *Nuclear Magnetic Resonance*, Cambridge University Press, 1955
4. C.G. Carter, L.H. Bennett, and D.J. Kahan, *Metallic Shifts in NMR*, Pergamon Press, 1977
5. T.J. Rowland, *Progr. Mater. Sci.*, Vol 9, 1961, p 1
6. I.D. Weisman, L.J. Swartzendruber, and L.H. Bennett, in *Techniques in Metals Research*, Vol 6, R.F. Bunshah, Ed., John Wiley & Sons, 1973, p 165-504
7. A. Abragam, *The Principles of Nuclear Magnetism*, Oxford University Press, 1961
8. F. Bloch, *Phys. Rev.*, Vol 70, 1946, p 460-474
9. R.K. Wangsness and F. Bloch, *Phys. Rev.*, Vol 89, 1953, p 728-739
10. G.C. Pake, *Solid State Phys.*, Vol 2, 1956, p 1-91.
11. E.L. Hahn, *Phys. Rev.*, Vol 80, 1950, p 580-594
12. L.H. Bennett and G.C. Carter, *Metall. Trans.*, Vol 2, 1971, p 3079
13. C. Froidevaux and D. Rossier, *J. Phys. Chem. Solids*, Vol 28, 1976, p 1197
14. I.D. Weisman, L.H. Bennett, A.J. McAlister, and R.E. Watson, *Phys. Rev. B*, Vol 11, 1975, p 82
15. P.S. Allen and E.F.W. Seymour, *Proc. Phys. Soc.*, Vol 85, 1965, p 509
16. R. Dupree, D.J. Kirby, W. Freyland, and W.W. Warren, Jr., *Phys. Rev. Lett.*, Vol 45, 1980, p 130
17. C. van der Marel, W. Geertsma, and W. van der Lugt, *J. Phys. F (Met. Phys.)*, Vol 10, 1980, p 2305
18. L.H. Bennett, G.G. Long, M. Kuriyama, and A.I. Goldman, in *Structure and Bonding in Noncrystalline Solids*, G.E. Walrafen, Ed., Plenum Press, 1986
19. T.J. Burch, J.I. Budnick, and S. Skalski, *Phys. Rev. Lett.*, Vol 22, 1969, p 846
20. L.H. Bennett, *Phys. Rev.*, Vol 188, 1969, p 1048
21. D. Shaw, *Fourier Transform NMR Spectrosopy*, Elsevier Scientific, 1976
22. R. Richards and K.J. Packer, *Nuclear Magnetic Resonance Spectroscopy in Solids*, Cambridge University Press, 1981
23. J. Preston, in *Kirk-Othmer Encyclopedia of Chemical Technology*, 2nd ed., Interscience, 1971, p 746
24. M.D. Sefcik, E.O. Stejskal, R.A. McKay, and J. Schaefer, *Macromolecules*, Vol 12, 1979, p 423
25. R.A. Assink, A.K. Hays, R.W. Bild, and B.L. Hawkins, *J. Vac. Sci. Technol. A*, Vol 3, 1985, p 2629

Mössbauer Spectroscopy

L.J. Swartzendruber and L.H. Bennett, National Bureau of Standards

General Uses

- Phase analysis
- Study of atomic arrangements
- Study of critical-point phenomena
- Magnetic-structure analysis
- Diffusion studies
- Surface and corrosion analysis

Examples of Applications

- Measurements of retained austenite in steel
- Analysis of corrosion products on steel
- Effects of grinding of the surface of carbon steel
- Measurement of δ-ferrite in stainless steel weld metal
- Curie and Neel point measurements

Samples

- *Form*: Solids (metals, ferrites, geological materials, and so on)
- *Size*: For transmission—powders or foils. Size varies, but of the order of 50 μm thick and 50 mg of material. For scattering—films, foils, or bulk metals with an area of the order of 1 cm² (0.15 in.²) or greater. As source—of the order of 1 to 100 mCi of radioactive material incorporated within approximately 50 μm of the sample surface

Limitations

- Limited to relatively few isotopes, notably ^{57}Fe, ^{119}Sn, ^{121}Sb, and ^{186}W
- Maximum temperature of analysis is usually only a fraction of the melting temperature
- Phase identification is sometimes ambiguous

Estimated Analysis Time

- 30 min to 48 h

Capabilities of Related Techniques

- *Optical metallography*: Shows morphology of the phases present
- *X-ray diffraction*: Faster; provides crystal structure information
- *Nuclear magnetic resonance*: Applicable to a wider range of isotopes, faster, more sensitive for nonmagnetic materials, applicable to liquids

Introduction

The Mössbauer effect (ME) is a spectroscopic method for observing nuclear γ-ray fluorescence using the recoil-free transitions of a nucleus embedded in a solid lattice. It is sometimes referred to as nuclear gamma-ray resonance (NGR). Most Mössbauer spectra are obtained by Doppler scanning, that is, by observing a count rate as a function of the relative velocity between the suitable γ-ray source and an absorber or scatterer. The spectrum then consists of a count rate versus relative velocity plot. The information in such a spectrum includes the amount of resonant absorption or scattering, line patterns characteristic of various phases or chemical species, the relative position of the spectrum (the isomer shift), and line splittings caused by nuclear hyperfine interactions. This information can then be interpreted to provide insight into the local atomic environment of those atoms responsible for the resonance. General information is provided in Ref 1 to 13.

Fundamental Principles

The Recoil-Free Fraction. The basis of the ME is the existence of a recoil-free fraction f for γ-rays emitted or absorbed by a nucleus embedded in a solid lattice. This recoil-free fraction, sometimes referred to as the Lamb-Mössbauer factor, yields the fraction of emitted or absorbed γ-rays that are unshifted by nuclear recoil. Only these unshifted γ-rays will be observed by the Mössbauer effect. The Lamb-Mössbauer factor is analogous to the Debye-Waller factor for x-ray diffraction in solids, in which the intensities of the Bragg reflection peaks decrease with increasing temperature. A temperature-dependent factor W that gives recoilless fraction is customarily defined as:

$$f = e^{-2W} \qquad \text{(Eq 1)}$$

In the Debye model for the spectrum of lattice vibrations, the solid is described as an isotropic medium that undergoes vibrations over a continuous range of frequencies up to a maximum cutoff frequency ω_{max}. A characteristic temperature θ_D, where $k\theta_D = \hbar\omega_{max}$, is introduced. For this model, W is:

$$W = \frac{3E_R}{k\theta_D}\left[\frac{1}{4} + \left(\frac{T}{\theta_D}\right)^2 \int_0^{\theta_D/T} \frac{x\,dx}{e^x - 1}\right]$$

(Eq 2)

where T is temperature, and E_R is the recoil energy of the free nucleus:

$$E_R = \frac{E_\gamma^2}{2Mc^2}$$

(Eq 3)

where E_γ is the energy of the γ-ray, M is the mass of the nucleus, and c is the velocity of light. Useful low- and high-temperature approximations for Eq 2 are:

$$W \cong \frac{3E_R}{4k\theta_D} \text{ for } T < \frac{\theta_D}{4}$$

(Eq 4a)

and

$$W \cong \frac{3E_R T}{k\theta_D^2} \text{ for } T > \frac{\theta_D}{2}$$

(Eq 4b)

Table 1 lists approximate Debye temperatures for elements used in ME. When the Mössbauer emitting or absorbing atom is an isolated impurity in a metallic matrix with Debye temperature θ_D, a useful approximation for an effective Debye temperature can be obtained using:

$$\theta_{eff} = \left(\frac{M_0}{M_I}\right)^{1/2} \theta_D$$

(Eq 5)

where M_0 is the atomic mass of the matrix atoms, and M_I is the atomic mass of the impurity atoms. Equation 5 neglects the effects of localized vibrational modes.

The Absorption Cross Section. The maximum cross section σ_m of a single nucleus for absorption of an incident Mössbauer γ-ray of energy E_γ is:

$$\sigma_m = f\sigma_0$$

(Eq 6)

where:

$$\sigma_0 = 2\pi \frac{\hbar^2 c^2}{E_\gamma^2} \frac{2I_e + 1}{2I_g + 1} \frac{1}{1 + \alpha}$$

(Eq 7)

where I_e is the spin of the excited nuclear state, I_g is the spin of the ground state, and α is the internal conversion coefficient. When the excited- and ground-state energy levels are split by a hyperfine field, the cross section is divided proportionally among the various possible transitions. Table 1 lists values for σ_0. As the energy of the γ-ray increases, f is reduced (Eq 1 and 2), and the absorption cross section is also reduced (Eq 7). Partly because of these two practical

considerations, ME has been observed only for γ-ray energies below 200 keV.

Selection Rules and γ-Ray Polarization. The relative intensities of the individual components of lines split by a hyperfine interaction depend on the selection rules governing the nuclear transition. The probability of the emission of the γ-ray also takes on an angular dependence, depending on the angle between the magnetic field at the nucleus and the direction of propagation of the γ-ray. The selection rules for ME transitions depend on the multipolarity of the nuclear transition between ground and excited states.

The laws of conservation of angular momentum and parity determine the possible transitions between the excited and ground states of a nucleus. Defining the momentum and parities of the excited nuclear state as I_e and P_e and of the ground state as I_g and P_g (the parities can have only one of two values, 1 or -1), the angular momentum L of the emitted (or absorbed) γ-ray can take on only the values $|I_e - I_g| < L < |I_e + I_g|$. The number 2^L defines the multipolarity of the transition, that is, $L = 1$ (dipole), $L = 2$ (quadrupole), $L = 3$ (octapole), and so on.

For each multipolarity L, there are two types of nuclear transitions—electric EL and magnetic ML. If P_e and P_g are equal, EL transitions are allowed only for even Ls, and ML transitions are allowed only for odd Ls. If P_e and P_g differ, EL transitions are allowed only for odd Ls, and ML transitions are allowed only for even Ls. For example, if $I_e = \frac{3}{2}$, $P_e = -1$, $I_g = \frac{1}{2}$, and $P_g = -1$, only $M1$ and $E2$ transitions are possible.

For a given energy of transition, the excited-state lifetime increases rapidly with multipolarity. Most usable Mössbauer transitions have energies of approximately 10 to 100 keV and have lifetimes from 10^{-6} to 10^{-10} s. This limits most Mössbauer transitions to pure $E1$, such as ^{237}Np; nearly pure $M1$, such as for ^{57}Fe and ^{119}Sn; $M1$ with a small mixture of $E2$, such as for ^{197}Au; or pure $E2$, such as for the even-even rare-earth nuclei that all have $I_g = 0$, $P_g = 1$, and $I_e = 2$, $P_e = 1$, for example, ^{178}Hf. The $E2/M1$ ratios have often been determined by internal conversion studies. For ^{197}Au, experimental values of ME line-intensity ratios correspond closely to the theoretical values for a 90% $M1$ plus 10% $E2$ transition.

In the presence of internal fields, the nuclear excited and ground state can be split into sublevels specified by a quantum number m, with $-I < m < I$. In this case, the γ-ray emissions will consist of a set of transitions between these sublevels. The relative intensities, I, of the various transitions are:

$$I = \left\{ \begin{matrix} I_f & L & I_i \\ m_f & m & -m_i \end{matrix} \right\}^2 G^L \Delta_m(\phi)$$

(Eq 8)

where the Wigner 3-j coefficient (the symbol in braces) is a function of the initial (I_i) and final (I_f) nuclear spins, the initial (m_i) and final (m_f) quantum numbers for the sublevels, and the multipolarity (L) of the transition. The function $G_m^L(\phi)$ determines the angular distribution of the radiation as a function of the angle ϕ between the internal field and the direction of γ-ray propagation. Table 2 lists the angular functions for the cases in which $L = 1$ and 2.

For the transition $2 \rightleftharpoons 0$, that is, $I_i = 2 \rightarrow I_f = 0$, or $I_i = 0 \rightarrow I_f = 2$, the square of all the Wigner coefficients is $\frac{1}{5}$, and relative emission intensities are given by $I = G^2 \Delta_m(\phi)/5$. Table 3 lists numbers proportional to the squares of the Wigner coefficients for the often encountered $\frac{3}{2} \rightleftharpoons \frac{1}{2}$ and $\frac{5}{2} \rightleftharpoons \frac{3}{2}$ cases.

A typical ME experiment uses a single-line unpolarized source. If the absorber is also unpolarized, that is, if the internal fields lie in directions random to the direction of γ-ray propagation, then all angular dependencies average to the same value, and the relative line intensities are proportional to squares of the Wigner coefficients. If the absorber is polarized, that is, if an internal magnetic field is aligned at a definite angle with the γ-ray propagation, then the angular dependencies must be included.

Population of the Excited Nuclear Level. Observation of the ME requires a source of γ-rays from an appropriate excited nuclear level. This excited level is usually obtained from a radioactive parent that populates the excited level during its natural decay. Table 4 lists radioactive parents and their principal means of production. A notable example is ^{57}Fe; the radioactive parent most often used is ^{57}Co, which has a 270-d half-life (Fig. 1). It is usually produced by bombarding ^{56}Fe with deuterons in a cyclotron and is commercially available, usually as a chloride in solution. The solution can be dried on a rhodium foil, reduced to cobalt metal in a hydrogen atmosphere, and diffused into the foil by heating. Usable activities range from several milliCuries for transmission experiments to more than 100 mCi for scattering experiments.

The Isomer Shift. If the source and absorber differ chemically, the center of a ME spectrum will be shifted away from zero relative velocity. This isomer shift is due to the Coulomb interaction between the nuclear charge and the electronic charge (Fig. 2). The magnitude of the isomer shift, S, is:

Table 1 Some properties of Mössbauer transitions

Atomic number, Z	Atomic weight, A	Element	E_γ, keV	Isotopic abundance, %	$t_{1/2}$, ns	I_e	I_g	σ_0, 10^{-20} cm²	W_0, mm/s	E_γ/k, K	θ_D, K
19 40	Potassium		29.6	0.0117	4.26	−3	−4	28.97	2.184	135	91
26 57	Iron		14.4125	2.19	97.81	−3/2	−1/2	256.6	0.1940	22.7	470
28 61	Nickel		67.42	1.25	5.06	−5/2	−3/2	72.12	0.8021	11.6	450
30 67	Zinc		93.32	4.11	9150	3/2	5/2	10.12	0.000320	810	327
32 73	Germanium		13.26	7.76	4000	5/2	9/2	361.2	0.005156	15.0	374
32 73	Germanium		68.75	7.76	1.86	7/2	9/2	22.88	2.139	403	374
36 83	Krypton		9.40	11.55	147	7/2	9/2	107.5	0.1980	6.63	72
44 99	Ruthenium		89.36	12.72	20.5	3/2	5/2	14.28	0.1493	503	600
44 101	Ruthenium		127.22	17.07	0.585	3/2	5/2	8.687	3.676	998	600
50 119	Tin		23.871	8.58	17.75	3/2	1/2	140.3	0.6456	29.8	200
51 121	Antimony		37.15	57.25	3.5	7/2	5/2	19.70	2.104	71.1	211
52 125	Tellurium		35.46	6.99	1.48	3/2	1/2	26.56	5.212	62.7	153
53 127	Iodine		57.60	100	1.9	7/2	5/2	21.37	2.500	163	...
54 129	Xenon		39.58	26.44	1.01	3/2	1/2	23.31	6.843	75.7	64
54 131	Xenon		80.16	21.18	0.50	1/2	3/2	7.183	6.825	306	64
55 133	Cesium		80.997	100	6.30	5/2	7/2	10.21	0.5361	307	38
59 141	Praseodymium		145.2	100	1.85	7/2	5/2	10.67	1.018	931	130
60 145	Neodymium		67.25	8.30	29.4	3/2	7/2	3.809	0.1384	194	140
60 145	Neodymium		72.50	8.30	0.72	5/2	7/2	5.916	5.240	226	140
62 147	Samarium		122.1	14.97	0.80	5/2	7/2	6.153	2.800	632	140
62 149	Samarium		22.5	13.83	7.12	5/2	7/2	7.106	1.708	21.2	140
62 152	Samarium		121.78	26.73	1.42	2	0	35.86	1.582	608	140
62 154	Samarium		81.99	22.71	3.00	2	0	30.08	1.112	272	140
63 151	Europium		21.64	47.82	9.7	7/2	5/2	11.42	1.303	19.3	140
63 153	Europium		83.3652	52.18	0.82	7/2	5/2	6.705	4.002	283	130
63 153	Europium		97.4283	52.18	0.21	5/2	5/2	17.97	13.37	387	130
63 153	Europium		103.1774	52.18	3.9	3/2	5/2	5.417	0.6798	434	130
64 154	Gadolinium		123.14	2.15	1.17	2	0	36.67	1.899	614	200
64 155	Gadolinium		60.012	14.73	0.155	5/2	3/2	9.989	29.41	145	200
64 155	Gadolinium		86.54	14.73	6.32	5/2	3/2	34.40	0.5002	301	200
64 155	Gadolinium		105.308	14.73	1.16	5/2	3/2	24.88	2.239	446	200
64 156	Gadolinium		88.967	20.47	2.22	2	0	30.42	1.385	316	200
64 157	Gadolinium		54.54	15.68	0.187	5/2	3/2	9.071	26.82	118	200
64 157	Gadolinium		64.0	15.68	460	5/2	3/2	44.79	0.009292	163	200
64 158	Gadolinium		79.51	24.87	2.46	2	0	27.88	1.399	249	200
64 160	Gadolinium		75.3	21.90	2.63	2	0	21.15	1.381	221	200
65 159	Terbium		58.0	100	13	5/2	3/2	9.827	0.3628	132	...
66 160	Dysprosium		86.788	2.29	1.98	2	0	29.42	1.592	293	210
66 161	Dysprosium		25.65	18.88	28.1	5/2	5/2	95.34	0.3795	25.2	210
66 161	Dysprosium		43.84	18.88	920	7/2	5/2	28.29	0.006782	74.4	210
66 161	Dysprosium		74.57	18.88	3.35	3/2	5/2	6.755	1.095	215	210
66 162	Dysprosium		80.7	25.53	2.25	2	0	26.09	1.507	251	210
66 164	Dysprosium		73.39	28.18	2.4	2	0	20.86	1.553	205	210
67 165	Holmium		94.70	100	0.0222	9/2	7/2	3.552	130.12	339	220
68 164	Erbium		91.5	1.56	1.73	2	0	28.10	1.728	318	220
68 166	Erbium		80.56	33.41	1.82	2	0	23.56	1.866	244	220
68 167	Erbium		79.321	22.94	0.103	9/2	7/2	7.715	33.48	235	220
68 168	Erbium		79.80	27.07	1.91	2	0	12.80	1.795	236	220
68 170	Erbium		79.3	14.88	1.92	2	0	24.31	1.797	220	220
69 169	Thulium		8.42	100	3.9	3/2	1/2	21.17	8.330	2.61	230
70 170	Ytterbium		84.262	3.03	1.60	2	0	23.93	2.029	260	120
70 171	Ytterbium		66.74	14.31	0.87	3/2	1/2	9.004	4.711	162	120
70 171	Ytterbium		75.89	14.31	1.7	5/2	1/2	13.14	2.120	210	120
70 172	Ytterbium		78.67	21.82	1.8	2	0	20.80	1.932	224	120
70 174	Ytterbium		76.5	31.84	1.76	2	0	20.69	2.032	210	120
70 176	Ytterbium		82.1	12.73	2.0	2	0	20.16	1.666	239	120
71 175	Lutetium		113.81	97.41	0.10	9/2	7/2	7.154	24.04	461	210
72 176	Hafnium		88.36	5.20	1.39	2	0	25.27	2.227	276	252
72 177	Hafnium		112.97	18.50	0.5	9/2	7/2	5.990	4.843	449	252
72 178	Hafnium		93.17	27.14	1.50	2	0	25.16	1.957	304	252
72 180	Hafnium		93.33	35.24	1.50	2	0	25.53	1.954	301	252
73 181	Tantalum		6.23	99.99	6800	9/2	7/2	167.6	0.006457	1.34	240
73 181	Tantalum		136.25	99.99	0.0406	9/2	9/2	5.968	49.45	639	240
74 180	Tungsten		103.65	0.135	1.47	2	0	25.88	1.795	372	400
74 182	Tungsten		100.102	26.41	1.37	2	0	25.17	1.995	343	400
74 183	Tungsten		46.4837	14.40	0.183	3/2	1/2	5.523	32.16	77.1	400
74 183	Tungsten		99.0788	14.40	0.692	5/2	1/2	14.95	3.990	334	400
74 184	Tungsten		111.192	30.64	1.26	2	0	26.04	1.953	419	400
74 186	Tungsten		122.5	28.41	1.01	2	0	31.35	2.211	503	400

(continued)

Note: E_γ is the γ-ray energy of the Mössbauer transition, $t_{1/2}$ is the half-life of the excited Mössbauer level, I_e and I_g are the spins of the excited- and ground-state nuclear levels, σ_0 is the resonant absorption cross section, W_0 is the full width at half maximum of the unbroadened line (twice the natural width), E_γ/k is the recoil energy of the free nucleus divided by the Boltzmann constant, and θ_D is the low-temperature limit. Source: Ref 14

Table 1 (continued)

Atomic number, Z	Atomic weight, A	Element	E_γ, keV	Isotopic abundance, %	$t_{1/2}$, ns	I_e	I_g	σ_0, 10^{-20} cm^2	W_0, mm/s	E_γ/k, K	θ_D, K
75	187	Rhenium	134.24	62.93	0.01	7/2	5/2	5.371	203.8	600	430
76	186	Osmium	137.157	1.64	0.84	2	0	28.39	2.374	630	500
76	188	Osmium	155.03	13.3	0.695	2	0	27.96	2.539	797	500
76	189	Osmium	36.22	16.1	0.50	1/2	3/2	1.151	15.10	43.2	500
76	189	Osmium	69.59	16.1	1.64	5/2	3/2	8.419	2.397	160	500
76	189	Osmium	95.23	16.1	0.3	3/2	3/2	3.503	9.575	299	500
76	190	Osmium	186.9	26.4	0.47	2	0	33.61	3.114	1146	500
77	191	Iridium	82.398	37.3	4.02	1/2	3/2	1.540	0.8258	222	420
77	191	Iridium	129.400	37.3	0.089	5/2	3/2	5.692	23.75	546	420
77	193	Iridium	73.028	62.7	6.3	1/2	3/2	3.058	0.5946	172	420
77	194	Iridium	138.92	62.7	0.080	5/2	3/2	5.833	24.61	623	420
78	195	Platinum	98.857	33.8	0.170	3/2	1/2	6.106	16.28	312	240
78	195	Platinum	129.735	33.8	0.620	5/2	1/2	7.425	3.401	538	240
79	197	Gold	77.35	100	1.90	1/2	3/2	3.857	1.861	189	164
80	201	Mercury	32.19	13.22	<0.2	1/2	3/2	1.935	42.49	32.1	75
90	232	Thorium	49.369	100	0.345	2	0	1.667	16.06	65.5	165
92	238	Uranium	44.915	99.27	245	2	0	0.917	0.2486	52.8	200
93	237	Neptunium	59.537	(radioactive)	68.3	5/2	5/2	32.55	0.06727	93.2	75

Note: E_γ is the γ-ray energy of the Mössbauer transition, $t_{1/2}$ is the half-life of the excited Mössbauer level, I_e and I_g are the spins of the excited- and ground-state nuclear levels, σ_0 is the resonant absorption cross section, W_0 is the full width at half maximum of the unbroadened line (twice the natural width), E_γ/k is the recoil energy of the free nucleus divided by the Boltzmann constant, and θ_D is the low-temperature limit. Source: Ref 14

$$S = \frac{2}{5}\frac{\pi c}{E_\gamma} Ze^2 [R_e^2 - R_g^2] [\rho_a(0) - \rho_s(0)]$$

$$\text{(Eq 9)}$$

where c is the velocity of light, Z is atomic number of the nucleus, e is the electronic charge, R_e and R_g are the radii of the excited- and ground-state nuclear levels, and $\rho_a(0)$ and $\rho_s(0)$ are the electronic densities at the nucleus in the absorber and in the source.

In ^{57}Fe, $R_e < R_g$; therefore, the isomer shift will be negative if the electronic density at the absorber nucleus exceeds that at the source nucleus. It is customary to refer to isomer shifts relative to a given absorber. For example, the isomer shift of pure iron as an absorber is arbitrarily assigned the value zero. The isomer shift for other absorbers (using the same source) is then given relative to pure iron. By convention, positive velocities refer to source and absorber approaching each other.

Quadrupole Interaction. The energy levels of the ground and excited nuclear states can be split by the hyperfine interaction between an electric-field gradient at the nuclear site and the electric quadrupole moment Q of the nucleus. This quadrupole interaction offers an opportunity to detect

Table 2 Angular distribution functions for nuclear transitions of multipolarity L = 1 and L = 2

Δm	$L = 1$, $G^1\Delta m(\phi)$	$L = 2$, $G^2\Delta m(\phi)$
±2	. . .	$(1 - \cos^4 \phi)$
±1	$(1 + \cos^2 \phi)$	$(4\cos^4 \phi - 3\cos^2 \phi + 1)$
0	$\sin^2 \phi$	$3 \sin^2 \phi \cos^2 \phi$

variations in crystal structure, local atomic environment, lattice defects, and conduction electron states.

Unless there is perfect cubic (or tetrahedral) symmetry, it is not generally possible to avoid nuclear quadrupole effects by selecting a suitable nucleus. This is because, even if the nuclear ground-state spin has no quadrupole moment, that is, $I_g = 0$ or 1/2, the excited state generally does (or conversely). Thus, even when the measurement of the quadrupole energy is not the object of the experiment, it is still often necessary to understand its effect on the spectrum to extract other parameters.

The electric-field gradient at the nucleus can be expressed using a symmetric tensor consisting of the components $-V_{i,j}$ ($i,j = 1$ to 3):

$$V_{i,j} = \frac{\partial^2 V}{\partial x_i\, \partial x_j} \qquad \text{(Eq 10)}$$

where x_1, x_2, and x_3 are equated to spatial coordinates ($x_1 = x$, $x_2 = y$, $x_3 = z$), and V is the electric potential. A set of axes, termed the principal axes, can be selected so that only V_{xx}, V_{yy}, and V_{zz} are different from zero. Further, the Laplacian of the electric potential vanishes:

$$V_{xx} + V_{yy} + V_{zz} = 0 \qquad \text{(Eq 11)}$$

Thus, there are only two independent parameters, and they are usually defined as q, the largest of the three components of the electric-field gradient (in units of the proton charge e), and η, the asymmetry parameter:

Table 3 Table of numbers proportional to the squared Wigner coefficients for multipolarity L = 1 and L = 2 and for 3/2 ⇌ 1/2 and 5/2 ⇌ 3/2 transitions

$I_1 = 3/2 \rightleftharpoons I_2 = 1/2$

		m_1			
	m_2	3/2	1/2	−1/2	−3/2
L = 1 . .	1/2	3	2	1	0
	−1/2	0	1	2	3
L = 2 . .	1/2	1	2	3	4
	−1/2	4	3	2	1

$I_1 = 5/2 \rightleftharpoons I_2 = 3/2$

		m_1					
	m_2	5/2	3/2	1/2	−1/2	−3/2	−5/2
L = 1 . .	3/2	10	4	1	0	0	0
	1/2	0	6	6	3	0	0
	−1/2	0	0	3	6	6	0
	−3/2	0	0	0	1	4	10
L = 2 . .	3/2	30	36	27	12	0	0
	1/2	40	2	6	25	32	0
	−1/2	0	32	25	6	2	40
	−3/2	0	0	12	27	36	30

$$eq = V_{zz} \qquad \text{(Eq 12)}$$

and

$$\eta = \frac{V_{xx} - V_{yy}}{V_{zz}} \qquad \text{(Eq 13)}$$

In addition, $|V_{zz}| \geq |V_{yy}| \geq |V_{xx}|$ are usually selected such that $0 \leq \eta \leq 1$. If the crystal-point symmetry is cubic or tetrahedral, then $V_{xx} = V_{yy} = V_{zz}$ and, by Eq 11, each component must be zero and the quadrupole interaction vanishes.

Table 4 Principal methods used for producing Mössbauer effect sources

Atomic number, Z	Atomic weight, A	Element	Radioactive parent (decay, half-life)(a)	Principal means of production	Favorable reaction energy, MeV	Convenient source hosts	Single-line absorbers
19	40	Potassium	Neutron capture	$^{39}K(n,\gamma)$	...	KF	KCl, KF
26	57	Iron	^{57}Co (EC, 270 d)	$^{56}Fe(d,n)$	9.5	Cr, Cu, Rh, Pd	$K_4Fe(CN)_6$
			^{57}Mn (β^-, 1.7 min)	$^{54}Cr(\alpha,n)$	21	Cr	
28	61	Nickel	^{61}Co (β^-, 99 min)	$^{64}Ni(p,\alpha)$	22	$NiV_{0.14}$	
30	67	Zinc	^{67}Ga (EC, 78 h)	$^{66}Zn(d,n)$	12	ZnO	Ni
32	73	Germanium	^{73}As (EC, 110 d)	$^{74}Ge(p,2n)$	24	Ge	Ge
32	73	Germanium	Coulomb excitation	$^{73}Ge(O^{4+})$	25	Cr	Ge
36	83	Krypton	^{83m}Kr (IT, 1.86 h)	$^{82}Kr(n,\gamma)$	...	Kr	Kr ice
			^{83}Br (β^-, 2.41 h)	$^{82}Br(n,\gamma)$	...	KBr	
44	99	Ruthenium	^{99}Rh (EC, 16 d)	$^{99}Ru(d,2n)$	20	Ru, Rh	Ru
44	101	Ruthenium	^{101}Rh (EC, 3 yr)	$^{101}Ru(d,2n)$	20	Ru	Ru
50	119	Tin	^{119m}Sn (IT, 250 d)	$^{118}Sn(n,\gamma)$	...	V, $CaSnO_3$	$CaSnO_3$
51	121	Antimony	^{121m}Sn (β^-, 76 yr)	$^{120}Sn(n,\gamma)$	...	SnO_2, $CaSnO_3$	InSb
52	125	Tellurium	^{125m}Te (IT, 58 d)	$^{124}Te(n,\gamma)$	...	Cu, ZnTe	ZnTe
53	127	Iodine	^{127}Te (β^-, 9.4 h)	$^{126}Te(n,\gamma)$	...	ZnTe	KI
			^{127m}Te (β^-, 109 d)	$^{126}Te(n,\gamma)$	...	ZnTe	
54	129	Xenon	^{129}I (β^-, 10^7 yr)	Fission product	...	$Na_3H_2IO_6$, KIO_4	Na_4XeO_6
54	131	Xenon	^{131}I (β^-, 8 d)	Fission product	...		Na_4XeO_6
55	133	Cesium	^{133}Ba (EC, 7.2 yr)	Fission product	...	$BaAl_4$	CsCl
59	141	Praseodymium	^{141}Ce (β^-, 33 d)	$^{140}Ce(n,\gamma)$	...	CeO_2	Pr_2O_3
60	145	Neodymium	^{145}Pm (EC, 17.7 yr)	$^{144}Nd(n,\gamma)$	...	Nd_2O_3	$NdCl_2$, Nd_2O_3
62	147	Samarium	^{147}Eu (EC, 22 d)	$^{148}Sm(p,2n)$	12	Sm_2O_3	SmB_6
62	149	Samarium	^{149}Eu (EC, 106 d)	$^{150}Sm(p,2n)$	12	Sm_2O_3	SmB_6
62	152	Samarium	^{152}Eu (EC, 9.3 h)	$Eu(n,\gamma)$	...	Gd_2O_3	SmB_6
62	154	Samarium	Coulomb excitation	$^{154}Sm(p)$	3	Sm_2O_3	...
63	151	Europium	^{151}Sm (β^-, 87 yr)	$^{150}Sm(n,\gamma)$	...	SmF_3, Sm_2O_3	$Cs_2NaEuCl_6$
63	153	Europium	^{153}Sm (β^-, 47 h)	$Sm(n,\gamma)$	...	Sm_2O_3	$EuPd_3$, EuF_3
63	153	Europium	^{153}Gd (EC, 242 d)	$^{152}Gd(n,\gamma)$	...	GdF_3, Gd_2O_3	EuF_3
63	153	Europium	^{153}Sm (β^-, 47 h)	$Sm(n,\gamma)$	...	$SmPd_3$, Sm_2O_3	$EuPd_3$, EuF
64	154	Gadolinium	^{154}Eu (β^-, 16 yr)	$^{153}Eu(n,\gamma)$	...	EuF_3	...
64	155	Gadolinium	^{155}Eu (β^-, 1.81 yr)	$^{154}Sm(n,\gamma)$	...	$SmPd_3$	$GdCo_2$, Cs_2NGdC
64	155	Gadolinium	^{155}Eu (β^-, 1.81 yr)	$^{154}Sm(n,\gamma)$	...	$SmPd_3$	$GdCo_2$, Cs_2NaG
64	155	Gadolinium	^{155}Eu (β^-, 1.81 yr)	$^{154}Sm(n,\gamma)$	...	$SmPd_3$	$GdCo_2$, Cs_2Na
64	156	Gadolinium	^{156}Eu (β^-, 15 d)	$^{154}Sm(n,\gamma)$	...	SmF_3	$GdCo_2$, $Cs_2NaGdCl_6$
64	157	Gadolinium	^{157}Eu (β^-, 15.2 h)	$^{158}Gd(\gamma,p)$	...	CeO_2, EuF_3	$CdCo_2$, $Cs_2NaGdCl_6$
64	157	Gadolinium	^{157}Eu (β^-, 15.2 h)	$^{158}Gd(\gamma,p)$	...	EuF_3, CeO_2	$GdCo_2$, $Cs_2NaGdCl_6$
64	158	Gadolinium	Neutron capture	$^{157}Gd(n,\gamma)$	...	YAl_2	$GdCo_2$, $Cs_2NaGdCl_6$
64	160	Gadolinium	Coulomb excitation	$^{160}Gd(Cl)$	64	...	$GdCo_2$, $Cs_2NaGdCl_6$
65	159	Terbium	^{159}Dy (EC, 144 d)	$^{158}Dy(n,\gamma)$	...	...	...
66	160	Dysprosium	^{160}Tb (β^-, 72.1 d)	$Tb(n,\gamma)$	...	$Tb_{0.1}Er_{0.9}H_2$	$Dy_{0.4}Sc_{0.6}H_2$
66	161	Dysprosium	^{161}Tb (β^-, 6.9 d)	$^{160}Gd(n,\gamma)$	...	GdF_3 (300 K)	DyF_3 (300 K)
66	161	Dysprosium	Coulomb excitation	$^{161}Dy(\alpha)$	3.3	DyF_3	...
66	161	Dysprosium	^{161}Tb (β^-, 6.9 d)	$^{160}Gd(n,\gamma)$	...	GdF_3	...
66	162	Dysprosium	Coulomb excitation	$^{162}Dy(\alpha)$	3	...	...
66	164	Dysprosium	Coulomb excitation	$^{164}Dy(\alpha)$	3	...	...
67	165	Holmium	^{165}Dy (β^-, 2.3 h)	$^{164}Dy(n,\gamma)$	...	...	...
68	164	Erbium	^{164}Ho (β^-, 39 min)	$Ho(\gamma,n)$	50	...	...
68	166	Erbium	^{166}Ho (β^-, 27 h)	$Ho(n,\gamma)$	...	$H_{0.39}Y_{0.61}H$	ErH_2
68	167	Erbium	^{167}Ho (β^-, 3.1 h)	$^{170}Er(p,\alpha)$	...	...	ErH_2
68	168	Erbium	^{168}Tm (EC, 86 d)	$Tm(\gamma,n)$	50	$TmAl_2$	ErH_2
68	170	Erbium	Coulomb excitation	^{166}Er ( )	3	...	...
69	169	Thulium	^{169}Er (β^-, 9.4 d)	$Er(n,)$	...	$ErAl_3$ (300 K)	$TmAl_2$ (300 K)
70	170	Ytterbium	^{170}Tm (β^-, 130 d)	$Tm(n,)$	...	$TmAl_2$, TmB_{12}	$YbAl_3$
70	171	Ytterbium	^{171}Tm (β^-, 1.92 yr)	$^{170}Er(n,)$	...	$ErAl_3$	$YbAl_3$
70	171	Ytterbium	^{171}Lu (EC, 8.3 d)	$^{169}Tm(,2n)$	23	$TmAl_3$	$YbAl_3$
70	172	Ytterbium	^{172}Lu (EC, 6.7 d)	$^{172}Yb(d,2n)$	15	$YbAl_3$	$YbAl_3$
70	174	Ytterbium	^{174}Lu (EC, 3.6 yr)	$Lu(\gamma,n)$	50	Lu	...
70	176	Ytterbium	Coulomb excitation	$^{176}Yb(\alpha)$	3	...	...
71	175	Lutetium	^{175}Yb (β^-, 101 h)	$^{174}Yb(n,\gamma)$	...	$YbAl_2$	...
72	176	Hafnium	^{176m}Lu (β^-, 3.7 h)	$Lu(n,\gamma)$	...	$LuAl_2$	$HfZn_2$
72	177	Hafnium	^{177}Lu (β^-, 6.7 d)	$^{176}Lu(n,\gamma)$	...	$LuAl_2$	$HfZn_2$
72	178	Hafnium	^{178}Ta (EC, 9.4 min)	$Ta(d,5n)$	...	Ta	$HfZn_2$
72	180	Hafnium	^{180m}Hf (IT, 5.5 h)	$^{179}Hf(n,\gamma)$	...	...	$HfZn_2$
			^{180m}Ta (EC, 8.1 h)	$Ta(\gamma,n)$	17	Ta	...
73	181	Tantalum	^{181}W (EC, 140 d)	$^{180}W(n,\gamma)$	...	W	Ta
73	181	Tantalum	^{181}Hf (β^-, 42.5 d)	$^{180}Hf(n,\gamma)$	...	$HfZn_2$	Ta
74	180	Tungsten	^{180m}Ta (β^-, 8.1 h)	$Ta(\gamma,n)$	17	Ta	W
74	182	Tungsten	^{182}Ta (β^-, 115 d)	$Ta(n,\gamma)$	...	Ta	W
74	183	Tungsten	^{183}Re (EC, 71 d)	$Ta(\alpha,2n)$	...	Ta	W
			^{183}Ta (β^-, 5.1 d)	$^{181}Ta(n,\gamma)$, $^{182}Ta(n,\gamma)$	...	Ta	...

(continued)

(a) The superscript m, as in ^{83m}Kr, represents the metastable state. EC, electron capture; β^-, β decay; IT, isomeric transition; α, α decay. Source: Ref 10

Table 4   (continued)

Atomic number, Z	Atomic weight, A	Element	Radioactive parent (decay, half-life)(a)	Principal means of production	Favorable reaction energy, MeV	Convenient source hosts	Single-line absorbers
74	183	Tungsten	^{183}Re (EC, 71 d)	Ta(α,2n)	...	Ta	W
			^{183}Ta (β^-, 5.1 d)	^{181}Ta (n,γ), ^{182}Ta(n,γ)	...	Ta	...
74	184	Tungsten	^{184}Re (EC, 38 d)	^{185}Re(p,pn)	32	Re	W
74	186	Tungsten	^{186}Re (EC, 90 h)	^{185}Re(n,γ)	...	Re	W
75	187	Rhenium	^{187}W (β^-, 23.9 h)	^{186}W(n,γ)	...	W	Re
76	186	Osmium	^{186}Re (β^-, 90 h)	^{186}Re(n,γ)	...	Re	K$_2$OsCl$_6$
76	188	Osmium	^{188}Re (β^-, 16.7 h)	^{187}Re(n,γ)	...	Re	K$_2$OsCl$_6$
76	189	Osmium	^{189}Ir (EC, 13.3 d)	^{189}Os(d,2n)	13	Ir	K$_2$OsCl$_6$
76	189	Osmium	^{189}Ir (EC, 13.3 d)	^{189}Os(d,2n)	13	Ir	K$_2$OsCl$_6$
76	189	Osmium	^{189}Ir (EC, 13.3 d)	^{189}Os(d,2n)	13	Ir	K$_2$OsCl$_6$
76	190	Osmium	^{190}Ir (EC, 11 d)	^{190}Os(d,2n)	13	Cu	
77	191	Iridium	^{191}Pt (EC, 3 d)	^{191}Ir(d,2n)	13	Ir	Ir
77	191	Iridium	^{191}Pt (EC, 3 d)	^{191}Ir(d,2n)	13	Ir	Ir
77	193	Iridium	^{193}Os (β^-, 31 h)	^{192}Os(n,γ)	...	Os, V, Pt, Nb	Ir
77	193	Iridium	^{193}Os (β^-, 31 h)	^{192}Os(n,γ)	...	Os	Ir
78	195	Platinum	^{195}Au (EC, 183 d)	^{195}Pt(d,2n)	13	Pt	Pt
78	195	Platinum	^{195m}Pt (IT, 4.0 d)	^{194}Pt(n,γ)	...	Pt	Pt
79	197	Gold	^{197}Pt (β^-, 18 h)	^{196}Pt(n,γ)	...	Pt	Au
80	201	Mercury	^{201}Tl (EC, 73 h)	Tl(γ,2n)	...	Tl$_2$O$_3$	...
90	232	Thorium	Coulomb excitation	^{232}Th(α)	6	Th, ThO$_2$	ThO$_2$
92	238	Uranium	^{242}Pu (α, 3.79 $\times$ 10^5 yr)	...	...	PuO$_2$	UO$_2$
93	237	Neptunium	^{237}U (β^-, 6.75 d)	^{236}U(n,γ), ^{238}U(γ,n)	...	UO$_2$	NpO$_2$
			^{237}Pu (EC, 45.6 d)	^{237}Np(d,2n)	15	...	...
			^{241}Am (α, 458 yr)	...	...	Am, Th	...

(a) The superscript m, as in ^{83m}Kr, represents the metastable state. EC, electron capture; β^-, β decay; IT, isomeric transition; α, α decay. Source: Ref 10

Fig. 1 Radioactive decay scheme showing the excited nuclear states of ^{57}Fe populated by decay of the radioactive precursor ^{57}Co

The ^{57}Fe Mössbauer effect uses the 14.4-keV transition between the first excited and the ground state.

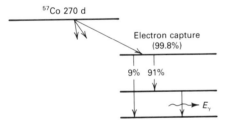

Spin (I)	Parity (P)	Energy, keV	Half-life, μs
5/2	-1	136	0.009
3/2	-1	14.4	0.098
1/2	-1	0	Stable

Fig. 2 Illustration of the isomer shift, S

(a) The ground- and excited-state energies are shifted by different amounts in source and absorber. The transition energy is larger in the absorber. (b) The shifted spectrum that results from such situations as (a)

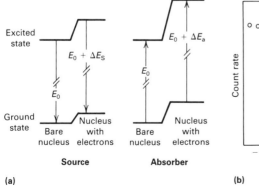

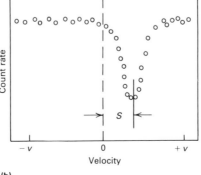

The quadrupole Hamiltonian is:

$$H_Q = \frac{e^2qQ}{4I(2I-1)}\left[3I_z^2 - I(I+1) + \frac{1}{2}\eta(I_+^2 + I_-^2)\right] \qquad \text{(Eq 14)}$$

where $I_+ = I_x + iI_y$ and $I_- = I_x - iI_y$ are, respectively, the raising and lowering operators for the spin angular momentum (i is the imaginary number $\sqrt{-1}$). The simplest case is axial symmetry ($\eta = 0$), for which the z-axis is the axis of symmetry, and the eigenvalues are:

$$E_m = \frac{e^2qQ}{4I(2I-1)}[3m^2 - I(I+1)] \quad \text{(Eq 15)}$$

where m is the same quantum number as for the magnetic case.

The relative transition probabilities and their angular distribution can be obtained from Tables 2 and 3 for the case in which $\eta = 0$. The angle referred to in Table 2 is the angle between the direction of γ-ray propagation and the principal axis. For example, the spin $I = \frac{1}{2}$ ground state of ^{57}Fe has $Q = 0$ and is not affected by an electric-field gradient. The excited state, with spin $I = \frac{3}{2}$, is split into two levels, one with $m = \pm\frac{3}{2}$ and the other with $m = \pm\frac{1}{2}$. The energy separation of the two levels is $eQV_{xx}/2$. For a single crystal whose z-axis is at an angle ϕ

Fig. 3 Transitions (a) and relative line intensities (b) for magnetic hyperfine interactions in ^{57}Fe

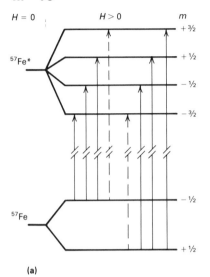

(a)

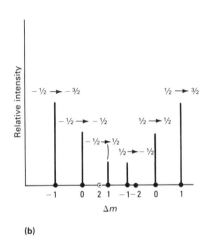

(b)

Fig. 4 Experimental arrangement showing four major components

1, Suitably prepared source of recoil-free γ-rays given a precisely controlled velocity by a transducer. 2, Absorber containing isotopes capable of recoil-free scattering of the γ-rays emanating from the source. 3, γ-ray detector, such as a proportional counter or a scintillation counter, with a suitable preamplifier and a single-channel analyzer to select only counts from the γ-ray energy range of interest. A shield and a filter are generally useful to exclude x-rays and scattered radiation out of the range of interest. 4, Storage device to monitor the number of counts as a function of the relative velocity between source and absorber. Earlier arrangements used a multichannel analyzer; newer systems use the capabilities of microcomputers.

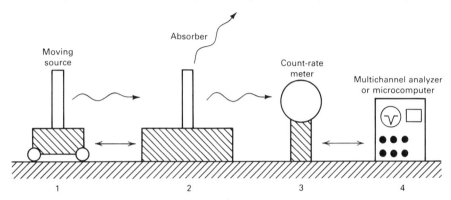

to the direction of γ-ray propagation, the ME spectrum consists of two lines with an intensity ratio:

$$\frac{I\left(\frac{3}{2} \to \frac{1}{2}\right)}{I\left(\frac{1}{2} \to \frac{1}{2}\right)} = \frac{1 + \cos^2 \phi}{\frac{5}{3} - \cos^2 \phi} \quad \text{(Eq 16)}$$

For a powder sample with no preferred orientation, the two transitions occur on the average with equal probability, assuming no anisotropy in the recoilless fraction. In ^{57}Fe, this results in the familiar doublet pattern.

Magnetic Interaction. The hyperfine interaction between the nuclear magnetic moment and a magnetic field at the nuclear site is useful for phase identification, for observing magnetic transitions, and for studying the local atomic environment of the resonating nucleus. This Zeeman effect is characterized by the Hamiltonian:

$$H = -\mu \cdot H_0 = -\gamma\hbar I \cdot H_0 \quad \text{(Eq 17)}$$

The equally spaced energy levels resulting from this Hamiltonian are given by $E = -\gamma\hbar m H_0$, where $m = -I, -I + 1, \dots, I - 1, I$; H_0 is the magnetic field at the nuclear site; $\hbar$ is Planck's constant over 2π; and γ is the gyromagnetic ratio of the nucleus.

Transitions and relative line intensities for the familiar and useful case of ^{57}Fe are illustrated in Fig. 3. For other cases, the relative line intensities of the transitions can be found using Tables 2 and 3.

Experimental Arrangement

Figure 4 shows a typical arrangement for obtaining Mössbauer effect spectra. To obtain the required γ-rays, a radioactive precursor, or parent, is used. For example, ^{57}Co is a suitable precursor for populating the 14.4-keV level of ^{57}Fe, the most heavily studied Mössbauer isotope. Figure 1 shows the appropriate decay scheme for ^{57}Fe. Table 1 lists isotopes that can be used for Mössbauer effect studies, along with some of their properties. Table 4 lists radioactive parents and their principal means of production. By far the two most frequently used isotopes are ^{57}Fe and ^{119}Sn.

Applications

Surface-Phase Detection. The ^{57}Fe Mössbauer spectrum obtained by counting conversion electrons provides information from a thin layer on the surface of a metal, the depth of the layer being limited by the range of these electrons within the metal. For iron-rich alloys, the depth being probed is of the order of 30 nm.

A sample of spheroidized iron carbide in ferrite, National Bureau of Standards Reference Material 493, contains approximately 14 vol% iron carbide, the remainder being α-iron containing a small amount of dissolved carbon. Appreciable amounts of austenite can be formed by coarse surface grinding of carbon steel; therefore, the standard material is subjected only to light surface grinding.

Conversion electron Mössbauer scattering (Ref 15) demonstrates that this procedure produces an extremely thin layer of austenite, which is apparent in Fig. 5. The 14.4-keV spectrum (spectrum A) probes a depth of approximately 30 μm and therefore represents the bulk sample. The inner two lines from the six-line iron spectrum and the six-line iron carbide spectrum are indicated (there is some overlap of the α-iron and Fe$_3$C lines). Spectrum B has an additional line identified as austenite. The austenite layer is too thin to be observed using conventional metallographic techniques, including glancing angle x-ray diffraction, and may be too strained to be readily observed using low-energy electron diffraction.

Phase Analysis of Hydrided TiFe. The intermetallic compound TiFe, with stoichiometric proportions of titanium and iron, has application as a hydrogen gas storage device. This compound readily absorbs and desorbs hydrogen, forming ternary TiFeH$_x$ phases. The ^{57}Fe Mössbauer transmission spectrum can be used to probe the phases formed (Ref 16).

Fig. 5 Backscattered ^{57}Fe Mössbauer spectra from the lightly ground surface of an iron-iron carbide alloy (NBS Standard Reference Material 493)

Only the central region of each spectrum is shown. A, 14.4-keV γ-rays counted; B, conversion electrons counted

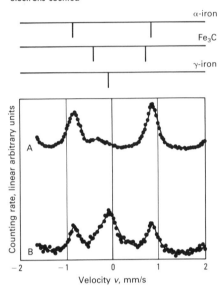

Fig. 6 ^{57}Fe Mössbauer absorption spectra for TiFeH$_x$

The lines shown through the data points are least square fits of the separate components. A, x = 0.1; B, x = 0.9; C, x = 1.7

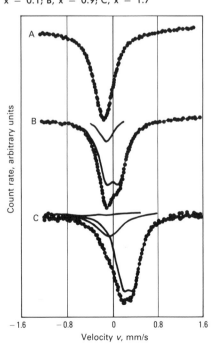

Fig. 7 Room-temperature ^{57}Fe Mössbauer absorption spectrum for a rapidly quenched Cu$_{0.97}$Fe$_{0.03}$ sample

The lines at the top indicate the positions of the lines that constitute the spectrum. The contribution from three types of iron (see text) are indicated. The zero of velocity represents the center of a pure iron absorption spectrum at room temperature. The source used was approximately 10 mCi of ^{57}Co in palladium.

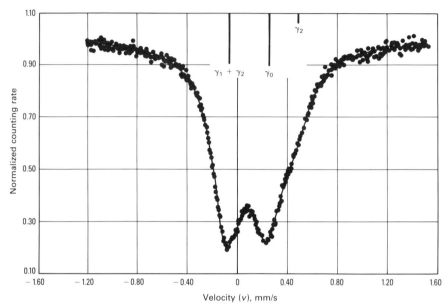

A small amount of hydrogen dissolves in the TiFe crystal structure (Fig. 6). Spectrum A shows that for a composition of TiFeH$_{0.1}$ the ^{57}Fe spectrum has a single peak, essentially identical to that of hydrogen-free TiFe. This cubic phase, based on TiFe, is termed α. The spectrum for a composition of TiFeH$_{0.9}$, Spectrum B, can be resolved into two lines: one identified with α and the second, a quadrupole doublet, associated with a noncubic β phase. The lever rule can be used to determine the location of this composition in the two-phase (α + β) region. Spectrum C is for a TiFeH$_{1.7}$ alloy and is in the two-phase region between β and a third noncubic phase γ. A small amount (approximately 2%) of TiFe is also evident. Because the spectra for TiFeH$_x$ are not completely resolved, this method of phase analysis is not unique, but it is quick and sensitive to the phases present.

Analysis of Phases of Iron in Copper. The Mössbauer effect readily distinguishes four types of iron in copper-iron alloys (Ref 17). Body-centered cubic (bcc) precipitates (α-iron) are characterized by a six-line magnetic hyperfine field pattern. Isolated iron atoms in solid solution, termed γ$_0$-iron, provide a single line centered at 0.24 mm/s. Iron atoms in solid solution with other iron atoms as near neighbors, termed

γ$_2$-iron, yield a quadrupole split doublet centered at 0.25 mm/s with a splitting of 0.58 mm/s. Iron in face-centered cubic (fcc) coherent precipitates, termed γ$_1$-iron, gives a single line centered at −0.10 mm/s (values given are at room temperature and are referenced to the center of a pure α-iron spectrum).

A room-temperature spectrum from a quenched sample of Cu$_{0.97}$Fe$_{0.03}$ is shown in Fig. 7. Two of the lines, the singlet line from γ$_1$-iron and one of the doublet lines from γ$_2$-iron, are coincident. Their relative magnitudes can be determined closely by assuming that the γ$_2$-iron doublet represents a powder pattern and is therefore symmetric. The transformations that occur upon cold working or annealing the sample can be readily observed from the spectra. The coherent γ$_1$-iron precipitates can grow quite large before they transform to α-iron.

Extended Solubility of Iron in Aluminum. The equilibrium solid solubility of iron in aluminum is extremely small (less than 0.01 wt% Fe at 500 °C, or 930 °F). However, a large supersaturation can be obtained by rapid solidification techniques. Supersaturated solid solutions containing up to 8 wt% Fe have been reported (Ref 18). Mössbauer measurements, combined with x-ray diffraction, have been performed (Ref

19) and confirm supersaturation up to this amount for splat quenched samples. The spectra show, however, that the number of iron-iron near neighbors is much greater than that expected for a random solid solution.

REFERENCES

1. A. Abragam, *L'effet Mössbauer*, Gordon and Breach, 1964
2. S.G. Cohen and M. Pasternak, Ed., *Perspectives in Mössbauer Spectroscopy*, Plenum Press, 1973
3. H. Frauenfelder, *The Mössbauer Effect*, Benjamin, 1962
4. U. Gonser, Ed., *Mössbauer Spectroscopy*, Springer-Verlag, 1975
5. N.N. Greenwood and T.C. Gibb, *Mössbauer Spectroscopy*, Chapman and Hall, 1972
6. L. May, Ed., *An Introduction to Mössbauer Spectroscopy*, Plenum Press, 1971
7. I.D. Weisman, L.J. Swartzendruber, L.H. Bennett, *Techniques in Metals Research*, Vol 6, R.F. Bunshah, Ed., John Wiley & Sons, 1973, p 165-504
8. G.K. Wertheim, *Mössbauer Effect: Principles and Applications*, Academic Press, 1964
9. J.G. Stevens and G.K. Shenoy, Ed., *Mössbauer Spectroscopy and Its Applications*, American Chemical Society, Washington, 1981
10. G.K. Shenoy and F.E. Wagner, Ed., *Mössbauer Isomer Shifts*, North Holland, 1978
11. J.G. Stevens, V.E. Stevens, and W.L. Gettys, *Cumulative Index to the Mössbauer Effect Data Indexes*, Plenum Press, 1979
12. I.J. Gruverman and C.W. Seidel, Ed., *Mössbauer Effect Methodology*, Vol 10, Plenum Press, 1976
13. A. Vertes, L. Korecz, and K. Burger, *Mössbauer Spectroscopy*, Elsevier, 1979
14. J.G. Stevens and V.E. Stevens, *Mössbauer Effect Data Index*, Plenum Press, 1973
15. L.J. Swartzendruber and L.H. Bennett, *Scr. Metall.*, Vol 6, 1972, p 737
16. L.J. Swartzendruber, L.H. Bennett, and R.E. Watson, *J. Phys. F (Met. Phys.)*, Vol 6, 1976, p 331
17. L.H. Bennett and L.J. Swartzendruber, *Acta Metall.*, Vol 18, 1970, p 485
18. T.R. Anatharaman and C. Suryanarayana, *J. Mater. Sci.*, Vol 6, 1971, p 1111
19. S. Nasu, U. Gonser, P.H. Shingu, and Y. Murakami, *J. Phys. F (Met. Phys.)*, Vol 4, 1974, p L24

Metallographic Techniques

Optical Metallography

M.R. Louthan, Jr., Department of Materials Engineering, Virginia Polytechnic Institute and State University

General Uses

- Imaging of topographic or microstructural features on polished and etched surfaces at magnifications of 1 to 1500×
- Characterization of grain and phase structures and dimensions

Examples of Applications

- Determination of fabrication and heat-treatment history
- Determination of braze- and weld-joint integrity
- Failure analysis
- Characterization of the effects of processing on microstructure and properties

Samples

- *Form*: Metals, ceramics, composites, and geologic materials
- *Size*: Dimensions ranging from 10^{-5} to 10^{-1} m
- *Preparation*: Specimens are usually sectioned and mounted, ground, and polished to produce a flat, scratch-free surface, then etched to reveal microstructural features of interest

Limitations

- *Resolution limit*: Approximately 1 μm
- Limited depth of field (cannot focus on rough surfaces)
- Does not give direct chemical or crystallographic information about microstructural features

Estimated Analysis Time

- 30 min to several hours per specimen, including preparation

Capabilities of Related Techniques

- *Scanning electron microscopy*: Provides better resolution (higher magnifications); greater depth of field (can image rough surfaces); qualitative elemental microanalysis
- *Electron probe x-ray microanalysis*: Provides quantitative elemental microanalysis
- *Transmission electron microscopy*: Provides much better resolution (much higher magnifications) on specially prepared specimens; semiquantitative elemental microanalysis; crystallographic information on microstructural features

Introduction

Optical metallography, one of three general categories of metallography, entails examination of materials using visible light to provide a magnified image of the micro- and macrostructure. In scanning electron microscopy (SEM), the second category, the surface of the specimen is bombarded with a beam of electrons to provide information for producing an image (see the article "Scanning Electron Microscopy" in this Volume). Lastly, transmission electron microscopy (TEM) consists of passing a beam of electrons through a very thin specimen and analyzing the transmitted beam for structural information (see the article "Analytical Transmission Electron Microscopy" in this Volume). Microscopy (microstructural examination) involves magnifications of approximately 50× or higher; macroscopy (macrostructural examination), 50× or lower.

Optical microscopy and, occasionally, SEM are used to characterize structure by revealing grain boundaries, phase boundaries, inclusion distribution, and evidence of mechanical deformation. Scanning electron microscopy is also used to characterize fracture surfaces, integrated circuits, corrosion products, and other rough surfaces, especially when elemental microanalysis of small features is desired. Transmission electron microscopy is used to examine dislocation arrangements or structures and other small defects in metals and alloys. Second-phase particles not observable using optical metallography can frequently be analyzed using TEM.

Because the macro- and microstructure of metals and alloys often determine the behavior of the material, characterization of the effects of composition, processing, service conditions, and other such variables on the macro- and microstructure is frequently required. Typical structure-property relationships that have been established using optical metallography include:

- A general increase in yield strength and hardness of a metal with decreasing grain size
- A general tendency for a decreased ductility with increasing inclusion content
- Correlations of weld penetration, heat-affected zone (HAZ) size, and weld-defect density with the nature and character of the welding

- Evaluation of such surface treatments as carburizing and induction hardening by determinations of the depth and microstructural characteristics of the hardened region
- Correlations of fatigue crack growth rates and fracture-toughness parameters with such structural variables as inclusion content and distribution
- Association of failure initiation sites with microstructural inhomogeneities, such as second-phase particles
- Correlations of anisotropic mechanical behavior with elongated grains and/or preferred grain orientations

The microstructures of metals and alloys are determined by composition, solidification processes, and thermomechanical treatment. Therefore, these process variables determine the response of metals and alloys to laboratory and service environments. Because of the relationships between structure and properties, metallographic characterization is used in materials specification, quality control, quality assurance, process control, and failure analysis.

Optical metallography is applicable to studies ranging from fundamental research to production evaluations. This article will discuss use of optical methods to evaluate structure and to relate that structure to process conditions and/or material behavior. Detailed information on the principles and instrumentation of optical microscopy is available in the article "Optical Microscopy" in Volume 9 of the 9th Edition of *Metals Handbook*.

Specimen Preparation

The first step in metallographic analysis is to select a sample that is representative of the material to be evaluated. This step is critical to the success of any subsequent study. The second, equally important step is to correctly prepare a metallographic specimen.

The region of the sample that is of interest must be sectioned from the component. For example, if a failure occurred because a steel pipe leaked during service, the metallographic analysis would probably involve at least three samples: one removed from the pipe such that a portion of the leak is contained in the sample, another removed near the leak, and a third taken far from the leak. Each of the samples would be mounted to facilitate handling. Selected surfaces would then be ground flat, polished, and etched to reveal the specific structure or structures of interest.

Sectioning of a metallographic sample must be performed carefully to avoid altering or destroying the structure of interest (see the article "Sectioning" in Volume 9 of the 9th

Edition of *Metals Handbook*). The most widely used sectioning device is the abrasive cutoff machine, ranging from units using thin diamond-rimmed wafering blades to those using wheels that are more than 1.5 mm ($\frac{1}{16}$ in.) thick, 30 to 45 cm (12 to 18 in.) in diameter, containing silicon carbide particles.

Heat is generated during abrasive cutting, and the material just below the abraded surface is deformed. To minimize burning and deformation, a lubricant or coolant is typically used. Wet cutting yields a flat relatively smooth surface. However, because of the abrasion associated with cutting, the structure of the metal or alloy is damaged to a depth of approximately 1 mm (0.04 in.). The exact depth of damage depends on the type of cutoff wheel used, the cutting speed, and the hardness of the specimen. The harder the specimen, the shallower the depth of damage. This damaged layer must be removed by grinding. However, before the specimen can be conveniently ground, it often must be mounted.

Mounting facilitates handling of the specimen. A procedure that does not damage the specimen should be selected. Because large specimens are generally more difficult to prepare than small ones, specimen size should be minimized. Standard or typical specimen mounts are right circular cylinders 25 to 50 mm (1 to 2 in.) in diameter. Mounting mediums should be compatible with the specimen regarding hardness and abrasion resistance. Two common mounting materials are thermosetting phenolics, such as Bakelite, and thermoplastic materials, such as methyl methacrylate (Lucite). A thermosetting polymer develops a rigid three-dimensional structure upon being heated and held at 200 to 300 °C (390 to 570 °F). A thermoplastic polymer softens when held at elevated temperatures.

Mounting involves placing the specimen in a mold and surrounding it with the appropriate powders. The mold and its contents are then heated under pressure to the thermal setting or the softening temperature. Once the powder sets, thermosetting mounts can be removed from the mold without lowering the temperature; thermoplastic mounts must be cooled to ambient temperature before removal. Mounting pressure or temperature may alter the structure of low melting temperature or soft and/or fragile specimens; therefore, castable (cold-mounting) techniques have been developed.

Plastics that set at room temperature are referred to as castable (cold-mounting) materials. The most widely used materials are epoxy resins. Epoxies resist acids and strong solvents effectively, a desirable characteristic in any mounting material. Epoxies and

Fig. 1 One method of mounting the sample to retain flatness for metallographic examination

The mount can also be filled with ground glass, pelletized Al_2O_3, or another hard material to maintain flatness.

Test specimen mounted in Bakelite

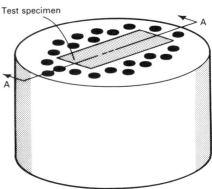

Test specimen

Hardened steel balls or chilled iron shot (typ)

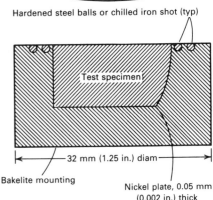

Test specimen

32 mm (1.25 in.) diam

Bakelite mounting

Nickel plate, 0.05 mm (0.002 in.) thick

Section A-A

thermoplastic materials are relatively soft mounting materials, and the specimen in such a mount must often be surrounded by a hard material, for example, hardened steel balls (Fig. 1). This material helps retain the edges of the sample by maintaining a flat surface during grinding and polishing. Additional information on mounting techniques and materials is available in the article "Mounting of Specimens" in Volume 9 of the 9th Edition of *Metals Handbook*.

Grinding is generally considered the most important step in specimen preparation. Care must be taken to minimize mechanical surface damage. Grinding is generally performed by the abrasion of the specimen surface against water-lubricated abrasive wheels (assuming water does not adversely affect the metal). Grinding develops a flat surface with a minimum depth of deformed metal and usually is accomplished by using progressively finer abrasive grits on the

Fig. 2 The effect of disturbed metal on the metallographic appearance of a plain carbon steel

(a) A layer of disturbed metal—an artifact structure caused by grinding damage—covers the polished surface. (b) The layer of disturbed metal is removed, and the structure is revealed to be lamellar pearlite. Etched using picral. 1000×

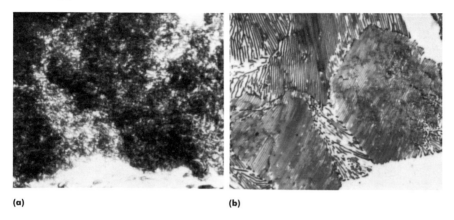

(a)   (b)

Fig. 3 The effect of improper polishing on AISI 1010 steel

(a) "Comet tails" from improper polishing. (b) The same material polished correctly, exhibiting small manganese sulfide inclusions

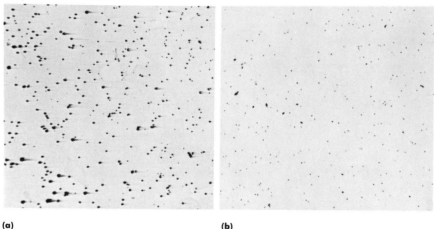

(a)   (b)

grinding wheels. A typical sequence might begin with 120- or 180-grit papers and proceed to 240, 320, 400, and 600 grits. Scratches and damage to the specimen surface from each grit must be removed by the next finer grinding step.

The surface damage remaining on the specimen after grinding must be removed by polishing. If this disturbed or deformed metal at the surface is not removed, microstructural observations may be obscured (Fig. 2). Because structure and properties are so closely related, conclusions based on the structure in Fig. 2(a) would lead to incorrect interpretation of the anticipated behavior of the metal. Grinding of metallographic specimens is discussed in the article "Mechanical Grinding, Abrasion, and Polishing" in Volume 9 of the 9th Edition of *Metals Handbook*.

Polishing of the metallographic specimen generally involves rough polishing and fine polishing. In rough polishing, the cloth covering on a wheel is impregnated with a fine (often as small as 1 μm) diamond paste or a slurry of powdered α-Al_2O_3 in water, and the specimen is held against the rotating wheel. The cloth for rough polishing is frequently napless, providing easy access of the polishing abrasive to the specimen surface. Fine polishing is conducted similarly, but with finer abrasives (down to 0.05 μm in diameter) on a napped cloth.

Although often automated, polishing can be performed by hand. Vibratory polishing and electropolishing techniques have also been developed for many metals and alloys (see the article "Electrolytic Polishing" in Volume 9 of the 9th Edition of *Metals Handbook*). Polishing should yield a scratch-

free specimen surface, in which inclusions and other second-phase articles may be visible. Polishing damage, such as that illustrated in Fig. 3, should be recognized and avoided when preparing metallographic specimens.

Etching includes any process used to reveal the microstructure of a metal or alloy. Because many microstructural details are not observable on an as-polished specimen, the specimen surface must be treated to reveal such structural features as grains, grain boundaries, twins, slip lines, and phase boundaries. Etchants attack at different rates areas of different crystal orientation, crystalline imperfections, or different composition. The resulting surface irregularities differentially reflect the incident light, producing contrast, coloration, polarization, etc. Various etching techniques are available, including chemical attack, electrochemical attack, thermal treatments, vacuum cathodic etching, and mechanical treatments (see the articles "Color Metallography" and "Etching" in Volume 9 of the 9th Edition of *Metals Handbook*). Chemical and electrochemical attack are the most frequently used. The details of the structure revealed by etching depend on the type of etchant used (Fig. 4).

Metallography involves many steps that can obscure or alter the structure observed during examination, leading to erroneous conclusions. Therefore, specimen preparation is not necessarily straightforward, and care must be taken to ensure that the structure observed is not an artifact. Good metallography is necessary in developing a correlation between the structure and the properties of metals and alloys.

Macroanalysis

Macrostructural characterization of metals and alloys is the detailed evaluation of large-scale inhomogeneities in composition, morphology, and/or density. These inhomogeneities may develop during such procedures as casting, extrusion, forging, rolling, and welding or during service. Figure 5 shows the macrostructure of a small relatively pure aluminum ingot exhibiting typical cast grain structure. To obtain the macrograph, the aluminum ingot was sectioned, then ground and polished to produce a flat reflective surface. The polished section was then etched by immersion in a solution that attacked the various grain orientations at different rates.

The etched structure was examined using a low-power microscope. The structural elements visible in this macrograph are grains. The small grains near the bottom of the ingot appear relatively equiaxed. This region of small equiaxed grains is the chill zone. During casting, such macrostructural defects

Fig. 4 Comparison of nital and picral for revealing a martensite structure

(a) Specimen etched using nital (nitric acid in ethanol or methanol). (b) Specimen etched using picral (picric acid in ethanol). Both 1000×

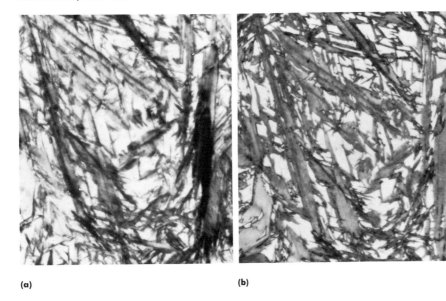

(a)   (b)

Fig. 5 Macrostructure of as-cast aluminum ingot

Transverse section shows outer chill zone and columnar grains that have grown perpendicularly to the mold faces. Etched using Tucker's reagent. 1.5×

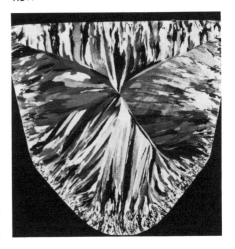

Fig. 6 Macrostructure of a continuous-cast copper ingot

(a) Spider cracks revealed using dye-penetrant inspection. Transverse section at top; longitudinal section at bottom. (b) Same ingot, etched using Waterbury's reagent. Cracks are not revealed. Both approximately 0.5×

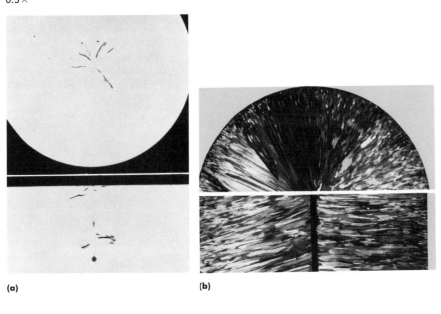

(a)   (b)

as gas or shrinkage porosity and center cracks can develop. Many of these defects can be characterized using macrostructural evaluation.

Figure 6(a) shows spider cracks in the center of a copper specimen. This specimen was sectioned, ground, and polished, but not etched. Chemical etching and subsequent evaluation of the macrostructure may fail to reveal this type of structural defect (Fig. 6b).

The cracks shown in Fig. 6(a) were revealed by applying a dye penetrant to the polished specimen. The dye was drawn into the cracks by capillary action, and the surface was then wiped clean. The specimen was then placed under a light that caused the dye to fluoresce, and the cracks became readily observable. Dye-penetrant techniques are excellent for examination of crack-like macrostructural defects in metals. However, grains and other microstructural features are visible only after etching, which frequently obscures the presence of the cracks. Therefore, different metallographic techniques are necessary to reveal various macrostructural elements.

Materials characterization by optical macrostructural examination can be divided into three categories. First, examination of the macrostructure of metallographically prepared sections removed from the component of interest is used to evaluate such structural parameters as:

- Flow lines in wrought products
- Solidification structures in cast products
- Weld characteristics, including depth of penetration, fusion-zone size and number of passes, size of heat-affected zone and type and density of weld defects
- General size and distribution of large inclusions and stringers
- Fabrication defects, such as laps, cold welds, folds, and seams, in wrought products
- Gas and shrinkage porosity in cast products
- Depth and uniformity of a hardened layer in a case-hardened product

Second, characterization of the macrostructural features of fracture surfaces is used to identify such features as:

Fig. 7 Flow lines in a forged 4140 steel hook

Specimen was etched using 50% HCl. 0.5×

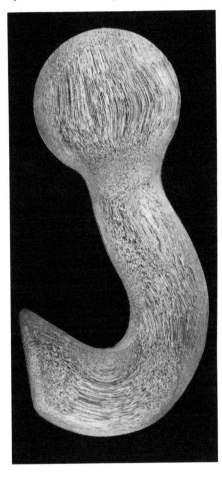

Fig. 8 Case-hardened layer in W1 tool steel

Specimens were austenitized at 800 °C (1475 °F), brine quenched, and tempered 2 h at 150 °C (300 °F). Black rings are hardened zones. Etched using 50% hot HCl. Approximately 0.5×

incomplete, represents the wide variety of features that can be evaluated and characterized using optical macroscopy. One of the major constraints of optical macroscopy is its limited depth of focus when the surfaces examined are very rough. If this lack of depth of focus is a problem, use of SEM is recommended.

Macroscopy of Metallographic Sections

Preparation of a metallographic section for examination requires careful selection of the area to be characterized. This area must be chosen to represent the unique features of a specific zone of interest or the general fea-

tures of a part or component selected for process characterization or quality assurance. The selected region of the specimen must then be removed from the component using techniques that do not damage or distort the features of interest. The section of interest is then prepared metallographically, and the prepared section is characterized using macroscopic examination.

Macroscopic examination generally does not require the extreme surface smoothness needed for microscopic examinations. Such surface preparation techniques as etching are frequently prolonged such that surface features are greatly enhanced; therefore, quantitative measurements should not be conducted on macroetched samples. Heavy etching accentuates any microstructural inhomogeneity (Fig. 7). The flow lines show the direction of metal flow during processing and frequently represent paths for easy fracture.

Figure 8 shows the use of similar macroscopic techniques to illustrate the depth of case hardening in a tool steel; Fig. 9, for examination of an arc weld. The weld macrograph shows the different etching characteristics of the various areas of the weld. The existence of the HAZ illustrates the effect of welding on the structure. The 2% nital etchant used to reveal the weld macrostructure is much less aggressive than the 50% hydrochloric acid etchants used on the specimens shown in Fig. 7 and 8 and reveals more structural detail.

Macroscopic examination of cast structures can be used to reveal various casting conditions. Solidification patterns are appar-

- Fracture initiation site
- Changes in crack propagation process

Third, characterization of surfaces and surface defects on parts and coupons is accomplished for purposes such as:

- Estimations of surface roughness, grinding patterns, and honing angles
- Evaluation of coating integrity and uniformity
- Determination of extent and location of wear
- Estimation of plastic deformation associated with various mechanical processes
- Determination of the extent and form of corrosive attack; readily distinguishable types of attack include pitting, uniform, crevice, and erosion corrosion
- Evaluation of tendency for oxidation
- Association of failure with welds, solders, and other processing operations

The above listing of uses for macrostructural characterization of materials, though

Fig. 9 Section through an arc butt weld joining two 13-mm (0.5-in.) thick ASTM A517, grade J, steel plates

The schematic shows the fusion zone, the heat-affected zone, and base metal. Etched using 2% nital. 4×

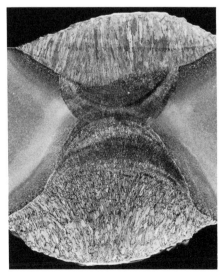 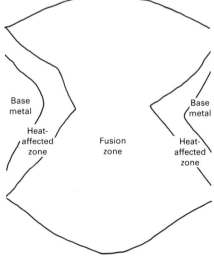

Fig. 10 Sketch of grains in a typical cast ingot

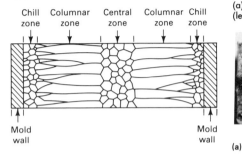

Fig. 11 Transverse fracture of an AISI 1075 steel railroad rail

Fracture nucleus (dark area near top of railhead) initiated a fatigue crack (large light area around nucleus).

Fig. 12 Example of how fracture surface features can point to the failure origin

(a) Fractograph of a high-velocity fracture in steel plate showing chevron pattern indicating the origin (left). (b) Schematic view of (a)

(a)

(b)

ent in the cross sections of macroetched ingots (Fig. 5 and 6). The outer chill zone depth, shape and size of the columnar or dendritic grains perpendicular to the mold wall, and size of the central equiaxed zone in a casting can be established (Fig. 10). One benefit of the macroscopy of cast structures is the ability to reveal the structure and associated defects.

Optical macroscopic examination of a fracture surface may reveal features that will help establish the failure process. For example, Fig. 11 illustrates a fracture in a railroad rail. The relatively smooth region in the photograph represents crack growth because of cyclic or fatigue loading. The dark spot (or fish eye) in the center of the reflective area represents the fracture-initiation site. The remainder of the surface failed by overload. This macroscopic observation of the failed rail shows that the failure was initiated because of the dark-appearing defect in the rail.

The macroscopic nature of many fractures is such that the fracture origin is easily recognizable. Brittle or low-ductility fractures have characteristic V-shaped markings on the fracture surface (Fig. 12) known as chevrons or herringbone marks. The tip of the V generally points to the origin of the failure. The origin of fatigue failures can also be isolated using macroscopic examination. For example, Fig. 13 shows a failure of a steel housing tube initiated in four regions. Each initiation region is observable in the macrographs, as shown by the four arrows. The position of the crack fronts at various times during the failure process is also visible as the so-called beach marks that are initially fairly concentric to the origin. The major problem with optical macroscopic or microscopic examination of fracture surfaces is the technique's inability to obtain favorable focus over the entire surface if the magnification exceeds 5 to $10 \times$. Therefore, SEM has become a standard metallographic tool in failure analysis.

Macroscopic evaluation of corroded parts can also provide considerable insight into corrosion processes. Each type of corrosion-induced failure causes a characteristic macrographic appearance; therefore, evaluation using optical macroscopy is generally effective. A frequent mistake in failure analysis is to neglect examination of the broken pieces at low magnifications. Too frequently the component is sectioned immediately, and the failure, casting, or other type of specimen examined at high magnification. Optical microscopic evaluation clearly is significant in any structural evaluation, but should not replace characterization by macroscopy.

These two types of metallography are complementary, but examination should always begin at low magnification and work upwards. Detailed information on sample preparation, equipment and etchants used in macroanalysis, and interpretation of results is available in Volume 9 of the 9th Edition of *Metals Handbook*.

Microanalysis

The importance of microstructure to the properties of metals and alloys has long been recognized. Grain size, twins, and the size, shape, and distribution of second-phase particles are important in determining the behavior of most structural metals. Therefore, characterization of the various microstructural elements in a metal or alloy is often necessary. Process-control parameters are established to provide specific grain sizes. The number, size, and distribution of second-phase particles, such as inclusions, are frequently specified, and quantitative metallographic procedures have been developed to describe microstructure.

The upper limit of useful magnification in the optical microscope is approximately $1500 \times$, and the fundamental limitations of light optic systems limit resolution to features which are ~ 1 μm or larger. Although this value is small, many microstructural features influencing the properties of metals and alloys are too small to be observed using optical microscopy. Dislocations, numerous

Fig. 13 Fractographs of a typical fatigue crack in a clamp

(a) The fatigue crack origin is marked by the arrow. The crack propagated to the right by continuous fatigue cracking (light) region, then continued alternately by rapid tearing and slow fatigue cracking. 2×. (b) Higher magnification view of the region near the arrow in (a). 10×

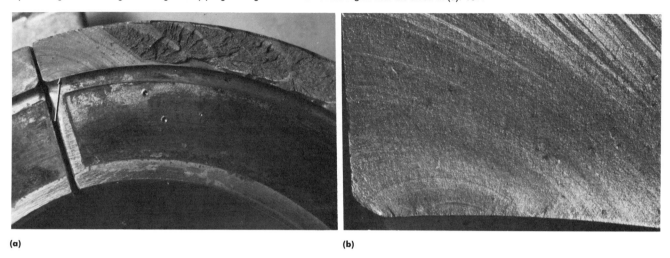

(a)   (b)

Fig. 14 Copper alloy 26000 (cartridge brass, 70%) sheet, hot rolled to a thickness of 10 mm (0.4 in.), annealed, cold rolled to a thickness of 6 mm (0.239 in.), and annealed to a grain size of 0.120 mm (0.005 in.)

At this reduction, grains are basically equiaxed. Compare with Fig. 15. Diagram in lower left of each micrograph indicates orientation of the view relative to the rolling plane of the sheet. Etched using NH_4OH plus H_2O_2. 75×

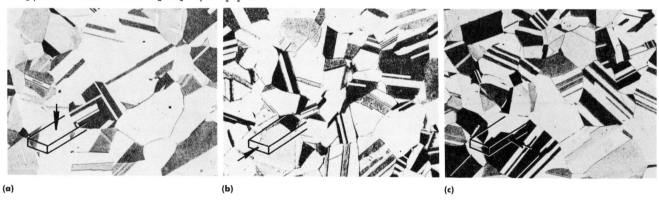

(a)   (b)   (c)

Fig. 15 Same alloy and processing as in Fig. 14, but reduced 50% by cold rolling from 6 mm (0.239 in.) to 3 mm (0.120 in.)

Grains are elongated in the rolling direction. Diagrams indicate same orientation of view as in Fig. 14. Etched using NH_4OH plus H_2O_2. 75×

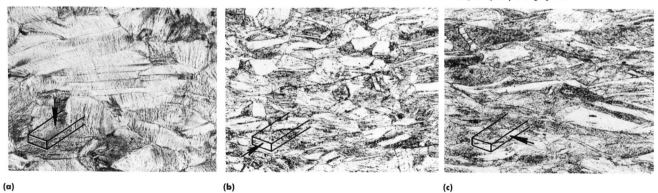

(a)   (b)   (c)

Fig. 16 Dendritic solidification structure in a Ni-5Ce (at.%) alloy

Nickel dendrites (light in b and c) are surrounded by a matrix of nickel-cerium eutectic. (a) 25×. (b) 75×. (c) 250×

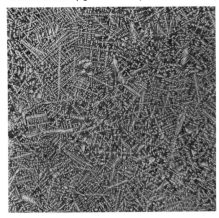

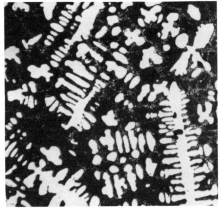

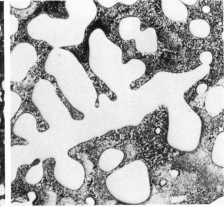

(a) **(b)** **(c)**

types of second-phase particles, spinodal and ordered structures, and many aspects of martensitic structures can be categorized as too small for optical microscopy. Therefore, metallographic observations of these very fine structural features is generally restricted to electron microscopy. Optical microscopy, then, is used primarily to examine grain structures and the morphology of large second-phase particles. Specialized optical metallographic techniques, such as polarized light microscopy and interference microscopy, can add significantly to the information obtained in a microscopic investigation, and interference microscopy can be used to identify height differences on a sample surface that are far smaller than 0.2 μm.

Optical characterization of the microstructures of metals and alloys involves determination of the size and shape of the grains, the extent of twinning, and some of the characteristics of grain boundaries and other observable defects. Solidification, solid-state transformation, deformation, and annealing microstructures are the four basic types in metals and alloys. Each of these has distinct characteristics.

Microstructural features exist in three dimensions, and in a typical metallographic observation, only two dimensions are observed. Therefore, effective microscopy frequently requires microstructural observations in two or more directions. Figures 14 and 15 illustrate the value of viewing the

microstructure in several directions. Figure 14 shows an annealed microstructure exhibiting similar grain shapes in all three views. Grain size is characterized by placing a line of known length (or preferably a circle of known circumference) on the magnified image of the microstructure and counting the number of intersections between the line and grain boundaries in the microstructure. The number of intersections, N, can be converted to a measure of grain size, d, using:

$$d = \frac{L}{NM} \qquad \text{(Eq 1)}$$

where M is the magnification of the image

Fig. 17 Typical defects observable using optical microscopy

(a) Shrinkage porosity in an aluminum alloy 5052 ingot. Note angularity. 50×. (b) Coarse primary CrAl$_7$ crystal in aluminum alloy 7075 ingot. 100×. (c) Oxide stringer inclusion in a rolled aluminum alloy 1100 sheet. 250×. All as-polished

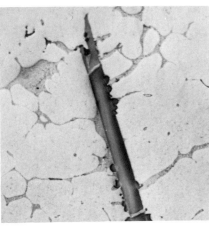

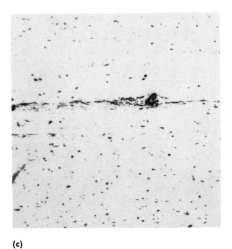

(a) **(b)** **(c)**

Fig. 18 Continuous grain-boundary precipitate in U-700 nickel-base heat-resistant alloy

Etched using HCl, ethanol, and H_2O_2. 500×

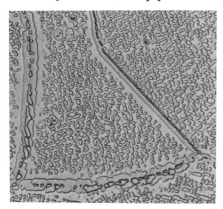

Fig. 19 Discrete precipitates along grain boundaries in a nickel-base heat-resistant alloy

Specimen was etched using 35 mL HCl, 65 mL ethanol, and 7 drops H_2O_2. 500×

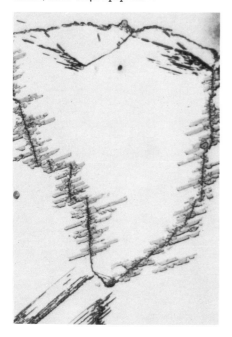

Fig. 20 The effect of prior cold work on recrystallized grain size

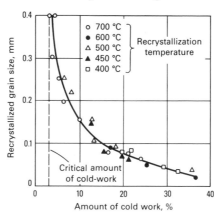

observed, and L is the length of line on the image.

The microstructure of the cold-rolled copper alloy shown in Fig. 15 differs from that of the annealed metal. Rolling elongated the grains in the rolling direction and flattened the grains in directions transverse or normal to the rolling directions. This change can render the grain structure—and the resulting mechanical properties—anisotropic. Because of the interrelationships between grain morphology (size and shape) and mechanical properties, characterization of the grain structure is a typical metallurgical function.

The most commonly observed solidification structure is dendritic. A dendritic structure usually exhibits compositional variations, with the dendrite arms containing less alloying element or impurity than interdendritic regions. Because of such compositional changes (termed coring), the rate of etching at interdendritic regions differs from that at dendrite arms. If the alloying element or impurity content is high, interdendritic regions may develop a two-phase structure (Fig. 16). Because dendrite arm spacing tends to decrease with increasing cooling rates, the properties of as-cast metals depend on the solidification rates.

Most metals shrink during solidification. Therefore, the liquid trapped between dendrite arms during solidification is frequently insufficient to fill the space between the arms when solidification is complete. This inability to fill the remaining space leads to shrinkage porosity, which can be observed microscopically. Porosity is generally easier to observe on as-polished specimens than on polished and etched ones. Figure 17(a) shows a typical example of shrinkage porosity.

Other structural defects, such as inclusions and stringers (Fig. 17b and 17c), can also be observed microscopically in as-polished specimens. Such defects as those shown in Fig. 17 can serve as failure-initiation sites in metals and alloys; therefore, characterization of their size, shape, and distribution is necessary to establish material properties and engineering reliability. Quality-assurance programs frequently

require controlling defects to regulate their number, size, and shape in a particular manner. For example, a component having a stringer distribution such as that shown in Fig. 17(c) would have better ductility if specimens or components were tested with the major stresses parallel to the stringer than if specimens were oriented with the major stresses perpendicular to the stringer.

Transformation structures almost always contain two phases. In such structures, the major phase is typically termed the matrix, or base structure, and the minor phase is termed the second phase. The size, shape, and distribution of second-phase particles are important in determining the properties of metals and alloys. Characterization of second-phase morphology can sometimes be accomplished using optical metallography. However, the second phase is sometimes so small that the resolution necessary to characterize the phase morphology exceeds the limits of the optical microscope. In these cases, transmission electron microscopy must be used. Age-hardenable or precipitation-hardened metals and alloys generally must be characterized using electron microscopy.

High-temperature phase transformations frequently nucleate at grain boundaries. The grain-boundary structures can be discrete or continuous. Continuous grain-boundary constituents (Fig. 18) provide easy fracture paths when the grain-boundary phase is less ductile than the matrix phase. For the material shown in Fig. 18, the expected failure would be fracture along the grain-boundary carbides. Figure 19 also shows discrete second-phase precipitates at grain boundaries. Comparison of the microstructures shown in Fig. 18 and 19 reveals differing second phase morphologies in two similar alloys. Therefore, the properties of these two alloys are also different, with the structure illustrated in Fig. 18 exhibiting the highest strength but the least ductility.

The microscopic details of deformation structures typically cannot be established using optical metallography. Deformation changes number and arrangement of dislocations (crystal defects) in the metal on an atomic scale. This dislocation substructure is best characterized using TEM. Optical metallography can be used to supplement TEM through characterization of the grain size and anisotropy in grain shape and distribution.

Microstructural changes due to annealing may be studied using TEM or optical microscopy. The most important structural changes that occur during annealing are recovery, recrystallization, and grain growth.

Recovery is the rearrangement and annihilation of imperfections (primarily vacancies and interstitials) within each grain of a cold-worked polycrystalline component. Because recovery deals mainly with point defects, any microstructural observations of it are difficult, and optical microscopy cannot be used because of its limited resolution.

Recrystallization is the formation of new strain-free grains within the previously cold-worked (strained) grains. The initial stages of recrystallization occur on such a fine scale that TEM is necessary; however, optical metallography can be readily used to study most of the recrystallization. The size of the recrystallized grains depends on the amount of cold working of the specimen before the recrystallization anneal. The greater the amount of cold work, the finer the grain size (Fig. 20). Because grain boundaries are a crystalline defect, continued annealing will cause this array of grains to be unstable, and grain growth will take place. Grain growth in a recrystallized specimen decreases the grain-boundary surface area to specimen volume ratio because the average grain size increases as grain growth takes place. The rate of grain growth depends on temperature and time. Figure 21 illustrates the time-temperature dependence of grain growth. Detailed information on all of these types of structures and on the metallography and microstructures of specific metals and alloys is available in Volume 9 of the 9th Edition of *Metals Handbook*.

SELECTED REFERENCES

- J.L. McCall and W.M. Mueller, Ed., *Metallographic Specimen Preparation*, Plenum Press, 1974
- *Metallography and Microstructures*, Vol 9, 9th ed., *Metals Handbook*, American Society for Metals, 1985
- *Metallography, Nondestructive Testing*, Vol 03.03, *Annual Book of ASTM Standards*, ASTM, Philadelphia, 1984
- G. Petzow, *Metallographic Etching*, American Society for Metals, 1978
- G.F. Vander Voort, *Metallography: Principles and Practice*, McGraw-Hill, 1984

Image Analysis

George F. Vander Voort, Carpenter Technology Corporation

General Uses

- Quantification of the morphological aspects of images obtained by optical metallography, scanning electron microscopy, and transmission electron microscopy

Examples of Applications

- Quantitative determination of grain size, grain shape, grain boundary area per unit volume, and so on, in single-phase metals and ceramics
- Quantitative determination of second-phase volume fractions, sizes, interfacial areas per unit volume, spacings, and so on, in multiphase metals and ceramics
- Quantitative determination of particle size distributions in powders

Samples

- Instrument can be interfaced with an optical microscope or a scanning electron microscope to permit direct analysis (without taking photographs). See the article "Optical Metallography" in this Volume for sample form, size, and preparation requirements

- Instrument also can be interfaced with macroviewer (epidiascope) for quantification of features on photographs (from optical microscope, scanning electron microscope, transmission electron microscope, and so on). Photographs must have sufficient contrast

Limitations

- Does not provide direct chemical information on microstructural features or particles and cannot generally discriminate between microstructural features or particles of different compositions
- Measures two-dimensional geometric quantities; third-dimensional parameters must be inferred

Estimated Analysis Time

- 5 min to several hours per sample

Capabilities of Related Techniques

- *Electron probe x-ray microanalysis*: Provides quantitative elemental compositions but no quantitative geometric characterization
- *Scanning electron microscopy*: Image contrast arises from different phenomena than for optical microscopy; discrimination of phases of differing compositions is possible

Introduction

Image analysis minimizes the influence of operator fatigue, which reduces the accuracy and reproducibility of manual measurements. In addition, although microstructural patterns, spatial relationships, and shapes are relatively easy to recognize in an image, reliable numerical data, such as counts, are far more difficult to obtain manually. Therefore, automation answers a long-recognized need in microstructural analysis for more precise data for quality control and structure-property studies.

Historically, most microstructural ratings, particularly in quality control studies and for specification compliance, have been performed using simple chart comparison ratings. Examples are grain-size measurements using ASTM E 112 (Ref 1) and inclusion ratings using ASTM E 45 (Ref 2) standard charts. In recent years, however, increased use has been made of manual and automated stereological relationships to describe microstructural characteristics. The mathematical relationships developed in quantitative metallography or quantitative stereology are described in the article "Quantitative Metallography" in Volume 9 of the 9th Edition of *Metals Handbook*. Other detailed treatments of the subject can be found in Ref 3 to 9.

The tedious nature of such measurements when performed manually has spurred development of automated procedures. The first approach was simply to develop devices to facilitate manual data collection. More recently, various semiautomatic and fully automatic devices have been developed that permit more rapid data collection, analysis, and formatting. The introduction of powerful, inexpensive minicomputers has greatly aided the development of these tools. The initial development of these devices concentrated on hardware-centered systems, but has since evolved to software-centered systems using faster, more powerful, inexpensive minicomputers. Today, various semiautomatic or fully automated systems are available.

Because use of automated devices eliminates operator fatigue and reduces analysis time, more measurements can be conducted more accurately. This is important because materials are not homogeneous. To obtain better-quality data, a larger sample area and more samples must be analyzed. Thus, image analysis can provide better statistical accuracy and more meaningful results. In addition, image analyzers can perform several measurements on each field within milliseconds, providing a more complete description of the microstructure. Finally, automation can be introduced in stage movement, focusing, data analysis, and formatting.

Image analyzers are often expensive, although several powerful, relatively inexpensive units are available. Another problem concerns the nature of the microstructural image. Not all structures lend themselves to accurate automatic detection; the structure must exhibit adequate contrast to allow the analyzer to distinguish its various components. For low-contrast samples, semiautomatic analyzers often provide more reliable feature discrimination at the loss of some measurement speed. Sample preparation procedures long used for qualitative assessment or manual measurements may be unsuitable for image analysis. Therefore, much more care must be exercised in sample preparation. The ability to prepare the sample properly is often the most critical and most difficult factor in image analysis. Obtaining maximum value from image analysis usually necessitates knowledge of sample preparation, stereology, machine operation, statistics, and computer programming.

Image analysis consists of sample selection and preparation, image preprocessing, measurement, and data analysis and output. Each step must be controlled properly to obtain accurate, reproducible results. Sample selection must be systematic and well-planned to ensure that the samples analyzed are representative. Image preprocessing refers to the manipulation of the detected image to improve the accuracy of measurements, for example, separating adjoining particles before counting, or to facilitate desired measurements, as in the fusing of aligned inclusion stringers for a length measurement. Although image-enhancement procedures are becoming prevalent and produce a more attractive picture, feature detection will probably not be improved.

Types of Image Analyzers

Image analyzers (Ref 10-13) have progressed considerably since their commercial introduction in 1963. The early systems used conventional television scanners for image detection. These scanners did not provide adequate resolution along and across the scan line; they exhibited poor signal-to-noise ratios, and the start, stop, and position of the scan lines were poorly controlled, which severely limited feature analysis. Modern image analyzers use several types of special-purpose scanners. These provide high resolution, low signal-to-noise ratios, and accurate control of the scan lines. Bandwidth restrictions are not as narrow as those associated with television scanners.

Each scan line or raster consists of horizontally aligned picture points, sometimes termed pixels; the quantity of pixels varies somewhat among different systems. Over the viewing screen are parallel scan lines whose quantity also varies among systems. The total number of picture points is defined by the number of picture points per scan line (horizontal) multiplied by the number of scan lines (vertical). The number of picture points in the measurement field varies among instruments from approximately 250 000 to 650 000. The picture points are used to detect the desired image features based on gray-level differences.

In addition to television-based systems, a second major type of device used for image analysis is the semiautomatic digital image analyzer (Ref 14-18). These relatively inexpensive systems are suitable for images that cannot be readily discriminated by gray-level differences. Feature detection is conducted using a cross-hair cursor viewed with the microscope or using a writing stylus with the image projected onto a digitizer tablet or on photographs attached to the tablet. The features to be measured are traced, or the intercepts are marked with a grid superimposed over the image. Therefore, detection is much slower than with the automatic television devices. Once the features are detected, analysis is rapid, and most stereological measurements can be performed. Many television-based systems can also detect features by operator-assisted light-pen image editing. However, light-pen tracing of structural features on a television screen is less precise than use of a digitizer tablet.

Image Analyzer Components

Although image analyzers are available at various levels of sophistication and cost, certain features are common. Images can be provided from diverse sources; however, the most common input peripheral is the optical microscope. All analyzers use a scanner to display the image on a television screen. Each system uses a central electronic processor for image detection and measurement of stereological and nonstereological parameters. Most systems incorporate data-handling devices, which range from desktop calculators to minicomputers. Finally, each system has a device to produce a hard copy of the data.

Input Devices. The most common source of images is an upright microscope, generally using bright-field illumination. For metallurgical investigations, reflected light is used; transmitted light is used for biological studies. The optical quality of the microscope is important in obtaining the optimum image. Colored filters can be useful in improving gray-level differences between constituents. Other illumination modes have been used infrequently in image analysis.

A macroviewer, or epidiascope, using transmitted or reflected light is a common input peripheral for handling photomicrographs or negatives. The field of view with such devices is in the macroscopic range and can usually be adjusted to accommodate different size prints.

In recent years image analyzers have been coupled to transmission or scanning electron microscopes using various procedures. Stereological measurement conducted on thin foils in transmission is a difficult task that usually requires knowledge of the foil thickness. Measurements of replicas using stereological procedures produce little difficulty, but measurement statistics suffer when high magnifications are involved.

Use of the scanning electron microscope involves special problems. For example, if the sample surface is not perpendicular to the beam, magnification will vary across the image, introducing considerable error. In addition, if the volume fraction, size, or spacing is to be measured, deep etching will introduce error. Use of backscattered images on as-polished samples, where applicable, can provide optimum results.

Scanners. The resolution capability of the scanner is the limiting factor in the system. The primary component in image resolution is the number of resolvable picture points in the image, which depends on the quality of the tube used and the magnification. In general, considerable inaccuracy attends measurements of particles smaller than approximately 2 μm viewed using the optical microscope as the input peripheral.

The scanner must have high light sensitivity to permit operation at low light levels. The scanner must also exhibit high differential sensitivity to permit discrimination of constituents having small gray-level differences. The various types of tubes have advantages and disadvantages. For example, one is better for discriminating pale features having similar contrast, but is less effective in the red end of the spectrum. Another requires more time to reach equilibrium be-

Fig. 1 Plot of the detected area fraction in 1% increments from black to white for five iron-carbon alloys

Microstructures consisted of varying amounts of ferrite and pearlite, ranging from the 0.003% C alloy (almost all ferrite) to the 0.8% C alloy (all pearlite).

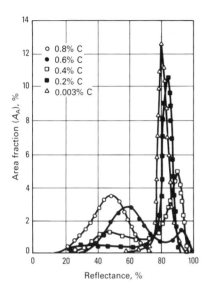

Fig. 2 Plot of cumulative detected area fraction in 1% increments from black to white for the five iron-carbon alloys in Fig. 1

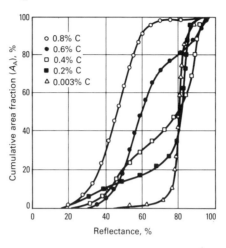

threshold device. As the carbon content increased to 0.6%, the size of the ferrite peak decreased, and the peak position increased slightly. For the 0.8% C alloy (all pearlite), no image was detectable above 76%. This suggests that the pearlite constituent is generally detected between approximately 16 and 76%, and the ferrite constituent is detected between approximately 76 and 91 to 99%, depending on the alloy. Figure 2 shows the same data plotted as a cumulative percentage of area fraction.

Setting the threshold to detect only gray levels within specific ranges enables selective detection of constituents. For example, Fig. 3 shows the microstructure of AISI type 416 stainless steel etched using Vilella's reagent. This is a resulfurized grade that has been heat treated to form tempered martensite but also contains δ-ferrite stringers. Figure 3(a) shows the live microscope image before phase detection. In Fig. 3(b), the threshold has been set to detect only the pale gray sulfides that appear white on the screen.

tween measurements, especially at low light levels.

Detection and Measurement. The primary mode of feature detection is gray-level thresholding. Several procedures, ranging from automatic to manual thresholding, may be available for feature detection. For optimum detection accuracy, the sample features of interest must be treated to have as narrow a contrast (gray-level) range as possible. The light source in the microscope must then be aligned for even illumination. Most image analyzers have circuits to provide shading correction to even out variations across the screen.

The gray-level range of the image from the darkest black to the lightest white feature can usually be segmented into 64 to 100 increments. As an example of gray-level feature detection, five iron-carbon alloys with carbon contents of 0.003 and approximately 0.2, 0.4, 0.6, and 0.8% were prepared metallographically and etched using picral. The microstructures consisted of varying amounts of ferrite and pearlite. The samples were scanned in 1% increments from black to white.

Figure 1 shows the area percent in the detected field area at each 1% portion in the gray-level scan for these alloys. The 0.003% C alloy, consisting almost entirely of ferrite, exhibits the highest ferrite peak, with maximum detection at approximately 81% on the

Fig. 3 Examples of preferential detection in an AISI 416 stainless steel sample

(a) Live image. (b) Preferential detection of manganese sulfides (white). (c) Preferential detection of tempered martensite (white). (d) Preferential detection of δ-ferrite (white). Sample etched using Vilella's reagent. 175×

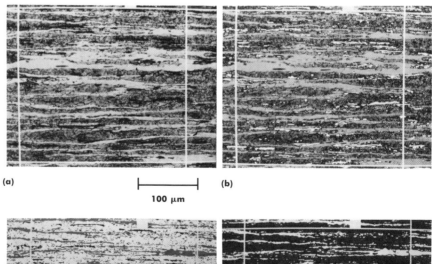

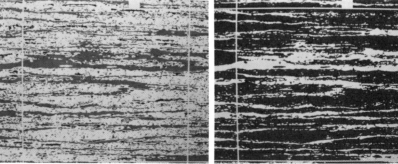

Fig. 4 Example of the influence of detection setting on the area fraction of pearlite detected in a low-carbon steel

(a) Live image showing ferrite and pearlite. (b) Pearlite underdetected (A_A = 28.1%). (c) Pearlite detected correctly (A_A = 34.05%). (d) Pearlite overdetected (A_A = 42.3%). Sample etched using 4% picral. 180×

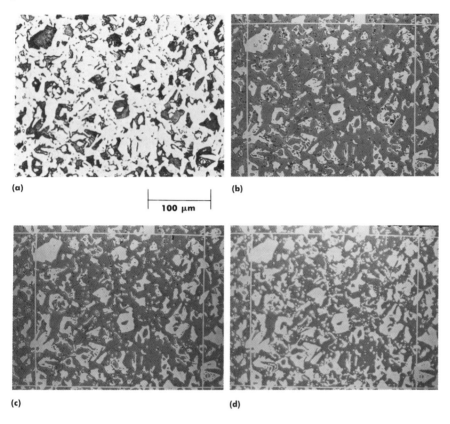

(a)

100 μm

(b)

(c)

(d)

Detection setting can be aided by alternating between the live image and the detected image (flicker mode) while observing the size correlation between these two images. If the gray-level ranges of two constituents overlap, detected (white) points will be visible in the undesired phase as the threshold setting is changed. If the degree of overlap is excessive, an alternate preparation procedure is required. In nearly all inclusion studies, the sample is examined unetched because detection of the inclusions is more reliable. Figure 3(c) shows detection of the martensite; Fig. 3(d) detection of the δ-ferrite. The optimum procedure for δ-ferrite detection is to etch the sample electrolytically using 20% aqueous NaOH, which colors only the δ-ferrite.

In attempting to detect all three constituents in this manner, it may be difficult, if not impossible, to have the three volume-fraction measurements add up to 100% on every measurement field. This example illustrates the ability to separate a complex image by thresholding. The preferred procedure would be to measure the sulfides in the as-polished condition, etch electrolytically and measure the amount of δ-ferrite, then determine the amount of martensite (major constituent) by difference.

Figure 4 illustrates the degree of error that can be encountered when thresholding is incorrect. Figure 4(a) shows the live image of a ferrite-pearlite sample etched using picral. Picral is far more accurate for such measurements because it does not etch the ferrite grain boundaries, which would be detected with the pearlite, and it produces more uniform darkening of the pearlite than nital. Figure 4(b) shows an underdetected image containing 28.1% pearlite. Some of the pearlite patches contain undetected regions. Figure 4(c) illustrates a correctly detected field with 34.05% pearlite. Figure 4(d) shows excessive detection, in which the features are enlarged and the volume fraction of pearlite was 42.3%.

The above examples illustrate field measurements; that is, all the features are measured simultaneously. More sophisticated image analyzers can perform feature-specific measurements; that is, each distinct feature in the field is measured individually. This technique is highly useful for particle sizing or shape measurements. When such capability is available, features with the same gray level can be further discriminated by differences in size or shape. For example the various graphite shapes of a cast iron sample can be sorted by size or shape, then measured.

Most image analyzers can perform measurements over the full screen (blank frame) or within a smaller live-frame region. In Fig. 3 and 4, the central screen area within the vertical and horizontal lines is the live-frame region, which is generally used when feature-specific measurements are conducted. Particles that intersect the live frame can be deleted from the detected region to prevent particle measurement errors. The region between the edge of the screen and the live frame is the guard region.

Sophisticated image analyzers can store several images in memory and use these images variously to enhance feature selection. The ability to erode or dilate features and compare these images to the original image can be useful in separating contiguous particles or fusing stringered features. Image analysis is much more precise than manual techniques for the counting of particles, but adjoining particles are difficult to handle without these special image-editing procedures. The alternative is to store the image in memory and use the light pen to cut contiguous particles. This is slower, but may be necessary with certain images. Accurate counting is also influenced by the shape of a particle and the counting procedure used. Spherical particles are easiest to count. More complex shapes require selection of the proper counting technique to obtain accurate counts.

Measurements are performed based on the number and distribution of detected picture points relative to the scan line and the total number of picture points. The area fraction is simply the ratio of the number of detected picture points to the total number of picture points in the measurement field, that is, the detected area divided by the measurement area. Therefore, the true size of the measurement field must be determined accurately using a stage micrometer for each magnification to operate in the calibrated mode. Some measurements can be performed in the uncalibrated mode, but this is less common.

Other measurements are more complex. For example, to count the number of detected particles in an image field of known size, that is, to obtain N_A, the number of particles per unit area, the image analyzer must first determine what portions of the detected image are discrete particles. A particle is any detected feature completely surrounded by undetected picture points. After this discrimination, the particles are counted, and the number is divided by the measurement area.

Sizing can be performed in several ways. The simplest procedure for determining the average particle area, $\bar{A}$, is to divide the area fraction by the number of particles per unit area, that is, A_A/N_A. This is the most direct procedure using field measurements. Feature-specific measurements provide several possible procedures. One is to measure the area of each feature and determine the average area of all the measured particles. Another involves measuring the area of each particle and computing the equivalent diameter based on some assumption about their shape. The projected height of the particles, the maximum and minimum length and thickness, and so on, could also be measured. More information on stereological measurement is available in the article "Quantitative Metallography" in Volume 9 of the 9th Edition of *Metals Handbook* and Ref 1 to 7.

Data Analysis. A major advantage of image analyzers is that the data produced, which may be extensive, can be analyzed statistically on-line using programs stored in the on-board minicomputer. For routine measurements, a predeveloped program can be stored in the computer, providing maximum effectiveness in usage. The program would include prompts for inputting information on the sample, calibration, stage movement, and detection. The program then controls these functions, obtains and stores measurement, and outputs the analyzed data. The program can also be set up to prompt the operator concerning the relative accuracy of the measurement and ask if more measurements are desired to improve accuracy. If this is necessary, more measurements are taken, added to those already obtained, and new results displayed. This procedure can be repeated until the desired accuracy is achieved.

Data analysis requires knowledge of statistics. This is not a simple task in all cases, and further investigation is necessary. In general, calculation of averages and the standard deviation of the measurements is the basic starting point of data analysis. From this data, the 95% confidence limit and relative accuracy of the data can be calculated. In more sophisticated investigations, it may be necessary to determine the nature of the data dispersion. Not all measurements exhibit normal (Gaussian) distributions; many show log-normal or other distributions. Histograms of data are useful for comparing results from different samples.

Data outputting must be controlled to provide the information in a convenient format for user examination. Pertinent sample identity data must also be included.

Possible Errors

Errors can arise in image analysis measurements from such sources as the representativeness of the sample, quality of sample preparation, operator bias in setting controls, and instrument errors. Errors can also result when assumptions upon which stereological formulas are based are invalid. A typical example of such a problem is the mathematical procedure for determining the number of grains per unit volume, N_V, based on planar grain-size measurements and grain-shape assumptions. The further the grains differ from the assumed shape, the greater the error in estimating N_V.

When a relatively small polished area of one or more samples is used to determine some quantity for a relatively large mass of material, errors will occur if sampling is inadequate or does not represent the mass. This problem is common in analyzing inclusions in a heat of steel. Because the quantity of inclusions is relatively or extremely low, and the inclusion distribution is not homogeneous, some degree of uncertainty is associated with such measurements. This error can be minimized by using a systematic sampling plan and by increasing the number of samples and area measured. In practice, compromise is necessary between the amount of time available for such measurements and the desired accuracy.

To illustrate the statistical nature of volume fraction measurements, Fig. 5 shows data for a resulfurized steel. In this experiment, the percentage of inclusions was determined using different magnifications (8, 16, 32, 50, 80, and 160× objectives) by automatic image analysis, as a function of the number of fields measured. For 50 or more fields, most of the measurements are between 0.5 and 0.7%. For ten or fewer fields, scatter is substantial. This scatter is typical for inclusion measurements due to the low volume fraction present and the nonuniform distribution of the inclusions. Figure 6 shows a plot of the percent relative accuracy of the measurements shown in Fig. 5 as a function of the number of fields measured. The relative accuracy of the measurements improves steadily as the number of fields increases. Figure 7 shows a more effective method of examining this data; the relative accuracy of the measurements is plotted as a function of the measurement area. For the example shown, appproximately 10 mm^2 (0.0155 in.^{2}) of surface area must be measured to obtain a

10% relative accuracy. The measurement area for 10% relative accuracy is a function of the volume fraction of the measured constituent and the homogeneity of its distribution.

The magnification selected significantly influences the measurement value and the statistics of the measurement. Simple guidelines have not been established for choosing the optimum measurement magnification. Although smaller features require higher magnifications, the field area decreases with increasing magnification. For example, the field area at 500× is one-twenty-fifth that at 100×. Therefore, to measure the same area at 500×, 25 times as many fields must be measured as at 100×. Choice of magnification is basically a compromise.

For the data shown in Fig. 5 to 7, a relatively high magnification would be desired to obtain favorable resolution. However, because there is a low volume fraction and inclusions are not uniformly distributed, a substantial area must be examined to obtain a workable estimate of the volume fraction. For such a sample, field-to-field volume fraction variation increases as the magnification increases, which produces a larger standard deviation, 95% confidence limit, and percent relative accuracy for a given number of fields. One method of assessing this is to examine the range of volume fraction measurements as a function of the number of fields for each magnification (Fig. 8). For this sample, the best compromise would be the 32× or 50× objective.

Sample preparation also influences measurement accuracy significantly. Samples must be polished with minimum relief, the desired constituents must be retained, and polishing artifacts must be controlled. Because sample volume can be high, automatic polishing equipment is generally necessary to provide the required sample throughput and quality.

Etching techniques used for qualitative structure assessment and manual measurements are frequently inadequate for image analysis. Instead, selective etching or staining techniques usually must be used (Ref 9, 19, 20). Color (tint) etching (Ref 9, 21) is extremely useful because of its high selectivity and near absence of etch relief (see the article "Color Metallography" in Volume 9 of the 9th Edition of *Metals Handbook*). Electrolytic etching techniques are also valuable. The optimum procedure darkens either the phase of interest or all other phases, distinguishing the constituents clearly by gray levels. In many studies, proper sample selection and careful polishing and etching are the most critical factors in obtaining favorable results. This is especially important in grain-size measurements, in which all

Fig. 5 Inclusion volume fraction as a function of magnification and number of fields measured

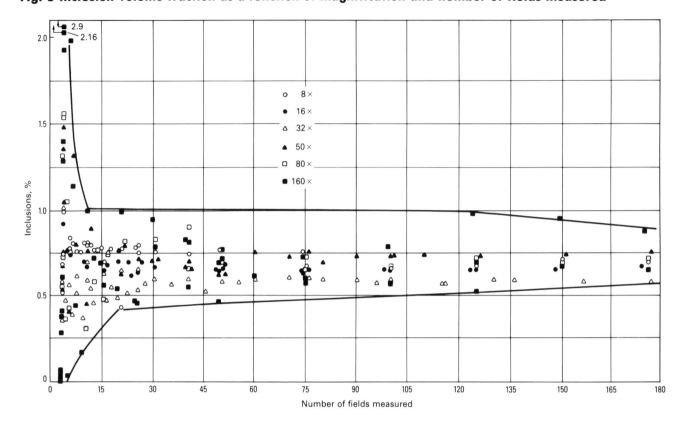

the grain boundaries must be revealed clearly.

When the above problems are resolved, the sample is ready for analysis. Attention must be given to the optical microscope to ensure that the best possible image is presented to the scanner tube. The microscope must be kept clean and properly aligned. The environment must also be controlled carefully. For example, during inclusion analysis, if dust settles on the sample, or if staining occurs because the humidity is too high, errors will be introduced. A clean, dry environment is also important for the on-board computer.

Many experiments have demonstrated that the setting of the detector threshold for feature discrimination is the most significant instrument error (Ref 22). Measurement reproducibility by different operators or by the same operator on different days can suffer significantly due to variations in the procedure used to establish detection. Several procedures have been recommended for setting the threshold, and most instruments have several optional procedures from fully automatic to manual for such settings. If relief is present at the edges of features, the gray-level reflectance at the edge will differ from that at the center and complicate detec-

tion. Additional research is necessary in this area.

The choice of magnification can also influence measurement results. Numerous cases have been documented in which the measured values were altered significantly as the magnification was changed (Ref 23).

The magnification effect has been observed in many studies involving various materials, measurements, and measuring devices. The problem is not simply one of poor technique. Examples of this problem have been summarized (Ref 23). Two basic types of magnification-affected data can be found in the literature. The first involves counting type data in which the count increases rapidly with initial increases in magnification, then levels off at high magnifications. The second involves spacing measurements in which there is an initial rapid drop in the spacing measurements with an increase in magnification, followed by a leveling off with further increases in magnification. Both situations arise from the observer's seeing more at the higher magnifications (Ref 23).

A somewhat different magnification problem may also be encountered in performing fully automated measurements, which is unique to such systems. To illustrate this problem, a medium-carbon hot-rolled steel

containing ferrite and pearlite was analyzed for the volume fraction of ferrite using 8, 16, 32, 50, 80, and 160× objectives. The sample was etched using picral. At low magnifications, the volume fraction of proeutectoid ferrite could be measured with favorable accuracy. However, as the magnification was increased, the structure of the pearlite became resolvable, and ferrite within the pearlite constituent was also detected. Thus, with increasing magnification and resolution, the volume fraction of ferrite increased. Figure 9 shows the measurement results as a function of the magnification and number of fields measured. The best determination of the volume fraction of proeutectoid ferrite was obtained using the 16× objective. This is not obvious from the data, but can be discerned while viewing the detection.

From a statistical viewpoint, lower magnifications enable measurement of large areas, lessening the influence of sample heterogeneity. As magnification increases, greater field-to-field measurement variations are encountered. Increasing the magnification improves resolution, but the area measured, if the number of fields is limited, may not be representative. Therefore, a compromise is necessary between the requirements for resolution and those for statistical sam-

Fig. 6 Relative accuracy of the inclusion volume fraction measurements as a function of magnification and the number of fields measured

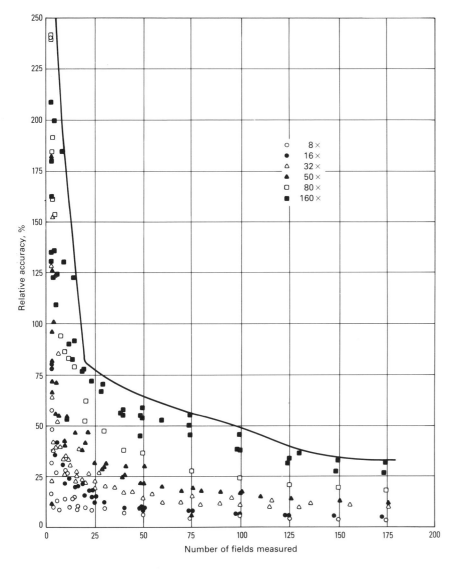

within the measurement area will be truncated and undersized. Two magnifications have been used for such measurements, and the analyses have been combined; however, this is a difficult procedure.

System resolution influences the ability to measure small particles accurately. For example, if the length of the particles is only ten times the system resolution, the accuracy of the length measurements will be no better than 10%. The orientation and shape of features also influences the ability to measure the features accurately.

Machine problems may also influence measurement accuracy. The degree of shading correction may limit gray-level discrimination ability. Noise or random variations of current or voltage with time will introduce gray-level thresholding problems by smearing out the ideal sharp cutoff. Small amounts of noise can be observed in a flickering of small features between the detected and live image with successive scans. This produces counting of features that should not be counted or lack of detection in areas that should be detected. Noise can also vary the size of features with successive scans. Distortion of image shape may also occur due to magnification variations in different directions across the screen. In general, the contribution of these errors is relatively small in modern image analyzers. Noise problems become important when measuring features with low contrast.

Measurements involving sizing are affected by the fact that the particles or grains intersecting the frame border will be undersized (Ref 24-27). A variety of solutions have been proposed to eliminate this problem. One of the simplest procedures is to delete all of the particles or grains that intersect the border. However, the measuring frame area must then be redetermined. Another approach measures fully all the particles or grains that intersect two of the four borders and conducts no measurements on those that intersect the other two borders.

The following example discusses two problems that can be encountered during image analysis of grain size—errors from improper etching and errors from undersizing grains that intersect the frame border. Grain-size measurements will be affected by the quality of etching and by the presence of other features with the same gray level, for example, inclusions. If the sample contains twin boundaries, they must be suppressed by the etchant; if this is not possible, a semiautomatic tracing device can be used where the operator ignores the twin boundaries. Some success has been achieved with development of electrolytic etchants that do not reveal twin boundaries in austenitic alloys (Ref 28, 29).

pling. Small features require a relatively high magnification for accurate measurements, particularly for size, shape, or perimeter measurements.

The choice of magnification influences the number of fields to be measured. As magnification increases, more fields are required to obtain a certain degree of accuracy. Automatic stage movement and automatic focusing facilitate increasing the number of fields. Automatic stage movement ensures selection of fields without introducing operator bias. Automatic focusing should not be taken for granted. At higher magnifications, the potential for improper focusing increases. The autofocus device must be operating properly. Calculating the relative accuracy of the mea-

surement enables determining if more fields must be measured. In general, a 10% relative accuracy is desired as a minimum. For volume-fraction measurements, as the volume fraction decreases, more fields must be measured to obtain this degree of accuracy. This problem becomes particularly acute when measuring volume fractions less than 0.01 (1%).

A serious problem is encountered when the feature to be sized exhibits a rather wide range of sizes or a bimodal size distribution. The larger particles are best measured at relatively low magnifications, but the smaller particles must be measured at a higher magnification. At a high magnification, the guard-frame procedure must be used, or any large feature not

Fig. 7 Relative accuracy of inclusion volume fraction measurements as a function of total measurement area

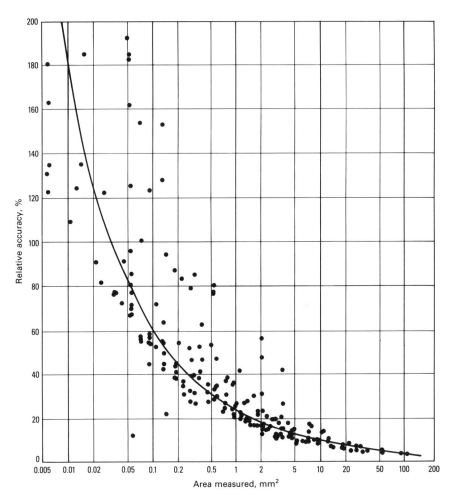

One procedure that has been used to measure grain size by automatic image analysis entails detecting the grain interiors, closing any holes in the grain interior to remove inclusions, then conducting chord measurements (Ref 30). The average chord length is equivalent to the mean lineal intercept, $\bar{L}_3$, used to assess grain size. However, grains that intersect the frame border will be undersized if they are not deleted. A sample with an ASTM grain size of approximately 5.2 was analyzed in this manner without deleting the grains that intersected the border. Three objectives were used with the following results:

Objective	L_3, μm	ASTM grain size
8×	.48.3	5.45
16×	.45.1	5.65
32×	.40.7	5.94

The error increased with magnification because a greater proportion of the grains in the image were undersized.

As another example of edge effects and of the influence of etching, a low-carbon sheet steel was etched for different times using 2% nital, an orientation-sensitive etchant (Ref 30). As the etch time increased from a few seconds to approximately 20 s, the mean lineal intercept length decreased from approximately 66 μm (ASTM grain size 4.5) to approximately 17 μm (ASTM 8.5). After an approximately 20-s etch, results were reasonably accurate and reproducible (Fig. 10). Heavy etching with nital is to be avoided, because etch relief will produce erroneous results. Consequently, etching time must be controlled carefully.

The low-carbon steel sample, with optimum etching, was measured by image analysis using the chord sizing method without deleting those grains that intersected the

border (Ref 30). Results using three objectives are shown below:

Objective	L_3, μm	ASTM grain size
16×	18	8.3
32×	12	9.5
50×	9	10.3

These examples demonstrate that the operator must be aware of the potential problems that can arise during measurement, particularly if a fully automatic system is used. In general, these problems are not as critical with the semiautomatic tracing devices, but errors can arise with either system if the operating and preparation variables are not under control.

Applications

Applications of image analysis are quite broad. Many image analyzers are in use in the electronics and textile industries simply as measurement devices (metrology). In materials science, the principal areas of application are measurement of microstructural features for evaluation of production processes, that is, quality control; quantifying parameters to understand how processing changes affect microstructure; and quantifying parameters to relate microstructure to properties or behavior.

In quality control, attention has been placed on inclusion analysis. This can be accomplished using stereological parameters or by simulating a chart method. Inclusion analysis presents considerable analysis difficulty due to the low amounts present, their nonuniform distribution, and the minor gray-level differences between inclusion types. Grain-size analysis has also received considerable attention. The primary problem is sample preparation, that is, delineation of all the grain boundaries without revealing other structure.

The use of stereological parameters to determine the influence of processing on microstructure or to relate microstructure to properties has progressed considerably. Such investigations require extensive knowledge of stereological principles and careful experimental design. Although much has been accomplished in these areas, a great deal remains to permit development of useful microstructural control models.

Example 1: Quantitative Metallographic Characterization of the Kinetics of Cellular Decomposition of Martensite in a Uranium Alloy.* The heat

*Example 1 was provided by K.H. Eckelmeyer, K.S. Vargo, and M.E. McAllaster, Sandia National Laboratories. This work supported by the U.S. Department of Energy under Contract No. DE-AC04-76DP00789.

Fig. 8 Range of inclusion volume fraction data as a function of the number of fields measured and magnification

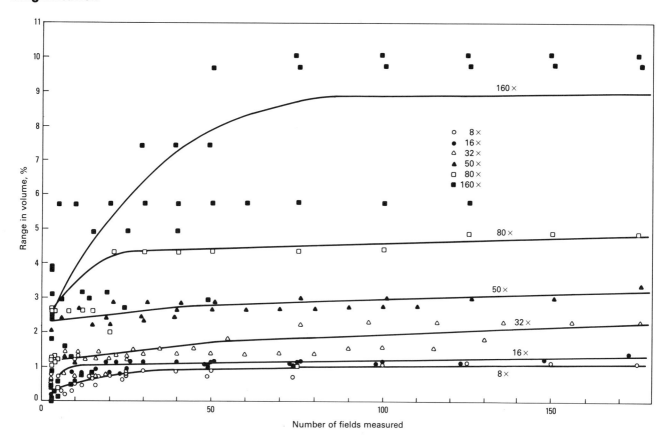

treatment of U-0.75Ti, a high-strength precipitation-hardenable uranium alloy, consists of quenching from the elevated temperature γ-phase field to obtain a supersaturated martensitic variant of the α phase, followed by age hardening of this α'-martensite. Age hardening occurs from 300 to 450 °C (570 to 840 °F) by the formation of coherent U_2Ti precipitates, which can be resolved only by transmission electron microscopy (TEM). Overaging occurs by cellular decomposition of the martensite to the equilibrium α plus U_2Ti phases. This reaction nucleates along the prior-γ grain boundaries and extends into the prior-γ grains, consuming the martensite (Fig. 11).

As part of a program to characterize the kinetics of overaging, samples were aged at several temperatures between 464 and 519 °C (867 and 966 °F) for times ranging from 1 to 224 h. After aging, the samples were prepared for metallographic examination using standard mounting and mechanical polishing techniques, followed by electrolytic etching in a 1:1 solution of phosphoric acid and water. This revealed the martensitic structure and etched the cellular decomposition product so that it appeared very dark when viewed with bright-field illumination (Fig. 11).

Metallographic samples corresponding to various aging temperatures and times were characterized using a light microscope interfaced with an image analyzer. The threshold intensity was adjusted to discriminate between the dark areas corresponding to cellularly decomposed material and the lighter areas corresponding to the as yet undecomposed martensite. The fraction of cellular decomposition f for each field was then taken to be:

$$f = \left(\frac{500\,000 - N}{500\,000} \right) \qquad \text{(Eq 1)}$$

where N is the number of picture points whose brightness exceeded the threshold intensity, 500 000 is the total number of picture points in the cathode-ray tube (CRT). Approximately 40 fields were viewed on each sample at $100 \times$. The fraction decom-

posed for each sample was calculated as the average for all fields viewed for that sample.

It can be shown from the theories of nucleation and thermally activated growth that isothermal phase transformations often proceed according to:

$$f = 1 - \exp\,[-kt^n] \qquad \text{(Eq 2)}$$

where f is the volume fraction transformed, t is time, and k and n are constants whose values depend on various aspects of the transformation. A considerable effort has been devoted to predicting the values of n that should correspond to particular combinations of transformation conditions. Equation 2 can be rearranged to yield:

$$\log \log \left[\frac{1}{1-f} \right] = \log \log e$$

$$+ \log k + n \log t \qquad \text{(Eq 3)}$$

Therefore, a plot of log log $[1/1 - f]$ versus log t should be a straight line whose slope

Fig. 9 Volume fraction of ferrite as a function of number of fields measured and magnification
At high magnifications, equiaxed ferrite and ferrite within the coarse pearlite were detected

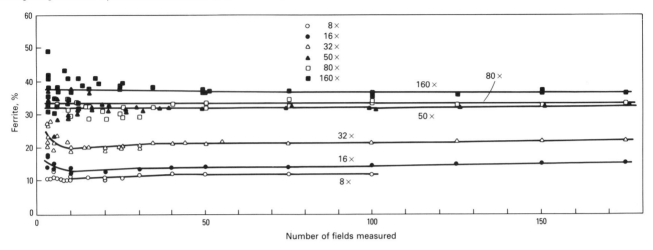

equals n. Based on this, the data were plotted as shown in Fig. 12. It can be seen that a good straight line fit is obtained with a slope equal to 1. This is consistent with theory, which predicts that such transformations nucleated along grain boundaries should exhibit $n = 1$ (after nucleation site saturation has occurred).

It is also well known that the effect of temperature on the rates of phase transformations and other thermally activated processes in metals follows:

Fig. 10 Influence of etch time on measurement of ferrite grain size
Etchant: 2% nital

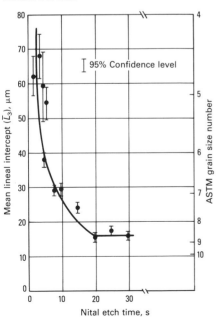

$$\text{Rate} = A \exp\left[\frac{-Q}{RT}\right] \qquad (\text{Eq 4})$$

where A is a constant, Q is the activation energy (a characteristic constant of the process under consideration), R is gas constant, and T is absolute temperature. Because the rate of transformation is related to the reciprocal of the time required to achieve a given fraction transformed, Eq 4 can be rewritten as:

$$\log_e t_f = -\log_e A + \frac{Q}{R}\left(\frac{1}{T}\right) \qquad (\text{Eq 5})$$

where t_f is the time required to reach a given fraction transformed. Therefore, a plot of $\log_e t_f$ versus $1/T$ should be a straight line whose slope equals Q/R. Based on this, the times required for 20% decomposition were plotted versus reciprocal temperature (Fig. 13). It can be seen that a good straight line fit was obtained. The value of activation energy calculated from this least square fit was $Q = 53$ kcal/mole °C.

Example 2: Combined Geometric and Elemental Analysis of Particles Produced by Explosive Detonation.*
As part of a study of the response of engineering components and materials to high-energy explosions, detonations were conducted near various structures containing components made of numerous materials. Debris were collected using several methods, one of which consisted of collecting and filtering the air near the experiment site at

*Example 2 was provided by W.F. Chambers, W.R. Sorenson, and K.H. Eckelmeyer, Sandia National Laboratories. Work supported by the U.S. Department of Energy under Contract No. DE-AC04-76DP00789.

various time increments following detonation. Part of the information desired from these tests was an analysis of the sizes, shapes, and chemistries of the particles collected on these filters. These analyses were performed using a scanning electron microscope equipped with an energy-dispersive x-ray detector and interfaced with an image analysis system.

Material was transferred from the collection filters onto metallographically polished beryllium stubs (for enhanced particle-to-background contrast in the backscattered electron imaging mode). A thin (approximately 20-nm-thick) layer of carbon was then evaporated onto each sample to make the particle surfaces electrically conductive, preventing imaging artifacts that would result if the sample became charged due to the impinging of the electron beam on nonmetallic particles.

A sample was placed in the scanning electron microscope, and approximately 20

Fig. 11 Microstructure of U-0.75Ti aged 12 h at 464 °C (867 °F)

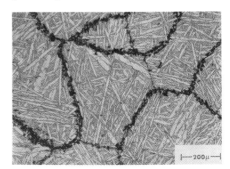

Fig. 12 Effect of time on cellular decomposition in U-0.75Ti

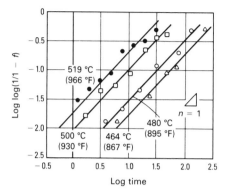

particles were analyzed manually to obtain the preliminary data needed to establish realistic parameters for subsequent automated analysis of much larger numbers of particles. Figure 14 shows several typical particles and an x-ray spectrum. The samples were imaged in the backscattered electron mode, in which signal strength is approximately proportional to atomic number. Because the backscattered electron output from the low atomic number beryllium stub was very low, the background appeared dark, and the particles, which consist of higher atomic number elements, appeared light. The intensity threshold was set at a level slightly above the background intensity. During subsequent analyses, then, any point exhibiting backscattered intensity above this threshold value was assumed to lie on a particle. Thresholding can also be used to detect dark particles on a light background or to detect particles whose intensities lie within a given range of intensities.

Fig. 13 Effect of temperature on time required for 20% cellular decomposition in U-0.75Ti

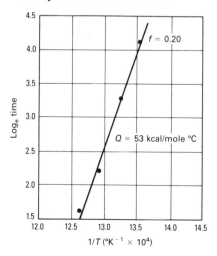

In the sample under discussion, the particles were found to range from one to several microns in diameter. Based on this, a magnification of 600× was chosen. In general, the magnification must be high enough that even the smallest particles present occupy at least one picture point or grid point during the normal scanning electron microscopy (SEM) raster; use of excessive magnification wastes time by having the same particle encountered on many adjacent line scans.

Energy-dispersive x-ray analyses of these particles revealed the presence of such elements as aluminum, chromium, copper, iron, phosphorus, silicon, sulfur, and zinc in widely varying concentrations in different particles. This was consistent with the elements known to be present in the explosive and in the test hardware. Therefore, the image analyzer was instructed to search each particle for these elements (using the x-ray analysis system of the scanning electron microscope) and to record the intensities of the x-ray energies that are characteristic of each of these elements (as a measure of the concentration of each element in the particle). In addition, a number of preliminary elemental categories were established into which the particle could be grouped, for

Fig. 14 SEM of particles (a) and energy-dispersive x-ray spectrum from a single particle (b)

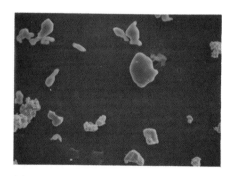

(a)

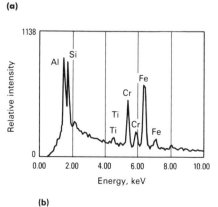

(b)

example, aluminum-rich (aluminum x-ray intensity >40% of sum of intensities of all x-rays), silicon-rich (silicon x-ray intensity >50% of sum of all x-ray intensities), iron-aluminum-rich (both iron and aluminum x-ray intensities >30% of sum of all x-ray intensities), and so on.

Data collecton for detailed analysis was performed by moving the sample from field to field in a predetermined pattern under computer control. Each field was imaged in the backscattered electron mode. As the electron beam rastered across the sample surface in the normal SEM mode, the backscattered electron signal was collected and analyzed at each grid point to determine whether its intensity exceeded the threshold intensity. As long as the intensity remained below the threshold, the system inferred that the beam was impinging on the beryllium stub rather than a particle, and the SEM raster was permitted to continue. When the signal intensity exceeded this threshold, the image analyzer inferred that the first particle had been encountered. At this point, the normal SEM raster was automatically discontinued, and a different beam motion mode was begun to define the size and shape of the particle.

Fig. 15 Schematic showing how particle location, size, and shape are established

(a) Finding a particle and locating the centroid. (b) Sizing of the particle. (c) Finding the next particle

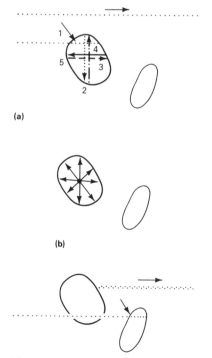

(a)

(b)

(c)

Fig. 16 Histogram for Example 2

Shown are average diameters of aluminum-rich particles.

```
AVE DIAMETER VS PARTICLE COUNT HISTOGRAM FOR CHEMICAL TYPE: AL RICH
SIZE OR SHAPE RANGE FROM:     0.10  TO    15.00
NO. OF PARTICLES IN HISTOGRAM  70        7.00 % TOTAL NO. PARTICLES
NO. OF PARTICLES OUTSIDE OF SIZE OR SHAPE RANGE    0


BIN MAX   NO.   %   00---10---20---30---40---50---60---70---80---90---100
   1.59    13  18.5 [*********
   3.08    24  34.2 [*****************
   4.57    20  28.5 [**************
   6.06     7  10.0 [*****
   7.55     4   5.7 [***
   9.04     0   0.0 [
  10.53     0   0.0 [
  12.02     1   1.4 [*
  13.51     0   0.0 [
  15.00     1   1.4 [*
```

In this mode, the beam automatically drew eight chords at 22.5° angles to one another across the particle (Fig. 15). The beam moved in much smaller steps than in the normal SEM raster, and the ends of the chords were defined by the points at which the backscattered electron signal dropped below the threshold intensity. Based on the end points of these chords, the image analyzer estimated the projected area, perimeter, average diameter, and shape factor (perimeter^2 divided by area/4π) for the particle and computed the location of its centroid. Chord-based calculations are quite accurate for regularly shaped particles, but accuracy decreases as the particles become irregular.

The electron beam was then repositioned to the particle centroid and was spread to cover a major portion of the particle surface; an x-ray spectrum was collected from which the chemistry of the particle could be inferred. The relative intensities of the characteristic x-rays corresponding to each element of interest were measured and recorded. This geometric and compositional information for the first particle was stored in the image analyzer. The normal SEM beam raster was then resumed.

This process was repeated for each particle encountered. Analysis of each particle required 5 to 10 s. Most of this time was required for collection of the x-ray spectrum. Whenever a particle was encountered, several chords were quickly drawn across it, and a quick test was performed to determine whether its size and location corresponded to those of a previously measured particle. If so, this particle was discounted, and the normal SEM raster was resumed.

Approximately 1000 particles were analyzed in this manner in about 100 fields during an 8-h day. The results were then sorted by elemental category, and listings were printed of the geometric and compositional characteristics of each particle in each category. In addition, a statistical summary was printed for each elemental category. Table 1 lists examples of the individual particle data and the statistical summaries for several elemental categories.

The individual particle data were stored on disk to permit additional off-line data analysis to be conducted at a later date. During this subsequent data analysis, several elemental categories were redefined, and some new categories were established. In addition, particle size and shape categories were defined, the fractions of particles meeting various geometric and/or chemical criteria were calculated, and histograms were drawn representing the size and shape distributions of particles within various elemental categories. Figure 16 shows an example of the data output. These other data were compared with the predictions of models for the behavior of materials under explosive conditions, and they provided a basis for refining these models.

Similar analyses could be performed to characterize inclusions and second-phase distributions in metals and ceramics. These analyses could be complicated by the fact that smaller atomic number differences may exist between the features of interest and the background, making detection by backscattered electron imaging more difficult.

REFERENCES

1. "Determining Average Grain Size," E 112, *Annual Book of ASTM Standards*, Vol 03.03, ASTM, Philadelphia, 1984
2. "Determining the Inclusion Content of Steel," E 45, *Annual Book of ASTM Standards*, Vol 03.03, ASTM, Philadelphia, 1984
3. R.T. DeHoff and F.N. Rhines, *Quantitative Microscopy*, McGraw-Hill, 1968
4. E.E. Underwood, *Quantitative Stereology*, Addison-Wesley, 1970
5. E.R. Weibel, *Stereological Methods*, Vol 1 and 2, Academic Press, 1979, 1980
6. R.T. DeHoff, Quantitative Microstructural Analysis, *STP 430*, ASTM, Philadelphia, 1968, p 63-95
7. R.T. DeHoff, Quantitative Metallography, in *Techniques of Metals Research*, Vol II, Part 1, Interscience, 1968, p 221-253
8. F.B. Pickering, *The Basis of Quantitative Metallography*, Institute of Metallurgical Technicians, London, 1976
9. G.F. Vander Voort, *Metallography: Principles and Practice*, McGraw-Hill, 1984
10. G.A. Moore, Recent Progress in Automatic Image Analysis, *J. Microsc.*, Vol 95, Part 1, Feb 1972, p 105-118
11. H.P. Hougardy, Instrumentation in Automatic Image Analysis, *The Microscope*, Vol 22, 1974, p 5-25
12. H.P. Hougardy, Measurement of the Performance of Quantitative Image Analyzing Instruments, *Pract. Metallogr.*, Vol 12, 1975, p 624-635
13. H.P. Hougardy, Recent Progress in Automatic Image Analysis Instrumentation, *The Microscope*, Vol 24, 1976, p 7-23
14. H.E. Exner, Programmable Semiautomatic Instruments for Quantitative Structure Analysis and Other Geometric Evaluations in the Materials Laboratory, *Pract. Metallogr.*, Vol 15, Jan 1978, p 15-22
15. M. Coster and J.L. Chermant, Image Analysis Using a Table Digitizer: I—Programming Fundamental Quantities in Local Analysis, *Pract. Metallogr.*, Vol 17, 1980, p 178-191
16. J.L. Chermant *et al.*, Image Analysis Using a Table Digitizer: II—Particle by Particle Analysis, and Study of Anisotropy, *Pract. Metallogr.*, Vol 18, August 1981, p 392-408
17. V. Smolej, Accuracy of Semiautomatic Measurements on Digitizing Equipment, *Pract. Metallogr.*, Vol 20, March 1983, p 138-149

18. V. Frith *et al.*, The Reliability of a Digitizer System for Image Analysis, *Pract. Metallogr.*, Vol 21, 1984, p 593-601

19. F. Hofer, Quantitative Metallographic Phase Analysis with the QTM, *The Microscope*, Vol 16, 1968, p 171-180

20. G.F. Vander Voort, Etching Techniques for Image Analysis, *Microstruc. Sci.*, Vol 9, Elsevier, 1981, p 137-154

21. G.F. Vander Voort, Tint Etching, *Metal Prog.*, Vol 127, March 1984, p 31-33, 36-41

22. C. Fisher, The Quantimet: Setting the Threshold and the Correction of Off-Set Threshold Error, *Pract. Metallogr.*, Vol 6, Nov 1969, p 659-672

23. E.E. Underwood, Practical Solutions to Stereological Problems, *STP 839*, ASTM, Philadelphia, 1984, p 160-179

24. G. Bockstiegel, A Calculation Technique for the Correction of Edge Errors Occurring in Determinations of the Size Distributions with Linear Scanning Instruments, *Pract. Metallogr.*, Vol 6, Oct 1969, p 596-602 (see also: Vol 7, Oct 1970, p 572-576, 577-586; Vol 9, June 1972, p 32-38; and Vol 9, May 1972, p 291-292)

25. G. Bockstiegel, A New Formula Permitting Straight-Forward Correction of Edge Errors in Size Distribution Measurements with Linear Scanning Instruments, *Pract. Metallogr.*, Vol 9, June 1972, p 329-341

26. H.E. Exner, Methods for Edge Error Correction in Lineal Analysis, *Pract. Metallogr.*, Vol 9, July 1972, p 383-392 (see also: Vol 10, Jan 1973, p 43-45)

27. T. Hersant *et al.*, Errors Due to Measuring Masks in Quantitative Metallography, *CDS CIT*, 1978, p 191-201

28. F.C. Bell and D.E. Sonon, Improved Metallographic Etching Techniques for Stainless Steel and for Stainless Steel to Carbon Steel Weldments, *Metallography*, Vol 9, 1976, p 91-107

29. J.M. Stephenson and B.M. Patchett, Grain-Boundary Etches for Austenitic And Ferritic Ni-Cr-Mo Corrosion-Resistant Alloys, *Sheet Metal Ind.*, Vol 56, 1979, p 45-50, 57

30. G.F. Vander Voort, Grain Size Measurement, *STP 839*, ASTM, Philadelphia, 1984, p 85-131

Table 1 Typical individual particle data and statistical summaries

Particle number	Area, μm^2	Perimeter	Max	Min	Avg	Shape factor	Mo	Zn	Cu	Fe	Cr	Ti	S	P	Si	Al	Na
Aluminum-rich particles																	
3	26.01	22.92	7.52	3.64	5.60	1.60	1	0	1	7	1	1	0	1	2	85	0
25	11.26	13.44	4.87	3.05	3.82	1.27	0	5	5	3	0	1	0	0	2	76	1
29	7.50	11.48	3.82	2.09	3.05	1.39	0	15	6	5	0	1	0	1	1	67	2
35	39.31	24.06	8.25	6.38	7.11	1.17	1	2	1	7	0	1	0	0	0	88	0
37	23.54	20.01	7.29	4.64	5.51	1.35	0	4	4	7	0	2	0	0	0	77	1
58	11.61	12.26	4.10	3.73	3.87	1.03	0	5	4	13	1	1	0	0	1	70	1
81	1.20	5.47	1.59	0.59	1.04	1.96	0	1	1	8	0	3	0	4	3	79	0
84	14.91	15.99	5.69	3.19	4.28	1.36	1	1	1	7	0	0	0	0	1	88	0
97	11.98	12.71	4.46	3.23	3.87	1.07	0	4	4	9	1	2	0	0	2	74	1
102	3.90	7.38	2.64	2.00	2.23	1.11	0	3	4	4	1	0	0	0	0	77	0
111	17.56	15.22	5.01	4.46	4.74	1.05	0	0	1	1	0	1	1	1	0	93	0
116	4.54	9.66	3.73	1.50	2.32	1.63	1	3	1	5	0	0	0	1	0	89	0
131	7.17	10.57	3.64	2.27	3.00	1.24	0	3	4	3	0	0	0	0	3	80	1
136	1.79	4.96	1.77	1.36	1.50	1.09	0	2	2	6	0	1	0	0	0	90	0
187	158.83	48.54	16.09	12.21	14.35	1.18	0	2	1	4	4	3	5	0	0	68	0
189	8.91	10.89	3.64	3.19	3.41	1.05	0	1	1	11	0	1	0	1	2	82	0
193	8.68	10.75	3.46	3.09	3.32	1.06	0	5	13	9	0	0	2	0	0	63	1
198	1.40	5.01	1.45	1.18	1.32	1.42	0	3	2	3	0	1	0	0	0	90	1
230	4.20	7.61	2.64	2.00	2.27	1.09	0	1	3	10	0	0	0	8	0	70	1
233	3.64	6.97	2.41	1.91	2.14	1.06	0	1	1	4	1	0	0	0	0	77	1
Number of particles, 70; 7% of total number of particles																	
Average values	13.20	11.75	4.00	2.97	3.42	1.23	0	3	3	6	0	0	0	0	1	78	0
Standard deviation	23.27	7.46	2.63	2.09	2.27	0.21	1	3	4	4	1	1	1	1	4	9	1
Iron-aluminum-rich particles																	
2	9.32	13.21	4.64	2.73	3.41	1.49	1	2	1	50	3	0	0	0	7	34	0
4	12.08	15.95	4.87	2.96	3.96	1.67	1	1	2	47	4	1	2	0	4	36	1
5	7.85	13.90	4.46	2.46	3.19	1.95	0	0	0	44	5	1	0	0	7	41	0
8	5.81	9.66	3.05	2.37	2.64	1.27	0	0	0	51	3	0	1	0	8	34	1
9	5.15	11.12	3.32	1.36	2.14	1.91	2	1	2	43	2	0	2	5	10	29	0
10	10.98	14.63	4.64	2.55	3.60	1.55	0	1	1	50	2	0	0	1	8	37	0
14	23.12	17.91	5.88	5.05	5.47	1.10	0	6	12	30	0	1	1	0	3	47	1
15	4.67	10.34	3.46	1.64	2.41	1.82	0	1	0	51	1	1	0	1	10	34	0
16	6.49	10.52	3.82	2.37	2.82	1.35	0	0	1	54	2	0	0	0	7	35	0
18	2.21	6.38	2.00	1.18	1.54	1.46	0	0	2	47	3	0	0	2	10	38	0
20	6.68	12.21	4.64	1.59	2.64	1.77	0	0	1	47	2	1	0	1	7	39	0
21	10.80	15.22	4.46	1.82	3.41	1.70	1	4	21	13	4	21	14	1	18	18	0
22	16.02	19.92	7.29	2.64	4.33	1.97	0	0	1	51	1	1	0	0	10	37	0
26	10.47	13.44	4.46	2.41	3.64	1.37	0	1	0	53	3	0	0	0	6	36	0
27	3.26	8.61	2.78	1.18	2.00	1.81	0	1	0	49	2	0	0	0	10	37	0
28	12.68	15.72	6.38	2.18	3.78	1.55	0	1	1	42	7	0	0	1	9	39	0
30	0.96	4.33	1.41	0.77	1.09	1.54	0	0	2	50	2	0	0	0	7	39	0
32	3.22	7.38	2.64	1.50	2.00	1.34	0	1	0	51	1	1	0	0	8	38	0
36	1.51	5.10	1.82	1.13	1.36	1.37	1	0	1	46	2	1	0	0	8	39	0
40	11.69	16.04	5.47	1.82	3.32	1.75	1	0	0	42	5	11	0	0	10	30	0

(continued)

Table 1 (continued)

Particle number	Area, μm²	Particle size and shape, μm					Elements (relative x-ray intensities)										
		Perimeter	Max	Min	Avg	Shape factor	Mo	Zn	Cu	Fe	Cr	Ti	S	P	Si	Al	Na
Number of particles, 474; 47.40% of total number of particles																	
Average values.......	4.99	8.83	3.02	1.53	2.16	1.61	0	0	1	44	2	2	0	0	8	35	0
Standard deviation	9.92	4.13	1.49	1.00	1.14	0.23	1	2	3	10	2	6	3	2	5	7	1
Particles with average diameters from 3 to 200 μm																	
2................	9.32	13.21	4.64	2.73	3.41	1.49	1	2	1	50	3	0	0	0	7	34	0
3................	26.01	22.92	7.52	3.64	5.60	1.60	1	0	1	7	1	1	0	1	2	85	0
4................	12.08	15.95	4.87	2.96	3.96	1.67	1	1	2	47	4	1	2	0	4	36	1
5................	7.85	13.90	4.46	2.46	3.19	1.95	0	0	0	44	5	1	0	0	7	41	0
6................	9.20	13.62	4.46	2.55	3.46	1.60	1	0	0	11	16	51	3	1	12	4	0
10................	10.98	14.63	4.64	2.55	3.60	1.55	0	1	1	50	2	0	0	1	8	37	0
12................	11.56	15.22	5.65	2.41	3.82	1.59	1	0	2	29	12	25	0	0	11	17	1
13................	7.93	11.35	4.05	2.41	3.19	1.29	0	0	0	1	1	0	0	0	98	0	0
14................	23.12	17.91	5.88	5.05	5.47	1.10	0	6	12	30	0	1	1	0	3	47	1
19................	10.68	13.53	4.87	2.59	3.64	1.36	1	0	1	4	18	60	1	0	12	1	0
21................	10.80	15.22	4.46	1.82	3.41	1.70	1	4	2	13	4	21	14	1	18	18	0
22................	16.02	19.92	7.29	2.64	4.33	1.97	0	0	1	51	1	1	0	0	10	37	0
23................	14.29	15.95	5.05	3.46	4.23	1.41	0	1	0	45	11	0	0	1	7	35	0
25................	11.26	13.44	4.87	3.05	3.82	1.27	0	5	5	3	0	1	0	0	2	76	1
26................	10.47	13.44	4.46	2.41	3.64	1.37	0	1	0	53	3	0	0	0	6	36	0
28................	12.68	15.72	6.38	2.18	3.78	1.55	0	1	1	42	7	0	0	1	9	39	0
29................	7.50	11.48	3.82	2.09	3.05	1.39	0	15	6	5	0	1	0	1	1	67	2
33................	14.92	14.95	4.87	3.73	4.37	1.19	0	0	0	4	18	63	0	0	12	3	0
34................	14.91	14.35	4.87	3.96	4.37	1.09	0	1	5	5	1	0	0	10	10	7	1
35................	39.31	24.06	8.25	6.38	7.11	1.17	1	2	1	7	0	1	0	0	0	88	0
Number of particles, 233; 23.30% of total number of particles																	
Average values.......	18.20	15.70	5.49	3.41	4.31	1.34	0	1	3	15	7	17	1	0	15	25	0
Standard deviation	27.93	6.80	2.42	1.98	2.05	0.25	1	4	6	18	9	24	5	2	21	28	2

Diffraction Methods

Introduction

Deane K. Smith, Department of Geosciences, The Pennsylvania State University

X-ray diffraction techniques are some of the most useful in the characterization of crystalline materials, such as metals, intermetallics, ceramics, minerals, polymers, plastics, or other inorganic or organic compounds. X-ray diffraction techniques can be used to identify the phases present in samples from raw starting materials to finished product and to provide information on the physical state of the sample, such as grain size, texture, and crystal perfection. Most x-ray diffraction techniques are rapid and nondestructive; some instruments are portable and can be transported to the sample. The sample may be as small as an airborne dust particle or as large as an airplane wing. This article will describe the methods of x-ray diffraction analysis, the types of information that can be obtained, and its interpretation.

In general, x-ray analysis is restricted to crystalline materials, although some information may be obtained on amorphous solids and liquids. These topics are discussed in the articles "Radial Distribution Function Analysis" and "Small-Angle X-Ray and Neutron Scattering" in this Volume. Similar information can often be obtained using electron diffraction or neutron diffraction, but the sample limitations are usually more severe and the equipment considerably more elaborate and costly.

Samples are acceptable in many forms, depending on the availability of the material and the type of analysis to be performed. Single crystals from a few microns to a few inches in diameter or loose or consolidated aggregate of many small crystals can be used. Although the overall size of the sample may be large, the actual area of the sample examined in a given experiment rarely exceeds 1 cm^2 (0.16 in.^{2}) and may be as small as 10 μm^2.

The type of information desired may range from the question of sample crystallinity or its composition to details of the crystal structure or the state of orientation of the crystallites. Crystal structure analysis is usually performed only on samples of single crystals, which are often approximately 100 μm

in diameter. Phase identification can be conducted on virtually all single crystal or powder samples. Also useful are measurements of the physical state of a sample that detect differences from the ideal crystal. The most common cause of crystal defects is deformation due to local or external applied stresses. Deformation or strain analysis is useful, especially in metallurgy. Table 1 lists types of x-ray diffraction analysis, indicates specific techniques, and describes the required form of the sample.

In general, the techniques are classified as single crystal or polycrystalline. The information obtainable can be categorized as position, intensity, and shape of the diffraction peaks. The spatial positions of the diffracted beams exiting the sample contain all the information on the geometry of the crystal. The intensities of the beams are related to the types of atoms and their arrangement in the crystal. The sharpness of the diffraction beams is a measure of the perfection of the crystal. Diffraction experiments can be designed to measure any or all of these features.

Theory

Nature and Generation of X-Rays.
X-rays are a portion of the electromagnetic spectrum having wavelengths from 10^{-10} to 10^{-8} m (1 to 100 Å), although only 0.3 to 2.5 Å is used for x-ray diffraction. As electromagnetic radiation, x-rays have wave and particle properties. Derivation of all angle-dependent phenomena is based on their wave characteristics. However, electronic detectors measure photon properties, with intensity measurements reported as counts per second.

Most commercial x-ray sources use a high-energy (50 kV) electron beam directed into a cooled metal target. As the electrons are decelerated in the target, several events produce x-radiation. Most of the electron beam energy is lost in collisions that set the atoms in motion and produce heat, which must be dissipated through the cooling water. Some electron energy is caught in the electric fields of the atom as the electrons decelerate and is reradiated as x-rays. Most of this radiation has energy near the excita-

Table 1 X-ray diffraction analysis

Type of analysis	Method	Sample
Crystal geometry	Moving crystal-spot pattern	Single crystal
	Computer positioned diffractometer	Single crystal
	Solution of *d*-spacing equations	Powder
Arrangement of atoms	Analysis of diffracted intensities	Single crystal
	Refinement of whole pattern	Powder
Symmetry	Moving crystal-spot pattern	Single crystal
	Stationary crystal-spot pattern	Single crystal
Identification of compound	Identification of cell parameters	Single crystal
	Matching of *d-I* set	Powder
Crystal orientation	Single-crystal back reflection	Large single crystal
	Texture analysis	Powder compact
Size of crystal	Line broadening	Powder
Magnitude of strain	Line shifts	Powder compact
Amount of phase	Quantitative analysis	Powder
Change of state	Special atmosphere chambers	Single crystal or powder
Crystal perfection	Direct imaging	Single crystal
	Line shape analysis	Powder

Fig. 1 Characteristic x-ray spectra

(a) Without a filter. (b) With a thin-foil monochromator and a crystal monochromator

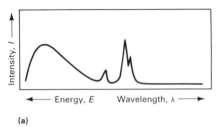

(a)

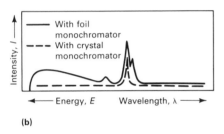

(b)

tion potential, 50 kV, but may have any value down to zero. This bremsstrahlung or white radiation, so termed because it is polychromatic, produces a continuum of all energies between the extremes.

A small but significant portion of the electron beam collides with the electrons of the target atoms. Some target electrons are knocked out of their orbitals, leaving the target atoms in a high-energy excited state. This excited state is brief, and the stored energy is released as the electrons from other orbitals drop into the vacant orbital. These electron transitions are of distinct energy jumps, that is, they are quantized, and the radiation emitted has specific wavelengths. Therefore, x-rays exiting the target have a few strong characteristic concentrations of specific wavelengths superimposed on the white radiation. The characteristic spectrum of an x-ray tube is simple, and few wavelengths have strong peaks (Fig. 1a).

Both the white radiation and the characteristic spectrum have utility in x-ray diffraction. For most experiments, the incident beam usually consists of only a single wavelength; that is, it is monochromatic. The output beam can be monochromatized variously. One of the simplest methods is to use a thin foil of an appropriate metal. The characteristic spectrum depends on the target element, but the white radiation does not. Copper is typically used as the target because the Kα characteristic radiation is a useful wavelength, 1.5406 Å, and the target is easily cooled for high efficiency. For copper radiation, a nickel foil absorbs most of the white radiation and the other characteristic

peaks, transmitting essentially pure Kα radiation (Fig. 1b).

An alternate method of monochromatizing the beam involves use of a single crystal as a diffractor that is set to allow diffraction of only the desired wavelength. Crystals of graphite, silicon, germanium, and quartz are often used for this purpose in modern devices. A third method is possible when the detector of the x-ray beam can discriminate the energies of the individual x-rays. Such a detector can be set electronically to accept only the energy corresponding to the characteristic radiation.

Some experiments use white radiation. This radiation is not characteristic of any specific target, and target materials whose characteristic spectrum is only partially excited by the 50-kV electron beam, such as tungsten, are commonly used. The small amount of characteristic radiation generated usually does not interfere with the experiment.

Detection of X-Rays. Use of x-rays in experiments necessitates detection of diffracted beams such that their positions in space and intensities are measurable. Photographic films and photon detectors are usually used. Special films, used as flat or cylindrical detectors, collect many beams simultaneously. The beam appears as a dark spot or line on the negative whose angular coordinates can be determined by its position on the film and the film geometry. The darkening of the spot is proportional to beam intensity. The photon detector measures only a single beam at any given time and must be repositioned to detect a different beam. Beam intensity is determined from the photon count rate.

The position-sensitive detector consists of a wire placed to intersect the beam over a range of angles. The location on the wire that detects a photon can be identified electronically. The photon interactions are totalled for each spot on the wire, providing intensity and position information simultaneously for a range of positions. A wavelength-dispersive detector operates on electronic energy discrimination of the components of a polychromatic beam, resulting in the simultaneous accumulation of the intensities of many different wavelengths.

The experiment often dictates selection of film or electronic collection of data. Film is useful when it is desirable to collect the entire diffraction pattern. Film images are easily interpreted in terms of the positions of diffraction beams, but are more difficult to use for quantitative intensity data. They are useful in experiments involving weak beams. Electronic methods, usually faster and more accurate, can be easily converted to computer readable information for data analysis.

The Crystalline State. A crystalline material is a three-dimensionally periodic arrangement of atoms in space. This arrangement is best depicted by describing a unit cell having all the fundamental properties of the crystal as a whole, that is, the basic repeating unit. This unit cell is always a parallelepiped having typical edge dimensions of 3 to 20 Å for most inorganic solids. Some proteins may have cell dimensions exceeding 1500 Å. Within the unit cell, the arrangement of atoms depends on the types of atoms, the nature of their bonds, and their tendency to minimize the free energy by a high degree of organization. This organization usually results in some degree of geometric symmetry and unit-cell shapes reflecting this symmetry.

The crystal as a whole consists of unit-cell building blocks packed like bricks in a wall. The resulting crystal exhibits shapes and symmetry controlled by the unit cell. Thus, a goal of x-ray diffraction is to characterize the unit cell, that is, to determine its size, shape, symmetry, and the arrangement of atoms. These characteristics can be determined from the collection of angles at which diffracted x-ray beams are detected. The arrangement of atoms and the details of symmetry require interpretation of the intensities of the diffracted beams. The former is the geometry of the unit cell; the latter, the crystal structure.

The Geometry of Unit Cells and Diffraction. A lattice is the arrangement of single geometric points at the center of each unit cell that represent the cell in space. The lattice reflects exactly the size and shape of the unit cells and their periodic arrangement in space. Where the shape of the unit cell is limited by the presence of symmetry, the lattice contains the same limitations. The lattice is fundamental to the geometry of any diffraction experiment.

Diffraction is a phenomenon of electromagnetic radiation scattered from a periodic arrangement of scattering centers with spacings of the same order of magnitude as the wavelength of the radiation. Interference of the scattered rays in most directions results in cancellation and absence of detectable beams; however, in a few selected directions, reinforcement of all the scattered rays occurs, and a strong beam results. The periodicity may be in one, two, or three dimensions. Figure 2 shows a wave incident on a one-dimensional row of scattering centers. The incident beam has all the rays in phase. At each scattering center, new rays emanate in all directions. The beams will not be in phase in most directions, and cancellation will occur. In the directions indicated, all wavefronts are in phase, and addition occurs, sending out strong beams. These are the diffracted beams.

Fig. 2 Diffraction of x-rays

(a) Diffraction conditions from a row of scattering centers. Most diffracted rays interfere and cancel each other; however, in some directions, reinforcement occurs, and a strong beam results. (b) Conditions for reinforcement

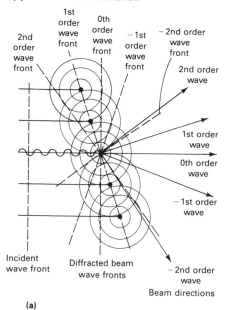

(a)

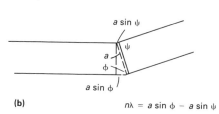

(b)

$n\lambda = a \sin \phi - a \sin \psi$

Although the incident beam and scattering centers lie in the plane of Fig. 2, the diffracted beams are not confined to this plane. Each scattering center emits rays in all directions, and the resulting diffracted rays define a family of cones in space (Fig. 3). This type of experiment is easy to conduct as an optical analog if a (the distances between equally spaced holes in an opaque mask) is approximately 50 μm or less. The row of equally spaced holes can be placed in a light beam, and the diffraction pattern observed on a screen positioned some distance beyond the mask. The diffraction pattern is a series of lines at which the cones intersect the screen.

This one-dimensional arrangement is only part of crystal diffraction. Because the crystal is periodic in three dimensions, the lattice sites act as the scattering centers. The conditions illustrated must then be satisfied simultaneously in three dimensions. Scattering must be considered from three noncolinear rows of the lattice; all the equations must be satisfied simultaneously:

$n_a\lambda = a(\sin \phi_a - \sin \psi_a)$ (Eq 1)

Fig. 3 Cones of diffraction

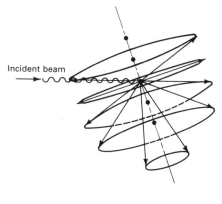

$n_b\lambda = b(\sin \phi_b - \sin \psi_b)$ (Eq 2)

$n_c\lambda = c(\sin \phi_c - \sin \psi_c)$ (Eq 3)

where a, b, and c are the lattice repeats; n_a, n_b, and n_c are the order numbers usually identified as the Miller indices h, k, and l; and ϕ and ψ are the incident and diffracted angles, respectively.

The three-dimensional lattice of scattering centers restricts a diffraction experiment severely. Few directions can diffract, and diffraction can only occur when the incident beam makes precisely the correct angle relative to the crystal. Equations 1, 2, and 3 define these restrictions. It is usually easier to visualize these conditions by reducing Eq 1, 2, and 3 to that shown in Fig. 4. The lattice is considered to be planes of lattice points, and the x-ray beam acts as if it reflects off these planes. Constructive interference occurs only when the incidence angle and diffraction angle, θ, satisfy the condition $\lambda = 2d \sin \theta$, where d is the perpendicular spacing between the lattice planes. The angle θ is a function of the ϕs and ψs, and d is a function of a, b, c, h, k, l and the lattice angles α, β, and γ. Equations 1, 2, and 3, being more realistic, identify diffraction as scattering and interference from the periodically arranged unit cells.

Determining Lattice Geometries.
Many diffraction experiments are implemented to identify lattice geometry. Lattice geometries are classified into six categories known as crystal systems (Table 2). The angles α, β, and γ are the interaxial angles $b \wedge c$, $c \wedge a$, and $a \wedge b$, respectively. Also in

Table 2 are the expressions for determining the possible d values for specific lattices. Single crystal diffraction experiments allow direct determination of all the lattice constants, including the angles, because the experiments separate the three-dimensional aspect of data. Powder diffraction produces only a set of d values, and the lattice constants must be determined by solving one of the d-spacing equations in Table 2, although it is not known *a priori* which equation to solve. This task is difficult unless the data are measured accurately.

The lattice constants of a crystal may be sufficient to identify an unknown compound when it is compared to a tabulation of the lattice data of all known compounds. Such compendia exist, for example, as Crystal Data and the Powder Diffraction File (PDF). Using the PDF, identification may be possible based only on the d spacings without knowledge of lattice constants. Accurate d-spacing or lattice data on experimental products can often indicate chemical and physical differences upon comparison with data from well-characterized related crystals. Changes in lattice constants as a function of temperature and/or pressure provide fundamental

Fig. 4 Diffraction in a crystal lattice and the derivation of the Bragg equation

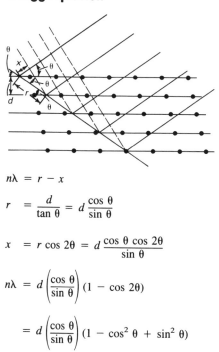

$n\lambda = r - x$

$r = \dfrac{d}{\tan \theta} = d\dfrac{\cos \theta}{\sin \theta}$

$x = r \cos 2\theta = d\dfrac{\cos \theta \cos 2\theta}{\sin \theta}$

$n\lambda = d\left(\dfrac{\cos \theta}{\sin \theta}\right)(1 - \cos 2\theta)$

$\quad = d\left(\dfrac{\cos \theta}{\sin \theta}\right)(1 - \cos^2 \theta + \sin^2 \theta)$

$\quad = d\left(\dfrac{\cos \theta}{\sin \theta}\right)(2 \sin^2 \theta) = 2d \sin \theta$

Table 2 Formulas for calculating interplanar spacing d_{hkl} (a)(b)

Crystal system	Axial translations	Axial angles	d_{hkl}
Cubic	$a = b = c$	$\alpha = \beta = \gamma = 90°$	$a(h^2 + k^2 + l^2)^{-1/2}$
Tetragonal	$a = b \neq c$	$\alpha = \beta = \gamma = 90°$	$[(h^2/a^2) + (k^2/a^2) + (l^2/c^2)]^{-1/2}$
Orthorhombic	$a \neq b \neq c$	$\alpha = \beta = \gamma = 90°$	$[(h^2/a^2) + (k^2/b^2) + (l^2/c^2)]^{-1/2}$
Hexagonal	$a = b \neq c$	$\alpha = \beta = 90°, \gamma = 120°$	$[(4/3a^2)(h^2 + k^2 + hk) + (l^2/c^2)]^{-1/2}$
Rhombohedral . . .	$a = b = c$	$\alpha = \beta = \gamma \neq 90°$	$a\left[\dfrac{(h^2+k^2+l^2)\sin^2\alpha + 2(hk+hl+kl)(\cos^2\alpha - \cos\alpha)}{1 + 2\cos^3\alpha - 3\cos^2\alpha}\right]^{-1/2}$
Monoclinic	$a \neq b \neq c$	$\alpha = \gamma = 90°, \beta > 90°$	$\left[\dfrac{(h^2/a^2) + (l^2/c^2) - (2hl/ac)\cos\beta}{\sin^2\beta} + \dfrac{k^2}{b^2}\right]^{-1/2}$
Triclinic	$a \neq b \neq c$	$\alpha \neq \beta \neq \gamma \neq 90°$	$\left[\dfrac{\dfrac{h}{a}\begin{vmatrix} h/a & \cos\gamma & \cos\beta \\ k/b & 1 & \cos\alpha \\ l/c & \cos\alpha & 1 \end{vmatrix} + \dfrac{k}{b}\begin{vmatrix} 1 & h/a & \cos\beta \\ \cos\gamma & k/b & \cos\alpha \\ \cos\beta & l/c & 1 \end{vmatrix} + \dfrac{l}{c}\begin{vmatrix} 1 & \cos\gamma & h/a \\ \cos\gamma & 1 & k/b \\ \cos\beta & \cos\alpha & l/c \end{vmatrix}}{\begin{vmatrix} 1 & \cos\gamma & \cos\beta \\ \cos\gamma & 1 & \cos\alpha \\ \cos\beta & \cos\alpha & 1 \end{vmatrix}}\right]^{-1/2}$

(a) Simpler expressions involving reciprocal lattice units are cited in Ref 1. (b) Source: Ref 2

---

thermodynamic data on the compound under study. Table 3 lists additional applications.

The Intensities of Diffracted Beams. The geometry of the crystal lattice controls the directions of diffracted beams. The intensities of these beams depend on the types of atoms in the crystal and their arrangement in the unit cell. If a unit cell were composed of a single electron, all the diffracted beams would have identical intensities. Real crystals consist of atoms having clouds of electrons. The scattering from all the electrons in the unit cell results in complex interference effects that enhance some beams and diminish others. These interference effects must be evaluated. In addition, the amplitude of the diffracted beam is the sum of the amplitudes of the component rays. The measured intensity is the square of this sum. Table 4 lists factors that control line intensity and information obtainable from the intensity of diffracted x-rays.

Figure 5 shows a single atom, within which are two electrons located at some instant at points 1 and 2. Each electron scatters equally in all directions, and the scattering does not modify the phase regardless of the scattering angle. The scattering amplitude of an individual electron is given by the Thompson scattering coefficient, e^2/mc^2, where e is the charge of an electron of mass m, and c is the velocity of light. All the rays in the incident beam are in phase, and the forward scattered rays, that is, a scattering angle of zero, from electrons 1 and 2 remain in phase. Thus, the total amplitude of the forward scattered beam is the sum of the contributions of all the electrons in the atomic system, $f_{\theta=0} = Z$, where Z is the number of electrons.

As the scattering angle deviates from zero, the path lengths of the rays from the source to the observation point change, and the scattered rays arrive at the wave front slightly out of phase. This phase difference

Table 3 Line position(a)

Controlled by:

1. Geometry of unit cell (lattice)
2. Wavelength of x-ray beam
3. Instrumental and sample aberrations

Applications:

Accurate lattice parameters
  Least-squares refinements
  Phase characterization
  Identification (qualitative analyses)
    Recognition by familiarity
    d-value searching (PDF Fink)
    Cell data (Crystal Data)

Lattice changes
  Lattice shifts
    Composition changes
    Thermal expansion
    Compressibility
    Homogeneous strain
    Phase changes (polymorphism)

(a) Source: Ref 3

Table 4 Line intensity(a)

Controlled by:

1. Types of atoms and atomic arrangement
2. Amount of sample which can diffract
3. Intensity correction factors

Applications:

Identification (qualitative analyses)
  d-I search/match (PDF Hanawalt)
  Intensity changes with element substitution

Crystal structure analysis
  Differences in fine grained state from
    single crystal state
  Structures of materials which only occur
    in fine grained state

Quantitative analysis
  Phase composition
  Order-disorder ratios
  Percent crystallinity
    polymers
    calcine reactions
  Chemical kinetics

State of polycrystalline aggregate
  Preferred orientation
  Texture

(a) Source: Ref 3

Fig. 5 Phase difference in scattering from different electrons within an atom

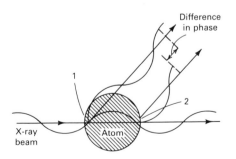

Fig. 6 Change in amplitude of the total diffracted beam as a function of the scattering angle

Higher scattering angles result in greater phase differences among the diffracted beams, decreasing the amplitude of the total diffracted beam.

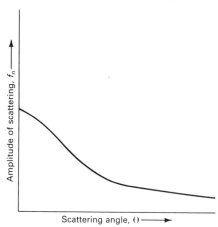

Fig. 7 Diffraction in a unit cell and the structure factor equation for the cell

The positions of atoms 1 and 2 are defined by their position coordinates based on fractions of the unit cell dimensions in directions a, b, and c.
$x_1 = X_1/a$, $y_1 = Y_1/b$, and $z_1 = Z_1/c$

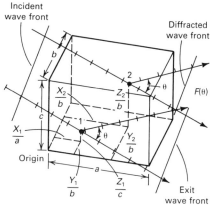

$$F_0 = f_1 + f_2$$

Several correction factors that enter into the intensity calculations are functions of the experimental technique and the nature of the sample. They correct for such components as atom vibrational motion due to temperature, beam polarization, varying diffraction times, and beam absorption in the sample. Considering these elements and the discussion above, the intensity I of a diffracted beam is:

$$I(hkl) = I_0 \times$$

$$(\text{electron scattering coefficient})^2 \times$$

$$(\text{experimental correction terms}) \times$$

$$(\text{structure amplitude})^2$$

Types of Diffraction Experiments

Single Crystal Methods—Polychromatic Beams. One of the simplest experiments involves placing a small crystal in a collimated beam of polychromatic x-rays and positioning a flat film on the other side (Fig. 8a). This transmission experiment, first performed in 1912, proved the wave nature of x-rays, but is rarely used. If the crystal is small enough to be x-ray transparent and if it is aligned with a symmetry element along the beam direction, the resulting diffraction pattern reveals the symmetry. Because the crystal is stationary, different wavelengths in the incident beam are required to satisfy the Bragg conditions from the various lattice planes that can diffract. Because neither the wavelength nor the d spacing are known *a priori*, Laue patterns are difficult to analyze.

An alternate arrangement involving large crystals and placement of the film on the source side of the crystal is used for crystal alignment. This is the back-reflection Laue method (Fig. 8b). In both techniques, the film can be replaced by direct imaging detectors that hasten the experiment significantly.

Single Crystal Methods Using Monochromatic Beams. Because a monochromatic beam can satisfy no more than one diffraction condition at a time, the crystal must be moved to observe the diffraction pattern. The most common movement is an oscillation or rotation about an axis perpendicular to the x-ray beam. If the crystal is aligned with a lattice row along the rotation axis, the resulting pattern of spots is easily interpreted. The film is usually placed like a cylinder around the rotation axis (Fig. 9). When the film is unrolled, the spots form rows that can be easily related to the lattice geometry. Figure 10 shows an example of a

causes some destructive interference that diminishes the amplitude of the total beam. Figure 6 illustrates the change with angle for a typical atom. The greater the angle, the larger the interference, but because the size of atoms is approximately the same as the wavelength of the radiation, total destruction is never reached.

The scattering factor from an atom may be measured experimentally using simple compounds of an element, or, typically, it may be calculated based on one of the electron orbital models of the atom. Tables of scattering values may be found in several sources for all the atoms and most of their ionic states. These scattering values are amplitudes normalized to the number of electrons involved at the scattering angle $\theta = 0$. Usually termed the atomic scattering factor or form factor, they are identified in intensity equations as f.

In a structure composed of a single atom in the unit cell, observed intensities decrease as the scattering angle increases proportionately to f^2. One of the forms of polonium has such a structure, but most metals and other compounds have more complex structures consisting of several atoms in the unit cell. The treatment of the phase interference of two or more atoms is similar to the treatment of the effect of every electron in the atomic cloud. The phase factor depends on the relative positions of the atoms in the unit cell.

Figure 7 shows a unit cell containing two atoms. The positions of these atoms are described by their position coordinates based on the fractions of the unit-cell dimensions in the three principal directions from some

origin. The choice of origin is not critical; it is usually selected on some symmetry element for convenience. Because the scattering effect of each atomic cloud has been considered in the atomic scattering factor f, each atom can be considered as a point atom concentrate at its center. The problem then reduces to determining the interference effect of the scattering from the atom centers due to their positions in space. For forward scattered beams, $\theta = 0$, all the rays are in phase, and their amplitudes are additive. At $\theta \neq 0$, the pathlengths of the scattered rays are different, and a phase difference necessarily results in some interference. The measure of this phase difference is contained in an exponential factor that expresses the amplitude shift in terms of the positions of the atoms. The combination of this phase factor and the atomic scattering factor is the structure factor (**F**):

$$\mathbf{F}(hkl) = \sum_n f_n e^{2\pi i(hx_n + ky_n + lz_n)}$$

where f_n is the atomic scattering factor for atom n; i is $\sqrt{-1}$; h, k, and l are the Miller indices of the diffracted direction; and x_n, y_n, and z_n are the position coordinates of atom n.

The amplitude of the total beam diffracted from the entire crystal is the sum of the contributions from each unit cell. In the directions of diffraction allowed by the lattice geometry, the resulting rays are always in phase and are additive. In any other direction, they interfere and totally cancel.

Fig. 8 Two types of single crystal diffraction experiments

(a) Transmission arrangement. (b) Back-reflection arrangement

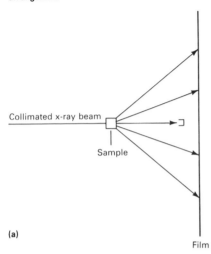

(a)

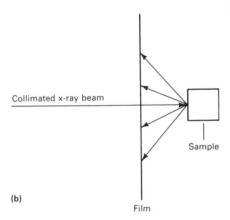

(b)

rotation pattern. This rotation method is usually used to characterize the lattice geometry and to check the quality of a crystal.

For symmetry analysis and measurement of intensities, the rotation method has some limitations that render it unsuitable. More useful patterns may be obtained by using a screen to limit the beams that can reach the film, then moving the film synchronously with crystal rotation. This is the Weissenberg method, which allows unequivocal identification of every diffracted beam. Figure 11 illustrates a Weissenberg pattern of the 0th row of the same crystal used for Fig. 10.

Several moving crystal/moving film techniques using different crystal and film motions are available. Another example is the precession method, whose pattern is shown in Fig. 12. All these methods can be used to obtain essentially the same type of informa-

Fig. 9 A single crystal experiment using monochromatic beams

The sample is rotated about an axis perpendicular to the beam, resulting in a pattern of spots on the cylindrical film.

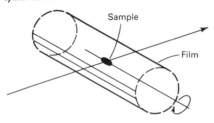

Fig. 10 A rotation pattern for an NaCl crystal

The pattern was obtained using the method shown in Fig. 9.

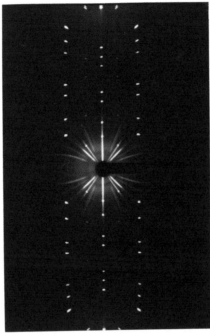

tion. Interpreting the patterns of spots in space enables determining both lattice periodicity dimensions, the angles between the lattice rows, and most of the symmetry information. By measuring intensity values using the relative darkness of the spots on the films, the data necessary to determine the crystal structure can also be obtained.

Electronic detectors have been used to replace the film. One- and two-dimensional position-sensitive detectors have been used in Weissenberg-like configurations. The most successful system is a computer-controlled device that positions a crystal and the detector to record one diffracted beam at a time. This approach is sufficiently rapid for

Fig. 11 Weissenberg pattern of the same crystal as in Fig. 10

In this method, the film is moved synchronously with the crystal rotation.

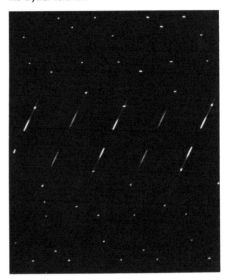

most studies, but problems arise for proteins, with their unusually large unit cells. Although counter techniques are best for measuring intensity values for crystal structure analysis, the film methods are preferred for determining lattice information. Film methods are indispensible for examining effects due to crystal defects or unusual aspects of a crystal structure.

Single Crystal Topography. X-ray topography is a unique application of single crystal analysis. It is essentially x-ray diffraction radiography in which a large area of

Fig. 12 A pattern for the NaCl crystal used in Fig. 10 and 11 obtained using the precession method

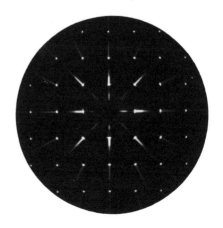

Fig. 13 The geometry of powder diffraction and several detection methods used in XRPD

(a) Cones of diffracted beams emanating from a powder sample. (b) The Debye-Scherrer detection method. (c) The diffractometer method of detection. (d) Position-sensitive detection. (e) Guinier method of detection. (f) Flat plate texture method of detection

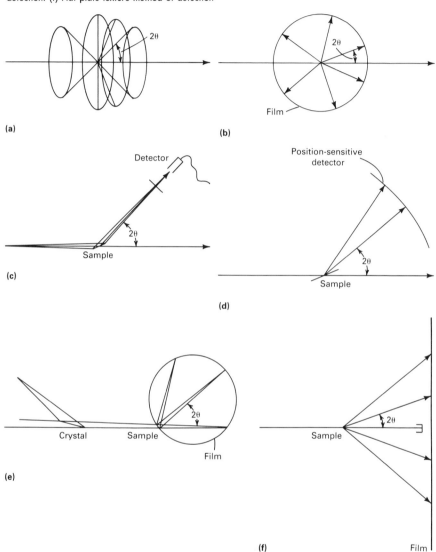

<table>
<tr><th colspan="2">Table 5   Line profile(a)</th></tr>
</table>

Controlled by:

1. State of crystallite perfection and sample homogeneity
2. Instrumental aberrations
3. Spectral distribution

Applications:

Crystallite size
   Size distributions

Lattice distortions
   Crystal defects
Inhomogeneous strain

Sample inhomogeneity

Crystallinity
   Amorphous state

(a) Source: Ref 3

The total collection of crystallites behaves like a single crystal that is moved into all possible orientations, diffracting all possible beams. The result is many coaxial cones of diffracted beams emanating from the sample (Fig. 13). There is a complete cone for every possible diffracted beam from the crystal. The cone half-angles are 2θ. Because the crystallites are oriented randomly in the sample, the only measurable position parameter is 2θ, which translates into a d value through the Bragg relation. No direct information on the lattice constants, the distances or the angles, is obtainable from the powder methods.

The powder method has several variations, depending on sample geometry and the method of detection (Fig. 13). In the Debye-Scherrer method, the sample is a ball or rod of powder on a fiber or in a rotated capillary tube, and the detector is a film forming a cylinder around the sample. All the diffracted beams are detected simultaneously. In the diffractometer method, the sample is flat, and the electronic detector is mounted on a movable arm. Only one beam at a time can be detected. Geometric focusing results in effective use of beam intensity. A modification of the diffractometer method incorporates a position-sensitive detector that can detect a range of beams simultaneously. The Guinier method uses a crystal monochromator to focus the incident beam. The sample is a thin foil, and film is the detector. A large range of beams can be diffracted simultaneously, but not all. A simple method using monochromatic radiation and a flat film located as in the Laue method mentioned above is used to analyze texture and to survey for grain size. If the crystallites in the sample are not oriented randomly, the diffraction cones are not complete, and arcs will be visible on its film

a single crystal produces a single diffracted beam that creates a 1:1 image of the diffracting volume of the sample crystal on an appropriate detector. This image may be detected by high-resolution film or special two-dimensional detectors. The image reveals the presence of such crystal defects as dislocations and subgrain boundaries. The technique is effective, because regions that contain defects scatter more strongly than defect-free regions. The real image produced shows the distribution of the defects in the crystal. Several experimental techniques that use this principle are considered in the article "X-Ray Topography" in this Volume.

Polycrystalline Diffraction Methods. Use of a single crystal is impossible or inappropriate for many samples. X-ray powder diffraction (XRPD) techniques use a sample composed of a powder of many small crystallites. Uses for XRPD techniques range from phase identification to quantitative analysis of mixtures to measuring strain in a weld joint. These applications are considered in the article "X-Ray Powder Diffraction" in this Volume.

The basic powder experiment uses a powder sample placed in a collimated monochromatic beam. Each crystallite behaves like a single crystal and may diffract one beam.

instead of rings. If the grain size is large, the rings appear spotty instead of smooth.

X-ray powder diffraction methods have many uses, although lattice information is more difficult to obtain from XRPD data and resolving every possible diffracted beam and accurately measuring their intensities is difficult. They are used extensively in the materials sciences for identification, crystal characterization, and physical state measurements. Sample chambers allow measurements to be made in controlled atmospheres, at temperatures from 4 to 3500 K, and at pressures from 1.3×10^{-6} Pa to 100 Pa. Modern instrumentation achieves pattern collection and analysis in seconds, allowing time-resolved studies of rapid reactions.

Crystal Imperfections. Crystals are rarely perfect. They contain deformed regions and mistakes in the way the structure fits together. Strain, dislocations, stacking faults, subgrain structure, and impurities dis-rupt the perfection of a crystal and thus affect the x-ray diffraction patterns. They affect the positions and shapes of the diffracted beams, that is, the distribution of intensity in space. This broadens the spots and peaks observed and shifts them from their ideal angular position. This broadening may be used to obtain information on the nature of the defects (see the article "X-Ray Topography" in this Volume). Table 5 lists factors that control the shapes of diffracted beams and applications of line broadening analysis.

Single crystal and powder experiments are affected by strain and defects. Spot patterns show misshapen spots and streaking; powder patterns show only broadening, which can be symmetric or asymmetric. Symmetric broadening is the effect of defects on the effective crystallite sizes. Asymmetric broadening and shifting are caused by deformation of the lattice due to strains from defect concentrations or forces from various causes. Under-standing the effects of these defects is important in allowing correct interpretation of the experimental data and in using the data to acquire information on the causes and nature of these defects.

REFERENCES

1. *International Tables for X-Ray Crystallography*, Vol II, Kynoch Press, 1959

2. H.P. Klug and L.E. Alexander, *X-ray Diffraction Procedures for Polycrystalline and Amorphous Materials*, 2nd ed., John Wiley & Sons, 1974

3. D.K. Smith, C.S. Barrett, D.E. Leyden, and P.K. Predecki, Ed., *Advances in X-Ray Analysis*, Vol 24, Plenum Press, 1981

X-Ray Powder Diffraction

Raymond P. Goehner, Siemens Corporation and Monte C. Nichols, Sandia National Laboratories

General Uses

- Identification of crystalline phases contained in unknown samples
- Quantitative determination of the weight fraction of crystalline phases in multiphase materials
- Characterization of solid-state phase transformations
- Lattice-parameter and lattice-type determinations
- Orientation of single crystals
- Stereographic projections
- Alignment for cutting along crystallographic planes

Examples of Applications

- Qualitative and quantitative analysis of crystalline phases in coal ash, ceramic powders, corrosion products, and so on
- Determination of phase diagrams
- Determination of pressure- and/or temperature-induced phase transformations
- Quantitative analysis of solid solutions from lattice-parameter measurements
- Determination of anisotropic thermal expansion coefficients

Samples

- *Form*: Crystalline solids (metals, ceramics, geological materials, and so on)
- *Size*: For powder samples 1 mg is usually adequate
- *Preparation*: Sometimes none; sample may require crushing to fit into the sample holder

Limitations

- Must be crystalline for phase identification
- Identification requires existence of standard patterns: JCPDS powder diffraction file of inorganic and organic phases, NBS Crystal Data (contains lattice constants for inorganic and organic phases), and Cambridge File of Organic Single Crystal Structural Data

Estimated Analysis Time

- Qualitative analysis requires less than 1 h for major phases, up to 16 h for trace phase confirmation
- Quantitative analysis, after a procedure is set up, requires several minutes to several hours

Capabilities of Related Techniques

- *X-ray spectrometry, inductively coupled plasma atomic emission spectroscopy, atomic absorption spectrometry, classical wet chemical analysis*: Quantitative and qualitative elemental information
- *Auger electron spectroscopy*: Elemental and structural data on small portions of the samples
- *Single-crystal x-ray diffraction*: Crystal structure using small single crystals
- *Infrared and Raman spectroscopy*: Molecular structure and sometimes crystal structure
- *Neutron diffraction*: Similar information, but can be applied in some cases in which x-ray powder diffraction fails

Introduction

X-ray powder diffraction (XRPD) techniques are used to characterize samples in the form of loose powders or aggregates of finely divided material. These techniques cover various investigations, including qualitative and quantitative phase identification and analysis, determination of crystallinity, microidentification, lattice-parameter determinations, high-temperature studies, thin film characterization, and, in some cases, crystal structure analysis. The powder method, as it is referred to, is perhaps best known for its use as a phase characterization tool partly because it can routinely differentiate between phases having the same chemical composition but different crystal structures (polymorphs). Although chemical analysis can indicate that the empirical formula for a given sample is FeTiO$_3$, it cannot determine whether the sample is a mixture of two phases (FeO and one of the three polymorphic forms of TiO$_2$) or whether the sample is the single-phase mineral FeTiO$_3$ or ilmenite. The ability of XRPD to perform such identifications more simply, conveniently, and routinely than any other analytical method explains its importance in many industrial applications as well as its wide availability and prevalence.

In general, an x-ray powder diffraction characterization of a substance consists of placing a powder sample in a collimated monochromatic beam of x-radiation. For crystalline materials, diffraction takes place as described in the "Introduction" to this Section to produce a diffraction pattern. The diffraction pattern is recorded on film or using detector techniques, then analyzed to provide x-ray powder data that can be used to solve such problems as those listed in the boxed summary on the first page of this article.

In XRPD analysis, samples usually exist as finely divided powder (usually less than 44 μm in size) or can be reduced to powder form. The particles in a sample comprise one or more independently diffracting regions that coherently diffract the x-ray beam. These small crystalline regions are termed crystallites. Consolidated samples, such as ceramic bodies or as-received metal samples, will likely have crystallites small enough to be useful for powder diffraction analysis, although they may appear to have considerably larger particle sizes. This occurs because a given grain or particle may consist of several crystallites (independently diffracting regions). Although larger grain sizes can sometimes be used to advantage in XRPD, the size limitation is important because most applications of powder diffraction rely on x-ray signals from a statistical sample of crystallites. The angular position, θ, of the diffracted x-ray beam depends on the spacings, d, between planes of atoms in a crystalline phase and on the x-ray wavelength λ:

$$n\lambda = 2d \sin \theta \qquad \text{(Eq 1)}$$

The intensity of the diffracted beam depends on the arrangement of the atoms on these planes.

X-ray powder diffraction techniques usually require some sample preparation. This may involve crushing the sample to fit inside a glass capillary tube, rolling it into a very thin rod shape for the Debye-Scherrer camera technique, spreading it as a thin layer on a sample holder, or packing it into a sample holder of a certain size for other XRPD techniques. In some cases, samples compatible with metallographic examination can be accommodated in powder diffractometers, but some form of sample preparation will usually be necessary. Preparation will depend on the equipment available and the nature of the examination.

A diffraction pattern can be recorded using film, analog, or digital methods. Whether film, analog, or digital data collection is used, the final data can be displayed as a graph of intensity, as a function of interplanar distance d, or as a function of diffraction angle 2θ. Many modern auto-

mated powder diffractometers can provide further data reduction, including peak finding, a tabular listing of peak intensity versus interplanar spacing, search/match software, and other computer utilities.

A powder pattern from a single-phase material will have maxima at positions dictated by the size and shape of its unit cell and will increase in complexity as the symmetry of the material decreases. For example, many metal patterns and those from simple compounds that tend to be mostly of cubic symmetry and have small unit cell edges will produce powder patterns having fewer lines or maxima than would be expected from a compound of lower symmetry or one having a very large unit cell. A pattern of a mixture of phases in which all the individual patterns are superimposed will produce a complex experimental pattern, especially when the number of phases present in the mixture exceeds approximately three or when the phases constituting the mixture are all of very low symmetry or have very large unit cell dimensions.

Phase identification using XRPD is based on the unique pattern produced by every crystalline phase. Much as a fingerprint is unique for each person, the diffraction pattern can act as an empirical fingerprint for that phase, and qualitative identification of phases can be accomplished by pattern-recognition methods that include established manual techniques and the newer methods that use computers, most of which implement programs based on heuristic algorithms. All of these methods make use of the database maintained by the JCPDS International Centre for Diffraction Data (Ref 1).

Instrumentation

Photographic film is the oldest detector of x-rays. It was first used in 1912 by Laue in his discovery of the wave nature of x-rays

Fig. 1 Schematic of a transmission pinhole camera

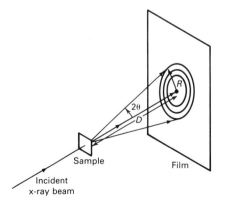

(Ref 2). Powder diffraction patterns were first recorded on film in 1913 (Ref 3, 4). Film remains in use as the detector of choice for various XRPD techniques.

Pinhole Camera/Laue Camera. The simplest photographic instrument is the pinhole camera (Fig. 1). This camera exists in four variations, depending on the placement of the film and the use of white radiation or monochromatic radiation. If the white radiation from the x-ray tube is used, the camera is usually referred to as a transmission Laue camera. The symmetry of the spot pattern can be used to determine the orientation of the single crystal relative to the x-ray beam. When monochromatic radiation is used, and the sample is polycrystalline, the film would show a set of concentric rings, known as Debye rings. In this case, the d-spacing (see the section "Introduction" in this article) can be calculated using:

$$\theta = \arctan \left(\frac{R}{D} \right) \qquad \text{(Eq 2)}$$

where R is the radius of the Debye ring, and D is the film-to-sample distance. Once θ is known, d can be calculated using Eq 1.

The principal disadvantage of the transmission pinhole camera is that the samples must be thin enough for the x-rays to penetrate. Metallic samples typically must be less than 0.1 mm (0.004 in.) thick. This severely limits the usefulness of the technique.

Figure 2 shows a back-reflection pinhole camera. If white radiation, that is, continuous variation of wavelengths, from the x-ray tube is used, the camera is usually referred to as a back-reflection Laue camera. This technique is widely used to determine the crystallographic orientation of single crystals. The back-reflection Laue technique and diffractometer methods can be used to align crystals for cutting. When monochromatic radiation is used for polycrystalline samples, the photograph will consist of concentric

Fig. 2 Schematic of a back-reflection pinhole camera

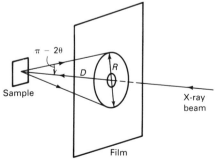

rings, as in the transmission pinhole camera. These Debye rings will be from the back-reflection ($2\theta > 90°$) region.

The major disadvantage with the back-reflection pinhole camera is that the reflections observed do not include the front-reflection lines ($2\theta < 90°$), which differ more in intensity and position between different phases than the back-reflection lines. Thus, the back-reflection results do not provide a useful characterization tool for phase identification. Another disadvantage with the front- and the back-reflection pinhole techniques is that the film-to-sample distance D usually cannot be measured with sufficient precision to provide accurate d-spacings. Transmission and back-reflection films are easily differentiated, because the back-reflection film has a hole in the center where the collimator went through, and the transmission film has a light spot if a beam stop was used or a very dark spot if there was no beam stop.

The monochromatic pinhole camera is used primarily in two areas. The first is the determination of preferred orientation (texture) in a sample. Preferred orientation occurs if certain crystallographic planes have a higher occurrence in certain directions in the sample. For example, cold-drawn aluminum wire has a [111] preferred orientation along its axis and a random orientation about its circumference. This type of preferred orientation is usually referred to as a fiber texture because it also occurs in natural and artificial fibers. Additional information is provided in the article "Crystallographic Texture Measurement and Analysis" in this Volume.

The second major use is in surveying the sample for crystallite size and plastic deformation. If the crystallite (grain) size of the sample exceeds approximately 30 μm, the Debye rings begin to appear grainy. When the crystallite size becomes less than a few thousand angstroms, the Debye rings broaden. Plastic deformation (microstress) will also broaden the rings in fine-grain samples. In single-crystal or coarse-grain samples, the spots will form streaks (asterism) due to the internal microstress in the grains. Additional information is available in the article "X-Ray Diffraction Residual Stress Techniques" in this Volume. The pinhole camera, particularly in the back-reflection mode, is an effective and inexpensive instrument for aligning single crystals and surveying polycrystalline samples for crystallite size and perfection.

Debye-Scherrer/Gandolfi Cameras. The Debye-Scherrer film technique is perhaps the most widely used XRPD technique because as a data-collection method it is inexpensive, flexible, and easy to use. Recent advances in the automated diffractome-

ter are making the powder diffractometer increasingly prevalent. However, the Debye-Scherrer technique will continue to be used extensively.

Figure 3 shows the Debye-Scherrer geometry and a typical film after development. In the Debye-Scherrer technique, the sample exists as a small cylinder of finely divided powder (with a random orientation of the crystallites) that is rotated about its long axis in a monochromatic x-ray beam. In this random assemblage, some of the particles will be oriented to the proper angle to diffract x-rays from their (100) planes; others will have an orientation that can allow diffraction from their (110) planes, etc. There is a continuum of orientations that allows a given set of planes to make the proper angle with the beam, producing a cone of x-rays coming from the sample for each set of planes diffracting. Figure 3 shows three such cones and their intersection with the film that has been placed around the sample. The Debye-Scherrer method has been widely used for such operations as the precision determination of lattice parameters, phase identification, and the determination of crystallinity.

The Gandolfi camera is an adaption of the Debye-Scherrer geometry that is useful for examining materials that may not exist as a random collection of finely divided powders. The principal difference from the Debye-Scherrer camera is in the motion of the sample. In the Debye-Scherrer geometry, the sample is rotated about an axis perpendicular to the x-ray beam. In the Gandolfi camera, the sample is mounted as a small sphere or assemblage of one or more grains on the end of a fiber mount. The mount is positioned such that it remains in the x-ray beam at all times, but it rotates about two axes rather than one. One of these motions rotates the sample about an axis as in the Debye-

Fig. 3 The Debye-Scherrer powder method

(a) Relationship of film to sample and incident beam. (b) Appearance of the film when laid flat. Source: Ref 11

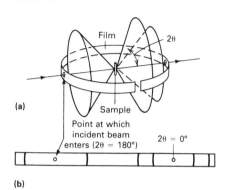

Scherrer geometry, but another axis of rotation exists at an angle with the normal Debye-Scherrer axis. Thus, the sample has two ways in which it is rotating in the x-ray beam, which presents more possible orientations to the beam. This increases the number of ways each grain or crystallite can diffract the x-ray beam. This method is excellent for examining samples that consist of just a few or even one crystal, such as might result from the extraction of grain-boundary precipitates from a metallurgical sample or the physical separation of one or more phases in a geological sample.

The Guinier camera combines a focusing monochromator and a focusing camera (Fig. 4). The curved crystal monochromator is tuned for $K\alpha_1$ radiation. Figure 5 illustrates the different arrangements for the Huber Guinier camera. The main advantage of the Guinier camera over the Debye-Scherrer camera is the much higher

Fig. 4 Schematic of a Guinier camera in the asymmetric transmission arrangement

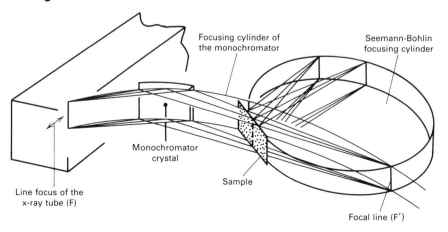

Fig. 5 Different arrangements of the Huber Guinier camera

(a) Symmetric transmission. (b) Asymmetric transmission. (c) Asymmetric back reflection. (d) Symmetric back reflection

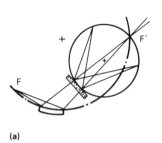

(a)

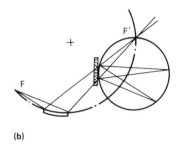

(b)

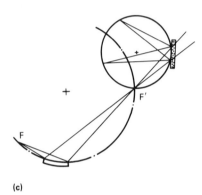

(c)

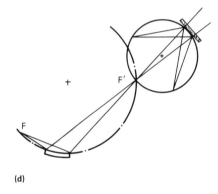

(d)

Fig. 6 Schematic of a Read camera

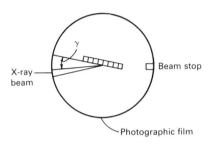

Fig. 7 Schematic of a G.E.C. x-ray texture camera

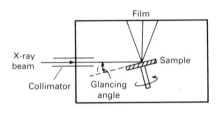

resolution, with full width at half maximum (FWHM) amplitude of 0.05 typically reported, as opposed to FWHM of 0.5 for the Debye-Scherrer camera and 0.15 for the diffractometer. Measurements conducted using a Guinier camera implementing an internal-standard technique exhibit excellent reproducibility and precision. The camera is well suited to studying complex diffraction patterns of mixtures of phases and low-symmetry materials. The Guinier method is often the only technique for obtaining precision lattice parameters from low-symmetry large-cell materials.

The Guinier technique has several disadvantages. First, alignment of the monochromator requires considerable effort, at least initially. This problem can be addressed by computer-assisted alignment. Second, the camera in any one setting cannot cover a large angle region. In the asymmetric transmission mode, the angle region is only approximately 50° in 2θ. Third, the camera requires the use of an internal standard to calculate peak positions. This is especially true in the asymmetric mode of operation. The Debye-Scherrer camera, having a geometry that can usually allow for absolute internal calibration, typically does not require an internal standard.

Microcameras. Back-reflection Laue, monochromatic pinhole, and Debye-Scher-

rer cameras can be equipped with very fine collimators of the order of 100 μm. These collimators are used when only a small amount of material is available, or a pattern is needed from a very small region of a sample. Diffraction patterns can be obtained with as little as 10 μg of sample. Back-reflection Laue cameras equipped with very fine collimators can often be used to obtain the orientation of small (0.5 mm, or 0.02 in.) grains in metallurgical samples. The micro-Laue camera is useful in the study of oxidation rates to determine, for example, why certain grains oxidize faster than others in the same sample or if an observed etching rate is dependent on crystallographic orientation. The microdiffractometer (see below) is a nonfilm device that is also used to obtain powder patterns from very small samples and small areas on samples.

Microcameras have several disadvantages. The first is the alignment of the microcollimator of the camera to the focal spot of the tube. The x-ray beam is no longer visible using a fluorescent screen, except when high-intensity sources are used. Second is the exceptionally long exposure time—one to two days using conventional tubes. Last is the positioning of the sample to the exact region of interest. For these reasons, microcameras are not used extensively.

Glancing Angle Camera. Several cameras using different geometries are referred to as glancing angle cameras. The Read camera (Ref 5-7) is a Debye-Scherrer type camera that uses 12.7- × 7.8-cm (5- × 7-in.) x-ray film, a special sample holder, and small collimators (Fig. 6). The sample holder allows flat samples, such as silicon wafers, to be mounted and the angle γ the sample makes to the entrance collimator to be set at any desired value. This camera is well suited to surveying deposited layers for crystallinity. The photographs obtained using the Read camera provide direct evidence as to whether the thin film layers are amorphous, polycrystalline, or single crystals. If the film is polycrystalline and has preferred orientation, the diffraction lines observed on the photograph will have discontinuous rather than continuous arcs. The extent of these arcs indicates the degree of preferred orientation of the crystalline layer. As the texture becomes stronger, the arcs become sharper until a spot will be observed for a single-crystalline layer instead of an arc.

The disadvantages of the Read camera are long exposure times (16 h or more) and the inaccuracy of the observed d-spacings. The d-spacings are difficult to measure accurately for three reasons. First, the zero angle position is not known. There are no diffraction lines on both sides of the hole to place the zero, unlike the Debye-Scherrer camera. The second reason is that the Read camera is a nonfocusing camera. Third, when the films are very thin and polycrystalline, the diffrac-

Fig. 8 Geometry of the Bragg-Brentano diffractometer

F, line source of x-rays from the anode of the x-ray tube; P, soller slits (collimator); D, divergent slit; A, axis about which sample and detector rotate; S, sample; R, receiving slit; RP, receiving soller slits; SS, scatter slit

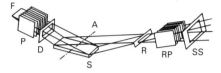

tion lines broaden and thus become more difficult to measure accurately. The primary advantage is the direct evidence obtained on the crystallinity and texture of thin films.

The G.E.C. x-ray texture camera (Fig. 7) is another type of glancing angle camera (Ref 8, 9). The x-ray beam is incident along the axis of the cylinder. In addition, the Debye cones intercept the film such that the pattern appearing on the film is a series of straight lines.

Conventional Diffractometers. Although film techniques have been in use since the inception of x-ray diffraction, the advent of powder diffractometers has been more recent. Powder diffractometers have been in use as a laboratory tool since the late 1950s and early 1960s. Automation of these devices began in the 1970s, but has become commonplace only in the 1980s. Initially, data were collected in analog form, with the results displayed and stored on chart recordings, then reduced manually. Automation of these instruments has enabled collection of digital data that can be displayed on a video screen, printer, or plotting device as raw digital data, smoothed data, or in tabular form. The computer programs included with most automated systems provide methods for such functions as peak finding, peak stripping, and phase identification.

The Bragg-Brentano geometry is used most commonly for powder diffractometers. Figure 8 shows this geometry as used for vertical diffractometers. In the vertical geometry, the axis A is horizontal. The Bragg-Brentano geometry is also widely used for horizontal diffractometers in which the apparatus shown in Fig. 8 is turned on its side such that the axis A is vertical. Both orientations have advantages and disadvantages, and some diffractometers can be used in either orientation.

An advantage of the vertical unit is the way in which a sample of loose powder is held essentially horizontal; in the horizontal diffractometer, such a sample can fall out. The principal advantage of the horizontal diffractometer is that any weight from the sample is directed down on the vertical axis,

Fig. 9 Schematic of a thin film diffractometer

A, line source of x-rays; B, axial divergence of soller slit; C, glancing angle; D, sample; E, equatorial divergence soller slit; F, detector

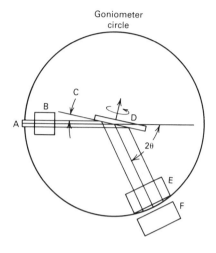

Fig. 10 Geometry of the Seeman-Bohlin arrangement

X, x-ray line source; M, curved monochromator crystal; S, sample; R, radius of focusing circle; D, focus-to-sample distance; P, receiving slits; C, counter

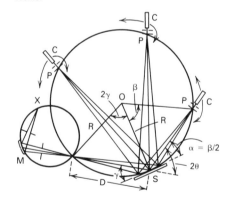

allowing heavy samples to be supported. In both units, the sample rotates at an angle θ, and the detector rotates at 2θ. In another variation of this Bragg-Brentano geometry, termed the θ-θ diffractometer, the sample is held stationary with its surface in a horizontal plane as the x-ray tube and the detector move. Such a system is useful for studying materials at high temperatures, especially for studies near or beyond the melting point of the material. The Bragg-Brentano diffractometer is discussed further in Ref 10 and 11.

Thin Film Diffractometers. The study of thin crystalline films has recently become important. Conventional powder diffraction

techniques lose their sensitivity because the penetration of x-rays into the sample generally exceeds the thickness of the film. In conventional diffractometers, the effective depth of penetration of the x-rays varies as $\sin(\theta)/\mu$. Thus, at low Bragg angle, the penetration depth is small, and at a Bragg angle of 90°, it is a maximum. The linear mass-absorption coefficient, μ, is a function of the wavelength of the x-rays. Generally, the longer the wavelength, the less penetration. Thus, a long wavelength radiation such as Cr Kα is used to increase sensitivity when thin films are studied.

If the surface of the sample is placed at a glancing angle of 5 to 10° to the x-ray beam, penetration of the x-rays into the sample is decreased by an order of magnitude. This can be accomplished in modern conventional diffractometers having independent θ and 2θ stepping drives by setting the angle θ at a glancing angle and stepping 2θ over the desired range (Fig. 9). Because θ remains fixed, the x-rays no longer focus at the receiving slit, and the diffraction peaks broaden as 2θ increases. At high 2θ angles, it is difficult to determine the presence of any peaks. The diffractometer optics can be modified by removing the conventional slits and replacing them with a set of soller collimators. This is usually referred to as parallel optics. The resolution of the instrument is determined by the distance between the soller baffles and the length of the assembly. Coarse soller slits are used for high intensity and low resolution, and fine soller slits for high resolution and lower intensity. This is often a simple modification to an existing instrument.

The Seeman-Bohlin x-ray diffractometer was designed to examine polycrystalline thin films. Figure 10 illustrates the Seeman-Bohlin arrangement with a curved crystal monochromator. The principal advantage of this geometry is its ability to study thin polycrystalline films down to a few hundred angstroms in thickness.

The Guinier diffractometer is an extension of the Guinier camera. The focusing circle is typically made the goniometer circle by using a scanning counter system with a receiving slit on the focusing circle. The counter then records counts as functions of 4θ. This arrangement has the advantage of direct digital data collection, allowing computer processing by essentially the same programs used to process automated diffractometer data. A moving-sample Guinier diffractometer with a position-sensitive detector has been designed (Ref 12). This system is capable of high resolution and high-speed analysis using small amounts of sample.

The microdiffractometer enables examination of very small areas of samples.

Collimators of 100, 30, and even 10 μm have been used with such an instrument. Its basic sample geometry is similar to that of a pinhole camera or a Debye-Scherrer camera (Fig. 3) in that a small beam of x-rays is impinged on what is ideally a random assemblage of very small grains, producing cones of diffracted radiation. The principal differences between the cameras and the microdiffractometers are in the nature of the detector system, which for the microdiffractometer consists of an annular detector that intercepts the entire cone of radiation. The motion of this annular detector toward and away from the sample allows the interception of individual cones of diffracted radiation by the annular detector at different distances from the sample. This interception of the entire cone of radiation and the small x-ray spot size contrast the microdiffractometer with the conventional diffractometer, in which the detector samples only a small section of a diffraction cone.

Figure 11 shows the essential geometry of the system, which operates in a transmission or reflection mode. This device is effective for phase characterization of very small areas and has been used to determine variations in residual stress over very small areas in microdevices. As with any of the microtechniques, care must be taken to ensure that the crystallite size of the material to be examined is small enough that meaningful statistics can be collected from the crystallites in the x-ray beam. Further development of two-dimensional position-sensitive detectors of high resolution will allow such a device to be used to examine all the diffraction cones simultaneously and will facilitate assessment of the sizes of the crystallites contributing to the diffraction cones; even single crystals or an aggregate of several crystals in the beam will be capable of examination.

Automation. Film methods have been automated in a sense by the use of automated film readers, which have been implemented most frequently in the area of Guinier film reading. In addition to film, the initial analog data collection using diffractometers has been replaced to a large extent in newer instruments by computer automation of data collection and the collection of digital rather than analog data. Automation has been extended to data reduction, display, qualitative phase identification, and quantitative analysis of the phases present in a given sample. Many instruments have automated sample changers available so that data collection can continue for a number of samples during off hours. Position-sensitive detectors also have been used extensively in some automated systems. A linear position-sensitive detector can be used on a conventional diffractometer to hasten data collection or to allow better counting statistics to be achieved in less time. The most common implementation of such an instrument uses a computer to scan a linear position-sensitive detector along 2θ. In addition to the one-dimensional position-sensitive detector for the conventional diffractometer, a two-dimensional position-sensitive detector may prove useful for applications discussed in the section "The Microdiffractometer" in this article and for the display of Laue patterns.

Qualitative Analysis

A significant feature of XRPD is the qualitative determination of crystalline phases present in a sample. Only XRPD provides general-purpose qualitative and quantitative information regarding crystalline phases present in an unknown mixture. Although other techniques, such as laser Raman (see the article "Raman Spectroscopy" in this Volume), differential thermal analysis, and x-ray absorption fine structure (see the article "Extended X-Ray Absorption Fine Structure" in this Volume), yield some information on specific phases or nearest-neighbor atoms from phases in a mixture, these methods cannot provide general-purpose, routine identification of phases.

The identification of phases using powder techniques is based on a comparison of the unknown pattern with a file of powder diffraction standards collected and maintained by the JCPDS. The data in this file come from many sources and may vary over considerable limits in the accuracy with which d-spacings and intensities are reported. The accuracy of the experimentally collected data that will be compared with the file must be assessed; limits of error within which a given spacing will be considered a match between standard and unknown must then be determined. Table 1 indicates the optimum resolution expected when data are collected using two different techniques. Data from a well-aligned powder diffractometer using an internal standard should be similar to the Guinier data in Table 1.

Manual and computer methods are the two principal ways the file can be used to identify crystalline phases from their powder patterns. The most widely used manual technique for the identification of phases from x-ray powder diffraction data is the Hanawalt method. A search manual, *The Hanawalt Manual*, lists standard phases from the JCPDS file, along with their eight most intense d-spacings and intensities. The search manual has been arranged into groups and subgroups based on pairs of lines from the standard patterns that are present as multiple entries based on different pairs of lines. For a single-phase unknown, the d value of the strongest line on the pattern is used to determine which group is to be consulted in the manual. The d value of the second strongest line in the unknown determines which subgroup to investigate to determine one or more patterns that match the other intense lines on the unknown pattern. If the other six lines of one of these standard patterns match lines of similar relative inten-

Fig. 11 Geometry of the microdiffractometer

(a) Reflection arrangement. (b) Transmission arrangement

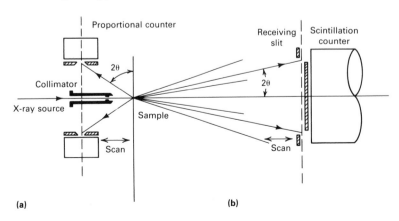

(a)　　　　　　　　　　　　　　(b)

Table 1　Possible deviation in d values

Interplanar spacing (d)	114-mm (4.5-in.) diam Debye camera (± Δd)	114-mm (4.5-in.) diam Guinier camera (± Δd)
1	0.002	0.001
2	0.004	0.002
3	0.010	0.003
4	0.018	0.005
5	0.025	0.007

sity in the unknown pattern, the standard selected is most likely a match for the unknown. To be more certain, the JCPDS data for the full pattern are then compared with the unknown pattern; any lines from the unknown that do not match lines of the standard may indicate the presence of a second phase and that the unknown pattern did not come from a single phase.

Problems can occur if the standard for the unknown pattern is not present in the file. In this case, a pattern similar to the unknown may possibly be found that has the same crystal structure as the unknown compound and thus can aid in the final identification of the unknown phase. This identification can be made more certain if the standard pattern found can be shown to have some chemical or crystal-chemical relationship with the composition of the unknown phase. A search of the file need not use any chemical information, although it is useful in making a final selection, especially if the data in the file or the data collected for the unknown could not be obtained with the highest possible accuracy.

A mixture of several patterns can complicate identification, because it is unclear whether the strongest lines in an unknown pattern represent the same unknown phase. The probability is high that the strongest lines from a multiphase unknown do not come from the same phase. Therefore, a search of the Hanawalt file for such an unknown must consider several permutations and combinations of the strongest unknown lines. As the nature of the unknown becomes increasingly complex, for example, when five or six phases are present in a mixture, use of manual methods to effect an identification can become tedious and subject to error. Therefore, one procedure recommends the use of a standard data form to assist in ensuring that all proper steps in the search have been taken and to allow all the bookkeeping associated with such a complicated search to be performed on paper.

The other common means of phase identification involves use of computer-based search/match programs. Such programs first appeared in the mid-1960s on mainframe computers and later on minicomputers. The major powder diffractometer manufacturers provide software packages with their automated powder diffraction systems. More recently, programs for personal computers also have become available.

In general, the computer approach to the search/match problem differs from manual methods. The manual search needs to compare lines from the unknown pattern in various permutations and combinations with the standard file; the most common computer technique involves the opposite, that is,

comparing the standards with the unknown. The computer asks whether a given standard could be a subset of the unknown, that is, could the standard being compared with the unknown be one phase comprising that unknown. If so, that standard pattern is ranked according to how well it matches the unknown, and another standard is compared with the unknown until all standards have been compared. Use of chemical information to aid in this type of search sacrifices the ability to locate structurally related compounds having chemistry different from the unknown. A collection of the best matches with the unknown is usually saved and displayed at the end of a search. The program or the investigator then selects one or more of the phases, examines them in greater detail, subtracts one or more standard patterns from the unknown, and then runs the residue through the searching process again.

Although computer search/match programs have been successful, they have not replaced a competent analyst who must still make the critical decisions. Nevertheless, such computer programs have proven valuable and expeditious. It is anticipated that laboratories soon will have the complete JCPDS file available on computer media with the ability to search and to interrogate a data base for powder data and auxiliary data, such as chemistry, color, hardness, unit cell edges, and density, that may help make an identification even more certain.

Quantitative Analysis

X-ray diffraction quantitative analysis of phase mixtures has been in use since 1925, when it was implemented to determine the amount of mullite in a fired ceramic (Ref 15). The technique has only recently become prevalent as an analytical tool for two reasons. The first is the need for quantitative phase analysis for such applications as government regulations on respiratory quartz, industrial quality control, and material research. X-ray diffraction is useful for bulk analysis on chemically similar phases. Diffraction is one of the few techniques that can identify and quantify crystalline polymorphs. For example, diffraction can quantify the amounts of rutile and anatase in a paint pigment mixture. These two minerals are TiO_2 polymorphs; that is, they have the same chemistry, but different crystal structures. For other analyses in which the information desired is elemental or the phases are elementally distinct, x-ray spectrometry (see the article ''X-Ray Spectrometry'' in this Volume) can provide the necessary quantification more easily and often more accurately (Ref 14).

The second reason for the increasing interest in quantitative XRPD is the availability of automated powder diffractometers. These instruments eliminate much of the tedium involved in collecting and reducing data for quantitative phase analysis. With the addition of automatic sample changers, the analysis can proceed unattended once the samples have been loaded. A third reason is the increased reliability and ease of use due to the work of Chung (Ref 15, 16).

Except for the lattice-parameter method, x-ray diffraction quantitative phase analysis is based on the premise that each crystalline material in the sample has a unique diffraction pattern and that the intensity of the peaks in that pattern varies directly with its concentration. Many factors prevent the direct comparison of concentration with peak intensity. The basic factor is the different x-ray absorption properties of the substances in the sample (Ref 17).

The lattice-parameter method of quantitative analysis is applicable to those compounds and metals that form solid continuous solid solutions often from one pure end member to the other (Ref 18). This technique is an accurate method of determining the chemical compositions of many types of materials by measuring accurate lattice parameters, particularly if the lattice constant varies linearly between the end members. It is especially useful when x-ray spectrometry cannot be easily used, for example, determining the amount of oxygen in AlN, or when the composition of a mullite is needed in the presence of quartz or corundum (Ref 14). Unlike typical quantitative diffraction techniques, the lattice-parameter method is used to determine the composition of a single phase, not the amounts of the different phases present. Use of the technique is limited, because lattice-parameter data versus composition is not readily available and in some cases is of dubious quality. Accuracy depends on the slope of the calibration curve and the precision of the lattice-parameter measurement.

The absorption diffraction method requires the measurement of the intensity from a diffraction peak in the mixture and from a pure standard of the material:

$$\frac{I}{I_{pure}} = \frac{(\mu/\rho)}{(\mu/\rho)_m} X \qquad (Eq\ 3)$$

where I_{pure} is the intensity of a peak from the pure phase, I is the intensity of the same peak of the phase in a mixture, X is the weight fraction of the phase in the mixture, (μ/ρ) is the mass-absorption coefficient of the phase, and $(\mu/\rho)_m$ is the mass-absorption coefficient of the entire sample. In general, the mass-absorption coefficient of the sample and the phase under analysis must be known. If the absorption coefficient of the sample is almost the same as each of its components, the ratio of intensity to the pure standards depends on the concentration of the phase in the sample. The accuracy of this technique depends strongly on consistent sample preparation procedures and operating conditions and on appropriate pure standards, which can be difficult to obtain.

The spiking method, sometimes referred to as the method of standard additions or the doping method (Ref 19), is applicable only to powder samples. It consists of measuring the diffraction-peak intensity from the phase of interest, then adding a small amount of this phase to the sample and remeasuring the intensities. The concentration C_0 of the phase of interest is then given by:

$$C_0 = \frac{I_1 C_1}{I_2 - I_1} \qquad \text{(Eq 4)}$$

where I_1 is the intensity of a diffraction line from the sample, I_2 is the intensity of the same line after the sample has been spiked, and C_1 is the amount of phase added to spike the sample. This procedure is useful when only one phase is to be quantified. It assumes a linear change in intensity with concentration; that is, the absorption coefficient is the same as that of the spiked material as that of the sample. If only small amounts are spiked, this assumption is generally valid. The accuracy of this technique depends on the difference in intensity between the spiked and unspiked sample, mixing procedure, and sample preparation techniques. Pure phases of the material of interest are required.

The internal standard method is one of the most accurate and widely used procedures for quantifying phase mixtures in powder samples. The technique involves adding a fixed amount of a known standard to a sample, then measuring the intensities of the phases of interest relative to the internal standard intensities:

$$\frac{I}{I_s} = KX \qquad \text{(Eq 5)}$$

where I is the intensity of the phase to be analyzed in the sample, I_s is the intensity of the internal standard, and K is the slope of the calibration curve of the pure phase material. If the diffraction peaks of the sample phases and the internal standard peak are close in 2θ, the sample preparation problems are less severe. The problem of obtaining a homogeneous mixture of the internal standard and the material to be analyzed remains (Ref 18).

The external standard method (Ref 15, 16, 20, 21) is similar to the internal standard method. In this case, the intensity ratio is measured against phases already contained in the sample:

$$\frac{X_a}{X_b} = K \frac{I_a}{I_b} \qquad \text{(Eq 6)}$$

where X_a is the weight fraction of phase a, X_b is the weight fraction of phase b, I_a is the intensity from a peak of phase a, I_b is the intensity from a peak of phase b, and K is a constant ($K = (I_b/I_a)$ for a 1:1 mixture). Calibration curves of single mixtures are used to obtain the K constant. If the appropriate ratios are measured on all the phases in the material, a complete quantification can be conducted. In general, this method is as accurate as the internal standard method and depends on measured intensities and the accuracy of K. Pure standards are needed to determine K.

The $I/I_{corundum}$ method (Ref 22-24) provides the ability to perform rapid semiquantitative phase analysis without pure standards. The weight fraction X_a of phase a is calculated using:

$$X_a = \frac{0.5(I_a/I_c)_{unk}}{(I_a/I_c)_{JCPDS}} \qquad \text{(Eq 7)}$$

where X_a is the weight fraction of phase a in the sample, $(I_a/I_c)_{unk}$ is the intensity of the 100 peak of phase a divided by the intensity of the 100 peak of corundum in a 1:1 mixture of sample and corundum, and $(I_a/I_c)_{JCPDS}$ is the reference intensity ratio. The (I/I_c) values for some phases can be found in the JCPDS data base, or they must be determined experimentally. This data base is currently incomplete and, because peak heights were used, subject to error, particularly if there is any broadening of the diffraction peaks. Because only single lines are used, internal checks cannot be conducted.

The direct comparison method is used mainly for retained austenite quantification (Ref 25). It can have more general utility for several materials, particularly those for which pure phase standards are difficult to obtain. Direct comparison is based on the ratio of intensities of phases in the sample:

$$\frac{I_a}{I_b} = \frac{X_a R_a}{X_b R_b} \qquad \text{(Eq 8)}$$

where I_a and I_b are the intensities of peaks from phases a and b, and X_a and X_b are weight fractions of phases a and b in the sample; R_a and R_b are constants of phase a and phase b calculated using crystal structure information and the fundamental intensity

equation. A computer program well suited to performing these calculations is described in Ref 26. The accuracy of this technique depends on calculation of R values and on the accuracy of the crystal structure information.

The standardless method has the potential of being able to quantify phase mixtures for which no standards exist and when the complete crystal structure is not known (Ref 27, 28). This technique requires extensive sample handling to produce different mountings of the sample in which the weight fractions of the phases in the original mixture are significantly modified. Accuracy depends on the efficiency of these phase separation techniques.

Computers for Quantitative Analysis. Computer programs have been developed for XRPD quantitative analysis (Ref 29). Coupled with a data-collection system (Ref 30, 31), these programs allow quantification of the phases in a sample using optional data-collection procedures. Three methods of quantitative analysis are implemented in the program: the spiking method, the absorption diffraction method, and the internal standard method and its variations, such as external standard, $I/I_{corundum}$, and direct comparison methods.

Sources of Error in XRPD

Crystal-particle statistics can be a major source of error. Favorable statistics require of the order of 6×10^8 crystallites (Ref 23). Therefore, a particle size of approximately 5 μm is necessary for a diffractometer sample. Rotating the sample in the diffractometer will bring more crystallites into the beam and provide improved intensities. One method of showing whether particle statistics are a problem is to conduct intensity measurements at different rotational placements of the sample. The intensity should remain constant as the sample is rotated. A second method is to rotate θ about its nominal value; there should be no sharp intensity changes when rotating over a range of a degree or two. A third method entails locating changes in relative intensity with different sample mountings.

Preferred orientation within the sample can invalidate the quantitative phase analysis. If only one peak from each phase is being used for the analysis, preferred orientation of the peak being measured can cause widely different answers. Preferred orientation is caused in a powder sample by the morphology of the particles constituting the sample. For example, if the particles have a platelike habit, the plates will tend to lie flat when a sample holder is packed from the top

Fig. 12 JCPDS card giving x-ray powder diffraction and other associated data for the mineral quartz

Source: Ref 1

d	3.34	4.26	1.82	4.26	SiO₂	★
I/I₁	100	22	14	22	Silicon Oxide	Quartz, low

Rad. CuKα₁ λ 1.540598 Filter Mono. Dia.
Cut off   I/I₁ Diffractometer I/I cor.
Ref. Nat. Bur. Stand. (U.S.) Monogr. 25, Sec. 18 (1981)

Sys. Hexagonal   S.G. P3₁21 (152)
a₀ 4.9133(2) b₀   c₀5.4053(4) A   C 1.1001
a   β   γ   Z 3   Dx 2.649
Ref. Ibid.

εa   nωβ 1.544   εγ   1.553   Sign +
2V   D 2.656   mp   Color Colorless
Ref. Ibid.

Sample from the Glass Section at the National Bureau
of Standards; ground single crystals of optical quality,
locality unknown. Pattern at 25°C.
Silicon (a₀=5.43088Å) used as internal standard.
F₃₀ = 76.6(0.0126,31). Quartz group.
To replace 5-490.

d A	I/I₁	hkl	d A	I/I₁	hkl
4.257	22	100	1.2285	1	220
3.342	100	101	1.1999	2	213
2.457	8	110	1.1978	1	221
2.282	8	102	1.1843	3	114
2.237	4	111	1.1804	3	310
2.127	6	200	1.1532	1	311
1.9792	4	201	1.1405	<1	204
1.8179	14	112	1.1143	<1	303
1.8021	<1	003	1.0813	2	312
1.6719	4	202	1.0635	<1	400
1.6591	2	103	1.0476	1	105
1.6082	<1	210	1.0438	<1	401
1.5418	9	211	1.0347	<1	214
1.4536	1	113	1.0150	1	223
1.4189	<1	300	0.9898	1	402
1.3820	6	212	.9873	1	313
1.3752	7	203	.9783	<1	304
1.3718	8	301	.9762	1	320
1.2880	2	104	.9636	<1	205
1.2558	2	302	6 reflections to 0.9089		

Table 2 Diffraction data from unknown phase(s) on silicon substrate

Interplanar spacing, d, Å	Relative intensity, I/I₀
4.25	3
3.34	10
2.45	1
2.28	1
2.23	1
2.12	1
1.98	1
1.81	3
1.67	1
1.54	2
1.38	1
1.37	3
1.29	1

or from the bottom. This tendency toward preferred orientation is a function of the amount, size, and shape of the other phases in the mixture and the packing pressure. If the degree of orientation can be controlled, calibration curves will yield favorable results. This approach is used to analyze clay minerals (Ref 32). Spray drying is a sample preparation technique that can eliminate preferred orientation problems (Ref 33-35). A suitable source of information on sample preparation techniques is provided in Ref 36.

Peak Broadening. Diffraction peaks can be broadened by samples having phases with very small crystallite sizes, microstresses, disorder, stacking faults, dislocations, and inhomogeneous solid solutions. If integrated intensity is measured, the errors caused by these effects are minimized.

Matrix absorption causes nonlinear change in intensity versus concentration when the matrix consists of phases having different absorption coefficients. Except when analyzing polymorphs, the calibration curves will generally not be linear.

Compositional Differences Between Standards and Samples. Cation substitutions and solid solution occur in many types of materials. The compositional changes alter the intensity and position of the peak. Laboratory standards are often not representative of similar phases found in naturally occurring or manufactured materials.

Primary Extinction. The intensity from perfect crystals is less than that for imperfect crystals. This effect is known as primary extinction. Quartz is notorious for demonstrating primary extinction. This effect is

usually related to particle size and increases with size.

Microabsorption and Particle Absorption. If the absorption coefficients of the phases in a sample are large, the highly absorbing phase will tend to mask the low-absorbing phase. The problem is alleviated by reducing the particle size.

Sample Preparation. Different sample preparation techniques can result in intensity changes due to such factors as the packing density of powder into the holder, the size and shape of the holder, and the thickness of the sample.

Instrumentation. The stability of the generator, x-ray tube, and counting electronics is important in obtaining suitable intensity data. Any changes in the slits, voltage, amperage, and counting electronics settings will cause variations in the intensity.

Intensity Measurement Procedures. Integrated intensity measurements, where possible, are preferred to peak height measurements. Poor crystallinity caused by defect structures, small crystallite size, or microstress alters the peak height, but not the integrated intensity. The background must be removed when the intensity is determined. Incorrect determination of the background can cause significant error, particularly if the background changes between the standards and the samples. Overlapping of peaks from one or more phases can cause large errors. This is true when deconvolution procedures are used, unless they are well controlled. The optimum procedure involves use of isolated peaks.

Other Possible Errors. Changes in barometric pressure and humidity can alter

the absorption characteristics of the air and thus the intensity of the peaks in a sample. Some samples can hydrate, oxidize, or carbonate when exposed to air. High humidity can also cause samples to pop out of their holders, raising the sample surface above its proper position. Grinding the samples to reduce the particle size will in some cases induce a phase transformation by causing the phases present to react with each other. In some materials, especially certain organics, the x-rays will damage the structure.

Applications

Example 1: Qualitative Analysis of a Surface Phase on Silicon. A small, oddly shaped sample was examined using x-ray analysis to determine the nature of a thin, powdery coating on its surface. The bulk sample was known to be elemental silicon. A very small amount (<0.01 mg) of the deposit was obtained by carefully abrading part of the sample surface and collecting the resulting material on a glass slide. The powder on the slide was incorporated into a mount suitable for a Debye-Scherrer camera by depositing it onto the end of a dampened gelatin fiber that had been cut from the side of a medicinal capsule as a narrow wedge shape ending in a sharp point.

The sample was mounted and exposed in the camera, the film developed, and the data (Table 2) obtained using a plastic overlay for quick reading of the d-spacings directly from the film. The intensities were estimated visually during determination of the d-spacings. Much greater accuracy in the determination of the d-spacings can be achieved by using a film reader followed by computation of d values or by using a technique such as the Guinier camera, which has higher inherent accuracy.

The JCPDS Data File (Ref 1) for the identification of unknown phases was then accessed. Use of the file involves computer-based search/match techniques or manual methods in which the most intense *d*-spacings of the unknown pattern are used to indicate one or more phases that are then examined in greater detail to identify the unknown.

Although manual techniques using the JCPDS Data File have been used since the 1940s, the method used for this unknown consisted of entering the *d*-spacings and intensities into a microcomputer for examination using a program that searches the appropriate JCPDS subfile (Ref 37). (An example of the cards used in a manual search is shown in Fig. 12.) A computer search was made, and the phase α-SiO_2 (quartz) was found to be the only possible phase that matched the submitted pattern. No other phases were found. The entire search process required only 2 s—considerably shorter than the approximately 2 min necessary to enter the experimental data into the computer.

Example 2: Alignment of a Silicon Boule for Cutting Along Crystallographic Planes.
Slices were desired from a silicon boule such that the (111) crystallographic plane is the flat of the slice and the axis of the boule is the [111] direction. The boule was mounted on a single-crystal cutting goniometer with the axis of the boule as the direction of the x-ray beam in the back-reflection Laue camera. The goniometer rotations were adjusted to center the zones (rows of spots) exactly in the photograph, indicating proper alignment. Once the sample was aligned, the cutting goniometer was mounted on a saw and the slices taken.

A common problem encountered with many types of materials, particularly when metallic crystals are sectioned, is that the crystal surfaces are cold worked. These surfaces give very poor Laue photographs that often defy interpretation. When cold work of the surface of the crystal is apparent, the sample must be prepared carefully by a combination of polishing and etching.

Example 3: Quantitative Analysis of ZnO in Calcite.
Many calcite ($CaCo_3$) and ZnO samples were analyzed over an extended period of time using a diffractometer equipped with a copper x-ray tube. The absorption diffraction method was selected because it yields a calibration curve against which the samples can be easily compared. First, the molecular weights of calcite and ZnO were calculated. The atomic weights for the elements are found in Appendix IV of Ref 18. Second, the mass-absorption coefficients of calcite and ZnO were calculated from the elemental mass absorption for copper radiation found in Appendix V of Ref 18. Table 3 shows calculated values of the concentration of ZnO in calcite versus the inten-

Table 3 Calculated absorption coefficients and relative intensities of ZnO in calcite

Zn, wt%	Absorption coefficient	Relative intensity of zinc, I/I_{pure}
0	75.6	0.00
10	73.0	0.07
20	70.4	0.14
30	67.8	0.22
40	65.2	0.30
50	62.6	0.40
60	60.1	0.50
70	57.5	0.61
80	54.9	0.72
90	52.3	0.86
100	49.7	1.00

sity of the strongest line of ZnO in the sample divided by the intensity of the line obtained from pure ZnO.

A graph can be produced from the data in Table 3 for use in determining the concentration of ZnO in an unknown sample. The graph does not have a linear relationship because of the difference in the absorption of copper radiation between calcite and ZnO. This technique is effective only when there is no preferred orientation and very reproducible sample preparation techniques are used.

REFERENCES

1. Joint Committee on Powder Diffraction Standards (JCPDS), International Centre for Diffraction Data, Swarthmore, PA
2. W. Friedrich, P. Knipping, and M.V. Laue, *Ann. Phys.*, Vol 411, 1912, p 971
3. W. Friedrich, *Phys. Z.*, Vol 14, 1913, p 317
4. H.B. Keene, *Nature*, Vol 91, 1913, p 607
5. M.H. Read, *Thin Solid Films*, Vol 10, 1972, p 123-135
6. R.W. Bower, R.E. Scott, and D. Sigurd, *Solid State Elec.*, Vol 16, 1973, p 1461
7. S.S. Lau, W.K. Chu, K.N. Tu, and J.W. Mayer, *Thin Solid Films*, Vol 23, 1974, p 205-213
8. C.A. Wallace and R.C.C. Ward, *J. Appl. Crystallog.*, Vol 8, 1975, p 255-260
9. C.A. Wallace and R.C.C. Ward, *J. Appl. Crystallog.*, Vol 8, 1975, p 545-556
10. J.L. Amoros, M.J. Buerger, and M. Canut de Amoros, *The Laue Method*, Academic Press, 1975
11. B.D. Cullity, *X-Ray Diffraction*, 2nd ed., Addison Wesley, 1978, p 175-177
12. H.E. Goebel, *Adv. X-Ray Anal.*, Vol 25, 1982, p 315-324
13. A.L. Navias, *Am. Ceram. Soc.*, Vol 8, 1925, p 296
14. M.F. Garbauskas and R.P. Goehner, *Adv. X-Ray Anal.*, Vol 25, 1982, p 283
15. F.H. Chung, *J. Appl. Crystallog.*, Vol 7, 1974, p 519
16. F.H. Chung, *J. Appl. Crystallog.*, Vol 8, 1975, p 17
17. L. Zwell and A.W. Danko, *Appl. Spectrosc. Rev.*, Vol 9, 1975, p 178
18. H.P. Klug and L.E. Alexander, *X-Ray Diffraction Procedures for Polycrystalline and Amorphous Materials*, John Wiley & Sons, 1974, p 562
19. S. Popovic and B. Grzeta-Plenkovic, *J. Appl. Crystallog.*, Vol 12, 1979, p 205
20. L.E. Copeland and R.H. Bragg, *Anal. Chem.*, Vol 30 (No. 2), 1958, p 196
21. R.P. Goehner, *Adv. X-Ray Anal.*, Vol 25, 1982, p 309
22. Alphabetic Index, JCPDS, Swarthmore, PA
23. C.R. Hubbard and D.K. Smith, *Adv. X-Ray Anal.*, Vol 20, 1977, p 27
24. F.H. Chung, *Adv. X-Ray Anal.*, Vol 17, 1974, p 106
25. C.F. Jatczak, J.A. Larson, and S.W. Shin, *Retained Austenite and its Measurements by X-Ray Diffraction*, SP-453, Society of Automotive Engineers, Warrendale, PA, 1980
26. D.K. Smith and M.C. Nichols, report SAND81-8226, Sandia National Laboratories, Livermore, CA, 1981
27. L.S. Zevin, *J. Appl. Crystallog.*, Vol 10, 1977, p 147
28. J. Fiala, *Anal. Chem.*, Vol 52, 1980, p 1300
29. C.R. Hubbard, C.R. Robbins, and R.L. Snyder, *Adv. X-Ray Anal.*, Vol 26, 1983, p 149
30. R.L. Snyder, C.R. Hubbard, and N.C. Panagiotopulos, *Adv. X-Ray Anal.*, Vol 25, 1982, p 245
31. R.L. Snyder, C.R. Hubbard, and N.C. Panagiotopoulos, NBS 81-2229, National Bureau of Standards, Washington, 1981
32. H.F. Shaw, *Clay Min.*, Vol 9, 1972, p 349
33. S.T. Smith, R.L. Snyder, and W.E. Browell, *Adv. X-Ray Anal.*, Vol 22, 1979, p 77
34. S.T. Smith, R.L. Snyder, and W.E. Browell, *Adv. X-Ray Anal.*, Vol 22, 1979, p 181
35. L.D. Calvert, A.F. Sirianni, and G.J. Gainsford, *Adv. X-Ray Anal.*, Vol 26, 1983, p 105
36. D.K. Smith and C.S. Barrett, *Adv. X-Ray Anal.*, Vol 22, 1979, p 1
37. Q. Johnson, MICRO-ID Program for SEARCH/MATCH, Materials Data Inc., Livermore, CA

SELECTED REFERENCES

- L.E. Alexander, *X-Ray Diffraction Methods in Polymer Science*, Wiley-Interscience, 1980
- L.V. Azaroff and M.J. Buerser, *The Powder Method in X-Ray Crystallography*, McGraw-Hill, 1958
- C.S. Barrett and T.B. Massalski, *Structure of Metals*, Pergamon Press, 1980
- B.A. Bellamy, *The APEX Goniometer as a Glancing Angle X-Ray Powder Diffractometer for the Study of Thin Layers*, AERE-R 10687, United Kingdom Atomic Energy Authority, Harwell, 1982
- S. Block and C.R. Hubbard, Ed., *Accuracy in Powder Diffraction*, NBS 567, National Bureau of Standards, Washington, 1980

- G.W. Brindly and G. Brown, *Crystal Structures of Clay Minerals and their X-Ray Identification*, Mineralogical Society of America, Washington, 1980
- A. Brown, J.W. Edmonds, and C.M. Foris, *Adv. X-Ray Anal.*, Vol 24, 1981, p 111-120
- B.D. Cullity, *Elements of X-Ray Diffraction*, Addison Wesley, 1978
- R. Feder and B.S. Berry, *J. Appl. Crystallog.*, Vol 3, 1970, p 372-379
- J.J. Fitzpatrick and J.S. Pressnall, *Adv. X-Ray Anal.*, Vol 27, 1984, p 317-330
- R.P. Goehner, *Adv. X-Ray Anal.*, Vol 19, 1976, p 725
- A. Guinier, *X-Ray Diffraction in Crystals, Imperfect Crystals, and Amorphous Bodies*, W.H. Freeman and Company, 1963

- P.B. Hirsch, in *X-Ray Diffraction by Polycrystalline Materials*, H.S. Peiser, H.P. Rooksby, and A.J. Wilson, Ed., Institute of Physics, London, 1955, p 278-297
- R.W. James, *The Optical Principles of the Diffraction of X-Rays*, Ox Bow Press, 1982
- H.P. Klug, and L.E. Alexander, *X-Ray Diffraction Procedures for Polycrystalline and Amorphous Materials*, John Wiley & Sons, 1974
- E. Preuss, B. Krahl-Urban, and R. Butz, *Laue Atlas*, John Wiley & Sons, 1974
- D.K. Smith and C.S. Barrett, *Adv. X-Ray Anal.*, Vol 22, 1979, p 1
- A. Taylor, *X-Ray Metallography*, John Wiley & Sons, 1961

Single-Crystal X-Ray Diffraction

Richard L. Harlow, E.I. DuPont de Nemours

General Uses

- Unit cell identification
- Formula weight determination from crystal class, space group, and density information
- Location of atoms within the unit cell, that is, the determination of the crystal structure: (1) atom coordination numbers and geometries, (2) interatomic bond distances and angles, (3) interactions between molecules and/or ions, and (4) absolute configurations

Examples of Applications

- Identification of previously studied crystalline phases by comparison of unit cell information
- Characterization of new crystalline compounds or phases
- Understanding physical properties of crystalline phases in terms of interatomic interactions

Samples

- *Form*: Single crystal, preferably with well-formed faces and, if transparent, without visible flaws when viewed under a microscope
- *Size*: Approximately the size of a salt grain, that is, 0.1 to 0.4 mm on a side
- *Preparation*: Generally, suitable crystals can be grown using various slow crystallization techniques. Air-stable crystals are usually mounted on glass fibers; air-sensitive crystals are sealed inside glass or quartz capillaries

Limitations

- Sample must be a single crystal. Crystals that appear to be single may consist of several domains with different orientations. In addition, the crystal selected for investigation may not be representative of the bulk sample

- For unit cell identification, literature or data base must be available
- Success in the determination of the atomic structure of a crystal can be impeded by subtle twinning effects, ambiguities in the assignment of the crystal class and/or the space group, the presence of a superlattice, disorder in the atoms at a particular site, partial occupancy of sites, and a host of other problems that may be related to data collection and reduction. Although a structure may appear well determined, the presumed precision is often much less than that suggested, for example, by the estimated standard deviations of the atomic coordinates

Estimated Analysis Time

- May vary from a few hours for a simple determination of the unit cell geometry to a few days for an average crystal structure determination. Problem structures can quickly turn into research projects

Capabilities of Related Techniques

- *Neutron single-crystal diffraction* can be used to determine the atomic structures of crystals. Advantages include higher accuracy for the positions of atoms with low atomic number and information about magnetic structure. Disadvantages include the requirement for larger single crystal (0.5 to 1.0 mm), limited number of neutron facilities, and longer data-collection times
- *Rietveld refinement of x-ray or neutron powder diffraction data* can also be used to determine crystal structures. Advantages include use of a crystalline powder rather than a single crystal. Disadvantages include limited number of atoms to be located and refined and less favorable precision

Introduction

Single-crystal x-ray diffraction has as its primary goal the determination of crystal structure, the arrangement of atoms within the unit cell. If the atoms are grouped into molecules, the molecular structure is an added benefit. Once the atoms are located, interatomic bond distances and angles can be calculated, coordination numbers and geometries determined, and unusual interatomic or intermolecular contacts observed. Crystal structures may be determined simply to identify new crystalline phases, or, in a broader context, they may lead to an understanding of the physical and chemical properties of the crystalline substances.

For example, consider the differences between diamond and graphite, two of the better known forms of elemental carbon. Diamond is extremely hard and transparent to light; graphite is soft and black. Only graphite conducts electricity. Diamond is, in a relative sense, chemically inert, but graphite absorbs many substances, including acids, salts, gases, and organic molecules. Because the atoms constituting these materials are the same, their differences must be related to the way in which the atoms pack or bond together. The crystal structures of the two substances are shown in Fig. 1.

In diamond, all the carbon atoms are equally bonded to four neighboring atoms, which ultimately produce a three-dimensional infinite network; the infinite nature of bonding accounts for the hardness of diamond. In contrast, graphite is characterized by planar hexagonal networks in which each carbon atom forms strong bonds to only three of its neighbors. These layers are held together by relatively weak C–C bonds. Slippage of one layer past another accounts for the soft texture of graphite and its use as a lubricant. Absorption of other substances into graphite crystals occurs because these materials can slide between the layers, a process termed intercalation. The variations in the optical and electrical properties of these two substances result from the differences in their bonding.

Principles

A diffraction pattern is used to determine the location of atoms within a unit cell and thus the crystal structure. This process is elucidated in a discussion of a one-dimensional optical-diffraction analog (Ref 2).

If a beam of monochromatic light is allowed to shine on a diffraction grating whose ruled lines are evenly spaced at some fixed distance t, a diffraction pattern will be produced where the spot separation is proportional to $1/t$ (Fig. 2a). The slits in the grating serve as scattering centers. Constructive interference of the scattered light waves produces the spots, the intensity of which decreases uniformly from the center spot.

A second grating is constructed by ruling another set of lines translated from the first set by some fixed distance, r (Fig. 2b). The repeat distance of the new grating is still t, and the diffraction pattern of this grating still has spot separations proportional to $1/t$. However, the intensities of the spots have been altered significantly. Moving the second set of lines on this new grating from $r = 0$ to $r = t$ would demonstrate the sensitivity of intensities to the position of the second set of lines relative to the first.

If a third set of lines were added to the grating, an entirely different pattern of intensities would emerge. If one set of lines were made slightly larger than the other sets, the intensities would change still further. It should now be clear that the positions of the diffraction spots depend only on the repeat distance of the grating; the intensities of the spots are sensitive to the number of ruled lines (scattering centers) within the repeating unit, their scattering ability, and their relative positions.

Demonstrating the analogy between optical diffraction and single-crystal x-ray diffraction requires several conversions. The scattering centers are no longer slits, but the electron clouds that surround every atom; the number of electrons that an atom has can be correlated with the size of the slit. The one repeat distance, t, in the optical grating is replaced with three repeat distances (a, b, c) and the angles between them (α, β, γ), that is, the unit cell. Thus, the single-crystal grating consists of a pattern of electron densities that repeats in three dimensions. X-radiation replaces visible light only because the repeat distances in a crystal are small (5 to 50 Å) and the wavelength, λ, required for diffraction to occur must also be small (λ for Cu Kα radiation is near 1.54 Å). Consequently, if a beam of monochromatic x-rays is allowed to strike a single crystal, a diffraction pattern will be produced in which the positions of the spots will be determined by the size and shape of the unit cell, while

Fig. 1 Crystal structures of two forms of carbon

(a) The structure of diamond results when each carbon atom bonds to four of its neighbors in a tetrahedral arrangement within a cubic unit cell. The C–C bond length is approximately 1.54 Å. (b) The crystal structure of graphite is described by a hexagonal unit cell. The bonds within the sheets are 1.42 Å, stronger than those of diamond; the bonds between the sheets are weak, with a length near 3.35 Å. Source: Ref 1

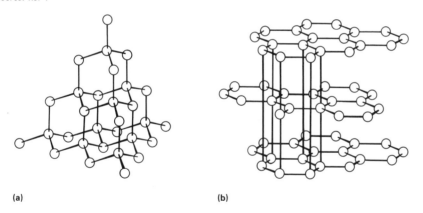

(a) (b)

Fig. 2 Diffraction of light by line gratings

(a) Grating of evenly spaced lines with diffraction pattern. (b) Grating consisting of pairs of lines (repeat distance same as in the first) with diffraction pattern. Source: Ref 2

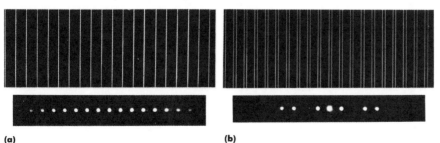

(a) (b)

Fig. 3 Examples of crystal symmetry in the tetragonal system

(a) Unit cell type. (b) Phloroglucinol diethyl ether, class 4/m. (c) Wulfenite (PbMoO₄), class 4. (d) Anatase (TiO₂), class 4/mmm. (e) Zircon (ZrSiO₄), class 4/mmm. The three digit codes are the Miller indices, *hkl*, of the crystal faces. Source: Ref 2

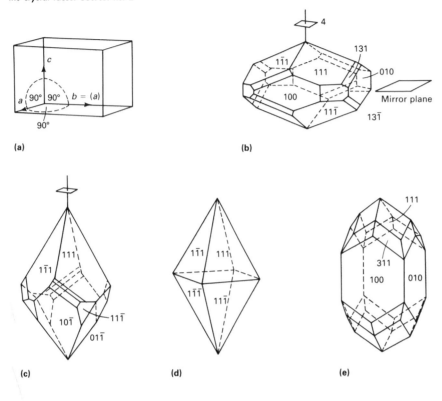

Fig. 4 Precession photographs showing three layers of a diffraction pattern

The layers contain the *hk*0, *hk*1, and *hk*2 reflections. The sixfold rotation axis through the center of each layer is visible. Not visible is a mirror plane coincident with the *hk*0 layer, which makes the *h,k,* −1 layer equivalent to the *hk*1 layer. The point group of this diffraction pattern is 6/m.

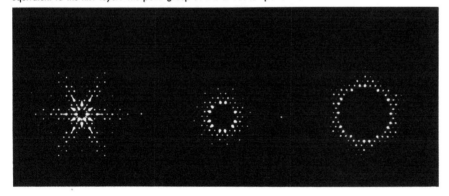

Crystal Symmetry

Crystals exhibit various forms and symmetries. Even before their atomic structures were known, crystals were classified according to the number and type of symmetry elements they exhibited. The 32 point groups, or crystal classes, of interest consist of individual elements—that is, an identity operation (1), a center of symmetry ($\bar{1}$), a mirror plane (*m*), a rotation axis (two-, three-, four-, sixfold), or an improper rotation axis ($\bar{3}$, $\bar{4}$, $\bar{6}$)—or a combination of these elements. Figure 3 shows an example of this method of classification. However, many crystals do not reveal their true symmetry, because they have been grown under less than ideal conditions.

Crystal Diffraction

In the optical analog, the one-dimensional grating produced a one-dimensional diffraction pattern. Because the single crystal used in x-ray diffraction is a three-dimensional grating, its diffraction pattern can be thought of as three dimensional. If all the diffraction spots are recorded on one piece of film, the pattern is generally unintelligible because the film records only the two-dimensional projection of the pattern. Special cameras, for example the Weissenberg and precession cameras, can be used to photograph the individual layers of the pattern. When such photographs are stacked one upon another, the three-dimensional nature of the diffraction pattern can be visualized (see Fig. 4).

Further, the point-group symmetry of the crystal is revealed by the pattern, except that an additional center of symmetry is often included. From the positions and symmetry of the spots, the crystal system (monoclinic, cubic, and so on) and the unit cell parameters can be determined. Once the unit cell is defined, each of the spots can be assigned a unique set of Miller indices (*hkl*), because each spot represents the reflected intensity from one set of Bragg planes. Thus, a table of *hkl*s and observed intensities, I_{obs}, can be constructed for use in determining the crystal structure.

Unit Cells

Unit cells are divided into triclinic, monoclinic, orthorhombic, tetragonal, hexagonal, trigonal (rhombohedral), and cubic crystal systems. A crystal system is assigned on the basis of its symmetry, not the shape of the unit cell. For example, a tetragonal unit cell is selected because the diffraction pattern exhibits 4/m or 4/mmm symmetry, not because $a = b \neq c$ and $\alpha = \beta = \gamma = 90°$. The presence of the fourfold symmetry

the intensities will be determined by the number of atoms, the atomic number of those atoms, and their relative positions within the unit cell.

In general, then, single-crystal x-ray diffraction concerns the extraction of atomic information from the positions and intensities of the spots found on the diffraction patterns made when a beam of monochromatic x-rays strikes a single crystal of a given substance. In the above optical experiment, changes in the diffraction pattern were observed as a function of changes in the grating. In a crystal structure analysis, the nature of the grating is unknown; the experiment is designed to determine its nature.

Fig. 5 The 14 symmetrical space lattices and their distribution among the five crystal systems

A, B, and *C* represent centering of the *bc, ac,* and *ab* faces, respectively. The points shown can represent one or more atoms. For example, in a body-centered lattice (symbol *I*), an atom at the origin with coordinates 0, 0, 0 has an equivalent at ½, ½, ½ (the center of the cell). More generally, an atom at *x, y, z* has an equivalent at ½ + *x,* ½ + *y,* ½ + *z.* Source: Ref 3

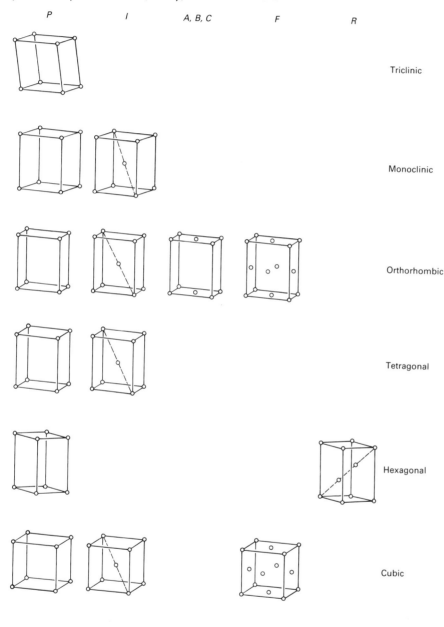

| P | I | A, B, C | F | R |

Triclinic

Monoclinic

Orthorhombic

Tetragonal

Hexagonal

Cubic

Space Groups

The symmetry that a crystal and its diffraction pattern exhibit as well as the symmetry suggested by the proper choice of a unit cell derive from the symmetry of the atomic arrangement. However, the symmetry that relates the atoms within the unit cell cannot be described in terms of a point group, that is, the symmetry about a point, but must be characterized by a space group that considers interactions between various point-group symmetry elements and the translational operations associated with the unit cell.

For example, in its simplest form, atoms clustered about an inversion center in one unit cell must have identical arrangements in every unit cell; thus, an inversion center must be present in all cells. Moreover, symmetry elements, when coupled with translational operations, produce additional symmetry elements at various locations in the unit cell. When the possible translations act on the various point-group symmetries, the result is 230 unique space groups that describe the ways in which atoms or molecules can pack in an organized symmetric fashion (Ref 4). Table 1 correlates the 230 space groups with the point groups and the crystal systems.

The concept of a space group is easily demonstrated. Each space group is designated with one capital letter indicating the basic arrangement of lattice points in the unit cell and numbers or small letters that provide information on the crystal symmetry. For example, *P*2 is a primitive unit cell with twofold axes parallel to the unique axis, which in the monoclinic system is generally the *b*-axis.

Figure 6 shows one layer of "cats" that have crystallized in the monoclinic space group *P*2. There are two "cats" per unit cell; each could represent one atom or a hundred. The first "cat" is located at fractional coordinates *x, y, z.* The second is related to the first by a twofold rotation axis at *x* = ½ and *z* = ½ and therefore is found at 1 − *x, y,* 1 − *z.* The locations of the other "cats" in the crystal can be produced by translational operations. The other twofold axes, for example, those at the corners of the cell, must be added to make the symmetry and translational operations self-consistent and complete. A "cat" crystal exhibits a twofold axis of symmetry and belongs to crystal class 2.

Space groups simplify conceptualization and reporting of crystal structures. To define a structure completely, all the atom positions within the unit cell must be specified. When symmetry elements exist to make some of the atoms equivalent, only the positions of the unique atoms need be specified if the sym-

makes the *a*-axis identical (rather than equal) to the *b*-axis.

Assignment of a crystal system must reflect the highest symmetry exhibited by the pattern; the unit cell should represent the smallest volume of the crystal consistent with that symmetry. The smallest unit cell that can be used to define a crystal structure is referred to as primitive. However, it is often found that a larger cell must be selected in order to comply with the highest symmetry principle. It can be shown that there are only 14 distinct unit cell types (see Fig. 5). Primitive unit cells are given the symbol *P*. Other unit cell types are *I* (inner centered or body centered), *F* (all faces centered), *C, B,* or *A* (single-face centered), and *R* (rhombohedral centering of a tetragonal unit cell). These are referred to as the 14 Bravais lattices.

Table 1   Relationships between the 230 space groups (atomic symmetry), 32 point groups (crystal symmetry), and the seven crystal systems

System	Point groups	Space groups					
Triclinic	1	$P1$					
	$\bar{1}$	$P\bar{1}$					
Monoclinic	2	$P2$	$P2_1$	$C2$			
	m	Pm	Pc	Cm	Cc		
	$2/m$	$P2/m$	$P2_1/m$	$C2/m$	$P2/c$	$P2_1/c$	$C2/c$
Orthorhombic	222	$P222$	$P222_1$	$P2_12_12$	$P2_12_12_1$	$C222_1$	$C222$
		$F222$	$I222$	$I2_12_12_1$			
	$mm2$	$Pmm2$	$Pmc2_1$	$Pcc2$	$Pma2$	$Pca2_1$	$Pnc2$
		$Pmn2_1$	$Pba2$	$Pna2_1$	$Pnn2$	$Cmm2$	$Cmc2_1$
		$Ccc2$	$Amm2$	$Abm2$	$Ama2$	$Aba2$	$Fmm2$
		$Fdd2$	$Imm2$	$Iba2$	$Ima2$		
	mmm	$Pmmm$	$Pnnn$	$Pccm$	$Pban$	$Pmma$	$Pnna$
		$Pmna$	$Pcca$	$Pbam$	$Pccn$	$Pbcm$	$Pnnm$
		$Pmmn$	$Pbcn$	$Pbca$	$Pnma$	$Cmcm$	$Cmca$
		$Cmmm$	$Cccm$	$Cmma$	$Ccca$	$Fmmm$	$Fddd$
		$Immm$	$Ibam$	$Ibca$	$Imma$		
Tetragonal	4	$P4$	$P4_1$	$P4_2$	$P4_3$	$I4$	$I4_1$
	$\bar{4}$	$P\bar{4}$	$I\bar{4}$				
	$4/m$	$P4/m$	$P4_2/m$	$P4/n$	$P4_2/n$	$I4/m$	$I4_1/a$
	422	$P422$	$P42_12$	$P4_122$	$P4_12_12$	$P4_222$	$P4_22_12$
		$P4_322$	$P4_32_12$	$I422$	$I4_122$		
	$4mm$	$P4mm$	$P4bm$	$P4_2cm$	$P4_2nm$	$P4cc$	$P4nc$
		$P4_2mc$	$P4_2bc$	$I4mm$	$I4cm$	$I4_1md$	$I4_1cd$
	$\bar{4}2m$	$P\bar{4}2m$	$P\bar{4}2c$	$P\bar{4}2_1m$	$P\bar{4}2_1c$	$P\bar{4}m2$	$P\bar{4}c2$
		$P\bar{4}b2$	$P\bar{4}n2$	$I\bar{4}m2$	$I\bar{4}c2$	$I\bar{4}2m$	$I\bar{4}2d$
	$4/mmm$	$P4/mmm$	$P4/mcc$	$P4/nbm$	$P4/nnc$	$P4/mbm$	$P4/mnc$
		$P4/nmm$	$P4/ncc$	$P4_2/mmc$	$P4_2/mcm$	$P4_2/nbc$	$P4_2/nnm$
		$P4_2/mbc$	$P4_2/mnm$	$P4_2/nmc$	$P4_2/ncm$	$I4/mmm$	$I4/mcm$
		$I4_1/amd$	$I4_1/acd$				
Trigonal/rhombohedral	3	$P3$	$P3_1$	$P3_2$	$R3$		
	$\bar{3}$	$P\bar{3}$	$R\bar{3}$				
	32	$P312$	$P321$	$P3_112$	$P3_121$	$P3_212$	$P3_221$
		$R32$					
	$3m$	$P3m1$	$P31m$	$P3c1$	$P31c$	$R3m$	$R3c$
	$\bar{3}m$	$P\bar{3}1m$	$P\bar{3}1c$	$P\bar{3}m1$	$P\bar{3}c1$	$R\bar{3}m$	$R\bar{3}c$
Hexagonal	6	$P6$	$P6_1$	$P6_5$	$P6_2$	$P6_4$	$P6_3$
	$\bar{6}$	$P\bar{6}$					
	$6/m$	$P6/m$	$P6_3/m$				
	622	$P622$	$P6_122$	$P6_522$	$P6_222$	$P6_422$	$P6_322$
	$6mm$	$P6mm$	$P6cc$	$P6_3cm$	$P6_3mc$		
	$\bar{6}m2$	$P\bar{6}m2$	$P\bar{6}c2$	$P\bar{6}2m$	$P\bar{6}2c$		
	$6/mmm$	$P6/mmm$	$P6/mcc$	$P6_3/mcm$	$P6_3/mmc$		
Cubic	23	$P23$	$F23$	$I23$	$P2_13$	$I2_13$	
	$m3$	$Pm3$	$Pn3$	$Fm3$	$Fd3$	$Im3$	$Pa3$
		$Ia3$					
	432	$P432$	$P4_232$	$F432$	$F4_132$	$I432$	$P4_332$
		$P4_132$	$I4_132$				
	$\bar{4}3m$	$P\bar{4}3m$	$F\bar{4}3m$	$I\bar{4}3m$	$P\bar{4}3n$	$F\bar{4}3c$	$I\bar{4}3d$
	$m3m$	$Pm3m$	$Pn3n$	$Pm3n$	$Pn3m$	$Fm3m$	$Fm3c$
		$Fd3m$	$Fd3c$	$Im3m$	$Ia3d$		

Source: Ref 5

orthorhombic (rather than hexagonal) unit cell and use only crystallographic inversion centers.

Crystal Structure Definition

Three items are necessary to define a crystal structure: (1) the space group (from which the crystal system, the crystal class, and the appropriate symmetry elements can be deduced), (2) the unit cell dimensions, and (3) a list of atomic coordinates. Such information as the crystal system, the number of molecules or formula units per unit cell (Z), and the volume of the unit cell (V) is redundant. The latter two quantities are useful for calculating the density of the crystalline substance, which is often compared with the measured density.

Diffraction Intensities

When x-rays interact with the electron clouds of the atoms in a crystal, each atom produces a diffracted wave whose amplitude is proportional to the number of electrons in the atom. These individual diffracted waves interfere with each other and ultimately produce the variations in the intensities visible in the diffraction pattern. The amount of interference depends on the positions of the atoms relative to each other and to the Bragg planes (Fig. 7).

Figure 7(a) shows a two-dimensional slice through a crystal containing only black atoms. The unit cell is described by vectors **a** and **b**, and a set of planes with indices hkl with a d-spacing (interplanar spacing) of d_{hkl} are illustrated. Also shown is an x-ray wave front of wavelength λ interacting with the atoms to produce a diffracted beam. A diffraction spot will occur only if the diffracted waves interfere in a constructive fashion, that is, when the phase of the bottom wave lags the top wave by 360° (2π radians). This diffraction condition is the basis of Bragg's law, which can be derived from the geometry illustrated in Fig. 7(a):

$$\lambda = 2d_{hkl} \sin \theta \qquad \text{(Eq 1)}$$

The diffraction spots are generally referred to as reflections, because the x-rays appear to be reflected from the plane.

If additional atoms—white atoms (Fig. 7b)—are added to the crystal structure, the same wave front that interacted with the black atoms must also interact with the white atoms. However, if the white atoms have fewer electrons, the amplitude of their diffracted beams is smaller than that of the black atoms. Although the addition of the white atoms does not change the Bragg angle

metry elements are also specified by the space group. In the case of the "cat" crystal, the location of the first "cat" is unique; however, the second "cat" is equivalent to the first by the twofold rotation axis. Only the coordinates of the first "cat" need be specified.

An atom may reside on a space-group symmetry element. For example, an atom could sit on the twofold axis of the space group $P2$.

A molecule having a twofold axis through it may have its molecular twofold axis align with a crystallographic twofold axis. In this case, because only half of the molecule is unique, only the locations of half the atoms in the molecule need to be specified. In general, molecules do not display their full symmetry when they pack together to form crystals; molecules of benzene, for example, have $6/mmm$ symmetry, but pack in an

Fig. 6 One layer of the "cat" crystal structure showing the *a* and *c* axes of the unit cell

The *b* axis is perpendicular to the *ac* plane. The other layers of cats sit directly above and below this layer. Each twofold axis is represented by the symbol ⬤ with the rotation axis parallel to the *b* axis.

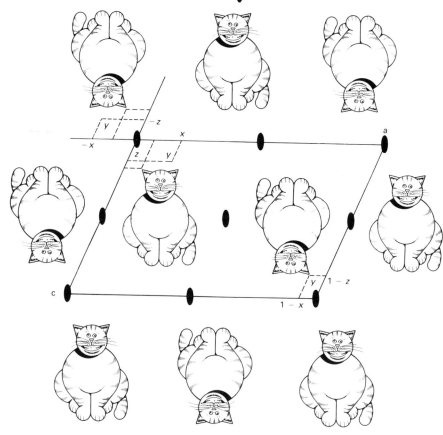

$$F_{hkl} = |F_{hkl}|\, e^{i\Phi_{hkl}}$$

$$= \sum_{j=1}^{N} f_j\, e^{2\pi i(hx_j\ +\ ky_j\ +\ lz_j)} \qquad \text{(Eq 5)}$$

where N is the total number of atoms in the unit cell. The resultant amplitude, $|F_{hkl}|$, is referred to as the structure factor amplitude, or structure amplitude. Figure 8 illustrates this summation.

Each set of *hkl* planes produces one spot on the diffraction pattern. The intensity I_{hkl} of the spot is proportional to the square of the amplitude of the resultant wave:

$$I_{hkl} \propto |F_{hkl}|^2 \qquad \text{(Eq 6)}$$

Thus, if the crystal structure—that is, the unit cell, the space group, and the atomic positions—is known, the relative intensities of all the diffraction spots can be calculated. The intensities are only a function of the atom positions and are not dependent on the repeat vectors that define the unit cell.

The Phase Problem

If the crystal structure is known, the intensities can be calculated. To determine the crystal structure, the process must be reversed. The intensities, or more accurately the structure factors, must be used to determine the positions of the atoms. For this purpose, a simple Fourier series relates the electron density (the number of electrons per Å^3), ρ, at a given point *xyz* within the unit cell and the structure factors, $\mathbf{F}_{hkl}$:

$$\rho_{xyz} = \frac{1}{V} \sum_h \sum_k \sum_l$$
$$\mathbf{F}_{hkl}\, e^{-2\pi i(hx\ +\ ky\ +\ lz)} \qquad \text{(Eq 7)}$$

Figure 9 shows a typical electron density map with contours at various levels of density to outline the atoms. The position of highest density is assumed to be the center of the atom and therefore the location of the nucleus. Thus, if the structure factors are known, calculation of a Fourier map is easy. However, $\mathbf{F}_{hkl}$ is composed of an amplitude and a phase:

$$\mathbf{F}_{hkl} = |F_{hkl}|e^{i\Phi_{hkl}} \qquad \text{(Eq 8)}$$

and only the amplitudes are obtained from the experimental diffraction pattern:

$$|F_{hkl}| \propto \sqrt{I_{hkl}} \qquad \text{(Eq 9)}$$

Without the phase information, the electron densities cannot be calculated and the structure cannot be determined.

θ at which the diffraction occurs, it alters the intensity of the reflection, because the diffracted wave from the white atom lags behind that from each black atom by some value ϕ between 0 and 360° (0 and 2π radians).

These two waves interfere with each other to a greater or lesser extent, depending on their relative positions. If the white atom were placed in the top plane of black atoms, ϕ would be 0° and the waves would constructively interfere. If the white atom were placed exactly in the middle of the two black-atom planes, ϕ would be 180°, or π, and the waves would destructively interfere. Ultimately, the intensity of the reflection could increase or decrease with the addition of the white atoms, depending on their placement. A simple proportionality exists between the phase and the position of the white atoms: $\phi/2\pi = \Delta d/d$, or:

$$\phi = 2\pi \frac{\Delta d}{d} \qquad \text{(Eq 2)}$$

A more detailed analysis of $\Delta d/d$ shows that it is equivalent to $hx + ky + lz$, where h, k, and l are the indices of the plane, and x, y, and z are the fractional coordinates of the atom. Thus, in more general terms:

$$\phi_j = 2\pi\, (hx_j + ky_j + lz_j) \qquad \text{(Eq 3)}$$

where j refers to the jth atom in the unit cell.

All the atoms in the unit cell must contribute to the final diffracted wave. In its classic mathematical form, a wave from any atom f_j, is:

$$\mathbf{f}_j = f_j\, e^{i\phi_j} = f_j\, e^{2\pi i(hx_j\ +\ ky_j\ +\ lz_j)} \qquad \text{(Eq 4)}$$

where the phase angle is part of a complex quantity, and f_j is the amplitude of the scattered wave for atom j. The value f_j is proportional to the number of electrons that the atom has; it is referred to as the scattering factor of the atom. Each of the contributions must be summed in vector form to yield the resultant, termed the structure factor:

Fig. 7 Basic principles of single-crystal diffraction

(a) A two-dimensional slice through a three-dimensional crystal containing only black atoms. (b) The same structures as in (a), but with white atoms added

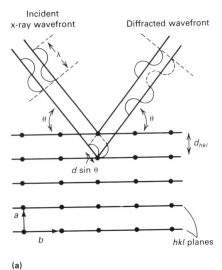

(a)

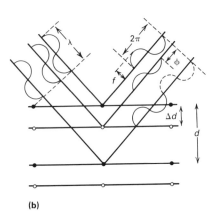

(b)

The phase problem can be avoided by simply guessing at a structure, then matching the calculated intensities with the measured intensities. If the proposed structure is correct, the intensities should match reasonably well. One useful indicator of the agreement between the calculated and observed structure amplitudes, $|F_c|$ and $|F_o|$, respectively, is known as the residual index, or R value:

$$R = \frac{\sum\limits_{hkl} \left| |F_o| - |F_c| \right|}{\sum\limits_{hkl} |F_o|} \quad \text{(Eq 10)}$$

Favorable matches yield low values of R, generally from 0.02 to 0.07.

Fig. 8 Derivation of the structure factor F

(a) Unit cell with eight atoms placed at random. (b) Vector diagram showing the amplitudes, f_i, and phases, $\phi_i = 2\pi(\Delta d_i)/d$, of all the individual atoms adding vectorially to give the resultant structure factor, **F**, with length $|F|$ and phase Φ. Source: Ref 3

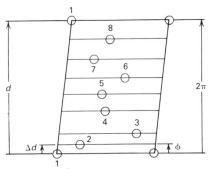

(a)

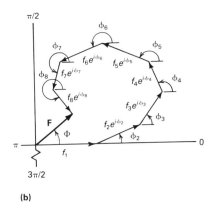

(b)

If a proposed structure has the atoms placed near their correct positions, an R less than 0.40 should be obtained. A crude structural model can be improved if an electron density map is calculated using the observed structure amplitudes $|F_o|$ and the calculated phases of the proposed structure; the resulting electron density peaks will be closer to the correct atomic positions. These improved positions can then be cycled to provide better phases, which further improves the electron density map. A refined crystal structure will eventually be obtained.

Guessing is rarely practical with complicated crystal structures, but it was used in the formative days of x-ray crystallography to solve a number of simple structures. Other techniques have since been developed to solve the phase problem. The key in each case is to find a set of starting phases that can be used with the observed structure amplitudes to produce an electron density map. The two techniques most widely used are the heavy-atom method and the direct method.

Fig. 9 Three-dimensional electron density map of potassium benzyl penicillin showing use of stacked plastic sheets to represent sections of the unit cell

Source: Ref 6

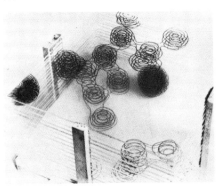

Fig. 10 The effect of atomic number on phases of structure factors

F is the vector sum of F_H, the contribution from the heavy atom(s), and a series of F_L's, the contributions of all the light atoms. Because F_H is the dominant contributor to **F**, $\Phi \cong \phi_H$.

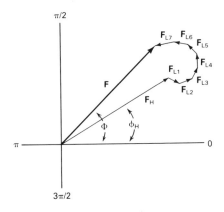

The heavy-atom method is predicated on the fact that one atom having many electrons will predominate in determining the phases of the structure factors (Fig. 10). Thus, if the heavy atom can be placed correctly in the unit cell, its phases ϕ_H will be close to the phases of the structure factors, Φ. An electron density map based on the heavy-atom phases and the observed structure amplitudes will often reveal the locations of many, if not all, of the lighter atoms. Locating the heavy atom involves techniques beyond the scope of this article. The inclusion of one heavy atom reduces the complexity of the structural solution—finding one atom in a unit cell is easier than finding 50 atoms.

Fig. 11 Mosaic structure of a crystal
Source: Ref 5

The direct method is based on the fact that the phases of the reflections, although not measurable, are not independent of each other. Phase information can be obtained by comparing the intensities of related reflections. In particular, if three intense reflections have indices $h_1k_1l_1$, $h_2k_2l_2$, and $h_3k_3l_3$, respectively, such that $h_1 + h_2 + h_3 = 0$, $k_1 + k_2 + k_3 = 0$, and $l_1 + l_2 + l_3 = 0$, then it is probably true that $\Phi(h_1k_1l_1) + \Phi(h_2k_2l_2) + \Phi(h_3k_3l_3) = 0°$. Thus, if two of the phases can be assigned, the phase of the third reflection can be calculated. By sorting the intense reflections and seeking these types of relationships, it is often possible to locate a favorable set of phases. The calculation of an electron density map with only the intense reflections will often reveal a significant portion of the atoms in the structure. These atoms can be used to phase all the structure amplitudes, and further maps can be prepared.

Experimental Procedure

A suitable structural determination begins with a single crystal. An ideal crystal is generally characterized by well-formed faces and uniform optical properties when observed using a polarizing microscope. In practice, crystals are often grown under less than ideal conditions and provide few recognizable faces—one side of a crystal may take the shape of the container in which it is grown, for example. Because crystals are often opaque, their optical properties cannot be studied. Therefore, the true test for any single crystal lies in the examination of its diffraction pattern; identification of a unit cell and space group(s) consistent with the diffraction spots is a necessary condition for a successful structural analysis.

The ideal crystal is not a perfect crystal. Perfect crystals have no impurities or defects; every unit cell is in precise alignment with each other. Most crystals are not perfect. Crystals used for x-ray diffraction are labeled ideally imperfect; they contain impurities and defects that produce small misalignments of the unit cell in various parts of the crystals. Such crystals

are said to be mosaic (Fig. 11), and this term applies to virtually all so-called single crystals. The diffraction pattern will generally not be affected by small amounts of impurities if they are distributed throughout the crystal. Crystals to be studied need not be large; most crystals used for analysis are 0.1 to 0.4 mm on a side, about the size of a grain of salt.

Until a decade ago, most crystals were examined by taking a series of precession or Weissenberg photographs to examine the diffraction pattern. This step is generally bypassed and the crystal mounted directly on an automated single-crystal diffractometer (Fig. 12). This instrument has computer-controlled angular motions that allow every set of planes to be placed in diffraction position. Although some photographic capability is usually available, the primary use of the diffractometer is the direct measurement of diffraction intensities using a scintillation counter. Intensities can be measured from films, but the process is more complex.

Using a camera or diffractometer, the first step is to determine the crystal system (triclinic, cubic, and so on), the unit cell dimensions, and the possible space group(s). If the density D_m of an unknown crystal is measured, the formula weight FW of the substance can be calculated from the unit cell volume, V:

$$FW = \frac{0.6225 D_m V}{Z} \qquad \text{(Eq 11)}$$

where the constant is derived by multiplying the inverse of Avogadro's number by 10^{-24}, the factor for converting cm^3 into $Å^3$; and Z is the number of formula units (molecules, for example) per unit cell. For an unknown substance, Z may not be known until the structural analysis is complete; however, $Z \times FW$ can be calculated. This may indicate the number and types of atoms constituting the unit cell. When the crystal structure is complete, the report will usually provide the calculated density, D_x, based on the determined values of FW, Z, and V; agreement with the measured density is expected.

The next step is to measure the intensities of the diffraction spots. Film techniques were originally used for this purpose, but diffractometers are now common, especially automated diffractometers, due to the tedium of collecting 1000 to 10 000 reflection intensities manually. Collection of all the intensities in the diffraction pattern is unnecessary. Because the pattern has symmetry, only the unique reflections must be measured.

The measured intensities, I_{hkl}, must be reduced to structure factor amplitudes, $|F_{hkl}|$, before the analysis can begin:

$$|F_{hkl}| = kC_{hkl} \sqrt{I_{hkl}} \qquad \text{(Eq 12)}$$

where k is a scale constant applied to every reflection, and C_{hkl} represents a collective group of correction factors that must be calculated separately for each reflection. The value k depends on such variables as the crystal size and the x-ray flux. The value C_{hkl} will include geometric terms and a correction for polarization of the diffracted beam; it may include a term to account for the absorption of the x-ray beam as it travels through the crystal.

Determination of the crystal structure depends entirely on finding a starting set of phases. The direct method is the technique of choice when all the atoms have approximately the same number of electrons (for example, organic compounds) or when there are many heavy atoms (for example, heteropolytungstates). When the structure contains few heavy atoms, the heavy-atom method may be used. By either means, the starting phases are coupled with the measured amplitudes to produce an electron density map. If the phases are nearly correct, this map will reveal the atomic number (number of electrons) and positions of many of the atoms. These atoms can be used to calculate improved phases; the process is cycled until all the atoms are located. Because of the space-group symmetry, only the atoms in a portion of the unit cell must be found; the others are generated by the symmetry elements of the space group.

During the solution of the structure, a least squares refinement of the atomic positions is often carried out to minimize the differences between the observed (measured) and calculated structure amplitudes:

$$D = \sum_{hkl} w \left(|F_o| - |F_c|\right)^2 \qquad \text{(Eq 13)}$$

Fig. 12 Conventional four-circle diffractometer
Source: Ref 7

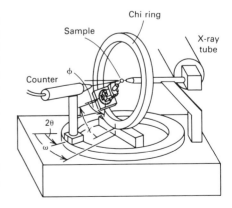

where w is a weighting factor intended to indicate the level of confidence in $|F_o|$. A better match between $|F_o|$ and $|F_c|$ is expected when the atoms are moved to better model the electron density. The least squares calculation yields refined positions, because $|F_c|$ and therefore D are dependent on the atomic coordinates. By a combination of least squares refinement and electron density maps, most crystal structures can be solved and refined quickly.

Atoms undergo vibrational motions. For example, one atom may be moving to the left as its equivalent in the next unit cell is moving to the right. The diffracted waves from these two atoms no longer interfere in a completely constructive fashion. A general decline in the intensities with increasing Bragg angle 2θ results. This decline must be considered when calculating the structure factor, or $|F_c|$ would never agree with $|F_o|$.

Although several expressions are used to account for these thermal motions, the motion is most commonly described as isotropic—spherical motion about an atom position (Eq 14)—or anisotropic, that is, ellipsoidal motion (Eq 15). Typical forms for these two types of motion are:

$$e^{-B\,\sin^2\,\theta/\lambda^2} \qquad (\text{Eq 14})$$

$$e^{-(\beta_{11}h^2\,+\,\beta_{22}k^2\,+\,\beta_{33}l^2\,+\,\beta_{12}hk\,+\,\beta_{13}hl\,+\,\beta_{23}kl)} \qquad (\text{Eq 15})$$

The B value of the isotropic form or the six βs of the anisotropic form may be variables in the least squares refinement. These are related to the root-mean-square motions of the atoms. If all the atoms are refined with isotropic thermal parameters, the complete equation for the structure factor becomes:

$$\mathbf{F}_{hkl} = \sum_{j=1}^{N} f_j e^{2\pi i(hx_j\,+\,ky_j\,+\,lz_j)}$$
$$e^{-B_j\,\sin^2\,\theta/\lambda^2} \qquad (\text{Eq 16})$$

The least squares refinement of the positional and thermal parameters will converge at R values of 0.02 to 0.05 (2 to 5%) if the crystal structure is straightforward and the intensity data are reliable. Slightly higher Rs will be obtained if some of the atoms of the structure are disordered or if the intensity data suffer from random errors (poor counting statistics) or systematic errors (absorption, poor diffractometer alignment, and so on).

Once the structure has been solved and refined, the fractional coordinates of all the atoms are known. Using the unit cell dimensions, these can be converted to Angstrom coordinates, from which bond distances, bond angles, mean planes for a group of atoms, and dihedral angles are easily calculated. The geometry around each atom can be examined (Fig. 1). The least squares refinement also produces a standard deviation σ for each of the variables, and these can be translated into standard deviations for the bond distances, and so on. Special programs, such as the Oak Ridge Thermal Ellipsoid Program (ORTEP), can be used to illustrate the crystal structure. Finally, if the atoms are clustered into molecules or complex ions, intermolecular or interionic contacts, such as hydrogen bonds, can be identified.

Reviewing the Results

A crystal structure analysis includes several assumptions. First, atoms are spherical in shape. Core electrons may have overall spherical symmetry, but bonding or nonbonding valence electrons do not. Second, the nucleus of the atom is located at the point of maximum electron density. For atoms with high atomic numbers, this assumption is valid. However, for light atoms, in which the valence electrons account for most of the scattering, the electron cloud is often distorted by the bonding environment. The worst deviations from this assumption occur for covalently bonded hydrogen atoms; the maximum in the electron density is often 0.10 to 0.20 Å from the nucleus toward the atom to which the hydrogen is bonded. Third, the thermal motions of atoms can be described by simple spherical or elliptical models. Most motions are more complex, particularly if the atoms are covalently bonded such that they "ride" on each other.

Accuracy denotes the measure of how close the structure is to the true structure. The above assumptions imply that the positions of heavy atoms (with many core electrons and little thermal motion) can be determined with high accuracy. Atoms as light as boron or carbon can be determined with reasonable accuracy; if a structure contains light and heavy atoms, the positions of the light atoms are in greater doubt, because the heavy atoms dominate the scattering. Hydrogen atom positions are almost always systematically in error. There are no indicators of accuracy that derive directly from a structural analysis.

Precision denotes the measure of how well the structural model reproduces the diffraction intensities. The R value is perhaps the most obvious indicator of the precision, but the standard deviations in the positional and thermal parameters as well as the bond distances and angles are also indicators.

These standard deviations have nothing to do with accuracy. However, an accurate structural analysis (within the limits noted above) has high precision as a prerequisite.

A well-determined structure implies high precision and freedom from other crystallographic problems, such as disordered atoms, atoms with very high thermal motions, and space-group ambiguities. There are several indicators of a well-determined structure. First, the R value should fall in the range of 0.02 to 0.05 (2 to 5%), perhaps lower if atoms with high atomic numbers are present. Second, the data-to-parameter ratio should exceed 7, preferably 10. The data refer to the number of reflections used in the least squares refinement; parameters refers to the total number of variables, including the positional and thermal parameters of all the atoms. Third, the accuracy of the structure, but not necessarily the precision, is improved if intensities are measured at very high Bragg angles. With Mo $K\alpha$ radiation, upper 2θ limits of 48 to 55° are commonly used, but for many inorganic structures, intensities can be measured to 70 to 80°. The higher the 2θ limit, the better the structure. Fourth, the thermal parameters should be reasonable; careful examination of the thermal ellipsoids shown in an ORTEP illustration may indicate problems with the data (for example, all ellipses elongated in the same direction) or with the structure (such as exceptionally large, small, or cigar-shaped ellipses), rather than actual vibrations of the atoms. Finally, and most importantly, the bond parameters (such as coordination geometries and bond lengths and angles) must make chemical sense (Ref 8, 9).

Cooling the crystal to low temperatures improves the intensities, especially for the high-angle reflections, and therefore the overall quality of the structure. The reduction in the thermal motions facilitates locating the atoms (sharpens the electron density around the atoms) and refining them (thermal motions are more spherical).

Crystallographic Problems

If a starting set of phases cannot be found, the crystal structure cannot be determined. What appear to be single crystals are sometimes subtle twins in which two or more single crystals in different orientations grow together. The intensities that result are then a combination of the intensities from the individual crystals, and these produce meaningless phase sets. Atoms or molecules may be badly disordered, with equivalent atoms in adjacent unit cells residing in disparate positions. Thus, even if a starting set of phases can be found, the electron density map will be unintelligible.

At other times, part of the structure can be identified, but other portions contain disordered atoms or sites that are partially occupied (nonstoichiometric compounds or unit cells containing solvent molecules that have partially evaporated) or occupied by different types of atoms in different unit cells (aluminum and silicon may substitute for each other in a zeolite structure). Some atoms in a structure may be highly mobile and therefore difficult to model; for example, solvent molecules in an open-cage zeolitic structure. Determination of the crystal system can be ambiguous, as illustrated by a crystal that appears orthorhombic but may in fact be monoclinic with a β angle of 90° within experimental error. In general, space groups are not unique. The true space group is often found only after the structure has been solved, refined, and reviewed. In many cases, an ambiguity can arise because the diffraction pattern may show the presence of a center of symmetry, although the unit cell of the crystal does not contain one.

Superlattices often occur in inorganic and organometallic crystals. In this case, the strong spots of the diffraction pattern suggest one unit cell, but a few weak spots suggest that the actual unit cell is much larger. The number of weak spots with measurable intensities is often insufficient to sort out the subtleties in the atom positions that caused them. A suitable structural analysis report will describe these and other potential problems that have been encountered. Finally, an incorrect structural model may refine to an acceptable R value and provide good, if not totally reasonable, bond distances and angles (Ref 10-12).

Applications

Example 1: Use of Unit Cell Information to Identify an Unknown Crystalline Phase. The recrystallization of an organic polysulfide, $C_9H_6N_2S_5$, formula weight (FW) 258.41, produced yellow crystals, one of which was placed on an x-ray diffractometer. The crystal was found to be orthorhombic with approximate unit cell dimensions of $a = 12.86$, $b = 24.35$, $c = 10.43$ Å. The space group was determined to be $Fddd$, an uncommon group. Furthermore, this space group generally has $Z = 32$, that is, 32 molecules per unit cell. If the molecule had a center of symmetry or a twofold axis, the molecular symmetry could be coincident with a space-group symmetry element, reducing Z to 16; however, this molecule was not expected to have any symmetry. A calculation of the expected density indicates a problem:

$$D_x = \frac{FW \cdot Z}{0.6225V} = \frac{FW \cdot Z}{0.6225 \cdot a \cdot b \cdot c} \quad \text{(Eq 17)}$$

The value D_x is 4.07 g/cm^3; expected densities would range from 1.3 to 1.5 g/cm^3. Although the density of the yellow crystals was not measured, the x-ray density deviates so much from the expected density that the proposed formula of the crystalline compound cannot be correct. Because of the possibility that the compound had decomposed to produce crystals of sulfur, the unit cell dimensions were checked against those listed in Ref 13, and a positive match was found for the orthorhombic form of S_8.

In general, cells should be matched against those reported in the literature to avoid repeating crystal structures that have already been determined. Crystals of the organic polysulfide were eventually obtained, and its structure was determined: monoclinic, space group $P2_1/c$, with an x-ray density of 1.42 g/cm^3.

Example 2: Analysis of a New Synthetic Substance. In an effort to synthesize the hexagonal polymorph of MoO_3, $(NH_4)Mo_5O_{15}(OH)\cdot2H_2O$ was heated under pressure in gold and copper tubes. A powder diffraction pattern of the product in the gold tube revealed that it had converted to the colorless orthorhombic form of MoO_3. A microscopic examination of the sample from the copper tube revealed two types of crystals, both of which were highly colored. The different crystals were isolated and ground into powders. From their powder diffraction patterns, one of the products was clearly identified as MoO_2; the second product appeared to match that of $Cu_6Mo_4O_{15}$, a previously reported phase. Chemical and mi-

croprobe analyses of the second product did not agree favorably with this formulation; therefore, a crystal structure analysis was performed. Consequently, the second phase was shown to be $Cu_6Mo_5O_{18}$. Some of the details of the structural work are given below.

The crystal used for this analysis had approximate dimensions of $0.09 \times 0.17 \times 0.45$ mm ($0.0035 \times 0.0067 \times 0.018$ in.). The crystal system was determined to be monoclinic with unit cell dimensions of $a = 14.676$ Å, $b = 6.280$ Å, $c = 15.254$ Å, and $\beta = 101.78°$ (for a monoclinic unit cell, α and $\gamma = 90°$ and are thus not listed in the structural report). The space group was ambiguous; Ic or $I2/c$ (body-centered lattices which are nonstandard settings of the C-face-centered space groups Cc and $C2/c$, respectively) were possible, the absence or presence of inversion centers being the fundamental difference in the two. The group $I2/c$ was selected because the atom positions were consistent with the presence of inversion centers.

The intensities of 1689 reflections were measured in the 2θ range of 4 to 50°. Of these, 1164 were considered observed and were used to refine the structure. A reflection is considered observed if its intensity exceeds n times the standard deviation in the intensity, which is usually based on counting statistics, although other factors are sometimes included. In the present case, $n = 3$.

The structure could have been solved using the direct method, because several atoms with high atomic number had to be located. However, it was solved using the heavy-atom method. By combining the phases calculated from the molybdenum and copper atoms with the observed structure ampli-

Table 2 Fractional coordinates *x*, *y*, and *z* (× 10 000) and isotropic thermal parameters B_{iso} for $Cu_6Mo_5O_{18}$

Atom(a)	x(b)	y	z	B_{iso}
Mo(1)	5000	9320(1)	2500	0.7(1)
Mo(2)	3389.6(3)	5820.5(8)	2421.9(3)	0.7(1)
Mo(3)	1586.8(3)	6356.9(7)	711.9(3)	0.7(1)
Cu(1)	3885.8(6)	6477.8(14)	378.1(6)	1.9(1)
Cu(2)	2143.6(6)	3799.2(12)	3692.5(6)	1.6(1)
Cu(3)	5031.0(6)	3043.1(14)	919.8(5)	2.0(1)
O(1)	4018(3)	3947(7)	3107(3)	1.3(1)
O(2)	2598(3)	6639(6)	3295(3)	0.8(1)
O(3)	868(3)	8497(7)	187(3)	1.2(1)
O(4)	4201(3)	6661(7)	1724(3)	1.1(1)
O(5)	923(3)	4076(6)	348(3)	1.2(1)
O(6)	5947(3)	8474(6)	1871(3)	0.9(1)
O(7)	2452(3)	6328(7)	65(3)	1.2(1)
O(8)	4346(3)	11 043(7)	1700(3)	1.2(1)
O(9)	2557(3)	4243(6)	1652(3)	1.1(1)

(a) The basic structural unit of unique atoms contains only half of the atoms in the empirical formula. That is, coordinates for only three, not six, copper atoms are given because the other three are generated by symmetry, in particular by the two-fold axis that passes through Mo(1). (b) The numbers in parentheses are the estimated standard deviations, σ, for each of the least squares variables. The x and z coordinates of Mo(1) do not have estimated standard deviations because the atom sits on a crystallographic two-fold axis located at $x = 1/2$ and $z = 1/4$; these coordinates cannot be varied. Source: Ref 13

Fig. 13 ORTEP illustration of the basic structural unit of $Cu_6Mo_5O_{18}$

Each atom is represented by an oval, a two-dimensional projection of its ellipsoidal thermal motion. The unique atoms have been labeled, and some of the symmetry-equivalent atoms have been added (as indicated by the small letters at the end of the label) to complete the coordination sphere around each atom. Source: Ref 14

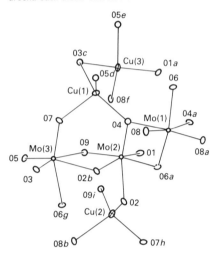

Fig. 14 Copper tetrahedra and molybdenum octahedra as packed into the unit cell

All the symmetry-equivalent units are included. Source: Ref 14

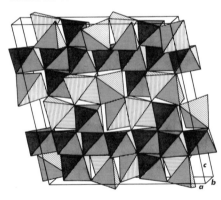

Fig. 15 Bond distances in angstroms and angles of the $CuCl_4^{2-}$ anion in the green (a) and yellow (b) modifications

The estimated standard deviations are given as single digits in parentheses after bond parameters. A prime is added to the labels of the symmetry-equivalent atoms. In the green form, the copper atom sits on a center of symmetry (indicated by ●); in the yellow form, a twofold axis passes through the copper atom (indicated by ◗). Source: Ref 15

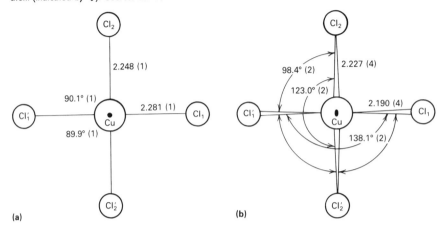

tudes, electron density maps were used to locate the oxygen atoms. A least squares refinement of the positional and isotropic thermal parameters was then carried out; results are listed in Table 2. The anisotropic thermal parameters were later refined; these are shown as the ellipsoidal representations of the atoms in the structure in Fig. 13.

The structure is clearly consistent with the formula $Cu_6Mo_5O_{18}$ and consists of copper atoms surrounded by a tetrahedral arrangement of oxygen atoms and molybdenum atoms in octahedral environments. Figure 14

shows the unit cell with the copper tetrahedra and molybdenum octahedra illustrated. The final R value for this structure was 0.027, which is very good. The data-to-variables ratio of 8.7 is acceptable—(1164 observed reflections)/(134 positional and thermal parameters plus other crystallographic factors).

Other structural details, including the bond distances and angles and a discussion of the short copper-copper contacts can be found in Ref 14. This example demonstrates the power of the technique to clarify uncertain chemical compositions in newly synthesized, crystalline substances. The ammonium molybdate had undergone an oxidation-reduction reaction with the copper tube in which it was placed:

$$(NH_4) \, Mo_5^{6+}O_{15} \, (OH)2H_2O \, + \, Cu^0 \rightarrow$$

$$Cu_6^+Mo_5^{6+}O_{18} \, + \, Mo^{4+}O_2 \quad (Eq \ 18)$$

Example 3: Determination of Coordination Geometry; Understanding Phase Changes.

The structure of the tetrachlorocuprate anion, $CuCl_4^{2-}$, had been investigated to the point where its average geometry was considered to be well established; the four chlorine atoms form a flattened tetrahedron about the central copper, with two chlorine-copper-chlorine angles increasing to approximately 130° and four angles decreasing to approximately 100° from the standard tetrahedral value of 109°. All the salts whose structures had been determined were yellow. However, the $(C_6H_5)CH_2CH_2NH_2CH_3^+$ salt of $CuCl_4^{2-}$ recrystallized from a yellow solution as a green crystalline solid. When the green phase was heated to 80 °C

(175 °F), it converted to the expected yellow form, a phase change which was found to be reversible.

Crystal structure studies of the two phases were then undertaken (Ref 15). Crystals of the low-temperature green phase were monoclinic, space group $P2_1/c$. The structure was refined to $R = 0.035$ and clearly demonstrated that the copper atom resided on a crystallographic center of symmetry with the four chlorines arranged around it in a square-planar configuration. Crystals of the high-temperature yellow form were also monoclinic, but belonged to space group $C2/c$. In this case, the well-established flattened tetrahedral geometry was found for the $CuCl_4^{2-}$ anion, with the copper atom residing on a crystallographic twofold axis. Because of some disordering in the cation and problems with high thermal motions in general (which limited the data set to low-angle reflections), the R value only decreased to 0.092. Although this structure cannot be considered well determined, it was sufficient to establish the geometry of the anion. The geometries of the green and yellow anions are shown in Fig. 15.

Some phase changes will reduce a single crystal to a powder. This was the case with the $CuCl_4^{2-}$ salt. The high-temperature form had to be grown carefully on the diffractometer from the melt. Other phase changes involve only subtle motions of atoms that do not destroy the crystals. The molecules in some crystals even undergo solid-state reactions with each other to produce dimers or polymers. Crystal structure analysis offers an opportunity to understand these changes in crystalline materials.

Example 4: Interatomic Bond Lengths and Physical Properties.

The differences in the physical properties of diamond and graphite are a direct result of their distinctive bonding patterns, which are made evident by their crystal structures. There are many other examples of the interrelationship between structure and properties, but one rather simple case is that of the nonstoichiometric salts of $[Pt(CN)_4]^{x-}$. These salts will conduct electricity only parallel to their needle axes and therefore are referred to as one-dimensional conductors. The reason for this property becomes clear when the crystal structures of these salts are known (Ref 16).

One example is that of $Rb_2[Pt(CN)_4]$ $(FHF)_{0.4}$ (Ref 17). Crystals belong to the tetragonal space group *I4/mcm* with $a = 12.689$ Å and $c = 5.595$ Å. Because of the *4/mmm* symmetry of the diffraction pattern, only 383 reflections had unique intensities. Because all the atoms reside at special symmetry-restricted sites, only a few atomic coordinates needed to be determined and refined. The final *R* value was 0.045. The positional and thermal parameters are given in Table 3; Fig. 16 shows an ORTEP illustration of the unit cell. The key feature is the short platinum-platinum interionic distance parallel to the *c* axis; this distance is only 0.03 Å longer than the platinum-platinum distance in the metal. Figure 17 illustrates the manner in which the platinum atoms interact with each other and allow electricity to flow along the *c* axis (the needle axis), but not along the *a* and *b* axes. In other salts, in which the platinum-platinum distance is somewhat longer, the conductivity is not as good.

Understanding the physical and chemical properties of a structure often necessitates observing many structures to compare their features (bond distances, bond angles, coordination geometries, intermolecular interactions). In this case, the conductivity is related not only to the platinum-platinum distance, but also to the partial oxidation states of the platinum atoms and the relative orientations of the $Pt(CN)_4^{4-}$ planes. Correlations of structures and properties are often major research projects.

Data Bases in Single-Crystal Analysis

An exponentially increasing number of crystal structures are being reported in the literature. Four data bases have been developed to store this data, and computer programs have been written to search the data bases for specific information:

- *Crystal Data*: Crystallographic Section, National Bureau of Standards, Washing-

ton, DC, 20234, USA. Reduced unit cell parameters. Most useful for identification of unknown crystalline phases or for finding phases with similar unit cells (isomorphous or isostructural materials)

- *Cambridge Crystallographic Data File*: Crystallographic Data Centre, University Chemical Laboratory, Lensfield Road, Cambridge, CB2 1EW, United Kingdom. Structural data (unit cell, space group, positional parameters, chemical connectivities) of all crystals containing organic carbon atoms. Uses include searching compounds to determine if structures have been analyzed, seeking structural fragments to determine their geometries, and locating structures related to those under determination

- *Inorganic Crystal Structure Data Base*: Fachinformationszentrum Energie Physik Mathematik, D-7514 Eggenstein-Leopoldshafen 2, West Germany. Structural data for all inorganic crystals except

those included in the Cambridge or Metals data bases. Uses are the same as those for the Cambridge File

- *Metals Data File*: National Research Council of Canada, Chemistry Division, Ottawa, Ontario, K1A OR9, Canada. Structural data for all metals and alloys. Uses are the same as those for the Cambridge File

Many of the these data bases are available on national computer facilities. Some of the

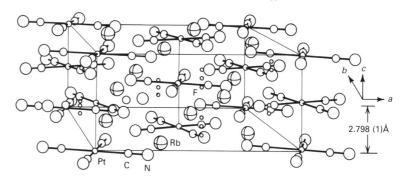

Fig. 16 Perspective view of the unit cell of $Rb_2[Pt(CN)_4](FHF)_{0.4}$

The small circles are the partially filled fluorine atom positions. The platinum-platinum spacing is the shortest known for any $Pt(CN)_4^{x-}$ 1-D metal complex. The corresponding platinum-chain conductivity is the highest ($\sim2000\ \Omega^{-1}\ cm^{-1}$ at 298 K) for any known complex of this type. Source: Ref 16

Table 3 Positional and thermal parameters for $Rb_2[Pt(CN)_4](FHF)_{0.40}$

Atom	x(a)	y	z	B Å²(b)
Pt	0.0	0.0	0.0	(c)
C	0.0550(8)	0.1480(8)	0.0	(c)
N	0.0871(8)	0.2325(8)	0.0	(c)
Rb. . . .	0.1555(3)	06555	0.0	(c)
F(1)	0.0	0.5	0.155(14)	4.9(11)
F(2)	0.0	0.5	0.25	5.7(13)

Anisotropic thermal parameters × 10 000(d)

Atom	β_{11}	β_{22}	β_{33}	β_{12}	β_{13}	β_{23}
Pt . . .	25.3(5)	25.3	84(2)	0	0	0
C . . .	48(7)	27(5)	117(29)	1(5)	0	0
N . . .	59(7)	51(7)	295(40)	−15(6)	0	0
Rb. . .	72(2)	72	382(8)	27(1)	0	0

(a) *x, y*, and *z* are fractional coordinates. (b) Isotropic temperature factor of the form exp $(−B^2 (\sin^2 \phi)/\lambda^2)$. (c) Atoms refined anisotropically. (d) Anisotropic thermal parameters of the form exp $−(h^2 \beta_{11} + k^2 \beta_{22} + l^2 \beta_{33} + 2hk\beta_{12} + 2hl\beta_{13} + 2kl\beta_{23})$. See Eq 14. Source: Ref 16

Fig. 17 Stacking of square-planar $[Pt(CN)_4]^{x-}$ groups showing the overlapping of platinum d_{z^2} orbitals

Source: Ref 16

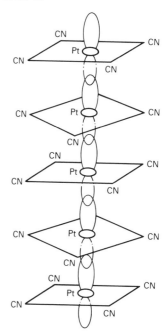

data-base information is also available in book form, although costs are prohibitive. Reference 18 is one source of information on metals and alloys, including carbides, nitrides, and hydrides.

REFERENCES

1. L. Bragg, Ed., *The Crystalline State*, Vol 4, *Crystal Structures of Minerals*, Cornell University Press, 1965
2. C.W. Bunn, *Chemical Crystallography*, Oxford University Press, 1946
3. M.J. Buerger, *Elementary Crystallography*, John Wiley & Sons, 1963
4. T. Hahn, Ed., *International Tables for Crystallography*, Vol A, *Space-group Tables*, Kluwer Academic Publishers, 1983
5. G.H. Stout and L.J. Jensen, *X-Ray Structure Determination*, MacMillan, 1968
6. D. Crowfoot, C.W. Burn, B.W. Rogers-Low, and A. Turner-Jones, in *The Chemistry of Penicillin*, H.T. Clarke, J.R. Johnson, and R. Robinson, Ed., Princeton University Press, 1949
7. D.P. Shoemaker, in *Critical Evaluation of Chemical and Physical Structural Information*, D.R. Lide, Jr., and M.A. Paul, Ed., National Academy of Sciences, Washington, 1974
8. P.G. Jones, *Chem. Soc. Rev.*, Vol 13, 1984, p 157-173
9. J.A. Ibers, in *Critical Evaluation of Chemical and Physical Structural Information*, D.R. Lide, Jr., and M.A. Paul, Ed., National Academy of Sciences, Washington, 1974, p 186-198
10. G. Zanotti, A. Del Pra, G. Bombieri, and A.M. Tamburro, *Acta Crystallogr. B*, Vol 34, 1978, p 2138-2141
11. J. Iball and S.N. Scrimgeour, *Acta Crystallogr. B*, Vol 33, 1977, p 1194-1196
12. C.J. Lock, R.A. Speranzini, and M. Avagulis, *Acta Crystallogr. B*, Vol 36, 1980, p 1789-1793
13. *Crystal Data Determinative Tables*, U.S. Department of Commerce, Washington, National Bureau of Standards, Washington; and the International Centre for Diffraction Data (JCPDS), Swarthmore, PA, 1973
14. E.M. McCarron III and J.C. Calabrese, *J. Solid State Chem.*, in press
15. R.L. Harlow, W.J. Wells III, G.W. Watt, and S.H. Simonsen, *Inorg. Chem.*, Vol 13, 1974, p 2106-2111
16. J.M. Williams, *Adv. Inorg. Chem. Radiochem.*, Vol 26, 1983, p 235-268
17. A.J. Schultz, D.P. Gerrity, and J.M. Williams, *Inorg. Chem.*, Vol 16, 1977, p 2129-2131
18. W.B. Pearson, *A Handbook of Lattice Spacings and Structures of Metals and Alloys*, Pergamon Press, 1985

SELECTED REFERENCE

- J.P. Glusker and K.N. Trueblood, *Crystal Structure Analysis: A Primer*, 2nd ed., Oxford University Press, 1985

Crystallographic Texture Measurement and Analysis

Brent L. Adams, Department of Mechanical Engineering, Brigham Young University

General Uses

- Quantitative determination of crystallographic preferred orientations in polycrystalline samples

Examples of Applications

- Quantitative description of deformation and recrystallization textures in metals and ceramics, including geological materials

Samples

- *Form*: Samples must be flat sections taken from the polycrystal. For transmission, samples must be thinned to a uniform thickness. The orientation of the surface normal must be precisely specified relative to the polycrystalline processing axes; another reference direction, such as the rolling direction, usually must also be known
- *Size*: The grain size of the polycrystal must be small compared to the x-ray beam diameter so that the beam irradiates a minimum of approximately 5000 grains; the sample may be oscillated to increase the area covered
- *Preparation*: The surface must be polished carefully to remove any possible disturbance from milling or cutting
- *Other requirements*: A random powder sample of the same shape as the textured sample usually must be prepared

Limitations

- Obtaining valid measurements of intensity is generally not possible when the x-ray source beam lies $\geq 70°$ from the direction normal to the sample surface because of geometric defocusing aberrations

- The crystallographic pole figure does not describe completely the orientation distribution for the sample; a complete description may be computed from a set of pole figures (the orientation distribution function)

Estimated Analysis Time

- Reliable pole figures can typically be measured in 10 to 100 min, depending on the diffraction equipment available. Because at least three pole figures are generally required to compute the orientation distribution function, this may require 30 to 180 min
- Computational time is usually insignificant compared to measurement time

Capabilities of Related Techniques

- *Neutron diffraction*: Increasingly prevalent as an alternative to x-ray measurement of pole figures, this technique can penetrate depths of up to four to five orders of magnitude larger than x-rays. Thus, true volume-averaged textures are measured. Sample preparation is simple in neutron experiments, and defocusing problems can usually be eliminated. However, suitable neutron sources are not readily accessible, and beam time may be expensive
- Some pole figures and orientation distribution functions can be determined from many single-crystal orientations, for example, single grain orientation by selected area channeling analysis using a scanning electron microscope. These methods are tedious, because measuring statistically reliable numbers of single orientations may involve over 3000 grains

Introduction

Crystallographic texture measurement and analysis, an important tool in correlating the properties of a material to its microstructural features, can be performed on any polycrystalline material. Polycrystalline materials consist of many small crystals, or grains, separated by thin boundaries assembled compactly in an aggregate. The individual crystals, or crystallites, are relatively free of defects compared to the boundary structure. Thus, a complete description of a polycrystal is complex. On a scale of the size of the crystallites (approximately 1 μm to 1 mm), at least the shape, volume, and crystallographic orientation of each grain must be prescribed. In a tensile sample of typical dimensions, up to 10^{10} grains may require characterization. There will also be an internal structure in each grain on a much finer scale (approximately 1 to 100 nm), including second phases, dislocation tangles, and point defects. These structural features also affect material behavior significantly. Therefore, complete structural characterization of the polycrystalline body is not feasible.

Correlating observed properties to microstructural features usually necessitates measuring parameters that represent a mean value of readily accessible microstructural features. Typical examples include the mean linear intercept measure of grain size and the average dislocation density in a grain. The scale of these parameters usually determines the difficulty of their measurement. For example, because accurate determination of dislocation densities is more difficult than measurement of mean grain size, microstructural correlations to material properties are more common on the larger scale of the crystallites. However, material properties are often governed by those microstructural features observed on a finer scale. For example, dislocation structure often dominates electrical resistivities in metals.

Crystallographic texture is a relatively accessible measure of average grain orientation in polycrystalline bodies. Straightforward methods of x-ray (or neutron) diffraction can be used to map grain orientations averaged over many grains to indicate prominent or most probable orientations. Texture measurement has become more prevalent over the past 20 years with the broadening of the analytical foundation for texture analysis and the documentation of numerous correlations of texture to material behavior. When control and analysis software is fully implemented, the time requirement for texture characterization using automated x-ray equipment and modest computational capability is of the same order as the effort required for an accurate grain

size measurement. Exceeding this is the complexity of texture analysis, as evident in the required computer algorithms; successful interpretation of the results requires a sound understanding of the analysis.

Preferred orientation is common in polycrystalline bodies. For example, preferred orientation is established in castings as preferred crystallographic orientations in freezing nuclei align themselves with the thermal gradient direction at the solid/liquid interface. Because crystalline powders are often nonspherical, powder compacts typically exhibit a preferred orientation reflecting the shape interaction of powders during compaction. Recrystallization textures are observed after annealing, suggesting the existence of complex orientation relationships between parent and daughter grains. Mechanical deformations exceeding approximately 30% strain begin to effect substantial texturing due to grain reorientations resulting from slip or twinning processes. Virtually all polycrystalline bodies exhibit some texturing; more difficult is the production of a material without texture.

Preferred orientations often alter property behavior, because crystals are inherently anisotropic. For example, Young's modulus varies with direction in most crystals. In face-centered cubic (fcc) crystals, Young's modulus is substantially lower in ⟨100⟩ directions than in ⟨111⟩ directions. Thus, when crystallographic texture is present in a sample, the observed Young's modulus is also anisotropic. The bulk value of Young's modulus can be predicted with acceptable accuracy by a simple average of the crystalline moduli over the distribution of crystal orientations in the direction of the applied stress.

Fig. 1 Construction of the stereographic projection

A point *P* on the surface of the reference sphere is projected to point *P'* on the projection plane

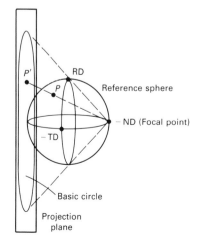

Consideration of the grain-to-grain interaction stresses that develop during loading will enhance the estimate.

The principal advantage of measuring crystallographic textures quantitatively is the possibility of predicting material behavior. This cannot be accomplished with models that predict crystalline response to various stimuli (mechanical, electrical, magnetic, and so on) in conjunction with models that predict the aggregate response from crystalline behavior. Quantitative texture data are fundamental in the equation, but little benefit will be realized without successful models.

This article is an introduction to texture analysis. Elements of the experimental techniques and the mathematical treatment will be covered. Also to be covered are x-ray diffraction methods, which will be compared with neutron diffraction. Information on modeling is cited in the Selected References.

Descriptions of Preferred Orientation

Orientations Represented in the Stereographic Projection. In describing the orientation of individual grains in a section of rolled sheet material, a useful selection of coordinate system for the sheet itself would be the rolling (length) direction, RD; the sheet normal (thickness) direction, ND; and the transverse (width) direction, TD. These axes are orthogonal, or mutually perpendicular. If the crystalline form is cubic, an appropriate set of coordinate axes for the crystallites would be the {100} plane normals [100], [010], and [001], which are also orthogonal. The sample axes (RD-TD-ND) or the crystal axes ([100], [010], and [001]) may be selected as the reference coordinate system. Specifying the other coordinate system relative to the reference system specifies the orientation completely.

The stereographic projection is readily visualized by centering a sphere of arbitrary radius (termed the reference sphere) about the origin of the reference coordinate system. With the sample axes as the reference, the stereographic projection is constructed as shown in Fig. 1. It is simply a projection of points on the top hemispherical surface of the reference sphere (representing vectors or directions) onto a plane parallel to the RD-TD plane. The focal point of the stereographic projection is commonly defined to be along the −ND direction. Figure 2 illustrates one possible orientation of a grain having three projected points representing the {100} family of plane. Also shown, for the [010] direction, are the spherical polar angles χ and η, which are frequently used to specify the orientation or individual axes or poles. These angles are clarified in Fig. 3.

Fig. 2 Crystal axes using the stereographic projection

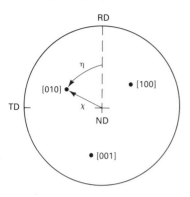

Fig. 4 Three consecutive Euler rotations defining an orientation

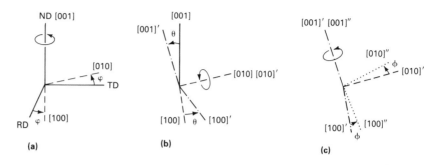

(a)   **(b)**   **(c)**

Fig. 3 Spherical polar angles defining directions in the RD-TD-ND coordinate system

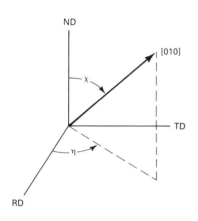

Only three angles are necessary to fix the orientation of a grain relative to the macroscopic reference axes. Although a pair of χ, η angles could be specified for each of the $\langle 100 \rangle$ directions, only three of this set of six angles would be independent. That is, two angles specify a direction, or the orientation of a plane, as shown in Fig. 3. The orientation of the crystal is then fixed by specifying the orientation of a direction in the plane. This requires only one additional angle. If the position of the (010) plane ([010] direction) is specified as shown in Fig. 2 using χ and η, directions [001] and [100] must lie on the same great circle centered about the origin. A single rotational angle of arbitrary origin will fix the location of the two directions. Therefore, specifying a pair of polar angles for each of the $\{100\}$ planes is not an efficient orientation determination. A more efficient system is that of Euler angles.

Specifying Orientation. Several choices of Euler angles are possible, and different selections alter important details of

texture analysis. One choice is the method developed by R.J. Roe, which is used extensively in England and America. The other system, commonly used in Europe, is that of H.J. Bunge.

Figure 4 shows a reference or starting position of the cubic crystal coincident with the macroscopic axes RD, TD, and ND. In Roe formalism, the crystal axes are first rotated counterclockwise to an angle φ about ND (Fig. 4a). The second rotation is about the new position of the [010] direction (Fig. 4b). The extent of this second counterclockwise rotation is θ. The new positions of the $\langle 100 \rangle$ directions are primed. Finally, the third rotation of ϕ is counterclockwise about [001]' (Fig. 4c). The final axis orientations are shown double primed. In Bunge formalism, the second rotation is counterclockwise about the [100] direction rather than [010]. The other two rotations are identical.

The rotations φ, θ, and ϕ define all possible orientation relationships between macroscopic and crystalline coordinate systems. The three Euler angles, the spherical-polar angles χ and η, and the spherical-polar angles Θ and Φ complete the set of angular parameters used in Roe formalism. The last two angles define directions or vectors relative to the crystalline axes. Figure 5 shows the complete set of angles; the original Roe notation for coordinate axes has been preserved. The equivalence usually is $z = \text{ND}$, $y = \text{TD}$, $x = \text{RD}$, $Z = [001]$, $Y = [010]$, and $X = [100]$ for consideration of rolled products with cubic crystal structure. The selection is arbitrary.

Metallurgical Specification of Preferred Orientation. A straightforward specification of the dominant components of preferred orientation is the metallurgical description. For wires or rods, one or more crystallographic planes will align themselves perpendicular to the fiber axis. These orientations frequently dominate the texture. Wires and rods are fabricated in axisymmetric dies during drawing, extrusion, or swaging; therefore, directions lying in the

preferred plane are randomly distributed about the wire or rod axis. Such textures are known as fiber textures. In the metallurgical description of fiber textures, the Miller index of the crystallographic direction aligned with the fiber axis designates the preferred orientation. Thus, in cubic materials in which $\{111\}$ and $\{100\}$ planes are predominantly oriented perpendicular to the wire axis, it is necessary only to indicate that the wire has a [111] and [100] fiber texture.

In rolled sheet materials, a two-component designation is commonly used. Miller indices are implemented. The dominant plane (hkl) lying parallel to the rolling plane and the dominant crystallographic direction $[uvw]$ lying parallel to the rolling direction are specified. Therefore, rolling textures are specified by the pair $(hkl)[uvw]$ or $\{hkl\}\langle uvw \rangle$. For example, in fcc metals, such as aluminum, copper, and nickel, the dominant texture orientations are $(123)[\bar{4}12] + (146)[\bar{2}\bar{1}1] + (112)[11\bar{1}]$, but

Fig. 5 The complete set of angles for Roe's analysis of orientation

The index i denotes different pole figures. The angles χ and η fix the diffracting plane normal, r_i, to specimen axes x, y, and z. The angles Θ_i and Φ_i fix this direction to the crystal axes X, Y, and Z. Also shown are the Euler angles φ, θ, and ϕ.

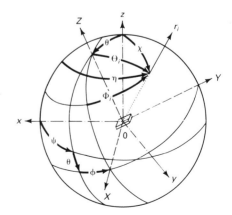

Fig. 6 Eulerian cradle mounted on the ω-axis of a diffractometer

The unit vectors S_0 and S depict the source and diffracted beams, respectively. The angles χ and η correspond to those shown in Fig. 2.

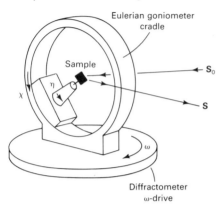

in cubic materials of lower stacking-fault energy, such as brass, silver, and stainless steel, the dominant components are $(110)[\bar{1}12] + (110)[001]$.

Pole Figures. Specifying individual preferred orientations has severe limitations, because texturing is never complete and a spread of preferred orientation is always observed. The pole figure, which can be measured using x-ray diffraction, helps to describe the spread of preferred orientations. The pole figure has long been a dominant form for representing crystallographic textures.

By fixing the Bragg angle, ϑ (usually Θ, which will be used below for a different quantity), and the wavelength of the probing radiation, λ, diffraction will occur only from planes with interplanar spacing d fixed by the Bragg equation $n\lambda = 2d \sin \vartheta$, where $n = 1, 2$, and so on. Bragg's law is discussed in the article "Introduction" in the Section "Diffraction Methods" in this Volume. In determining pole figures, a sample is prepared with a flat surface. The direction normal to the surface and a direction in the surface are identified in some fixed relationship to the macroscopic processing axes. For sheet materials, common practice is to prepare the sample surface parallel to the rolling plane, then identify in that plane the rolling direction, perhaps using a scribe mark. Measuring a pole figure then consists of fixing the wavelength, λ, and the Bragg angle, ϑ, to examine a single plane, followed by rotation of the sample in numerous orientations covering the hemisphere of the stereographic projection. This rotation is typically performed using a Eulerian goniometer attached to an x-ray diffractometer (Fig. 6).

In Fig. 6, the diffraction angle, ω, is fixed relative to the Bragg angle such that the plane of the goniometer bisects the diffraction vectors S_0 and S. Thus, grains with crystallographic planes of interplanar spacing d lying in the direction $S - S_0$ will diffract. Other grains in the polycrystal not satisfying this condition do not contribute to the diffracted intensity along S. Therefore, by scanning the range of $0 \leq \chi \leq \pi/2$ and $0 \leq \eta \leq 2\pi$, a distribution of plane-normal intensities referred to as a pole figure is measured over the stereographic projection. Changing the Bragg angle or the wavelength implies observing a new plane, d, and therefore a new pole figure.

To illustrate, diffraction conditions are fixed such that the {111} planes will diffract in an fcc material, and a sheet material, such as Cu-3Zn, that exhibits dominant {112}⟨111⟩, {123}⟨634⟩, and {110}⟨112⟩ preferred orientations is examined. Figure 7(a) shows the expected positions of ⟨111⟩ poles for three variants of the preferred orientations.

Fig. 7 Expected pole orientations of preferred orientations in Cu-3Zn

(a) Expected positions of ⟨111⟩ poles for three specific variants of the preferred orientations. (b) Expected ⟨111⟩ orientations when two mirror planes are introduced. Figure 8 shows the measured ⟨111⟩ pole figure for the same alloy; note similarities between Fig. 7(b) and 8.

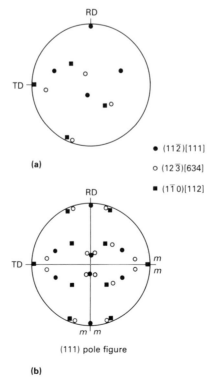

- (11$\bar{2}$)[111]
- (12$\bar{3}$)[634]
- (1$\bar{1}$0)[112]

(a)

(111) pole figure

(b)

Fig. 8 Measured (111) pole figure for Cu-3Zn

Source: Ref 2

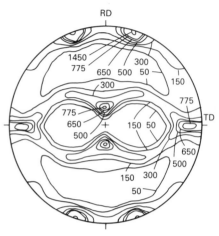

Figure 7(b) presents a more complete set of ⟨111⟩ orientations when two mirror planes typical of sheet-rolled materials are introduced. Three mirror planes are expected in rolling perpendicular to the RD, TD, and ND directions; only two are visible in Fig. 7(b). The measured (111) pole figure for rolled Cu-3Zn is shown in Fig. 8. The similarities between the idealized construction and the measured pole figure are apparent.

Most pole figures are measured using a thick-sample reflection technique that requires specialized geometrical and defocusing corrections when the angle χ exceeds approximately 70°. Thin transmission samples are sometimes used where $S + S_0$ passes through the thin section, necessitating a correction for x-ray absorption. Additional information on pole-figure determination is cited in Ref 1.

Euler Plots and the Orientation Distribution Function. The pole figure, which specifies distributions of crystallographic plane poles, is ambiguous in that only two of the three angles necessary for complete orientation specification are given. The pole is fixed, but directions in the plane are not. Several pole figures, providing distributions of several different plane poles, can be used to clarify the picture of preferred orientations, but this method is qualitative and sometimes misleading.

The orientation distribution function (ODF) is a function defined over the range of Euler angles φ, θ, and φ. It provides the probability that a grain has a particular orientation given by the three Euler angles. If a range of angles is defined as $d\varphi \, d\theta \, d\phi$, referred to as an incremental volume in Euler space, the volume fraction of grains having

Fig. 9 Euler space in Roe's notation

Points in the cube represent discrete orientations. For materials of cubic symmetry, regions I, II, and III represent equivalent orientations.

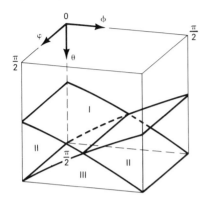

an orientation in a range $d\varphi\ d\theta\ d\phi$ around φ, θ, and ϕ is:

$$\frac{dV}{V} = w\ (\varphi,\theta,\phi)\ \sin\theta\ d\varphi\ d\theta\ d\phi$$

where $w(\varphi,\theta,\phi)$ is the ODF.

Figure 9 shows the Euler space. For cubic materials with rolling symmetry only the range of 0 to $\pi/2$ need be considered for each of the three Euler angles. All possible orientations are in this range. In addition, because of the high degree of symmetry exhibited in cubic crystals, only a portion of the cube representing Euler space is required. Each of the three regions shown within the cube contains equivalent orientation information. Thus, specifying a point in region I fixes on points in regions II and III of equivalent orientation. A volume of Euler space is a subvolume in the cube.

Identified with each point in the cube of Euler space is a number representing $w(\varphi,\theta,\phi)$, the ODF. Different materials exhibit diverse values of the ODF at each point. Because it is impossible to illustrate such functions as the ODF in two dimensions, Euler plots, which are sections through Euler space at evenly spaced intervals of a single angle, are commonly used. Figure 10 shows sections of copper 10100 tubing at discrete, evenly spaced values of ϕ (10° increments). The contour levels represent equipollent (equal strength) values of the ODF. For tubing, the angle φ must be permitted to vary from 0 to π rather than from 0 to $\pi/2$ for sheet materials, because tube processing operations do not impose the triad of mirror symmetries typical of sheet rolling. Rather, only a single mirror plane containing the tube axis and the radial direction of the tube wall is required.

The range of Euler angles necessary for varying processing conditions must be carefully evaluated.

The Series Method of ODF Analysis

The series method predominates for calculation of the ODF, $w(\varphi,\theta,\phi)$, from pole figures. This method uses series expansions to represent the ODF and the pole figures. The expansions are of specialized complete orthogonal functions weighted by coefficients. Background information on spherical harmonics, crystallographic symmetry, and group theory can be obtained in the selected references listed at the end of this article. Software is available in Roe and Bunge formalisms for cubic sheet-formed materials. More complex software packages that treat hexagonal or lower symmetry polycrystals and less highly symmetric forming operations, such as tube extrusion, are less common. Figure 5 defines angles discussed below.

Series Representations. In this technique, $I(\chi,\eta)$ represents the intensity distribution measured in the pole-figure experi-ment (measurements of intensity in the pole-figure experiment generally require corrections for sample geometry, defocusing at large χ angles, and absorption for transmission samples). A plane-normal orientation distribution $q(\chi,\eta)$ is then defined by normalizing the intensity distribution:

$$q(\chi,\eta) = \frac{I(\chi,\eta)}{\int_0^{2\pi}\int_0^{\pi} I(\chi,\eta)\ \sin\chi\ d\chi\ d\eta} \quad \text{(Eq 1)}$$

The term pole density is used for the function $(4\pi)q(\chi,\eta)$.

This function can be readily expanded in a series of spherical harmonics, P_l^m (cos χ)$e^{-im\eta}$, where the functions P_l^m (cos χ) are the associated Legendre functions used extensively in quantum mechanics. The spherical harmonics form a complete set of orthogonal functions over the surface of a sphere, that is, $0 \leq \chi \leq \pi$ and $0 \leq \eta \leq 2\pi$. Thus, any function in χ and η can be represented in a series of spherical harmonics weighted with appropriate coefficients, including the plane-normal distribution:

Fig. 10 Orientation distribution function for copper 10100 tubing using method of Euler plots

θ and φ vary as shown in lower right-hand corner. The value of φ for each slice is given in each rectangle.

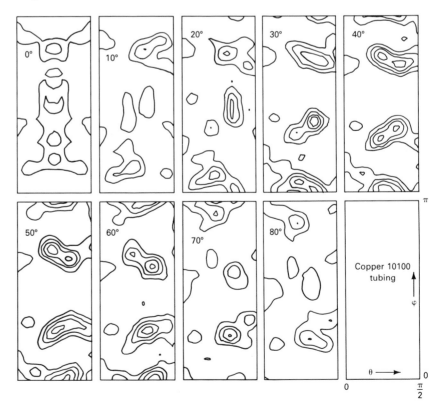

$$q(\chi, \eta) = \sum_{l=0}^{\infty} \sum_{m=-l}^{l} Q_{lm} P_l^m (\cos \chi) \, e^{-im\eta}$$

(Eq 2)

The coefficients Q_{lm} are usually complex numbers that may be evaluated from the orthogonality property of the spherical harmonics:

$$\int_0^{2\pi} \int_0^{\pi} P_{l'}^{m'} (\cos \chi) \, e^{-i(m-m')\eta}$$

$$\sin \chi \, d\chi \, d\eta = 2\pi \, \delta_{ll'} \, \delta_{mm'} \quad \text{(Eq 3)}$$

The term $\delta_{ll'}$, the Kronecker Delta, is 1 if $l = l'$ and 0 if $l \neq l'$. Multiplying both sides of Eq 2 with the harmonic $P_{l'}^{m'}(\cos \chi) e^{im'\eta}$ and integrating over the range of χ and η yields an expression suitable for calculating the relevant coefficients Q_{lm}:

$$Q_{l'm'} = \frac{1}{2\pi} \int_0^{2\pi} \int_0^{\pi} q(\chi, \eta) \, P_{l'}^{m'}$$

$$(\cos \chi) \, e^{im'\eta} \, \sin \chi \, d\chi \, d\eta \quad \text{(Eq 4)}$$

Similarly, the ODF, $w(\varphi, \theta, \phi)$, can be expanded in a series of generalized spherical harmonics, $Z_{lmn} (\cos \theta) e^{-im\psi} e^{-in\phi}$:

$$w(\varphi, \theta, \phi) = \sum_{l=0}^{\infty} \sum_{m=-l}^{l} \sum_{n=-l}^{l} W_{lmn} \, Z_{lmn}$$

$$(\cos \theta) \, e^{-im\psi} \, e^{-in\phi} \quad \text{(Eq 5)}$$

Once the series coefficients, W_{lmn}, are known, the ODF is specified. They are generally complex numbers. A simple relationship exists between the three-angle generalized spherical harmonics and the two-angle type used to represent the plane-normal distribution:

$$P_l^m (\cos \chi) = Z_{lm0} (\cos \chi) \quad \text{(Eq 6)}$$

Determination of ODF Coefficients. The Lengendre addition theorem is used to relate the W_{lmn} coefficients to the coefficients for several pole figures. By distinguishing between pole figures using

an index, i, the addition theorem produces:

$$Q_{lm}^i = (2\pi)\left(\frac{2}{2l+1}\right)^{1/2} \sum_{n=-l}^{l} W_{lmn} \, P_l^n$$

$$(\cos \Theta_i) e^{in\Phi_i} \quad \text{(Eq 7)}$$

As shown in Fig. 5, the angles Θ_i and Φ_i represent the spherical-polar angles fixing the ith diffraction vector r_i, or $\mathbf{S} - \mathbf{S}_0$, relative to the crystal coordinate axes. Thus, using Eq 7, if sufficient pole figures are available, a system of linear equations may be solved for W_{lmn}.

The number of pole figures required to determine these coefficients depends on the quantity that is linearly independent. In Roe formalism, this relies explicitly on the crystal symmetry. For example, in cubic materials for $l \leq 22$, the only independent W_{lmn} may be W_{lm0} and W_{lm4}. Similarly, the number of m subscripts required in the analysis depends explicitly on the symmetry of the forming operation. For sheet materials, only even values of m are required, and for fiber or wire textures, only the coefficients Q_{l0}^i and W_{l0n} require consideration. That is, selection rules are established in Roe formalism based on considerations of symmetry.

In the Bunge formulation, the series expansions are similar, except (1) the Euler angles selected to represent orientations are different, altering formulation of the spherical harmonics used, and (2) all the crystallographic and statistical (polycrystalline) symmetry is placed into the spherical harmonics. This second point causes difficulties in comparing the two methods.

The relationships in Eq 1 to 7 are typically used in texture analysis when complete pole figures are available. Defocusing aberrations limit the range of χ over which reflection pole figures can be measured. Techniques of analysis are available that allow the more difficult calculation of W_{lmn} coefficients from incomplete pole figures.

The limitation Friedel's law imposes on all diffraction experiments, such as measuring the pole figure, is that observed diffraction data exhibit centrosymmetry, a symmetry of reflection through the origin of the stereographic projection. This symmetry element is not imposed by nature on the polycrystal, but is an artifact of the diffraction experiment. Therefore, in the series expansion of the ODF, certain secondary peaks observed in the Euler plots are illusory "ghost" peaks. The several methods for their removal that have been proposed remain under development. In materials property prediction, the "ghost" portion of the ODF cannot significantly affect averaging

Fig. 11 (111) pole figure for copper 10100 tubing taken from the midwall

Fig. 12 (111) pole figure for copper 10100 tubing taken from the inside wall

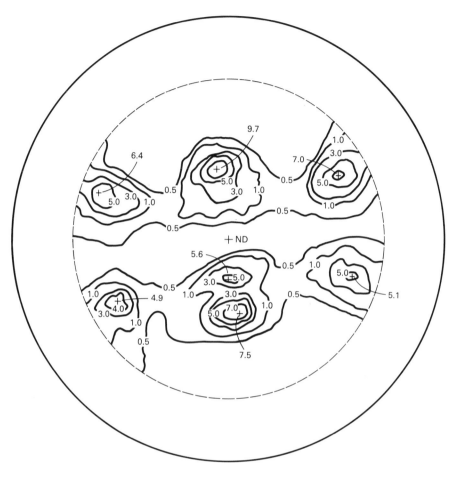

Fig. 13 α- and β-fibers in rolled copper

Courtesy of Jürgen Hirsch, Aachen

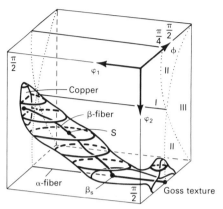

calculations for most properties of interest. Other limitations of the series method are related to experimental uncertainties, computational precision, and error introduced by truncating the series expansions to a finite order of *l*.

Applications

Example 1: (111) Pole Figures From Copper Tubing. Figures 11 and 12 show (111) pole figures from copper 10100 tubing. Figure 11 illustrates the midwall of the tubing; Fig. 12, the inside wall.

Samples were prepared by chemically etching selected layers of the tube wall using a solution containing nitric acid (HNO_3). The selected layer was thinned to a thickness of approximately 0.1 mm (0.004 in.), then opened by slitting the tube. Care was taken to introduce only elastic strains in the

thinned layer to ensure that the texture was not altered.

A random sample of copper was prepared by mixing a fine copper powder (~100 μm mesh size) in an epoxy binder. The powder sample was prepared to have the same geometric shape as the thin-layer samples taken from the tubing. The density of this powder compact was found to be approximately half that for fully dense copper.

This random sample was used to prepare a geometric defocusing correction, because the intensity of pole-figure measurements is usually found to decrease with increasing angle χ during sample rotation. This decrease cannot be a texture effect, because the sample is random. The rotation in χ was terminated at $\chi \leq 75°$ because of excessive intensity loss due to defocusing at larger angles.

For the pole figures shown in Fig. 11 and 12, a high-voltage rotating anode source of

Cu Kα radiation was used. Recorded intensities were first corrected for background by subtracting the average measured noise levels adjacent to the peak.

Figures 11 and 12 illustrate the nonuniformity of texture through the wall thickness of tubing. Similar differences are visible in rolled materials. Particularly noticeable are the variations in symmetry between the midwall texture and the inside wall texture. Figure 11 (midwall) shows a well-developed mirror symmetry across the AD (axial length direction of the tube) and ND (thickness direction of the tube) planes. In Fig. 12, however, an additional mirror plane perpendicular to the previous one is almost completely formed. In contrast to the midwall texture, the symmetry of the texture near the inside diameter of the tube is almost orthotropic, as in sheet-rolled materials. The Euler plots in Fig. 10 were calculated on the basis of the midwall texture shown in Fig. 11 when the (111) was combined with (200) and (220) pole figures. An incomplete pole-figure analysis was used.

Example 2: Features of Rolling Textures in fcc Materials. Rolled fcc materials characteristically develop fibers in the space of Euler angles. That is, the ODF develops a fibrous or tubelike structure common to many fcc polycrystals. Figure 13 shows a representation of Euler space. The Euler angles are those of Bunge, φ_1, ϕ, and φ_2, showing the location of the α and β fibers characteristic of rolled materials. The ODF is shown only for points in region I.

The details of the structure of the α and β fibers in the ODF depend strongly on the percent reduction imposed during the rolling operation. Figure 14 shows plots of peak value of the ODF along the fiber lines as a function of rolling reduction. For these plots,

Fig. 14 Orientation distribution function along fiber lines as a function of percent rolling reduction

(a) α-fiber. (b) β-fiber. (Courtesy of Jürgen Hirsch, Aachen)

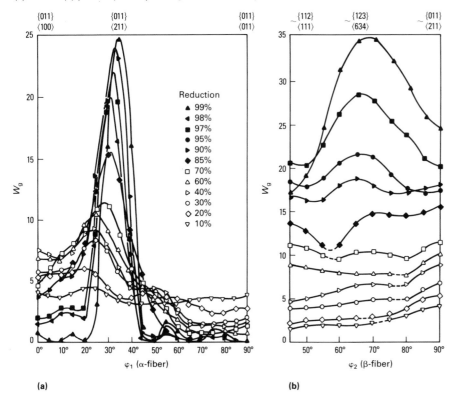

only a single variable in Euler space (φ_1 for the α fiber or φ_2 for the β fiber) is necessary, because the position of the central skeletal line of the fibers is well established. The plots show the occurrence of the preferred orientations, given in their metallurgical description, across the top of the figure. For example, with rolling reduction increases from 10 to 99%, the occurrence of the {011}⟨211⟩ preferred orientation is observed to increase approximately 25-fold (Fig. 14a).

REFERENCES

1. H.J. Bunge and C. Esling, Ed., *Quantitative Texture Analysis*, Deutsche Gesellschaft fur Metallkunde, Adenauerallee, GDR, 1982
2. A. Merlini and P.A. Beck, *Trans. AIME*, Vol 203, 1955, p 385

SELECTED REFERENCES

- H.J. Bunge, *Texture Analysis in Materials Science, Mathematical Methods*, Butterworths, 1982
- B.D. Cullity, *Elements of X-Ray Diffraction*, Addison-Wesley, 1967
- J. Szpunar, *At. Energy Rev.*, Vol 14 (No. 2), 1976, p 199-261

X-Ray Topography

Robert N. Pangborn, Department of Engineering Science and Mechanics, The Pennsylvania State University

General Uses

- Imaging of individual lattice defects, such as dislocations, twins, and stacking faults, in near-perfect crystals
- Nondestructive characterization of surface relief, texture, lattice distortion, and strain fields due to defects and defect accumulations in imperfect single crystals and polycrystalline aggregates
- Measurement of crystal defect densities as well as crystallite/subgrain sizes and shapes
- Evaluation of tilt angles across subgrain boundaries, interfacial defects and strains, domain structures, and other substructural entities

Examples of Applications

- Study of crystal growth, recrystallization, and phase transformations, focusing on crystal perfection and attendant defects
- Characterization of deformation processes and fracture behavior
- Correlation between crystal defects and electronic properties in solid-state device materials
- Synchrotron radiation extends the use of topography to permit the study of dynamic processes, such as magnetic domain motion, *in situ* transformations (solidification, polymerization, recrystallization), radiation damage, and yielding

Samples

- *Form*: For defect imaging (transmission or reflection case), flat, relatively perfect ($<10^6$ dislocations/cm^2) single crystals with uniform thickness or wedge shape. Evaluation of lattice distortions, texture, substructure, and surface relief in monocrystals, polycrystalline aggregates, ceramic or metal alloys, or composites
- *Size*: 1 × 1 cm (0.4 × 0.4 in.), 1 μm to several millimeters thick, up to 5-cm (2-in.) diam or larger wafers; thin films 100 nm and thicker
- *Preparation*: Usually desirable to remove surface damage due to cutting, abrading, and so on, from virgin material by chemical or electrolytic polishing

Limitations

- Sample must be crystalline
- Relatively defect-free crystals required for defect imaging techniques
- Thickness of single-crystal or polycrystalline samples that can be studied in transmission arrangement is limited by intensity and wavelength of incident radiation used as well as absorption by the sample
- Direct images are actual size. Further magnification must be obtained optically; that is, grain size of photographic plate emulsion must be small enough to allow substantial enlargement

Estimated Analysis Time

- Several minutes to hours exposure time for conventional photographic (plate or film) methods, in addition to developing/enlarging time
- Milliseconds to several seconds using synchrotron radiation and/or electronic or electro-optical imaging systems

Capabilities of Related Techniques

- *Optical metallography*: Characterization of grain size and shape, subgrains, phase morphology, and slip traces using suitable etchants; estimation of low dislocation densities and determination of slip systems by etch pit techniques
- *Scanning electron microscopy*: Observation of irregular surfaces, surface relief, and various features induced by deformation, such as slip bands and rumpling; examination of fracture surfaces to evaluate crack initiation and propagation
- *Electron channeling*: Qualitative evaluation of crystal perfection over shallow surface layer of crystals with high symmetry orientations
- *Transmission electron microscopy*: Imaging of line and planar defects and estimation of defect densities; substructural and morphological characterization of thin foils prepared from bulk sample or replicas taken from the surface
- *Neutron diffraction and topography*: Study of very thick or heavy metals in transmission arrangement and of magnetic domain structure

Introduction

X-ray topography is a technique that comprises topography and x-ray diffraction. The term topography refers to a detailed description and mapping of physical features in a region. In the context of x-ray diffraction, topographic methods are used to survey the lattice structure and imperfections in crystalline materials. The method and procedure used depend largely on the density of defects present and the nature of the crystalline material to be examined, but all methods share the capability for nondestructive application. Research in the semiconductor/device and structural/mechanical materials industries, both of which use topographic techniques extensively, is focused on the study of similar features of the crystal lattice, but on different levels.

For large, nearly perfect crystals, images of individual defects may be obtained and recorded on photographic plates or film. Defects near the surface can be completely characterized and defined using reflection topography (the Bragg case); defects in the bulk can be probed using transmission techniques (the Laue case) (Fig. 1). For relatively imperfect crystals, reflection topography can be applied to evaluate surface relief, small changes in crystallographic orientation, and the strains associated with the accumulation and/or interaction of various types of lattice defects in the near surface layer. X-ray topography can also be used to study the microstructural changes, lattice defects, strain distribution, and texture induced by thermal and deformation processing and during the service of polycrystalline aggregates, including metal alloys, ceramics, and composites.

Kinematical Theory of Diffraction.

Many x-ray diffraction techniques, such as those used for crystal structure determination, rely on uniformity in the sample, and any incidental nonuniformity in the diffraction spot is intentionally averaged using a suitable method. However, in x-ray topography, this intensity variation within the diffraction spot is of interest. The various topographic methods depend on the capability to record the microstructural detail of the diffraction spot as a diffraction profile or in a photographic image.

In theory, the diffracted intensities are attributed to a combination of kinematical and dynamical effects. The kinematical theory of diffraction accounts for the intensities reflected by ideally imperfect crystals. Such crystals are mosaic in structure, consisting of many small misaligned blocks (Ref 1). Only a single Bragg reflection takes place in the crystal, with waves scattered by each block interacting no further with each other

Fig. 1 Arrangements for x-ray topography

(a) Reflection topography (the Bragg case).
(b) Transmission topography (the Laue case). P, primary beam; R, diffracted beam; n, normal to diffraction planes; θ_B, Bragg angle

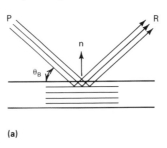

(a)

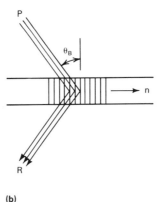

(b)

or with the lattice. This readily explains the origin of contrast in a reflection topograph of a highly distorted crystal. For example, if a white (polychromatic) beam of x-rays from a point source impinges on a crystal surface, any imperfections that introduce tilts between adjacent regions cause the reflected rays to overlap partially (Fig. 2a). A line source of monochromatic radiation used as shown in Fig. 2(b) produces much the same result. The primary beam has some divergence, and the deviations from a parallel lattice cause nonuniformity in the reflected intensity.

Many topographic characterizations involving metal alloys and other mechanical/structural materials require only consideration of kinematical diffraction. Rather than imaging materials on the basis of differences in x-ray absorption, as in x-ray radiography, the topographic techniques applied to polycrystals exploit the elastically (diffracted) and inelastically scattered x-rays. This allows diverse structural features, usually associated with the particular crystal structure and orientation, to be imaged in materials exhibiting only minor variations in x-ray absorption.

Fig. 2 Two methods for obtaining reflection topographs

(a) Polychromatic x-rays from a point source. The misoriented crystal domains are numbered 1 to 3 and separated by tilt boundaries I and II. (b) Top and side views of the line source of characteristic x-rays

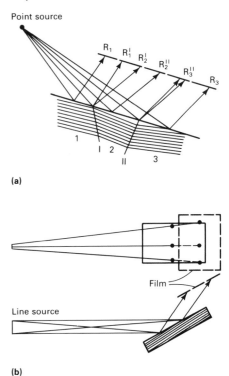

(a)

(b)

The dynamical theory of diffraction

treats the stronger wave interaction present in near-perfect crystals, for which multiple diffraction occurs. This contribution to x-ray diffraction phenomena enables the imaging of individual crystal defects, making x-ray diffraction topography a useful tool for characterizing and evaluating solid-state device materials.

The first predictions based on dynamical theory, and later observed experimentally using double-crystal diffractometry, were that the angular range of reflection for a perfect crystal would be narrow (seconds of arc) and that the integrated intensity would be orders of magnitude less than that for a similar but imperfect crystal (Fig. 3a). The latter phenomenon was rationalized by accounting for the attenuation of the incident beam due to the normal photoelectric absorption and to coherent scattering and multiple diffraction—the so-called primary extinction effect associated with successive reflections by many perfectly parallel places (Fig. 3b).

The two- and many-beam cases considered the refraction, absorption, and propaga-

Fig. 3 Diffraction in a near-perfect crystal

(a) Reflected intensity distribution (rocking curve) for a near-perfect absorptionless crystal rotated through its angle for Bragg reflection, θ_B. (b) Attenuation of the incident beam by simple (R_h) and multiple (R_0) reflection. R_0' is $180°$ out of phase with R_0.

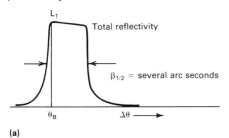

(a)

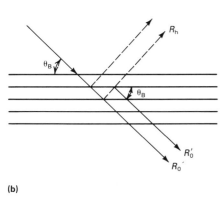

(b)

Fig. 4 The flow of x-ray energy in crystals of different thicknesses

(a) Borrmann fan in a thin crystal. (b) Fan with reduced effective width in a thick crystal. P is the primary beam defined by slits S; $\mathbf{k}_0$ and $\mathbf{k}_h$ are the outermost wave vectors; R_0 and R_h, the transmitted and reflected directions (toward the reciprocal lattice origin and the reciprocal lattice point $n(hkl)$. Reduced effective absorption in (b) results in anomalous transmission.

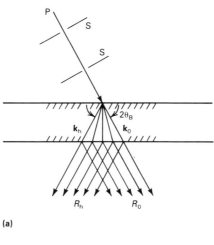

(a)

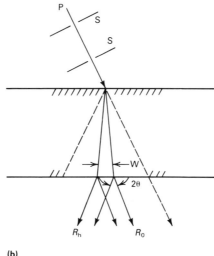

(b)

tion directions of the wave fields (Ref 1-3). Several significant consequences are evident regarding the flow of x-ray energy in and through perfect crystals. In the two-beam case (only the incident and reflected waves are considered), the portion of the primary beam entering, or accepted by, the crystal when set at an angle satisfying the Bragg condition consists of a wave bundle with a small divergence (limited to several seconds of arc). By virtue of dynamical interaction, the forward (0) and reflected (h) waves generate four wave fields within the perfect crystal—two wave fields for the σ and π polarization modes, respectively. The angular spread of the wave fields, termed the Borrmann fan, extends through the angle of $2\theta_B$ (Fig. 4a). For thin crystals, that is, $\mu t < 1$, where μ is the linear absorption coefficient and t is the crystal thickness, the energy flows through the entire Borrmann fan. Because each wave field propagates through the crystal with different phase velocity, a periodic exchange of energy takes place between the 0 and h waves. The minimum distance required to convert completely the energy of the incident 0-beam

into the reflected h-beam is the extinction distance. The intensities pertaining to the beams emerging from the exit surface of the crystal, designated R_0 and R_h, depend on the extinction distance and crystal thickness.

Anomalous Transmission. For sufficiently thick crystals, that is, $\mu t \geq 10$, the x-ray energy is confined to a much narrower fan situated about the reflecting plane halfway between $\mathbf{k}_0$ and $\mathbf{k}_h$, as if the wave were being diffracted repeatedly by two adjacent lattice planes (Fig. 4b). Further, of the four

wave fields in the crystal, those with maximum field intensity (antinodes) at the atomic planes are absorbed strongly, but those with intensity minima (nodes) at these planes suffer substantially less attenuation. As a result of the reduced effective absorption, the transmitted beam emerges from the crystal with nearly the same intensity as the reflected beam, a phenomenon known as anomalous transmission, or the Borrmann effect (Ref 4-7).

Defect Imaging. If crystals are considered thin relative to the photoelectric penetration distance $1/\mu$, but thick relative to extinction distance, the capability to visualize defects derives primarily from kinematical contrast, but is made possible only through the dynamical effects associated with diffraction. In reflection topography (the Bragg case), the coupling of the incident and reflected waves as a wave field, typical of dynamical interaction, is destroyed by the severe lattice distortion associated with the defect. Thus, the primary extinction effect is suppressed in this vicinity, and kinematic diffraction prevails. Only an incident wave bundle with a narrow angular divergence is accepted into the wave fields constituting the Borrmann fan. In practice, the primary beam has a considerably larger divergence of several minutes of arc. Distorted areas of the crystal, such as the dislocation core, can reflect some portion of this substantial intensity, producing dark contrast where normally only weak diffracted intensities would be measured. Thus, this direct image has a kinematic origin.

Contrast is also affected by the particular orientation of the defect and its strain field. The reflecting planes incurring the maximum contrast will lie perpendicular to the displacement due to strain. Therefore, for a dislocation, the plane with reciprocal vector parallel to the Burgers vector provides the greatest contrast. Because some atomic displacement also occurs perpendicular to the slip plane, planes with lattice normal in this direction contribute to the contrast. Only those lattice planes having reciprocal vectors lying normal to the plane containing the Burgers vector and the slip plane normal are devoid of contrast due to the dislocation.

A similar kinematic origin accounts for the direct image of a defect in transmission topography (the Laue case), as illustrated for a dislocation in Fig. 5. Passage of the dislocation through the Borrmann fan contributes to the contrast in two other ways. First, changes in the beam path and absorption caused by the strains about the dislocation weaken the wave field at a point such as C in Fig. 5. The wave is diverted to either side of its original direction FC. Second, interaction of the wave fields caused by the larger

Fig. 5 Origin of direct (1), dynamical (2), and intermediate (3) image contrast for a dislocation

Source: Ref 8

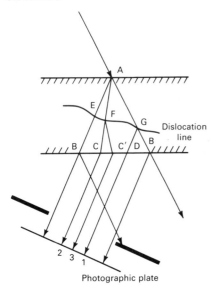

Photographic plate

Fig. 6 Origin of fringes caused by a fault plane between crystals I and II

Source: Ref 9, 10

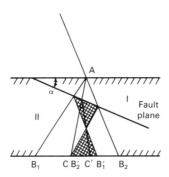

Fig. 7 Schulz x-ray topograph of a niobium single crystal revealing its intrinsic microstructure

$8 \times$. Source: Ref 13

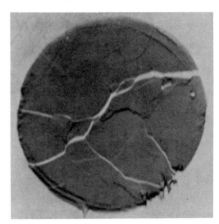

strains near the dislocation core result in the excitation of a new wave in the direction FC′ and further attenuates the wave field at C. The resultant shadow in the reflected beam from C is the dynamic image; the enhanced intensity from C′ associated with the new wave path produces the intermediate image.

Pendellösung Fringes. Energy transfer between the two humming waves in the crystal, k_0 and k_h, and the thickness of the crystal control the intensities of the reflections R_0 and R_h. When a photographic plate or film intercepts the reflected beam from a wedge-shaped crystal, interference, or Pendellösung fringes are recorded, lying parallel to the edge of the crystal. Pendellösung fringes (Ref 2) can also be obtained for crystals of uniform thickness by using Lang section topography (in traverse topographs of crystals with rectangular cross section, superposition of the fringes causes smearing of the intensity contrast, preventing their disclosure). The fringes are sensitive to lattice distortion; small elastic strains bend and/or alter the fringe spacing in traverse topographs of wedge-shaped crystals, and additional fringes may appear in section topographs upon introduction of elastic strain fields to a crystal. However, plastic deformation destroys the dynamical interaction, and the fringe patterns disappear.

In thick crystals, fringe patterns are absent, because only waves subject to reduced effective absorption traverse the crystal.

However, should a fault plane, such as those associated with a stacking fault or twin, lie near the surface, excitation of new waves can occur. Fringes are produced in the Borrmann fan at the exit surface due to the interference between newly scattered waves (II) and between waves that maintain the propagation directions from the original crystal orientation (I) (Fig. 6). Superposition of the two sets of fringes produces a pattern, or image, characteristic of the fault.

Another pattern, the x-ray analog to bend contours in transmission electron microscopy, can be exploited to characterize strain fields in a crystal (Ref 11). A band(s) of enhanced intensity is typically obtained for a distorted crystal when irradiated with a monochromatic beam, owing to the limited region of the crystal that is oriented for diffraction. These equi-inclination contours occur in different locations when the crystal is rotated to a new angular position. Rotating the crystal in discrete angular increments and recording successive positions of a band in a multiple exposure produces a mapping of the contour with angle of rotation. The patterns are particularly useful for studying crystals deformed to a level at or above the macroscopic yield point, for which the dislocation density generally is too high ($>10^6$ cm^{-1}) for imaging individual dislocations by conventional topography.

Methods and Instrumentation

Topographic methods are employed for two primary reasons. Some methods are intended principally for use in characterizing defects in single crystals and are applied routinely in studying semiconductor substrates, thin films, and other device materials. Other techniques are useful in studying a broader spectrum of engineering materials.

Appropriate selection of technique, procedure and instrumentation affords disclosure of surface relief; topological and deformation features, such as slip lines and subgrains; grain morphology; crystallographic texture; and various combinations of lattice distortion and plastic strain/cold work. These techniques can be applied nondestructively, require little or no preparation of the sample, and often permit easy and rapid scanning of relatively large areas.

Reflection Topography. The most widely used reflection arrangements for x-ray topography are the Schulz and Berg-Barrett methods. These techniques are suited to the evaluation of substructure in all crystalline materials, particularly as associated with cold work, recovery, recrystallization, and precipitation hardening.

In the Schulz method (Ref 12), the white radiation from a fine-focus x-ray tube or microfocus generator impinges on the sample (Fig. 2a). The sample is angled approximately 25° to the direction of the diverging x-ray beam. Uniform magnification in the horizontal and vertical directions is achieved if the photographic plate is placed parallel to the crystal surface. The technique has numerous applications in crystal growth and recrystallization studies for evaluation of subgrain size and misorientations. Figure 7 shows a topograph of a niobium single crystal in which the lines of enhanced or deficient intensity disclose subgrain boundaries. The width of each line can be used to calculate the misorientation angle across the boundary.

Fig. 8 Camera for Berg-Barrett topography

Sample is mounted on a tilting stage (right), and the film plate is held close to the sample surface by a supporting plate that also screens the film plate from scattered incident radiation. Source: Ref 15

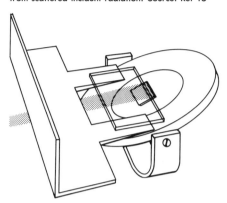

Fig. 9 Berg-Barrett topographs of a Vickers hardness indentation on MgO cleavage surface

(a) (022) reflection. (b) (202) reflection. Both 45×. Source: Ref 17

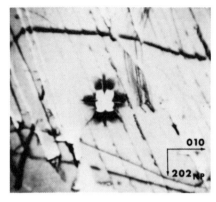

(a)   (b)

The Berg-Barrett method (Ref 14, 15) uses monochromatic radiation and a line source increases the observation range (Fig. 2b). Attainment of optimum resolution requires a narrow line width as well as maintenance of a long source-to-monochromator distance and a short sample-to-photographic plate distance. If the reflecting planes are inclined to the surface such that the angle of x-ray incidence is small and the angle of reflection approximately of 90°, the plate can be as close as 0.1 mm (0.004 in.) to the surface. In addition, penetration of the x-rays is minimized with the asymmetrical reflection, providing a sharper image. Figure 8 illustrates the reflection camera. The reduction in primary extinction caused by the strains about dislocations can be studied by observing the contrast effects for various crystallographic planes (Ref 16). The distribution of dislocations and the strains due to intersecting slip systems can be investigated by preparing topographs from several different reflections from the same family of planes. Another contribution to the contrast in the image derives from surface relief inherent in the sample. Any departure from a perfectly smooth surface, such as that caused by cleavage steps, leads to shadowing, as illustrated in the topographs of a magnesium oxide (MgO) single crystal shown in Fig. 9, which also displays the characteristic features of a hardness impression.

A Berg-Barrett arrangement also can be used for topography of polycrystals. Only suitably oriented grains will diffract the incident x-rays and the shapes and intensities of the grain reflections are influenced by the inclination of the reflected rays relative to the photographic plate, the distance of each of the grains from the plate, and the partic-

ular crystallographic planes diffracting the incident rays. Nevertheless, the technique is useful in preliminary investigations of texture and of grain size and shape; special surface preparation is unnecessary.

Transmission Topography. Figure 10(a) shows a transmission arrangement for a divergent beam. Parallel planes, each choosing incident rays with the appropriate wavelength for diffraction, focus the polychromatic rays impinging on the thin crystalline wafer. The existence of substructure featuring relatively perfect, polygonized domains tilted slightly relative to one another causes the focal points for the domains to be displaced from each other along the focusing circle. Figure 10(b) illustrates a transmission arrangement for the Berg-Barrett method.

In the Lang transmission arrangements (Ref 19), x-rays from a point focus source pass through a set of narrow slits before incidence on the sample at an angle that satisfies the Bragg diffraction for a particular set of transverse planes (Fig. 11a). For a thin crystal ($\mu t < 1$), the direct beam is pre-

vented from intercepting the photographic plate while the reflected beam passes through an appropriately located slit on the back side of the sample. An exposure taken with the assembly held stationary (Fig. 11b) is a section topograph, in which the imaged area is confined to the width of the Borrmann fan. Synchronized translation of the sample crystal and photographic plate yields a projection, or traverse, topograph. Either Lang technique can be used to image defects.

A fault in the sample causes the fringe pattern in the section topograph shown in Fig. 12; the fault excites new wave fields which interact with the wave field already present in the crystal. Projection topography is an effective method for scanning a crystal for possible defects. Various degrees of crystal imperfection may be imaged, from the collection of individual dislocations shown in Fig. 13, which includes a Frank-Read source, to the intense distortion about a notch in silicon bent at elevated temperature (Fig. 14). In the latter, the Pendellösung fringes resulting from the wedge-shaped

Fig. 10 Configurations for transmission topography

(a) Using white radiation from a point source. (b) Using characteristic radiation from a line source. Source: Ref 18

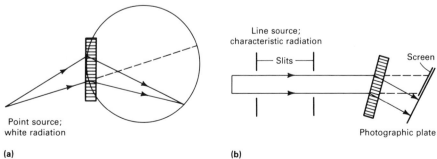

(a)   (b)

Fig. 11 Defect imaging with transmission topography

(a) Lang arrangement. (b) Borrmann arrangement

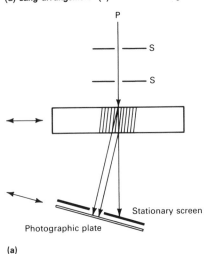

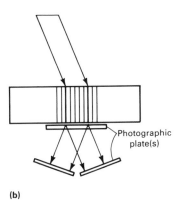

cross section of the sample are bent in the regions subject to elastic strains. The dense accumulations of dislocations in the plastically deformed regions at and approximately opposite the notch result in a direct image (black) bordered by dynamical (white) contrast due to local lattice curvature.

In crystals of medium thickness ($1 < \mu t < 4$) kinematical and dynamical effects are observed; in thick crystals ($\mu t > 4$), dynamical contrast predominates. Figure 11(b) shows the diffraction geometry for Borrmann topography and the shadows cast by dislocations in the R_0 and R_h reflections in the topographic image are shown in Fig. 15.

A technique that preserves the scanning feature of Lang but uses a line focus, with a Soller slit to limit divergence, can be used to image large area crystals rapidly (Ref 23). Oscillating the sample while scanning it is effective when extreme warpage of the crys-

Fig. 12 Topograph of a 1-mm (0.04-in.) thick dolomite plate with an inclined stacking fault near the exit surface

Source: Ref 9

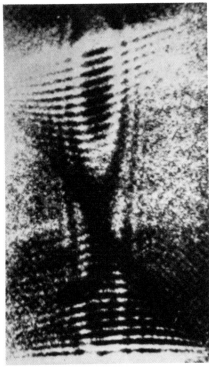

tal otherwise prevents obtaining a large area image.

Divergent Beam Method. Anomalous transmission is important to an arrangement that incorporates a divergent beam. In this experimental setup, a thin metal foil on the end of an evacuated tube is the target of an

Fig. 13 Lang topograph of a silicon crystal showing dislocations, including a Frank-Read source and thickness fringes

Source: Ref 20

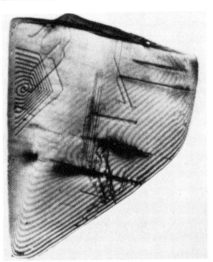

electron gun (Fig. 16). The foil is situated near the sample and bombarded with electrons to produce a divergent spray of characteristic radiation on the sample. An advantage of this method is that significant elastic strain can be tolerated, because the lattice planes always reflect some of the diverging rays and therefore produce the anomalous transmission pattern (R_0 and R_h of nearly equal intensity). Translation of the sample past the x-ray source enables scanning of the crystal for regions with defects that interrupt the wave interactions responsible for anomalous transmission. The divergent beam ar-

Fig. 14 X-ray topographs of a wedge-shaped silicon crystal showing Pendellösung fringes

(a) Section topograph of the undeformed crystal. (b) Traverse (projection) topograph of the undeformed crystal. (c) Topograph of the notched crystal bent at elevated temperature. Source: Ref 21

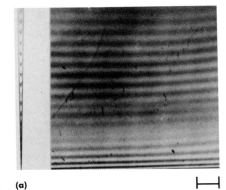

(a)

1 mm

(b)

1 mm

Fig. 15 Borrmann (anomalous transmission) topograph of a silicon crystal showing contrast caused by dislocations
Source: Ref 22

Fig. 16 Divergent beam anomalous transmission method of x-ray topography
Source: Ref 24

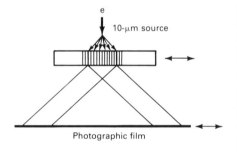

Fig. 17 X-ray interferometer
Source: Ref 25

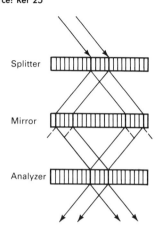

Fig. 18 Double crystal diffractometer arrangements

(a) $(+,-)$ setting. (b) $(+,+)$ setting. Source: Ref 27

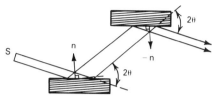

(a)

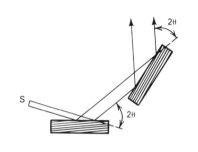

(b)

rangement also creates conditions under which deficiency and diffraction cones are recorded. Deficiency cones are caused by the removal of radiation from the original cone due to diffraction from oblique planes; diffraction cones, by diffraction in the direction of the film. Imperfection degrades the contrast inherent in these conical sections, known as pseudo-Kossel lines. Discontinuities in the lines and modifications of the shape of the patterns are useful for deducing the localized and uniform strain components, respectively.

X-Ray Interferometry. Figure 17 shows an x-ray interferometer that exploits anomalous transmission. The interaction of the waves as they pass through and between the three crystals depends strongly on the perfection of the crystals. Distortions and displacements in the third (analyzer) crystal as small as 0.001 seconds of arc and 0.01 nm respectively, are detectable (Ref 26). Other applications include observation of moiré fringes for edge dislocations, x-ray phase contrast microscopy, and precise measure-

ment of x-ray refractive indices, x-ray scattering factors, and lattice constants.

Double-Crystal Spectrometry and Polycrystal Rocking Curve Analysis. The double-crystal spectrometer, or diffractometer, is used to determine precisely the degree of imperfection of crystalline samples. To achieve the desired sensitivity to small localized strains, reflection from the first "perfect" crystal produces a monochromatic and highly parallel beam of x-rays used to probe the test crystal. Monitoring of the x-ray intensity diffracted by the test crystal as it is slowly rotated, or rocked, through the Bragg angle for the reflecting planes yields a rocking curve. Two settings for the first and second crystals are possible (Fig. 18a and b). If the first and test crystals are identical in type and crystallographic orientation, the $(+,-)$ setting has no dispersion effect, and the width of the rocking curve does not depend on the spectral spread of the incident radiation.

When the monochromator and test crystals are not identical, the arrangement is a nonparallel $(+m,-n)$ setting, and the rocking curve is no longer independent of the spectral intensity distribution. This also holds for the $(+,+)$ setting, for which all wavelengths reflected by the first crystal, that is, the small band of wavelengths the monochromator crystal accepts as a result of the inevitable horizontal divergence of the primary beam, will not be simultaneously reflected by the second crystal. Therefore, the breadth of the rocking curve is partly due to the extent of the spectrum of the incident radiation and therefore can be used to study the widths and fine structure of x-ray lines.

The $(+m,-n)$ arrangement typically provides narrow rocking curves for near-perfect crystals (a few seconds of arc) and is extremely sensitive to elastic deformations. If

the crystal contains numerous defects, is plastically bent, or is composed of misaligned blocks, the rocking curve is broader (Fig. 19a and b). Under certain circumstances, the tilt angle between adjacent misoriented crystals may be accurately determined from a multimodal rocking curve (Fig. 19c). Several models for dislocation distributions have been proposed and used to derive expressions for calculating the dislocation density from broadened x-ray diffraction profiles (Ref 30-32). Rocking curve profiles have also been used extensively to study semiconductor materials or thin films on supporting substrates (Ref 33-37). Detailed analysis of the main peaks and subsidiary intensity fluctuations provides information on strain and defects in single or multiple surface layers as well as their composition and thickness.

The double-crystal arrangement becomes a true topographic technique if a film is interposed between the test crystal and the detector as in Fig. 20. Optimum resolution is obtained if the film is placed near the surface of the test crystal to prevent the rays emanating from distorted regions with different inclinations from crossing one another and deviating from their true spatial relationship on the surface. This is most conveniently accomplished by using asymmetric reflections. To eliminate the effect of dispersion, the $K\alpha_2$ component of the radiation

Fig. 19 Intensity profiles (rocking curves)

(a) Bent crystal. (b) Crystal composed of misaligned independently reflecting domains. (c) Crystal containing a tilt boundary. Source: Ref 28, 29

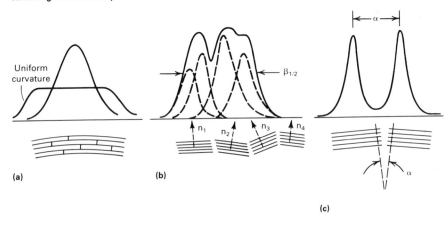

(a)   (b)   (c)

Fig. 20 Double crystal diffractometer (a) and beam expansion by reflection from two asymmetrically cut crystals in succession (b)

Source: Ref 24, 38

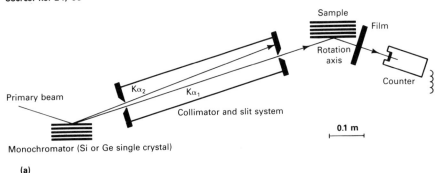

(a)

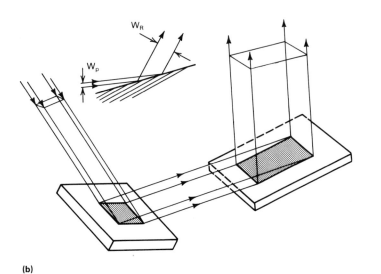

(b)

reflected by the first crystal must be removed using a suitably positioned slit.

Adjustment of the second (test) crystal slightly off the maximum intensity position of the diffraction peak maximizes sensitivity to near-surface distortions and elastic strains. In highly perfect crystals, single dislocations may be resolved. For imperfect crystals, the physical origin of intensity fluctuations in the rocking curve profile can be conveniently determined by taking several topographs, each at a different angular position along the rocking curve (Fig. 21). Use of a position-sensitive detector parallel to the long dimension of the beam enables determination of the variation in rocking curve width along this direction on the sample. Similar measurements, made after incremental translation of the sample, allow generation of a two-dimensional mapping of the surface distortion (Ref 39).

To image larger areas of test crystals in a single exposure, an asymmetrically cut monochromator crystal can be used to expand the primary x-ray beam. By using two such crystals in succession, rotated 90° from one another about an axis parallel to the diffraction plane, the primary beam can be expanded and made parallel relative to the horizontal and vertical directions (see Fig. 20b).

The principles of double-crystal diffractometry have been successfully extended to study diverse polycrystalline materials. As shown in Fig. 22, an x-ray micrograph, or reflection topograph, can be obtained by intercepting the reflected rays from the sample material on a photographic plate positioned close to and as nearly parallel as possible to the sample surface. Only those grains suitably oriented for diffraction reflect incident radiation. Because the normals to the reflecting planes of the individual grains make different angles relative to the plane of diffraction, the images of the grains tend to become interposed in photographs taken at increasing distances from the sample surface (Fig. 23). At a distance of 27.5 mm (1.1 in.) the diffracted spots are visible along Debye arcs, which are portions of the diffraction cones intercepted by a cylindrical film surrounding the sample. These arcs would normally be continuous, but because of the highly parallel and monochromatic incident radiation, only selected grains are oriented for reflection.

The rocking curves of the individual grains can be evaluated (Fig. 24) by rotating the sample in small angular increments (several seconds to minutes of arc, depending on the material condition) and recording the grain reflections at each position. A slight rotation of the film after each exposure prevents superimposition of the reflected

Fig. 21 Rocking curve and topographs of a gold single crystal

(a) Rocking curve with (311)⟨123⟩ orientation strained 5% in tension. (b) Topographs taken at angular positions 1 through 5

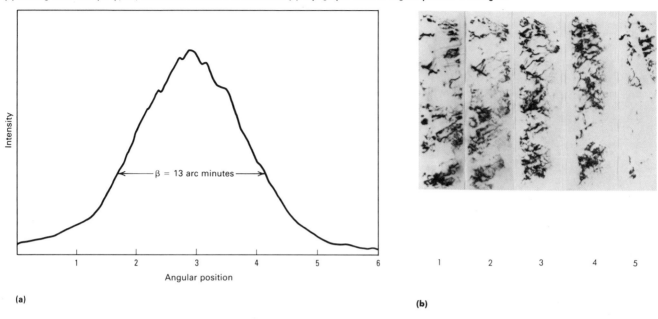

(a)

(b)

Fig. 22 Double crystal diffractometer for polycrystalline samples

Source: Ref 40, 41

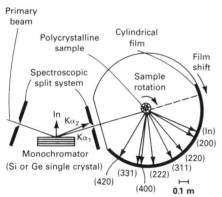

spots from each grain. Thus, as each grain is rotated through its diffraction angle, an array of spots of increasing and decreasing intensity reveal the angular range over which the grain diffracts measurable intensities. Each of the arrays of spots, as recorded on film, can then be scanned using a microdensitometer to facilitate construction of conventional diffracted intensity profiles for the various grains. The widths of the rocking curves indicate the inherent lattice distortion within the grains. A more convenient method is computer-assisted rocking curve analysis (CARCA), in which a position-sensitive detector (PSD) is substituted for the film. The PSD is placed tangent to the diffraction arc

Fig. 23 Outward tracing of individual grain reflections from the surface to the diffraction pattern

(a) At the sample surface. (b) 2.5 mm (0.1 in.) from the surface. (c) 27.5 mm (1.1 in.) from the surface

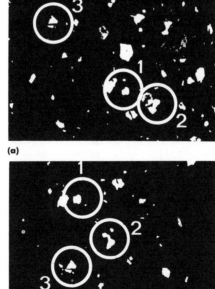

(a)

(b)

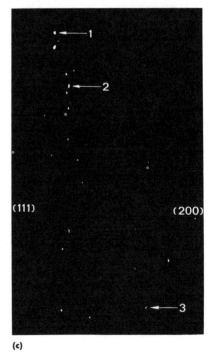

(c)

of interest and coupled with a multichannel analyzer (MCA). A microcomputer is used to evaluate the rocking curves for many individual grains from the intensity data retrieved from the MCA (Ref 42). A principal application of CARCA is evaluation of the degree and spatial distribution of plastic deformation incurred by polycrystalline materials subjected to various types of mechanical stressing.

Fig. 24 Rocking curves for individual grains of a polycrystalline sample

Arrays of spots correspond to reflection range of each grain and are obtained by multiple exposures after incremental sample rotations of 3 arc minutes each. (a) Annealed and undeformed type 304 stainless steel. (b) Same sample after subjection to stress-corrosion. (c) Detail of rock curve of grain 3 in (a). (d) Detail of rocking curve in grain 3 in (b)

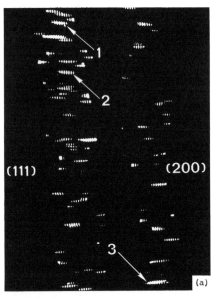

(111)   (200)

(a)

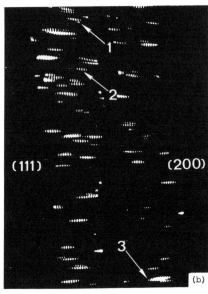

(111)   (200)

(b)

(c)

(d)

Fig. 25 Basic principle of polycrystal scattering topography

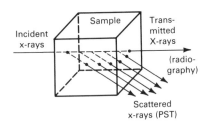

Line Broadening Analysis and the Microbeam Method.

Several methods for evaluating and imaging the substructure of polycrystalline materials use the typical Debye-Scherrer diffracted x-rays. These methods assist characterization of various types of strain, defect structures, and crystallographic orientation effects introduced or eliminated during material processing, treatment, or service. X-ray line broadening and integrated intensity measurements, for example, are widely used to determine microstrains, crystallite (particle) size, and fault densities. Because these methods do not provide information on the portion of the sample responsible for each component of the diffracted image, they are not topographic techniques. Additional information on these methods is available in Ref 43 and 44.

The x-ray microbeam method is another approach for studying microstructural changes in polycrystalline materials (Ref 45). Like the double-crystal diffractometer method for polycrystalline materials, the microbeam technique allows resolution of the individual grains. Instead of using a highly

parallel and monochromatic beam, the incident beam is simply restricted in size to control the number of resultant grain reflections. A microfocus generator is usually used with a 50-μm-diam aperture (pin hole). The irradiated area on the sample is approximately 150 μm, and the resolving power of the microbeam camera is approximately 1 μm. The site analyzed is confined to a small area, for example, the crack initiation site in a sharp-notched fatigue specimen (Ref 46), but only a few grains can be imaged in a single exposure. Careful examination of the radial and tangential broadening of the reflection spot for each grain, that is, in directions normal to and along the diffraction ring, and the subdivision of the spot reveals the misorientation, lattice strain, and subgrain size within the grain.

Polycrystal Scattering Topography.

The polycrystal scattering topographic (PST) methods sacrifice some of the resolving power of the methods described above for the capability to image considerably larger areas (Ref 47, 48). Rather than exploiting variable absorption to produce an image, as is typical of radiographic tech-

niques, these methods make use of elastic and inelastic scattering for image formation (Fig. 25). Therefore, the contrast does not rely on the presence of materials having large differences in x-ray absorption, but is derived from variations in crystal structure and material distribution. One of several Soller slit arrangements is used to maintain the spatial relationship of the scattered rays, providing a one-to-one correlation between the sample and the image on the emulsion plate (Fig. 26).

One geometry incorporates two Soller slits rotated 90° relative to each other and oscillated to prevent shadows from being visible. Oblique incidence of the beam on the sample, synchronous translation of the sample and slit/film cassette assembly, or expansion of the incident beam by reflection from an asymmetrically cut monochromator crystal can be used to increase the viewing area. Conventional sealed x-ray tubes are used, and a resolution of approximately 0.1 mm (0.004 in.) is obtained for transmission and reflection arrangements. Several methods implement white radiation incident on the sample; a thin pencil of rays may be used with a cone-shaped slit and x-y scanning (Ref 51), or dual asymmetrically cut crystals may be arranged to intercept and resolve spatially diffracted rays at a selected range of azimuthal angles and to magnify the resultant image. Use of a position-sensitive detector, multichannel analyzer, and CRT display allow more rapid and convenient image generation. Polycrystal scattering topography is particularly useful for evaluating the development and modification of deformation texture due to mechanical processing.

Synchrotron Radiation.

Synchrotron sources produce intense radiation, tunable to various wavelengths, that is advantageous for x-ray topography (Ref 52, 53). A white beam used in the Laue setting allows analysis of curved crystals without compensation for the varying orientation (usually facilitated by instrumentation for automated Bragg angle control). Rapid characterization of the displacement vectors associated with

Fig. 26 Two arrangements for polycrystal scattering topography
(a) Cross Soller slit method. (b) Soller slit oscillating method. Source: Ref 49, 50

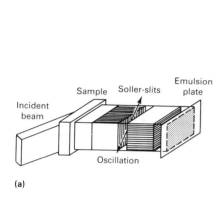

(a)

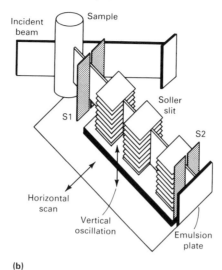

(b)

various defects is possible using white beam topography. Coupled with position-sensitive or electro-optical detectors, synchrotron radiation affords the capability for monitoring dynamic processes, such as the movement of magnetic, ferroelectric, subgrain or twin domains and boundaries. Because the divergence of the incident beam is small, superior resolution is obtained even if the sample-to-detector distance is great. Therefore, ample space is available for locating furnaces, magnets, and other equipment about the sample.

A high-intensity monochromatic beam from a synchrotron source also enhances the potential for probing small areas (approximately 1-μm spot sizes) in much the same way as electron microscopy, but nondestructively. Even thin layers produce sufficiently strong diffracted intensity, and there is less concern over intensity losses associated with attempts to expand the incident beam with a system of multiple asymmetrically cut monochromator crystals. In general, synchrotron radiation should be the next option considered when short exposure times or other special criteria demand intensities greater than those furnished by more conventional high-power laboratory generators, such as rotating anodes.

Applications

X-ray topography is well suited to three principal areas of research. The first is crystal growth and characterization of electronic device materials. Interest in single crystals is highest in the electronics industry, but single crystals—or at least highly oriented crystalline materials—are also of interest because

of their favorable creep or corrosion resistance and high stiffness, for example, directionally solidified metals and alloys or fiber reinforcements in composites. In the electronics industry, an appropriate topographic method or combination of methods can reveal much about thin film and surface modified structures. The second area of research is material transformations and kinetics of crystal processes. Synchrotron radiation is particularly advantageous for these studies, because the bright beam allows the dynamic processes to be followed *in situ*. In the third field of application, materials deformation and fracture behavior, the nondestructive nature of x-ray diffraction can be exploited to afford repetitive observations and measurements during deformation.

Crystal Growth and Electronic Device Material Studies. X-ray topography has been used extensively to study defects produced during crystal growth. Information on the methodology for correlating defects to growth processes is cited in Ref 54. X-ray topography is useful for assessing all the microstructural features (growth bands, dislocations, faults, twins, point clusters, inclusions, and so on) that accompany crystal growth from solution or by melt, solid-state, or vapor techniques. The information gained through topographic studies enables modifications in technique, procedure, and operating conditions that enhance production of highly defect-free crystals.

The activity in electronic device development has prompted extensive application of x-ray topography. The perfection of the substrate material, the structure of any overlying films, and the defects in the interfacial re-

gion between them influence the behavior and the performance of the device components. For example, dislocations and grain boundaries in the substrate result in device degradation by substantially reducing the minority carrier lifetime (Ref 55). X-ray topographic imaging and measurements of reflected intensities can be used to monitor their generation or prevalence during growth, cutting, surface preparation, and other processing/treatments of semiconductor substrates (Ref 34, 56, 57).

Rocking curve profiles obtained by double-crystal diffractometry, on the other hand, are most effective for characterizing thin films grown, deposited, or similarly produced on the surface of the substrates (Ref 33, 35). Figure 27 illustrates the basic features of a diffraction scan from a sample with a thin (100-nm to several microns thick)

Fig. 27 Illustration of rocking curve profiles for epitaxial films of different thicknesses
(a) Relatively thin film. (b) Relatively thick film. Peak positions and breadths, peak separations, number and spacing of subsidiary peaks, and interpeak intensities yield information useful in characterizing the junction.

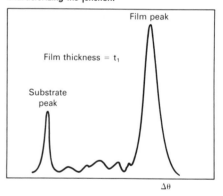

(a)

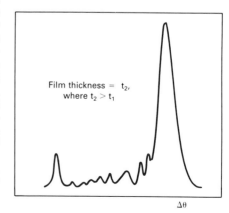

(b)

epitaxial film. The information that can be extracted from the pattern includes (1) the misfit of the film and substrate lattices, determined from the angular separation of the diffraction peaks produced by the two lattices, (2) the composition of the film, calculated from the misfit, (3) the film thickness, which controls the spacing and widths of the subsidiary peaks (the Pendellösung maxima located between the two primary peaks), (4) the local strain in the layer(s) is/are measured from the angular shifts of the primary peaks from the positions expected for known composition, and (5) the inherent nonuniform distortions of the layer(s) and substrate as evidenced by broadening of the respective diffraction peaks. The modification of surface layers by such processes as ion implantation affects the diffraction profiles in ways similar to those observed for newly deposited layers (Ref 36, 37). For surface modification, emphasis is on evaluation of the damage, which includes atom displacements (defects, disorder, and/or amorphism) and macroscopic strains due to the ion distribution.

Topographic imaging techniques aid investigation of heterojunctions. Topographs can be taken of samples prepared with single or multiple films to reveal the misfit dislocations and other interfacial defects. The defect distribution can then be correlated with the quantitative information from rocking curve analysis and the measurements of electrical properties and behavior (Ref 58). Damage due to implantation (Ref 59) or the intentionally introduced defects on the backside of wafers, an industrial process for "gettering," can also be monitored using x-ray topography. In addition to its use in establishing the quality of the as-fabricated substrate and disclosing defects or strain due to subsequent processing, automated topographic scanning can be used to analyze completed devices rapidly (Ref 60). For example, the diffraction contrast at the boundary lines of silicon/silicon oxide junctions is an indication that precipitation has occurred there, while the heightened contrast within devices prepared on a silicon wafer is frequently caused by faulting, the result of phosphorus diffusion and defect generation in the silicon (Ref 23).

Material Transformations and Crystal Kinetics. Many recent studies involving x-ray topography, particularly the dynamic experiments conducted using synchrotron sources, have focused on material transformations and crystal processes. These include solidification/crystallization, ordering/disordering, recrystallization, precipitation, polymerization, and ferroelectric and magnetic domain formation.

Fig. 28 Photographs from video monitor of Laue transmission patterns of aluminum

(a) During recrystallization. (b) During coarsening. Enlargement of Laue spot in lower right hand corner of (b) shows structure of recrystallized grains. Source: Ref 62

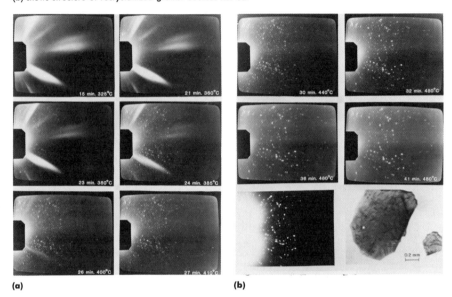

(a)   (b)

Although considerable data have been generated to help model the kinetics of recrystallization, much remains to be learned about the mechanisms of solid-state nucleation and growth. X-ray topography can be used to probe bulk samples rapidly and nondestructively in order to monitor the structure of moving interfaces, including attendant defects, during recrystallization (Ref 61). Studies of aluminum demonstrated that the boundaries of the growing recrystallized grains were planar and became curved only when they encountered precipitates or impinged upon other recrystallized grains. In addition, the faces of the faceted grains exhibiting the lowest velocities corresponded to crystallographic planes with the densest packing of atoms. Finally, the dislocation density within the nucleated grains was found to be high immediately following nucleation, to decrease during growth, then to increase during coarsening.

Figure 28 shows white beam synchrotron topographs taken in the transmission Laue arrangement that distinguish clearly the recrystallization and coarsening stages in aluminum (Ref 62). The structure of the growing grain is visible in the enlargement of one of the Laue spots. This type of study enables evaluation of the growth rate of an individual grain relative to its counterparts with different sizes. It was noted that although smaller grains generally shrink and the larger ones grow, large grains may suddenly disappear or small grains may begin to grow rapidly.

The use of x-ray topography to study phase transformations and precipitation yields information similar to that for recrystallization. For example, contrast changes at the particle/matrix boundary can be used to evaluate interfacial distortions and defect structure. The method of equi-inclination contours has been used to determine selected components of the strain tensor about β-NbH precipitates in niobium (Fig. 29). The distortions within Ti$_3$Al particles and the β phase of a titanium-aluminum-molybdenum precipitation-hardening alloy have also been evaluated, and the rocking curves obtained by double crystal diffractometry for the two constituents compared (Ref 24). The results could be interpreted in terms of the dislocation-particle interaction and resultant effect on slip distribution during deformation.

Deformation and Fracture Behavior. Topographic methods have been found to be extremely useful in studying deformation and fracture behavior of various materials subjected to diverse loading and environmental conditions. Fracture surfaces, free surfaces, and small volumes featuring localized deformation, such as those near notches, crack tips, or sites of contact loading, can be examined.

X-ray fractography has been used to investigate the failure modes for refractory metals and alloys by implementing the bright, polychromatic low-divergence radiation from a synchrotron source (Ref 63). Precracked molybdenum single crystals,

Fig. 29 Topographs showing equi-inclination contours in a niobium crystal containing β-niobium hydride precipitates

Plate 0 is a multiple exposure. Plates 1 to 16 are single exposures taken 140 arc minutes of rotation about the [110] direction. OM is an optical micrograph showing hydride locations. Source: Ref 11

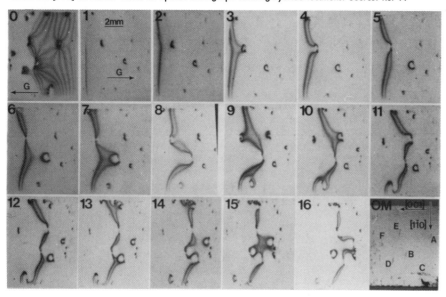

Fig. 31 Traverse x-ray topographs of a silicon sample deformed in tension at 800 °C (1470 °F) showing distribution of microplastic zones; AgKα₁, (200) reflection

(a) Without surface removal. (b) After removal of a 125-μm surface layer by chemical polishing. Source: Ref 66

(a)

(b)

cleaved by mechanical straining in tension, were examined optically and topographically (Fig. 30). Because the crack tip image persisted for topographs taken with various **g** (diffraction) vectors, the region of plastic relaxation at the tip of the precursor crack was concluded to be characterized by a dense tangle of dislocations from different slip systems. Other features included the streaks emanating from the crack tip image, which were correlated to the sites of macroscopic twins. Further, incremental removal of 5- to 20-μm layers from the cleavage surface caused a monotonic reduc-

Fig. 30 Fracture surface of a molybdenum crystal

(a) Synchrotron topograph of the fracture [(001) cleavage] surface; (2̄2̄2̄) reflection. Dark band at the top of the image shows the crack initiation site, gray band through the midsection of the crystal corresponds to the path of fast fracture, and dark banding at the bottom of the image is the location of twinning. (b) Optical micrograph. (c) Scanning electron micrograph of the cleavage surface

 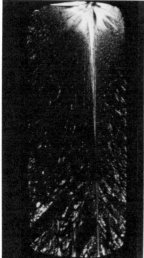 

(a)   **(b)**   **(c)**

tion in the width of the crack tip image and in the contrast due to twins. On the basis of these and other observations, a detailed description of the crack propagation behavior and underlying mechanisms could be proposed.

Several techniques have been used to study the deformation of silicon crystals at elevated temperatures (Ref 64, 65). Figure 31 shows Lang projection topographs of a crystal lightly deformed at 800 °C (1470 °F) before and after chemical removal of a 125-μm layer from the surface. The disappearance of microplastic zones that accompanies such polishing indicates that the zones are generated primarily in the near-surface layers of material. Double-crystal diffractometry provided a quantitative measure of the distortion. A similar crystal, plastically deformed 10% at 650 °C (1200 °F), was used as the second crystal of the diffractometer in the (+m,−n) setting. The halfwidth (full width at half maximum intensity) of the rocking curve was found to decline as the surface layers were removed, indicating a reduction in the misalignment of the diffracting planes.

Use of a position-sensitive detector produced a complete mapping of the lattice distortion in plastic zones formed about and between notches in tensile-deformed silicon crystals (Ref 39). Lang topography vividly disclosed the polygonization associated with elastic strain relaxation that occurred upon annealing of a notched and bent wedge-shaped crystal (Fig. 14). Similar combinations of techniques can be used to study localized deformations caused by other forms of loading, such as the distortion about a microhardness impression. The slip and surface relief caused by indentation of MgO was studied using Berg-Barrett topography (Fig. 8). Measurements made using double-crystal diffractometry allowed construction of a contour map on a sectioned surface of the lattice distortions beneath the indentation (Ref 67).

The growth of the crack tip plastic zone in silicon was investigated *in situ* using synchrotron radiation (Ref 68, 69). A threshold value of the stress-intensity factor was measured for dislocation nucleation at the crack tip, and the size of the zone was monitored using topography in the double-crystal spectrometer arrangement. By evaluating the speed of the leading dislocation, the effective local stress could be determined. The fraction of dislocations with various orientations could also be estimated (Ref 70). Lang topography revealed the predominance of dislocations having Burgers vector parallel to the crack front that are therefore incapable of blunting the crack. The increase in the critical fracture stress produced by prestraining was concluded to result not from blunting, but rather from shielding of the crack tip; that is, long-range stresses exist that oppose the opening of the crack.

Application of x-ray diffraction to evaluate deformations in polycrystalline materials of engineering importance is particularly effective in view of (1) its potential for nondestructive application so that multiple examinations can be conducted as the deformation progresses, (2) the large areas that may be scanned in comparison to some other techniques, (3) the subsurface information that can be obtained using penetrating radiation, and (4) the capability for dynamic processes using intense synchrotron sources and rapid detection systems. For example, fatigue deformation in diverse metal alloys has been studied using line broadening (Ref 71-74), microbeam techniques to probe the root of a starter notch (Ref 46), and the modified form of rocking curve analysis for polycrystalline materials (Ref 42, 66, 74, 75). These techniques, along with polycrystal scattering topography, have great potential for application in the field to evaluate cumulative damage in structural members and mechanical components. As portable x-ray generators, robotic manipulation, rapid and position-sensitive detection systems, and computer automation and data analysis are set to the task, nondestructive evaluation of the deformation state, before crack initiation and in the absence of other more microscopic flaws, will be possible outside the laboratory.

REFERENCES

1. C.G. Darwin, *Philos. Mag.*, Vol 27, 1914, p 315
2. P.P. Ewald, *Ann. Phys.*, Vol 54, 1917, p 519
3. M. von Laue, *Ergeb. Exackt. Naturw.*, Vol 10, 1931, p 133
4. G. Borrmann, *Physikal. Z.*, Vol 42, 1941, p 157
5. G. Borrmann, *Z. Phys.*, Vol 127, 1950, p 297
6. M. von Laue, *Acta Crystallogr.*, Vol 2, 1949, p 106
7. M. von Laue, *Acta Crystallogr.*, Vol 5, 1952, p 619
8. F. Balibar and A. Authier, *Phys. Status Solidi*, Vol 21, 1967, p 413
9. A. Authier, *Adv. X-Ray Anal.*, Vol 10, 1967, p 9
10. N. Kato, K. Usami, and T. Katagawa, *Adv. X-Ray Anal.*, Vol 10, 1967, p 46
11. S.R. Stock, H. Chen, and H.K. Birnbaum, in *Applications of X-ray Topographic Methods to Materials Science*, S. Weissmann, F. Balibar and J.-F. Petroff, Ed., Plenum Press, 1984, p 140
12. L.G. Schulz, *Trans. AIME*, Vol 200, 1954, p 1082
13. M.R. Achter, C.L. Vold, and T.G. Digges, Jr., *Trans. AIME*, Vol 236, 1966, p 1597
14. W. Berg, *Naturwissenschaften*, Vol 19, 1931, p 391
15. C.S. Barrett, *Trans. AIME*, Vol 161, 1945, p 15
16. J.B. Newkirk, *Trans. AIME*, Vol 215, 1959, p 483
17. R.W. Armstrong and C.Cm. Wu, *J. Am. Cer. Soc.*, Vol 61, 1978, p 102
18. A. Guinier and J. Tennevin, *Acta Crystallogr.*, Vol 2, 1949, p 140
19. A.R. Lang, *Acta Metall.*, Vol 5, 1957, p 358
20. A. Authier and A.R. Lang, *J. Appl. Phys.*, Vol 35, 1964, p 1956
21. Y. Tsunekawa and S. Weissmann, *Met. Trans.*, Vol 5, 1974, p 1585
22. G. Borrmann, W. Hartwig, and H. Irmler, *Z. Naturforsch.*, Vol 13A, 1958, p 423
23. G.H. Schwuttke, *J. Appl. Phys.*, Vol 36, 1965, p 2712
24. S. Weissmann, in *Nondestructive Evaluation of Materials*, J.J. Burke and Y. Weiss, Ed., Plenum Press, 1979 p 69
25. U. Bonse and M. Hart, *Appl. Phys. Lett.*, Vol 6, 1965, p 155
26. U. Bonse and M. Hart, *Z. Phys.*, Vol 190, 1966, p 455
27. R.W. James, *The Optical Principles of the Diffraction of X-rays*, G. Bell and Sons, 1950
28. S. Weissmann, *J. Appl. Phys.*, Vol 27, 1956, p 389
29. S. Weissmann, L.A. Gorman, and L. Zwell, *J. Appl. Phys.*, Vol 33, 1962, p 3131
30. P. Gay, P.B. Hirsch, and A. Kelly, *Acta Metall.*, Vol 1, 1953, p 315
31. P.B. Hirsch, *Progress in Metal Physics*, Vol 6, B. Chalmers and R. King, Ed., Pergamon Press, 1956, p 282
32. M. Wilkins, *Phys. Status Solidi (a)*, Vol 2, 1970, p 359
33. W.T. Stacy and M.M. Jannsen, *J. Cryst. Growth*, Vol 27, 1974, p 282
34. A. Fukuhara and Y. Takano, *Acta Crystallogr.*, Vol A33, 1977, p 137
35. W.J. Bartels and W. Nijman, *J. Cryst. Growth*, Vol 44, 1978, p 518
36. Y.S. Speriousu, H.L. Glass, and T. Kobayashi, *Appl. Phys. Lett.*, Vol 34, 1979, p 539
37. W.H. de Roode and J.W. Smits, *J. Appl. Phys.*, Vol 52, 1981, p 3969
38. W.J. Boettinger, H.E. Burdette, and M. Kuriyama, *Rev. Sci. Instrum.*, Vol 50, 1979, p 26
39. W.E. Mayo and S. Weissmann, in *Applications of X-Ray Topographic Methods to Materials Science*, S. Weissmann, F. Balibar and J.F. Petroff, Ed., Plenum Press, 1984, p 311
40. A.J. Reis, J.J. Slade, Jr., and S. Weissmann, *J. Appl. Phys.*, Vol 22, 1956, p 655
41. S. Weissmann, in *Accuracy in Powder Diffraction Patterns*, Special Publication 567, National Bureau of Standards, Gaithersburg, MD, 1979, p 411
42. R. Yazici, W. Mayo, T. Takemoto, and S. Weissmann, *J. Appl. Crystallogr.*, Vol 16, 1983, p 89
43. J.B. Cohen, *Diffraction Methods in Materials Science*, Macmillan, 1966
44. B.E. Warren, *X-Ray Diffraction*, Addison Wesley, 1969
45. S. Taira, K. Tanaka, T. Shimada, and Y. Kato, *Proceedings of the 16th Japan Congress on Materials Research*, 1973, p 174
46. S. Taira, J. Ryu, H. Tamaiwa, and K. Tanaka, *Proceedings of the 16th Japan Congress on Materials Research*, 1973, p 77
47. Y. Chikaura, Y. Yoneda, and G. Hildebrandt, *J. Appl. Crystallogr.*, Vol 15, 1982, p 48

48. E. Born and H. Schwarzbauer, *Kristall. Tech.*, Vol 15, 1980, p 837
49. T. Horiuchi and Y. Yoneda, *Proceedings of the 32nd Annual Conference of Applied Physics*, Japan, 1971, p 343
50. S. Oki and K. Futagami, *Jpn. J. Appl. Phys.*, Vol 8, 1969, p 1569
51. Y. Yoneda, T. Horiuchi, and N. Hiramatsu, *Jpn. J. Appl. Phys.*, Vol 19, 1980, p 353
52. M. Kuriyama, W.J. Boettinger, and G.G. Cohen, *Ann. Rev. Mater. Sci.*, Vol 12, 1982, p 23
53. W.J. Boettinger, R.C. Dobbyn, H.E. Burdette, and M. Kuriyama, *Nucl. Instrum. Methods*, Vol 195, 1982, p 355
54. B.K. Tanner, *X-Ray Diffraction Topography*, Pergamon Press, 1976
55. A.D. Kurtz, S.A. Kulin, and B.L. Averbach, *Phys. Rev.*, Vol 101, 1956, p 1285
56. B.W. Batterman, *J. Appl. Phys.*, Vol 30, 1959, p 4
57. J.R. Carruthers, R.B. Hoffman, and J.D. Ashner, *J. Appl. Phys.*, Vol 34, 1963, p 3389
58. J.-F. Petroff and M. Sauvage, *J. Cryst. Growth*, Vol 43, 1978, p 626
59. B.K. Tanner, *X-Ray Diffraction Topography*, Pergamon Press, 1976, p 123
60. B.K. Tanner, *X-Ray Diffraction Topography*, Pergamon Press, 1976, p 109-110
61. J. Gastaldi and C. Jourdan, in *Applications of X-Ray Topographic Methods to Materials Science*, S. Weissmann, F. Balibar, and J.-F. Petroff, Ed., Plenum Press, 1984, p 273
62. W.J. Boettinger, H.E. Burdette, and M. Kuriyama, in *Applications of X-Ray Topographic Methods to Materials Science*, S. Weissmann, F. Balibar, and J.-F. Petroff, Ed., Plenum Press, 1984, p 283
63. A.B. Hmelo, J.C. Bilello, S.T. Davies, and D.K. Bowen, *Mater. Lett.*, Vol 2, 1983, p 6
64. S. Weissmann, in *STP 557*, ASTM, Philadelphia, 1974, p 4
65. H.Y. Liu, G.J. Weng, and S. Weissmann, *J. Appl. Crystallogr.*, Vol 15, 1982, p 594
66. R.N. Pangborn, S. Weissmann, and I.R. Kramer, *Met. Trans. A*, Vol 12, 1981, p 109
67. T. Larchuk, T. Kato, R.N. Pangborn, and J.C. Conway, Jr., *Applications of X-Ray Topographic Methods to Materials Science*, S. Weissmann, F. Balibar, and J.-F. Petroff, Ed., Plenum Press, 1984, p 301
68. A. George and G. Michot, *J. Appl. Crystallogr.*, Vol 15, 1982, p 412
69. G. Michot and A. George, *Scr. Metall.*, Vol 16, 1982, p 519
70. G. Michot, K. Badawi, A.R. Abd el Halim, and A. George, *Philos. Mag.*, Vol A42, 1980, p 195
71. R.W. Gould and C.F. Pittella, *Adv. X-Ray Anal.*, Vol 16, 1973, p 354
72. C.M. Wan and J.G. Byrne, *Int. J. Fract.*, Vol 11, 1975, p 251
73. V. Weiss, A. Wu, and Y. Oshida, *Fatigue Eng. Mater. Struct.*, Vol 1, 1979, p 333
74. R. Khatri and R.N. Pangborn, *J. Mater. Sci. Eng.*, in press
75. T. Takemoto, S. Weissmann, and I.R. Kramer, in *Fatigue*, J. Burke and V. Weiss, Ed., Plenum Press, 1983, p 71

X-Ray Diffraction Residual Stress Techniques

Paul S. Prevey, Lambda Research, Inc.

General Uses

Macrostress measurement
- Nondestructive surface residual stress measurement for quality control
- Determination of subsurface residual stress distributions
- Measurement of residual stresses associated with failures caused by fatigue or stress corrosion

Microstress measurement
- Determination of the percent cold work at and below the surface
- Measurement of hardness in steels in thin layers

Examples of Applications
- Determination of the depth and magnitude of the compressive layer and hardness produced by carburizing steels
- Investigation of the uniformity of the surface compressive residual stresses produced by shot peening in complex geometries
- Measurement of surface residual stresses and hardness on the raceway of ball and roller bearings as functions of hours of service
- Study of the alteration of residual stress and percent cold work distributions caused by stress-relieving heat treatment or forming
- Measurement of surface and subsurface residual stresses parallel and perpendicular to a weld fusion line as a function of distance from the weld
- Determination of the direction of maximum residual stress and percent cold work gradient caused by machining

Samples
- *Form*: Polycrystalline solids, metallic or ceramic, moderate to fine grained
- *Size*: Various, with limitations dictated by the type of apparatus, the stress field to be examined, and x-ray optics
- *Preparation*: Generally, none. Large samples and inaccessible areas may require sectioning with prior strain gaging to record the resulting stress relaxation. Careful handling or protective coatings may be required to preserve surface stresses

Limitations
- Expensive, delicate apparatus generally limited to a laboratory or shop
- Only a shallow (<0.025-mm, or 0.001-in.) surface layer is measured, requiring electrolytic polishing to remove layers for subsurface measurement
- Samples must be polycrystalline, of reasonably fine grain size, and not severely textured

Estimated Analysis Time
- 1 min to 1 h per measurement, depending on the diffracted x-ray intensity and technique used. Typically, 1 h per measurement for subsurface work, including material removal and sample repositioning

Capabilities of Related Techniques
- *General dissection techniques*: Generally good for determination of gross residual stress distributions extending over large distances or depths. Restricted to simple geometries
- *Hole drilling*: Applicable to a variety of samples with stress fields uniform over dimensions larger than the strain-gage rosette and depth of the drilled hole and with magnitudes less than nominally 60% of yield strength. Serious errors are possible due to local yielding for higher stresses, variation in the stress field beneath the rosettes, eccentricity of the hole, or as a result of residual stresses induced in drilling the holes
- *Ultrasonic methods*: Require relatively long gage lengths and stress-free reference standards. Of limited practical application due to errors caused by transducer coupling, preferred orientation, cold work, temperature, and grain size. Sensitivity varies greatly with material
- *Magnetic (Barkhausen or magnetostrictive) methods*: Limited to ferromagnetic materials and subject to many of the limitations and error sources of ultrasonic methods. Highly nonlinear response with low sensitivity to tensile stresses

Introduction

In x-ray diffraction residual stress measurement, the strain in the crystal lattice is measured, and the residual stress producing the strain is calculated, assuming a linear elastic distortion of the crystal lattice. Although the term stress measurement has come into common usage, stress is an extrinsic property that is not directly measurable. All methods of stress determination require measurement of some intrinsic property, such as strain or force and area, and the calculation of the associated stress.

Mechanical methods (dissection techniques) and nonlinear elastic methods (ultrasonic and magnetic techniques) are limited in their applicability to residual stress determination. Mechanical methods are limited by assumptions concerning the nature of the residual stress field and sample geometry. Mechanical methods, being necessarily destructive, cannot be directly checked by repeat measurement. Spatial and depth resolution are orders of magnitude less than those of x-ray diffraction.

All nonlinear elastic methods are subject to major error from preferred orientation, cold work, temperature, and grain size. All require stress-free reference samples, which are otherwise identical to the sample under investigation. Nonlinear elastic methods are generally not suitable for routine residual stress determination at their current state of development. In addition, their spatial and depth resolutions are orders of magnitude less than those of x-ray diffraction.

To determine the stress, the strain in the crystal lattice must be measured for at least two precisely known orientations relative to the sample surface. Therefore, x-ray diffraction residual stress measurement is applicable to materials that are crystalline, relatively fine grained, and produce diffraction for any orientation of the sample surface. Samples may be metallic or ceramic, provided a diffraction peak of suitable intensity and free of interference from neighboring peaks can be produced in the high back-reflection region with the radiations available. X-ray diffraction residual stress measurement is unique in that macroscopic and microscopic residual stresses can be determined nondestructively.

Macroscopic stresses, or macrostresses, which extend over distances that are large relative to the grain size of the material, are of general interest in design and failure analysis. Macrostresses are tensor quantities, with magnitudes varying with direction at a single point in a body. The macrostress for a given location and direction is determined by measuring the strain in that direction at a single point. When

Fig. 1 Principles of x-ray diffraction stress measurement

(a)$\psi = 0$. (b)$\psi = \psi$ (sample rotated through some known angle ψ). D, x-ray detector; S, x-ray source; N, normal to the surface

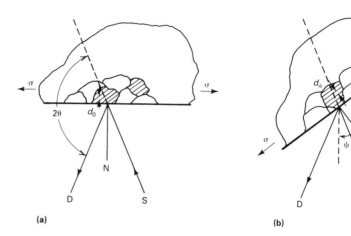

(a)   (b)

macrostresses are determined in at least three known directions, and a condition of plane stress is assumed, the three stresses can be combined using Mohr's circle for stress to determine the maximum and minimum residual stresses, the maximum shear stress, and their orientation relative to a reference direction. Macrostresses strain many crystals uniformly in the surface. This uniform distortion of the crystal lattice shifts the angular position of the diffraction peak selected for residual stress measurement.

Microscopic stresses, or microstresses, are scalar properties of the sample, such as percent of cold work or hardness, that are without direction and result from imperfections in the crystal lattice. Microstresses are associated with strains within the crystal lattice that traverse distances on the order of or less than the dimensions of the crystals. Microstresses vary from point to point within the crystal lattice, altering the lattice spacing and broadening the diffraction peak. Macrostresses and microstresses can be determined separately from the diffraction-peak position and breadth.

Principles of X-Ray Diffraction Stress Measurement

Figure 1 shows the diffraction of a monochromatic beam of x-rays at a high diffraction angle (2θ) from the surface of a stressed sample for two orientations of the sample relative to the x-ray beam. The angle ψ, defining the orientation of the sample surface, is the angle between the normal of the surface and the incident and diffracted beam bisector, which is also the angle between the

normal to the diffracting lattice planes and the sample surface.

Diffraction occurs at an angle 2θ, defined by Bragg's Law: $n\lambda = 2d \sin \theta$, where n is an integer denoting the order of diffraction, λ is the x-ray wavelength, d is the lattice spacing of crystal planes, and θ is the diffraction angle. For the monochromatic x-rays produced by the metallic target of an x-ray tube, the wavelength is known to 1 part in 10^5. Any change in the lattice spacing, d, results in a corresponding shift in the diffraction angle 2θ.

Figure 1(a) shows the sample in the $\psi = 0$ orientation. The presence of a tensile stress in the sample results in a Poisson's ratio contraction, reducing the lattice spacing and slightly increasing the diffraction angle, 2θ. If the sample is then rotated through some known angle ψ (Fig. 1b), the tensile stress present in the surface increases the lattice spacing over the stress-free state and decreases 2θ. Measuring the change in the angular position of the diffraction peak for at least two orientations of the sample defined by the angle ψ enables calculation of the stress present in the sample surface lying in the plane of diffraction, which contains the incident and diffracted x-ray beams. To measure the stress in different directions at the same point, the sample is rotated about its surface normal to coincide the direction of interest with the diffraction plane.

Because only the elastic strain changes the mean lattice spacing, only elastic strains are measured using x-ray diffraction for the determination of macrostresses. When the elastic limit is exceeded, further strain results in dislocation motion, disruption of the crystal lattice, and the formation of microstresses, but no additional increase in macroscopic stress. Although residual stresses re-

Table 1 Recommended diffraction techniques, x-ray elastic constants, and bulk values for various ferrous and nonferrous alloys

Alloy	Radiation	Lattice plane, (hkl)	Diffraction angle (2θ), degrees	Elastic constants(a) ($E/1 + \nu$), GPa (10^6 psi) (hkl)	Bulk	Bulk error, %	K_{45}(b) MPa	ksi	Linear absorption coefficient (μ) cm^{-1}	in.$^{-1}$
Aluminum-base alloys										
2014-T6	Cr Kα	(311)	139.0	59.4 ± 0.76 (8.62 ± 0.11)	54.5 (7.9)	−8.3	387	56.2	442	1124
2024-T351	Cr Kα	(311)	139.3	53.8 ± 0.55 (7.81 ± 0.08)	54.5 (7.9)	+1.1	348	50.5	435	1105
7075-T6	Cr Kα	(311)	139.0	60.9 ± 0.48 (8.83 ± 0.07)	53.8 (7.8)	−11.4	397	57.6	...	...
7050-T6	Cr Kα	(311)	139.0	57.1 ± 0.41 (8.28 ± 0.06)	53.8 (7.8)	−5.8	372	54.0	443	1126
Iron-base alloys										
Incoloy 800	Cu Kα	(420)	147.2	148.2 ± 2.8 (21.5 ± 0.4)	147.5 (21.4)	−0.4	758	110.0	1656	4205
304L	Cu Kα	(420)	147.0	157.2 ± 2.8 (22.8 ± 0.4)	151.0 (21.9)	−3.9	814	118.0	2096	5321
316	Cu Kα	(420)	146.5	132.4 ± 1.4 (19.2 ± 0.2)	153.8 (22.3)	+16.0	696	101.0	2066	5245
Invar	Cu Kα	(420)	147.0	108.2 ± 4.1 (15.7 ± 0.6)	112.4 (16.3)	+3.8	560	81.2	1706	4330
410 (22 HRC)	Cr Kα	(211)	155.1	176.5 ± 0.7 (25.6 ± 0.1)	155.8 (22.6)	−11.7	680	98.6	840	2129
410 (42 HRC)	Cr Kα	(211)	155.1	173.1 ± 1.4 (25.1 ± 0.2)	155.8 (22.6)	−9.9	667	96.7	840	2129
1050 (56 HRC)	Cr Kα	(211)	156.0	184.1 ± 2.1 (26.7 ± 0.3)	148.2 (21.5)	−19.4	683	99.0	885	2244
4340 (50 HRC)	Cr Kα	(211)	156.0	168.9 ± 2.8 (24.5 ± 0.4)	156.5 (22.7)	−7.3	627	90.9	909	2307
6260	Cr Kα	(211)	155.5	169.6 ± 2.8 (24.6 ± 0.4)	158.9 (23.0)	−6.5	643	93.2	894	2271
9310	Cr Kα	(211)	155.5	172.4 ± 2.8 (25.0 ± 0.4)	160.0 (23.2)	−7.2	653	94.7	894	2271
52100	Cr Kα	(211)	156.0	173.7 ± 2.1 (25.2 ± 0.3)	153.8 (22.3)	−11.5	645	93.5	714	1807
M50 (62 HRC)	Cr Kα	(211)	154.0	179.3 ± 2.1 (26.0 ± 0.3)	157.9 (22.9)	−11.9	724	105.0	1000	2490
17-4PH	Cr Kα	(211)	155.0	180.0 ± 0.7 (26.1 ± 0.1)	158.9 (23.0)	−11.9	696	101.0	888	2254
Nickel-base alloys										
Inconel 600	Cu Kα	(420)	150.8	159.3 ± 0.7 (23.1 ± 0.1)	165.5 (24.0)	+3.9	724	105.0	896	2275
Inconel 718	Cu Kα	(420)	145.0	140.0 ± 2.1 (20.3 ± 0.3)	156.5 (22.7)	−8.9	772	112.0	1232	3127
Inconel X-750	Cu Kα	(420)	151.0	160.6 ± 1.4 (23.3 ± 0.2)	160.6 (24.0)	+3.0	724	105.0	813	2062
Incoloy 901	Cu Kα	(420)	146.0	134.4 ± 3.4 (19.5 ± 0.5)	158.6 (23.0)	+17.9	717	104.0	1408	3569
Rene 95	Cu Kα	(420)	146.7	168.9 ± 0.7 (24.5 ± 0.1)	164.1 (23.8)	−2.8	882	128.0	935	2370
Titanium-base alloys										
Commercially pure Ti	Cu Kα	(21.3)	139.5	90.3 ± 1.4 (13.1 ± 0.2)	84.8 (12.3)	−6.1	581	84.3	917	2320
Ti-6Al-4V	Cu Kα	(21.3)	141.7	84.1 ± 0.7 (12.2 ± 0.1)	84.8 (12.3)	+0.8	509	73.9	867	2203
Ti-6Al-2Sn-4Zr-2Mo	Cu Kα	(21.3)	141.5	102.0 ± 1.4 (14.8 ± 0.2)	86.2 (12.5)	−15.5	622	90.2	866	2200

(a) Constants determined from four-point bending tests. (b) K_{45} is the magnitude of the stress necessary to cause an apparent shift in diffraction-peak position of 1° for a 45° angle tilt

sult from nonuniform plastic deformation, all residual macrostresses remaining after deformation are necessarily elastic.

The residual stress determined using x-ray diffraction is the arithmetic average stress in a volume of material defined by the irradiated area, which may vary from square centimeters to square millimeters, and the depth of penetration of the x-ray beam. The linear absorption coefficient of the material for the radiation used governs the depth of penetration, which can vary considerably. However, in iron-, nickel-, and aluminum-base alloys, 50% of the radiation is diffracted from a layer approximately 0.005 mm (0.0002 in.) deep for the radiations generally used for stress measurement. This shallow depth of penetration allows determination of macro- and microscopic residual stresses as functions of depth, with depth resolution approximately 10 to 100 times that possible using other methods.

Although in principle virtually any interplanar spacing may be used to measure strain in the crystal lattice, availability of the wavelengths produced by commercial x-ray tubes limits the choice to a few possible planes. The choice of a diffraction peak selected for residual stress measurement impacts significantly on the precision of the method. The higher the diffraction angle, the greater the precision. Practical techniques generally require diffraction angles, 2θ, greater than 120°.

Table 1 lists recommended diffraction techniques for various alloys. The relative sensitivity is shown by the value of K_{45}, the magnitude of the stress necessary to cause an apparent shift in diffraction-peak position of 1° for a 45° ψ tilt. As K_{45} increases, sensitivity decreases.

Plane-Stress Elastic Model

X-ray diffraction stress measurement is confined to the surface of the sample. Elec-tropolishing is used to expose new surfaces for subsurface measurement. In the exposed surface layer, a condition of plane stress is assumed to exist. That is, a stress distribution described by principal stresses σ_1 and σ_2 exists in the plane of the surface, and no stress is assumed perpendicular to the surface, $\sigma_3 = 0$. However, a strain component perpendicular to the surface ϵ_3 exists as a result of the Poisson's ratio contractions caused by the two principal stresses (Fig. 2).

The strain, $\epsilon_{\phi\psi}$, in the direction defined by the angles φ and ψ is:

$$\epsilon_{\phi\psi} = \left[\frac{1 + \nu}{E} (\sigma_1 \, \alpha_1^2 + \sigma_2 \, \alpha_2^2) \right] - \left[\frac{\nu}{E} (\sigma_1 + \sigma_2) \right] \quad \text{(Eq 1)}$$

where E is the modulus of elasticity, ν is the Poisson's ratio, and α_1 and α_2 are the angle cosines of the strain vector:

$$\alpha_1 = \cos \phi \sin \psi$$
$$\alpha_2 = \sin \phi \sin \psi \quad \text{(Eq 2)}$$

Substituting for the angle cosines in Eq 1 and simplifying enables expressing the strain in terms of the orientation angles:

Fig. 2 Plane-stress elastic model

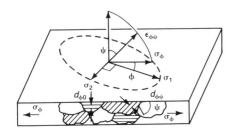

$$\epsilon_{\phi\psi} = \left[\frac{1+\nu}{E}(\sigma_1 \cos^2 \phi + \sigma_2 \sin^2 \phi)\right.$$

$$\sin^2 \psi\left.\right] - \left[\frac{\nu}{E}(\sigma_1 + \sigma_2)\right] \qquad \text{(Eq 3)}$$

If the angle ψ is taken to be 90°, the strain vector lies in the plane of the surface, and the surface stress component, σ_ϕ, is:

$$\sigma_\phi = (\sigma_1 \cos^2 \phi) + (\sigma_2 \sin^2 \phi) \qquad \text{(Eq 4)}$$

Substituting Eq 4 into Eq 3 yields the strain in the sample surface at an angle ϕ from the principal stress σ_1:

$$\epsilon_{\phi\psi} = \left[\frac{1+\nu}{E}\sigma_\phi \sin^2 \psi\right] -$$

$$\left[\left(\frac{\nu}{E}\right)(\sigma_1 + \sigma_2)\right] \qquad \text{(Eq 5)}$$

Equation 5 relates the surface stress σ_ϕ, in any direction defined by the angle ψ, to the strain, ϵ, in the direction (ϕ,ψ) and the principal stresses in the surface.

If $d_{\phi\psi}$ is the spacing between the lattice planes measured in the direction defined by ϕ and ψ, the strain can be expressed in terms of changes in the linear dimensions of the crystal lattice:

$$\epsilon_{\phi\psi} = \frac{\Delta d}{d_0} = \frac{d_{\phi\psi} - d_0}{d_0}$$

where d_0 is the stress-free lattice spacing. Substitution into Eq 5 yields:

$$\frac{d_{\phi\psi} - d_0}{d_0} = \left[\left(\frac{1+\nu}{E}\right)_{(hkl)}\sigma_\phi \sin^2 \psi\right] -$$

$$\left[\left(\frac{\nu}{E}\right)_{(hkl)}(\sigma_1 + \sigma_2)\right] \qquad \text{(Eq 6)}$$

where the elastic constants $(1 + \nu/E)_{(hkl)}$ and $(\nu/E)_{(hkl)}$ are not the bulk values but the values for the crystallographic direction normal to the lattice planes in which the strain is measured as specified by the Miller indices (hkl). Because of elastic anisotropy, the elastic constants in the (hkl) direction commonly vary significantly from the bulk mechanical values, which are an average over all possible directions in the crystal lattice.

The lattice spacing for any orientation, then, is:

$$d_{\phi\psi} = \left[\left(\frac{1+\nu}{E}\right)_{(hkl)}\sigma_\phi d_0 \sin^2 \psi\right] -$$

$$\left[\left(\frac{\nu}{E}\right)_{(hkl)}d_0(\sigma_1 + \sigma_2) + d_0\right] \qquad \text{(Eq 7)}$$

Equation 7 describes the fundamental relationship between lattice spacing and the biaxial stresses in the surface of the sample. The lattice spacing $d_{\phi\psi}$ is a linear function of $\sin^2 \psi$. Figure 3 shows the actual dependence of $d(311)$ for ψ, ranging from 0 to 45° for shot peened 5056-O aluminum having a surface stress of −148 MPa (−21.5 ksi), to which a straight line has been fitted by least squares regression.

The intercept of the plot at $\sin^2 \psi = 0$ is:

$$d_{\phi 0} = d_0 - \left(\frac{\nu}{E}\right)_{(hkl)}d_0(\sigma_1 + \sigma_2) =$$

$$d_0\left[1 - \left(\frac{\nu}{E}\right)_{(hkl)}(\sigma_1 + \sigma_2)\right] \qquad \text{(Eq 8)}$$

which equals the unstressed lattice spacing, d_0, minus the Poisson's ratio contraction caused by the sum of the principal stresses. The slope of the plot is:

$$\frac{\partial d_{\phi\psi}}{\partial \sin^2 \psi} = \left(\frac{1+\nu}{E}\right)_{(hkl)}\sigma_\phi d_0$$

which can be solved for the stress σ_ϕ:

$$\sigma_\phi = \left(\frac{E}{1+\nu}\right)_{(hkl)}\frac{1}{d_0}\left(\frac{\partial d_{\phi\psi}}{\partial \sin^2 \psi}\right) \qquad \text{(Eq 9)}$$

The x-ray elastic constants can be determined empirically, but the unstressed lattice spacing, d_0, is generally unknown. However, because $E \gg (\sigma_1 + \sigma_2)$, the value of $d_{\phi 0}$ from Eq 8 differs from d_0 by not more than ±1%, and σ_ϕ may be approximated to this accuracy using:

$$\sigma_\phi = \left(\frac{E}{1+\nu}\right)_{(hkl)}\frac{1}{d_{\phi 0}}\left(\frac{\partial d_{\phi\psi}}{\partial \sin^2 \psi}\right) \qquad \text{(Eq 10)}$$

The method then becomes a differential technique, and no stress-free reference standards are required to determine d_0 for the biaxial stress case. The three most common methods of x-ray diffraction residual stress measurement, the single-angle, two-angle, and $\sin^2 \psi$ techniques, assume plane stress at the sample surface and are based on the fundamental relationship between lattice spacing and stress given in Eq 7.

The single-angle technique, or single-exposure technique, derives its name from early photographic methods that require a single exposure of the film (Ref 1).

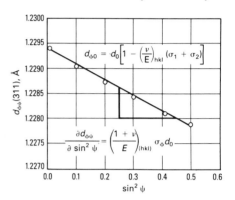

Fig. 3 A $d(311)$ versus $\sin^2 \psi$ plot for a shot peened 5056-O aluminum alloy having a surface stress of −148 MPa (−21.5 ksi)

The method is generally considered less sensitive than the two-angle or $\sin^2 \psi$ techniques primarily because the possible range of ψ is limited by the diffraction angle 2θ.

Figure 4 shows the basic geometry of the method. A collimated beam of x-rays is inclined at a known angle, β, from the sample surface normal. X-rays diffract from the sample, forming a cone of diffracted radiation originating at point 0. The diffracted x-rays are recorded using film or position-sensitive detectors placed on either side of the incident beam. The presence of a stress in the sample surface varies the lattice spacing slightly between the diffracting crystals shown at points 1 and 2 in Fig. 4, resulting in slightly different diffraction angles on either side of the x-ray beam. If S_1 and S_2 are the arc lengths along the surface of the film or detectors at a radius R from sample surface, the stress is:

$$\sigma_\phi = \left(\frac{E}{1+\nu}\right)_{(hkl)}\left(\frac{S_1 - S_2}{2R}\right)$$

$$\left(\frac{\cot \theta}{\sin^2 \psi_1 - \sin^2 \psi_2}\right)$$

The angles ψ_1 and ψ_2 are related to the Bragg diffraction angles θ_1, θ_2, and the angle of inclination of the instrument, β, by:

$$\psi_1 = \beta + \theta_1 - \frac{\pi}{2}$$

and

$$\psi_2 = \beta + \theta_2 - \frac{\pi}{2}$$

Fig. 4 Basic geometry of the single-angle technique for x-ray diffraction residual stress measurement

N_p, normal to the lattice planes; N_s, normal to the surface. See text for a discussion of other symbols. Source: Ref 2

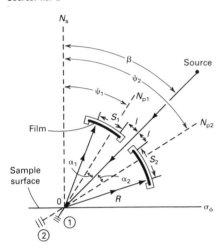

The precision of the method is limited by the principle that increasing the diffraction angle 2θ to achieve precision in the determination of lattice spacing reduces the possible range of $\sin^2 \psi$, lessening sensitivity. The single-angle technique is generally not used, except for film and position-sensitive detector apparatuses designed for high-speed measurement.

Two-Angle Technique. Equation 7 and Fig. 3 show that if the lattice spacing, $d_{\theta\psi}$, is a linear function of $\sin^2 \psi$, the stress can be determined by measuring the lattice spacing for any two ψ angles, originating the term two-angle technique. The technique has been thoroughly investigated by the Society of Automotive Engineers (SAE) and finds wide acceptance in the United States (Ref 3). Selecting ψ angles to provide as large a range of $\sin^2 \psi$ as possible within the limitations imposed by the diffraction angle 2θ and the sample geometry maximizes sensitivity of the method. Lattice spacing is determined precisely at two extreme values of ψ, typically 0 and 45°, and the stress is calculated using Eq 10.

The $\sin^2 \psi$ technique (Ref 4) is identical to the two-angle technique, except lattice spacing is determined for multiple ψ tilts, a straight line is fitted by least squares regression (as shown for the shot peened aluminum sample in Fig. 3), and the stress is calculated from the slope of the best fit line using Eq 10. The method, a standard procedure in Japan and Germany, provides no significant improvement in precision over

the two-angle technique if the two data points are selected at the extreme ends of the $\sin^2 \psi$ range.

The primary advantage of the $\sin^2 \psi$ technique, considering the additional time required for data collection, is in establishing the linearity of d as a function of $\sin^2 \psi$ to demonstrate that x-ray diffraction residual stress measurement is possible on the sample of interest.

The Marion-Cohen technique characterizes the dependence of lattice spacing on stress in highly textured materials (Ref 5). The method assumes a biaxial stress field with an additional dependence of the lattice spacing on a texture distribution function $f(\psi)$, a measure of the (hkl) pole density calculated from the diffracted intensity over the range of ψ tilts used for stress measurement. The model assumes a lattice spacing dependence of:

$$d_{\psi\phi} = \left(\frac{1 + \nu}{E}\right)_{(hkl)} \sigma_\phi d_0 \sin^2 \psi +$$

$$(d_{max} - d_B) \, f(\psi) + d_B$$

where d_{max} and d_B are the maximum and minimum lattice spacings in the range investigated. The method requires simultaneous determination of the preferred orientation, or texture, in the sample to determine $f(\psi)$ along with lattice spacing and is solved by multiple linear regression over the functions $f(\psi)$ and $d_{\psi\phi}$ as functions of $\sin^2 \psi$ to determine σ_ϕ, d_{max}, and d_B.

The assumption that the lattice spacing and preferred orientation present at the time of measurement resulted entirely from the same origin limits practical application of the method. Residual stresses measured by the Marion-Cohen, two-angle, and $\sin^2 \psi$ methods yield virtually identical results for stress produced by shot peening, grinding, or machining in most materials of practical interest (Ref 6).

Full-Tensor Determination. An expression for the lattice spacing can be formulated as a function of ϕ and ψ, assuming stresses exist normal to the surface. This state of stress in the surface layers penetrated by the x-ray beam is a possible explanation for nonlinear dependence of the lattice spacing on $\sin^2 \psi$. Nonlinearities in the form of elliptical curvature of the d $\sin^2 \psi$ plots resulting in ψ splitting are attributable to stresses normal to the surface or large shear stresses near the sample surface. Psi splitting results in different values of the lattice spacing for positive and negative ψ tilts and potential error in stress calculation.

In principle, the full-tensor method (Ref 7, 8) can be used to determine surface

stresses nondestructively in the presence of large subsurface stress gradients, such as those found on machined or ground samples; however, extensive data collection is required, generally exceeding that acceptable for routine testing. Unlike the plane-stress methods, determination of the full stress tensor requires absolute knowledge of the unstressed lattice spacing, d_0, at the accuracy required for strain measurement (1 part in 10^5) to calculate the stress normal to the sample surface. In many cases, such as for plastically deformed surfaces generated by machining or carburized steels, the lattice spacing varies as a result of deformation or heat treating, precluding independent determination of the unstressed lattice spacing with sufficient precision. The extensive data collection and dependence on absolute knowledge of d_0 limit the full-tensor method primarily to research applications. If measurements can be performed destructively, by electropolishing to remove layers, surface results obtained using the plane-stress method can be corrected for the presence of the subsurface stress gradient (Ref 9).

Basic Procedure

Sample preparation, if the geometry of the sample does not interfere with the incident or diffracted x-ray beams, is generally minimal. Preparation of the sample surface depends on the nature of the residual stresses to be determined. If the stresses of interest are produced by such surface treatments as machining, grinding, or shot peening, the residual stress distribution is usually limited to less than 500 μm of the sample surface. Therefore, the sample surface must be carefully protected from secondary abrasion, corrosion, or etching. Samples should be oiled to prevent corrosion and packed to protect the surface during handling. Secondary abrasive treatment, such as wire brushing or sand blasting, radically alters the surface residual stresses, generally producing a shallow, highly compressive layer over the original residual stress distribution.

If the stresses of interest are those produced by carburizing or heat treatment, it may be advisable to electropolish the surface of the sample, which may have undergone finish grinding or sand blasting after heat treatment. Electropolishing eliminates the shallow, highly stressed surface layer, exposing the subsurface stresses before measurement.

To measure the inside surface of tubing, in bolt holes, between gear teeth, and other restrictive geometries, the sample must be sectioned to provide clearance for the incident and diffracted x-ray beams. Unless prior experience with the sample under investigation indicates that no significant stress relaxation occurs upon sectioning, electrical resistance strain-gage rosettes should be applied to the measurement area to record the strain relaxation that occurs during sectioning. Unless the geometry of the sample clearly defines the minimum and maximum directions of stress relaxation, a full rectangular strain-gage rosette should be used to calculate the true stress relaxation in the direction of interest from the measured strain relaxation.

Following x-ray diffraction residual stress measurements, the total stress before sectioning can be calculated by subtracting algebraically the sectioning stress relaxation from the x-ray diffraction results. If only near-surface layers are examined on a massive sample, a constant relaxation correction can be applied to all depths examined. If a significant volume of material is removed, as in determination of the stress distribution through the carburized case of a thin bearing race, a more accurate representation of sectioning relaxation can be achieved by applying strain-gage rosettes to the inner and outer surfaces and by assuming a linear relaxation of stress through the sample.

Sample Positioning. Because the diffraction angles must be determined to accuracies of approximately ±0.01°, the sample must be positioned in the x-ray beam at the true center of rotation of the ψ and 2θ axes, and the angle ψ must be constant throughout the irradiated area. Therefore, extremely precise positioning of the sample to accuracies of approximately 0.025 mm (0.001 in.) is critical. Further, the size of the irradiated area must be limited to an essentially flat region on the sample surface. Small-diameter samples or such sample geometries as small-radius fillets, the roots of threads, and fine-pitched gears may contribute to major sources of error if the x-ray beam is not confined to an essentially flat region at a known ψ tilt on the curved surface. If the irradiated area is allowed to span a curved surface, ψ will not be constant during determination of lattice spacing. These restrictions imposed by the sample geometry may prohibit x-ray diffraction residual stress measurement in many areas of primary concern, such as the roots of notches.

Irradiated Area and Measurement Time. The residual stress determined by x-ray diffraction is the arithmetic average stress in the area defined by the dimensions of the x-ray beam. Consideration must be given to an appropriate beam size for the nature of the stress to be investigated. If average stresses over significant areas are of interest, the maximum beam size allowed by the geometry of the sample would be an appropriate choice. If local variations in

Fig. 5 Range of Kα doublet blending for a simulated steel (211) Cr Kα peak at 156.0°

A, fully annealed; B and C, intermediate hardness; D, fully hardened

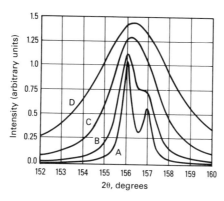

residual stress, such as those produced by individual passes of a grinding wheel, are of interest, a smaller irradiated area with a geometry appropriate for the investigation should be selected. Practical dimensions of the irradiated area may range from circular zones 1.25 mm (0.050 in.) in diameter to a range of rectangular geometries from approximately 0.5 to 13 mm (0.020 to 0.5 in.). The maximum irradiated area generally feasible is approximately 13 × 8 mm (0.5 × 0.3 in.).

As the irradiated area is increased, the data collection time necessary to achieve adequate precision for residual stress measurement diminishes. The precision with which the diffracted intensity can be determined varies as the inverse of the square root of the number of x-rays collected. To determine the intensity to an accuracy of 1% at a single point on the diffraction peak, 10^4 x-rays must be counted, regardless of the time required. With diffracted intensities typically available on a fixed slit diffractometer system, this may require collection times of approximately 30 s for each point on the diffraction peak. If seven data points are collected on each diffraction peak for a two-angle technique, total measurement time may be 10 to 15 min. Reducing the irradiated area sufficiently to decrease the diffracted intensity by an order of magnitude increases the data collection time proportionally for the same precision in measurement. If fluorescence is not a problem, position-sensitive detectors can be used to collect data simultaneously at numerous points across the diffraction peak, with some sacrifice in angular precision, reducing data collection time by an order of magnitude.

Diffraction-Peak Location. The transition metal target x-ray tubes used for stress measurement produce a continuous spectrum of white radiation and three monochromatic high-intensity lines. The three lines are the $K\alpha_1$, $K\alpha_2$, and $K\beta$ characteristic radiations with wavelengths known to high precision. The $K\alpha_1$ and $K\alpha_2$ lines differ too little in wavelength to allow separation of the diffraction peaks produced. The $K\alpha_1$ line, the highest intensity, is nominally twice that of the $K\alpha_2$ line. The $K\beta$ line is produced at a substantially shorter wavelength and can generally be separated from the $K\alpha$ lines by filtration, the use of high-energy resolution detectors, or crystal monochromators. The $K\beta$ line is typically one fifth the intensity of the $K\alpha_1$ line and is generally too weak for practical x-ray diffraction residual stress measurement on plastically deformed surfaces.

Because the $K\alpha$ doublet is generally used for residual stress measurement, the diffraction peaks produced consist of a superimposed pair of peaks, as shown in Fig. 5 for four cases, indicating the various degrees of broadening that may be encountered. The variable blending of the $K\alpha$ doublet typical of an annealed sample is indicated by curve A; a fully hardened or cold-worked sample, curve D. Because the accuracy of x-ray diffraction residual stress measurement depends on the precision with which the diffraction peak can be located, the method used to locate broadened doublet peaks is of primary importance.

Precise determination of the position of the diffraction peak at each ψ tilt begins with collection of raw intensity data at several points on the peak. The diffracted intensity (x-rays counted per unit time) or inverse intensity (time for a fixed number of x-rays to be counted) is determined to a precision exceeding 1% at several fixed diffraction angles, 2θ, spanning the diffraction peak. Depending on the method to be used for peak location, 3 to 15 individual data points and 2 background points are measured using standard diffractometer techniques. If data are collected using a position-sensitive detector, the diffracted intensity can be determined at dozens of data points spanning the diffraction peak. Sharp diffraction peaks, such as those shown in curve A in Fig. 5, may be located using intensity data of lower precision than that required for broad peaks, as shown in curve D. The number of x-rays to be collected, and therefore the time required for stress measurement to a fixed precision, increases as the diffraction peaks broaden.

Before determining a diffraction-peak position, the raw measured intensities must be corrected for Lorentz polarization and absorption. A sloping background intensity is then corrected by subtracting the back-

Fig. 6 Comparison of *d* (21.3) versus sin² ψ data taken 0.176 mm (0.0069 in.) below the surface for a ground Ti-6Al-4V sample using two diffraction-peak location methods

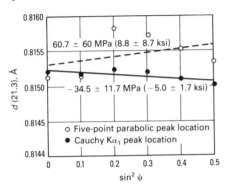

ground, assuming a linear variation beneath the diffraction peak. Various numerical methods are available to calculate the position of the diffraction peak. The simplest method, incorporated in early automated diffraction equipment, is to locate 2θ positions on either side of the peak at which the intensity is equal and assume the peak position to be at the midpoint. A straight line can be fitted to the opposing sides of the diffraction peak and the point of intersection of the two lines taken as a peak position (Ref 10). Early SAE literature recommends calculating the vertex of the parabola defined by three points confined to the top 15% of the peak (Ref 11). A significant improvement in precision can be achieved, approaching the 0.01° resolution of most diffractometers, by collecting 5 to 15 data points in the top 15% and fitting a parabola by least squares regression before calculation of the peak vertex.

If the intensity is measured at many points ranging across the entire Kα doublet, the peak position can be calculated as the centroid of the area above the background or by autocorrelation. Both of these area-integration methods are independent of the peak shape, but are extremely sensitive to the precision with which the tails of the diffraction peak can be determined.

All the above methods are effective, regression fit parabola being superior, if applied to a single symmetrical diffraction-peak profile, such as the simple Kα₁ peak shown in curve A in Fig. 5 or the fully combined doublet shown in curve D. All can lead to significant error in the event of partial separation of the doublet, as shown in curve B (Fig. 5). Partial separation commonly results from defocusing as the sample is tilted through a range of ψ angles. If residual

stresses are measured as a function of depth, diffraction peaks can vary from breadths similar to curve D (Fig. 5) at the cold-worked surface through a continuous range of blending to complete separation beneath the cold-work layer, as shown in curve A. All the techniques of peak location discussed can lead to significant error in stress measurement as the degree of doublet separation varies.

The Rachinger correction (Ref 12) can be applied to separate the Kα doublet before fitting parabolas, but the precision of the correction diminishes on the Kα₂ side of the combined profile and is generally inadequate for precise residual stress measurement. Fitting Pearson VII distribution functions (Cauchy to Gaussian bell-shaped, as described in Ref 13 and 14) separately to the Kα₁ and Kα₂ diffraction peaks, assuming a doublet separation based on the difference in wavelength, provides a method of peak location that overcomes most of the problems outlined above.

Figures 6 and 7 show the effect of the peak-location method on the results obtained. Figure 6 illustrates comparison of the same data reduced using Pearson VII distribution functions and a five-point least squares parabolic fit for ground Ti-6Al-4V using the (21.3) planes for residual stress measurement. Apparent nonlinearities in *d* versus sin² ψ for the parabola fit are due to inaccurate diffraction-peak location in the presence of partial blending of the Kα doublet. Figure 7 shows the errors in stress measurement by the two methods of peak

location applied to the identical data for the entire stress profile. The errors for the distribution function fit are smaller than the plotting symbols at all depths.

Microstress Determination and Line Broadening. Diffraction peak broadening caused by microstresses in the crystal lattice can be separated into components due to strain in the crystal lattice and crystallite size. Separation of the broadening, which is of instrumental origin, from that due to lattice strain and crystallite size is performed using Fourier analysis of the diffraction-peak profile and data collection sufficient to define precisely the shape of the entire diffraction peak. Analysis of the Fourier series terms allows separation of the components of the broadening attributable to lattice strain from that caused by reduction in the crystallite size. However, this method requires extensive data collection and depends on the precision with which the tails of the diffraction peak can be separated from the background intensity.

For most routine analyses of microstresses associated with cold working or heat treatment for which separation of the strain and size components is not necessary, much simpler determinations of diffraction-peak breadth are adequate. The diffraction-peak width can be quantified precisely as the integral breadth (total area under the peak divided by diffraction-peak height) or the width at half the height of the diffraction peak. The width of the diffraction peak can be measured directly from strip-chart recordings or calculated from the width of the

Fig. 7 Comparison of residual stress patterns derived using Cauchy and parabolic peak location for a ground Ti-6Al-4V sample using a six-angle sin² ψ technique

Errors in stress measurement by two methods of diffraction-peak location are shown.

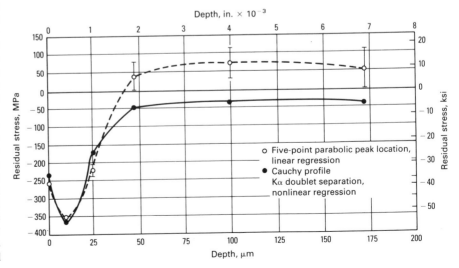

Fig. 8 Diffraction-peak breadth at half height for the (211) peak for M50 high-speed tool steel as a function of Rockwell hardness

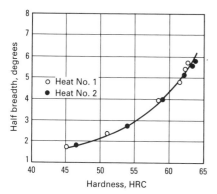

Fig. 9 Diffraction-peak breadth at half height for the (420) peak for René 95 as a function of cold-working percentage

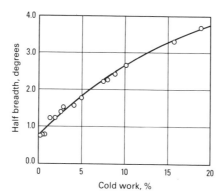

function fitted to the diffraction-peak profile during macrostress measurement. Micro-stresses and macrostresses can then be determined simultaneously from the peak breadth and position.

Figures 8 and 9 show empirical relationships established between diffraction-peak breadth at half height for the (211) peak for M50 high-speed tool steel as a function of hardness and for the (420) peak breadth as a function of percent cold work for René 95, respectively. These empirical curves can be used to calculate the hardness or cold work in conjunction with macroscopic residual stress measurement. For the preparation of the hardness curve, a series of coupons are quenched and tempered to known hardness. The peak breadth is then measured using the same slit system and peak-location method used for macrostress measurement. For the percent cold work curve, samples are heat treated, then pulled in tension to produce a series of coupons with various known amounts of cold work. Because the initial heat treatment may alter significantly the initial peak breadth before cold work, the coupons must receive the same heat treatment as the samples to be measured before inducing known amounts of cold work.

Sample fluorescence complicates the selection of radiation to be used for residual stress measurement. The radiation necessary for the highest precision techniques may cause fluorescence of the elements present in the sample under investigation. The use of Cu Kα radiation for residual stress measurement in alloys containing iron, chromium, or titanium can result in fluorescent background intensities many times as intense as the diffracted radiation, greatly reducing the

signal-to-noise ratio. Problems with fluorescence may be overcome in some cases by use of metal foil filters, but generally require use of a crystal monochromator or high energy resolution solid-state detector. Failure to eliminate fluorescence can degrade severely the precision with which the diffraction peak can be located accurately, increasing random experimental error significantly. Diffracted-beam monochromators and solid-state detectors can be used only on standard laboratory diffractometers. The position-sensitive detectors available for residual stress measurement are the gas-filled proportional counter or fluorescence screen type and have insufficient energy resolution to overcome fluorescence.

Sources of Error

Instrumental and Positioning Errors. The principal sources of error in x-ray diffraction residual stress measurement are related to the high precision with which the diffraction-peak position must be located. Errors of approximately 0.025 mm (0.001 in.) in alignment of the diffraction apparatus or positioning of the sample result in errors in stress measurement of approximately 14 MPa (2 ksi) for high diffraction angle techniques and increase rapidly as the diffraction angle is reduced.

Instrument alignment requires coincidence of the θ and ψ axes of rotation and positioning of the sample such that the diffracting volume is centered on these coincident axes. If a focusing diffractometer is used, the receiving slit must move along a true radial line centered on the axes of rotation. All these features of alignment can be checked readily using a stress-free powder sample

(Ref 15). If the diffraction apparatus is properly aligned for residual stress measurement, a loosely compacted powder sample producing diffraction at approximately the Bragg angle to be used for residual stress measurement should indicate not more than ± 14 MPa (± 2 ksi) apparent stress. Alignment and positioning errors result in systematic additive error in residual stress measurement.

Effect of Sample Geometry. Excessive sample surface roughness or pitting, curvature of the surface within the irradiated area, or interference of the sample geometry with the diffracted x-ray beam can result in systematic error similar to sample displacement. Coarse grain size, often encountered in cast materials, can lessen the number of crystals contributing to the diffraction peak such that the peaks become asymmetrical, resulting in random error in diffraction-peak location and residual stress measurement. Rocking of coarse-grained samples about the ψ axis through a range of a few degrees during measurement can be used to increase the number of crystals contributing to the diffraction peak in coarse-grained samples to allow residual stress measurement on samples with a grain size as large as ASTM No. 1 (Ref 16). Residual stress generally cannot be measured reliably using x-ray diffraction in samples with coarser grain sizes.

X-Ray Elastic Constants. A major source of potential systematic proportional error arises in determination of the x-ray elastic constants $(E/1 + \nu)_{(hkl)}$. The residual stress measured is proportional to the value of the x-ray elastic constants, which may differ by as much as 40% from the bulk value due to elastic anisotropy. The x-ray elastic constant must be determined empirically by loading a sample of the material to known stress levels and measuring the change in the lattice spacing as a function of applied stress and ψ tilt (Ref 17). The x-ray elastic constant can then be calculated from the slope of a line fitted by least squares regression through the plot of the change in lattice spacing for the ψ tilt used as a function of applied stress.

Figure 10 shows data obtained for determination of the x-ray elastic constants in Inconel 718. With instrumented samples placed in four-point bending, the x-ray elastic constant can typically be determined to an accuracy of ± 1%. Table 1 lists elastic constants determined in four-point bending for various alloys along with the bulk elastic constants and the potential systematic proportional error that could result from use of the bulk values. X-ray elastic constants should be determined whenever possible to minimize systematic proportional error.

Subsurface Measurement and Required Corrections

Measuring residual stress distributions as functions of depth into the sample surface necessitates electropolishing layers of material to expose the subsurface layers. Electropolishing is preferred for layer removal because no residual stresses are induced, and if properly performed, preferential etching of the grain boundaries does not occur. Any mechanical method of removal, regardless of how fine the abrasive or machining method, deforms the surface and induces residual stresses, altering severely the state of stress present in the sample. Such methods must be avoided. Thick layers can be removed using a combined machining or grinding procedure, followed by electropolishing to remove at least 0.2 mm (0.008 in.) of material to eliminate the machining or grinding residual stresses.

Subsurface Stress Gradients. Although the x-ray beam penetrates only to shallow depths (approximately 0.005 mm, or 0.0002 in.) beneath the exposed surface, the residual stress distributions produced by machining and grinding may vary significantly

over depths of this order. Because the x-ray beam is attenuated exponentially as it passes into and out of the sample, stress measurements conducted in the presence of such a subsurface stress gradient yield an exponentially weighted average of the stress at the exposed surface and in the layers below. The intensity of the radiation penetrating to a depth x is:

$$I(x) = I_0 e^{-\mu x}$$

where I_0 is the initial intensity, μ is the linear absorption coefficient, and e is the natural logarithm base (2.71828...). If the linear absorption coefficient is known, this exponential weighting can be unfolded provided measurements have been conducted at a sufficient number of closely spaced depths to define the stress gradient adequately. Correction for penetration of the radiation into the subsurface stress gradient requires calculating the derivative of the lattice spacing at each ψ tilt as a function of depth. The linear absorption coefficient is calculated from the chemical composition, mass absorption coefficients for the elemental constituents of the alloy, density of the alloy, and radiation

Fig. 11 Effect of the stress gradient correction on the measurement of near-surface stresses for ground 4340 steel, 50 HRC

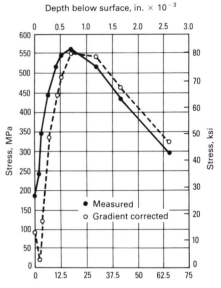

used. Failure to correct for penetration of the radiation into the stress gradient can lead to errors as large as 345 MPa (50 ksi).

Figure 11 shows an example of the effect of the correction on the residual stress profile produced in ground 4340 steel. Errors due to the subsurface stress gradient are generally maximum at the surface of the sample and become minimal beneath the highly deformed surface layer. Nondestructive surface residual stress measurements are subject to significant error on machined or ground surfaces due to the presence of the subsurface stress gradient.

Significant relaxation of stress in the surface exposed by layer removal can occur in determination of subsurface residual stresses. If the sample geometry and nature of the residual stress distribution conform to the simple symmetries of flat plates or cylindrical bodies, closed-form solutions are available to correct the results obtained on the surfaces exposed by electropolishing for removal of the stressed layers above (Ref 18). These corrections involve integration over the residual stress measured in the layers removed from the exposed layer back to the original surface. The accuracy of these corrections depends on the depth resolution with which the stress distribution is measured. Correction for layer removal can be combined with correction for sectioning to

Fig. 10 X-ray elastic constant determination for Inconel 718, (220) planes

$\Delta\psi = 45°$, $d_0 = 1.1272$ Å

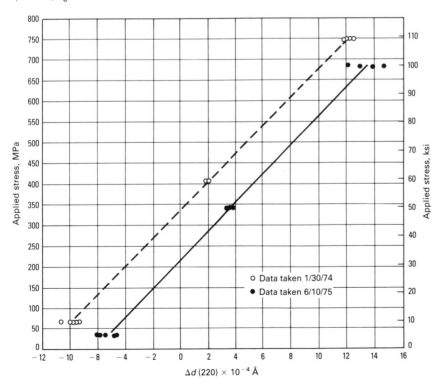

Fig. 12 Longitudinal residual stress distribution with and without correction for removal of the carburized case from a 16-mm (⅝-in.) diam 1070 steel shaft

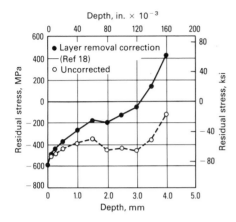

Fig. 13 Longitudinal residual stress distribution in an induction-hardened 1070 carbon steel shaft

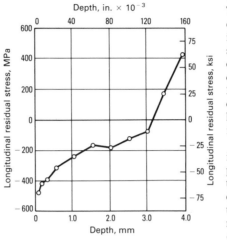

determine the total state of residual stress before dissection of the sample.

The magnitude of the layer-removal stress-relaxation correction, which depends on the stress in the layers removed and the sample geometry, increases with the total strain energy released. For massive samples from which only thin layers have been removed or for any sample geometry in which no significant stresses are present, correction will be insignificant. However, the correction can be large for some combinations of stress distribution and geometry. Figure 12 shows the longitudinal residual stress distribution with and without correction for complete removal of the carburized case on a 16-mm (⅝-in.) diam steel shaft.

Many components, such as gear teeth and turbine blades, do not conform to the simple geometries and assumed stress fields to which the closed-form layer-removal corrections apply. For these geometries, electropolishing in a confined pocket to minimize stress relaxation, which is assumed to be negligible, is the only practical approach.

Applications

The following examples result from investigations performed on horizontal laboratory diffractometers modified for stress measurement and instrumented with a lithium-doped silicon solid-state detector for suppression of sample fluorescence. The examples implement the two-angle technique and the fitting of a parabola to the top 15% or a Cauchy profile of the entire diffraction peak, as appropriate for the symmetry of the diffrac-

tion peaks produced. Results were corrected for Lorentz polarization and absorption as well as a sloping background intensity. Subsurface results were corrected for penetration of the radiation into the subsurface stress gradient and for sectioning and layer removal stress relaxation, as appropriate.

The elastic constants used to calculate macroscopic stress from strain in the crystal lattice were obtained empirically by loading an instrumented beam of the alloy under investigation in four-point bending. The samples were positioned to the center of the diffractometer using a feeler gage capable of repeat positioning precision of ±0.05 mm (±0.002 in.). The alignment of the diffractometers was established and checked using

Fig. 14 Hardness (Rockwell C scale) distribution in an induction-hardened 1070 carbon steel shaft

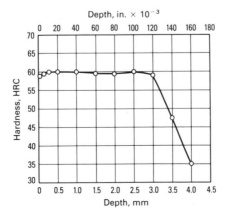

nickel or iron powder in accordance with ASTM E 915 (Ref 15).

Example 1: Subsurface Residual Stress and Hardness Distributions in an Induction-Hardened Steel Shaft. The longitudinal residual stress and hardness distributions through the case produced by induction hardening of a 1070 carbon steel shaft were investigated to qualify a modification of the induction-hardening procedure. The sample consisted of a nominally 205-mm (8-in.) long shaft of complex geometry; a 16-mm (⅝-in.) diam induction-hardened bearing surface was the region of interest.

The sample was first sectioned to approximately 100 mm (4 in.) in length to facilitate positioning on the diffractometer. Because the sample was cut a distance of several diameters from the area of interest, no attempt was made to monitor sectioning stress relaxation, assumed to be negligible. X-ray diffraction macroscopic residual stress measurements were performed using the two-angle Cr Kα (211) technique in the longitudinal direction as a function of depth to approximately 4 mm (0.16 in.) beneath the original surface, fully removing the hardened case. The material was removed by electropolishing complete cylindrical shells as necessary to correct for layer removal stress relaxation using closed-form solutions (Ref 18). Simultaneous determinations of the breadth of the Cauchy diffraction-peak profile fitted to the Kα₁ peak were used to calculate the hardness of the material using an empirical relationship similar to that shown in Fig. 8, which was previously established for 1070 steel.

Figure 13 shows the longitudinal residual stress distribution corrected for penetration of the radiation into the stress gradient, essentially negligible for the gradual stress gradient produced by induction hardening, and for layer removal, which builds to corrections as large 550 MPa (80 ksi) at the maximum depth. The fully corrected results show surface compression of approximately −550 MPa (−80 ksi) diminishing initially in a near-exponential fashion, then more gradually beyond depths of approximately 1.5 mm (0.060 in.). The stress distribution crosses into tension at a nominal depth of 3 mm (0.125 in.) and rises to relatively high tension in the core of the shaft, approaching 517 MPa (75 ksi) at the maximum depth of 4 mm (0.160 in.) examined.

Figure 14 illustrates the hardness distribution calculated from the breadth of the (211) diffraction-peak profile fitted using a Cauchy distribution function to separate the Kα doublet. The hardness was found to be extremely uniform, varying between 59 and 60 HRC to a depth of 3 mm (0.120 in.). At

Fig. 15 Longitudinal residual stress and percent cold work distributions in belt-polished Inconel 600 tubing

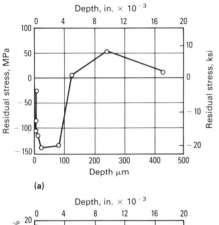

(a)

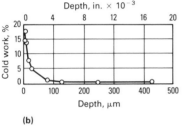

(b)

Fig. 16 Longitudinal residual stress as a function of the quantity (1 + cos θ) for a 63-mm (2.5-in.) Inconel 600 U-bend

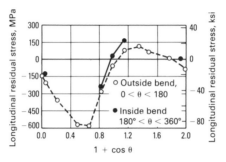

approximately the depth at which the longitudinal residual stress distribution goes into tension, the hardness begins to diminish linearly, dropping to approximately 35 HRC at the maximum depth examined in the core of the shaft.

Example 2: Residual Stress and Percent Cold Work Distribution in Belt-Polished and Formed Inconel 600 tubing. Inconel 600 tubing of the type used for steam generators subject to potential stress corrosion cracking is fabricated by cross roll straightening and belt polishing of the outer diameter surface. Belt polishing induces subsurface residual stress and cold-work distributions, which can impact on the state of residual stress present in the tubing when it is formed into U-bends.

A single sample of mill-annealed and belt-polished straight tubing was investigated to determine the longitudinal subsurface residual stress and percent plastic strain distribution as functions of depth produced by belt polishing. X-ray diffraction macro- and microstress measurements were performed using a Cu Kα (420) two-angle technique. The Kα₁ diffraction peak was separated from the doublet by fitting a Cauchy diffraction-peak profile. The X-ray elastic constant required had been determined previously by loading a sample of the alloy in four-point bending. An empirical

relationship was established by annealing, then drawing samples of tubing to plastic strain levels in excess of 20%, generating an empirical relationship similar to that shown in Fig. 9.

The subsurface longitudinal residual stress and percent plastic strain distributions were determined by electropolishing thin layers of material in complete cylindrical shells from around the circumference of the 16-mm (0.625-in.) nominal diameter tubing. Layer removal began with 0.005-mm (0.0002-in.) thick layers near the sample surface, the increment between layers increasing with depth to nominally 0.4 mm (0.017 in.) beneath the original surface. Corrections were applied for the stress gradient and layer removal.

Figure 15 illustrates the results of the longitudinal residual stress and percent plastic strain distributions. The residual stress distribution shows a pronounced gradient from approximately −35 MPa (−5 ksi) at the surface to a maximum compressive value of approximately −150 MPa (−20 ksi) at a nominal depth of 0.05 mm (0.002 in.). With increasing depth, the stress distribution rises back into tension at approximately 0.13 mm (0.005 in.), with a low-magnitude tensile profile peaking at nominally 55 MPa (8 ksi) at greater depths. The plastic strain distribution shows a slight hook near the surface of the sample; the percent cold work approaches 19% at a nominal depth of 5 μm (0.0002 in.). With increasing depth, the cold-work distribution decreases nearly exponentially to negligible values beyond approximately 0.13 mm (0.005 in.) beneath the belt-polished surface.

A 63-mm (2.5-in.) U-bend manufactured from Inconel 600 tubing was strain gaged at the apex and sectioned to remove approximately a 50 mm (2 in.) arc length. This portion of the U-bend was mounted in a special fixture providing precision orienta-

tion around the circumference of the tubing to an accuracy of 0.1°. X-ray diffraction residual macrostress measurements were made on the existing surface as a function of angle θ around the circumference of the tubing.

Figure 16 shows the results of these measurements; the longitudinal surface residual stress has been plotted as a function of the quantity (1 + cos θ) to expand the central portion of the plot, at which the sharp transition occurs between maximum compression and tension. The position around the circumference of the tubing ranges from the outside of the bend at the origin around the flank, or neutral axis, at 1(1 + cos θ) and around to the inside of the bend. The results shown as open circles indicate the longitudinal residual stress around one side of the tubing; closed circles, comparable measurements made on the opposing side.

The x-ray beam was limited to a height of 0.5 mm (0.020 in.) and a width of 2.5 mm (0.1 in.) along the axis of the tubing. The small beam size was necessary to optimize spatial resolution in the presence of the pronounced stress gradient occurring on the flank of the tubing. The compressive stresses produced around the outside of the bend exceed −550 MPa (−80 ksi) in a material with a nominal annealed yield strength of 240 MPa (35 ksi). The presence of these high stresses after forming result from cold working at the tubing induced during belt polishing. Cold working of Inconel 600 to 20% increases yield strength to approximately 690 MPa (100 ksi). Cold-worked surface layers in components subjected to subsequent forming frequently result in complex residual stress distributions having magnitudes often exceeding the yield strength of the undeformed material.

Example 3: Local Variations in Residual Stress Produced by Surface Grinding. The high spatial resolution of x-ray diffraction residual stress measurement was applied to determine the longitudinal surface and subsurface residual stress variation near grinder burns produced by traverse grinding of a sample of 4340 steel with a hardness of 50 HRC. Three samples were initially investigated: two were ground abusively to produce grinder burn, and one was ground gently using adequate coolant. X-ray diffraction residual stress measurements were performed initially on only the surfaces of the three samples using a Cr Kα (211) two-angle technique. The diffraction-peak positions were located using a five-point parabolic regression procedure, assuming the Kα doublet to be completely blended into a single symmetrical peak for all measurements performed in the hardened material. The irradiated area was 0.5 by 6.4 mm

Fig. 17 Variations in longitudinal surface residual stress produced by surface grinding 4340 alloy steel (50 HRC) samples

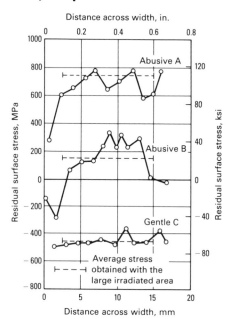

Fig. 18 Subsurface residual stress profiles produced in burned and unburned regions of abusively ground 4340 alloy steel (50 HRC)

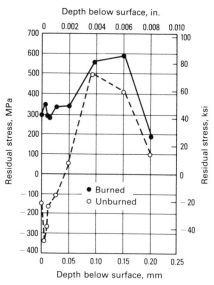

Fig. 19 Longitudinal residual stress distribution across a flash butt welded induction-hardened railroad rail head

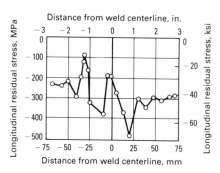

(0.020 by 0.250 in.), with the long axis aligned in the grinding direction. Measurements were conducted using the narrow irradiated area as a function of distance across the surface of each sample. A single measurement using a 12.5- by 6.4-mm (0.5- by 0.250-in.) irradiated area spanning nearly the entire region covered by the series of measurements made with the smaller irradiated zone was then performed on each sample.

Figure 17 shows the results of the surface measurements. The individual measurements made using the 0.5-mm (0.02-in.) wide irradiated area are shown as open circles. The single result obtained using the 13-mm (0.5-in.) wide beam is plotted as a dashed line; the bounds on the line indicate the approximate extent of the large irradiated area. The gently ground sample was found to be uniformly in compression, with surface stresses ranging from approximately −400 to −520 MPa (−60 to −75 ksi) at all points examined. The abusively ground sample A was found to be entirely in tension; the values range from 275 to 825 MPa (40 to 120 ksi) across the width of the sample. Abusively ground sample B shows regions of compression and tension, with visible grinder burn associated with the tensile peaks occurring above approximately 275 MPa (40 ksi) near the center of the sample.

The results for the large irradiated area provide nominally the arithmetic average of the small area results.

The subsurface residual stress distribution was then determined at the point of maximum compression and maximum tension on the abusively ground sample B using the 0.5-mm (0.020-in.) irradiated area. The sample was electropolished completely across the width as measurements were conducted at the two locations of interest. The subsurface results shown in Fig. 18 indicate compressive stresses near the edge of the unburned sample at the point of maximum compression that extend to a nominal depth of 0.05 mm (0.002 in.) and rise into tension approaching 500 MPa (70 ksi) at greater depths. The burned region shows entirely tensile stresses ranging from approximately 275 to 345 MPa (40 to 50 ksi) to a depth of 0.05 mm (0.002 in); it rises into tension approximately 600 MPa (90 ksi) further below the surface.

The residual stresses produced by many grinding and machining operations can vary significantly over local distances, particularly if there is significant heat input, loss of coolant, or tool dulling. Further, use of a nondestructive surface measurement of residual stress or a nital etch to reveal grinder burn may not reveal subsurface tensile residual stresses that could degrade fatigue performance severely.

Example 4: Longitudinal Residual Stress Distribution in Welded Railroad

Rail. Continuously welded railroad rail may be subject to high tensile or compressive applied stresses resulting from thermal contraction and expansion in the field. The presence of significant residual stresses in the flash butt welded joints of such rail could contribute to failure near the welds.

To determine the longitudinal residual stresses in the hardened head of welded rail near the weld, a nominally 200 mm (8 in.) portion of rail containing the weld was band sawed from a section of continuous rail after welding. Sectioning stress relaxation was assumed to be negligible.

The surface of the rail head was prepared by electropolishing to a nominal depth of 0.25 mm (0.010 in.) to remove any surface residual stresses that may have originated from sources other than welding. X-ray diffraction longitudinal residual stress measurements were then conducted using the two-angle technique at a series of positions across the center line of the weld, which was located by etching with nital before electropolishing. A Cr Kα (211) technique was used, locating the diffraction peak using a parabolic regression procedure. The rail head was induction hardened, and the Kα doublet was completely blended and symmetrical throughout the hardened head portion of the rail.

Figure 19 illustrates the results of the longitudinal measurements, which reveal an entirely compressive longitudinal residual stress distribution at the top of the head of the rail near the weld and an asymmetrical oscillating pattern of residual stress different from that which would have been predicted by analytical solution. The results of repeat measurements confirmed the nature of the stress distribution.

The analytical methods for predicting the residual stresses produced by welding generally predict a symmetrical residual stress distribution around the weld fusion line;

Fig. 20 Minimum and maximum principal residual stress profiles and their orientation relative to the longitudinal direction in a turned Inconel 718 cylinder

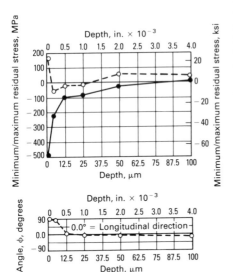

however, the actual stress distributions revealed by measurement are often substantially more complex than those predicted.

Example 5: Determination of the Magnitude and Direction of the Maximum Residual Stress Produced by Machining. The direction of maximum residual stress, that is, most tensile or least compressive, is assumed to occur in the cutting or grinding direction during most machining operations. This is frequently the case, but the maximum stress often occurs at significant angles to the cutting direction. Furthermore, the residual stress distributions produced by many cutting operations, such as turning, may be highly eccentric, producing a highly tensile maximum stress and a highly compressive minimum stress.

The residual stress field at a point, assuming a condition of plane stress, can be described by the minimum and maximum normal principal residual stresses, the maximum shear stress, and the orientation of the maximum stress relative to some reference direction. The minimum stress is always perpendicular to the maximum. The maximum and minimum normal residual stresses, shown as σ_1 and σ_2 in Fig. 2, and their orientation relative to a reference direction can be calculated along with the maximum shear stress using Mohr's circle for stress if the stress σ_ϕ is determined for three different values of ϕ.

To investigate the minimum and maximum normal residual stresses and their orientation produced by turning an Inconel 718 cylinder, x-ray diffraction residual stress measurements were performed in the longitudinal, 45°, and circumferential directions at the surface and at subsurface layers to a nominal depth of 0.1 mm (0.004 in.), exposing the subsurface depths by electropolishing complete cylindrical shells around the cylinder. The cylinder was nominally 19 mm (0.75 in.) in diameter and uniformly turned along a length of several inches. The irradiated area was limited to a nominal height of 1 mm (0.05 in.) around the circumference by 2.5 mm (0.10 in.) along the length. Measurements were conducted using a Cu Kα (420) two-angle technique, separating the Kα_1 peak from the doublet using a Cauchy peak profile.

The measurements performed independently in the three directions were combined using Mohr's circle for stress at each depth to calculate the minimum and maximum normal residual stresses and their orientation defined by the angle ϕ, which was taken to be a positive angle counterclockwise from the longitudinal axis of the cylinder. Figure 20 illustrates the results, showing the maximum and minimum principal residual stress profiles and their orientation relative to the longitudinal direction. The maximum stresses are tensile at the surface, in excess of 140 MPa (20 ksi), dropping rapidly into compression at a nominal depth of 0.005 mm (0.0002 in.). The maximum stress returns into tension at depths exceeding 0.025 mm (0.001 in.) and remains in slight tension to the maximum depth of 0.1 mm (0.004 in.) examined. The minimum residual stress is in compression in excess of −480 MPa (−70 ksi) at the turned surface and diminishes rapidly in magnitude with depth to less than −138 MPa (−20 ksi) at a depth of 0.013 mm (0.0005 in.). The minimum stress remains slightly compressive and crosses into tension only at the maximum depth examined. The orientation of the maximum stresses is almost exact in the circumferential direction (90° from the longitudinal) for the first two depths examined. For depths of 0.013 mm (0.0005 in.) to the maximum depth of 0.1 mm (0.004 in.), the maximum stress is within approximately 10° of the longitudinal direction.

The results appear to indicate that stresses within approximately 0.013 mm (0.0005 in.) of the sample surface are dominated by machining, which resulted in a maximum stress direction essentially parallel to the cutting action. At greater depths, the stress distribution may be governed not by the machining as much as by stresses that may have been present due to forging or heat treatment.

REFERENCES

1. M.E. Hilley, Ed., *Residual Stress Measurement by X-Ray Diffraction*, SAE J784a, Society of Automotive Engineers, Warrendale, PA, 1971, p 21-24
2. B.D. Cullity, *Elements of X-Ray Diffraction*, Addison Wesley, 2nd ed., 1978, p 470
3. M.E. Hilley, Ed., *Residual Stress Measurement by X-Ray Diffraction*, SAE J784a, Society of Automotive Engineers, Warrendale, PA, 1971, p 19
4. M.E. Hilley, Ed., *Residual Stress Measurement by X-Ray Diffraction*, SAE J784a, Society of Automotive Engineers, Warrendale, PA, 1971, p 20
5. R.H. Marion and J.B. Cohen, *Adv. X-Ray Anal.*, Vol 18, 1975, p 466
6. P.S. Prevey, *Adv. X-Ray Anal.*, Vol 19, 1976, p 709
7. H. Dölle and J.B. Cohen, *Met. Trans.*, Vol 11A, 1980, p 159
8. H. Dölle, *J. Appl. Cryst.*, Vol 12, 1979, p 498
9. M.E. Hilley, Ed., *Residual Stress Measurement by X-Ray Diffraction*, SAE J784a, Society of Automotive Engineers, Warrendale, PA, 1971, p 61
10. A.L. Christenson and E.S. Rowland, *Trans. ASM*, Vol 45, 1953, p 638
11. D.P. Koistinen and R.E. Marburger, *Trans. ASM*, Vol 51, 1959, p 537
12. W.A. Rachinger, *J. Sci. Instr.*, Vol 25, 1948, p 254
13. S.K. Gupta and B.D. Cullity, *Adv. X-Ray Anal.*, Vol 23, 1980, p 333
14. P.S. Prevey, *Adv. X-Ray Anal.*, Vol 29, to be published
15. "Standard Method for Verifying the Alignment of X-ray Diffraction Instrumentation for Residual Stress Measurement," E 915, *Annual Book of ASTM Standards*, Vol 03.01, ASTM, Philadelphia, 1984, p 809-812
16. "Standard Methods for Determining Average Grain Size," E 112, *Annual Book of ASTM Standards*, Vol 02.01, ASTM, Philadelphia, 1984, p 1073-1107
17. P.S. Prevey, *Adv. X-Ray Anal.*, Vol 20, 1977, p 345
18. M.G. Moore and W.P. Evans, *Trans. SAE*, Vol 66, 1958, p 340

Radial Distribution Function Analysis

J.H. Konnert, J. Karle, and P. D'Antonio, Laboratory for the Structure of Matter, Naval Research Laboratory

General Uses

- Determination of interatomic distance distributions and coordination numbers of amorphous materials, polycrystalline materials, liquids, and gases
- Determination of long-range order in amorphous materials

Examples of Applications

- Structural ordering in amorphous carbon
- Coordination numbers for liquids
- Bonding topologies in silicate glasses
- Variation of long-range order of glasses as a function of preparation
- Three-dimensional structure of gas molecules

Samples

- *Form*: Solid, liquid, or gas
- *Size*: 1 mm^3 (0.00006 in.^{3}) for x-ray diffraction; 1 cm^3 (0.06 in.^{3}) for neutron diffraction; 100 Å thick for electron diffraction
- *Preparation*: Flat for reflection geometry; cylindrical for transmission geometry; weakly scattering thin-wall container for polycrystalline or liquid samples. For example, Mylar is used for flat samples

Limitations

- The radial distribution function is a one-dimensional display of distances in a three-dimensional sample. Therefore, the peaks in the radial distribution function beyond approximately 4 Å usually consist of several components or different types of distances. Consequently, the radial distribution function does not generally contain enough information to determine uniquely the arrangement of atoms in a sample. However, the radial distribution function provides a stringent test for the accuracy of any proposed model

Estimated Analysis Time

- X-ray or neutron diffraction data can be collected in several days with any powder or single-crystal diffractometer
- High-intensity sources, such as synchrotrons, permit faster data collection or use of smaller samples
- Electron diffraction data can be collected within seconds
- Obtaining an accurate radial distribution function usually requires a day of interactive computation on a mainframe computer
- Interpretation of the radial distribution function may take several days to several weeks, depending on the number of model radial distribution functions considered

Capabilities of Related Techniques

- *Single-crystal diffraction study*: This should almost always be the method of choice if a single crystal can be obtained; it takes less time and yields much more structural information
- *Extended x-ray absorption fine structure*: Can be useful for studying the stereochemistry of a minor constituent; such a study requires use of a radiation source, such as a synchrotron, that can be tuned to an absorption edge of the element of interest and the collection of data for model compounds

Introduction

The diffraction pattern of any material can be analyzed directly to obtain interatomic distance information. When the sample of interest contains a random orientation of atomic configurations, as is normally the case for so-called amorphous materials, it is necessary to collect only a one-dimensional data set consisting of intensity versus the scattering angle to obtain the maximum amount of information available in a diffraction experiment. The accuracy and extent of the diffraction data determine the accuracy of the distance information obtainable.

The appropriate Fourier transform of the intensity data yields the radial distribution function (RDF). The RDF gives the distribution of interatomic distances present in the sample and also gives information concerning the frequency with which particular distances occur. Figure 1 illustrates the RDF for silica glass (fused quartz, SiO_2). The sharp peak at 1.61 Å represents the bonded silicon oxygen distance; the area of the peak is

Fig. 1 The radial distribution function, $r^2 G(r)$, for silica glass with the first three peaks reintroduced without associated termination effects

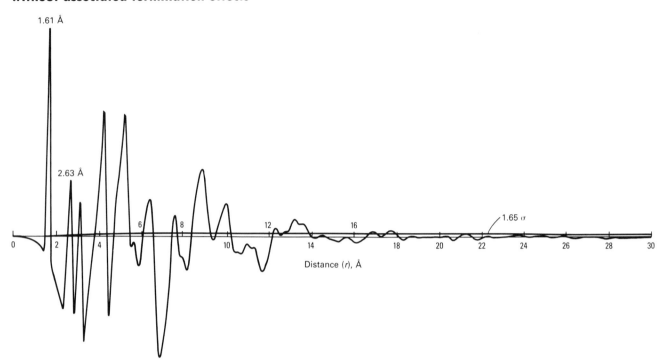

related to the number of such distances in the sample. The peak width illustrates, after experimental resolution is accounted for, the variation in this distance due to the distribution of equilibrium distances and thermal motion. The second peak at 2.63 Å represents the nonbonded oxygen-oxygen distances. Therefore, interpretation of the first two peaks yields information concerning the oxygen-silicon-oxygen bond angles. Thus, the RDF provides information on bond distances and angles and the number of atoms in various coordination spheres.

Because only the shorter distances in the RDF are resolved (Fig. 1), the RDF for an amorphous material does not generally contain enough information to uniquely determine the extended three-dimensional arrangement of the atoms. However, the degree of long-range order present may be observed from the extent to which the interatomic distances continue to persist in the RDF. For some amorphous materials, this may be less than the 20 Å shown for silica glass in Fig. 1. The order will be considerably greater for samples that are partially or completely crystalline. The extent and shape of the long-range detail also provide a stringent test for the accuracy of any proposed model.

A radial distribution analysis generally involves the collection of data, the calculation of an accurate experimental RDF,

and then a comparison of the goodness-of-fit with RDFs computed for proposed models.

When sample volumes of the order of cubic centimeters are available, neutron and x-ray diffraction can be used. Volumes of the order of cubic millimeters are amenable to some x-ray techniques. X-ray or neutron diffraction data can be collected from smaller sample volumes using high-intensity radiation sources. Thin samples (several hundred angstroms or less) are suitable for electron diffraction studies.

Sufficiently accurate x-ray and neutron data can be collected in several hours to several days, depending on the intensity of the source and the type of detection system. High-intensity synchrotron sources enable collection of data in minutes. Collection of electron-diffraction data requires seconds to minutes.

Diffraction patterns suitable for RDF analysis can be obtained with any diffractometer (powder or single crystal) that is equipped with a source producing radiation of about 0.7 Å or shorter wavelength (Mo Kα radiation = 0.71 Å, Cu Kα = 1.54 Å). A mainframe computer or equivalent is required to carry out the computations necessary both for obtaining accurate interatomic distance information and for calculating RDFs from models for comparison purposes.

Diffraction Data

Amorphous materials produce diffuse diffraction patterns characterized by relatively few broad features. This contrasts with diffraction patterns from polycrystalline materials characterized by many relatively sharp diffraction rings, unless the crystallite size is very small.

The total diffracted intensity from a randomly oriented sample (polycrystalline, amorphous, or liquid) consists of three components. Assuming correction of the data for such effects as polarization and absorption, the total scattering (or total diffracted intensity), I_t, consists of the interatomic interference scattering, I, and the smooth, featureless terms I_c and I_i representing coherent and incoherent atomic scattering. The distance information of interest is contained in I. Figure 2 shows a total intensity curve for silica glass. The related equations follow:

$$I_t(s) = I(s) + I_c(s) + I_i(s)$$
$$= I(s) + I_b(s) \qquad \text{(Eq 1)}$$

where $s = (4\pi \sin \theta / \lambda)$ (2θ is the angle between the incident and diffracted beams, and λ is the wavelength) and I_b is the background intensity. One purpose of data reduction is to separate I from I_t.

It is convenient to define a reduced intensity, $i(s)$:

$$i(s) = \frac{[I_t(s) - I_b(s)]}{\Sigma f(s)^2} \qquad (Eq\ 2)$$

The sum of the atomic scattering factors squared in the unit of composition, that is, SiO_2, is Σf^2. Division by this term largely removes the effect of the atomic electron distributions on the scattering and results in an intensity corresponding approximately to vibrating point atoms.

The RDF, $rG(r)$, is obtained by taking the Fourier sine transform of $si(s)$:

$$rG(r) = 4\pi r^2(\rho r - \rho_0)$$

$$= \frac{2r}{\pi} \int_0^\infty si(s)\ \sin(sr)\ ds \qquad (Eq\ 3)$$

where $4\pi r^2 \rho(r)$ represents the probability, weighted by the product of the scattering factors, of finding atoms separated by distance r in the sample. The bulk density parameter is ρ_0.

Equation 3 can be used to illustrate several important considerations for data collection. The integral is to be taken from $s = 0$ to $s = \infty$. Although this is not experimentally possible, collection of data to as large a value of s as possible is important for optimizing the resolution of distances in the RDF and their accuracy. The ultimate resolution of a sampled Fourier transform is $2\pi/s_{max}$ in angstroms. Thus, resolution of distances separated by 0.5 Å necessitates accurate data collection at least as far as $s = 2\pi/0.5 = 12.6$ Å^{-1}. Higher resolution than this is generally desirable. Because $s_{max} = 4\pi/\lambda$, the resolution is $\lambda/2$. Silver Kα (0.54 Å) with an associated resolution of 0.27 Å is the shortest wavelength generally available in a standard x-ray apparatus. Copper Kα radiation (1.54 Å) with an associated resolution of only 0.77 Å ($s_{max} = 8.1$) is not usually acceptable.

Data are generally collected in linear increments of s (Δs). A useful Δs for amorphous materials is 0.05. The diffraction data must be collected to a high degree of accuracy to prevent introduction of spurious details into the RDF. The total intensity minus the background intensity divided by the sum of the atomic scattering factors squared and multiplied by s, $si(s)$, must be accurately derived from the measured data. An error of approximately 1% in the total intensity is generally acceptable, except for x-ray data of light atom samples, in which incoherent atomic scattering may dominate at large values of s. The pattern illustrated in Fig. 2 includes much incoherent scattering and the data at large values of s were collected to an

Fig. 2 The total x-ray diffraction pattern for silica glass

I_t is the total diffracted intensity; I_b is the background intensity; and $s = 4\pi \sin\theta/\lambda$. The ordinate is multiplied by a factor of 1, 3, and 9 in the three sets of curves.

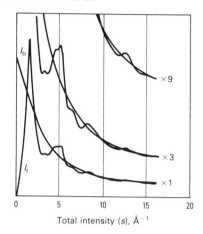

accuracy of 0.2% to obtain the desired accuracy for the interference term. Additional information on the theory of diffraction can be found in Ref 1 to 4.

Instrumentation

Collection of a set of diffraction data entails a measurement of scattered intensity versus $\sin\theta/\lambda$. Thus, in principle, a data set can be obtained by using a fixed wavelength and scanning θ (angle dispersive) or by fixing θ and scanning the wavelength (energy dispersive). Most instruments scan θ; however, new radiation sources for x-rays and neutrons composed of a broad spectrum of high-intensity wavelengths permit energy-dispersive measurements. Significant absorption effects may complicate the analysis of energy-dispersive data, because absorption and scattering depend on wavelength in a complicated fashion. The effect of absorption on the diffraction data can be used by collecting angular data at various well-selected wavelengths. This can provide more information than is obtained at a single wavelength and thus facilitate the analysis and afford more structural details. The time required for the diffraction experiment will depend significantly on the intensity of the source and the efficiency of the detection system.

X-ray Sources. Various x-ray sources differ by a factor of 10^5 in the intensity produced at a given wavelength. The least intensity derives from a conventional tube in which electrons of approximately 50 keV strike a stationary target and produce x-rays characteristic of the target material. The Kα

radiation from a molybdenum target (0.71 Å) or silver target (0.54 Å) is suitable for collecting intensity data as a function of scattering angle using a conventional source. These sources are available in many laboratories and permit data collection in one to several days if sufficient sample is available.

Rotating anode sources differ in that the target material is rotated rapidly to produce a tenfold increase in intensity without overheating. Much greater intensity can be obtained from a synchrotron, in which x-rays are produced by the acceleration of electrons. A broad range of wavelengths at high intensity results, facilitating angle-dispersive and energy-dispersive measurements. A valuable feature of synchrotron radiation is that angular data can be collected readily at several tunable wavelengths within minutes to hours. Although few synchrotron facilities are available, their number is increasing.

Neutron Sources. Nuclear reactors generally produce the neutrons used for diffraction studies (see the article "Neutron Diffraction" in this Volume). The neutrons from the reactor are moderated (slowed) to produce a broad spectrum of wavelengths. The desired wavelength is then selected using a monochromator crystal, and intensity data are collected over the range of scattering angles. Data collection may require one to several days. Intense beams of neutrons can be produced in conjunction with some particle accelerators in which a pulse of protons is used to produce a pulse of neutrons containing a broad spectrum of wavelengths (Ref 5). These spallation sources are particularly useful in energy-dispersive data collection. The bursts are of short duration, and the wavelengths of the neutrons are determined by their momenta or, equivalently, by the times required for the neutron to reach a detector at fixed angle.

Electron Sources. Several laboratories possess equipment devoted exclusively to electron-diffraction studies of gases and solids. Such equipment contains long electron path lengths necessary for favorable resolution in s and special rotating sectors to level the rapidly falling I_b experimentally. Diffraction patterns can generally be obtained within seconds.

Electron microscopes, although not designed to collect undistorted diffraction data to large values of s, are widely available and can obtain electron-diffraction patterns. Microscopes operating with an accelerating voltage of 100 keV produce electrons with a wavelength of 0.037 Å. Therefore, observation of a sufficient range of diffraction data is not difficult; however, the distortions that a magnetic lens can introduce into the data should be recognized. The diffraction patterns are collected on film; several exposures are necessary to obtain the desired range of s without exceeding the density range of the film. Optical densitometer measurements must then be performed.

An important future source of high-quality electron-diffraction data will be scanning transmission electron analytical microscopes equipped with electron energy loss (EELS) detectors (see the article "Analytical Transmission Electron Microscopy" in this Volume). Slight alteration of the conventional microscopes permits scanning of the diffraction pattern across the electron energy loss detector. In principle, diffraction data could be obtained from elastically scattered (zero energy loss) and inelastically scattered electrons.

Variable 2θ Geometry. Radiation from the source (polychromatic to varying degrees) passes through a monochromator and collimation system before striking the sample. The sample is generally a cylinder or a flat plate. For samples composed of atoms of low atomic weight that do not absorb the x-rays strongly, it is often preferable to use a cylindrical sample with dimensions small enough to avoid large geometric aberrations due to the angle the sample subtends to the detection system. This cylindrical geometry is often used to collect neutron-diffraction data. A sample so strongly absorbing that the radiation penetrates only a fraction of a millimeter requires the sample geometry of a flat plate, whose normal is maintained in a position to bisect the angle between the incident and diffracted radiation. The considerations are the same as those discussed in the article "X-Ray Powder Diffraction" in this Volume.

However, the radiation used for RDF analyses (0.7 Å or less) is absorbed much less by most samples than the Cu Kα (1.54 Å) used in many powder diffractometers. The scattered radiation can be directed to pass through another collimation system and monochromator before entering the detector. This monochromator is desirable if none is present in the incident beam and can also be used to remove inelastically scattered radiation from the detector. A linear detector or a linear array of detectors may hasten data collection by permitting simultaneous measurement over a range of angles.

Variable Wavelength Geometry. Polychromatic radiation is collimated, strikes the sample, and is scattered into a detector positioned at a fixed angle. For x-rays, a solid-state detector capable of energy discrimination measures the scattered energy at each wavelength. For neutron diffraction, wavelength is related to neutron

velocity. Thus, when a spallation source produces a broad spectrum of wavelengths within approximately an instant of time, only the number of neutrons arriving versus time need be measured. Data are collected from a series of nonoverlapping pulses.

Data Reduction

Data reduction should optimize the accuracy and amount of interatomic distance information obtainable from the diffraction experiment. Several strategies for accomplishing this are available. The one described here produces an RDF with minimal error by requiring the I_b and the resultant RDF to satisfy various physical and mathematical criteria (Ref 8).

First, the inner region of the RDF should be featureless where distances are known not to exist. The precise calculation of Eq 3 to obtain an RDF requires experimental data that extends to an effective infinity, although it actually extends to an experimental s_{max}. An effective infinity is a value for s beyond which the contribution of the integrand is negligible. For amorphous materials, this would occur at an experimentally measurable s_{max} if contributions from the first few distances were removed from the diffraction data. This is performed in data reduction, thus removing termination error, and is facilitated by the requirement that the RDF be featureless in its inner region and in the region from which the distances are removed. Second, the outer region of the RDF should exhibit a uniform distance distribution. Termination errors and errors in the experimental data can cause spurious features in this region. Third, the scaling of the data should be consistent with density measurements, known coordination numbers, or both. Lastly, the background intensity, I_b, should be a smoothly changing function whose shape is compatible with that expected from theory.

The procedure developed on the basis of these criteria affords rapid convergence of data reduction, producing an RDF of suitable form. In achieving this, the RDF is expressed explicitly as a function of parameters that define the background intensity and short distances. For the portion of the intensity that contains the distance information to be separated accurately from the total intensity, I_b must be represented by a smooth flexible function, because the exact shape is not precisely known theoretically but adjusted to satisfy the criteria by the resulting RDF.

Parameters Defining the Background. It is convenient to express I_b in the form of overlapping exponential functions:

$$I_b(s) = \Sigma\, W_n(s)\, \exp\,(a_n +$$
$$b_n\, s^{c_n} + ds^e) \qquad \text{(Eq 4)}$$

where W_n is a smoothly varying weighting function in the overlap region, and d and e define a ramp that is useful when dealing with neutron diffraction data. Each exponential function overlaps to the midpoint of the adjacent function, and the functions are constrained to be equal at points of abutment. The parameters, a_n, b_n, and c_n, are altered during data reduction. The line through the oscillations in Fig. 2, for example, was constructed in this manner.

Parameters Defining the Short Distances. The reduced intensity $i(s)$ can be expressed in terms of the interatomic distances:

$$si(s) = \Sigma N_{ij} f_i f_j \exp\,(-l_{ij}^2\, s^2/2)$$
$$\sin sr_{ij}/r_{ij}\, \Sigma f^2 \qquad \text{(Eq 5)}$$

where r_{ij} is the distance between the ith and jth atoms, N_{ij} is the coordination number, and l_{ij} is the disorder parameter.

Elimination of spurious details due to termination effects from the RDF is based on the recognition that generally only the shortest distances contribute significantly to the experimental intensity beyond an s value of 15 to 20 Å^{-1}. This holds because the short distances normally have small values for l_{ij}, the disorder parameter in Eq 5; longer interatomic distances have greater disorder parameters, causing the exponential functions in Eq 5 to have values near zero at s_{max}. Subtracting appropriately the contributions of the short distances from the intensity function before taking the Fourier transform enables obtaining a new RDF, $rG'(r)$, that does not contain spurious details due to termination of the integration at s_{max}.

The radial distribution function, $rG'(r)$, can be expressed in terms of parameters defining the experimental intensity, the flexible background, the short-distance parameters, the scale factor, and the bulk density. Data reduction consists of determining those values of the parameter that satisfy the four mathematical and physical criteria stated above. This can be accomplished using a least squares procedure. The equations used in least squares data reduction are:

$$rG'(r) = 4\pi r^2[\rho'(r) - \rho_0]$$
$$= \frac{2r}{\pi} \int_0^{smax} si'(s)\, \exp\,(-\alpha s^2)\, \sin srds$$
$$\text{(Eq 6)}$$

$$i'(s) = i(s) - \sum_{sd} N_{ij} f_i f_j$$

$$\exp\left(\frac{-l_{ij}^2 s^2}{2}\right) \cdot \sin sr_{ij} / sr_{ij} \Sigma f^2 \quad \text{(Eq 7)}$$

$$i(s) = \{I(s) - A \, [\sum_n W_n(s)$$

$$\exp(a_n + b_n s^{c_n}) + ds^e]\}/\Sigma f^2(s) \quad \text{(Eq 8)}$$

$$\rho_0 = \frac{\rho_0'(\Sigma f_{(s=0)})^2}{\sum_{uc} f_{(s=0)}^2} \quad \text{(Eq 9)}$$

$$I(s) = \frac{I(s) \text{ measured}}{K} \quad \text{(Eq 10)}$$

where the refinable parameters are r_{ij}, l_{ij}, N_{ij}, and ρ_0'; the background parameters are a_n, b_n, c_n, and the factor K that places the intensity on the absolute scale; and uc is the unit of composition (SiO_2 for silica glass). The short distances are sd; α is an artificial damping factor that may be given a small value, if necessary, to remove residual termination effects; A scales I_b; and ρ_0' is the bulk density in units of composition per cubic angstrom.

Least Squares Refinement of RDF. The procedure is to minimize:

$$\left\{\sum_{p<r<q} [G'(r) + 4\pi r \, \rho_0]^2 + w \sum_{u<r<v} [G'(r)]^2\right\}$$

(Eq 11)

where p and q delineate the inner region having zero probability for an interatomic distance, u and v delineate the outer region where all distances are equally probable, and w fixes the relative weight of the two regions. Only the first sum normally requires minimization while monitoring the behavior of the inner and outer portion of the RDF.

Table 1 Initial and final short-distance parameters for the silica glass refinement

Material	Cycle	r_{ij}, Å	l_{ij}, Å
Si-O	0	1.608	0.03
	5	1.610	0.06
O-O	0	2.626	0.10
	5	2.639	0.10
Si-Si	0	3.060	0.10
	5	3.083	0.09

Fig. 3 The intensity functions of $si(s)$ and $si'(s)$ for silica glass and the RDFs associated with $si'(s)$ at various stages of refinement

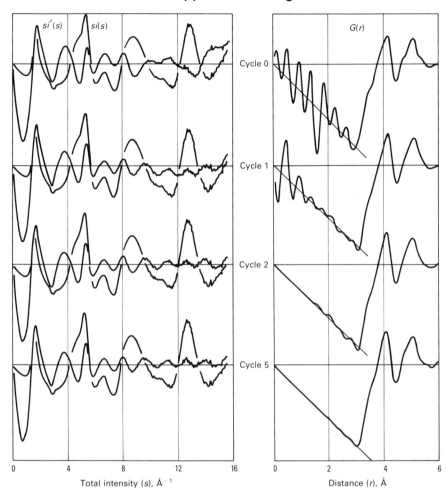

Optimum values for the a, b, and A defining I_b and for K, r_{ij}, l_{ij}, and N_{ij} are obtained (Ref 9).

Data Reduction for Silica Glass. Obtaining the path of the RDF for silica glass illustrated in Fig. 1 from the intensity function illustrated in Fig. 2 (Ref 10) necessitated subtracting the three shortest distances, consisting of the covalent bonded Si-O, the O-O within the tetrahedra, and the Si-Si of adjacent tetrahedra, to rid the integral of Eq 3 of termination errors. Figure 3 illustrates cycles of minimization required to obtain an accurate RDF. The inner region of the RDF is illustrated at several stages of refinement along with the corresponding intensity functions, $si'(s)$ and $si(s)$. Table 1 lists the short-distance parameters at various stages. Scaling the theoretical background shape so that positive and negative areas of $si(s)$ were equal provided I_b for cycle 0. Cycles 1, 3, and 5 refined the short-distance parameters,

r_{ij}, l_{ij}, K, A, and ρ_0. Cycles 2 and 4 refined the I_b shape.

For silica glass, the shortest distances, approximately 1.6 Å, contribute a sine wave to $si(s)$ with periodicity of approximately 4 s units. Introduction of an incorrect I_b with this periodicity or less must be avoided. The ρ_0 refined to 0.0212 uc/Å^3 compared to the measured value of 0.02205 uc/Å^3. Because the parameters defining the short distances have been determined, these distances may be introduced back into the RDF as Gaussian functions, as in Fig. 1. The σ in Fig. 1 represents the standard deviation in the RDF, which is estimated from the counting statistics associated with the intensity measurements.

Separation of RDF Into Pair Distribution Functions. The RDF just calculated contains three types of distances, or pair functions. One consists of all the Si-Si distances; another, all the O-O distances; and the third, all the Si-O distances. In general, if NT types of atomic species are present in the sample, $NT(NT + 1)/2$ types of pair distribution functions are present $[2(2 + 1)/2 = 3$ for $SiO_2]$. These pair functions can be separated from one another only if $NT(NT + 1)/2$ diffraction experiments can be conducted in which the relative values for the scattering factors are different. This is accomplished by changing isotopes in neutron diffraction and by using anomalous dispersion measurements with x-ray diffraction.

In the general case in which scattering factors in Eq 7 may be complex, the scattering factor for the jth atom is $f_j + if_j''$, where i is the square root of -1. The term $f_i f_j$ is replaced with $(f_i F_j + f_i'' f_j'') = A_{ij}$, and the term Σf_k^2 is replaced with $\Sigma (f_k^2 + f_k^2)$. The intensity for a pair function IP is:

$$IP_{ij} = \Sigma \, N_{k,m} \exp{(l_{k,m}^2 \, s^2/2)}$$
$$\sin{sr_{k,m}}/(sr_{k,m}) \qquad \text{(Eq 12)}$$

where k,m represents all atoms of types i and j.

For simplicity in comparing different experiments, $I(s)$ will be discussed rather than the reduced intensity $i(s)$. The interference intensity, $I(s)$, obtained from the experimental data using data reduction and placed on an absolute scale is:

$$I(s) = \Sigma \, A_{ij} \, IP_{ij} \qquad \text{(Eq 13)}$$

If the material of interest has N different pair distribution functions, N experiments in which the values of A_{ij} were different would provide N equations, such as Eq 13, with N unknown quantities (the N different intensity distributions associated with the pair functions, IP_{ij}). Such a linear set of equations can be readily solved for the desired pair functions.

Different relative values for the scattering factors can be obtained using neutron diffraction by preparing a sample with different isotopes. The relative scattering factors in x-ray experiments differ from those in the neutron experiments. An effective method is available using synchrotron radiation to vary the x-ray scattering factors. Selecting the appropriate wavelengths enables the analyst to significantly change the scattering factor for some types of atoms. An alternative for obtaining additional information is to substitute one type of atom for another without altering the structure. This is isomorphous replacement.

Interpretation of an RDF

An RDF, or any single pair distribution function, consisting of the superposition of interatomic distances that arise from the many configurations in a large sample volume, does not provide the basis for a unique determination of the atomic coordinates of an amorphous material. However, the RDF is an important criterion for judging the validity of any proposed model. A proposed model must agree with all the features of the experimental RDF to within acceptable limits of error to be considered correct.

A model consists of a set of coordinates specifying the positions of all the atoms in the model. Calculation of the corresponding RDF consists simply of computing all the interatomic distances. Expressing each interatomic distance as a Gaussian function, the RDF is:

$$4\pi\rho(r) = 1/(r\sqrt{2\pi}) \, \Sigma \, \Sigma \, w_i w_j f_i f_j$$
$$\exp{[-(r - r_{ij})^2/(2l_{ij}^2)]}/(r_{ij} l_{ij} \Sigma f^2) \qquad \text{(Eq 14)}$$

For crystalline materials, the sum over i need include only those atoms with uniquely different environments. Crystallographically, this is the asymmetric unit. It includes only those atoms in a portion of a single unit cell that yield all the atoms in the crystal when acted on by the space group operations and the cell translations of the crystal. The sum over j must include all atoms in the crystal located within the distance range of interest from the asymmetric unit.

For a model of finite dimensions, sums over i and j include all atoms of the model. If the finite model is spherical, the RDF that this type of bonding topology would produce for a larger model can be approximated by dividing by the RDF for a sphere, $\epsilon(r,R)$, the same size as the model. The RDF in this case is:

$$G(r) = 4\pi r \left[\frac{\rho(r)}{\epsilon(r,R)} - \rho_0 \right] \qquad \text{(Eq 15)}$$

where

$$\epsilon(r,R) = 1 - \frac{3}{4}\left(\frac{r}{R}\right) + \frac{1}{16}\left(\frac{r}{R}\right)^3, \, r \le 2R$$

and

$$\epsilon(r,R) = 0, \, r \ge 2R \qquad \text{(Eq 16)}$$

It is sometimes useful to consider the RDF for a small region of radius t. This is:

$$G(r) = 4\pi r \left[\frac{\rho(r)}{\epsilon(r,R)} - \rho_0 \right] \epsilon(r,t) \quad \text{(Eq 17)}$$

More elaborate RDFs can be constructed by combining regions of different sizes (Ref 11).

The experimental and model RDFs can be compared by calculating a correlation function, $F(calc,exp)$:

$$F(calc,exp) = \int [rG(r)]_{calc}[rG(r)]_{exp}dr/$$
$$(\int [rG(r)]_{calc}^2 dr \int [rG(r)]_{exp}^2 dr)^{1/2} \qquad \text{(Eq 18)}$$

The function may range in value from 1.0 to -1.0. A value of 1.0 corresponds to perfect positive correlation; a value of 0, no correlation.

Applications

Example 1: Silica Glass. Analysis of the x-ray diffraction pattern of silica glass obtained with Mo Kα (0.71 Å) radiation illustrates the considerations required for obtaining an accurate RDF. The experimental RDF for silica glass will be compared with those calculated from the bonding topologies of quartz, cristobalite, tridymite (all crystalline polymorphs of SiO_2) and a 1412

Table 2 Correlation coefficients comparing the silica glass radial distribution function with those for various bonding topologies defined in the text

Range, Å	1412 atom model	Tridymite	Cristobalite	Quartz
0–20	0.91	0.82	0.69	0.26
0–10	0.91	0.83	0.68	0.28
10–20	0.87	0.90	0.76	0.10
0–2	1.00	1.00	0.97	1.00
2–4	0.95	0.89	0.87	0.46
4–6	0.90	0.83	0.53	0.44
6–8	0.96	0.83	0.65	−0.17
8–10	0.90	0.75	0.49	0.00
10–12	0.92	0.96	0.92	−0.32
12–14	0.80	0.86	0.82	0.31
14–16	0.86	0.69	−0.01	0.33
16–18	0.86	0.84	0.85	0.76
18–20	0.75	0.40	0.70	0.72

Fig. 4 The experimental RDF curve obtained for silica glass and the corresponding curves calculated from the atomic coordinates of a 1412 atom model and spherical regions within the crystal structures of tridymite, cristobalite, and quartz

For the small details in $G(r)$ at large r to be evident on the same plot as much larger details at small r, the function $r^2G(r)$ is illustrated.

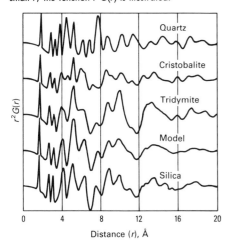

Fig. 5 Diffraction data for an activated carbon (Amoco PX-21)

I_t is the total diffracted intensity, SAXS is the small-angle x-ray scattering obtained from the Fourier transform of the average density envelope, and I_t − SAXS represents the total intensity with the small-angle contribution removed.

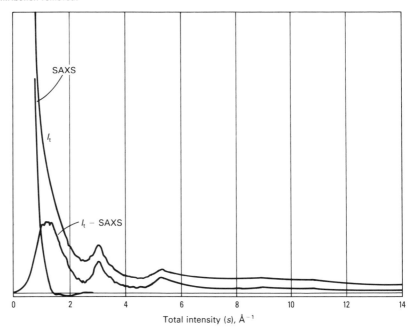

Fig. 6 The interatomic distance distribution function, $4\pi r(\rho(r) - \rho_0)$, of an activated carbon is shown along with the average density envelope $4\pi r \rho_c$ and the bulk density term $-4\pi r \rho_0$

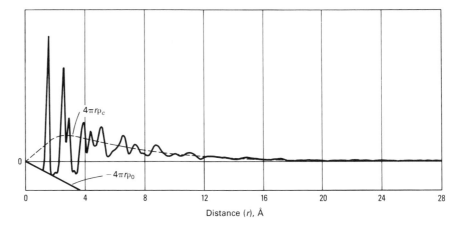

atom model of silica glass 35 Å in diameter (Ref 12).

The model RDFs (Fig. 4) were calculated using Eq 16, with t values representing ordered regions of 6.5 and 12 Å in radius present in a ratio of 7:3. Table 2 lists the correlation values for the range $0 < r < 20$ Å that compare $r^2G(r)$ functions. The values for quartz, cristobalite, tridymite, and the 1412 atom model are 0.26, 0.69, 0.82, and 0.91, respectively.

Cristobalite and tridymite consist entirely of six-membered rings of silicate tetrahedra. The 1412 atom model contains six- and five-membered rings in a ratio of 2.6:1. Thus, the correlation coefficients suggest that the six-membered rings predominate in silica glass, but that other ring sizes are important and result in the higher correlation for the 1412 atom model. The correlation coefficient of 0.90 between the model and the silica glass curves in the range $4 < r < 6$ Å suggests that the model does not have the correct proportion of the various ring sizes. A much larger model, possibly approximately 200 Å in diameter, may be required to represent adequately the distribution of configurations present in the glass.

Example 2: An Activated Carbon. A carbon prepared from petroleum coke (Amoco PX-21) possesses a large surface

area for adsorption of nitrogen (3500 m²/g). One gram of conjugated carbon atoms (graphite-like planes) possesses a surface area of only 2600 m²/g. X-ray diffraction data were collected using Mo Kα radiation for the range $2.5 < s < 15$ Å⁻¹ and using Cu Kα radiation for the range $0.05 < s < 5.0$ Å⁻¹. The longer wavelength Cu Kα measurements were required to accurately obtain the low-angle scattering data arising from the voids, small carbon

particles, or both. This carbon experiment illustrates the simultaneous analysis of low- and high-angle scattering data (Ref 13).

The I_t in Fig. 5 represents the total intensity for the carbon. The RDF shown in Fig. 6 was obtained using the methods described above. The dotted envelope, $4\pi r \rho_c$, represents deviations of the average local density from the bulk density. These deviations produce small-angle scattering. The envelope rises rapidly from the origin and falls back to

Fig. 7 Definitions of the *a* and *b* directions in a graphite layer

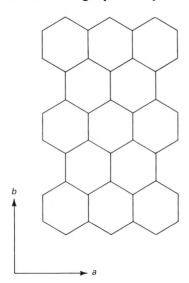

Fig. 8 RDFs for an activated carbon and five models defined in the text

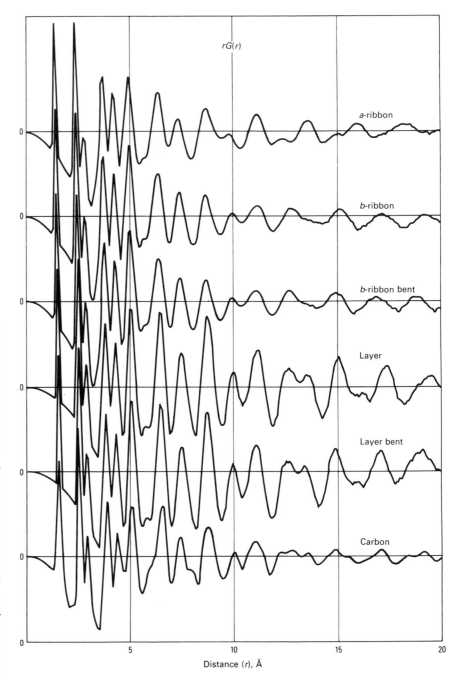

the average density by approximately 20 Å, indicating the size of the voids or particles. The small-angle scattering component to the intensity can be obtained by taking the Fourier transform of the envelope. This contribution has been subtracted, and the result is designated as $I_t(s) - SAXS$ (small-angle x-ray scattering). The peak appearing at 1.6 $Å^{-1}$ could be associated with the 002 Bragg reflection. If this association is made, the width of the peak indicates that on average few graphite-like layers are combined to provide structural ordering.

The features in the RDF resemble those of a single graphite layer (Fig. 7). However, some distortion of this layer is necessary to obtain a favorable match in the outer region of the RDFs. Figure 8 shows the experimental RDF along with those for the graphite layer and several distortions of it. The *a*-ribbon extends infinitely in the *a* direction but only 10 Å in the *b* direction. The *b*-ribbon extends similarly in the *b* direction. The bent *b*-ribbon has been constructed by giving a flat *b*-ribbon a radius of curvature of 25 Å relative to the axis parallel to *a*. The effect is to shift the peaks in the outer portion of $rG(r)$ to progressively smaller *r* values. The bent layer was also given a 25 Å radius of curvature. Table 3 lists the correlations and includes a correlation function $F'(calc,exp)$ sensitive to the shape and the relative scale of the two curves under comparison:

$$F'(calc,exp) = \int [rG(r)]_{calc}[rG(r)]_{exp}dr/$$

$$(\int[rG(r)]^2 \, dr) \qquad \text{(Eq 19)}$$

Table 3 Comparison of the correlation functions $F(calc,exp)$ and $F'(calc,exp)$ for carbon with five models

Range, Å	b-ribbon bent		Layer bent		Layer		b-ribbon		a-ribbon	
	(a)	(b)	(a)	(b)	(a)	(b)	(a)	(b)	(a)	(b)
0–20	0.92	0.90	0.87	0.67	0.86	0.67	0.91	0.89	0.89	0.85
0–10	0.92	0.91	0.90	0.74	0.90	0.74	0.92	0.90	0.93	0.88
10–20	0.73	0.70	0.82	0.27	0.56	0.21	0.43	0.39	0.04	0.04

(a) $F(calc,exp)$. (b) $F'(calc,exp)$

The denominator is the larger of $[rG(r)]^2_{calc}$ and $[rG(r)]^2_{exp}$.

The data suggest that this material consists of distorted graphite-like ribbons elongated in the b direction. The intensity profile indicates that at most a few of these ribbons are associated closely enough to provide for the structural ordering indicated by the RDF in Fig. 8. This open structure results in the large surface area and the extensive small-angle scattering.

REFERENCES

1. P. Debye, *Ann. Phys.*, Vol 46, 1915, p 809-823
2. F. Zernicke and J.A. Prins, *Z. Phys.*, Vol 41, 1972, p 184-194
3. A. Guinier, *X-ray Diffraction*, W.H. Freeman, 1963
4. B.E. Warren, *X-ray Diffraction*, Addison-Wesley, 1969
5. Spallation neutron sources, Argonne National Laboratory, Argonne, IL
6. R. Kaplow, S.L. Strong, and B.L. Averbach, *Phys. Rev.*, Vol 138A, 1965, p 1336-1345
7. A.J. Leadbetter and A.C. Wright, *J. Non-Cryst. Solids*, Vol 7, 1972, p 141-155
8. J.H. Konnert and J. Karle, *Acta Cryst.*, Vol A29, 1973, p 802-810
9. P. D'Antonio and J.H. Konnert, *J. Appl. Cryst.*, Vol 12, 1979, p 634-635
10. J.H. Konnert, P. D'Antonio, and J. Karle, *Advances In X-ray Analyses*, Vol 24, D.K. Smith, C.S. Barrett, D.E. Leyden, and P.K. Predecki, Ed., Plenum Press, 1981, p 63-72
11. P. D'Antonio and J.H. Konnert, *J. Appl. Cryst.*, Vol 13, 1980, p 459-461
12. J.H. Konnert, P. D'Antonio, and J. Karle, *J. Non-Cryst. Solids*, Vol 53, 1982, p 135-141
13. J.H. Konnert and P. D'Antonio, *Carbon*, Vol 21 (No. 3), 1983, p 193-196

Small-Angle X-Ray and Neutron Scattering

D.G. LeGrand, Polymer Physics and Engineering Branch, Corporate Research and Development, General Electric Company

General Uses
- Detection of heterogeneities in solids and liquids
- Monitoring of phase separations

Examples of Applications
- Phase separation in multicomponent metallic and polymer alloys, ceramics, and glasses
- Microphase separation in block copolymers
- Nucleation in metals
- Structure of crazes in glassy polymers
- Defects in metals

Samples
- *Form*: Solid or liquid
- *Size*: 1 to 20 mm (0.04 to 0.8 in.) on a side; thickness depends on mass-absorption coefficient

Limitations
- Sensitivity depends on wavelength, mass-absorption coefficient, and electron density contrast between scattering entities and surroundings
- The cause of the scattering and the shape of the scattering species cannot be determined uniquely in most materials without extensive modifications to the sample. Alternative methods must be used

Estimated Analysis Time
- 1 to 8 h

Capabilities of Related Techniques
- *Scanning electron microscopy*: Imaging and qualitative identification of microstructural features in solids as small as 3×10^{-8} m
- *Transmission electron microscopy*: Imaging and qualitative analysis of features smaller than those resolved using scanning electron microscopy; crystallographic data can be obtained
- *X-ray diffraction*: Identification and quantification of phases or compounds in unknown samples; measurement of crystal defect densities, residual stresses, and so on

Introduction

Small-angle x-ray scattering (SAXS) and small-angle neutron scattering (SANS) used to characterize the periodic, quasiperiodic, and random structures of matter should be helpful in the study of all materials because they can provide information on as-received samples over large sample volumes at microstructural sizes comparable to the electron microscope and can indicate the sample morphology. However, the experimental data can be fraught with artifacts and/or errors.

Small-angle scattering (SAS) has been used to study and distinguish between the different mechanisms of phase separation (spinodal versus nucleation) and to evaluate long-range periodic order, voiding, random spatial correlations, internal surface area, orientation, deformation, molecular configuration, the effects of fatigue on the nucleation and growth of defects, the effects of annealing in terms of long period spacing, dislocation density and line shape, bulk compressibility, and so on. Examination of almost any material using the appropriate SAS technique will provide some information about its morphology and homogeneity that can be used to support other experimentation or to aid in understanding its behavior. A unique interpretation of SAS is frequently not possible, and many of the other techniques discussed in this Volume must be used in support of the interpretation. This article will present the experimental and theoretical aspects of SAS and discuss specific applications (Ref 1-10).

Experimental Aspects

Small-angle scattering demands the use of a highly collimated beam to determine the spatial dependence of the scattered beam in the presence of the incident beam. For low-energy and low-flux x-ray sources (stationary and rotating target tubes), several collimation techniques are used. X-rays are normally collimated by tubes and slits or by reflection; this is in contrast to light and electrons, which are collimated by lenses and magnetic fields, respectively. An exception is use of the Bormann effect, which results in a highly collimated and monochromatic beam.

Figure 1 shows the basic methods for collimation. The higher the level of resolution, that is, the smaller the angle of scattering, the greater the degree of collimation required. This results in a significantly lower incident intensity and, correspondingly, lower scattered intensity. Frequently, as with the Kratky camera (Fig. 1c), line rather than point collimation is used to increase the level of available scattered radiation and to reduce parasitic scattering. This method can smear the observed scattering as a result of the collimation optics (Ref 1, 11-13).

Procedures for desmearing the observed scattering into its idealized state have been given (Ref 11-13). The underlying cause of the smearing of the scattered radiation (Fig. 2) is that the measured intensity at a point (x, y) is a summation of scattered rays that come from different points across the line source and whose scattering vectors are distributed over a range defined by the height

Fig. 1 Basic methods of collimating x-rays

(a) Slit and pinhole collimation. (b) Kratky collimation using beam stops B1, B2, and B3. (c) Curved mirror focusing camera. Source: Ref 5

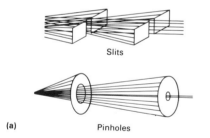

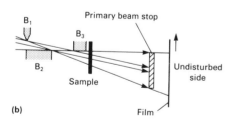

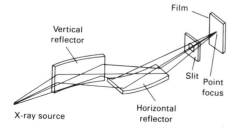

Fig. 2 The cause of smearing from a line source

See text for explanation

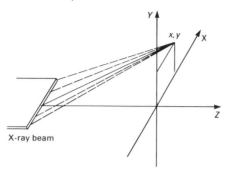

and width of the beam. Desmearing involves characterization of the incident x-ray beam along its height and width (Fig. 3).

High-energy and high-flux synchrotron sources provide a reliable means of obtaining x-ray intensities several orders of magnitude greater than those previously possible. Beam divergences of the order of 0.2 mrad provide resolution of the order of 100 nm. However, these sources are expensive and will not soon become part of the materials science laboratory. Under special circumstances and in collaboration with the appropriate personnel at national and university laboratory sites, they can be used to perform SAXS experiments; many synchrotron laboratories also have sources for SANS experiments. Use of such facilities is decided by a committee. Some proposals are refused because of limited time, personnel, and equipment. How-

ever, most good proposals are accepted for which synchrotron sources are necessary.

Photographic and electronic detection of the scattered radiation are used in SAS measurements. Multichannel data acquisition, in conjunction with mainframe and personal computers, allows data manipulations in terms of corrections and data analysis, reduction, or enhancement. The latter may reveal structural information that is buried within noise. Such procedures represent the state of the art, and their use necessitates caution.

Theoretical Aspects

In general, the observed scattering may consist of a series of maxima, a single maximum, a gradual decrease in intensity, or a constant level of scattering (Fig. 4a to c). The scattering may be anisotropic. The occurrence of discrete maxima may be viewed as a manifestation of a periodic or at least quasiperiodic structure and may under some circumstances be interpreted using the techniques discussed in the article "Introduction" in this Section. However, the observation of a single maximum or a set of maxima is not sufficient to prove periodicity because they can occur for other reasons.

The SAXS from materials can be treated in terms of two limiting theories. The first, which can be referred to as the particle approach, involves calculating the scattering by summing the scattering amplitudes from all the volume elements within a given particle, such as a sphere or a rod. The second is the statistical approach, in which the

Fig. 3 Desmearing parameters

(a) The cross section of the incident beam. The intensity of the incident beam at $P(x,y)$ is $i(x,y)dxdy$. The coordinates of $P(x,y)$ are $x = 2\pi OPx/s\lambda$ and $y = 2\pi OPy/s\lambda$, where s is the sample-to-detector distance. Radiation scattered from $P(x,y)$ to point M will be scattered through an angle defined by these parameters. (b) To correct for the beam height, the contribution to the scattering from a point in the incident beam R to the point of observation M must be considered. Source: Ref 1

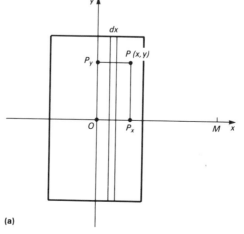

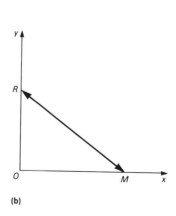

Fig. 4 Types of scattering curves

(a) Widely separated homogeneous spheres.
(b) Phase separated blend, block copolymer, a metallic alloy, or a glass. (c) A random structure.
(d) A liquid or glass with no structure.

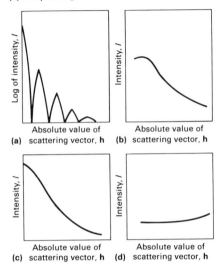

(a) Absolute value of scattering vector, **h**

(b) Absolute value of scattering vector, **h**

(c) Absolute value of scattering vector, **h**

(d) Absolute value of scattering vector, **h**

structure of the material is characterized in terms of correlation functions used to describe the fluctuations in density within the material. The initial theory for x-ray scattering (discussed in the article "Introduction" in this Section) was based on the particle approach; that is, the atoms are the particles (Ref 14). In materials for which the shape and size of such particles and the number density are not known, the statistical approach allows evaluation of such parameters as correlation distance and internal surface area that can be used to characterize the material.

For example, when an x-ray (neutron) beam of wavelength λ passes through a material with an average electron density ρ_{av} and with local electron densities $\rho(\mathbf{r}_i)$ ($\mathbf{r}_i$ is a vector from an arbitrary origin to the ith position), the incident field undergoes absorption and scattering as a result of its interaction with the material. At a large distance R from the ith element and within the material, the scattered wave is:

$$E(\mathbf{h}) = E_0 \exp(-ikR) \frac{k^2 \sin^2 \psi}{4\pi} \int \rho(\mathbf{r})$$

$$\exp[i\mathbf{k}(\mathbf{Sr})]d\mathbf{r} \qquad (Eq\ 1)$$

where $\mathbf{k} = 2\pi/\lambda$, ψ is the angle between E_0 and R, and $\mathbf{S}$ is a vector that is the difference between a unit vector $\mathbf{S}$ along the scattered wave and $\mathbf{S}_0$ along the incident wave. The angle between these two vectors is the scattering angle. To take the absorption into account, $\mathbf{k}$ should be written as a complex

quantity, that is, $\mathbf{k} = k' + ik''$. The refractive index for materials in the x-ray region is less than unity and is complex (Ref 3). The scattered intensity is obtained by multiplying $E(\mathbf{h})$ by its complex conjugate, then summing over all volume elements. This procedure leads to the relation:

$$\frac{I(\mathbf{h})}{I_0} = \mathbf{C} \exp\left(\frac{-t}{\tau}\right) \int \int \rho(\mathbf{r}_i)\, \rho(\mathbf{r}_j)$$

$$\exp i\mathbf{k}(\mathbf{Sr}_{ij})d\mathbf{r}_i d\mathbf{r}_j \qquad (Eq\ 2)$$

where $\mathbf{C} = (\mathbf{k}^2 \sin^2 \psi)/(16\pi R^2)$. Equation 2 is used to define the optimum sample thickness, t_0:

$$t_0 = \frac{1}{\tau} \qquad (Eq\ 3)$$

where τ is the mass-absorption coefficient.

If $\rho(\mathbf{r}_i)$ and $\rho(\mathbf{r}_j)$ are assumed to be spatially periodic and are inserted into Eq 2, the resultant intensity of scattering will yield periodic minima and maxima. In contrast, if the local values of the ρ_i's are random, it is assumed that (Ref 15):

$$\rho_k(\mathbf{r}) = \rho_{av} + \Delta\rho_k(\mathbf{r}) \qquad (Eq\ 4)$$

where $\Delta\rho$ is the fluctuation from the average and may be positive or negative (Ref 15, 16). Substitution of this expression into Eq 2 for both ρ terms followed by an expansion of the terms yields:

$$I(\mathbf{h}) = \mathbf{C} \int\int \Delta\rho_i \,\Delta\rho_j \exp(-i\mathbf{k}\mathbf{s} \cdot \mathbf{r})d\mathbf{r}_i d\mathbf{r}_j$$

$$(Eq\ 5)$$

because the terms involving the product of average electron densities and the cross terms between the average electron densities and the fluctuations must average to zero. If only isotropic mediums are considered, a correlation function $\gamma(r)$ defined by:

$$\gamma(r) = \frac{(\Delta\rho_i\, \Delta\rho_j)}{(\Delta\rho^2)_{av}} \qquad (Eq\ 6)$$

may be introduced in Eq 5. The result is:

$$I(\mathbf{h}) = \mathbf{C}[(\Delta\rho^2)_{av}] \int \gamma(r) \frac{\sin ksr}{ksr}\, dr \quad (Eq\ 7)$$

Because a random distribution of the electron density is assumed, the correlation function should decrease monotonically from a value of unity at $r = 0$ to a value of zero at $r = \infty$. A simple exponential possesses proper behavior:

$$\gamma(r) = \exp-\left(\frac{r}{a}\right) \qquad (Eq\ 8)$$

where a is defined as a correlation length or a persistence distance (Ref 15). Substituting this function into Eq 7 and performing the required integration yields:

$$I(\mathbf{h}) = \mathbf{C}(\Delta\rho)^2 \frac{8\pi a^3}{[1 + (ksa)^2]^2} \qquad (Eq\ 9)$$

Equation 9 can be used to evaluate the correlation length a by plotting $I(\mathbf{h})^{-0.5}$ against $\mathbf{h}^2$. Alternatively, the correlation function $\gamma(r)$ can be obtained from the Fourier transform of Eq 7 and graphical integration of the scattering data. An alternate use of the correlation function approach has been presented for the scattering of spheres of radius R, which are separated by a distance r. A simple geometric argument yields:

$$\gamma(r) = 1 - \frac{(3r)}{(4R)} + \frac{1}{16}\left(\frac{r}{R}\right)^3 \qquad (Eq\ 10)$$

which if substituted into Eq 7 provides the classic Rayleigh equation for scattering from a sphere:

$$I(\mathbf{h}) = 9\left[\frac{\sin(\mathbf{h}R) - \mathbf{h}R \cos(\mathbf{h}R)}{(\mathbf{h}R)^3}\right]^2 \ (Eq\ 11)$$

For small values of $\mathbf{h}$, the trigonometric terms in Eq 11 can be expanded, and the equivalent of the classic Guinier approximation obtained (Ref 1):

$$I(\mathbf{h}) = I_0 \exp\left(\frac{-k^2R^2}{3}\right) \qquad (Eq\ 12)$$

A plot of the log of the scattered intensity as a function of $\mathbf{h}^2$ yields a measure of the radius of gyration of the scattering entity.

The theory for interpreting the scattering from multicomponent materials undergoing phase separation depends on the assumed mechanism, that is, nucleation and growth versus spinodal decomposition. Because nucleation involves the formation of nuclei and growth at random locations within the material, Eq 4 can be used. The formal analogy between the theory of SAS and the mathematical solutions of spinodal decomposition has been documented (Ref 17). The basic difference between the expected scattering for these two mechanisms is that nucleation and growth will shift the observed scattering to smaller angles (a maximum may or may not be observed) as the new phases grow in size, but the latter will result in a maximum that will increase in magnitude but not change its position.

Applications

Metals. Small-angle diffraction has been used to study heterogeneities in unstable metallic solutions known as Guinier-Preston (G-P) zones (Ref 1). More recently, SAXS and SANS have been used to study the heterogeneities in metallic glasses, emphasizing the effects of thermal annealing and neutron irradiation in terms of their number and size (Ref 7, 9, 10). Small-angle neutron scattering studies on ferromagnetic spin glasses of composition Fe_xCr_{1-x} exhibit a peak at the Curie temperature over a broad range of composition. For those exhibiting spin-glass behavior, there is an increase in intensity below the T_c (Ref 9, 10, 18).

Small-angle x-ray scattering has been used to determine the miscibility gap in binary metallic alloys, such as aluminum-silver, aluminum-zinc, and so on, and in ternary systems (Ref 18). It has been observed that the SAXS from cold-worked metals can be explained in terms of double Bragg scattering. That is, the incident beam is diffracted by a crystalline grain, and the diffracted beam is then rediffracted by a second crystal. This problem can be eliminated by using SANS because of the longer wavelengths of the neutron beam (0.8 to 1.0 nm). Small-angle x-ray scattering has also been used to study critical phenomena in binary alloys (Ref 2, 7) and to determine particle sizes in rapidly solidified alloys.

In one experiment, a thin ribbon of an iron-nickel alloy with additions of phosphorus and boron was prepared by ejecting a stream of liquid metal onto a rapidly moving surface. The film was mounted on a holder and placed on a Kratky-type small-angle x-ray instrument. Molybdenum $K\alpha$ x-rays were used in all measurements. The x-ray beam was monochromatized using a pulse height discriminator and a zirconium foil filter.

The linear absorption coefficient of the sample was measured by placing the ribbon in front of the collimator and the detector (a xenon proportional counter). The detector was placed at zero angle, and the intensity was measured with and without the sample. The linear absorption coefficient τ was calculated using:

$$I_{abs} = I_0 \exp(-\tau d) \qquad \text{(Eq 13)}$$

where d is the sample thickness in centimeters. The optimum thickness was determined using Eq 3. The sample was then thinned down to this dimension by polishing. The sample was placed in the scattering position of the Kratky camera, and the intensity of scattering was measured for 100 s at approximately 100 angles. The raw data were then corrected for absorption and background scattering using:

$$I_{cor} = I_s - I_b \exp(-\tau d) \qquad \text{(Eq 14)}$$

where I_s is the measured intensity, and I_b is the background intensity, which was determined by placing the sample in the absorp-

tion position and measuring the scattering as a function of angle. The logarithm of the corrected scattering intensity was plotted as a function of $\mathbf{h}^2$ (Guinier plots), and the dimensions of the scattering particles were determined from the slope at the origin. Electron microscope studies were then conducted on the sample. Randomly distributed particles of approximately the size determined from the small-angle x-ray measurements were found.

Glasses. The use of SAXS and SANS in the study of inorganic glasses has focused on the detection of long-range order, on the mechanisms of phase separation, on the internal surface area in porous samples, on detection of the presence of heterogeneities, and on the characterization of the microstructure (Ref 19-23). As with other materials, it is found that spinodal decomposition governs the early stage of phase separation, but nucleation and growth control the later stages (Ref 21).

Polymers. Small-angle x-ray scattering has been used to study the quasiperiodicity and orientation in such semicrystalline polymers as polyethylene and polypropylene, phase and microphase separation in polymer blends and block copolymers, and the structure of crazes and fracture surfaces of glassy polymers (Ref 24-26). Small-angle neutron scattering has been used to study the conformation of single polymer chains within their matrix under static and time-dependent conditions and in the strained state (Ref 27). Small-angle x-ray scattering has also been used to characterize the degree of dilatation that occurs when filled polymers and polymer blends are stressed (Ref 28).

In positional small-angle x-ray scattering (PSAXS), the scattering across the breadth of a sample is measured at a constant scattering angle as the sample is moved incrementally along its length. This technique has been used to study the nucleation and growth of defects and flaws in mechanically fatigued samples and to study the structure of crazes (Ref 29, 30). The technique allows the detection and evaluation of subtle changes in macroscopic materials for large volumes. Positional small-angle neutron scattering (PSANS) could also be used.

Ceramics. The use of SAS techniques in the study of ceramics has been limited, as evidenced by the quantity of published papers over the past 20 years (Ref 31). This may be a result of the key words used in abstracting and classifying the papers. This situation is expected to change. Table 1 summarizes the above results in terms of material, applications, and techniques.

Table 1 Some applications of SAS techniques

Materials	Subject	Technique(s)	References
Metals	Spinodal decomposition	SAXS	32, 33, 34
	Nucleation	SAXS, SANS, TEM	2, 9, 10
	Guinier-Preston zones	SAXS	35, 36
	Miscibility	SAXS, SANS	18
	Dislocations	SAXS	2, 7
	Dilation/voiding	SAXS	37
Metallic glasses	Correlated fluctuations	SAXS, SANS	18, 38
	Annealing	SAXS, SANS	18, 39–42
	Heterogeneities	SAXS	41–43
	Miscibility	SAXS	44
Glasses/ceramics	Phase separation	SAXS, TEM	19, 21, 31
	Heterogeneities	SAXS	20, 31
Crystalline polymers	Long period	SAXS, WAXS	24–26
	Annealing	SAXS, SANS	24–26
Block polymers	Microphase separation	SAXS, SANS, TEM	45
	Structure	SAXS, SANS, TEM	11, 46
Polymer blends	Phase separation	SAXS, SANS, TEM	46, 47
	Dilation, voiding	SAXS	48, 49
Polymer glasses	Crazing	SAXS, PSAXS	28, 30, 50, 51
	Densification	SAXS	29
	Annealing	SAXS, SANS	26
Polymer molecules	Configuration	SANS	27

REFERENCES

1. A Guinier, G. Fournet, C.B. Walker, and K.L. Yudowitch, *Small-Angle Scattering of X-rays*, John Wiley & Sons, 1955
2. H. Brumberger, Ed., *Small-Angle X-ray Scattering*, Gordon and Breach, 1967
3. A.H. Compton and S.A. Allison, *X-rays in Theory and Experiment*, D.H. Van Nostrand, 1954
4. H.P. Klug and L.A. Alexander, *X-ray Diffraction Procedures*, John Wiley & Sons, 1954
5. W.O. Statton, in *Newer Methods of Polymer Characterization*, B. Ke, Ed., Interscience, 1964
6. R. Hosemann and S.N. Bagchi, *Direct Analysis of Diffraction by Matter*, North Holland, 1962
7. V. Gerold and G. Kostorz, *J. Appl. Crystallogr.*, Vol 11, 1978, p 516
8. J.S. Higgins and R.S. Stein, *J. Appl. Crystallogr.*, Vol 11, 1978, p 346
9. J. Schelten and R.W. Hendrick, *J. Appl. Crystallogr.*, Vol 11, 1978, p 297
10. M.K. Wilkinson, A. Bienenstock, M. Blume, W.L. Clinton, J.J. Rush, and J.M. Rowe, *Mater. Sci. Eng.*, Vol 35, 1978, p 33
11. P.W. Schmidt and R. Hight, Jr., *Acta Crystallogr.*, Vol 13, 1960, p 480
12. O. Kratky, I. Pilz, and P.J. Schmidt, *J. Coll. Int. Sci.*, Vol 21, 1966, p 24
13. R.J. Roe and J.J. Curro, *Macromolecules*, Vol 16, 1983, p 428
14. P. Debye, *J. Math. Phys.*, Vol 4, 1925, p 133
15. P. Debye, and A.M. Bueche, *J. Appl. Phys.*, Vol 20, 1949, p 518
16. G. Porod, *Kolloid. Zh.*, Vol 124, 1951, p 83; Vol 125, 1952, p 51
17. K.B. Rundman and J.E. Hilliard, *Acta Metall.*, Vol 15, 1967, p 1025
18. E.A. Kramer, W.L. Johnson, and C. Cline, *Appl. Phys. Lett.*, Vol 35, 1979, p 815

19. E.D. Zannotto, A.F. Craierich, and P.F. Jones, *J. Phys.*, Vol 43, Conf C9, 1982, p 107
20. M. Tomozawa and S. Copella, *J. Am. Ceram. Soc.*, Vol 66, 1983, p C/24-25
21. M. Tomozawa, R.K. Mcrone, and H. Herman, *Phys. Chem. Glasses*, Vol 11, 1970, p 136
22. J.A. Williams, G.E. Rudone and H.A. McKinstry, *Phys. Chem. Glasses*, Vol 64, 1981, p 709
23. A. Benedetti, G. Cocco, G. Fagherazzi, S. Meriai, and G. Scarinci, *J. Mater. Sci.*, Vol 18, 1983, p 1099
24. M.J. Shanker Narayanaon and J.H. Magill, *J. Poly. Sci. Poly. Phys.*, Vol 22, 1984, p 223
25. D.T. Grubb, J.J. Liu, M. Caffrey, and D.H. Bilderback, *J. Poly. Sci. Poly. Phys.*, Vol 22, 1984, p 367
26. D.G.H. Ballard, G.D. Wignall, and J. Schelten, *Eur. Poly.*, Vol 9, 1973, p 965; Vol 10, 1974, p 801
27. J.A. Miller, S.L. Cooper, C.C. Han, and G. Pruckmayr, *Macromol.*, Vol 17, 1984, p 1063
28. F. Hamada, H. Hayashi, and A. Nakajima, *J. Appl. Crystallogr.*, Vol 11, 1978, p 514
29. D.G. LeGrand, G.R. Tryson, W.V. Olszewski, and C.M. Forth, *Poly. Eng. Sci.*, Vol 22, 1982, p 928
30. C.M. Forth and D.G. LeGrand, *J. Poly. Sci. Poly. Lett.*, Vol 21, 1983, p 853
31. K. Frye and H. Nickel, Report 1662, Kernforschungslage, July 1980
32. T. Ungar, *Z. Metallkd.*, Vol 70, 1979, p 739
33. O. Lyon, C. Severac, and C. Servant, *Philos. Mag. A*, Vol 48, 1983, p 825
34. J.E. Epperson, B.A. Loomis, and J.S. Lin, *J. Nucl. Mater.*, Vol 108-109, 1982, p 476
35. B. Gueffray-Oettez and H. Loffler, *Phys. Status Solidi*, Vol 73, 1982, p 153

36. K. Osamura, K. Murakami, T. Sato, T. Takahashi, T. Abe, and K. Hirano, *Acta Metall.*, Vol 31, 1983, p 1669
37. K. Meada., S. Kobayashi, S. Takachi, T. Chiba, and K. Osamura, *Phys. Status Solidi (A)*, Vol 83, 1984, p 219
38. A. Naudau and A.M. Frank, *J. Phys.*, Vol 43, Conf C9, 1982, p 79
39. S. Ceresara, A. Benedetti, G. Cocco, and S. Enzo, *Philos. Mag. A*, Vol 43, 1981, p 1093
40. T. Ungar, J. Lendrai, and I. Kovacs, *Philos. Mag. A*, Vol 43, 1981, p 927
41. J.R. Walter, D.G. LeGrand, and F.E. Luborsky, *IEEE Trans.*, Vol 12, 1976, p 930
42. U. Koster and U. Herold, in *Topics in Applied Physics*, Vol 46, H.J. Guntherodt and H. Beck, Ed., Springer-Verlag, 1981, p 225
43. W. Yuming and M. Chaote, *J. Non-Cryst. Solids*, Vol 5t, 1983, p 187
44. G. Cocco, G. Faghorazzi, and F. Schiffini, *J. Appl. Crystallogr.*, Vol 10, 1977, p 255
45. T.P. Russel and J.T. Koberstein, *J. Appl. Crystallogr.*, Vol 23, 1985, p 1109
46. J.T. Koberstein and R.S. Stein, *Poly. Eng. Sci.*, Vol 24, 1984, p 293; J.J. Curro and R.J. Roe, *J. Poly. Sci. Poly. Phys.*, Vol 21, 1983, p 1785
47. T.P. Russel and R.S. Stein, *J. Poly. Sci. Poly. Phys.*, Vol 20, 1982, p 1593; Vol 21, 1983, p 999
48. S. Kaneko, J.E. Frederick, and D. McIntyre, *J. Appl. Poly. Sci.*, Vol 26, 1981, p 4175
49. J. Elad and J.M. Schultz, *J. Poly. Sci. Poly. Phys.*, Vol 22, 1984, p 781
50. P.A. Westbrook, J.F. Fellers, M. Cakmak, J.S. Lin, and R.W. Hendricks, *J. Poly. Sci. Poly. Phys.*, Vol 21, 1983, p 1913
51. W.S. Rothwell, R.H. Martinson, and R.L. Gorman, *Appl. Phys. Lett.*, Vol 42, 1983, p 422

Extended X-Ray Absorption Fine Structure

Joe Wong, Corporate Research and Development, General Electric Company

General Uses

- Determination of local structure (short-range order) about a given atomic center in all states of matter
- For crystals and oriented surfaces, structural information on next-nearest and further-out neighbors can also be determined
- Identification of phases and compounds containing a specific element
- Orientation of adsorbed molecules on single-crystal surfaces
- Combined with near-edge structure, bonding and site symmetry of a constituent element in a material can be determined

Examples of Applications

- Bond distance, coordination, and type of nearest neighbors about a given constituent atomic species in disordered systems, such as glasses, liquids, solutions, and random alloys, or complex systems, such as catalysts, biomolecules, and minerals
- In ordered systems, such as crystals and oriented surfaces, structural information on the next-nearest neighbors can also be obtained
- Structural evolution in amorphous to crystalline transformation can be followed
- Geometry of chemisorbed atoms or molecules on single-crystal surfaces
- *In situ* structure determination of active sites in catalysts
- *In vivo* structure determination of active sites in metalloproteins
- Combined with x-ray absorption near-edge structure, bonding and local structure of trace impurities in natural materials (for example, coal) and synthetic materials (for example, diamond) can be determined

Samples

- *Form*: Solids, liquids, and gases. Solids should ideally be in thin foil (metals and alloys) or uniform films of fine powders (~400 mesh or finer)
- *Size*: Area—25 × 5 mm (1 × 0.2 in.) minimum. Thickness—bulk samples: 1 to 2 absorption lengths at the absorption edge of the element of interest; dilute samples: up to a few millimeters thick
- *Preparation*: Mainly required for solid samples—rolled metal foil, sputtered or evaporated thin films, uniformly dispersed powder films. Aerobic or anaerobic environments must be used for biological materials and checks for radiation damage (loss of biological activity)

Limitations

- Nonunique results if the element of interest exists in multiple nonequivalent sites or valence states
- Structural results can depend strongly on model systems used in quantitative analysis
- Low concentration limit is near 100 ppm or a few millimolar in favorable cases
- For dilute and surface systems, synchrotron radiation is necessary

Estimated Experimental Scan Time

- 30 min to 1 h for bulk samples (single scan)
- 5 to 10 h or more for dilute samples and surfaces (multiple scans)

Estimated Data Analysis Time

- 2 to 20 h or more per spectrum

Capabilities of Related Techniques

- *X-ray or neutron diffraction*: Identification of bulk crystalline phases; radial distribution functions of bulk amorphous phases
- *X-ray anomalous scattering*: Characterization of bulk amorphous materials
- *Electron energy loss spectroscopy*: Extended fine structure in solids; sample must withstand vacuum
- *Magic-angle spinning nuclear magnetic resonance*: For solid-state studies

Introduction

Extended x-ray absorption fine structure (EXAFS) (Ref 1) is associated experimentally with the oscillatory modulation of the absorption coefficient on the high-energy side of an x-ray absorption edge of a given constituent atom in a material. Figure 1 shows the K-edge EXAFS of nickel metal. When an x-ray beam passes through a medium, its intensity is attenuated exponentially:

$$I = I_0 \exp(-\mu x) \qquad \text{(Eq 1)}$$

where I and I_0 are the transmitted and incident intensities, respectively; μ is the linear absorption coefficient; and x is sample thickness. In general, μ is a function of photon energy. When the x-ray energy $h\nu$ equals or exceeds the binding energy E_b of a core electron, the latter is emitted by a photoelectric process from the atom with kinetic energy E, conserving energy:

$$E = h\nu - E_b \qquad \text{(Eq 2)}$$

For pure nickel, when $h\nu = 8332.8$ eV (the binding energy of the inner most K-electron in nickel), μ increases sharply, producing a characteristic K-absorption edge (Fig. 1). On the high-energy side of the absorption edge, μx fluctuates with increasing photon energy extending to a few hundred electron volts beyond the edge. These oscillations are understood theoretically to be a final-state electron effect resulting from

the interference between the outgoing photoejected electron and that fraction of the photoejected electron that is backscattered from the neighboring atoms. The interference directly reflects the net phase shift of the backscattered electron near the central excited atom, which is largely proportional to the product of the electron momentum k and the distance traversed by the electron. The type of central absorbing atom and backscattering neighboring atoms (that is, their positions in the periodic table) also affect the interference event. Therefore, EXAFS is considered effective for probing the atomic environment of matter, particularly since the advent of intense continuous synchrotron radiation in the x-ray region.

The fine structure above x-ray absorption edges had been reported as early as 1920 (Ref 2, 3) based on studies with the K-edges of magnesium-, iron-, and chromium-containing compounds and with the L-edges of elements from cesium to neodymium, respectively. Progress was slow before 1970 primarily because the physical processes associated with EXAFS were not well understood; therefore, there was no adequate theory to account for the observed spectra. In addition, the experiments were tedious before the availability of synchrotron radiation.

The early theories proposed to explain EXAFS can be classified as long-range order (LRO) and short-range order (SRO). The LRO theories require the existence of lattice periodicity characteristic of crystalline solids and assume transition to quasistationary states to explain the fine structure (Ref 4, 5). However, the LRO theories do not predict the shape of the experimental absorption curve adequately, because the dominant matrix element effects are neglected (Ref 6, 7). The early LRO Kronig theory (Ref 4) also failed to explain EXAFS in polyatomic in gases and amorphous materials.

However, ample experimental evidence supports the SRO approach (Ref 7). Extended x-ray absorption fine structure has been observed in simple gaseous molecular systems, such as $GeCl_4$ (Ref 8), and, more recently, Br_2 (Ref 9). Figure 2 shows the germanium EXAFS above its K-edge in $GeCl_4$ taken using synchrotron radiation. The fine structure arises from backscattering of the germanium K-photoelectron by the four chlorine atoms bonded to germanium in the tetrahedral molecule. In another early study, a similarity was observed between the EXAFS spectra of a series of chromium, manganese, and cobalt crystalline compounds and those of their aqueous solution; the region of influence in an EXAFS event was concluded to only 4-5 Å from the center of the atom being excited (Ref 11).

Fig. 2 Experimental EXAFS scan of germanium in $GeCl_4$ molecule taken using synchrotron radiation above the K-absorption edge of germanium at 11 103.3 eV

Source: Ref 10

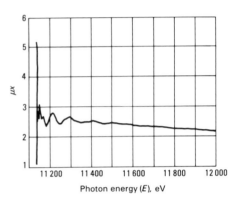

In solids, perhaps the first convincing experiments to demonstrate the SRO effects associated with EXAFS were conducted in 1962 (Ref 12). The EXAFS was measured above the germanium K-edge in glassy GeO_2 to 350 eV and compared to those of the hexagonal and tetragonal crystalline polymorphs shown in Fig. 3. The extended absorption fine structures of glassy and hexagonal GeO_2, in which germanium is 4-fold coordinated by oxygen, were similar, but differed notably from that of tetragonal GeO_2, in which germanium is 6-fold coordinated by oxygen. These observations were reconfirmed in 1965 (Ref 1). The measurement was extended to 1100 eV beyond the K-absorption edge of germanium. Because LRO, that is, lattice periodicity, does not exist in the amorphous phase, the fine structure must be concluded to be strongly influenced by the arrangement of neighboring atoms about the germanium. An account of the history and modern practice of EXAFS since 1970 is cited in Ref 13.

EXAFS Fundamentals

Recent interest in EXAFS began in 1970 (Ref 14). A single-scattering approximation was used to show that the observed fine structure oscillations can be understood in terms of interference between the outgoing photoelectron wave near the central atom and that portion of it backscattered from neighboring atoms. Furthermore, the problem can be inverted to obtain interatomic

Fig. 1 Experimental EXAFS scan of nickel metal taken using synchrotron radiation above the K-absorption edge of nickel at 8332.8 eV

The energy is labeled regarding the K-edge of nickel as zero.

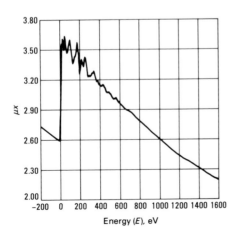

Fig. 3 Experimental K-edge EXAFS spectrum of germanium in crystalline and glassy GeO₂

The energy is labeled regarding the K-edge of germanium at 11 103.3 eV as zero. Source: Ref 12

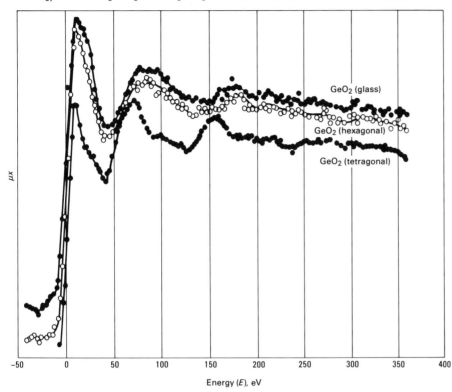

distances r_j from a Fourier analysis of EXAFS data. A Fourier transform of EXAFS data in k-space for crystalline and amorphous germanium revealed that peaks in the transforms correspond to various atomic shells (Ref 15). Analysis of the EXAFS can yield the distance, number, and type of nearest-neighbor atoms about the central atom.

Another milestone in the development of EXAFS was the availability of synchrotron radiation in the x-ray region (Ref 6). The 10^4 to 10^6 increase in intensity in tunable x-rays over a broad spectral region enables obtaining EXAFS spectra with excellent signal-to-noise ratios within minutes. In the past decade, EXAFS has become prevalent as a structural tool for studying various materials for which such conventional techniques as x-ray diffraction and conventional electron microscopy are less useful or ineffective.

The Physical Mechanism. The attenuation of x-rays traversing a medium occurs by scattering, pair production, and photoelectric absorption. In the EXAFS regime, photoelectric absorption dominates attenuation. In this process, a photon provides its full energy to electrons according to Eq 2.

Understanding the mechanism that produces the EXAFS oscillations necessitates considering the K-edge fine structure. In the dipole approximation (Ref 16), the probability p of x-ray absorption is:

$$p = 2\pi^2 e^2 \, (\omega c^2 m)^{-1} \, |M_{fs}|^2 \rho(E_f) \qquad \text{(Eq 3)}$$

where $M_{fs} = \langle f | \boldsymbol{\epsilon} \cdot \mathbf{p} | s \rangle$, $|s\rangle$ is the K-shell s state, $\langle f |$ is the final unoccupied state of p symmetry, $\rho(E_f)$ is the density of states per unit energy at the energy E_f of the final state, $2\pi\omega$ is the frequency of the x-ray, $\mathbf{p}$ is the momentum operator, and $\boldsymbol{\epsilon}$ is the electric field vector of the x-ray. For x-ray energies well above the edge, $\rho(E_f)$ provides a monotonic contribution and can be approximated by that of a free electron of energy $E = \hbar^2 \mathbf{k}^2 (2m)^{-1} + E_0$. In this case, E_0 is the energy of free electrons with $\mathbf{k} = 0$ and is the effective mean potential experienced by an excited electron. It is often termed the threshold energy. With this assumption for $\rho(E_f)$, M_{fs} is the only remaining factor that can contribute to the EXAFS signal. The initial state $|s\rangle$ is fixed and does not vary with ω. However, the final state $\langle f |$ varies with ω and produces the fine structure.

Further, the wave function $\langle f |$ is a sum of two contributions. If the atom is isolated, the excited photoelectron would be in a solely outgoing state from the central atom, as shown in Fig. 4 by the outgoing solid rings. In this case, M_{fs} exhibits no fine structure, and the x-ray absorption coefficient would vary monotonically with ω. This is the case for a monatomic gas such as krypton, whose spectrum beyond the K-edge at 14 326 eV follows a decay predicted by the photoelectric effect and reveals no fine structure (Fig. 5).

If the x-ray absorbing atom is surrounded by other atoms, as in a molecule such as GeCl₄ (Fig. 2) or in a condensed phase, whether liquid, glassy, or crystalline, the outgoing electron is scattered by the surrounding atoms producing incoming waves, as depicted by the dashed lines in Fig. 4. These incoming or backscattered waves can interfere constructively or destructively with the outgoing wave near the origin where $|s\rangle$ exists. As shown in Fig. 4(a), the amplitudes of the outgoing and backscattered waves add at the central A-atom site, leading to a maximum in x-ray absorption probability. In Fig. 4(b), the x-ray energy has been increased to E_2, leading to a shorter photoelectron wavelength for which the outgoing and backscattered waves interfere destructively at the absorbing A-atom site with a resulting minimum in absorption. This interference produces an oscillatory variation in M_{fs} as ω is varied, changing the electron wavelength and thus the phase between the outgoing and backscattered waves. Constructive interference increases M_{fs}; destructive interference decreases M_{fs} from the isolated atom value.

The total absorption $\mu(\mathbf{k})$ above the absorption edge is then:

$$\mu(\mathbf{k}) = \mu_0(\mathbf{k})[1 + \chi(\mathbf{k})] \qquad \text{(Eq 4)}$$

where $\mu_0(\mathbf{k})$ is the smooth varying portion of $\mu(\mathbf{k})$ and corresponds physically to the absorption coefficient of the isolated atom (Ref 17). Therefore, the fine structure $\chi(\mathbf{k}) = [\mu(\mathbf{k}) - \mu_0(\mathbf{k})]/\mu_0(\mathbf{k})$ is due to interference between backscattered and outgoing photoelectron waves in the photoabsorption matrix element.

The Single-Scattering Approximation. The first successful working theory of EXAFS was derived based on the above physical mechanism (Ref 14). It was subsequently modified to a more general form (Ref 7) and further refined (Ref 18, 19). For an unoriented sample, the fine structure above the K or L₁ edge can be described using:

$$\chi(\mathbf{k}) = -\frac{1}{\mathbf{k}} \sum_j \frac{N_j}{r_j^2} \exp\left(\frac{-2r_j}{\lambda}\right)$$

$$\exp\left(-2\sigma_j^2 \mathbf{k}^2\right) f_j(\pi, \mathbf{k})$$

$$\sin\left[2\mathbf{k}r_j + \delta_j(\mathbf{k})\right] \qquad \text{(Eq 5)}$$

where $\mathbf{k} = [2m(E - E_0)/\hbar^2]^{1/2}$ is the wave vector of the ejected photoelectron of energy E, and E_0 is the inner potential or threshold energy caused by the atomic potentials and represents the threshold above which the kinetic energy must be added to determine the total energy E. The summation is over shells of atoms that are at a distance r_j from the absorbing atom and that contain N_j atoms (the coordination number). Lambda is the mean free path of the photoelectron. The second exponential containing σ_j^2 is a Debye-Waller term in which σ_j^2 is not the usual mean-square vibrational amplitude of an atom, but the mean-square relative positional fluctuation of the central and backscattering atoms. The fluctuations can be static (structural disorder) or dynamic (thermal) in origin.

In this form, the resultant EXAFS is a sum of sine waves with periods $2\mathbf{k}r_j$ from each jth shell with an amplitude that represents the number of neighbors modified by an envelope due to the scattering amplitude $f_j(\pi, \mathbf{k})$, the Debye-Waller damping, and the mean-free-path damping. Besides the usual $2\mathbf{k}r_j$ that accounts for the phase difference of a free electron returning to the neighbor, additional phase shifts $\delta_j(\mathbf{k})$ are necessary to account for the potentials due to the central atom and backscatterers. The factor r_j^{-2} arises from the product of the amplitudes of the outgoing and backscattered waves, both of which decay as r_j^{-1} because of their spherical nature. For a single-crystal sample, the factor $3\cos^2\theta_j$ must be included in the summation, where θ_j is the angle the jth neighbor makes with polarization vector of the x-ray. This factor averages to one for polycrystalline or amorphous materials. Conceptually, EXAFS can be considered a mode of electron diffraction in which the source of electrons is generated from within a particular atomic species participating in the absorption event.

The derivation of Eq 5 is based on two assumptions. First, because the atomic radius is small enough for the curvature of the incident wave on the neighboring atoms to be neglected, the incident wave can be approximated using a plane wave. This is achieved mathematically by replacing the Hankel function with its asymptotic form (Ref 19, 20), which yields the factor $1/\mathbf{k}$ in Eq 5. Second, only single scattering by the

Fig. 4 Schematic representation of EXAFS event

The excited electronic state is centered about the A-atom. The solid circles represent the crests of the outgoing part of the electronic state. The surrounding B-atoms backscatter the outgoing part as shown by the dotted circles. (a) Constructive interference. (b) Destructive interference

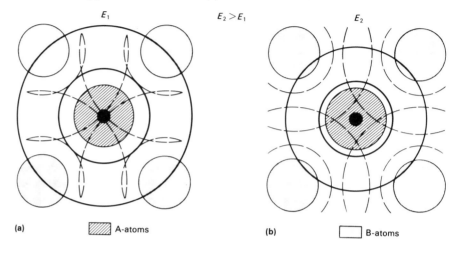

neighboring atoms is included. These assumptions have been examined in detail for face-centered cubic (fcc) copper (Ref 19); electron scattering was first treated using a spherical wave expansion to take account of the finite size of the atoms. Although large, the effects appear to make quantitative but not qualitative changes on the single-scattering description. As the size of the scattering atoms increases, significant deviations in phase and amplitude are noted between the spherical wave calculation and the asymptotic plane wave approximation (Ref 21).

Multiple-Scattering Effects. Extended x-ray absorption fine structure has been reduced to the problem of the scattering of photoelectrons by atoms analogous to low-energy electron diffraction (LEED), in which an electron beam with several hundred electron volts of energy is scattered by a crystal. Because multiple scattering is important in the interpretation of LEED data (Ref 22), this calls into question the adequacy of the single-scattering description for EXAFS.

Each multiple-scattering process can be described by an effective interference path length equal to the sum of the scattering paths (Ref 19). In $\mathbf{k}$-space, they give rise to rapidly oscillating terms that tend to average out. Multiple scattering (band-structure and chemical bonding effects) becomes important only near the absorption edge within approximately 30 eV, the x-ray absorption near-edge structure (XANES) (Ref 23). This is because at low energy the scattering becomes more isotopic, and the electron mean free path becomes long. Alternatively, if the data are Fourier transformed, the multiple-

scattering contribution will appear farther out in the transformed spectrum. In particular, because the path length for multiple scattering must be larger than that for the dominant first-shell interaction, its contribution will not influence the nearest-neighbor distance that is a predominant feature in the radial structure function of such disordered systems as glasses and isolated impurities.

However, multiple scattering in EXAFS is important when an inner-shell atom shadows an outer-shell atom, as was first realized when the fourth shell in the copper EXAFS was seen to have an anomalously large amplitude and phase shift. The reason for this observation is that in a fcc lattice a nearest-neighbor atom is directly in the line of sight of the fourth-shell atom. The outgoing electron is strongly forward scattered, enhancing the electron amplitude in the fourth shell (Ref 19). This produces the

Fig. 5 K-edge absorption spectrum of krypton gas

Source: Ref 10

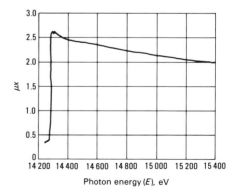

focusing effect analogous to an amplifying relay system. This focusing effect has been used in developing a formalism to determine bond angle of nearly-colinear systems, such as those of M–C–O in metal carbonyl complexes (Ref 24). It has also been used to "see" hydrogen atoms in EXAFS studies of metal-hydrogen systems (Ref 25).

Synchrotron Radiation as X-Ray Source for EXAFS Experiments

The two sources of continuous x-radiation used for EXAFS experiments are the bremsstrahlung output from a rotating-anode x-ray tube and the synchrotron radiation produced from electron storage rings or synchrotrons. Extended x-ray absorption fine structure deals with the fine attenuation, 5 to 10% of the main absorption increase in relative magnitude, on the high-energy side of an absorption edge. To ensure that an EXAFS signal is being measured, reliable signal counting statistics must be obtained to yield a high signal-to-noise ratio (>300:1). Achieving this with a conventional x-ray tube and a flat dispersing crystal necessitates an experimental scan, such as that shown in Fig. 3 for the GeO_2 polymorphs, that typically requires a week or more. Source instability over such an extended period of operation compounds the problem. With the advent of synchrotron radiation sources in the x-ray region, particularly that at the Stanford Synchrotron Radiation Laboratory (SSRL) (Ref 26), a second important milestone has been reached in the development of modern EXAFS.

Synchrotron radiation is the major energy-loss mechanism of accelerated charged particles, such as electrons and positrons, traveling at relativistic velocities. The properties of synchrotron light emitted from electrons with velocities near that of the light are drastically different from classical dipole radiation (Ref 27) and constitute the importance of synchrotron radiation as an effective light source (Ref 28). Having been measured (Ref 29) and studied theoretically (Ref 26), the properties can be summarized (Ref 26) as follows:

- Continuous spectral distribution from the infrared to the x-ray region, which is ideal as a light source for ultraviolet (UV) and x-ray spectroscopies
- Higher intensity, permitting use of monochromators with narrow band pass
- Plane polarized, with the electric vector in the orbital plane of the circulating particles

- Extremely high collimation, which is important to lithography of submicron structure
- Sharply pulsed-time structure

Synchrotron radiation was discovered experimentally at the General Electric 70 MeV betatron in 1947 (Ref 29). A detailed historical account of this discovery is cited in Ref 30.

The spectral distribution of synchrotron radiation from the Stanford Position Electron Accelerator Ring (SPEAR) (Ref 26) is shown in Fig. 6, with the electron-beam energy E as the parameter from 1.5 to 4.5 GeV. It is an intense continuous distribution extending from the infrared into the x-ray region. With this spectral distribution and the transmission characteristic of the beryllium window assembly, useful x-ray fluxes from 3.5 to approximately 30 keV for a 3.5 GeV electron beam are available in SPEAR. This permits routine measurement of the K-edge EXAFS of potassium (K-edge energy = 3.60 keV) to cadmium (K-edge = 26.71 keV) and the L-edge of indium (L_3 edge = 3.70 keV) to uranium (L_3 edge = 17.17 keV).

Compared with the bremsstrahlung output of a 12-kW standard x-ray tube, synchrotron radiation is higher in intensity by a factor of approximately 10^6. This reduces the measurement time for a typical EXAFS experiment from a week or more to an hour or less. Figure 7 compares the K-edge EXAFS spectrum of arsenic in glassy As_2Te_3 taken with a conventional x-ray tube and with synchrotron radiation. The spectrum shown in Fig. 7(a) is the summation of seven individual scans; each required three days of continuous scanning. The synchrotron spectrum shown in Fig. 7(b) was taken in 1.3 h. The product of the increase of resolution × measurement time × signal-to-noise ratio of the two spectra shows an improvement of ~3 × 10^4 of the synchrotron data over that obtained using a conventional source (Ref 30).

As shown in Fig. 8(a), the x-ray beam from the SPEAR vacuum chamber passes successively through a helium chamber; a beryllium window; a slit; a channel-cut crystal monochromator; a mask; ion chamber No. 1, which measures I_0; a sample; and ion chamber No. 2, which measures I. The experiment is controlled by a PDP-11/34 minicomputer, with interfaces to control the angle of the crystal monochromator, digitize the ion-chamber currents, and store and plot the ratio I_0/I.

For dilute systems, a fluorescence technique (Ref 33) has been devised to enhance experimentally the relatively weak EXAFS signal from the bulk absorption background of the matrix. This detection technique uses

Fig. 6 Spectral distribution of synchrotron radiation from SPEAR

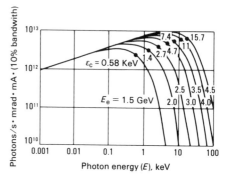

the principle that an inner-shell vacancy may relax by undergoing a radiative transition from a higher energy occupied shell. The fluorescence yield is a monotonically increasing function of atomic number and is expected to be independent of excitation energy for above threshold, but may vary slightly near threshold. Thus, the fluorescence intensity is a direct measure of absorption probability, the mechanism of interest in EXAFS. Figure 8(b) shows a typical fluorescence EXAFS set up. The original configuration (Ref 33) has been further modified for improved solid-angle collection, filtering of Compton and elastic scattering of the incident beam by the sample (Ref 34) and discriminative energy detection (Ref 35, 36).

Further experimental details associated with EXAFS measurements have been documented (Ref 37-43). Since SSRL opened in 1974, requests for beam time for x-ray experiments have doubled every year. This has revived interest (Ref 44) in in-house laboratory EXAFS apparatus constructed using more powerful rotating-anode sources for

Fig. 7 K-edge EXAFS spectra of arsenic in As_2Te_3 glass

(a) Taken with a conventional x-ray tube. (b) With synchrotron radiation. The sharp white line in (b) is due to higher resolution (approximately 2 eV) compared with approximately 8 eV for the data taken with the x-ray tube. Source: Ref 31

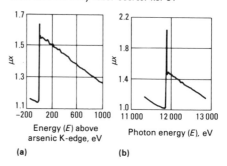

Fig. 8 EXAFS experimental apparatus at SSRL

(a) Transmission mode of detection. (b) Fluorescence mode of detection. Source: Ref 32

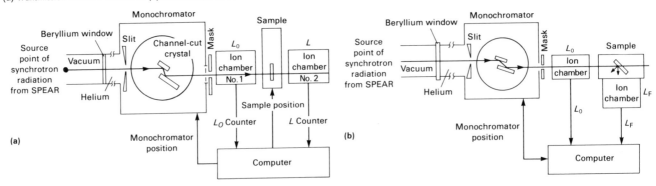

x-ray generation in conjunction with curved-crystal optics (Ref 45-48). Also as a consequence of the demand of the scientific community, various synchrotrons around the world are now being updated, and new facilities built as dedicated sources for synchrotron radiation research (Ref 49). Table 1 lists synchrotron radiation sources.

Data Analysis

General Considerations. Experimentally, the EXAFS spectrum shown in Fig. 1 appears as low-intensity oscillations (relative to the jump at the absorption edge) superimposing on the smooth atomic absorption background that decays with increasing energy above the absorption edge. Therefore, the fine structure according to Eq 4 is $\chi(\mathbf{k}) = [\mu(\mathbf{k}) - \mu_0(\mathbf{k})]/\mu_0(\mathbf{k})$, where $\mu(\mathbf{k})$ is the total absorption measured above the edge, and $\mu_0(\mathbf{k})$ is the smooth atomic contribution. A fairly standardized procedure has been established to extract the EXAFS signal $\chi(\mathbf{k})$ from the experimental x-ray absorption spectrum (Ref 37, 40, 50, 51). It consists of correcting for spectrometer shift, deglitching, pre-edge and post-edge background removal, edge normalization, extraction of the EXAFS signal $\chi(\mathbf{k})$, Fourier transform of $\chi(\mathbf{k})$, and inverse transform to isolate the EXAFS contribution from a selected region in real space.

Background Removal. Because the smooth absorption of an isolated atom $\mu_0(\mathbf{k})$ is not generally available experimentally, and present theoretical calculations of $\mu_0(\mathbf{k})$ are not sufficiently accurate for most EXAFS investigations (approximately 0.1%), the smooth part of $\mu(\mathbf{k})$ is assumed to represent the desired $\mu_0(\mathbf{k})$. With this assumption, the remaining oscillatory part of $\mu(\mathbf{k})$ is taken as $\Delta\mu = \mu(\mathbf{k}) - \mu_0(\mathbf{k})$ to yield $\chi(\mathbf{k}) = \Delta\mu(\mathbf{k})/\mu_0(\mathbf{k})$. The post-edge background above 30 eV in the EXAFS region can then be generated analytically by fitting $\mu(\mathbf{k})$ (in-cluding the EXAFS) with a series of cubic splines of equal segments (Ref 52). The ends of each segment are connected such that the derivatives are continuous across the ends. Three to five such splines are adequate for data extending 1000 eV above the absorption edge. When the number of segments is too small, the background is not separated well enough; when too large, the background follows the EXAFS oscillations, especially at low energy, and reduces its intensity (Ref 51).

A least squares fit with such a spline function enables removal of low-frequency background components from $\mu(\mathbf{k})$ without affecting the higher frequency EXAFS oscillations. Spline fitting is essentially a local fitting procedure in that the polynomial function within each interval is determined mainly by the local quality of the fit. The pre-edge background from -200 to -20 eV is obtained by a linear regression analysis of the first ten raw data points.

Figure 9 shows the result for nickel. The solid line in Fig. 9(a) is the raw experimental K-edge EXAFS scan of a 5-μm thick nickel foil taken at 90 K. The spectrum was recorded at SSRL, with SPEAR operating at 2.6 GeV electron energy and beam current at approximately 30 mA. The broken line is the smooth post-edge background derived from a cubic spline fitting with five segments from 30 to 1200 eV.

Other background removal methods have been used, such as a single polynomial fit over the whole range of the data and the sliding box-car window fitting (Ref 41). However, in all these procedures, a single bad data point, noise, or end-point effects can introduce systematic errors.

EXAFS Extraction. The energy scale is converted to $\mathbf{k}$-scale using $\mathbf{k} = [0.263(E - E_0)]^{1/2}$, where E_0, the energy threshold of the absorption edge, is located experimentally by the first maximum in the derivative spectrum of the absorption curve.

The EXAFS $\chi(\mathbf{k})$ at energies above approximately 30 eV is obtained by subtracting the smooth post-edge background $\mu_0(\mathbf{k})$ from the measured absorption $\mu(\mathbf{k})$ and dividing by the step jump S at the absorption edge with the McMaster correction (Ref 17), $M(\mathbf{k})$, as a function of energy:

$$\chi(\mathbf{k}) = \frac{\mu(\mathbf{k}) - \mu_0(\mathbf{k})}{S \cdot M(\mathbf{k})} \qquad \text{(Eq 6)}$$

This procedure yields the normalized $\chi(\mathbf{k})$, which is then weighted by $\mathbf{k}$ to yield the familiar $\mathbf{k} \cdot \chi$ versus $\mathbf{k}$ plot shown in Fig. 9(b). The $\mathbf{k}$-weighting or, more generally, the $\mathbf{k}^n$-weighting will be discussed below in conjunction with Fourier analysis.

Fourier Transform to r Space. The expression for $\chi(\mathbf{k})$ (Eq 5) can be Fourier transformed to yield a radial structure function $\phi(r)$ that contains structural information on the absorbing atom. The Fourier inversion (Ref 15), a significant step in the development of modern EXAFS, converts the technique from a qualitative to a quantitative effect (Ref 37):

$$\phi(r) = (2\pi)^{-1/2} \int \chi(\mathbf{k}) \exp(2i\mathbf{k})d\mathbf{k} =$$

$$\sum_j N_j \int \frac{dr'}{r^2 T(r - r')}$$

$$\exp\left(\frac{-2(r - r'_j)^2}{\sigma_j^2}\right) \qquad \text{(Eq 7)}$$

where $\phi(r)$, the Fourier transform of the EXAFS, consists of a sum of radial peaks located at r_j and determines the spatial variation of the scattering matrix. Because in practice an EXAFS spectrum is taken over a finite energy range (hence $\mathbf{k}$-space), the Fourier transform taken is:

$$\phi(r) = (2\pi)^{-1/2} \int_{k_{min}}^{k_{max}} W(\mathbf{k})\mathbf{k}^n \chi(\mathbf{k})$$

$$\exp(2i\mathbf{k}r)d\mathbf{k} \qquad \text{(Eq 8)}$$

Table 1 Synchrotron radiation sources

Machine	Location	Energy, GeV	Current, mA	Bending radius, m	Critical energy, keV	Remarks
PETRA	Hamburg, Germany	15	50	192	39.0	Possible future use for synchrotron radiation research
PEP	Stanford, CA	15	50	165.5	45.2	Synchrotron radiation facility planned
CESR (Cornell)	Ithaca, NY	8	50	32.5	35.0	Used parasitically
VEPP-4	Novosibirsk, Soviet Union	7	10	16.5	46.1	Initial operation at 4.5 GeV
		4.5	. . .	(18.6)	(10.9)	(From 8-kG wiggler)
DORIS	Hamburg, Germany	5	50	12.1	22.9	Partly dedicated
		2.5	300	. . .	2.9	. . .
SPEAR	Stanford, CA	4.0	50	12.7	11.1	50% dedicated
		3.0	100	. . .	4.7	. . .
		3.0	. . .	(5.5)	(10.8)	(From 18-kG wiggler)
SRS	Daresbury, England	2.0	500	5.55	3.2	Dedicated
		. . .	. . .	(1.33)	(13.3)	(For 50-kG wiggler)
VEPP-3	Novosibirsk, Soviet Union	2.25	100	6.15	4.2	Partly dedicated
		. . .	. . .	(2.14)	(11.8)	(From 35-kG wiggler)
DCI	Orsay, France	1.8	500	4.0	3.63	Partly dedicated
ADONE	Frascati, Italy	1.5	60	5.0	1.5	Partly dedicated
		. . .	. . .	(2.8)	(2.7)	(From 18-kG wiggler)
VEPP-2M	Novosibirsk, Soviet Union	0.67	100	1.22	0.54	Partly dedicated
ACO	Orsay, France	0.54	100	1.1	0.32	Dedicated
SOR Ring	Tokyo, Japan	0.40	250	1.1	0.13	Dedicated
SURF II	Washington, DC	0.25	25	0.84	0.041	Dedicated
Tantalus I	Wisconsin	0.24	200	0.64	0.048	Dedicated
PTB	Braunschweig, Germany	0.14	150	0.46	0.013	Dedicated
N-100	Karkhov, Soviet Union	0.10	25	0.50	0.004	. . .
Photon factory ..	Tsukuba, Japan	2.5	500	8.33	4.16	Dedicated
		. . .	. . .	(1.67)	(20.5)	(For 50-kG wiggler)
NSLS	Brookhaven National Lab, NY	2.5	500	6.88	5.01	Dedicated
		. . .	. . .	(1.67)	(20.5)	(For 50-kG wiggler)
BESSY	West Berlin, Germany	0.80	500	1.83	0.62	Dedicated; industrial use planned
NSLS	Brookhaven National Lab, NY	0.70	500	1.90	0.40	Dedicated
ETL	Electrotechnical Lab Tsukuba, Japan	0.66	100	2	0.32	Dedicated
UVSOR	Institute of Molecular Science, Okatabi, Japan	0.60	500	2.2	0.22	Dedicated
MAX	Lund, Sweden	0.50	100	1.2	0.23	Dedicated
Kurchatov	Moscow, Soviet Union	0.45	. . .	1.0	0.21	Dedicated

where k_{max} and k_{min} are the maximum and minimum k values of the usable experimental data, and k^n is a weighting function used to compensate for amplitude reduction as a function of k (Ref 37), especially for low-Z scatterers. Values of n = 1, 2, and 3 have been suggested (Ref 52) for backscatterers with $Z > 57$, $36 < Z < 57$, and $Z < 36$, respectively. The $\chi \cdot k^1$-transform is sensitive to k_{min} between the origin and r_1, the first peak in $\phi(r)$ (Ref 50). The $\chi \cdot k^3$-transforms can be approximated to a pseudo-charge density insensitive to k_{min} and E_0. The k^3 transform weights less at low k and

more at high k, at which the EXAFS effect is better approximated by the single-scattering expression given in Eq 5, but experimentally is of poorer quality because of a poorer signal-to-noise ratio.

The factor $W(k)$ on the right-hand side of Eq 8 is a window function that when multiplied by the integrand converts the finite data set to an infinite set necessary for Fourier transform. This is accomplished by selecting functions that smoothly set the raw data points to zero at k_{min} and k_{max}. An example of $W(k)$ is a Hanning function (Ref 53) defined in terms of k:

$$W(k) = \frac{1}{2} \frac{(1 - \cos 2\pi)(k - k_{min})}{(k_{max} - k_{min})} \quad (Eq\ 9)$$

It is easily seen that $W(k) = 0$ at $k = k_{min}$ and k_{max}. This window function is applied to the first and last 5% of the normalized nickel data discussed above and plotted as $\chi \cdot k$ versus k in Fig. 9(b). The Fourier transform thus obtained is shown in Fig. 9(c). The transform is conducted relative to $\exp(2ikr)$ without including the phase shift $\delta_j(k)$. This shifts all the peaks in $\phi(r)$ closer to the origin to $r_j - \delta'$, where δ' is some average of the first derivative of $\delta_j(k)$ relative to k. In Fig. 9(c), the first peak is the nearest-neighbor position in fcc nickel shifted to 2.24 Å. The crystallographic value from diffraction is 2.492 Å, so that δ' for j = 1 is 0.25 Å.

In general, the effect of $\delta_j(k)$ on the transform can be corrected for empirically by measuring the EXAFS spectrum of a standard or model compound of known structure. As in the case of complex biomolecules, several such model compounds are used on a trial and error basis to deduce a model of the unknown structure. Alternatively, theoretical values of $\delta_j(k)$ (Ref 52) can be used in the Fourier transform, and r_j obtained directly.

Figure 9(d) shows an inverse transform of the first shell in Fig. 9(c) from 1 to 2.8 Å. This essentially isolates the EXAFS contribution due to the 12 nearest neighbors. The inverse signal in k-space can then be used to derive structural parameters by simulation.

Structural Information in k-Space. In addition to interatomic distances r_j, EXAFS contains other structural information, such as the coordination number N_j and type of jth atoms in the shell at r_j and their relative mean square disorder σ_j^2 about the average distance r_j. These structural parameters can be obtained by measuring the EXAFS of model compounds under identical conditions and using the transferability of phase shifts (Ref 54). The structure of the unknown is then modeled by curve-fitting procedures to arrive at a calculated EXAFS that best fits the experimental values. Modelling can be performed effectively in combination with back Fourier transforming, especially in systems in which the coordination shells are well separated in r-space or whose $\phi(r)$ is dominated by the nearest-neighbor shell, as in amorphous materials. The shell-by-shell back Fourier transform enables determination of a self-consistent phase shift and experimental envelope function for each jth shell. Various curve-fitting techniques for extracting structural information from EXAFS data have been prescribed (Ref 20, 42, 50, 55-57). A more widely-used procedure is described below (Ref 57).

Fig. 9 Typical EXAFS data analysis

(a) Experimental scan of nickel K-edge EXAFS in pure nickel at 90 K. The dotted line denotes a spline fit of the smooth post-edge background absorption above the absorption edge. (b) Normalized EXAFS plotted as $\chi \cdot k$ versus k, with a Hanning window applied to the first and last 5% of the k-space data. (c) Fourier transform of (b) according to Eq 8. (d) Inverse transform of the first shell in (c) from 1 to 2.8 Å

Fig. 10 Experimental (line) and simulated (points) EXAFS of the first shell of 12 neighbors from 1 to 2.8 Å about a nickel atom in fcc nickel at 90 K

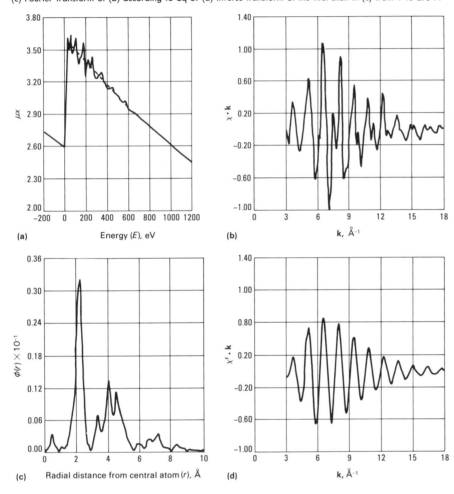

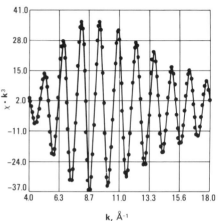

Using the single-scattering expression given in Eq 5, the observed EXAFS $\chi(\mathbf{k})$ can be described by:

$$\chi(\mathbf{k}) = \frac{-1}{\mathbf{k}} \sum_j A_j \sin \left[2r_j\mathbf{k} + \phi_j(\mathbf{k}) \right]$$

$$\text{(Eq 10)}$$

having oscillatory terms with frequencies $[2r_j\mathbf{k} + \phi_j(\mathbf{k})]$ and amplitude terms A_j given by:

$$A_j = \frac{N_j}{r_j^2} f_j (\pi,\mathbf{k})$$

$$\exp \left(\frac{-2r_j}{\lambda} \right) \exp \left(-2\sigma_j^2\mathbf{k}^2 \right) \quad \text{(Eq 11)}$$

The parameters on the right-hand side of Eq 10 and 11 can be classified as scattering parameters (phase shift $\phi_j(\mathbf{k})$, backscattering

amplitude $f_j(\pi,\mathbf{k})$, and mean free path λ) and structural parameters (coordination number N_j, bond distance r_j, and Debye-Waller factor σ_j). The summation is over all coordination shells j participating in the EXAFS event. In a model system for which N_j and r_j are known crystallographically, EXAFS can be used to generate a set of self-consistent scattering parameters; this information can then be applied to an unknown system of similar chemical nature, for example, a glass of the same composition, to determine structural parameters.

A least squares procedure (Ref 57) is set up to minimize the variance S:

$$S = \sum_i^n (\chi_i^F - \chi_i)^2 \quad \text{(Eq 12)}$$

where χ_i^F represents the Fourier-filtered experimental data, and χ_i is the analytical

expression given in Eq 10 that describes χ_i^F for n data points. Because $\chi(\mathbf{k})$ is not a linear function of the various parameters, a Taylor series expansion is used that expresses $\chi(\mathbf{k})$ in terms of approximate parameter values, P_j, and parameter adjustments, $\Delta P_j = P_j - P_j'$. Applying the least squares condition yields a set of simultaneous equations in terms of ΔP_j rather than P_j. The equations are solved for the adjustment, ΔP_j, and the parameters were adjusted by ΔP_j to provide a new set of estimates. The procedure was then repeated with the new estimates P_j' and so on until the new solution differed from the last by less than a desired value, usually 1%.

The phase and envelope function for the nickel-nickel pair (Ref 58) is generated by performing a self-fitting of the filtered EXAFS (Fig. 9d) of the first shell of 12 nearest neighbors in fcc nickel with the following fixed inputs: $N_1 = 12$, $r_1 = 2.492$ Å, $\Delta E_0 = 0$, and $\sigma_1^2 = 0$. The fitting was performed in $\chi \cdot \mathbf{k}^3$ space to weigh the contribution of nickel at high $\mathbf{k}$. The results are shown in Fig. 10; the curve denotes the filtered experimental EXAFS, and the points denote the simulated spectrum. This simulation has a standard deviation of 5% of the maximum amplitude of the experimental $\chi^F \cdot \mathbf{k}^3$ spectrum. The nickel-nickel phase parameters thus obtained can then be used as initial inputs to simulate the filtered transform arising from the nickel-nickel subshells in crystalline Ni_2B. The nickel-nickel phase shifts as derived from crystalline Ni_2B have in turn been transferred directly to determine nickel-nickel bond distances and coordination numbers of the various subshells in amorphous Ni_2B. Details of such systematic simulations are cited in Ref 58 to 60.

Near-Edge Structure

In EXAFS analysis for structural determination, the data within approximately 30 eV of the absorption edge are generally ignored because their interpretation is complicated by multiple scattering and chemical bonding effects. Phenomenologically, as the region near an x-ray absorption edge is scanned in energy, the ejected photoelectron probes the empty electronic levels of the material sequentially. The resulting XANES (Ref 23) spectrum within 30 eV of threshold has been realized to be rich in chemical information and is receiving increasing attention. Although the study of XANES has a long history (Ref 61), these spectra can now be measured more quickly and simply and with greater resolution due to the availability of intense and well-collimated synchrotron x-ray sources and improved experimentation.

Vanadium forms a series of oxides over a range of formal oxidation states. The crystal structures of VO, V_2O_3, V_4O_7, V_2O_4, and V_2O_5 are known. These oxides provide a useful series of materials for systematic study of the effects of valence-site symmetry and coordination geometry on the XANES spectrum of the central metal atom coordinated by the same ligand (Ref 62).

The NaCl structure of VO has regular octahedral VO_6 units. In the corundum structure of V_2O_3, V^{3+} ions are six-fold coordinated by oxygen ions at two distinct distances 1.96 Å and 2.06 Å. A mixed-valence oxide, V_4O_7 consists of V^{3+} and V^{4+} ions. The structure consists of a distorted hexagonal close-packed (hcp) oxygen array with vanadium atoms occupying the octahedral sites (distorted) to form rutile blocks extending indefinitely in the triclinic a-b plane. The rutile blocks are four octahedra thick along the perpendicular to this plane. There are four crystallographic nonequivalent vanadium sites with V-O distances 1.883 to 2.101 Å. The crystal structure of V_2O_4 is monoclinic and is a distorted form of rutile. The vanadium atoms are again six-fold coordinated by oxygens, but are much displaced from the center of the octahedron, resulting in a short V-O bond of 1.76 Å. In V_2O_5, the vanadium is five-fold coordinated in a distorted tetragonal pyramid of oxygen. The apex oxygen distance is only 1.585 Å, but the basal V-O distances vary from 1.78 to 2.02 Å. The site symmetry of the vanadium atom decreases from O_h to VO to C_3 in V_2O_3, C_1 in V_4O_7 and V_2O_4, and C_s in V_2O_5.

The vanadium K-edge XANES spectra in these oxides (Fig. 11) exhibit a pre-edge absorption feature that grows in intensity from V_2O_3 to V_2O_5, followed by a weak shoulder on a rising absorption curve (the absorption edge) that culminates in a strong peak near approximately 20 eV. This strong peak has been assigned as the allowed transition $1s \rightarrow 4p$ (Ref 63), the lower energy shoulder as the $1s \rightarrow 4p$ shakedown transition, and the pre-edge feature at threshold as the forbidden transition $1s \rightarrow 3d$ (Ref 63). At energies equal to and above the $1s \rightarrow 4p$ transition, absorption features may arise from transition to higher np states, shape resonances (Ref 64), and/or multiple scattering (Ref 65). The latter two effects are much more complicated to analyze.

Because the initial $1s$ state is a ground state, the $1s \rightarrow 3d$ transition is strictly dipole forbidden, as it is for VO, which contains regular octahedral VO_6 units having a center of inversion. When the symmetry of the ligands is lowered from O_h, the inversion center is broken, as in V_2O_3, V_4O_7, and V_2O_4 with distorted octahedral VO_6 groups and in V_2O_5 with distorted square pyramidal VO_5 groups. The pre-edge absorption becomes dipole allowed due to a combination of stronger $3d$-$4p$ mixing and overlap of the metal $3d$ orbitals with the $2p$ orbitals of the ligand (Ref 63).

The intensity variation of the pre-edge peak across the oxide series is noteworthy. As shown in Fig. 12, the oscillator strength increases with progressive relaxation from perfect octahedral symmetry, as in VO, to distorted octahedral VO_6 groups, as in V_2O_3, V_4O_7, and V_2O_4, and to a lower coordination with a short V-O bond in a square pyramidal symmetry, as in V_2O_5. The molecular-cage effect on the oscillator

Fig. 11 The vanadium K-edge XANES spectra of a series of vanadium oxides

The zero of energy is taken at the K-edge of vanadium metal at 5465 eV in all cases.

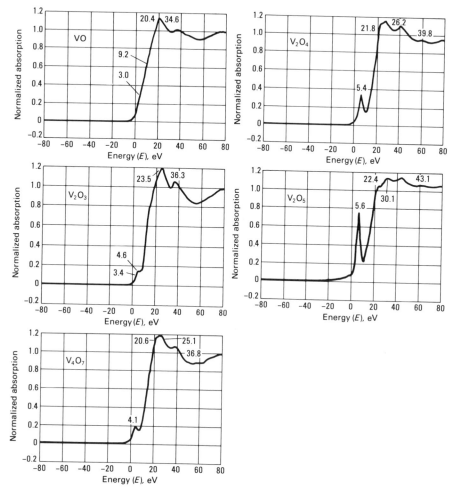

strength of this transition to the 3d orbitals in K-edge spectra (Ref 66) appears to be operative in this case.

Closer examination of the V_2O_3 spectrum reveals a multiplet structure in the pre-edge peak region. The multiplet structure exhibits splitting of approximately 1.3 and 2.0 eV. The splitting in the $1s \rightarrow 3d$ transition is caused by crystal-field splitting of the ground state (Ref 65), and in the case of V_2O_3, the d levels of V^{3+} ions in C_3 sites are split into $A + 2E$ symmetries.

The energy positions of various absorption features correlate with the oxidation state (formal valency) of vanadium in the oxides. With increases in oxidation state, the absorption threshold as defined by the position of the first peak in the derivative spectrum, the absorption edge as defined by the second peak in the derivative curve, the energy of the pre-edge peak, and the $1s \rightarrow 4p$ transition above the absorption edge shift to higher energies. The energy shifts, or chemical shifts, follow Kunzl's law (Ref 67) and vary linearly with the valence of the absorbing vanadium atoms (Fig. 12). The positive shift in the threshold energy with valence increase can be understood conceptually to be due to an increase in the attractive potential of the nucleus on the 1s course electron and a reduction in the repulsive core Coulomb interaction with all the other electrons in the compound.

The lines shown in Fig. 12 are least squares fitted lines with slopes of 1.4, 1.1, 2.5, and 3.2 eV per valence increase for the threshold, the pre-edge peak, the absorption edge, and the $1s \rightarrow 4p$ transition, respectively. The increase in slope reflects tighter binding of the inner 3d and 4s levels relative to the outermost 4p levels, which are more easily perturbed by valence change.

Unique Features of EXAFS

Figure 13(a) shows the EXAFS above the K-edges of iron and nickel in a bcc iron-nickel alloy containing 80 at.% Fe. These were obtained in one experimental scan by tuning the synchrotron radiation near the K-absorption edge of iron at 7.11 keV, scanning the iron EXAFS over a 1000-V range, and continuing scanning another 1000 eV beyond the nickel K-edge to obtain its EXAFS. Iron and nickel are separated by two units in atomic number, yet their K-absorption edges are far apart in energy so the EXAFS of iron is not overlapped by the onset of the K-absorption of nickel. Therefore, structural information extracted from analyzing each EXAFS spectrum is atom specific in that the central atom is defined;

Fig. 12 Oxidation state versus energy positions of various absorption features in the vanadium K-edge XANES spectra of various vanadium oxides shown in Fig. 11

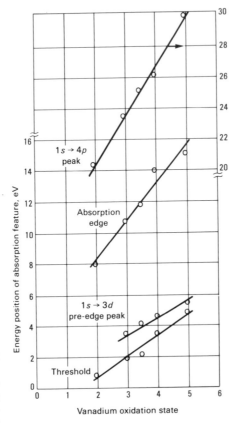

consequently the origin of each of the $\phi(r)$ is known. This demonstrates the atomic selectivity of EXAFS for studying multiatomic systems.

Using the data-reduction procedure described above in the section "Data Analysis" in this article, the normalized EXAFS for nickel is obtained and plotted as $\chi \cdot k$ versus k (Fig. 13b). This is then Fourier transformed relative to $\exp(2ikr)$ to obtain $\phi(r)$ (Fig. 13c). The Fourier transform is dominated essentially by a strong radial structure peak above 2 Å. Higher coordination shells are also visible to 5 to 6 Å. The oscillations in the low-r side of the first peak are due to termination errors of the transform and are not structural in origin. The transform shown in Fig. 9(c) for pure nickel, which is fcc and has 12 nearest neighbors, differs significantly from the transform pattern shown in Fig. 13(c) for nickel in the bcc iron-nickel alloy. The latter is characteristic of a bcc structure such as iron, which has eight nearest neighbors (Ref 41). This is also

Fig. 13 bcc iron-nickel alloy containing 80 at.% Fe

(a) Experimental EXAFS spectra above the K-edges of iron and nickel. (b) Normalized EXAFS plotted as $\chi \cdot k$ versus k for the EXAFS. (c) Fourier transform of (b). The peaks on the low-r side of the first main peak at 2.2 Å are spurious effects of the transform and therefore nonphysical. This radial structure function for nickel in a bcc environment differs from that for pure fcc nickel shown in Fig. 9(c).

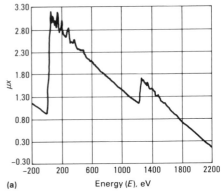

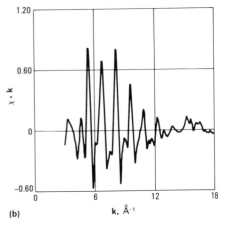

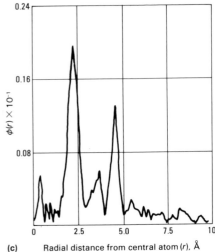

Fig. 14 Normalized nickel K-edge EXAFS plotted as $\chi \cdot k$ versus k and corresponding Fourier transform

(a) Nickel impurity in synthetic diamond. (b) fcc nickel. (c) Ni_3B. r is the radial distance (phase shift not included) from a central x-ray absorbing nickel atom.

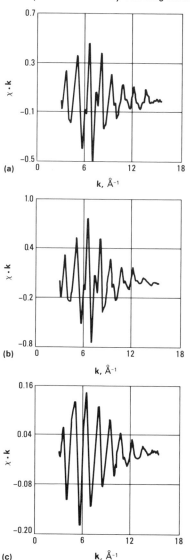

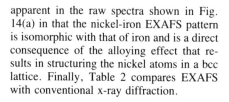

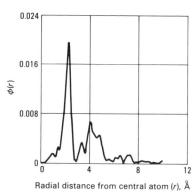

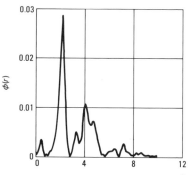

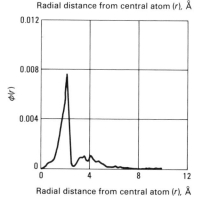

Table 2 Comparison of EXAFS and x-ray diffraction

	EXAFS	X-ray diffraction
r-space range	Short, because $\chi(k) \sim 1/r^2$ and $\lambda \leq 10$ Å	Long
k-space range	$0 < k < 50$ Å^{-1}	$0 \leq q \leq 25$ Å^{-1}
Selectivity	Atom specific	All atoms diffract
N_j	$\pm 10\%$	$\pm 1\%$ or better
r_j	± 0.02 Å for first shell; ± 0.1 Å for second shell	0.001
σ_j	Two-body average	One-body average
ϕ_j	Contains phase information	No phase
Material systems	All states of matter, bulk and dilute	Crystalline solids, bulk

apparent in the raw spectra shown in Fig. 14(a) in that the nickel-iron EXAFS pattern is isomorphic with that of iron and is a direct consequence of the alloying effect that results in structuring the nickel atoms in a bcc lattice. Finally, Table 2 compares EXAFS with conventional x-ray diffraction.

Applications

Application of EXAFS to various materials characterization problems is rapidly evolving. The most fully developed applications are in disordered systems, catalysis, and biology. As the technique extends to other materials, whether in different states or

configurations, new detection techniques develop to enable more efficient extraction of the EXAFS signal in terms of signal-to-noise ratio. General information on EXAFS is cited in Ref 40, 42; EXAFS as applied to Biology, Ref 38, 68; catalysts, Ref 69; amorphous materials, Ref 41, 70, 71; and Geology, Ref 72.

Characterization of Metal Impurities in Synthetic Diamond. Characterization of metal impurities incorporated in synthetic diamond crystals during growth at high temperature and high pressure illustrates use of EXAFS as a phase identification tool (like powder x-ray diffractometry) (Ref 73). In Fig. 14(a), the room temperature nickel K-edge EXAFS from the nickel im-

purity in synthetic diamond is plotted as $\chi \cdot k$ versus k. The corresponding Fourier transform, shown on the right hand side, is plotted as $\phi(r)$ versus r, where r is radial distance from the central atom. The corresponding results for nickel and Ni_3B are shown in parts (b) and (c) of Fig. 14. The spectrum of nickel in the synthetic diamond is directly identifiable as that of pure nickel, which yields a radial structure function (right-hand side of Fig. 14b) characteristic of the fcc structure and consists of four resolved peaks associated with the first four coordination shells about the central atom (compare with Fig. 9 for nickel at 90 K). Like Ni_3C, Ni_3B has a cementite structure (Schoenflies symbol V_h^{16}; Hermann-Mauguin space group *Pbnm*; 4 molecules per unit cell) (Ref 74). There are two nonequivalent nickel sites: Ni(I) has 11 nickel neighbors at distances from 2.43 to 2.74 Å, two boron atoms at approximately 2.0 Å and one boron at 2.30 Å; Ni(II) has 12 nickel atoms at distances from 2.50 to 2.79 Å, two boron atoms at 2.05 Å and one at 2.60 Å. The nickel EXAFS in Ni_3B shown in Fig. 14(c) differs from that found in the synthetic diamond. The Fourier transform shown on the right-hand side of Fig. 14(c) consists basically of a radial peak centered at approximately 2 Å, which is rather broad, reflective of the distribution of nickel-nickel distances in the structure. No dominant features are evident beyond 3 Å in the radial structure function. Thus, EXAFS can be used to fingerprint an unknown phase containing a selectively known constituent element.

Other Detection Techniques. The modern EXAFS technique has been built on two major milestones in 1970. The first is elucidation of the basic physics of the phenomenon in terms of the single scattering formalism and Fourier transform of the ex-

Table 3 Other EXAFS detection techniques

Detection technique	Year	Remarks
Fluorescence	1977	Uses fluorescent x-ray photons to monitor μx of dilute species
Surface EXAFS	1978	Uses Auger electrons to monitor μx of surface atoms
Dispersive	1982	Rapid scan for kinetic studies
Double fluorescence ..	1983	For heavy impurities in slightly lower Z matrix
Reflection EXAFS	1984	Probes buried interfaces
Electron detection	1984	Applicable for use at atmospheric pressure, avoiding ultrahigh vacuum conditions

perimental signal to yield quantitative structural information (Ref 15); second is availability of intense well-collimated synchrotron radiation in the x-ray region (Ref 26) as a light source for high quality and fast acquisition of experimental spectra. Several detection techniques have since been developed to explore application of EXAFS to other materials in various states and configurations not amenable to conventional transmission measurement. These techniques include electron detection in ultrahigh vacuum for surface structure studies (of adsorbates) (Ref 75), fluorescence for dilute systems (biomolecules) and trace impurities (Ref 33), dispersive EXAFS for kinetic studies under-a-minute time scale (Ref 76, 77), double fluorescence for discriminating dilute impurities in a slightly lower Z matrix (Ref 78), reflection EXAFS for subsurface (buried interface) characterization (Ref 79), and electron detection in nonvacuum condition (Ref 80). Table 3 summarizes each technique and outlines its application.

REFERENCES

1. F.W. Lytle, in *Physics of Non-Crystalline Solids*, J.A. Prins, Ed., North-Holland, 1965, p 12-25
2. H. Fricke, *Phys. Rev.*, Vol 16, 1920, p 202
3. G. Hertz, *Z. Phys.*, Vol 21, 1920, p 630; Vol 3, 1920, p 19
4. R. De L. Kronig, *Z. Phys.*, Vol 70, 1921, p 317; Vol 75, 1932, p 191
5. T. Hayashi, *Sci. Rep. Tohoku Univ.*, Vol 33, 1949, p 123, 183
6. L.V. Azaroff, *Rev. Mod. Phys.*, Vol 35, 1963, p 1012

7. E.A. Stern, *Phys. Rev. B*, Vol 10, 1974, p 3027
8. J.D. Hanawalt, *Phys. Rev.*, Vol 37, 1931, p 715
9. B.M. Kincaid and P. Eisenberger, *Phys. Rev. Lett.*, Vol 34, 1975, p 1361
10. B.M. Kincaid, Ph.D. thesis, Stanford University, Stanford, CA, 1975
11. R.A. Van Ordstrand, in *Non-Crystalline Solids*, V.D. Frechette, Ed., John Wiley & Sons, 1960, p 108
12. W.F. Nelson, I. Siegel, and R.W. Wagner, *Phys. Rev.*, Vol 127, 1962, p 2025
13. F.W. Lytle, D.E. Sayers, and E.A. Stern, in *Advances in X-ray Spectroscopy*, C. Bonnelle and C. Mande, Ed., Pergamon Press, 1982, p 267
14. D.E. Sayers, F.W. Lytle, and E.A. Stern, *Adv. X-ray Anal.*, Vol 13, 1970, p 248
15. D.E. Sayers, E.A. Stern, and F.W. Lytle, *Phys. Rev. Lett.*, Vol 27, 1971, p 1204
16. H. Bethe and E. Salpeter, *Quantum Mechanics of One- and Two-electron Systems*, Springer Verlag, 1959
17. W.H. McMaster, N. Nerr del Grande, J.H. Mallett, and J.H. Hubbell, "Compilation of X-ray Cross Sections," Report UCRL-50/74, Sec. 2, Rev. 1, Lawrence Radiation Laboratory, Berkeley, 1969
18. C.A. Ashley and S. Doniach, *Phys. Rev. B*, Vol 11, 1975, p 1279
19. P.A. Lee and J.B. Pendry, *Phys. Rev. B*, Vol 11, 1975, p 2795
20. P.A. Lee and G. Beni, *Phys. Rev. B*, Vol 15, 1977, p 2862
21. R.F. Pettifer and P.W. McMillan, *Philos. Mag.*, Vol 35, 1977, p 871
22. F. Jona, *Surf. Sci.*, Vol 68, 1977, p 204
23. A. Bianconi, *Appl. Surf. Sci.*, Vol 6, 1980, p 392
24. B.K. Teo, *J. Am. Chem. Soc.*, Vol 103, 1981, p 3390
25. B. Lengeler, *Phys. Rev. Lett.*, Vol 53, 1984, p 74
26. A.D. Baer, R. Gaxiola, A. Golde, F. Johnson, B. Salsburg, H. Winick, M. Baldwin, N. Dean, J. Harris, E. Hoyt, B. Humphrey, J. Jurow, R. Melen, J. Miljan, and G. Warren, *IEEE Trans. Nucl. Sci.*, NS-22, 1975, p 1794; S. Doniach, I. Lindau, W.R. Spicer, and H. Winick, *J. Vac. Sci. Technol.*, Vol 12, 1975, p 1123
27. J. Schwinger, *Phys. Rev.*, Vol 75, 1949, p 1912
28. H. Winick, in *Synchrotron Radiation Research*, H. Winick and S. Doniach, Ed., Plenum Press, 1980, p 11
29. F.R. Elder, R.V. Langmuir, and H.D. Pollock, *Phys. Rev.*, Vol 74, 1948, p 52

30. H.C. Pollock, *Am. J. Phys.*, Vol 51 (No. 3), 1983, p 278
31. R.F. Pettifer, Ph.D. thesis, University of Warick, U.K., unpublished, 1978
32. S.H. Hunter, Ph.D. thesis, Stanford University, Stanford, CA, unpublished, 1977
33. J. Jaklevic, J.A. Kirby, M.P. Klein, A.S. Robertson, G.S. Brown, and P. Eisenberger, *Solid State Commun.*, Vol 23, 1977, p 679
34. E.A. Stern and S.M. Heald, *Rev. Sci. Instrum.*, Vol 50 (No. 12), 1979, p 1579
35. J.B. Hasting, P. Eisenberger, B. Lengeler, and M.C. Perlman, *Phys. Rev. Lett.*, Vol 43, 1979, p 1807
36. M. Marcus, L.S. Powers, A.R. Storm, B.M. Kincaid, and B. Chance, *Rev. Sci. Instrum.*, Vol 51, 1980, p 1023
37. F.W. Lytle, D.E. Sayers, and E.A. Stern, *Phys. Rev. B*, Vol 11, 1975, p 4825
38. S.P. Cramer and K.O. Hodgson, *Prog. Inorg. Chem.*, Vol 25, 1979, p 1
39. G.S. Brown, in *Synchrotron Radiation Research*, H. Winick and S. Doniach, Ed., Plenum Press, 1980
40. P.A. Lee, P.H. Citrin, P. Eisenberger, and B.M. Kincaid, *Rev. Mod. Phys.*, Vol 53 (No. 4), 1981, p 769
41. J. Wong, in *Topics in Applied Physics*, Vol 46, H-J. Guntherodt and H. Beck, Ed., Springer-Verlag, 1981
42. T.M. Hayes and J.B. Boyce, *Solid State Phys.*, Vol 37, 1982, p 173
43. E.A. Stern and S.M. Heald, in *Handbook on Synchrotron Radiation*, Vol 1, E.E. Koch, Ed., North-Holland, 1983
44. A.L. Robinson, *Science*, Vol 205, 1979, p 1367
45. G.S. Knapp, H. Chen, and T.E. Klippert, *Rev. Sci. Instrum.*, Vol 49, 1978, p 1658
46. G.G. Cohen, D.A. Fischer, J. Colbert, and N.J. Shevchik, *Rev. Sci. Instrum.*, Vol 51 (No. 3), 1980, p 273
47. A. Williams, *Rev. Sci. Instrum.*, Vol 54 (No. 2), 1983, p 193
48. W. Thulke, R. Haensel, and P. Rabe, *Rev. Sci. Instrum.*, Vol 54 (No. 3), 1983, p 277
49. H. Winick, in *Synchrotron Radiation Research*, H. Winick and S. Doniach, Ed., Plenum Press, 1980
50. E.A. Stern, D.E. Sayers, and F.W. Lytle, *Phys. Rev. B*, Vol 11, 1975, p 4836
51. B. Lengeler and P. Eisenberger, *Phys. Rev. B*, Vol 21, 1980, p 4507
52. B.K. Teo and P.A. Lee, *J. Am. Chem. Soc.*, Vol 101, 1979, p 2815

53. C. Bingham, M.D. Godfrey, and J.W. Turkey, *IEEE Trans.*, Vol Aug-15 (No. 2), 1967, p 58
54. P.H. Citrin, P. Eisenberger, and B.M. Kincaid, *Phys. Rev. Lett.*, Vol 36, 1976, p 1346
55. B.K. Teo, P. Eisenberger, J. Reed, J.K. Barton, and S.J. Lippard, *J. Am. Chem. Soc.*, Vol 100, 1978, p 3225
56. S.P. Cramer, K.O. Hodgson, E.I. Stiefel, and W.R. Newton, *J. Am. Chem. Soc.*, Vol 100, 1978, p 2748
57. G.H. Via, J.H. Sinfelt, and F.W. Lytle, *J. Chem. Phys.*, Vol 71, 1979, p 690
58. J. Wong and H.H. Lieberman, *Phys. Rev. B*, Vol 29, 1984, p 651
59. K.J. Rao, J. Wong, and M.J. Weber, *J. Chem. Phys.*, Vol 78, 1983, p 6228
60. J.H. Sinfelt, G.H. Via, and F.W. Lytle, *J. Chem. Phys.*, Vol 72, 1980, p 4832
61. M.C. Srivastava and H.L. Nigam, *Coord. Chem. Rev.*, Vol 9, 1972, p 275
62. J. Wong, F.W. Lytle, R.P. Messmer, and D.H. Maylotte, *Phys. Rev. B*, Vol 30, 1984, p 5596
63. R.G. Shulman, Y. Yafet, P. Eisenberger, and W.E. Blumberg, *Proc. Nat. Acad. Sci.*, Vol 13, 1976, p 1384
64. J.L. Dehmer, *J. Chem. Phys.*, Vol 56, 1972, p 4496
65. P.J. Durham, J.B. Pendry, and C.H. Hodges, *Solid State Commun.*, Vol 38, 1981, p 159
66. F.W. Kutzler, C.R. Natoli, D.K. Misemer, S. Doniad, and K.O. Hodgson, *J. Chem. Phys.*, Vol 73, 1980, p 3274
67. V. Kunzl, *Collect. Trav. Cjim. Techecolovaquie*, Vol 4, 1932, p 213
68. S. Doniach, P. Eisenberger, and K.O. Hodgson, in *Synchrotron Radiation Research*, H. Winich and S. Doniach, Ed., Plenum Press, 1980, p 425-458
69. F.W. Lytle, G.H. Via, and J.H. Sinfelt, in *Synchrotron Radiation Research*, H. Winich and S. Doniach, Ed., Plenum Press, 1981, p 401-424
70. S.J. Gurman, *J. Mater. Sci.*, Vol 17, 1982, p 1541
71. S.J. Gurman, in *Extended X-ray Absorption Fine Structure*, R.W. Joyner, Ed., Plenum Press, 1985
72. K.O. Hodgson, B. Hedman, and J.E. Penner-Hahn, Ed., *Part VII: Geology and Geochemistry of EXAFS and Near-Edge Structure III*, Spring-Verlag, 1984, p 336-390
73. J. Wong, E.F. Koch, C.I. Hejna, and M.F. Garbauskas, *J. Appl. Phys.*, Vol 58, 1985, p 3388
74. S. Rundquist, *Acta. Chem. Scand.*, Vol 12, 1958, p 658
75. P.H. Citrin, P. Eisenberger, and R.C. Hewitt, *Phys. Rev. Lett.*, Vol 41, 1978, p 309
76. A.M. Flank, A. Fontain, A. Jucha, M. Lommnier, and C. Williams, *J. Phys. Lett.*, Vol 43, 1982, p L315
77. R.P. Phizackerley, Z.U. Rek, G.B. Stephenson, S.D. Conradson, K.O. Hodgson, T. Matsushita, and H. Oyanagi, *J. Appl. Crystallog.*, Vol 16, 1983, p 220
78. J. Wong and K.J. Rao, *Solid State Commun.*, Vol 45 (No. 9), 1983, p 853
79. S.M. Heald, E. Keller, and E.A. Stern, *Phys. Lett.*, Vol 103A, 1984, p 155
80. M.E. Kordeseh and R.W. Hoffman, *Phys. Rev. B*, Vol 29, 1984, p 491

Neutron Diffraction

W.B. Yelon and F.K. Ross, University of Missouri Research Reactor
A.D. Krawitz, Department of Mechanical and Aerospace Engineering, University of Missouri—Columbia

General Uses

- Determination of atomic arrangements (for example, crystal structure, short- and long-range order), especially for structures containing light (low atomic number) atoms in the presence of heavier atoms or neighboring elements
- Determination of magnetic structures
- Determination of structural changes as a function of temperature, pressure, magnetic field, etc.
- Quantitative analysis of multiphase materials
- Determination of residual stress and texture in polycrystalline engineering materials

Examples of Applications

- Location of hydrogen atoms in organometallic compounds or hydrogen-containing intermetallic compounds
- Observation of site preference for metals in intermetallic compounds
- Observation of ferri-, ferro-, antiferro-, or complex magnetic ordering
- Observation of phase transitions
- Refinement of structural parameters and phase fractions in mixed catalyst systems
- Determination of three-dimensional residual and applied stress tensors as a function of depth in engineering materials
- Study of grain interaction stresses in composites and hexagonal metals
- Quantitative measurement of texture and texture gradients
- Determination of radial distribution functions in liquid and amorphous materials

Samples

- *Form*: Polycrystalline solids, powders, single crystals, amorphous solids, liquids
- *Size*: 1 to 10 cm^3 for powder structure determination, single crystals of 0.5 to several hundred mm^3. Low absorption allows large samples of powders, liquids, and amorphous solids (for radial distribution function studies), typically 1 to 50 g
- *Preparation*: Minimal preparation necessary; insensitive to sample geometry; often tall, narrow specimens desirable (5 $\times$ 0.2 cm)

Limitations

- Relatively low intensity, which may require large sample volumes and/or long counting times
- Strong absorbers (Gd, Cd, Sm, Li, B) must be avoided or kept at low concentrations
- X-ray studies usually must precede neutron diffraction analysis for structure modeling
- Substitution of deuterium for hydrogen may be necessary to reduce incoherent scattering contributions to backgrounds
- In the U.S., only seven centers provide neutron beams of sufficient strength for scattering research; worldwide, about 30 centers are active in neutron scattering

Estimated Analysis Time

- *Acquisition*: Typically 12 h for powder diffraction with optimized instrumentation; days to weeks for single-crystal and texture studies
- *Analysis*: Time is highly variable. Rietveld and single-crystal studies require hours to days to weeks

Capabilities of Related Techniques

- *X-ray diffraction*: Highly complementary but most sensitive to heavy elements, insensitive to magnetism. X-ray diffraction primarily a near-surface probe compared with bulk penetration by neutrons

Introduction

The thermal neutron is a unique probe of condensed matter whose utility has been demonstrated in a wide variety of applications. There are numerous aspects that make neutron scattering a valuable tool in materials science.

First, the scattering factor of nuclei for neutrons varies randomly across the periodic table (see Table 1). Consequently, contrast between nearby elements in the periodic chart may be extremely good, and "light" atoms are almost always observable even in the presence of "very heavy" atoms, which would dominate in x-ray or electron scattering. The range of scattering amplitude for neutrons varies only by a factor of approximately 4 (with a few exceptions) compared to a factor of nearly 100 between hydrogen and uranium for x-rays. Thus, the neutron scattering length, b, for hydrogen ($b_H = -0.374 \times 10^{-12}$ cm) is a significant contributor in a neutron diffraction study of Ta_2H (Ref 1), where $b_{Ta} = 0.691 \times 10^{-12}$ cm, but produces almost no measurable diffraction contribution for x-rays. Of particular importance for neutrons is the difference in scattering for isotopes of the same element, because this permits scattering patterns to vary without changes in chemistry. This allows the extraction of partial scattering factors for each element, which is particularly useful for studying amorphous materials, but also has applications in crystalline systems. Some of the most important isotope effects are those for hydrogen ($b_H = -0.37 \times 10^{-12}$ cm, $b_D = +0.67 \times 10^{-12}$ cm), chlorine ($b_{35Cl} = 1.17 \times 10^{-12}$ cm, $b_{37Cl} = 0.31 \times 10^{-12}$ cm), and nickel ($b_{58Ni} = 1.44 \times 10^{-12}$ cm, $b_{60Ni} = 0.28 \times 10^{-12}$ cm), but many other elements show significant (if smaller) effects with isotopic substitution.

Second, the neutron possesses a magnetic moment and interacts with the magnetic fields present within the condensed phase. It is the most direct probe of magnetic ordering in solids. Although recent x-ray studies at synchrotrons have demonstrated some potential for x-ray studies of magnetic ordering, almost all known magnetic structures have been determined by neutron diffraction.

Third, the form factor is essentially constant with diffraction angle, unlike those for x-ray or electron diffraction. Fourth, the neutron is an uncharged particle that interacts weakly with matter. The resulting high penetrability in most materials enables excellent volume sampling, insensitivity to surface condition, the possibility of depth profiling, and ease of measurement in special environments, for example, high-temperature furnaces, low-temperature cryostats, and high-pressure cells. In fact, the mass absorption coefficient $\mu/\rho < 1$ cm^{-1} for all but seven naturally occurring elements (lithium, boron, cadmium, samarium, europium, gadolinium, and dysprosium), and in all cases, weakly absorbing isotopes can be found to substitute for these when needed. Linear absorption coefficients and thicknesses required to absorb 50% of a thermal neutron beam for a variety of elements are listed in Table 1. Corresponding values for CuKα x-rays are also included.

Fifth, peak shapes from steady-state neutron sources (reactors) are essentially Gaussian, and no complications due to the Kα_1, Kα_2 doublet are present as for x-rays. This makes peak fitting simpler and more accurate than in the x-ray case. The situation is more complicated for the spectrum of neutrons necessary for measurements made at pulsed neutron sources.

Finally, the neutron energy and wavelength simultaneously match characteristic phonon energies and interatomic distances.

In contrast, x-rays or electrons with comparable wavelengths have energies orders of magnitude higher (10^6 and 10^3, respectively), while inelastic photon scattering (Raman or infrared) uses sources with wavelengths very poorly matched to the interatomic distances in solids. Thus, neutrons are a principal tool for the study of lattice vibrational spectra in materials.

Neutron Production

Although various methods of neutron production exist, only two produce sufficient intensity to be useful in neutron scattering research: fission (of ^{235}U or ^{239}Pu) and spallation.

The fission process occurring in high flux reactors produces approximately two neutrons per fission, and one of these is absorbed to induce a subsequent fission event. The fission neutrons with ~14-MeV energy are slowed by collisions with the moderator (typically H_2O or D_2O) and diffuse outward from the reactor core. For a room-temperature moderator, the Maxwellian distribution of neutron energy peaks at about 60 meV (1.2 Å). The neutrons are transported from the reactor core to the experiment in evacuated or helium-filled beam tubes. Alternate high-temperature (hot source) or low-temperature (cold source) moderators can be placed in front of the beam tube near the reactor core. These shift the peak in the neutron spectrum to higher or lower energies, respectively. Neutron scattering at steady-state sources is most commonly performed with monochromatic beams and continuous data collection, although polychromatic beam methods can be carried out using choppers to pulse the beam, allowing time-of-flight to differentiate the neutron energy spectrum.

In spallation neutron sources, high-energy protons (~500 to 800 meV) collide with a heavy metal target, producing approximately 5 to 30 neutrons per proton. These are moderated in a fashion similar to that of steady-state reactors. However, the proton beam is normally pulsed, leading to pulsed neutron production, and experiments are most commonly performed in the time-of-flight mode with polychromatic beams impinging on the sample, separated in energy by the arrival time. One further notable difference between reactor and spallation neutron production is the relative richness in intermediate energy (~1 to 100 eV) neutrons for the latter method, leading to special applications utilizing these higher fluxes.

Table 1   Comparison of neutron and x-ray scattering and absorption characteristics(a)

Element	Neutrons b, 10^{-12} cm	μ, cm^{-1}	$t_{50\%}$, cm	X-rays f, 10^{-12} cm	μ, cm^{-1}	$t_{50\%}$, cm
$C_{Graphite}$	0.66	0.62	1.11	1.69	9.6	0.72×10^{-1}
Al	0.35	0.10	7.05	5.69	131	0.53×10^{-2}
Ti	−0.34	0.45	1.55	9.12	938	0.74×10^{-3}
V	−0.05	0.56	1.25	9.63	1356	0.51×10^{-3}
Cr	0.35	0.47	1.47	10.1	1814	0.38×10^{-3}
Fe	0.96	1.12	0.62	11.5	2424	0.29×10^{-3}
Co	0.25	2.40	0.29	12.2	2980	0.23×10^{-3}
Ni	1.03	1.86	0.37	12.9	407	0.17×10^{-2}
Mo	0.69	0.48	1.44	21.6	1618	0.43×10^{-3}
W	0.47	1.05	0.66	42.3	3311	0.21×10^{-3}

Note: b is the neutron scattering length; μ is the linear absorption coefficient; $t_{50\%}$ represents the thickness required to absorb 50% of a thermal neutron beam; and f is the x-ray form factor.
(a) X-ray f and μ values calculated for CuKα at sin $\theta/\lambda = 0.5$.

Neutron Powder Diffraction

The fundamental equations governing neutron powder diffraction are essentially the same as for x-rays, except that the neutron scattering length b replaces the x-ray form factor f. Furthermore, neutrons produced in reactors or pulsed neutron sources are most prevalent at nearly the same wavelength as copper x-rays; consequently, powder diffraction is observed at roughly the same angles and over the same range of d-spacings as with x-rays. For the reasons cited in the introduction to this article, neutron powder diffraction data have been more amenable to reliable analysis of intensities for the extraction of structural information than x-ray data.

Instrumentation. Neutron powder diffraction is carried out in either of two modes: (1) a fixed-wavelength mode in which the scattering is observed as a function of the angle 2θ or (2) a fixed-angle mode with the scattering observed as a function of the wavelength λ. In principle, either method can be used with steady-state or pulsed neutron sources; in fact, however, constant-wavelength data is the preferred method at the former, while constant-angle data are collected in the time-of-flight mode at pulsed neutron sources. For reactors, data are generally collected in a Debye-Scherrer geometry with a highly collimated, monochromatic beam impinging on the sample from a Bragg reflecting monochromator crystal.

Two different detection schemes are commonly employed. The first, the multidetector method (see Fig. 1), uses Soller slit collimators to define the scattered angle and can utilize large samples without resolution loss. The second (Fig. 2) uses position-sensitive detection to define the scattered angle and collects data simultaneously over many angles. Both methods use vertically extended samples and detectors to improve data acquisition rates. The most advanced instruments of each type have approximately equal data acquisition rates and resolutions ($\sim$0.1% $\Delta d/d$).

With crystal monochromators, the resolution depends on collimation, the Bragg angle, and the mosaic spread of the monochromator (Ref 2). Time-of-flight instruments generally utilize long distances between sources and sample to give a large time spread between differing wavelength neutrons, which travel at different velocities (Fig. 3). One or more detector banks at fixed angles are utilized, with the best resolution provided by detector banks located at large scattering angles ($2\theta \sim 160°$). However, such a bank will only collect data for relatively small d-spacing, because long neutron wavelengths ($\gtrsim$2 Å) are not used. Therefore, data for longer spacings must be collected on detector banks positioned at low angles and, when necessary, these data sets are combined. One advantage of pulsed-source compared to fixed-wavelength diffraction is that the resolution ($\Delta d/d$) is approximately constant with d-spacing, which permits data collection to very small d-spacings ($<$0.5 Å^{-1}). This is further enhanced by the relative richness of short-wavelength neutrons available at pulsed neutron sources compared to reactors.

Samples. To compensate for the low fluxes available from neutron sources ($\sim$10^5 to 10^7 neutrons/cm^2/s on sample), samples

Fig. 1 Schematic diagram of a neutron powder diffractometer equipped with a multidetector bank

M, monochromator

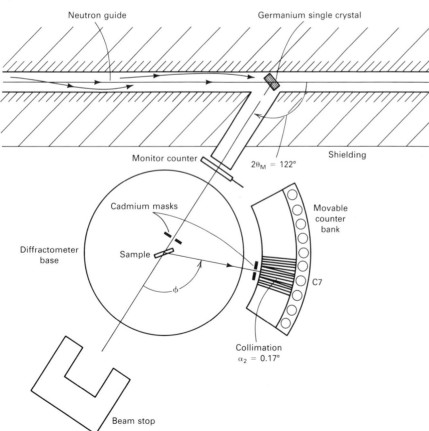

Fig. 2 Position-sensitive detector that replaces the multidetector bank in Fig. 1

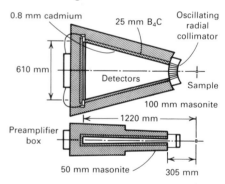

Fig. 3 Schematic diagram for a time-of-flight powder diffractometer

Incident wavelength is a function of time (rotor velocity) and detectors are stationary.

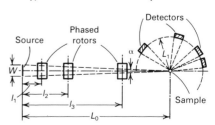

for neutron powder diffraction have generally been large (~10 cm³). Making use of tall detectors and matching samples, typical experiments have used approximately 5-cm-high × 1.5-cm-diam (2-in.-high × 0.6-in.-diam) cylindrical containers. With the exceptions noted, absorption is not a problem, the scattering power is not large, and the aberrations common to x-ray diffraction are absent, even with large work pieces. Although compacted, uncontained masses are ideal for neutron scattering, samples are most often contained in aluminum or vanadium containers, which scatter weakly or almost not at all, respectively. For reasons of cost and ease of fabrication, aluminum remains the most common container material.

The low absorption of neutrons in a variety of engineering materials has allowed relatively easy production of special sample environments, including low (~10 mK) and high (3000 K) temperatures and pressures up to approximately 45 kbar (with aluminum oxide cells). The Soller slit collimators used with multidetectors or the oscillating radial collimators used with position-sensitive detectors define the volume from which scattering is observed, and thus can be used to eliminate the signals from the outer shrouds of the environment chambers.

The Rietveld Method. Neutron powder diffraction has undergone a revolution in the past decade due to the introduction of the Rietveld method (Ref 3) and related computer methods for analyzing structures from powder diffraction data. Although x-ray powder diffraction has great utility for the identification of phases and for related "fingerprinting" tasks, it has not been particularly successful in evaluation of powder intensities to extract structural models. For neutrons, on the other hand, it was demonstrated in the late 1960s that the detailed powder diffraction diagram could be modeled using expressions of the type:

$$I(2\theta) = \sum_{i=n}^{m} F_i^2 \chi_i(2\theta_i - 2\theta) C_i$$

where $I(2\theta)$ is the intensity observed at the angle 2θ, F_i is the structure factor for the ith reflection, χ_i is the normalized peak shape function for the ith reflection with center at $2\theta_i$, and C_i is a geometric factor including multiplicity, Lorentz factor, and so on. The summation is over those reflections $(n \rightarrow m)$ that contribute intensity at the angle 2θ. The peak shape function for monochromatic diffraction is usually taken as a simple Gaussian:

$$\chi(2\theta_i - 2\theta)\alpha e^{-(2\theta_i - 2\theta)^2/\Gamma_i^2}$$

where Γ_i is the half-width of the ith reflection. The peak shape for time-of-flight diffraction is a more complicated function, but unlike x-ray diffraction with characteristic radiation, neither neutron case has multiple peaks contributing to a single reflection.

Analysis of the data consists of (1) parameterizing the structure factors in terms of positional parameters, temperature factors, etc., as well as the half-width, zero point, and cell parameters and (2) calculating, in a least squares method, the difference between observed and calculated intensities. Although such a method is most often applied to the refinement of atomic coordinates, increasingly it has been applied to the solution of structures by trial and error or Patterson methods.

In addition to refinement of atomic coordinates and temperature factors, the original Rietveld code was established for the refinement of magnetic structures. Newer versions of the code can be used to simultaneously refine multiple phases, in terms of the phase fractions and coordinates of each phase. This is especially useful for multiphase catalytic systems where the interaction between phases is of particular interest.

As the resolution of neutron instrumentation has improved, effects of particle size and strain have become more visible, causing deviation of the lineshape from pure Gaussian to a mixture of Gaussian and Lorentzian. This can be represented in Rietveld code by a Voigt, Pearson VII, or pseudo-Voigt function. Refinements with these models are slower than those using a pure Gaussian, but ultimately provide additional information about the sample.

The present generation of instruments has the capability of successfully refining problems with as many as 100 parameters, although many factors may reduce that maximum for a given sample. Such factors include poor diffracting power, high symmetry (which reduces the number of measurable reflections), and so on. The most advanced designs ($\Delta d/d = 0.03\%$) could permit structure solutions with as many as 300 parameters in the structural model. This compares favorably with many single-crystal diffraction problems, but contains the advantage of not requiring a macroscopic single-crystal specimen (such specimens are difficult to obtain for many important new materials). Due to the limits imposed by the particle size and by strain, however, this may be the limit of structural modeling with powders. The next major step in powder diffraction will be the application of "direct-method" structure solution techniques to permit routine structural analysis from powder data alone.

Texture

The use of neutrons for texture measurement is based on the same analytical principles as for x-rays (see the article "Crystallographic Texture Measurement and Analysis" in this Volume). The differences lie in the experimental capabilities and are primarily due to the increased penetrability of thermal neutrons in engineering materials (Ref 4). Measurements are usually made with instruments that are designed for single-crystal applications and that use conventional single-slit detectors. However, a dedicated texture instrument using position-sensitive detectors has been constructed that is capable of obtaining full pole figures in as little as 10 min (Ref 5). At the present time, steady-state sources are more appropriate for neutron texture studies.

Volume sampling is dramatically increased with neutrons. An incident beam of a cross-sectional area of 1 cm² will sample volumes of the order of 1 cm³ for neutrons, compared to 10^{-3} cm³ for x-rays. This enables two special cases of importance to be addressed: (1) large grain sizes for which a large volume is required for statistical reliability (for example, electrical steels), and (2) heavy elements for which x-ray beam penetration is restricted to only a few microns (for example, uranium and tungsten). Generally, the correlation of bulk measurements with texture is facilitated by the ability to measure the same volume as is physically used, for example, the entire cross section of tensile samples.

The entire full pole figure may be recorded out to $\chi = 90°$, unlike the x-ray case, for which measurements beyond approximately 70° are not practical. This makes composite specimens unnecessary. Also, absorption corrections are much less important, although they should generally be employed.

Pole figures from multiphase systems are more readily obtainable. This is principally due to the fact that neutron scattering cross sections do not decrease with diffraction angle, so one is more likely to access peaks of interest from all phases.

Nondestructive measurement of texture as a function of depth below the surface is possible. This consists of defining a volume in space at the center of the goniometer, using apertures in the incident and diffracted beams, and varying the position of the sample relative to the beam. The sampling volume and maximum depth that can be probed depend on the elements scattering and the geometry of the specimen (Ref 6). General guidelines are that volumes of a few cubic millimeters can be probed to a depth of a few centimeters. This method is appropriate for the study of long-wavelength texture variations due, for example, to processing of a plate. It is complementary to x-ray methods, which can be used to study near-surface regions as well as steep gradients over shallow depths by systematic removal of material.

Kinetics of texture development can be studied due to the ease of using special environments with neutron spectrometers. Thus, for example, the evolution of recrystallization texture may be monitored *in situ* (Ref 7).

Residual Stress

Neutron diffraction can be used to investigate residual stress states in crystalline materials. The technique is based on x-ray methodology, which is discussed in the article "X-Ray Diffraction Residual Stress Techniques" in this Volume. However, differences in types of applications and experimental procedures arise due to differences in beam penetration, peak shape, instrumental resolution, and geometrical considerations (Ref 6). For texture, the property of neutrons on which the technique is based is penetrability, which is of the order of millimeters for neutrons, compared to microns for x-rays (see Table 1). This makes two classes of residual stress problems—macrostresses and microstresses—particularly amenable for study.

Macrostress states extending into the bulk can be measured at depths up to a few centimeters (Ref 8-10). This enables, in principle, nondestructive characterization of interior stress tensors and gradients in large specimens. As for the x-ray case, accurate values for unstressed interplanar spacings are required for absolute determinations of stress tensors. Measurements are made with slits (uniaxial or biaxial stress state) or apertures (triaxial state). Interior probing restricts measurements to intermediate angles (60° to 110° 2θ) due to geometrical considerations; 90° is an ideal working angle.

Microstresses (grain interaction stresses) are volumetric in nature in contrast to the near-surface stresses traditionally studied using x-rays. Thus, a large volume is irradiated as in conventional powder diffraction. Microstresses arise from single-phase anisotropy (for example, plastically deformed Zircaloy) (Ref 11) or property differences in multiphase systems (for example, differential thermal stress in composites or ceramics) (Ref 12). In such cases, the use of neutrons may be essential due to relaxation near the surface or effects of surface preparation, particularly in the presence of heavy elements (Ref 13). Absolute magnitudes of stress require accurate values of unstressed interplanar spacings; however, relative

changes due, for example, to mechanical conditioning or heat treatment may be determined.

Peak fitting of all or nearly all of a measured peak is generally straightforward, because peak shapes are essentially Gaussian. They are typically fit in 0.1° 2θ steps across the peak. Although instrumental peak breadths are broad for reactor spectrometers relative to x-rays, the accuracy of peak fit is generally high (less than 0.01° 2θ). Thus, changes of about 1 in 10^4 are measurable. Peaks at pulsed sources are sharper, but more complex in shape.

Single-Crystal Neutron Diffraction

The ability to resolve diffracted intensities in all directions of diffraction space produces a wealth of information that cannot be obtained by any other technique. The intensities alone are usually sufficient to define a detailed model for the structure. As described in the article "Single-Crystal X-Ray Diffraction" in this Volume, for x-rays such a model contains the precise location and the individual anisotropic thermal motion of every atom. The intensities are also sensitive to the complete magnetic structure (for neutron diffraction only, note that the magnetic unit cell may differ from the crystallographic cell), to small structural changes which may precede the onset of a phase transition, and to anisotropy in the crystal mosaic via secondary extinction effects. Information on the mosaic structure may also be available by directly comparing lineshapes for reflections within a given form, that is, {*hkl*}.

Single-crystal methods may require a minimum specimen size of 0.5 mm³ for very simple materials and 1 to 10 mm³ for more complex structures. When adequate specimens are available, single-crystal neutron diffraction is unparalleled for locating "light" atoms (especially hydrogen), for revealing complex three-dimensional magnetic structures, for orienting and characterizing large samples, and for making diffraction measurements through sample environment containers (cryostats, furnaces, pressure cells, and so on).

To compensate for the low neutron flux on samples, instrumentation is being constructed to greatly increase the volume of diffraction space that can be sampled at one time. The single-crystal diffractometer at Argonne National Laboratory's Intense Pulsed Neutron Source, for example, has a 30- × 30-cm (12- × 12-in.) detector mounted 32 cm (12.6 in.) from the sample and at a diffracting angle of 90° (Fig. 4). This instrument accepts neutrons of wave-

lengths from 0.7 to 4.2 Å to simultaneously record 5% of reciprocal space by Laue's method. A total of about 35 overlapping settings provide all the information available; for many samples, the individual histograms require several hours each and the experiment can be completed in three days. The single-crystal diffractometer combines all the qualitative advantages of x-ray film techniques with the quantitative power of diffractometers. For example, a recent study of yttria-stabilized zirconia (Ref 14) revealed the dc charge-induced mobility of oxygen atoms at 1040 K. The furnace used for this study is shown in Fig. 5, and Fig. 6 displays data measured at 1040 K in a 7.8 V

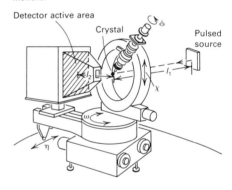

Fig. 4 Time-of-flight single-crystal diffractometer at a pulsed neutron source

Detector is usually fixed at 90° 2θ, and diffraction is recorded in Laue's geometry. The sample (a single crystal) is positioned by Eulerian angle motions.

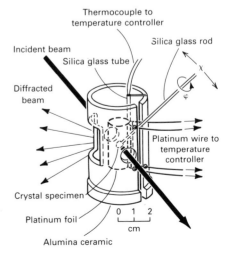

Fig. 5 Furnace designed for single-crystal neutron diffraction

Note that the beam readily penetrates the platinum foil heat shield. Source: Ref 14

Fig. 6 One histogram of data for Zr(Y)O$_{1.862}$ at 1040 K and 7.8 V dc across the crystal

(a) The Laue pattern for all 112 time channels (λ = 0.70 to 3.60 Å). (b) Time resolution of the *hhh* reflections at *y* = 63. TOF, time-of-flight. Source: Ref 14

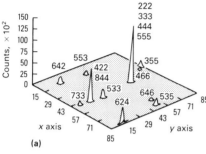

(a)

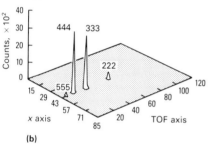

(b)

Fig. 7 Plot of measured diffraction intensity (points) versus calculated (solid line) for Nd$_2$(Co$_{0.1}$Fe$_{0.9}$)$_{14}$B powder sample

Regions near 9°, 14°, 67°, and 78° 2θ are rejected due to presence of alpha-iron contamination. The lower curve is the difference between the observed, I_{obs}, and the calculated, I_{calc}, intensity.

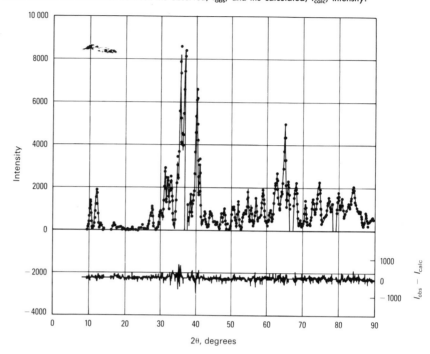

dc field. Note that Fig. 6(b) shows the time-resolved contributions for *y* = 63 expanded from Fig. 6(a). Currently, no parallel capability exists for x-ray diffraction, although some area detectors are available for fast data acquisition from proteins and other large molecules.

Applications

Example 1: Rietveld Analysis of Nd$_2$(Co$_{0.1}$Fe$_{0.9}$)$_{14}$B. Powder neutron diffraction data were collected from a 2-g sample of Nd$_2$(Co$_{0.1}$Fe$_{0.9}$)$_{14}$B at room temperature in 24 h using a position-sensitive detector diffractometer. Thirty-eight parameters were refined, including 14 position parameters, six occupancy factors, and eight magnetic moments. Several regions of the diagram were excluded due to the presence of a small contamination of alpha-iron. Observed, calculated, and difference curves are shown in Fig. 7. The results of the refinement are given in Table 2. The occupancies are normalized to 1 for each site, and a pronounced cobalt deficiency is noted on the j_2 site (which persists for all cobalt concentrations). At the same time, an unusually large magnetic moment (μ_z) is seen on the same j_2 site. Position parameters agree well with those for pure Nd$_2$Fe$_{14}$B as deter-

mined both by single-crystal x-ray diffraction and by neutron powder diffraction (Ref 15).

Example 2: Texture Measurement and Analysis. Three (110) full pole figures from Fe-3Si electrical steels of various grain sizes are shown in Fig. 8. The texture is seen to vary with grain size. This application illustrates the penetration power of neutrons and the resultant capabilities of recording the entire stereographic hemisphere and handling large grain sizes.

Example 3: Residual Stress Measurement. Residual stresses in a section cut from a double-V test weld were profiled (Fig. 9). The sample dimensions were 13.5 × 240 × 42 mm in the *x*-, *y*-, and *z*-directions, respectively. The probe volume was approximately a 3-mm cube. The zero strain level was determined by measuring at a position well away from the weld. Measurements of the stress in the *y*-direction with variation in depth *z* are also indicated. The sample configuration and neutron

Table 2   Structural parameters for the refined model for Nd$_2$(Co$_{0.1}$Fe$_{0.9}$)$_{14}$B

| Element/site | Atomic coordinates(a) | | | n(b) | μ$_z$(c) |
	x	y	z		
Nd 4f	0.2692(6)	0.2692(6)	0	1	0.3(2)
Nd 4g	0.1409(6)	−0.1409(6)	0	1	1.4(2)
Co 16k$_1$	0.2227(4)	0.4675(4)	0.1275(3)	0.06(1)	1.3(1)
Co 16k$_2$	0.0373(4)	0.3593(4)	0.1754(3)	0.15(2)	2.9(1)
Co 8j$_1$	0.0984(4)	0.0984(4)	0.2046(3)	0.17(2)	3.0(2)
Co 8j$_2$	0.3176(3)	0.3176(3)	0.2469(4)	0.03(2)	3.7(2)
Co 4e	0.5	0.5	0.1142(6)	0.15(2)	1.2(2)
Co 4c	0	0.5	0	0.12(3)	1.3(3)
B 4g	0.3719(12)	−0.3719(12)	0	1	

R_{nuc}(d) = 3.3%
R_{mag}(e) = 5.6%
S (chi-square) = $(R_{wp}/R_{exp})^2$ = 3.0(f)

Note: Numbers in parentheses represent the error on the least significant digit.
(a) Coordinates in the *a*, *b*, and *c* directions, respectively. (b) *n*, fractional occupancy of the sites. (c) μ$_z$, magnetic moment. (d) R_{nuc}, goodness-of-fit for the nuclear part of the model. (e) R_{mag}, goodness-of-fit for the magnetic part of the model. (f) The subscripts wp and exp represent the weighted profile and expected profiles, respectively.

stress and strain gage results are shown in Fig. 9.

REFERENCES

1. H. Asano, Y. Ishikawa, and M. Kirabayashi, *J. Appl. Cryst.*, Vol 11, 1978, p 661
2. G. Cagliotti, A. Paoletti, and F.P. Ricci, *Nucl. Instrum. Meth.*, Vol 3, 1958, p 233
3. H.M. Rietveld, *J. Appl. Cryst.*, Vol 2, 1969, p 65
4. J.A. Szpunar, *J. Mater. Sci.*, Vol 19, 1984, p 3467
5. D.J. Jensen and J.K. Kjems, in *Textures and Microstructures*, Vol 5, Gordon and Breach, 1983, p 239-251
6. A.D. Krawitz, J.E. Brune, and M.J. Schmank, in *Residual Stress and Stress Relaxation*, E. Kula and V. Weiss, Ed., Plenum Press, 1982 p 139-156
7. N. Hansen and D.J. Jensen, *Metall. Trans. A*, Vol 17, 1986, p 253-259
8. M.J. Schmank and A.D. Krawitz, *Metall. Trans. A*, Vol 13, 1982, p 1069-1076
9. L. Pintschovius, V. Jung, E. Macherauch, and O. Vohringer, *Mater. Sci. Eng.*, Vol 61, 1983, p 43-50
10. A.J. Allen, M.T. Hutchings, and C.G. Windsor, *Adv. Phys.*, Vol 34 (No. 4), July-Aug 1985, p 445-474
11. S.R. MacEwen, J. Faber, and A.P.L. Turner, *Acta Metall.*, Vol 31, 1983, p 657-676
12. A.D. Krawitz, R. Roberts, and J. Faber, *Advances in X-ray Analysis*, Vol 27, Plenum Press, 1984, p 239-249
13. A.D. Krawitz, *Mater. Sci. Eng.*, Vol 75, 1985, p 29-36

Fig. 8 (110) pole figures for Fe-3Si electrical steels of various grain sizes

(a) Up to 20 mm diam. (b) Up to 5 mm diam. (c) Up to 0.4 mm diam. Source: Ref 16

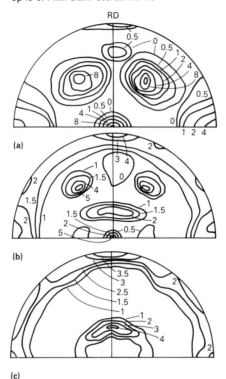

14. H. Horiuchi, A. Schultz, P. Leung, and J. Williams, *Acta Cryst.*, Vol B40, 1984, p 367-372
15. J.F. Herbst and W.B. Yelon, *J. Appl. Phys.*, to be published

Fig. 9 Variation of residual stress with position through a double-V weld

Strain gage results for variation in *y*-direction with depth *z* are also shown. Source: Ref 10

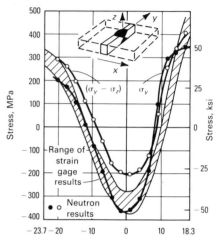

16. J. Szpunar, *At. Energy Rev.*, Vol 14 (No. 2), 1976, p 199-261

SELECTED REFERENCES

• U. Arndt and B. Willis, *Single Crystal Diffractometry*, Cambridge University Press, 1966
• G.E. Bacon, *Neutron Diffraction*, 3rd ed., Clarendon Press, 1975
• D.L. Price and K. Skold, Ed., *Experimental Methods in Physics: Neutron Scattering*, Academic Press, 1986

Electron Optical Methods

Analytical Transmission Electron Microscopy

A.D. Romig, Jr., Sandia National Laboratories

General Uses

- Imaging of microstructural features at 1000 to 450 000×. Microstructural detail resolution of <1 nm
- Qualitative and quantitative elemental analysis of microstructural features as small as 30 nm
- Crystal structure and orientation determination of microstructural features as small as 30 nm
- Lattice imaging of crystals with interplanar spacings >0.12 nm

Examples of Applications

- Very high magnification characterization of the microstructure of metals, ceramics, geologic materials, polymers, and biological materials
- Identification (composition and crystal structure) of inorganic phases, precipitates, and contaminants

Samples

- *Form*: Solids (metals, ceramics, minerals, polymers, biological, and so on)
- *Size*: An approximately 5-μm-thick, 3-mm-diam disk
- *Preparation*: Bulk specimens must be sectioned and electrothinned or ion milled to produce regions that permit transmission of the electron beam. Electron-transparent regions typically less than 100 nm thick. Powdered samples are often dispersed on a thin carbon substrate

Limitations

- Sample preparation is tedious, and development of a suitable procedure may take weeks
- Imaging resolution is approximately 0.12 nm
- *Elemental microanalysis*: Typical minimum size of region analyzed is 30 nm in diameter. Threshold sensitivity is approximately 0.5 to 1 wt%. Accuracy of quantification routinely is 5 to 15% (relative). Quantification is possible only for elements with atomic number ≥11. Some instruments can detect (qualitatively) only elements with atomic number ≥11
- *Electron diffraction*: Minimum size of region analyzed is approximately 30 nm in diameter. Crystal structure identification is limited to phases or compounds tabulated in powder diffraction file (approximately 40 000 phases or compounds). Orientation relationship between two coexisting phases can be determined only if phase crystal structures are known or can be determined. Determination of full space and point groups is possible only using specialized microdiffraction techniques

Estimated Analysis Time

- 3 to 30 h per specimen (does not include sample preparation)

Capabilities of Related Techniques

- *X-ray diffraction*: Gives bulk crystallographic information
- *Optical metallography*: Faster; lower magnification (up to approximately 1000×) overview of sample microstructure. No chemical information
- *Scanning electron microscopy*: Faster; lower magnification than transmission electron microscopy (up to approximately 20 000× in bulk samples), with image resolution routinely as good as approximately 50 nm in bulk samples. Qualitative chemical information only. Limited crystallographic information through electron channeling
- *Electron probe x-ray microanalysis*: Faster; gives more accurate (better than 1%, relative) quantitative elemental analysis for elements as light as boron. Poorer spatial resolution (approximately 1 μm). No crystallographic information

Introduction

Analytical transmission electron microscopy (ATEM) is unique among materials characterization techniques in that it enables essentially simultaneous examination of microstructural features through high-resolution imaging and the acquisition of chemical and crystallographic information from small (submicrometer) regions of the specimen. This article will illustrate the effectiveness of the technique in solving materials problems. The treatment is intended to be as practical as possible, with little emphasis on the associated mathematical theories. Sufficient background information will be provided for an understanding of the basic principles of the technique, including the physics of signal generation and detection, the rudiments of data analysis, and the preparation of samples, specifically the ways in which sample preparation can limit the analysis of an engineering material.

In the past 50 years, the transmission electron microscope has become a well-established research instrument for the microstructural analysis of metallic, ceramic, and organic materials. Electrons, the source of illumination, are transmitted through the sample, which is very thin ("electron transparent"), to generate some form of contrast that enables observation of the internal structure of the sample. The resulting image displays structural detail at very high resolution, of the order of fractions of a nanometer, allowing examination of the structure on a microscopic scale.

In the early years of transmission electron microscopy (TEM), the most common application was the simple imaging of the structure. In the last 35 years, additional quantitative information generated from the electron/specimen interactions has been used to analyze materials. The first quantitative information routinely obtained was due to electron diffraction in thin crystalline samples. Using electron diffraction, it is possible to enhance image contrast by imaging with the transmitted (undiffracted) electrons or the electrons diffracted from a given family of atomic planes. Certain crystallographic details of the sample, such as crystal orientation and matrix-precipitate orientation relationships, may also be obtained. The newest generation of microscopes can generate electron-diffraction patterns from small volumes (<50 nm in diameter) in the sample by electron microdiffraction.

In the past 10 years, energy-dispersive x-ray spectrometers have been added to transmission electron microscope columns, allowing determination of the elemental composition of small volumes (<50 nm in diameter) in the sample. With the ability to extract a wide range of quantitative information from the sample, modern fully capable (implying the capability for x-ray microanalysis and electron microdiffraction) transmission electron microscopes are often referred to as analytical electron microscopes. To maintain the relationship to the analysis of thin electron-transparent samples, the instruments are occasionally referred to as analytical transmission electron microscopes. In this article, to be consistent with the most frequently used terminology, the instrument will be referred to as the analytical electron microscope, and the technique as analytical electron microscopy (AEM). In one specific operational configuration, the electron beam is focused to a fine probe and scanned over the thin specimen, generating an image on a cathode-ray tube (CRT) in a manner similar to that of a scanning electron microscope. In this configuration, the instrument is often referred to as a scanning transmission electron microscope.

This article is divided into two major sections. The first introduces the analytical electron microscope and its basic operational characteristics, electron optics, electron beam/specimen interactions and the generation of a signal, signal detectors, electron diffraction, imaging, x-ray microanalysis, electron energy loss spectroscopy, and sample preparation. The second section consists of 12 examples, each illustrating a specific type of materials problem that can be solved, at least in part, with AEM. Detailed information on TEM and AEM can be found in Ref 1 to 7.

The Instrument

The analytical electron microscope is a classical electron optical instrument. The instrument is built around the electron column, which can be divided into two principal subassemblies: the electron gun, or source of high-energy electrons, and the electromagnetic lenses, which are used to control the beam and thus generate an image. Figures 1(a) and (b) are schematic representations that compare the electron optical systems of the scanning electron microscope and the conventional transmission electron microscope, respectively.

The scanning electron microscope typically operates at 2 to 50 kV; a range of 15 to 25 kV is common for most metallurgical and ceramic applications. The electromagnetic lenses in the column are used to form a small-diameter electron probe (>5 nm in diameter for most scanning electron microscopes). A set of scan coils raster the electron probe over the specimen surface as an electron beam scans the inside of the CRT screen. At each point in the sample struck by the incident electron beam, several electron/specimen interactions occur that produce a number of different measurable signals, such as secondary electrons, backscattered electrons, and characteristic x-rays.

The intensity of the emitted signal is a function of the specimen. The intensity may vary as a function of surface topography or composition, depending on the signal in question. The signals are collected, amplified, and displayed on a CRT. Regions in the specimen that emit an intense signal will appear bright on the CRT; those regions emitting a weaker signal will appear dark. A bulk specimen that is not electron transparent is examined in the scanning electron microscope. Therefore, the scanning electron microscope has no post-specimen lenses. The ultimate image resolution in the scanning electron microscope is of the order of the electron probe diameter. Additional information is provided in Ref 8 and in the article "Scanning Electron Microscopy" in this Volume.

The conventional transmission electron microscope typically operates at voltages exceeding 60 kV; 100, 120, or 200 kV are most common for inorganic samples. Both 300- and 400-kV instruments are now commercially available. The electron lens configuration in the transmission electron microscope is also different from that found in the scanning electron microscope. The electron-ray path through a transmission electron microscope is analogous to the visible light ray path through the ground glass lenses in an optical microscope configured to operate in the transmitted-light mode (except that the electron follows a spiral path through the lens as it is focused, while light is focused through the lens in a plane in an optical microscope). Consequently, the electrons "flood" the sample and thus illuminate the entire area of interest.

The electrons are provided by the illumination system, which includes the electron gun and the prespecimen lenses (the electron gun is discussed in the section "Electron Optics" in this article). The prespecimen lenses include one or more condenser lenses that form the initial beam and the upper half of the objective lens. The electrons strike the thin film specimen and may undergo any of several interactions with the specimen. One of these interactions, diffraction of the electrons by the periodic array of atomic planes in the specimen, ultimately produces the contrast that most commonly enables observation of structural detail in crystalline materials. The electrons that pass through the thin crystal without being diffracted by the atomic planes are referred to as transmitted electrons. The electrons that have been diffracted from a given (*hkl*) plane are the (*hkl*)

Fig. 1 Comparison of the electron optical columns used in analytical electron microscopes

(a) SEM electron optical column. In the scanning electron microscope, the electron lenses are used to focus the electron beam to a small-diameter probe. To form an image, the scan coils raster the beam over the specimen surface. The sweep of an electron beam in the CRT is synchronized with the electron-beam sweep over the specimen surface. The beam is shown at three points on the specimen surface during the raster sequence. (b) Electron optical column in a conventional transmission electron or analytical electron microscope operated in the TEM mode. (c) Electron optical column in a modern analytical electron microscope operated in the STEM mode. Source: Ref 3

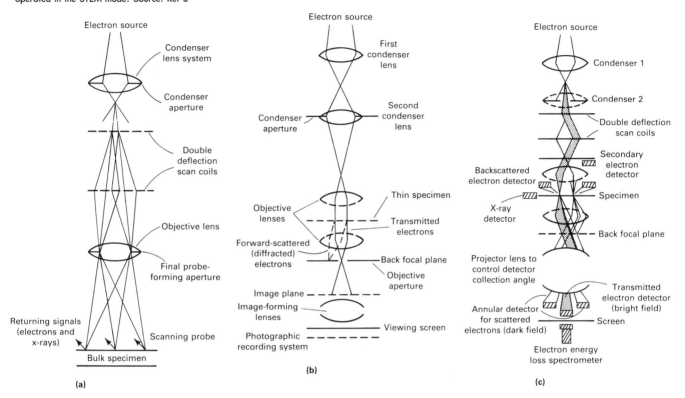

(a) (b) (c)

diffracted electrons. Contrast in noncrystalline materials is primarily due to electron-absorption effects, which increase with atomic number. Therefore, organic samples are often stained with a heavy metal to enhance contrast.

Following the specimen are several post-specimen lenses, including the lower half of the objective lens, the magnifying lens, the intermediate lens, and a projection lens. The series of post-specimen lenses is often referred to as the image-formation system. These post-specimen lenses, acting in series, magnify the image. After passing through the image-formation system, the electrons form an image on a fluorescent screen or a photographic film. The theoretical resolution in a TEM image approaches the wavelength of the incident electrons, although this resolution is not attained absolutely due to such lens defects as spherical and chromatic aberration and aperture diffraction. Typical line-to-line resolution limits in modern transmission electron microscopes are approximately 0.15 nm. Additional information on the electron optical column and lens defects can be found in Ref 1 to 7.

The conventional transmission electron microscope is capable of simple imaging of the specimen and the generation of selected-area diffraction patterns (SADPs). Images formed using only the transmitted electrons are known as bright-field images; images formed using specific diffracted (*hkl*) beams are known as dark-field images. A special aperture in the microscope column, the selected-area aperture, can be used to limit the area of the thin film specimen from which the SADP is obtained. Using the selected-area aperture, it is possible to generate diffraction patterns from areas of the specimen as small as 1 μm in diameter. Selected-area diffraction patterns can be used to identify the crystal structure of a given phase, determine the identity and orientation of a given crystal in the sample, or determine the orientation relationship between two coexisting phases.

The modern analytical electron microscope, shown schematically in Fig. 1(c), is capable of all the functions of a conventional transmission electron microscope. In addition, several capabilities exceed those of the conventional transmission

electron microscope. The lenses are designed to allow focusing of the beam to a diameter of 2 nm or less. An electron-diffraction pattern can be generated using this small probe. This technique is referred to as a type of electron microdiffraction. Because the finely focused beam is highly convergent, the electron-diffraction pattern thus generated is termed a convergent-beam electron-diffraction pattern (CBEDP). The CBEDP is generated from a specimen volume many times smaller than the conventional SADP. The diameter of the region of the specimen sampled using CBED is routinely smaller than 50 nm.

An energy-dispersive x-ray spectrometer is mounted on the side of the column, allowing collection of x-rays generated by interactions between the focused electron beam and the specimen; therefore, chemical/elemental characterization of submicrometer volumes of the sample is possible. Conventional energy-dispersive spectrometers can detect only elements with an atomic number, Z, greater than or equal to 11 (sodium). A new energy-dispersive spectrometry (EDS) detector, the ultrathin window detector, has been developed. This unit enables detection of elements as light as $Z = 6$ (carbon). Although it is possible to perform quantitative chemical analysis for elements as heavy as or heavier than sodium, the ability to perform quantitative analysis for lighter elements using the EDS ultrathin window detector has yet to be developed. As with the scanning electron microscope or the electron probe microanalyzer, the x-ray spectrum is the raw information used to perform qualitative and/or quantitative x-ray microanalysis.

Some transmitted electrons that pass through the specimen will lose a certain amount of energy due to interactions with the atoms in the specimen. The amount of energy lost will be characteristic of the atomic species with which the electron has interacted. A spectrometer can be mounted on the bottom of the analytical electron microscope to collect these electrons. Analysis of the energy distribution of these transmitted electrons can be used for chemical analysis of the specimen. This technique, referred to as electron energy loss spectroscopy (EELS), is especially suited to the detection of light elements ($Z < 10$). As such, it complements EDS as a technique for chemical microanalysis. The capability of performing quantitative microanalysis routinely using EELS has yet to be perfected.

Due to the ability to collect quantitative analytical data (SAD, CBED, EDS, and EELS), the modern instrument is referred to as an analytical transmission electron microscope, or analytical electron microscope. Solving materials problems often necessitates simultaneous use of several analytical capabilities of the analytical electron microscope. The technique enables characterization of the microstructure of the specimen in several ways, including high-resolution imaging to examine the fine structural detail of the specimen, high spatial resolution microanalysis using EDS and EELS to determine the chemical/elemental composition of small (submicrometer) regions of the specimen, and high spatial resolution crystallographic analysis by electron diffraction.

Electron Optics

Electron Guns. All electron optical instruments require a source of high-energy electrons. The high-energy electrons are produced by an electron gun. The simplest, least expensive, most reliable, and therefore most common electron gun uses a tungsten hairpin filament (W-hairpin). A current of the order of fractions of an ampere is passed through a thin tungsten wire (approximately 50 μm in diameter) shaped like a hairpin. The radius of curvature at the tip is approximately 5 to 100 μm. The filament is heated (2700 K) by electrical resistance, and electrons are emitted from the filament by thermionic emission. The emitted electrons are focused to a coarse spot, perhaps 50 μm in diameter, by a negatively biased (by a few hundred volts) cap termed a Wehnelt cylinder. Below the Wehnelt cylinder is the anode cap or anode plate. The anode is biased to some large positive voltage (80 to 200 kV in a typical analytical electron microscope). The anode accelerates the electrons down the column of the instrument. Typical beam currents in a W-hairpin-equipped analytical electron microscope are of the order of 100 μA.

Some modern instruments use a filament made of lanthanum hexaboride (LaB_6), a brighter source of electrons. A few modern instruments use field emission guns (FEG). In the case of an FEG, electrons are emitted from the filament by overcoming the work function barrier of the filament material in a large electric field rather than by thermionic emission. The FEG is many hundreds of times brighter than a conventional W-hairpin source. Both LaB_6 and field emission sources offer advantages in AEM, but they have not replaced tungsten filaments to a great extent, because modification of the analytical electron microscope vacuum system is required for ultrahigh vacuum (UHV). Special care must be exercised in the operation and maintenance of these guns, and both are expensive options.

As the intensity of the electron beam increases, smaller electron probe sizes can be used, and the resolution attainable in the analysis (imaging, electron diffraction, and x-ray microanalysis) increases; that is, the region under analysis decreases. Analytical electron microscopy electron sources are discussed further in Ref 4.

Electromagnetic Lenses. In both the conventional TEM mode and the scanning transmission electron microscopy (STEM) mode, the beam produced by the electron gun is controlled by a system of electromagnetic lenses. The electromagnetic lens operates on the principle that the path of a moving charged particle, in this case an electron, is deviated by a magnetic field. Thus, the magnetic field provides focusing/defocusing capability. A perfect electromagnetic lens could focus the incident probe to an infinitely small spot. However, electromagnetic lenses have several aberrations. The focusing of electrons by modern electromagnetic lenses is far inferior to the focusing of visible light by modern ground glass lenses. Ultimately, the performance of these lenses limits the image resolution achievable in AEM. Additional information on electron lenses can be found in Ref 3, 4, and 8.

Electron Beam/Specimen Interactions

The signals generated, collected, and analyzed in the analytical electron microscope are produced by interactions between the electrons in the high-energy incident beam and the material in the thin film target. Electron beam/specimen interactions, or scattering events, can be divided into two categories: (1) elastic events, which affect the trajectories but do not significantly affect the velocities or kinetic energies of the incident electrons, leading to emission of forward diffracted and transmitted electrons as well as backscattered electrons, and (2) inelastic events, which result in a transfer of energy to the solid with very little change in the electron trajectory, leading to generation of secondary electrons, Auger electrons, characteristic and continuum x-rays, long-wavelength electromagnetic radiation in the visible, ultraviolet, and infrared regions, electron-hole pairs, lattice vibrations (phonons), and electron oscillations (plasmons).

A number of these signals produced by the interaction of the incident electrons with the thin foil specimens are used in AEM, including unscattered and inelastically scattered transmitted electrons, diffracted electrons, secondary electrons, backscattered electrons for imaging and the generation of channeling patterns, emitted x-ray spectra, and energy loss electrons. These signals can be used individually or in various combinations to characterize microstructure, crystallography, and compositional variations in engineering materials.

Elastic Scattering. When elastic scattering occurs, the direction component of the velocity of the electron, v, is changed, but the magnitude of the velocity remains essentially constant. Because the velocity is unchanged, the kinetic energy of the electron, $E = \frac{1}{2}m_e v^2$, where m_e is the electron mass, is also essentially unchanged. Less than 1 eV of energy is typically transferred from the electron to the specimen during an elastic scattering event. A loss of 1 eV is insignificant relative to the incident-beam energy of 100 keV or more. During the elastic scattering event, the electron is deviated from its incident path through an angle θ_e, where e implies an elastic scattering angle. The elastic scattering angle can vary from 0 to 180°, but typically is ≤2°.

Elastic scattering is due to interactions of the energetic electrons with the nuclei of the atoms in the target, partially screened by the bound electrons. The extent of the elastic scattering is related to the square of the atomic number of the target material and

Fig. 2 Inner-shell ionization and subsequent de-excitation by Auger electron emission or characteristic x-ray photon emission

Source: Ref 8

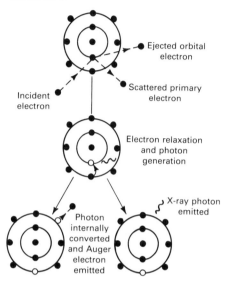

inversely related to the square of the incident-beam energy. Therefore, for a specified thickness of a given material, elastic scattering is more probable in high atomic number materials at low beam energy.

Elastic scattering is responsible for both electron diffraction (thin foils) and the generation of backscattered electrons (bulk specimens and thin foils). Coherent elastic scattering of electrons in the forward direction produces the form of electron diffraction commonly encountered in TEM and AEM. The origin and use of electron diffraction will be discussed in the section "Electron Diffraction" in this article. Backscattered electrons, also produced by elastic scattering events, have some use in AEM (STEM mode) analysis. The yield of backscattered electrons depends strongly on atomic number so the signal can be used for qualitative elemental mapping. Backscattered electrons also generate electron-channeling patterns, which are useful in crystallographic studies of the material.

Inelastic scattering is the second category of scattering. During an inelastic scattering event, energy is transferred to the target atoms, and the kinetic energy of the incident electrons is decreased. There are several possible inelastic scattering processes.

Inner-Shell Ionization. A sufficiently energetic electron can interact with an atom and cause the ejection of a tightly bound inner-shell electron, leaving the atom in an ionized and highly energetic state (Fig. 2). During subsequent de-excitation, an electron transition occurs in which an electron from an outer shell drops inward to fill the inner-shell vacancy. The electron transition involves a change in energy. The energy released will be in the form of a characteristic x-ray or an ejected outer-shell electron termed an Auger electron. Because the electron structure of each atom is unique, the spectrum of possible characteristic x-rays and Auger electrons is also unique. The name assigned to a given characteristic x-ray, for example, Kα, depends on the electron shells involved in the transition.

Figure 3 shows a schematic of the energy-level diagram for an atom. The characteristic emissions resulting from certain electron-shell transitions are shown. The relationship between characteristic x-ray wavelength or energy and atomic number is given by Mosely's law, which states that the x-ray photon wavelength is inversely proportional to the atomic number. The relationship between atomic number and x-ray wavelength (or energy, because $E = hc/\lambda$, where E is the x-ray energy, h is Planck's constant, c is the speed of light, and λ is the x-ray wavelength) is illustrated in Fig. 4. Therefore, the wavelength of each family of x-ray photons is related linearly to the square of the atomic number. Because each atomic species has a unique characteristic x-ray spectrum, this signal is useful for qualitative and quantitative chemical microanalysis. By identifying all the x-ray lines in the spectrum, it is possible to determine what elements are present in the volume of the specimen in which the x-rays were generated. The intensity of the x-ray lines can be subsequently used to determine quantitatively the amount of each element present in that volume of the specimen.

Bremsstrahlung or Continuum X-Rays. An energetic incident-beam electron can undergo deceleration in the Coulombic field of an atom. The energy lost from the beam electron in this deceleration is converted into an x-ray photon known as a bremsstrahlung (braking radiation) x-ray. Deceleration is a continuous process, with most electrons losing their energy through several interactions. The most energetic continuum x-ray possible has the energy of the incident electron. In this case, the electron has lost all its energy in one scattering event. Consequently, the bremsstrahlung x-rays form a continuous spectrum from zero energy up to the incident-beam energy. The continuum x-ray spectrum must be considered in quantitative x-ray microanalysis. Because only the characteristic x-ray intensity above the continuum is important, the continuum must be removed to obtain only the characteristic

Fig. 3 Energy-level diagram for an atom showing the excitation of the K, L, M, and N shells and the formation of Kα, Kβ, Lα, and Mα x-rays

Source: Ref 8

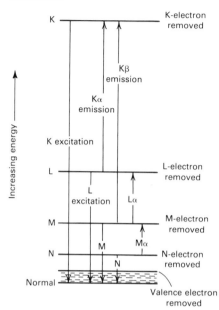

Fig. 4 Representation of Mosely's law showing the relationship between characteristic x-ray wavelength and atomic number

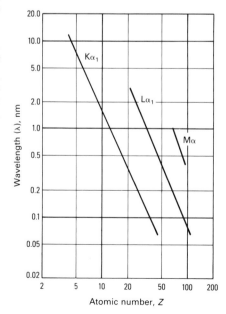

Fig. 5 Comparison of electron beam spreading in thin foils and bulk targets

(a) Thin foil specimen, AEM. (b) Bulk specimen, SEM

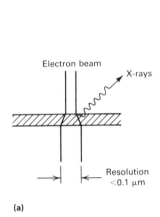

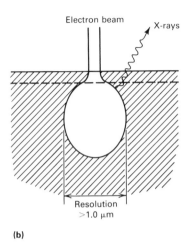

Fig. 6 Positioning of signal detectors in the analytical electron microscope column

Source: Ref 3

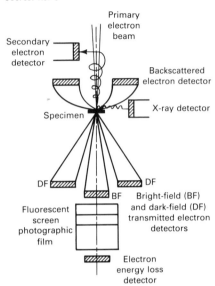

intensities. As such, the continuum serves no useful purpose in microanalysis.

Excitation of Conduction Electrons Leading to Secondary Electron (Low-Energy) Emission. The interaction of the electron beam with the solid can lead to the ejection of loosely bound electrons in the conduction band. These ejected electrons are referred to as secondary electrons, and most have a kinetic energy of <50 eV. The resulting secondary electron distribution is peaked at 3 to 5 eV, with the distribution decreasing sharply as the energy increases above 5 eV. The emission of secondary electrons is extremely sensitive to surface topography. Secondary electrons in the analytical electron microscope enable generation of scanning images in the STEM mode that are analogous to scanning images in the scanning electron microscope. However, much higher resolution is possible in such scanning images in the scanning transmission electron microscope relative to the scanning electron microscope due to the smaller volume of electron interaction in thin foil targets relative to bulk specimens.

Excitation of Phonons. Much of the energy deposited into the specimen by the incident electron beam is transferred to the solid by the excitation of lattice oscillations (phonons), that is, heat. If the specimen is a good thermal conductor, as are most metals, the specimen and the specimen holder will serve as an effective heat sink, and significant heating will not occur. For nonconductors, such as ceramics and polymers, heating can be more significant. In some cases, beam-induced heating is sufficient to cause phase transformations or recrystallization in specimens.

Plasmon Excitation. The incident electrons can excite waves in the free-electron gas that exists between the ionic cores in a solid, especially a metal. Plasmon excitation is a highly probable scattering event. In a metal such as aluminum, excitation of a plasmon involves the transfer of approximately 15 eV to the solid.

Electron Scattering Volume. The most striking difference between electron scattering in bulk targets and thin foils is the difference in electron scattering volume (Fig. 5). In bulk targets and thin foil specimens, the lateral extent of scattering is due primarily to elastic scattering. In the case of bulk targets, the electrons will scatter in the target until they are either backscattered out of the target or lose all of their kinetic energy and come to rest. For a small-diameter beam (<10 nm), the electron scattering volume and therefore the volume in which all of the signal is generated will be of the order of 1 μm in diameter. The diameter of the scattering volume is a function of the average atomic number, atomic weight, density, and the energy of the incident electrons.

The volume of electron scattering is important in the analysis of solid specimens because it limits the spatial resolution for chemical analysis. X-rays are generated essentially throughout the entire electron scattering volume; therefore, it is not possible to generate a unique x-ray spectrum from a submicrometer volume of the sample (a small precipitate, for example), making determination of the composition of these submicrometer-diameter volumes in the scanning electron microscope or electron probe microanalyzer impossible. A thorough mathematical treatment of electron beam/specimen interactions is provided in Ref 9.

Signal Detectors

The modern analytical electron microscope is often equipped with a wide variety of signal detectors. All the emissions discussed above can be collected using various types of signal detectors. In the STEM mode, any of these signals—transmitted electrons, diffracted electrons, backscattered electrons, secondary electrons, and characteristic x-rays—can be used to modulate the input signal to the CRT and thus produce an image. In the conventional TEM mode, images of the microstructure can be produced directly on a fluorescent screen or photographic film. Microanalysis can be performed using the inelastically scattered electrons or characteristic x-rays for EELS or EDS analysis, respectively. Figure 6 shows schematically how these various signal detectors are interfaced with the analytical electron microscope.

Transmitted and Scattered Electrons (TEM Mode). In the conventional TEM mode, in which the entire region of the specimen is flooded with incident electrons, the diffraction pattern and associated bright-field and dark-field images can be viewed directly on a fluorescent screen or recorded on photographic film. The photographic film used to record these images is very fine grained and has very good image resolution. Therefore, it is often possible to observe detail in the photographic record that is not visible on the fluorescent screen. Some lab-

Fig. 7 Magnetic spectrometer and detector used in EELS
Source: Ref 3

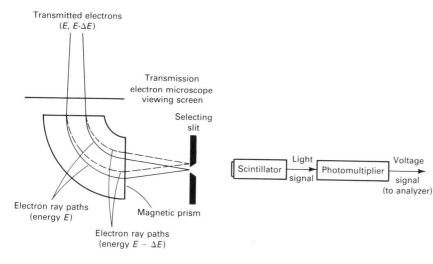

Fig. 8 Cross section of conventional EDS detector

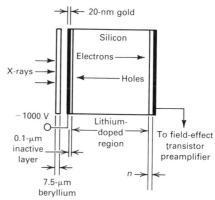

oratories have attached video cameras to the microscopes. The video attachment allows large groups of people to view the image, provides an alternative to sheet film for image recording, and allows continual recording of microstructural changes that might occur during *in situ* experiments.

Transmitted and Scattered Electrons (STEM Mode). The high-energy electrons, those that have not been scattered in the specimen or only elastically scattered in the forward or backward direction, can be detected using a solid-state electron detector or a scintillator/photomultiplier detector. Detailed information on the different detectors used in commercial analytical electron microscopes is provided in Ref 3 and 8.

Secondary Electrons (STEM Mode). The low-energy secondary electrons emitted from the top and bottom surfaces of the thin foil specimen are collected using a scintillator/photomultiplier detector. In the STEM mode, the signal from the photomultiplier is used to modulate the signal into the CRT to produce a scanning image. Therefore, secondary electron imaging in the analytical electron microscope is available only in the STEM mode. Further details on secondary electron detectors are provided in Ref 8.

Energy Loss Electrons. Some electrons will have undergone only inelastic scattering; that is, they will have lost some amount of energy without a significant change in trajectory and will therefore be contained in the transmitted beam along with the unscattered electrons. The amount of energy the electrons have lost during inelastic scattering will be a function of the scattering event they have undergone. These electrons are termed energy loss electrons and can be used for

imaging in the STEM mode or for chemical microanalysis.

To collect these electrons for imaging or microanalysis, a magnetic-sector spectrometer and scintillator/photomultiplier detector are placed at the bottom of the microscope column (Fig. 7). By scanning over the entire range of electron energies, an energy loss spectrum can be collected for microanalysis. By using the spectrometer to collect only electrons of a given energy, the collected signal can be used to modulate the CRT and produce a scanning image in the STEM mode. Because there is a relationship between some of the energy loss electrons and the atomic species with which they interacted, scanning elemental maps can be generated.

The characteristic x-rays produced when the incident electrons interact with the specimen can be used for microanalysis or elemental mapping. The x-rays generated in the analytical electron microscope are detected and sorted by the energy dispersive spectrometer; they are collected by a solid-state detector and sorted by energy by a multichannel analyzer, which is part of the modern EDS computer system. The detector (Fig. 8) is made from a chip of lithium-doped silicon. A thin gold film is used as an electrical contact, and a thin (7.5-μm-thick) beryllium window isolates the delicate detector from the microscope column. Most x-rays (with energies ≥ 1.5 keV) pass unaffected through the beryllium window.

When an x-ray strikes the silicon chip, a number of electron-hole pairs are produced, the number being directly proportional to the energy of the incident x-ray. The electrons and holes are swept apart by an applied bias and induce a current that is converted to a

voltage pulse in a field-effect transistor (FET) preamplifier. The voltage is further amplified, then discriminated into specific channels using the multichannel analyzer. The output on a CRT plots the x-ray intensity versus x-ray energy, which is directly related to the voltage. Therefore, an entire x-ray spectrum can be collected simultaneously, allowing for rapid qualitative analysis of unknowns. The acquired spectrum can be processed to determine compositions quantitatively.

Energy-dispersive x-ray spectrometry has several limitations. First, the resolution of a solid-state x-ray detector is approximately 150 eV; therefore, it may be impossible, or at least very difficult, to resolve two characteristic x-ray peaks whose energy difference is less than the resolution of the spectrometer.

A second limitation of conventional AEM-EDS is the inability of the conventional energy-dispersive spectrometer to detect elements lighter than sodium. The characteristic x-rays emitted from these elements are very low in energy (<1 keV) and are totally absorbed by the beryllium window of the detector. Ultrathin window and windowless EDS detectors have recently become available. The windowless detectors can be used only on UHV analytical electron microscopes, which are typically ion pumped and have metal-to-metal seals. The ultrathin window detectors use a thin polymer window in place of the beryllium window. The polymer window is far more transparent to low-energy x-rays. The ultrathin window is sufficient for isolating the delicate vacuum inside the detector from the environment inside the microscope column, but it is far more fragile than the standard beryllium window and must be treated carefully. Ultrathin window and windowless detectors offer enormous potential for qualitative analysis, although quantification may be difficult due to complicated x-ray/specimen effects. Additional information on EDS detectors can be found in Ref 8.

Electron Diffraction

Coherent Bragg Diffraction. In the case of a thin foil specimen of a crystalline material, most of the electrons will pass through the specimen and exit at the bottom. Some of the electrons will not undergo any scattering and will exit the foil with the same velocity and trajectory with which they entered. Other electrons will undergo only inelastic scattering; that is, they will suffer a loss in energy, but their trajectory will be essentially unchanged. The unscattered electrons and the electrons that have undergone only inelastic scattering will form the transmitted electron beam. Other electrons will undergo elastic scattering with essentially no loss in energy but a significant change in trajectory. Some of these electrons will be scattered through very large angles and exit back through the top of the foil as backscattered electrons. Many of these electrons will undergo elastic scattering in the foil through smaller angles and exit through the bottom of the foil.

The directions in which electrons are elastically scattered from a crystal are not random, but depend on the geometric arrangement of the atomic planes. The scattering off of specific atomic planes is coherent; that is, the electrons will be scattered in specific directions determined by the crystallography (orientation between the given atomic planes and the incident beam) of the specimen. Coherent scattering of backscattered electrons leads to the formation of electron-channeling patterns in the STEM mode, assuming the electron lenses are properly configured. The formation of channeling patterns in thin crystalline foils in STEM is analogous to channeling-pattern formation in bulk specimens in the scanning electron microscope. A more detailed description of channeling patterns in bulk specimens and thin foils is given in Ref 10.

Coherent elastic scattering in the forward direction is responsible for the formation of the diffracted beams in the transmission electron microscope and therefore produces the conventional electron-diffraction patterns in TEM. The angles through which the electrons are scattered are given by Bragg's law:

$$n\lambda = 2\,d\sin\theta$$

where n is an integer, λ is the wavelength of the electrons (0.0037 nm and 0.0025 nm for 100- and 200-keV electrons, respectively), d is the interplanar spacing for the family of diffracting planes, and θ is the diffracting angle.

Only certain atomic planes will diffract the electron beam. The atomic planes that will diffract are a function of the crystal structure: all planes can diffract in a simple Bravais lattice; only planes in which h and k (of the Miller indices) are both odd or even can diffract in a base-centered Bravais lattice; only planes in which $(h + k + l)$ is even can diffract in a body-centered Bravais lattice; and only planes in which h, k, and l are all even or odd can diffract in a face-centered Bravais lattice. (Crystal structures, diffracting conditions, a description of permissible reflections, reciprocal lattices, and stereographic projections are reviewed in Ref 11 and 12.)

Diffraction of electrons by crystals is mathematically identical to the diffraction of x-rays by a crystal. The difference between x-ray diffraction and electron diffraction lies primarily in the wavelength of the diffracting radiation. X-rays have a wavelength of the order of tenths of a nanometer; 100- to 200-keV electrons have a wavelength of the order of 10^{-3} nm. Consequently, the diffracting angles for x-rays are typically tens of degrees, but the diffracting angles for electrons are typically tenths of a degree. For small angles, $\theta = \sin\theta$, and considering only first-order reflections ($n = 1$), Bragg's law for electron diffraction reduces to:

$$n\lambda = 2\,d\theta$$

The geometry of the transmission electron microscope is such that Bragg's law can be further modified. The distance from the transmitted beam to the diffracted beam, r, at the plane of the photographic film is related to the camera constant of the microscope. The camera constant is the product of the electron wavelength, λ, and the effective distance from the specimen to the film, L (the derivation of this geometrical construction is provided in Ref 1). Therefore, Bragg's law, as typically written for electron diffraction in the transmission electron microscope, is:

$$rd = \lambda L$$

where d is still the atomic interplanar spacing. The camera constant can be determined for a specific microscope at a specific operating voltage (which determines the electron wavelength) from a diffraction pattern obtained from a known standard. For the standard for which the values of d are known, r

can be measured and therefore λL can be calculated.

Selected-Area Diffraction. The standard method for generating diffraction patterns using conventional TEM is by SAD. In SAD, an aperture appropriately termed the selected-area aperture is moved into the column to limit the area of the specimen from which a diffraction pattern is obtained. Proper positioning of the aperture selects the region from which the pattern will be obtained. The diameter of the selected-area aperture can be varied, but diffraction effects from the edge of the aperture limit the minimum area of the specimen from which a SADP can be generated to a region approximately 0.5 μm in diameter.

Any of three types of electron-diffraction patterns can be generated in an SADP: (1) ring patterns from fine-grained polycrystalline materials in which diffraction occurs simultaneously from many grains with different orientations relative to the incident beam; (2) spot patterns in which diffraction occurs from a single-crystal region of the specimen; and (3) Kikuchi line patterns in which diffraction occurs from a single-crystal region of the specimen, which is sufficiently thick that the diffracting electrons have undergone simultaneous elastic and inelastic scattering, known as Kikuchi scattering.

Ring patterns arise when many randomly oriented fine grains contribute to the observed diffraction pattern. Ring-pattern analysis, like powder x-ray analysis, can be used to identify unknowns or to characterize the crystallography of a new crystalline material. Ring patterns are commonly used to assist identification of fine precipitates in a matrix. The fine particles would typically be removed from the matrix by chemical dissolution or by using extraction replicas (see the section "Sample Preparation" in this article). Similarly, ring patterns might be used to aid identification of a surface corrosion product that could be removed from its substrate using a chemical process or extraction replicas. Ring patterns can also be generated from a fine polycrystalline matrix, such as might be produced by certain chemical or vapor-deposition processes. In any of these cases, the crystal structure and lattice parameters of the material producing the ring pattern can be determined.

In its applications and mechanics of use, an electron-diffraction ring pattern is analogous to a Debye-Scherrer x-ray diffraction pattern. Figure 9 shows a ring pattern generated from a thin polycrystalline specimen of aluminum. The ratio of ring diameters proves that the crystal has the fcc structure: $(h^2 + k^2 + l^2) = 3, 4, 8, 11, 12, 16, \ldots$ for (111), (200), (220), (311), (222), (400),

Fig. 9 Ring pattern from polycrystalline aluminum

The rings show the permissible reflections for the fcc crystal structure. The rings (beginning with the innermost) index as (111), (200), (220), (311), (222), and so on. The lattice parameter can be determined from the radii of the diffraction rings. The microscope was operated at 200 keV. Camera constant, $\lambda L = 2.49$ Å · cm. Courtesy of C.R. Hills

Fig. 10 Spot diffraction pattern from a single crystal of aluminum

The transmitted and diffracted spots are shown. The spots are indexed in the key. The beam direction, B, is parallel to the zone axis, z. Courtesy of C.R. Hills

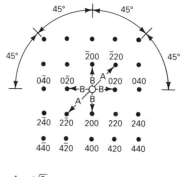

$$\frac{A}{B} = \frac{\sqrt{2}}{1} = 1.414 \qquad B = z = [001]$$

and so on. A more detailed discussion of the relationship between crystal structure and permissible (*hkl*) reflections can be found in Ref 11. The interplanar spacings are related to the ring radii by the camera constant of the microscope. The camera constant is the product of the electron wavelength and the distance from the specimen to the photographic recording film. For ring patterns, Bragg's law retains the form:

$$rd = \lambda L$$

where *d* is still the (*hkl*) interplanar spacing, but *r* is the radius of the given (*hkl*) diffraction ring. From the camera constant, λL, of the microscope, the (*hkl*) interplanar *d*-spacings are obtained, and the lattice parameter(s) can then be calculated from standard crystallographic relationships. Alternatively, a common technique for identifying an unknown from its ring pattern involves measuring the *d*-spacings of the various rings and comparing the results to the spacings of suspected candidates listed in the x-ray diffraction card file of the Joint Committee on Powder Diffraction Standards (Ref 13).

Spot patterns arise when the incident electron beam irradiates a portion of a single crystal within the specimen. The spot pattern is qualitatively analogous to the single-crystal x-ray diffraction patterns obtained using the Laue technique (the diffraction from single crystals is discussed further in Ref 2 and 11). Figure 10 shows a simple spot pattern from a single-crystal region of pure aluminum. The sample has been tilted such that a simple crystallographic direction, [100], is aligned parallel to the incident beam. This is often referred to as the [100] zone axis. The transmitted spot appears at

the center, and the various (*hkl*) reflections appear at specific distances and angles from the transmitted spot.

The transmitted spot corresponds to the point at which the transmitted beam intersects the photographic film, and each diffracted spot corresponds to the point at which a given diffracted beam intersects the photographic film. The crystal structure and orientation of the single-crystal region of the specimen being irradiated can be identified from its spot pattern. These patterns can be indexed, and the (*hkl*) plane that produced each diffraction spot determined. The pattern is solved using the modified form of Bragg's law:

$$rd = \lambda L$$

where *r* is the radial distance from the transmitted spot to the given (*hkl*) diffracted spot, and *d* is the (*hkl*) interplanar spacing. The procedure used to solve a diffraction pattern is discussed further in Example 2 in the section "Applications" in this article. Simple crystal structures and orientations can often be identified by comparing the unknown spot pattern to standard tabulations. Diffraction patterns, their solutions, and their applications are further discussed in Ref 2.

Kikuchi patterns arise when the single-crystal SADP is taken from a thick region of the thin foil. If the foil is sufficiently thick, some electrons will undergo inelastic and elastic scattering. Some inelastically scattered electrons will be subsequently elastically scattered by Bragg diffraction from the various (*hkl*) atomic planes. Two cones of diffracted electrons will be generated from each set of (*hkl*) planes, and these will intersect the fluorescent screen or photographic

film and produce two lines termed Kikuchi lines.

The lines are actually arcs of intersection with very large radii. One cone of radiation will be more intense than the general background and will produce a bright line on the film. The bright Kikuchi line is the excess line. The second cone of radiation will be less intense than the inelastic background and will produce a dark line on the film. The dark Kikuchi line is the defect line. Figure 11 shows a typical Kikuchi pattern. The symmetry apparent in the pattern indicates that the pattern was taken with the electron beam exactly parallel to the [111] zone axis. Kikuchi patterns provide much information about the crystallography of the specimen. The geometry of Kikuchi patterns is much more precise than spot patterns, allowing for very accurate determination of crystal orientation.

The Kikuchi pattern is also invaluable in establishing the proper diffracting conditions for obtaining high-contrast images. Very near the exact Bragg condition for a set of (*hkl*) planes, the excess (*hkl*) Kikuchi line will pass through the (*hkl*) spot, and the defect (*hkl*) Kikuchi line will pass through the (000) transmitted spot. This relative positioning of the diffraction spots and Kikuchi lines occurs under dynamical conditions for which high-contrast bright-field or dark-field images can be obtained. Under kinematical conditions, far from the exact Bragg condition, the excess and defect Kikuchi lines do not pass near the (*hkl*) and (000) spots, respectively (Fig. 12). Under kinematical conditions, images of low contrast are obtained. Because kinematical versus dynamical conditions are important within the context of image contrast rather than formation or use of electron-diffraction patterns, the

Fig. 11 Kikuchi pattern from [111] single-crystal silicon

The three-fold symmetry is visible in the pattern. The crystal orientation is such that each set of (*hkl*) planes parallel to the beam deviates from the Bragg condition through exactly the Bragg angle. The symmetry of the Kikuchi lines about the transmitted beam proves that the incident electron beam was parallel to the [111] zone axis. Courtesy of T.J. Headley

Fig. 12 Kikuchi pattern near the [111] zone in single-crystal silicon

The specimen has been tilted approximately 0.87° (the Bragg angle) from the exact Bragg condition for the (220) and ($\bar{2}\bar{2}0$) reflections. The spot pattern alone could indicate that the incident beam was parallel to the [111] zone axis. However, the higher precision Kikuchi pattern demonstrates that the beam is actually tilted 3.2° (the angular distance from the transmitted beam to the [111] zone) from the [111] zone axis. The Kikuchi lines converge about the actual [111] zone. Courtesy of T.J. Headley

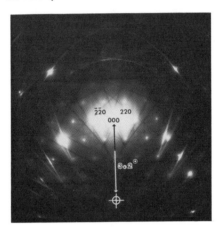

two conditions will be discussed in more detail in the section "Imaging in the Analytical Electron Microscope" in this article.

The analysis of ring, spot, and Kikuchi patterns reveals a great deal about the nature of the specimen. These patterns can be indexed to determine the crystal structure and lattice parameters of an unknown material. The advantages of such determinations using the analytical electron microscope relative to x-ray diffraction are the use of much smaller volumes of material, the use of small volume fractions of a second phase in a matrix, and simultaneous very high resolution examination of the microstructure and crystallography of the material.

Fine Structure Effects. Other useful information related to the solid-state nature of a material, in addition to the crystal structure and lattice parameters, can be determined by analyzing pattern geometry and orientation of fine structure diffraction effects in SADPs (ring, spot, and Kikuchi). Examples are (1) the determination of orientation relationships between coexisting phases, (2) the determination of dislocation Burgers vectors, (3) the determination of defect habit planes, (4) the characterization of order/disorder in the crystal, (5) the characterization of coherent precipitation, and (6) the characterization of spinodal decomposition. Points (1), (2), and (3) are discussed further in Examples 1 and 5 in the section "Applications" in this article.

Orientation Relationships. Even on a very fine microstructural scale, it is possible to

determine the orientation relationship between two coexisting phases from an examination of the relative orientation of their spot SADPs. Orientation relationships are typically expressed as a pair (one in each phase) of parallel directions in a pair of parallel planes. A common example is the Kurdjumov-Sachs relationship between martensite and austenite in a low-carbon steel: $(111)_\gamma \parallel (011)_M$ and $[10\bar{1}]_\gamma \parallel [11\bar{1}]_M$ (Ref 14). This relationship has been expanded to include the same general relationship between coexisting face-centered cubic (fcc) and body-centered cubic (bcc) phases (Ref 6). These relationships are best illustrated using stereograms or stereographic projections. Figure 13 shows the general Kurdjumov-Sachs relationship for fcc/bcc materials. The orientation relationship determination is discussed in Example 1 in the section "Applications" in this article. A more thorough description of stereograms is provided in Ref 2 and 11.

Atomic order in alloys or compounds can be detected readily by analyzing SADPs. For example, in an fcc material, the only permissible diffracted reflections are those in which $N = (h^2 + k^2 + l^2)$ and h, k, and l are all even or all odd, that is, for $N = 3, 4, 8, 11, 12, 19, 20, \ldots$. Thus, the (020) ($N = 4$) reflections are permitted, but the (010) reflections are not. Examination of the spot

pattern for an unordered fcc alloy will uncover no (010) reflections. If the lattice is ordered, the (010) and other superlattice reflections will appear. Therefore, ordered crystals can almost always be identified by the presence of superlattice spots in the spot pattern.

Figure 14 shows the image, spot diffraction pattern, and indexed schematic diffraction pattern from an iron-base superalloy sample containing an ordered fcc precipitate, γ'-$Ni_3(Ti,Al)$, in an unordered fcc austenitic matrix. The presence of ordered precipitates can be identified unambiguously by imaging the structure with one of the suspected superlattice diffraction spots. If ordered, the phase will be illuminated in the image created using the diffracted beam. This image-verification procedure is illustrated in Fig. 15.

Strain-Induced Defects. The lattice strain associated with crystal defects or precipitation can lead to streaking of some spots in the diffraction pattern. One use of elastic strain induced streaking is the study of coherent precipitation (Ref 15, 16). Figure 16 shows a diffraction pattern in which elastic strains due to coherent precipitation have streaked the diffraction spots. Although streaking is helpful in identifying the presence of coherent precipitation, it is difficult to quantify precipitation through diffraction-pattern analysis alone. Streaking of diffraction spots has several other causes, including precipitate-shape effects, stacking faults, twins, and surface films. Additional information on streaking in diffraction patterns can be found in Ref 2 and 5.

Satellite spots are another feature sometimes observed in diffraction patterns. Satellites are small additional diffraction spots occurring near the major diffraction spots. Composition modulations, such as those from spinodal decomposition, are one source of satellite spots. These satellite spots lie in the same crystallographic direction as the composition fluctuation and are due to a variation in the lattice parameter and the nature of the elastic scattering of the electrons. The spacing of the satellite spots is related to the wavelength of the compositional modulation. The elastic strain induced by the composition modulation can also induce streaking in the diffraction pattern. Satellite spots also form due to regular arrays of dislocations, twins, antiphase domain boundaries, and magnetic domains.

Convergent-Beam Electron Diffraction. The advent of the modern analytical electron microscope with STEM capability and the ability to form STEM-like fine probes in the TEM mode enables examination of the crystallographic nature of materials on a very small spatial scale through the

Fig. 13 Stereographic projection representing the Kurdjumov-Sachs orientation relationship between bcc and fcc materials

Source: Ref 6

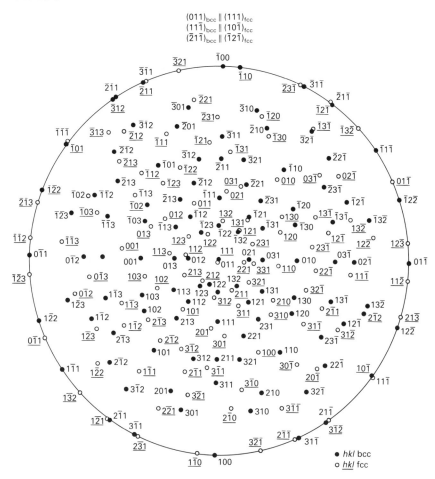

$(011)_{bcc} \parallel (111)_{fcc}$
$(11\overline{1})_{bcc} \parallel (10\overline{1})_{fcc}$
$(\overline{2}1\overline{1})_{bcc} \parallel (\overline{1}2\overline{1})_{fcc}$

• hkl bcc
○ hkl fcc

use of microdiffraction. Microdiffraction can generally be defined as any diffraction technique that allows the collection of diffraction data from volumes of the specimen less than approximately 0.5 μm in diameter. The most common microdiffraction technique in use is CBED.

In standard SAD using the conventional TEM mode, the specimen is illuminated by essentially parallel rays of electrons, producing the standard SADP with sharply defined diffraction spots. In the STEM mode, a diffraction pattern will also be produced by the scanning probe. The diffraction pattern produced by a scanning transmission electron microscope probe is a stationary diffraction pattern. To generate a diffraction pattern from a specific small volume of the specimen area, the scanning probe can be stopped and placed at the position of interest. However, because the electron probe is now highly convergent, the diffraction pattern

will be a series of disks rather than sharp spots, and the diameter of the disks is proportional to the beam convergence angle. Diffraction patterns produced by convergent beams are termed convergent-beam electron-diffraction patterns (CBEDP). Figure 17 shows a comparison between a conventional SADP and a CBEDP generated from the same specimen. The CBEDPs that have spot arrangements analogous to conventional SADPs are termed zero-order Laue zone CBED patterns (ZOLZ-CBEDPs). The procedure for indexing ZOLZ-CBEDPs is the same as that used to index conventional SADPs.

Convergent-beam electron-diffraction patterns can be used in a number of ways to extract quantitative crystallographic information from the specimen. Perhaps the most routine application of CBED is the crystallographic analysis of small volumes, such as fine precipitates, in thin foil specimens. The

CBEDP will be formed from only the electron scattering volume around the fine-beam probe. The electron scattering volume in thin foils is typically <50 nm in diameter. Therefore, CBEDPs can be generated easily from these small volumes. This type of CBEDP (ZOLZ-CBEDP) does not inherently contain more information than a conventional SADP, but it may be more convenient to perform the desired analysis using CBED because extraneous spots generated elsewhere in the larger region and illuminated during SAD will be eliminated. Thus, using CBED, it is possible to determine the structure and lattice parameter of small regions.

If the analytical electron microscope is properly configured, the ZOLZ-CBEDP will contain additional information. Using appropriately sized condenser apertures, it is possible to produce a CBEDP with large, yet nonoverlapping, diffraction disks. If the region from which the pattern is being generated is sufficiently thick, dynamical diffraction contrast information will appear in the disks; that is, it will be possible to observe thickness fringes in each disk. This form of CBEDP is referred to as a Kossel-Mollenstaedt (K-M) pattern (Ref 17, 18) (Fig. 18). Kossel-Mollenstaedt conditions are required to form discrete bright-field (transmitted electron only) and dark-field (a given group of diffracted electrons only) images in the STEM mode (further discussion is provided in the section "Imaging in the Analytical Electron Microscope" in this article).

If the size of the condenser lens aperture is increased, or the strength of the condenser and objective lens adjusted, which increases the convergence angle of the probe, the size of the diffraction disks will increase. When the disks become large enough to overlap, the resulting CBEDP is termed a Kossel pattern (Fig. 19). This term is taken from the analogous x-ray diffraction phenomenon that produces Kossel x-ray patterns. Convergent-beam electron-diffraction patterns also contain Kikuchi lines, enabling precise orientation determinations of specimen volumes too small to analyze using conventional SAD.

If there is sufficient electron scatter into diffracted beams in higher order Laue zones (HOLZ), that is, $n = 2, 3, \ldots$ in the Bragg equation, three-dimensional crystallographic information can be determined from a single CBEDP. The higher order zones appear as rings around the ZOLZ-CBEDP. The first-order Laue zone (FOLZ) corresponds to $n = 1$, the second-order Laue zone to $n = 3$, and so on. Such a pattern is often referred to as a HOLZ pattern (Fig. 20). Usually, only the FOLZ is present in the CBEDP. The HOLZ pattern shown in Fig.

Fig. 14 Bright-field image and diffraction pattern from an fcc matrix (austenite) containing precipitates having the ordered fcc (L_{12}) superlattice, $Ni_3(Ti,Al)$

The fcc spot pattern is indexed in the schematic key, and the superlattice reflections are indicated by an arrow in the diffraction pattern. The beam direction, B, and the zone axis, z, are parallel. Courtesy of T.J. Headley

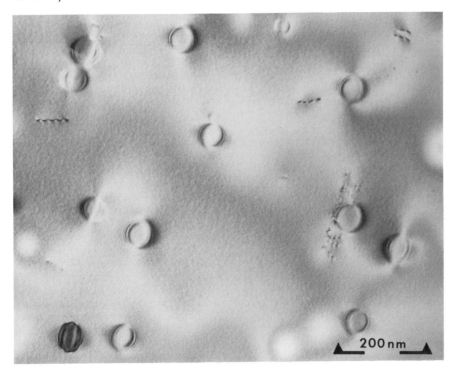

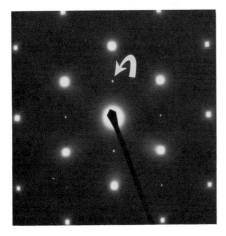

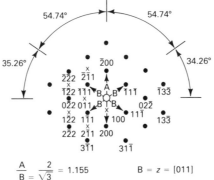

$$\frac{A}{B} = \frac{2}{\sqrt{3}} = 1.155 \qquad\qquad B = z = [011]$$

Fig. 15 Image of ordered $Ni_3(Ti,Al)$ precipitates

Image formed with the superlattice spot indicated by the arrow in Fig. 14. Courtesy of T.J. Headley

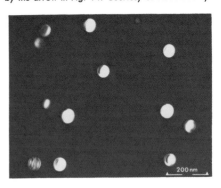

Fig. 16 Diffraction pattern from a specimen of shock-loaded Nitronic 40

The streaking is due to precipitation of a coherent second phase and deformation-induced twinning. The shape of the coherent precipitates and the elastic strain they induce has caused streaking of the precipitate diffraction spots. Courtesy of C.R. Hills

crystal. Additional information on CBEDPs, HOLZ patterns, and crystal structure determination can be found in Ref 3 and 4.

Imaging in the Analytical Electron Microscope

Imaging in the TEM Mode. In the conventional TEM mode, the electron microscope can be operated to produce either a diffraction pattern or any of several types of images on the fluorescent screen or photographic film. The diffraction pattern and the associated images are intimately related in that either the transmitted beam or any of the diffracted beams can be used to form the image. Extraction of quantitative information on the microstructure of the material

20 contains only the FOLZ ring and is typical of many published HOLZ patterns.

Higher order Laue zone patterns are obtained by operating under K-M conditions. Observation of the HOLZ rings requires a wide-angle view (typically greater than ± 10 to 12°) of the diffraction pattern. Diffraction disks within the HOLZ rings and the 000 transmitted disk may also contain HOLZ

lines, which are essentially extensions of the Kikuchi lines formed in the ZOLZ pattern. Analysis of the HOLZ lines enables lattice-parameter determination accurate to 5×10^{-4} nm. Complete analysis of the HOLZ rings, the HOLZ lines, and the intensity distribution in the ZOLZ disks in the HOLZ pattern allows complete determination of the full point and space group of the

Fig. 17 Conventional SADP (a) and ZOLZ-CBEDP (b) in 316 stainless steel

The diffraction patterns were taken along the [111] zone axis. The two diffraction patterns are essentially identical and can be indexed using the same procedure. If the beam convergence angle in the CBEDP is increased, the pattern will appear as an array of disks as opposed to discrete points. Courtesy of M. Kersker

(a)   (b)

necessitates combined use of imaging and diffraction-pattern analysis.

When the incident electron beam strikes the specimen, some of the electrons pass through the foil without undergoing elastic or inelastic scattering and form the major part of the transmitted beam. Other electrons that have undergone only inelastic scattering, and have therefore not had their trajectory significantly altered, form the remaining portion of the transmitted beam. An image can be produced with the transmitted electrons by inserting an aperture in the plane (known as the back focal plane) at which the diffraction pattern is first formed just below the objective lens and the specimen. This aperture is termed the objective aperture. When the objective aperture is positioned to allow only the electrons in the transmitted beam to pass through and contribute to the image, the resulting image is termed a bright-field image. Bright-field imaging is commonly used for routine examination of the microstructural features of a specimen.

If the specimen is crystalline, many of the electrons will undergo coherent elastic scattering from the various (hkl) planes, resulting in one or more additional electron beams termed diffracted beams. Each diffracted beam will contain only electrons scattered elastically from a given set of (hkl) crystallographic planes. If any one of these

Fig. 18 K-M CBEDP from pure aluminum

The diffraction disks are large, but do not overlap. (a) The specimen is very thin, and no detail is visible in the disks. (b) The specimen is sufficiently thick to induce dynamical contrast so that the image of the microstructure is visible in the diffraction disks. Source: Ref 3

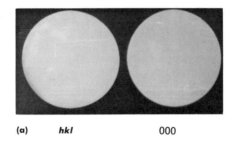

(a)   *hkl*   000

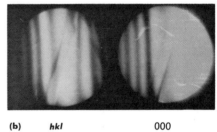

(b)   *hkl*   000

diffracted beams is permitted to pass through the objective aperture to create an image, the result is termed a dark-field image. To improve the resolution in a dark-field image, it is standard practice to deflect the diffracted beam of interest such that it lies along the optic axis of the microscope column, minimizing the effects of the magnetic lens aberrations (especially spherical aberration and astigmatism). Under these conditions, the result is termed a centered dark-field image.

If, under examination, the microstructure contains more than one crystalline phase, overlapping diffraction patterns can occur in the SADP. If such a structure is imaged in

dark field, only the crystalline phase that has scattered electrons into the particular diffracted beam selected for imaging will be illuminated in the dark-field image. Thus, imaging in dark field often enables distinguishing microstructural detail that cannot be observed in bright-field images.

For example, Fig. 21 shows the diffraction-pattern, bright-field, and dark-field images from an iron-base superalloy. The alloy, similar to A-286, has an austenitic matrix (fcc) with coherent γ' precipitates, $Ni_3(Ti,Al)$. The precipitates have an ordered fcc structure (L_{12}) and are approximately 2 to 3 nm in diameter. In bright field, the γ' precipitates are only

Fig. 19 Kossel CBEDP from 316 stainless steel in which the diffraction disks overlap

Only the zero-order Laue reflections are visible in this image. Courtesy of M. Kersker

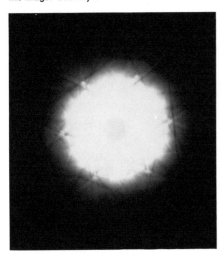

Fig. 20 HOLZ pattern taken from 316 stainless steel

Only the FOLZ ring is present in the CBEDP. The HOLZ lines are also visible. Analysis of these patterns allows for precise determination of the three-dimensional crystallography of the specimen. Courtesy of M. Kersker

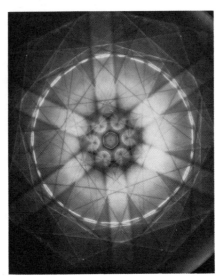

marginally visible, although the elastic strain fields they generate are apparent. However, selecting a diffracted beam from the γ′ enables observation of the precipitates in the dark-field image.

Dark-field imaging is also commonly used to delineate regions of different crystallographic orientation. Such regions also produce overlapping diffraction effects in the SADP. Figure 22 shows an example in a crystal of rutile (TiO$_2$) containing an annealing twin. In the bright-field image, the difference in contrast between the matrix and twin is small. However, by imaging in dark field with one of the diffracted beams from

the twin, the twinned region is illuminated.

Imaging in the STEM mode also allows for generation of bright-field and dark-field images. These images contain the same information contained in their conventional TEM analogs. When the electron probe is rastered over the crystalline specimen surface in the STEM mode, a stationary diffraction pattern will form below the specimen. By moving the transmitted electron detector under any beam exiting from the bottom of

the foil, a STEM image is created. If the detector is positioned to intercept only the electrons in the transmitted beam, a bright-field image will result. If the detector is positioned to intercept only one diffracted beam, an image equivalent to a conventional centered dark-field image will result.

Imaging of only one unique beam requires a K-M CBEDP in which the diffraction disks do not overlap. If a Kossel pattern in which the diffraction disks overlap is used, the resulting image will be a multibeam image, and some degree of diffraction contrast may be lost. Many analytical electron microscopes are also equipped to form annular dark-field images. The annular dark-field detector is a solid-state detector in the shape of a ring that surrounds the normal bright-field electron detector. With the annular detector, it is possible to create a dark-field image using several diffracted beams, all of which lie at approximately the same radial distance from the transmitted beam.

Relationship Between TEM and STEM Images. It is possible in the STEM mode to form images that are essentially equivalent to the conventional TEM images. Obtaining equivalent images in conventional TEM and STEM is termed the principle of reciprocity (Ref 3). For crystalline materials, the STEM images offer no advantage over the equivalent image obtained using TEM. The principal use of STEM imaging in crystalline materials is as an aid in locating a given area to analyze microchemically (EDS, EELS) or crystallographically (CBED). However, for amorphous materials in which contrast in the image is not due to a diffraction effect but to differential absorption, STEM images are often superior. Proper setting of the lens in the STEM condition allows use of more electrons to

Fig. 21 Diffraction pattern and bright-field and centered dark-field images of an iron-base superalloy

(a) The diffraction pattern is a [100] fcc zone axis pattern. (b) By imaging with the transmitted beam, the γ′ precipitates are not visible. Only the strain fields associated with the precipitates are visible. (c) In centered dark field, using the [100] reflection from the γ′ precipitates as indicated by the arrow in (a), the precipitates are clearly visible. Courtesy of T.J. Headley

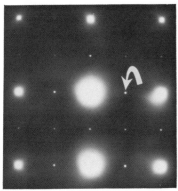

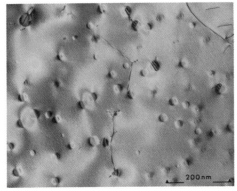

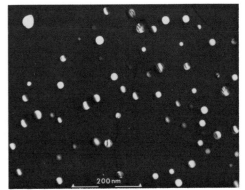

(a)   (b)   (c)

Fig. 22 Bright-field and dark-field images of an annealing (growth) twin in rutile

(a) Bright-field image of twinned grain (arrow) in strong contrast. (b) Diffraction pattern of twinned grain showing [111] zone twinned on (ī01). (c) Dark-field image of matrix spot a (see Fig. 22b). (d) Dark-field image of twin spot b (see Fig. 22b). Courtesy of M.J. Carr

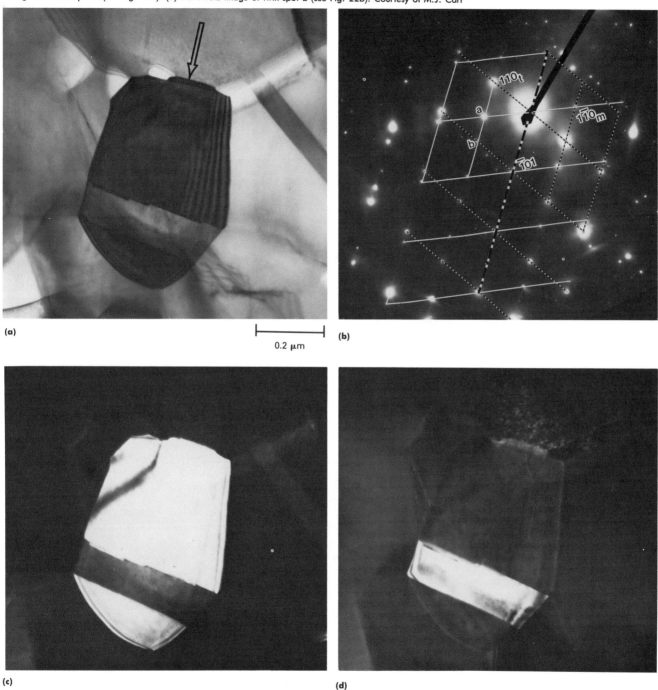

(a)

0.2 μm

(b)

(c)

(d)

produce the image than can be obtained in conventional TEM.

In crystalline materials, images and diffraction patterns can be generated under kinematical and dynamical diffracting conditions. Two theories of diffraction contrast, termed the kinematical theory and the dynamical theory, have been developed to account for the image contrast observed when kinematical or dynamical conditions apply. A thorough understanding of kinematical and dynamical diffracting conditions is essential for the microscopist, but not necessarily the materials engineer or scientist who wishes to apply AEM to a given problem. Therefore, no further discussion of the mathematical theory or use of these diffracting conditions is warranted. A discussion of

Fig. 23 Bright-field image of polycrystalline aluminum showing dislocations as they often appear in metallic crystals

The dislocations appear as dark curved lines and exhibit dark contrast relative to the matrix due to the distortion of the atomic planes near the dislocations. The dislocations must be oriented properly relative to the incident beam to be visible in the image. If the specimen is tilted relative to the beam, these dislocations will "go out of contrast" and disappear from the image; other dislocations will "come into contrast" and appear in the image. Courtesy of C.R. Hills

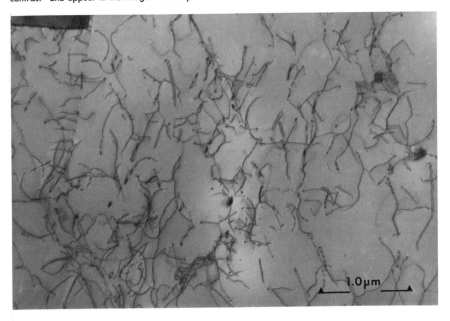

1.0 μm

these diffracting conditions and how they influence imaging and defect analysis is provided in Ref 2. The formal mathematical treatment of kinematical and dynamical diffracting conditions is covered in Ref 5. Kinematical and dynamical diffraction conditions are also discussed in the article "Transmission Electron Microscopy" in Volume 9 of the 9th Edition of *Metals Handbook*.

Contrast Mechanisms. The details of the microstructure of a material can be observed using TEM because the electrons interact with the material in one of several ways to create image contrast. Three important mechanisms produce image contrast in AEM micrographs: diffraction contrast; absorption, amplitude, or mass-thickness contrast; and phase contrast.

Diffraction contrast is the dominant mechanism in crystalline materials, revealing structural features larger than approximately 1.5 nm. When an electron enters a material, it may undergo scattering. In thin crystalline materials, the dominant form of scattering is coherent elastic scattering, in which the electrons are scattered into specific directions. These directions depend on the crystallographic orientation of the various atomic planes in the scattering volume of the material relative to the incident beam. Coherent scattering is re-

sponsible for the formation of the diffraction pattern.

Regions of different crystallographic orientation in the specimen will diffract the electrons differently. For example, one region may not scatter strongly, leaving a large portion of the incident electrons in the transmitted beam, but another region may scatter strongly into one or more diffracted beams, leaving far fewer electrons in the transmitted beam. When imaged in bright field, the weak-scattering region will appear bright, and the strongly scattering region will appear much darker.

Many different physical features can produce regions of different crystallographic orientation relative to the incident electron beam. Examples are different grains and precipitates within a matrix. If the crystal lattice is strained, such as it might be by a dislocation or a small coherent precipitate, the atomic planes in the strained region will be oriented differently relative to the incident electrons than are planes in unstrained regions. Therefore, diffraction conditions will be different in the strained region, producing diffraction contrast in the image. Figure 23 shows diffraction contrast generated by dislocations in a crystalline material. Diffraction contrast is discussed further in Examples 5 and 6 in the section "Applications" in this article.

In addition to microstructural features that can create diffraction contrast, several artifacts can also induce contrast in the image. One of the most common is the bend contour. Thin regions of the foil are usually bent, causing a continuous variation in the crystal/beam orientation. This condition will cause varying diffraction contrast in the image. Typical bend contours in a polycrystalline molybdenum-rhenium alloy are shown in Fig. 24. Other contrast artifacts occur in crystalline materials, for example, thickness fringes that appear near the edge of a wedge-shaped thin foil and interference fringes that appear at grain boundaries and incoherent phase interfaces.

Absorption Contrast. Amorphous materials exhibit a different form of image contrast known as absorption, amplitude, or mass-thickness contrast. Such amorphous materials as biological thin sections, fully amorphous polymers, or replicas of fracture surfaces do not exhibit diffraction contrast. An electron-diffraction pattern from such a material will show the transmitted beam and only a weak general dispersion of scattered electrons. No electrons are diffracted into any specific directions. Any contrast visible in the image of such a material is due to absorption of the electrons as they pass through the specimen. Regions of the specimen with higher mass density and greater thickness will absorb more electrons and therefore exhibit dark contrast.

To enhance the contrast in these images, the biological or polymeric specimens are often stained with a heavy metal that will attach itself only to specific areas of interest. Replicas of fracture surfaces are often obliquely shadowed with metals to enhance absorption contrast. Replicas will be discussed in the section "Sample Preparation" in this article.

Some amorphous materials possess a degree of short-range order. The classic example of this type of amorphous material is a glass, both ceramic glasses and amorphous metals. These materials are not crystalline and therefore do not have long-range order, but they do possess some degree of short-range order. The diffraction patterns generated from these materials contain the transmitted beam and one or more diffuse rings due to the short-range order. When the objective aperture is positioned to exclude the outer diffuse rings from the image, the contrast exhibited in these materials is a combination of absorption contrast and diffraction contrast. Images and diffraction patterns from a glass-ceramic are shown in Fig. 25 to illustrate diffuse halo diffraction contrast. Image contrast in amorphous (short-range ordered)

Fig. 24 Bend contours in a polycrystalline molybdenum-rhenium alloy

The bend contour is an artifact due to local bending of the specimen. Note that bend contours are not continuous across grain boundaries because each grain has a different crystallographic orientation and therefore the diffracting conditions near the bend are different in each grain. Courtesy of C.R. Hills

1.0 μm

lattice images shown in Fig. 26. To produce a lattice image, the transmitted beam and one diffracted beam are passed through the objective aperture and combined. The phase interference between these two beams yields the periodic intensity fringes present in the image. Under the appropriate imaging conditions, there is a one-to-one correspondence between the intensity fringes in the image and the atomic planes from which the electrons were diffracted. In this case, the spacing of the fringes in the image is equivalent to the spacing of the atomic planes.

Using lattice images, it is possible to examine the atomic detail of grain boundaries and phase interfaces and to image edge dislocations. Under special conditions verifiable using image calculations based on electron scattering, it is possible to produce a phase-contrast image with a two-dimensional variation in intensity (the image appears as an array of bright and dark spots). In this image, there is a one-to-one correspondence between individual atoms or groups of atoms, such as tetrahedra, in the material and the intensity maxima in the image. The resulting images, known as structure images, represent what is essentially atomic resolution electron microscopy. Individual atoms have not been imaged using conventional TEM, but free heavy-metal atoms supported on thin carbon films have been imaged using specialized STEM techniques (Ref 19, 20).

Special Techniques. Several special techniques can be used to image the microstructural details of a material. Diffraction contrast in standard bright-field and dark-field images often suffices for examination of crystal defects, such as dislocations,

materials is discussed further in Example 12 in the section "Applications" in this article.

Phase contrast is another important AEM image-contrast mechanism, in which electrons that illuminate the specimen are coherent and therefore in phase. As the electrons pass through the foil, some interact with atoms, are scattered, and undergo a phase shift. Thus, electrons leaving the bottom surface of the foil contain small differences in phase. When these scattered electrons are allowed to pass through the objective aperture and are recombined to form an image, the phase differences produce intensity variations in the image and thus image contrast.

Phase contrast is often used to observe structural detail at a scale less than 1 nm and was the mechanism used to produce the

Fig. 25 Conventional TEM bright-field images and associated diffraction patterns from a ceramic containing crystalline and amorphous phases

(a) A TEM bright-field image of a crystal of Li$_3$PO$_4$ in a matrix of Li$_2$O-Al$_2$O$_3$-SiO$_2$ glass containing P$_2$O$_5$. (b) The diffraction pattern from the crystal is typical of that produced by materials with long-range order. (c) The diffraction pattern from the glassy matrix shows the transmitted beam and a diffuse diffraction halo that arises as a consequence of the short-range order present in glassy materials. Courtesy of T.J. Headley

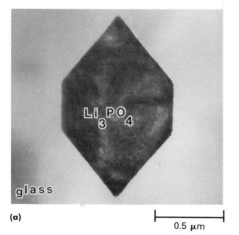

(a)

0.5 μm

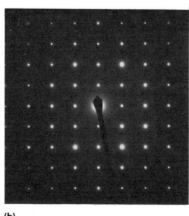

(b)

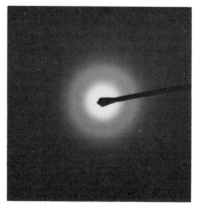

(c)

Fig. 26 Lattice image of zinc oxide formed by combining the transmitted beam and (002) diffracted beam

The interplanar spacing is 0.26 nm. A grain boundary, inclined relative to the incident electron beam, is visible in the upper portion of the photomicrograph. Courtesy of T.J. Headley

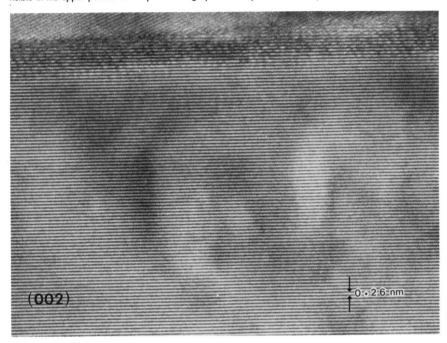

misfitting precipitates, and stacking faults. However, in some cases, the difference in contrast between the normal matrix and the strained matrix is small, or the strain contrast images of closely spaced defects overlap, making it difficult to resolve microstructural details.

To produce high-resolution diffraction contrast images of crystal defects, it is often desirable to use the weak-beam technique. In this technique, only diffraction contrast from very near the defect core is used to form the image. Consequently, the image contrast and resolution are exceedingly high. The weak-beam technique and its applications are discussed in more detail in Example 5 in the section "Applications" in this article.

A useful special case of phase contrast permits examination of the magnetic microstructure of the material. The imaging of magnetic domain boundaries using low-resolution (not atomic-scale) phase-contrast microscopy is termed Lorentz microscopy. Lorentz microscopy allows examination and characterization of the magnetic domain walls, the direction of domain magnetization, and interactions between the magnetic domains and fine-scale structural crystal defects. Further details on Lorentz microscopy and its applications are provided in Ref 2.

Individual atoms have also been imaged by using a special field emission dedicated scanning transmission electron microscope (Ref 19). To visualize the atoms in this instrument, electrons elastically and inelastically scattered by the atoms are collected with the electron energy loss spectrometer and annular dark-field detector, respectively. The ratio of these signals is used to modulate the CRT, and the atoms can be visualized because the elastic and inelastic scattering have different functional dependencies on the atomic number of the atoms being imaged.

X-Ray Microanalysis in the Analytical Electron Microscope

The advantage of AEM-EDS relative to other electron beam microanalytical techniques (SEM, electron probe microanalysis, and Auger electron spectroscopy) is its ability to generate x-ray spectra from, and therefore determine the composition of, very small volumes of the specimen. As discussed in the section "Electron Beam/Specimen Interactions" in this article, one product of the inelastic scattering of electrons in a target is the generation of characteristic x-rays. Modern analytical electron microscopes are equipped with solid-state energy-dispersive spectrometers to collect these characteristic x-rays (see the section "Signal Detectors" in this article).

Qualitative analysis is one of the most common uses of EDS in the analytical electron microscope. The energy-dispersive spectrometer is ideal for qualitative analysis because characteristic x-rays can be determined from approximately 1 keV (for a beryllium-window energy-dispersive spectrometer) to 20 keV, allowing rapid qualitative identification of the elements present in the specimen at the point of beam impingement. Detectors for EDS are essentially 100% efficient for the collection of x-rays from 3 to 17 keV. X-rays less energetic than 3 keV are partially absorbed in the detector; x-rays more energetic than 17 keV may pass through the spectrometer and may not be counted. Because detector efficiency decreases sharply at energies above 25 keV, it is not practical to collect x-rays exceeding 25 keV. When performing a qualitative analysis in the analytical electron microscope, collection of a spectrum from 0 to 20 keV is typical.

Identifying unknown elements in the specimen necessitates considering the appearance of K, L, and M x-ray line families in the spectrum. All the lines in the spectrum must be identified when analyzing the spectrum. Several aids are available to assist identification of the peaks in the spectrum and therefore the elements in the specimen (the x-ray as it is generated in the specimen is usually referred to as an x-ray line, but the x-ray line as displayed on the CRT is usually referred to as an x-ray peak). Modern multichannel analyzers, as discussed in the section "Signal Detectors" in this article, are often integral components of the computers on analytical electron microscopes. The computer systems have software that assists identification of the peaks in the x-ray spectrum. Figure 27 illustrates the qualitative analysis of two coexisting phases in an iron-base superalloy.

Qualitative EDS can be performed in any of several operating modes. Energy-dispersive spectrometry is usually performed in the analytical electron microscope to identify the composition of some small volume (a precipitate or inclusion) in the specimen. To collect the spectrum from this small volume, the instrument can be operated in the TEM or STEM mode. In TEM, the beam can be focused to a spot and placed on the region of interest. In STEM, the beam raster can be halted, and the beam then placed on the point of interest. In most cases, the capabilities for qualitative EDS are the same for operation in the TEM or STEM mode.

One useful qualitative application of EDS is the generation of x-ray scanning maps, sometimes termed elemental-distribution maps or elemental-concentration maps. Such maps show the spatial distribution of a se-

Fig. 27 AEM-EDS spectra collected from the iron-base superalloy Haynes Alloy 556

(a) Bright-field image of precipitates that decorate the grain boundaries. (b) and (c) show EDS spectra from the matrix and particles, respectively. Iron, chromium, nickel, cobalt, molybdenum, tungsten, and titanium are detected in the matrix. Only tantalum in the form of Ta(C,N) is detected in the precipitates. Carbon and nitrogen cannot be detected using a conventional beryllium-window EDS detector. Courtesy of W.R. Sorenson

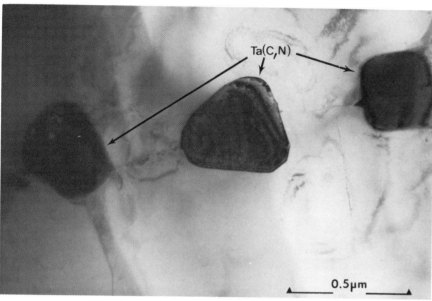

(a)

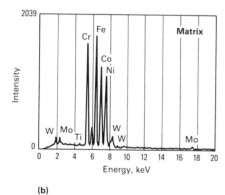

(b)

(c)

lected element in the region of the specimen being scanned by the electron beam. As discussed in the article "Electron Probe X-Ray Microanalysis" in this Volume, x-ray scanning maps can be produced in an analog or digital mode. Analog and digitally recorded images are compared in Fig. 28. Additional information on digital imaging can be found in Ref 21.

Quantitative analysis of the composition of a region in the thin foil is often desired. Quantification of x-ray intensity data and determination of a chemical composition necessitate calculation of the composition of the specimen from the x-ray

intensity measured by the spectrometer. The x-ray intensity emitted by the specimen and the x-ray intensity measured by the spectrometer are related through detector efficiency. For x-rays from 2 to approximately 18 keV, the emitted and measured x-ray intensities are related linearly. For lower energy x-rays, a correction for absorption in the detector must be included (Ref 22). X-rays with energies exceeding 18 keV are rarely used for quantitative analysis.

The intensity of the x-rays generated in the target is directly related to the number of atoms of a given species (the atomic fraction of the element of interest) that interact with

the beam as well as the efficiency of the electron beam at stimulating x-ray emission from the atoms in the target. If the efficiency is known, the atomic fraction of each species should be easy to calculate, assuming the generated x-ray intensity can be determined. In thin foils, the emitted x-ray intensity and the generated x-ray intensity are essentially equal. Therefore, determining compositions from the measured x-ray intensities is generally straightforward.

Cliff and Lorimer recognized this relationship and proposed a simple technique to determine the composition of thin foils (Ref 23). To ensure that variations in x-ray intensity were due only to composition variations in the specimen and not thickness variations in the foil, Cliff and Lorimer suggested using ratios of the measured x-ray intensities. The data-analysis technique they proposed is termed the Cliff-Lorimer, or standardless ratio, technique:

$$\frac{C_A}{C_B} = k_{AB} \frac{I_A}{I_B}$$

where C_A and C_B are the concentrations of A and B in the specimen, respectively; I_A and I_B are the background-corrected x-ray intensities for elements A and B, respectively; and k_{AB} is the Cliff-Lorimer sensitivity factor. The constraining condition is that $C_A + C_B = 1$ for an A-B binary alloy. The standardless ratio equation is easily solved arithmetically because k_{AB} is known (see below) and is not a function of composition. An iterative procedure is not required, and compositions can be calculated using a desktop calculator. If the unknown contains more than two elements, the compositions can be determined by simple matrix algebra. A series of uncoupled equations can be written for each pair of elements, that is, k_{AB}, k_{AC}, k_{AD}, . . . , k_{An}, with the final equation being $C_A + C_B + C_C + \ldots + C_n = 1$.

The value of the sensitivity factor, k_{AB}, can be determined experimentally or from first-principle calculations. For quick one-time-only analyses, theoretically determined values of k_{AB} can be used, although the accuracy of the results is poorer than that achieved using experimentally determined values of k_{AB}. Theoretically determined values of k_{AB} are usually assumed to be accurate to 10% (relative) for Kα x-rays and 15 to 20% (relative) for Lα x-rays. More detailed studies require use of standards of known composition and determination of k_{AB} for a given set of experimental conditions. Experimentally determined values of k_{AB} can be as accurate as 2 to 3% (relative).

Limitations of Quantitative EDS. Despite the apparent mathematical simplicity of quantitative EDS analysis of thin foils,

Fig. 28 Analog (a) and digitally filtered (b) x-ray maps for iron in an aluminum matrix

The definition and clarity of the digitally processed image is apparent. The contrast between the matrix and the iron-rich particles is enhanced in the digitally acquired image relative to the analog image. Courtesy of C.E. Fiori

(a)

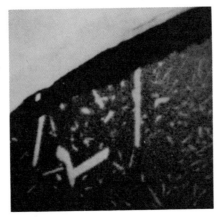

(b)

several limitations of analysis must be considered. Two limitations (discussed above) are the inability of the beryllium-window detector to detect x-rays emitted from elements lighter than sodium and the 150-eV energy resolution of an energy-dispersive spectrometer, which limits the ability of the spectrometer to resolve x-rays of similar energy. Other limitations include spectrum artifacts, specimen-generated x-ray/specimen effects (x-ray absorption and fluorescence), x-ray spatial resolution, elemental detectability limits, and the accuracy and precision of AEM-EDS.

Artifact peaks may arise in the x-ray spectrum. These artifacts must be identified unambiguously; they could be attributed erroneously to some element not present in the specimen. Three of the most common spectral artifacts are the silicon fluorescence peak, the silicon escape peak, and summation (or pile-up) peaks. The critical requirement of EDS qualitative analysis is that all peaks, real and artifact, must be identified. The procedure for EDS qualitative analysis is identical for spectra collected from the analytical electron microscope or the scanning electron microscope (Ref 8). For details on EDS qualitative analysis, see the article "Electron Probe X-Ray Microanalysis" in this Volume.

X-Ray Absorption and Fluorescence. The derivation of the standardless ratio, or Cliff-Lorimer, equation assumed that the measured x-ray intensity ratio was equal to the generated x-ray intensity ratio. The assumption is valid only if absorption or fluorescence of x-rays does not occur in the specimen. Specimens in which there is no significant absorption or fluorescence are said to obey the thin film criterion (Ref 24).

The thin film criterion is violated if the generated and measured x-ray intensity ratios differ by more than 5% (relative). The thickness at which the thin film criterion is violated can be calculated from the mass-absorption coefficients of the x-rays in the specimen, the x-ray path length through the specimen, and the average specimen density. The thickness at which the specimen violates the thin film criterion is a strong function of the elements in the specimen. The range of thicknesses can extend from 10 to 20 nm for Ni-Al to several micrometers for other systems.

The opposite problem to absorption, x-ray fluorescence, is usually not encountered in thin film analyses. X-ray fluorescence occurs when specimen-generated high-energy x-rays, rather than electrons, excite other atoms in the specimen and produce secondary x-ray emission. Specimens containing iron and chromium are among those that show a measurable effect. In general, if fluorescence effects occur, the absorption problems are too severe to correct, and a thinner region of the foil should be examined. Additional information on x-ray absorption and fluorescence and methods for their correction is provided in Ref 4, 8, and 11.

X-ray spatial resolution is defined as the volume from which the characteristic x-ray spectrum is generated. It is not possible to determine uniquely the composition of any volume smaller than the x-ray generation volume. In bulk analysis—for example, using the scanning electron microscope or electron microprobe—the electron scattering volume and therefore the volume of x-ray generation are of the order of 1 μm in

diameter. Electron scattering dominates the size of the volume, not the diameter of the incident beam. A 1- or 200-nm-diam incident beam will yield the same x-ray generation volume and therefore x-ray spatial resolution of approximately 1 μm. Therefore, it is usually impossible to measure the composition of submicrometer particles with bulk specimens in the scanning electron microscope or electron microprobe.

As discussed in the section "Electron Beam/Specimen Interactions" in this article, the volume of electron scattering in thin foils is much smaller than in bulk targets. The scattering volume is sufficiently small that the diameter of the incident beam significantly influences the size of the scattering volume. An incident beam diameter of 5 to 10 nm is typical in many instruments. For that size incident beam and, for example, a 150-nm-thick specimen of steel, the volume of x-ray generation and therefore the x-ray spatial resolution are approximately 40 nm.

In general, the composition of volumes (small particles, precipitates, inclusions, and so on) as small as 50 nm can be measured using AEM-EDS. Consequently, it is possible to determine the composition of precipitates as small as 50 nm in diameter or to measure concentration gradients over submicrometer distances. Using analytical electron microscopes designed to generate fine beams (0.5 nm, such as in an FEG-dedicated scanning transmission electron microscope) and very thin specimens, volumes less than 10 nm in diameter can be examined. Analysis of small particles is discussed in Examples 2 and 10 in the section "Applications" in this article. Spatially short concentration gradients are discussed in Example 9.

The volume of x-ray generation in thin foils can be measured experimentally or calculated (Ref 25). The most accurate calculations are performed using Monte Carlo techniques, such as those described in Ref 26 and in the article "Electron Probe X-Ray Microanalysis" in this Volume. Several simple scattering models have also been developed that allow rapid calculation of the scattering volume (Ref 24, 27-29). The ability to calculate x-ray scattering volumes is valuable in materials science because it indicates the scale of microstructural evaluation possible using AEM-EDS for the given specimens in question. Under certain conditions, it is possible to determine the composition of smaller particles if they can be removed from the matrix. One method of removing such particles is through the use of extraction replicas. In this case, that some electrons will scatter out of the particle is not experimentally significant. Particles less than 100 nm in diameter should be removed from the surrounding matrix if possible.

Elemental Detectability Limits. The minimum mass fraction (MMF) is defined as the smallest concentration of a trace element present in the matrix that can be detected statistically. The minimum detectable mass (MDM) is defined as the smallest quantity of a concentrated element, for example, a small free particle or a small metal particle in a polymeric matrix, that can be detected. The values of the MMF and MDM are statistical. Therefore, smaller values of MMF and MDM are obtainable for larger numbers of x-ray counts.

The total number of x-ray counts obtained from thin foils in the analytical electron microscope is smaller than that obtained for bulk particles analyzed in the electron microprobe; the electron-beam current in the analytical electron microscope is smaller than in the electron microprobe, and the volume of x-ray generation in thin foils is smaller than in bulk specimens. In thin metallurgical specimens in which the elements have similar atomic weights, it is possible to obtain MMF as low as 0.1 wt%, although 0.3 to 0.5 wt% is more typical for routine analyses. The MMF is higher for light elements in a heavy matrix. For heavy elements in a light matrix, the MMF may be smaller. Under ideal conditions, such as iron in an organic matrix, the MDM is of the order of 10^{-20} g. For metallurgical samples, such as concentrations of bismuth in copper, an MDM of ~5×10^{-18} is typical (Ref 30).

The accuracy of quantification is the final limitation of AEM-EDS analysis. Accuracy is the closeness of the measured composition to the actual composition. The accuracy of a quantitative analysis, like the MMF and MDM, is statistical. Because the total counts obtained using AEM-EDS will be far smaller than those obtained in the electron probe microanalyzer, it is unreasonable to expect the accuracy of AEM-EDS to approach that obtainable in the electron probe microanalyzer.

The error in any given analysis is the result of any error in k_{AB} and in I_A and I_B. Optimum values of k_{AB} are accurate to ±3%. For any data point, it is difficult to measure I_A/I_B to an accuracy exceeding 2 to 3%. It is reasonable to assume that the errors add in quadrature; therefore, the total error is approximately 5% (relative). This low a percentage of total error is often impossible to achieve in practice. Lack of time in collecting large numbers of counts and potential problems with x-ray peak overlap may limit the accuracy of the analysis severely. A more conservative and routinely more reliable limit of accuracy is of the order of 10 to 15% (relative). Energy-dispersive

spectrometry x-ray analysis in the analytical electron microscope is discussed further in Ref 3 and 4.

Solution of many materials problems often necessitates combining results from EDS microanalysis with results obtained from other AEM techniques. Electron-diffraction data and EDS data are often used in a complementary manner. Complementary EDS and electron-diffraction analysis are discussed further in Examples 2 and 4 in the section ''Applications'' in this article.

Electron Energy Loss Spectroscopy

The electrons in the transmitted beam either pass through the thin foil specimen without undergoing any energy loss, or they suffer only inelastic scattering, imparting a loss in energy without a significant change in trajectory. Electron energy loss spectroscopy involves analysis of the energy distribution of the inelastically scattered electrons in the transmitted beam. Theoretically, EELS should be an effective technique for quantitative analysis. Ideally, hydrogen could be detected using EELS, but boron is a more realistic practical limit.

During EELS, all the inelastically scattered electrons are detected. Therefore, the signal intensity should be much higher than the x-ray intensity, because only a small fraction of inelastic scattering events produces characteristic x-ray emission. In addition, the spatial resolution for analysis should approach the diameter of the incident beam (the elastic scattering responsible for the relatively large volume of x-ray production does not produce energy loss electrons that are collected).

However, limitations due to specimen thickness and difficulties in quantification have prevented EELS from attaining its potential. For example, it is not possible to measure carbon or nitrogen dissolved in steel using EELS. The physics of energy loss favor strong EELS signal generation for light elements relative to x-rays. As such, EELS can be a useful complement to EDS analysis of thin foils, because EDS is usually insensitive to light elements. It may be, for example, an ideal technique for determining if the tantalum-containing precipitates shown in Fig. 27 are TaC, TaN, or Ta(C,N).

Magnetic Spectrometer. As discussed in the section ''Signal Detectors'' in this article, the EELS detector is a magnetic sector spectrometer that discriminates the energy loss electrons on the basis of their absolute energy. Electrons with different energies and therefore different velocities are bent through different radii of curvature by the magnetic field of the spectrometer. Once

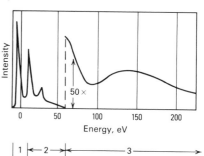

Fig. 29 Typical EELS spectrum
The zero-loss (1), low-loss (2), and core-loss (3) regions are shown. Ionization edges that can appear in region 3 can, under proper conditions, be used to determine the composition of the sample volume from which the EELS spectrum was generated. Note the scale amplification by 50× in region 3.

spatially separated by the spectrometer, the electrons can be detected and processed. The signal from the electron energy loss spectrometer can be used to generate an EELS spectrum, which allows determination (at least qualitatively) of the composition of the volume from which the energy loss electrons originated. Alternatively, the spectrometer can be used to produce a compositional map, with the analytical electron microscope operating in the STEM mode. The signal from a select portion of the EELS spectrum, for example, that corresponding to carbon, can be used to modulate the CRT and produce a carbon map.

The EELS spectrum shown in Fig. 29 is divided into three regions. Each region arises due to a different group of electron/sample interactions.

Region 1 (0 to 10 eV) is the zero-loss region. The zero-loss peak contains the unscattered electrons, elastically scattered electrons that excite the specimen in the transmitted beam, and electrons that generate phonon excitations (atomic vibrations) in the specimen. The energy loss due to the excitation of a phonon vibration is only approximately 0.02 eV, which cannot be resolved using the electron energy loss spectrometer. The zero-loss peak is the most intense portion of the EELS spectrum, often containing over 70% of the total number of electrons in the spectrum. It has little value for microanalysis, but is used to calibrate the energy scale of the electron energy loss spectrometer.

Region 2 (10 to 60 eV) is the low-loss region. The total number of electrons in the low-loss region is typically only 5 to 10% as intense as the zero-loss region. The peaks contained in the low-loss region are due to plasmon excitations. The intensity of the

Fig. 30 Preionization and postionization structure in a typical K-shell ionization edge

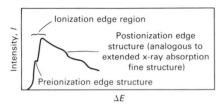

plasmon peaks depends on and increases with the thickness of the specimen. Consequently, the number of visible plasmon peaks also increases with specimen thickness.

Analysis of the plasmon spectrum has proved to be an accurate method of foil-thickness determination (Ref 4). In a few metallic systems with many free electrons, such as aluminum, analysis of the plasmon spectrum can be used to determine chemical composition (Ref 31). Because the plasmon spectrum is sensitive to the interactions of the incident electrons with the molecular orbitals involved in bonding, it is also useful in quantifying the composition of organic materials (Ref 32). Although qualitative analysis of these materials has been demonstrated, quantification of the data is not yet possible.

Region 3 (>60 eV), the core-loss region, is the most important region of the EELS spectrum for microanalysis. The signal in the core-loss region is very weak relative to that in the zero-loss and low-loss regions. Therefore, the core-loss region of the spectrum is often amplified 50 to 100 times to highlight the detail in this portion of the spectrum.

The peaks, or edges, arise because of interactions between the incident electrons and the inner-shell electrons of atoms in the specimen. These are the same inner-shell electrons responsible for the generation of characteristic x-rays. When an incident electron ionizes an atom, it relinquishes a specific amount of energy. The amount of energy lost in ionizing the target atoms is the electron energy loss. If the energy lost by an incident electron is measured, it is possible to determine which ionization event occurred in the specimen and therefore which element(s) is present in the specimen. Because every atom has a unique electron-shell structure, the electron energy losses suffered by the beam electrons are also unique. Each atom contains several electron shells and subshells. Each element produces a family of ionization edges that are visible in the EELS spectrum.

If the ionization edges present in the EELS spectrum are analyzed closely, fine detail may be visible in the spectrum immediately before and after the ionization edge. This detail is termed fine structure. The detail before the edge is the preionization edge fine structure, and the detail on the tail of the edge is the postionization edge structure (Fig. 30).

Only the postedge structure has shown potential utility for AEM materials analysis. The entire range of detail included in the postionization structure is termed the extended x-ray absorption fine structure (EXAFS). The phenomenon is analogous to the extended absorption structure that appears after an x-ray absorption edge. Theoretically, analysis of the EXAFS spectrum should enable calculation of the position of the atoms in the material, that is, the radial distribution function about the atom, and determination of the nature of bonding between atoms. Specimen-thickness effects and difficulties in deconvoluting EXAFS spectra have prohibited routine use of the technique in AEM. If AEM-EXAFS fulfills its potential, it may become an effective tool in determining atomic configuration in crystalline materials. Additional information on EXAFS is provided in Ref 33 and in the article "Extended X-Ray Absorption Fine Structure" in this Volume.

Qualitative EELS. The most frequent use of AEM-EELS is the qualitative determination of the composition of precipitates containing light elements (too light to detect using a conventional energy-dispersive spectrometer). Metallurgical analysis typically necessitates differentiating among carbides, nitrides, and carbonitrides. This problem is discussed in Example 3 in the section "Applications" in this article.

The quantification of EELS spectra remains challenging. Quantification can be divided into three steps. The first requires the removal of the background from beneath the ionization edges, the second the integration of area within the edge, and the third determination of composition from the integrated intensities. Detailed information on quantification of EELS is provided in Ref 4.

Limitations of EELS Analysis. Despite the theoretical ease with which an EELS spectrum can be collected and analyzed, several limitations have prevented the technique from becoming commonplace in AEM. A severe limitation of EELS is specimen thickness. The background below the ionization edges increases rapidly with specimen thickness. The increase in background is due to the heightened probability of multiple scattering as the electron passes through the specimen. For aluminum, the usable thickness for EELS analysis is of the order of

10 to 20 nm. For heavier materials, such as steels, the limiting thickness is even less. The limitation imposed by specimen thickness is fundamental and cannot be overcome by more sophisticated analysis techniques.

Higher voltage analytical electron microscopes (upon availability) will allow EELS analysis of thicker specimens. The MMF detectable using AEM-EELS, even with ideal specimens, is far inferior to the values quoted above for AEM-EDS. Experimentally, 3 at.% C and 6 at.% O in iron have been detected (Ref 34). However, that level of detectability is insufficient for studying carbon partitioning during phase transformations in steel, for example. These values are appropriate only under ideal experimental conditions. With currently used 100- to 200-keV analytical electron microscopes and quantification methods, the primary advantage of AEM-EELS will likely remain its ability to identify carbides, nitrides, and oxides in metallic and perhaps ceramic matrices. A more thorough review of AEM-EELS is provided in Ref 3 and 4.

Sample Preparation

Samples for AEM can be divided into three broad groups: samples from the bulk, fine particles, and thin films. Detailed information on the first two types of samples is provided in Ref 35.

Bulk Samples. In many conventional metallurgical and ceramic applications, the starting material is a bulk sample. Use of a bulk sample is advisable for studies of such phenomena as phase transformations, diffusion, recrystallization, and grain growth. If analysis begins with material in the form of a thin disk, such surface effects as nucleation at the free surface may dominate and produce misleading results. Once the bulk sample is available, a suitable specimen must be obtained.

The first step in preparing an electron-transparent specimen is to section the bulk sample into wafers. Sectioning is generally performed mechanically with a low-speed diamond saw or by electric discharge machining (EDM). The wafers produced by mechanical or EDM sectioning are usually >250 μm thick. Most current AEM studies are performed with specimens referred to as self-supporting disks. Self-supporting disks are usually obtained by mechanically punching or electric discharge machining from the sectioned wafers. These disks are typically 3 mm (0.12 in.) in diameter, which will fit most modern AEM specimen holders.

The 3-mm (0.12-in.) disks are then mechanically ground to a thickness of approximately 125 to 150 μm. Grinding to specimen

Fig. 31 Electrojet thinning for TEM examination

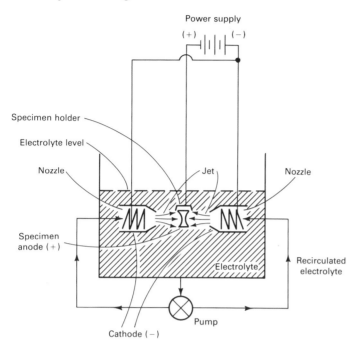

Fig. 32 The window technique

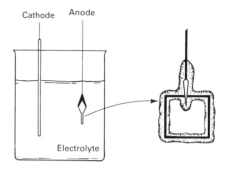

thicknesses less than 100 μm is not advisable, because it may introduce mechanical damage into the microstructure of the specimen. The 100-μm, 3-mm (0.12-in.) diam thin disk is now ready for final thinning. Final thinning can be performed electrochemically, chemically, or by ion beam milling.

Electrojet thinning is the most frequently used technique for producing electron-transparent regions in a self-supporting foil. Despite the widespread use of electrochemical thinning, hazards attend its implementation; proper instruction is essential. Many of the electrolytes are aggressive acids and oxidizers capable of inflicting severe burns. Some electrolytes are explosive and must be handled with care. The technique is quite safe in experienced hands, but should not be attempted by a novice.

Figure 31 is a schematic diagram of an electrojet thinner. The specimen is clamped into a holder that is typically fabricated of a fluorocarbon polymer. A cathode, often constructed of platinum, will be in the system. The specimen acts as the anode. A pump forces electrolyte through two orifices so that a stream of electrolyte impinges on each side of the specimen. During thinning, a current flows between the anode and cathode. An electrochemical reaction occurs that removes metal from the surface of the specimen. Thinning is permitted to continue until the sample perforates. After perforation, the sample is

quickly removed from the thinner, then rinsed.

Several conditions of thinning must be controlled, including the choice of the electrolyte, the applied voltage, the pump speed (rate of fluid flow), and the electrolyte temperature. The electrolyte is often cooled to below 0 °C (32 °F) with dry ice or liquid nitrogen to slow the reaction rate; if not cooled, thinning may occur so rapidly that polishing cannot be halted quickly enough to preserve a thin area in the specimen. To be considered usable, the foil must have thinned evenly and must contain a large region of electron-transparent material around the perforation. The thin area should be many micrometers wide.

Determining the appropriate polishing conditions often requires many attempts. If only a limited amount of material is available for investigation, specimen preparation by electrojet thinning may not be advisable. Once the appropriate conditions are established, electrojet polishing is the fastest method of producing thin foils and is the method of choice when a large amount of material is available and many specimens must be analyzed. In some cases, the electrochemical process leaves a residue on the foil that could be mistaken for an internal structure. The experienced microscopist can often determine if structural features are real or artifact. Electrojet thinning is widely used for metals, but is not useful for ceramic

materials because they are electrical insulators.

The Window Technique. The most straightforward and least expensive polishing cell is a beaker of electrolyte into which the cathode and the sample are dipped. The cathode is a sheet of the same material as the specimen or an inert material, such as platinum or stainless steel. The specimen acts as the anode, and a 10- to 20-mm (0.4- to 0.8-in.) square sheet is generally held in metal tweezers to allow application of the potential using alligator clips (Fig. 32). The edges of the sample and the tweezers must be coated with an acid-resistant lacquer for protection against attack. A "window" of metal remains exposed, from which the technique derives its name (Fig. 32). The tweezers are held by hand so that the specimen is submerged and the potential is applied.

Using this technique, the specimen can be viewed during polishing, because most electrolytes are transparent. Further, polishing can be quickly halted by switching off the power supply after a hole forms. Upon removal from the electrolyte, the specimen should be immersed in a beaker containing solvent, then washed thoroughly. Despite its simplicity, the window technique is not commonly used.

Ion beam milling provides an alternate method of producing electron-transparent regions in self-supporting disks. Figure 33 is a schematic diagram of the ion milling process. Two high-energy beams (4 to 10 keV) of Ar^+ ions are used to sputter material from the foil until a perforation results. The specimen is mounted into a holder and placed inside a vacuum chamber. The holder is tilted approximately 10 to 15° relative to the incident ion beams. During thinning, the specimen holder rotates to ensure uniform thinning.

If the ion milling machine is operating properly, thinning is reliable. The probability of obtaining a usable specimen for the

Fig. 33 Typical ion milling machine

Source: Ref 35

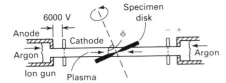

Fig. 34 Procedure used to produce single-stage extraction replicas for the analysis of small particles originally embedded in a matrix

(a) The original material with particles embedded in a matrix. (b) The particles have been etched to stand in relief. (c) The specimen is coated with a carbon film, usually by vacuum evaporation. (d) The specimen is immersed in an aggressive solution to release the particles from the matrix. Source: Ref 35

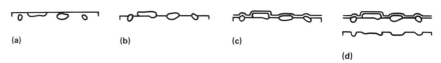

(a)   (b)   (c)   (d)

analytical electron microscope on the first attempt is very high. The only difficulty arises when different phases or regions in the foil are thinned at vastly different rates. The thinning rate is proportional to the average atomic number of the material being thinned. If two phases have widely different average atomic numbers, achieving uniform thinning may be difficult.

In the thinning of carbides in steel, for example, the thinning rates are not significantly different; these specimens can be produced reliably. The thinning of nickel-aluminum diffusion couples, however, is an example in which different regions have vastly different thinning rates, complicating production of suitable AEM specimens. Certain steps are often successful, such as masking, predimpling with an electrojet thinner, or preferential placement of the sample such that the most intense regions of the ion beam impinge its slowest thinning region. Ion milling is reliable for metals and ceramics. Because ceramics are usually impossible to thin electrochemically, ion milling is often the sample preparation technique of choice.

Despite the tremendous reliability of the ion thinner, it has some disadvantages. Ion thinning is slow, requiring several hours to several days to produce a specimen. The specimen heats during ion thinning, potentially to a temperature sufficiently hot to crystallize some amorphous materials or to age certain precipitation-hardenable aluminum alloys. The heating problem can be minimized by use of a liquid nitrogen cooled stage. The ions introduce radiation damage and defects into the material. Ion milling may not be suitable for determining the defect density of a metal or ceramic. Ion milling does not leave surface residues on the specimen. Consequently, specimens that have been electrojet thinned with the ion milling machine should be cleaned (approximately 5 min), especially if a compositional analysis of the specimen with EDS or EELS is anticipated.

Microtomes. In a few limited cases, it is possible to produce a suitable specimen for AEM directly from the bulk using a microtome. The microtome is a mechanical device with a diamond blade that can take sections less than 1 μm thick from bulk materials. The technique is effective for polymeric and biological specimens. It is often not appropriate for metallic or ceramic materials, because it damages the microstructure severely.

Small-Particle Examination. Many research programs require the microstructural evaluation of small particles. Several techniques are available to examine particles. If the particles are small enough (submicrometer), scattering them on a thin carbon film supported by a copper TEM grid is sometimes sufficient. The grid may receive an additional coating of carbon after the particles are placed onto it to help keep the particles attached to the grid and help prevent charging by the electron beam. The particles can be examined morphologically in the imaging mode. The structure can be examined using electron diffraction. The composition of the particles can be examined using EDS and, and in some cases, EELS.

If the particles are too large for the procedure described above, it may be possible to grind them to a smaller size and disperse the fragments on a TEM grid. The larger particles may be examined morphologically in the scanning electron microscope, then ground for crystallographic and chemical analysis in the analytical electron microscope. Depending on the particle size, special analysis routines may be necessary to determine the composition of the particles. If the diameter of the particles is less than the thickness limit specified by the thin film criterion, the x-ray data can be analyzed using the standardless ratio technique. If they are larger, alternate data-reduction techniques are required (Ref 36, 37). Examination of the internal structure, crystallography, or composition of particles that cannot be ground to sufficiently small sizes requires a different approach. The particles can be mixed with epoxy, and the resulting epoxy/powder mixture compacted into a mold with a centrifuge, wafered, ground, and ion milled (Ref 38).

Extraction Replicas. Characterization of small particles imbedded in a matrix, such as small second-phase particles in a steel, is often necessary. If the particles are large enough (>100 nm in diameter), it should be possible to examine them directly in the thin foil. If the particles are smaller, it is best to extract them from the matrix using extraction replicas (Fig. 34).

The first step in producing an extraction replica is to etch the alloy heavily to leave the particles of interest in relief. A carbon film is then deposited on the surface. A second etch is then implemented to dissolve the matrix further, leaving only the particles attached to the carbon film. The film, which contains the particles, can then be examined in the analytical electron microscope. The replicating procedure may alter the extracted particles and may produce spurious oxide particles. To assist in distinguishing detail from artifacts induced by specimen preparation, it is advisable to prepare the extraction replicas using several etchants and compare the results.

Fine structural detail of a surface can also be examined using a two-stage replication technique. A piece of solvent-softened polymeric film is pressed onto the surface. After hardening, the film is removed and shadowed obliquely with metal, then carbon coated. The polymer is then dissolved with a solvent, leaving a shadowed carbon film with the morphology of the original surface. The metal shadowing generates absorption contrast at edges when the sample is examined in the analytical electron microscope. A common application is the examination of fracture surfaces. Analysis of fracture surfaces is currently performed almost exclusively using SEM. Replicas are used occasionally to examine the fine structural detail produced by crack propagation during cyclic fatigue. Additional information on replication is provided in Ref 39.

Thin Film Examination. Some applications necessitate examination of materials that are originally in the form of thin films. Examples include thin deposited films, films produced by ion implantation and other surface modification techniques, and electronic microcircuits. Fundamental to the examination of deposited films is the removal of the film from the substrate. The most straightforward method of acquiring a free-standing film is to deposit the film on a substrate that can be easily removed. One common practice is to deposit the film onto salt (NaCl) or glass, then remove the substrate by dissolution in water or hydrofluoric acid, respectively.

In some cases, the films may not adhere to the substrate, allowing simple mechanical removal. If the thin film is adherent and the substrate cannot be removed mechanically or chemically, a suitable specimen may be prepared by thinning (electrojet or ion milling) from only one side. Thinning from only one side is also the commonly used technique for examining the layers formed by a surface modification process, such as ion implantation. Thinning from one side is discussed in further detail in Example 12 in the section "Applications" in this article.

Much work has been performed on analyzing electronic circuits in cross section using AEM. Several groups at commercial electronic laboratories are active in this area. A thorough review of the subject is provided in Ref 40.

Applications

Several examples in which AEM can be used to solve materials problems are discussed in the following sections. These examples have been grouped into two topical areas. The first group, which details AEM techniques and procedures, consists of:

The second group of examples is applications oriented. These examples are intended to demonstrate the extensive capability of AEM for materials characterization rather than review the electron microscopy of a given material:

ACKNOWLEDGMENT

The author wishes to express his appreciation to the following individuals for their assistance: M.J. Carr, T.J. Headley, C.R. Hills, M. Kersker, and W.R. Sorenson for providing many of the sample micrographs, diffraction patterns, and other data used in this article; to the authors who contributed examples of AEM applications; and to T.J. Headley, K.H. Eckelmeyer, M.J. Carr, J.G. Speer, and C.E. Lyman for their thorough and constructive manuscript review. This work performed at Sandia National Laboratories supported by the U.S. Department of Energy under Contract No. DE-AC04-76DP00789.

Example 1: Orientation Relationships and Habit Plane Determination

T.J. Headley
Sandia National Laboratories

During a phase transformation, the lattice of the product phase often orients itself in a fixed manner relative to the parent lattice to minimize interfacial energy. This fixed orientation between parent and product lattices is termed the orientation relationship. It is usually expressed as a pair of parallel directions lying in a pair of parallel planes. Parent/product orientation relationships are commonly observed in precipitation from solid solution, martensitic transformation, twinning, epitaxy, and interdendritic solidification of second phases. Furthermore, when the product phase takes the form of thin platelets, these platelets usually lie parallel to certain low-index planes in the matrix. The matrix plane on which the platelets lie is termed the habit plane. The crystallographic information necessary to identify orientation relationships and habit planes can be obtained from electron-diffraction and stereographic analyses.

Orientation Relationship Determination

In the first portion of this example, the orientation relationship is determined for a Ni-Mo-Cr-rich σ phase that formed in interdendritic regions of welds in the nickel-base alloy Hastelloy C-22. The alloy matrix is fcc austenite (γ), with $a_0 \simeq 0.36$ nm; σ phase is tetragonal, with $a_0 = 0.908$ nm, $c_0 = 0.475$ nm. Figure 35(a) shows a σ-phase particle in the γ matrix. Using electron diffraction, the foil was tilted to locate a low-index matrix zone on which was superimposed a low-index σ zone (Fig. 35b). In Fig. 35(c), the patterns have been indexed correctly. Therefore, $[001]_\sigma$ is parallel to $[111]_\gamma$. Furthermore, the row of σ reflections that include $(1\bar{1}0)_\sigma$ and higher order reflections lies parallel to $(2\bar{2}0)_\gamma$, as indicated by the arrow. Consequently, $(1\bar{1}0)_\sigma$ is parallel to $(1\bar{1}0)_\gamma$, and the orientation relationship may be expressed as $[001]_\sigma \parallel [111]_\gamma$ and $(1\bar{1}0)_\sigma \parallel (1\bar{1}0)_\gamma$. The consistency of this relationship must be confirmed by tilting in a known sense to one or more additional zone axes and verifying the patterns obtained.

First, the $[001]_\sigma$ and $[111]_\gamma$ standard projections are superimposed in the same orientation as the diffraction patterns shown in Fig. 35(b). This is illustrated in Fig. 36, in which the $(1\bar{1}0)_\sigma$ and $(1\bar{1}0)_\gamma$ poles have been aligned. All other points in this stereogram are projected directions. Along great circle AB, the $[11\bar{1}]_\sigma$ and $[110]_\sigma$ zones fall on or very near the $[11\bar{1}]_\gamma$ and $[11\bar{2}]_\gamma$ zones, respectively, as indicated by arrows. Therefore, tilting about the normal to this great circle, that is, about the normal to $(1\bar{1}0)_\gamma$, should bring these diffraction patterns into view for inspection. Figures 37(a) and 38(a) show the patterns thus obtained. The indexed schematics shown in Fig. 37(b) and 38(b) verify that the correct zones have superimposed. Therefore, the orientation relationship is confirmed as $[001]_\sigma \parallel [111]_\gamma$ and $(1\bar{1}0)_\sigma \parallel (1\bar{1}0)_\gamma$.

Habit Plane Determination

In the next portion of this example, the habit plane is determined for thin η-Ni₃Ti platelets in the γ-austenite matrix of an iron-base superalloy using the method of trace analysis discussed in Ref 2. Figure 39 shows two η platelets inclined through the foil. To determine their habit plane, the foil normal (FN), trace direction (TD), or crystallographic direction of intersection be-

Fig. 35 AEM analysis of a nickel-base specimen

(a) σ-phase particle in Hastelloy C-22 weld. (b) Electron-diffraction pattern. (c) Indexed schematic. The zone axes are $[001]_\sigma$ and $[111]_\gamma$.

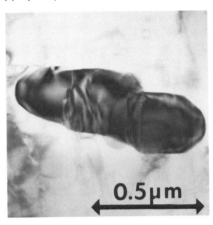

(a)

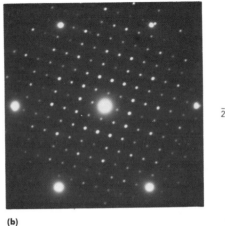

(b)

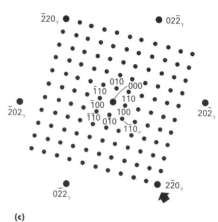

(c)

Fig. 36 Superposition of $[001]_\sigma$ and $[111]_\gamma$ standard projections

Underlined *hkl* refers to σ phase.

Fig. 37 Effect of tilting on electron-diffraction pattern

Diffraction pattern (a) and indexed schematic (b) after tilting about $[1\bar{1}0]_\gamma$. The zone axes are $[11\bar{1}]_\gamma$ and $[111]_\sigma$. Compare with Fig. 38.

(a)

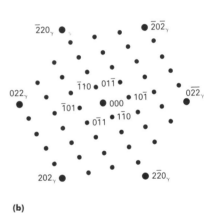

(b)

Fig 38 Effect of tilting on electron-diffraction pattern

Diffraction pattern (a) and indexed schematic (b) after further tilting about $[1\bar{1}0]_\gamma$. The zone axes are $[11\bar{2}]_\gamma$ and $[110]_\sigma$. Compare with Fig. 37.

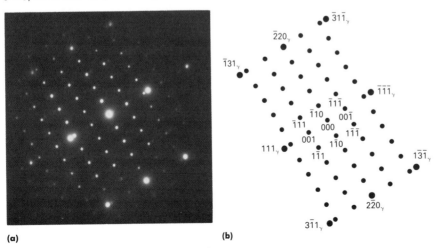

(a)

(b)

tween the habit plane and foil plane as well as the angle, ϕ, between the habit plane and foil plane must be known (Fig. 40).

The FN was determined from a diffraction pattern obtained at zero specimen tilt and is within approximately 1° of $[001]_\gamma$ (Fig. 39b). The diffraction pattern shown in Fig. 39(b) has been rotated through the proper angle of rotation that exists between the image and the diffraction pattern due to lens rotations in the microscope. Therefore, the TD can be transferred directly from diffraction pattern to image and is within approximately 1° of $[110]_\gamma$. Angle ϕ can be determined from the projected width, *w*, of the platelets if the foil thickness, *t*, is known. The foil thickness was determined to be approximately 405 nm using the contamination-spot-separation method (Ref 3). The projected width is approximately

Fig. 39 AEM analysis of an iron-base superalloy

(a) η-Ni₃Ti platelets. (b) Electron diffraction pattern in nearby γ matrix at zero specimen tilt. Zone axis is close to [001]ᵧ.

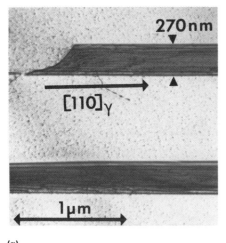

(a)

(b)

Fig. 40 Platelet geometry in foil

HN, habit plane normal

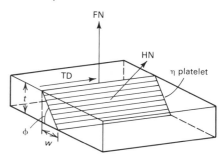

Fig. 41 Stereographic projection for determining the habit plane normal, HN

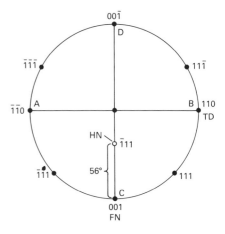

270 nm. Thus, tan $\phi = 405/270$ and $\phi = 56°$.

In the stereographic projection shown in Fig. 41, circle AB represents all directions in the foil plane with FN [001], including the [110] TD. The habit plane normal (HN) is perpendicular to TD and therefore lies in circle CD at the angle $\phi = 56°$ from the [001] FN. The habit plane normal HN is thus found to fall within 1.5° of $[\bar{1}11]_\gamma$. The uncertainty in this method of analysis is typically 5°.

Example 2: Unknown Phase Identification by Electron Diffraction/EDS

Martin J. Carr
Sandia National Laboratories

Identification of "unknown" phases or particles is often necessary. However, the "unknown" is often not a new material, but rather is typically found to match a compound whose characteristics have been cataloged in a data base. This example will describe a stepwise method of analysis for the identification of unknowns by combined electron diffraction and energy-dispersive x-ray spectroscopy. The instrument require-

ments include a relatively modern analytical electron microscope and involve the ability to obtain SADPs and qualitative compositional information. The data base is the JCPDS Powder Diffraction File (PDF), a commonly used data base containing over 36 000 inorganic compounds (Ref 13).

Assessment of Experimental and Reference Data

Search/match methods that are effective with electron microscopy data must take into account the positive and negative aspects of the data obtainable from the instrument. Crystallographic information from electron diffraction is limited by the relatively low precision inherent in the technique. Diffraction vector lengths can normally be measured to no better than approximately 1%, and angles between vectors can rarely be measured to better than 1°. The primary advantage of electron diffraction is that it is a single-crystal method that can be used to obtain three-dimensional information on the reciprocal lattice. Acquiring a set of related patterns by controlled tilting about a single axis can provide information on angles between zone axis directions; these are a measure of the three-dimensional relationships among planes and directions in the crystal lattice of the unknown. Three-dimensional angular information compensates for much of the low precision of the technique. Polycrystalline (ring) patterns can be analyzed successfully, but will frequently defy identification if they represent a mixture of phases. It is usually best to disperse the unknown

particles or to reduce the area selected sufficiently to obtain single-crystal information.

This analysis requires only qualitative chemical information. This information is best obtained using EDS. As discussed in the section "X-Ray Microanalysis in the Analytical Electron Microscope" in this article, obtaining qualitative, that is, presence/absence, compositional information for elements of atomic number 11 or greater is relatively easy; knowing which elements are absent can be as useful as knowing which ones are present. In laboratories in which EDS is not available, qualitative chemical information can often be generated by obtaining a history of the sample from the requestor and making reasonable assumptions based on the physics and chemistry of the situation.

The qualities of the data base also affect searching. The PDF evolved from the ASTM card file and consists primarily of a compilation of experimental x-ray powder diffraction patterns. Each record contains a list of interplanar distances (d-spacings) and intensities of peaks observed by Debye-Scherrer, diffractometer, or other x-ray powder techniques as well as a compound name, formula, and usually some lattice-parameter information. The *d*-spacing information is more precise than can be achieved using electron diffraction, and the intensity information is not applicable. Double diffraction, common in electron diffraction, usually does not occur in x-ray powder patterns; therefore, special processing is required during the search to avoid false rejections because these double-diffracted reflections are not in the data base. Many compounds that are derived from material from different sources or measured to different degrees of precision by different methods have multiple entries. Most materials of interest are represented in the PDF. Because of the vast quantity of possible combinations, most solid-solution series are represented by end members.

Strategy of Analysis

Successful analysis requires (1) obtaining reliable data, (2) searching the data base for potential matches, (3) testing matches against experimental data, and (4) confirming the identification.

Obtaining Reliable Data. With modest care, it is possible to achieve repeatability of diffraction data routinely within 0.5 to 1% over years of operation. This greatly facilitates simulation of diffraction patterns and many other operations. It is best to obtain several patterns from low-index zones, that is, closely spaced spots, tilted such that the intensities of the spots are as symmetrical as possible about the transmitted beam. Closely spaced spots in diffraction patterns are derived from widely spaced planes (high *d*-spacings) and are the most diagnostic spacings for a given lattice. Symmetrical patterns suffer the least from the host of distortions and artifacts that can plague electron diffraction patterns. Six to ten different reflections are usually sufficient for search purposes.

The optimum compositional data is obtained from isolated areas of the unknown, such as fragments of a pure bulk specimen, or from small particles on a clean extraction replica. When the unknown is a small particle embedded in a matrix, a reasonable qualitative measure of the major constituents can be obtained by subtracting a matrix-only spectrum from a matrix-plus-unknown spectrum. Without other information, all of the unobserved light elements ($Z < 11$) should be tentatively considered possible. Care should be taken to identify instrumental background peaks (for example, those arising from pole pieces, apertures, and grids) and obvious contaminants (such as

solvent residues) and eliminate them from the data.

Searching the Data Base for Potential Matches. The search is conducted initially on the basis of composition. Compositional information is divided into three categories for this purpose:

- *Observed elements*: This category includes all elements that are or may be qualitatively present in the unknown, as determined by direct observation (EDS) or by inference ($Z < 11$). Successful matches to this data will contain one or more of these elements

- *Required elements*: This optional category is applied when circumstances reasonably suggest that the unknown will contain specific elements and that it is necessary to limit the scope of the search. For example, carbon may be required when trying to identify precipitates in a tempered steel, or silicon and oxygen when working on a mineral sample from a silicate mineral vein

- *Elements that are absent*: Reference compounds containing one or more of these elements are excluded from consideration as possible matches. This is a powerful category that allows passing over large portions of the data base that cannot contain valid matches, reducing the number of compounds that require detailed examination

The initial phase of the search consists of retrieving from the data base only those compounds that contain one or more of the observed elements and no excluded elements. In addition, if required elements are specified, only compounds containing the required elements pass this screen and advance to the next stage of the procedure. The search can be conducted manually in the alphabetical index to the PDF (Ref 13), in the MAX-D index (Ref 13, 41), or by a computerized method (Ref 42). Searching an appropriate JCPDS subfile, such as Metals and Alloys or Commonly Encountered Phases (Ref 13), can also facilitate manual searching.

Applying compositional criteria usually reduces the number of possible compounds from 36 000 to approximately 100. The experimental diffraction data are next applied to the possible matches in two steps. First, the number of experimental reflections not found in a given reference are counted, and if the number of missed reflections exceeds some fraction of the total number of experimental reflections, the compound is rejected. No allowance should be made for double diffraction at this point. Experience has shown that if one third to one half of the experimental lines are missed in a given

reference compound, that compound should be rejected. Approximately one third of the compounds that passed the compositional search will be eliminated in this step. A more detailed evaluation is conducted of the compounds that remain, in which a figure-of-merit is computed, with which the remaining possible matches may be ranked in terms of goodness-of-fit to the experimental data.

Many valid techniques are possible, but any should include assigning a higher relative weight to high *d*-spacing reflections and counting a given reflection as a hit if it matches a reflection in the reference pattern directly or matches a reflection at *d*/2. The latter procedure accounts for the most common aspect of double diffraction. Successful matches are those that exceed some empirically defined level of figure-of-merit. The usual result of searching the 36 000 compounds in the PDF in this manner is a relatively short list, discounting multiple entries for the same compound.

Testing Matches Against Experimental Data. Crystallographic data for the remaining candidate compounds must be obtained before proceeding. Several compilations of such data are available (Ref 43, 44). These data are then used to generate tables of *r*-spacings or *d*-spacings of allowed reflections for these compounds, which are subsequently used to attempt to index the experimental patterns in terms of each remaining candidate compound. Indexing patterns by comparison to compilations of standard zone axis patterns will frequently fail unless the unknown happens to be cubic or hexagonal with an ideal *c*/*a* ratio, structures for which such compilations are available. The vast number of zone axis patterns required to extend the comparison technique to all lower symmetry crystal types prevents its use for the indexing of patterns from unknowns; therefore, each pattern must be indexed directly. A general method for indexing diffraction patterns is detailed in Ref 2. A computer technique for indexing electron diffraction patterns has also been devised (Ref 45). Direct indexing consists of:

- Assigning tentative Miller indices to several of the reflections closest to the transmitted beam in a given pattern based on the *d*-spacing tables computed for each candidate compound
- Permuting the tentative indices and changing signs to arrive at a set of indices that are self-consistent when added vectorially
- Obtaining the vector cross product of any two indexed spots in a self-consistent set to find the zone axis of the pattern

Fig. 42 Metal/ceramic brazing assembly interface

(a) Cross section of the metallized layer, reaction layer, and 94% Al₂O₃ substrate. Note that unknown surface particles are connected to the reaction layer. (b) SEM micrograph showing unknown particles on the molybdenum metallized surface

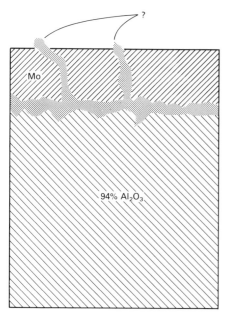

(a)

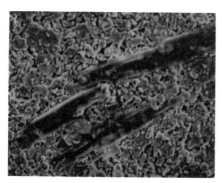

(b)

- Computing the diffraction pattern for the zone axis determined. Methods for the computation of diffraction patterns from arbitrary zone axis directions in any crystal structure have been discussed (Ref 46)
- Checking the consistency between all of the spots in the experimental and computed patterns in terms of spacings and angles between spots

After testing all the candidate compounds in this manner, the list of possible compounds will usually be reduced to a single match or to a few related or isomorphous compounds.

Fig. 43 TEM bright-field image showing two types of particles on a carbon support film

Unknown particle denoted by X is a single crystal, as indicated by the bend contours that cross it.

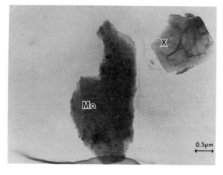

Confirming the Identification. Agreement between individual experimental patterns and computed patterns as shown above merely demonstrates consistency and should not be considered a positive identification. Confirmation of the identification requires obtaining a series of diffraction patterns by tilting a single crystal of the unknown phase about an axis to obtain a systematic series of zone axis patterns and the angles between them. Quantitative agreement between the interzonal angles obtained in a systematic tilting experiment and computed patterns and interzonal angles for a compound may be considered proof of identification.

At this point, it is appropriate to apply quantitative compositional information, if any is available, to the rationalization of the unknown as a solid solution between two or more isomorphous compounds. This can be accomplished only on the basis of composition, because electron diffraction data are rarely precise enough to detect the change in lattice parameter with composition.

Analysis of a Metallized Ceramic

To produce an assembly composed of a 94% alumina ceramic insulator brazed to a metal component, the ceramic part is metallized in a separate operation (Ref 47). Metallization consists of painting a slurry composed of molybdenum powder, titanium hydride, and organic binders onto the ceramic part through a stencil. The 94% alumina is a technical grade of alumina consisting of α-alumina grains bonded together with a glassy or crystallized grain-boundary phase containing calcium, aluminum, and magnesium silicates. When the coated ceramic part is fired at 1495 °C (2725 °F) under

Fig. 44 EDS spectra of a typical unknown particle

Particle contains primarily titanium and aluminum with a trace amount of magnesium.

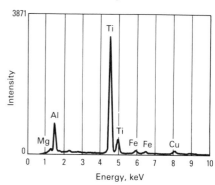

a partially oxidizing, wet hydrogen atmosphere (dew point, 30 °C, or 85 °F), the titanium hydride reacts with the intergranular phase, producing a phase that wets the porous sintered molybdenum layer, binding it to the ceramic. The organic binder burns off. The clean molybdenum surface is subsequently nickel plated to provide a surface suitable for brazing.

Occasionally, the molybdenum surface is not clean after firing, but is littered with blocky particles connected with the reaction layer at the metal/ceramic interface (Fig. 42). These particles apparently do not conduct electricity and do not accept the nickel plating, causing a weak braze joint later in the process. The first step in controlling the problem was to identify the particles to understand their nature and prevent their occurrence.

Combined SEM/EDS and microprobe analysis were attempted first and showed that the particles contained titanium, but were too thin to provide clean spectra without interference from the molybdenum substrate. Analytical TEM was the logical next step.

Specimens were prepared simply by scraping a pin across the contaminated molybdenum surface and collecting the fragments onto a carbon support film on a copper grid. Bright-field images produced by TEM disclosed two types of particles (Fig. 43), which EDS analysis showed to be molybdenum or the unknown phase. Energy-dispersive x-ray spectrometry spectra from several particles showed a consistent composition, of which Fig. 44 is typical. The unknown was found to contain primarily titanium, some aluminum, and a trace of magnesium. The other peaks in the spectrum are instrument artifacts. No other elements above atomic number 10 were present. Symmetrical diffraction patterns were obtained

Fig. 45 Symmetrical diffraction patterns obtained from different unknown crystals

Eight unique *r*-spacings were selected. Original camera constant was 2.49 Å · cm.

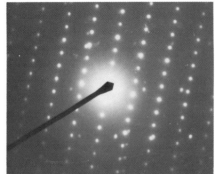

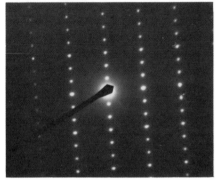

r-spacings

0.75	1.07
0.52	0.25
0.98	0.94
0.58	0.72

from several crystals exhibiting the proper composition, and eight unique *r*-spacings were selected (Fig. 45).

The full inorganic PDF was searched by a computerized method (Ref 42) that used the principles discussed above and the following input data and conditions:

- Titanium and aluminum were observed. All light elements ($Z < 11$) were allowed to be present as well, because EDS could not deny their presence
- No elements were specifically required
- All unobserved elements above atomic number 10 were excluded
- Eight observed *r*-spacings, at a camera constant of 2.49 Å · cm, were used

Approximately 40 references matched the input data sufficiently well to pass the initial search. Several were duplicate entries in the file. Twenty-four compounds remained when duplicate entries were discounted. Of these, 16 compounds contained unlikely light elements, such as lithium or boron. After consulting with the requestor, these were eliminated on the basis of a bulk chemical analysis that showed the absence of these elements in all of the materials used in the metallizing process. Results of the coarse search/match to the JCPDS data base are:

- *Best matches*: Al_2TiO_5 and Ti_3O_5
- *Considered, but rejected*: Ti_9O_{17}, Al_2O_3, TiH, Ti_5O_9, Ti_3Al, and Ti_2Al
- *Rejected on the basis of light-element bulk analysis*: 16 others, including Li_2TiO_3 and $Al_{14}B_2O_9$

Lattice-parameter data were obtained for the remaining eight compounds. After attempting to index the experimental diffraction patterns in terms of the remaining compounds, it was found that six of the compounds were inconsistent with the angular information in the experimental data in Fig. 45, and they were rejected. The two remaining, Al_2TiO_5 and Ti_3O_5, were found to be isomorphous compounds, both members of the pseudobrookite class of metal-titanium suboxides (Table 1). Because the lattice parameters for these two orthorhombic compounds were only slightly different, either fit the experimental data well.

To confirm the identification of the unknown as one of these compounds, a controlled tilting experiment was performed in which five diffraction patterns were obtained by tilting through approximately 35° about the normal to the (200) plane (Fig. 46). The angles between the zones were recorded as they were found. The three similar patterns, Fig. 46(a), (c), and (e), were indexed as [012], [011], and [010]. The interzonal angles for both candidate compounds were computed and compared to the measured values. As shown in Table 2, the agreement was favorable for both compounds, with Ti_3O_5 fitting slightly better. The slight difference in the agreement of the angular data may have been fortuitous, but it also agrees with the EDS data that quantitatively showed more titanium than aluminum and therefore is closer to Ti_3O_5 than to Al_2TiO_5. Magnesium also forms a mixed oxide with titanium, $MgTi_2O_5$, which also has the pseudobrookite structure. A small amount of magnesium was found in the unknown, which was probably a ternary solid solution. The identification of the compound as a suboxide of titanium led engineers to increase the oxidizing potential of the furnace atmosphere, that is, to raise the dew point, and thus prevent the formation of the compound in subsequent runs.

ACKNOWLEDGMENT

Work performed at Sandia National Laboratories supported by the U.S. Department of Energy under Contract No. DE-AC04-DP00789.

Table 1 Crystal data for the two best matches of the search/match to the JCPDS data base

Compound	Orthorhombic	Space group: c2/m	M = 12 (96 atoms/unit cell)
Al_2TiO_5	a = 9.429 Å	b = 9.636 Å	c = 3.591 Å
Ti_3O_5	a = 9.474 Å	b = 9.734 Å	c = 3.754 Å

Note: *M* represents the number of molecules (structural units) in the total unit cell.

Table 2 Comparison between measured and calculated interzonal angles

Compound	Zone axis [012]	[023]	[011]	[021]	[010]
Measured	7.8°	9.5°	9.9°	11.3°	
Al_2TiO_5	7.5°	8.8°	9.9°	10.6°	
Ti_3O_5	7.7°	9.0°	10.2°	10.9°	

Fig. 46 Diffraction patterns obtained by tilting a single crystal about the normal to the (200) plane

Zone axes: (a) [012], (b) [011], (c) [010], (d) [023], (e) [021]

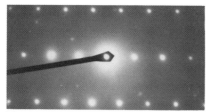

(a)

(b)

(c)

(d)

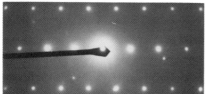

(e)

Example 3: Light-Element Analysis by EDS/UTW-EDS/EELS

L.E. Thomas
Westinghouse Hanford Company

Many problems in materials analysis can be solved by identifying the chemical elements in small precipitate particles or other specimen regions visible in the analytical electron microscope. The technique most widely used for this purpose is EDS, although an increasing number of analytical electron microscopes are also equipped for EELS. Typically, EDS and EELS are used in conjunction with electron diffraction and imaging techniques to obtain complementary information on composition, crystal structure, crystal orientation, and microstructure of selected specimen microareas.

Although both EDS and EELS detect most elements, EDS is generally preferred because it offers nearly equal sensitivity for all but the lightest elements, provides more easily interpreted spectra from multielement materials, and operates with less ideal (thicker) specimens than EELS. The detectors used in EDS are much less expensive than those for electron spectrometers. However, EELS detects light elements that are inaccessible using conventional EDS detectors and yields chemical bond information. Recently developed ultrathin window (UTW) and windowless x-ray detectors have extended EDS analysis from the normal cutoff at sodium ($Z = 11$) down to elements as light as boron ($Z = 5$). However, the complementary capabilities of EELS are such that use of both methods remains advantageous.

This example illustrates an application of combined EDS and EELS to solve a typical metallurgical problem. The example is selected to emphasize the qualitative capabilities of EDS and EELS without introducing the added complexities of quantitative compositional analysis or of other AEM techniques.

Precipitate Identification in Stainless Steel

To develop long-life cores for nuclear reactors, high-strength swelling-resistant alloys have been tested for fuel cladding and duct

Fig. 47 Optical micrograph of stainless steel tube showing a band of precipitates and cracks formed during stress-rupture testing

Arrows A and B indicate representative locations of subsequently prepared TEM specimens.

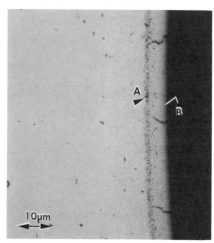

component applications. In one such test, pressurized tubes of a titanium-modified 316 stainless steel exhibited poor stress rupture life at 650 °C (1200 °F). Optical metallographic examination of the transversely sectioned tubing revealed that precipitate particles had formed in a narrow band near the inner wall and that fractures were initiated from the tubing inner diameter. Figure 47 shows an optical micrograph of a tube section. Because poor stress-rupture behavior appeared to be associated with precipitate formation, attention was given to identifying the precipitate phases and their chemical components. A STEM microbeam analysis was used because the precipitate particles were too small and too locally concentrated for most other compositional analysis methods.

A selective backthinning method was used to prepare suitably thin TEM specimens from regions within the band of precipitates and from near the tube inner surface. Preparation consisted of punching 3-mm (0.12-in.) diam TEM disks from the tubing, jet electropolishing the disks from both sides to expose the desired layer and produce polished surfaces, protecting one side of the specimen with lacquer and polishing from the other side until the specimen was perforated, and cleaning the protective lacquer from the specimen.

Figure 48 shows a transmission electron micrograph of the region within the precipitate band (region A in Fig. 47). The micrograph was taken in dark field with an austenite matrix reflection to emphasize particles near the thin edge of the specimen.

Fig. 48 Dark-field transmission electron micrograph from specimen region containing a band of precipitate particles (region A in Fig. 47)

Phases are identified using SAD.

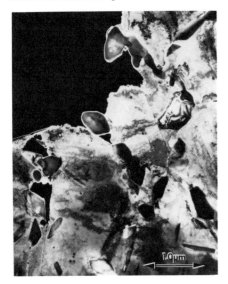

Fig. 49 Characteristic EELS edge shapes for amorphous carbon and carbon in a metal carbide

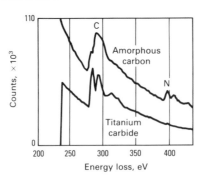

Fig. 50 Simultaneously acquired EDS/EELS spectra from an M₂X particle in a sample area similar to Fig. 49

The phase is Cr_2N, with no detectable carbon. (a) EDS spectrum. (b) EELS spectrum

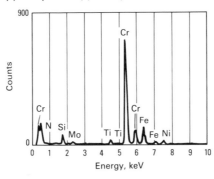

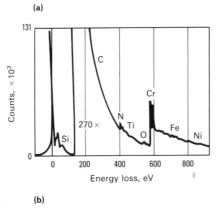

Fig. 51 Simultaneously acquired EDS/EELS spectra from an M₆X particle (region A in Fig. 47)

The phase is η-silicide, nominally $Cr_2NiMoSi$ but containing nitrogen and possibly carbon. (a) EDS spectrum. (b) EELS spectrum

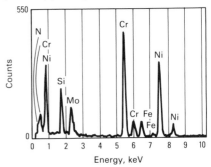

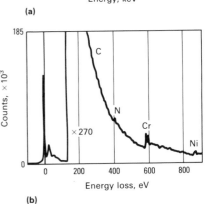

Selected-area diffraction showed that three types of particles, all carbides or nitrides commonly formed in stainless steels, were present. The precipitate phases were of type MX, M_6X, and M_2X, where M is usually one or more transition-metal elements and X may include carbon, nitrogen, and sometimes boron. The combination of EELS and EDS (with an ultrathin window x-ray detector) was used to ensure identification of all elements in the particles (above detectability limits for these methods) and to determine whether the particles were carbides or nitrides.

Combined EDS/EELS analysis was performed using an FEG scanning transmission electron microscope equipped with an ultrathin window x-ray detector and a double-focusing second-order aberration-corrected magnetic-sector electron spectrometer. The scanning transmission electron microscope provides a 1- to 2-nm-diam electron probe with sufficient intensity for EDS/EELS and a clean UHV environment. Given the relatively large precipitate size (0.1 to 0.3 μm), a conventional transmission electron microscope/scanning transmission electron microscope with a 10- to 20-nm-diam probe and a cooling stage for specimen decontamination could have been used. Because EDS and EELS data were collected simultaneously, both analyses refer to essentially the same specimen region and analysis conditions.

Microbeam analysis of carbides requires a clean specimen and a noncontaminating specimen environment, because any hydrocarbon contamination accumulated on the specimen surfaces during analysis will obscure carbon signals from the specimen. A primary advantage of EELS over EDS for carbide analysis is that the characteristic shapes of the core-loss edges in EELS spectra facilitate distinguishing bonded carbon from the amorphous carbon in specimen surface contamination. Figure 49 shows characteristic carbon K-edge shapes for amorphous carbon and a metal carbide (TiC).

Simultaneously collected EDS/EELS spectra from particles in the precipitate band region of the specimen showed that all the particles were nitrides. The spectra from an M_2X particle (Fig. 50) indicate that the particle is chromium nitride with minor concentrations of iron, titanium, nickel, molybdenum, and silicon. No carbon was detected in this phase, although the carbon K-edge position is marked in the EELS spectrum. The oxygen edge is attributed to the presence of thin surface oxide layers on the specimen. The spectra illustrated in Fig. 51 show that the M_6X phase is a chromium nickel molybdenum silicide (known as η-silicide) with nitrogen and possibly carbon. Silicide precipitation in this class of radiation-resistant steels is not unusual. However, because the initial nitrogen content of the steel was too low for nitride precipitation, it appeared that the tubing was nitrided accidentally.

Further analysis revealed the presence of particles of aluminum nitride in the specimen

Fig. 52 The EDS/EELS spectra from an aluminum nitride particle found near the tubing inner diameter (region B in Fig. 47)

(a) EDS spectrum. (b) EELS spectrum

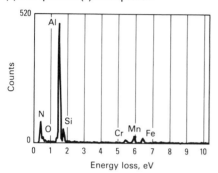

(a)

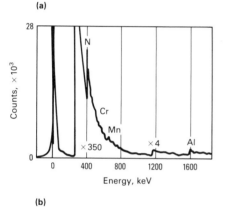

(b)

from the inside wall of the tubing. Figure 52 shows spectra from one of these particles. A check of the processing history of the tubing revealed the source of the aluminum nitride contaminant and helped to explain its presence inside the tubing.

Results. This example shows one method of using qualitative EDS/EELS elemental analysis to help solve materials problems. In this case, EELS or EDS could have identified the occurrence of nitriding and the aluminum nitride contaminant as the probable cause of alloy mechanical property degradation. However, the combination of the two methods provided useful additional information that would not have been obtained from the individual techniques. If carburization had been involved, the ability of EELS to differentiate bonded carbon from carbon contamination produced in the electron microscope would have been essential for the analysis. The TEM/STEM microbeam analysis was preferred over other methods in this case because of the relatively small particle sizes and limited extent of the region containing the precipitates. However, surface analytical methods, such as Auger electron spectroscopy, x-ray photoelectron spectros-

copy, or Rutherford backscattering spectrometry, may also have provided a solution to the problem.

The EDS spectra from an ultrathin window detector usually exhibit peaks from carbon at 283 eV (when carbon is present) and a noise peak at 0 eV. The 0-eV noise peak does not appear in this example, because the spectra were cut off below 160 eV by a discriminator setting in the counting electronics. The carbon peak does not appear, because the carbon concentrations in the particles were too low. In the EELS spectra, the zero-loss peak has a low-energy tail due to afterglow in the electron detector. By scanning the electron spectrometer from high to low energy loss, the afterglow is made to appear below zero energy loss rather than superimposed on the low-loss spectral region. The gain change at approximately 180 eV in the EELS spectra is due to a change in counting mode; the $4\times$ gain change at approximately 1200 eV in the aluminum nitride spectrum shown in Fig. 52 was included to enhance visibility of the aluminum K-edge at 1560 eV. The exponentially falling background (with increasing energy loss) in EELS spectra is a normal feature of this method.

The spectra shown in this example illustrate the complementary nature of EDS and EELS in terms of qualitative elemental analysis. In the Cr_2N particles, both methods detected the major elements chromium and nitrogen, but minor constituents iron, titanium, molybdenum, nickel, and silicon were best detected using EDS. Although EELS has relatively high sensitivity for transition-metal elements, the small iron, titanium, and nickel L-edges in the EELS spectrum shown in Fig. 50(b) are partly obscured by structure in the high-energy tails of the relatively large nitrogen and chromium K- and L-edges, respectively. Molybdenum produces a very broad $M_{4,5}$ edge at approximately 230 eV energy loss, but it is difficult to discern against the exponentially decreasing spectral background. Although molybdenum is difficult to detect in the EELS spectrum, EDS quantitative analysis showed that the M_6X phase contains 10 wt% Mo. Structure on the broad molybdenum $M_{4,5}$ edge also obscures the superimposed carbon K-edge shown in Fig. 51(b) and makes the identification of carbon in the η-silicide phase uncertain. Sharp molybdenum $M_{2,3}$ edge features also superimpose on the nitrogen K-edge. In addition, silicon is difficult to detect using EELS; the silicon L-edge at 100 eV energy loss is not apparent in Fig. 50(b) or 51(b), and the silicon K-edge at 1839 eV (not shown) was barely detectable, although silicon-K x-ray peaks are prominent in the corresponding EDS spectra.

There are also spectral overlaps in the EDS spectra, particularly at low energies at which peaks from the light elements appear. The nitrogen-K and chromium-L x-ray peaks in Fig. 50(a) and 51(a) are sufficiently overlapped that small nitrogen concentrations in the presence of chromium are difficult to detect. In Fig. 50(a), the nitrogen-K x-ray peak also superimposes with the titanium-L peak, and the oxygen-K peak is hidden by the chromium-L peak. Thus, the oxygen detected using EELS would be undetected using EDS in the presence of chromium (unless the oxygen concentration was very high). It would also be difficult to detect nitrogen in the presence of titanium or vanadium with only an ultrathin window x-ray detector. However, these are special cases; in the aluminum nitride there are no spectral interferences, and the nitrogen is readily detected using both methods.

Example 4: Diffusion-Induced Grain-Boundary Migration Analysis by EDS/CBED

J.R. Michael
Homer Research Laboratory
Bethlehem Steel Corporation

A primary advantage of AEM is the ability to combine many techniques to study a given problem. An interesting combination of techniques is x-ray microanalysis using EDS and structural analysis through CBED. X-ray microanalysis allows determination of compositional variation on an extremely fine scale; one aspect of CBED allows the measurement of small changes in lattice parameters of the order of 0.0002 nm in alloy systems that are difficult or impossible to analyze by x-ray microanalysis, that is, high-absorption or light-element analysis (Ref 48). Many phenomena of metallurgical interest involve compositional and structural changes that can be studied using AEM.

Grain-Boundary Migration in Al-4.7Cu

Diffusion-induced grain-boundary migration (DIGM), which has been observed in many polycrystalline materials, occurs when there is a diffusional flux of atoms in the grain-boundary plane that induces boundary

Fig. 53 TEM micrograph of a grain boundary in Al-4.7Cu aged 30 min at 250 °C (480 °F)

The boundary has bowed between the two large θ (CuAl₂) precipitates. The dark spots indicate the probe positions during x-ray microanalysis.

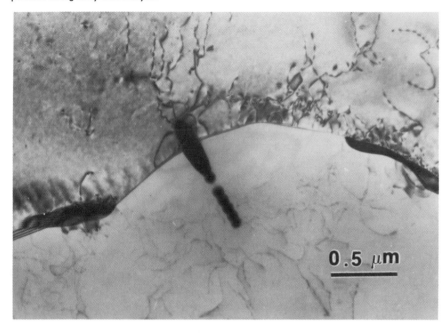

0.5 μm

Fig. 54 Compositional profile made by moving a 5-nm probe sequentially across the grain boundary (see Fig. 53) that shows the redistribution of copper

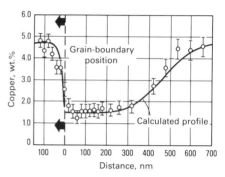

migration in a direction normal to the diffusional flux (Ref 49). A related phenomena to DIGM is discontinuous precipitation, in which precipitation accompanies boundary migration and may result in a degradation of high-temperature properties in many alloys. Attempts to describe these processes have resulted in controversy concerning the solute redistribution during grain-boundary motion (Ref 50). This example describes the results of an AEM study of grain-boundary migration in Al-4.7 Cu. The results illustrate determination of the compositional and lattice-parameter changes that accompany migration using combined x-ray microanalysis and CBED.

X-Ray Microanalysis. Figure 53 shows a bright-field TEM micrograph of a grain boundary in an aluminum-copper alloy. It is apparent that grain-boundary migration has occurred between the two θ (CuAl₂) precipitates. This bowing motion must be accompanied by some copper redistribution to the growing grain-boundary precipitates. To determine the copper redistribution, x-ray microanalysis was carried out by sequentially placing a 5-nm probe at 20-nm intervals across the area swept by the grain boundary. The raw x-ray data were then converted to compositions using the Cliff-Lorimer ratio technique, implementing an experimentally determined k-factor of 1.07 ± 0.02 (Ref 51). Calculations showed that the corrections

for absorption and fluorescence effects were less than the error in the counting statistics at a 99% confidence level.

Figure 54 shows the result of one such compositional profile as determined using x-ray microanalysis. As is apparent from the compositional profile, some solute depletion occurs immediately in front of the migrating boundary. Immediately following the grain boundary, the x-ray data show that the composition remains constant in the volume swept by the grain boundary, then increases smoothly to the bulk composition at the initial boundary position. No other analytical technique would have a sufficiently high spatial resolution to measure these small-scale compositional changes. The entire profile occupies approximately 900 nm, with 24 individual measurements occurring in that distance. In comparison, an electron probe microanalyzer may obtain one data point in a distance interval of 1 μm (1000 nm).

Also shown in Figure 54 with the experimental data is the result of a computer simulation of copper diffusion in aluminum during boundary migration. The simulation was carried out using a Crank-Nicholson finite difference technique. The agreement between the theoretically calculated curve and the experiment is very good. The proper application of x-ray microanalysis to this study requires several precautions. During specimen preparation, a number of artifacts

may arise. In the case of a thin foil, as in this study, it is important to ensure that the surface composition has not been modified by electrolytic polishing (Ref 52, 53). In addition, microanalysis must be performed in the thinnest portion of the specimen to maximize the spatial resolution and minimize the effect of x-ray absorption.

Convergent-beam electron diffraction may also be used to determine lattice-parameter changes that occur across the grain boundary. These lattice-parameter changes can be related to compositional changes by using a calibration curve based on Vegard's law (Ref 54). This technique involves the formation of a probe on the sample, followed by observation of the diffracted electrons.

Figure 55 shows a CBEDP for an aluminum-copper alloy. The central portion of the pattern corresponds to a normal SADP pattern; the outer ring of the pattern represents diffraction from a HOLZ, which normally is not visible in SADPs. These HOLZ lines also appear in the central disk of the pattern. Figure 56 shows an enlarged central disk (termed the 000 disk) from a (114) pattern. The central disk consists of several fine intersecting lines. The position of these lines varies with the lattice parameter. Thus, different lattice parameters will result in slightly different patterns of HOLZ lines in the 000 disk. Therefore, the criterion for selecting a specific zone axis for analysis is the presence of a sufficient number of intersecting HOLZ lines. Other commonly used orientations are (111) and (233).

Figures 56(a) and (b) show 000 disks from CBEDPs taken across the grain boundary shown in Fig. 53. Because the lattice parameter of aluminum changes with copper concentration, the two patterns are different.

Fig. 55 Typical (114) CBEDP obtained for the matrix of Al-4.7Cu

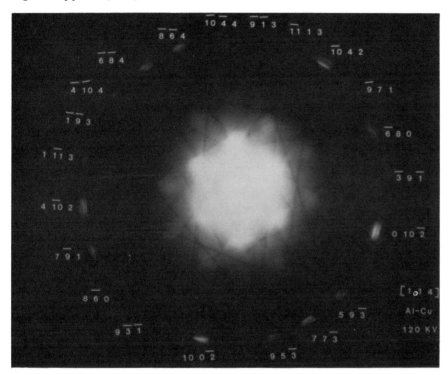

Fig. 57(a) Computer simulation matching the HOLZ pattern of Fig. 56(a)

Indicates that the lattice parameter is 0.4020 nm, which is consistent with Al-4.7Cu

Fig. 57(b) Computer simulation matching the HOLZ pattern of Fig. 56(b)

Indicates that the lattice parameter is 0.4026 nm, which is consistent with Al-1.5Cu

Fig. 56(a) Enlargement of the 000 disk of a (114) pattern taken from in front of the advancing grain boundary shown in Fig. 53

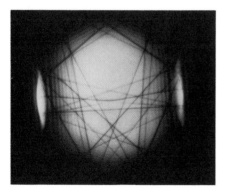

Fig. 56(b) Enlargement of the 000 disk of a (114) pattern taken from the solute-depleted region behind the grain boundary shown in Fig. 53

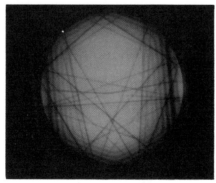

The pattern taken in front of the migrating interface (Fig. 56a) represents the lattice parameter of aluminum with 4.7 wt% Cu, but the pattern taken behind the boundary (Fig. 56b) represents a lattice parameter of aluminum with approximately 1.5 wt% Cu. To obtain sharp patterns in aluminum alloys, it is necessary to cool the sample. In this example, the sample was cooled to −180 °C (−290 °F). Therefore, the lattice parameters must be corrected for the effects of the thermal contraction (Ref 55). The differences in Fig. 56(a) and (b) are most easily visible where there are intersections of three lines. The small polygons that are formed show large changes with small changes in lattice parameters. The lattice parameter for each pattern can be obtained by comparison with computer-drawn simulations. These simulations use a simple geometric construction of the diffraction process to generate the HOLZ patterns (Ref 56).

Figures 57(a) and (b) show two simulations that correspond to Fig. 56(a) and (b). If the areas at which a number of HOLZ lines converge are compared with the actual patterns, the agreement is good. The change in lattice parameter from 0.4020 nm (Al-4.7Cu) to 0.4026 nm (Al-1.5Cu) is consistent with the 3.2 wt% change in copper contents as determined by EDS x-ray microanalysis. As in EDS x-ray microanalysis, certain precautions must be taken when performing lattice-parameter measurement by CBED. The specimen must be clean and free of surface films that may cause strains. Any bending of the foil will also tend to cause distortions in the CBEDP. Any strains present in the specimen will tend to broaden the HOLZ lines and, in the extreme, make them impossible to observe. When obtaining the CBEDPs, it is important not to tilt the specimen too far, because this will also distort the HOLZ patterns. Finally, cooling of the specimen can sometimes allow the HOLZ lines to be observed in samples that do not show HOLZ lines at room temperature (Ref 57).

Example 5: Defect Analysis by TEM/STEM

John B. Vander Sande
Department of Materials Science and Engineering
Massachusetts Institute of Technology

This example presents the various ways in which TEM and STEM can be used to generate diffraction-contrast information from defects in thin crystalline specimens. Background information on this contrast mechanism was provided in the section "Imaging in the Analytical Electron Microscope" in this article. This example will treat only the analysis of extended defects in crystals, which for the most part can be classified in terms of their dimensions.

These include line defects, such as dislocations; planar defects, such as antiphase boundaries, stacking faults, and grain boundaries; and volume defects, such as point defect clusters and small precipitates. Only precipitate contrast generated from elastic strain in the matrix due to the presence of the precipitate will be covered. A precipitate can also be observed through contrast from the precipitate body itself or through observation of the interface between precipitate and matrix.

A displacement field is commonly associated with a crystal defect. This displacement field describes the deviation of atomic positions near the defect from those characteristic of the perfect crystal. This distortion of atomic positions leads to the displacement or translation of atomic planes near the defect, which in turn affects the diffracting conditions near the defect and allows observation of the defect using electron microscopy.

Experimental Parameters

Before discussing the details of the contrast developed from specific defects, it is important to note the experimental parameters that must be defined to interpret electron microscopy images quantitatively from thin specimens. Most of the important parameters can be determined directly or indirectly from the selected-area diffraction pattern taken from the region in the foil that contains the defect(s) of interest. The electron-diffraction pattern from a grain having many defects will appear similar to a perfect single-crystal electron-diffraction pattern. This becomes less true as the dimension of the defect(s) increases (planar defects typically yield more structure in

electron-diffraction patterns than linear defects) and as the number density of such defects increases. However, a single-crystal pattern from the perfect part of the matrix can always be observed.

By establishing a two-beam diffracting condition (the two beams are the forward scattered beam and one strong diffracted beam from the planes in the object (*hkl*) that have a reciprocal lattice vector g_{hkl}) in the diffraction pattern, the reciprocal lattice vector for the diffracting planes, g_{hkl}, is established, and the proximity of those planes to the exact Bragg condition can determined from the Kikuchi pattern, yielding information on the deviation parameter, s. Knowledge of g and s is imperative for quantitative analysis because they appear in the theory, and knowledge of g is required to calculate extinction distance, ξ_g. In addition, a complete cross-grid diffraction pattern is useful in providing a qualitative feel for the crystallographic viewing direction. Lastly, the specimen thickness sometimes must be known at least to the nearest whole number of extinction distances.

Once a two-beam condition has been established in the diffraction pattern, the objective aperture can be centered about the optic axis of the microscope, and the instrument operated in magnification mode to generate an image at high magnification. If the beam on the optic axis is the forward scattered beam, the result is bright-field microscopy. Dark-field microscopy requires the strongly diffracted beam to be on the optic axis. If a weakly diffracted beam is on the optic axis, this is weak-beam microscopy. Additional information on bright-field, dark-field, and weak-beam microscopy is provided in the section "Imaging in the Analytical Transmission Electron Microscope" in this article.

Fig. 58 Elastic displacement field associated with dislocations

(a) An edge dislocation at which the perfect part of the crystal is oriented far from the Bragg angle. (b) The transmitted intensity, I_t, as a function of depth, z, below the entrance surface of the thin crystal for the position x shown in (a). (c) Transmitted intensity as a function of x across the bottom surface of the thin crystal. The core of the dislocation is at $x = 0$.

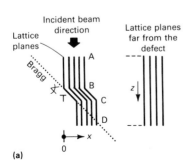
(a)

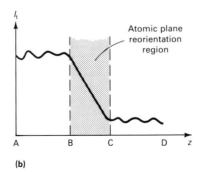
(b)

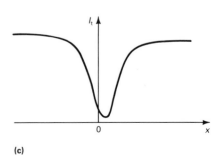
(c)

Fig. 59 A dislocation array associated with a low-angle grain boundary in an aluminum alloy

The diffraction vector is **g** = (200).

One-Dimensional Defect Analysis

Dislocations present in a crystalline lattice have an associated elastic displacement field. That is, near the core of the dislocation, the planes of atoms have been distorted relative to the planes in the perfect crystal. At ≥20 nm from the core of the dislocation, the displacement field has been reduced to such an extent that the crystal can be considered perfect. However, near the core of the dislocation the lattice-plane bending or lattice-plane reorientation can be considerable. Figure 58(a) illustrates the plane bending around an edge dislocation. The lattice-plane bending has a different sense on either side of the dislocation, and the perfect part of the crystal is deviated from the exact Bragg condition by the amount shown.

Figure 58(a) shows the history of an electron as it travels down a narrow column through the crystal labeled ABCD. In this example, only the history of forward scattered electrons will be considered. From A to B, the lattice planes are far from the Bragg condition, and little diffraction of electrons is expected. However, from B to C, the atomic planes are locally at the Bragg angle, and strong diffraction will occur, removing electrons from the forward scattered beam. This reduction in forward scattered intensity remains from C to D. Figure 58(b) shows this intensity change with position through the foil.

If a similar exercise is conducted for other columns at other positions that are a distance x from the dislocation core, a plot of transmitted electron intensity can be produced (Fig. 58c). The image of this dislocation is a depression in intensity (this corre-

sponds to a black line in a TEM photomicrograph) and is rather wide. Figure 59 shows an image of dislocations in an aluminum alloy.

Burgers Vector Determinations. A dislocation is characterized by its Burgers vector, **b**, and its tangent vector, **u**. An important parameter describing the displacement field of a dislocation is **b**. Because the plane bending due to the displacement field, **R**, of the dislocation locally changes the diffracting condition, that is, locally reorients **g**, it is not surprising that in the theory the term **g** · **R** appears. This term, which can be reduced to **g** · **b** for the case of a dislocation, governs the contrast. In the case in which **g** · **b** = 0 for a screw dislocation (for an edge dislocation **g** · **b** and **g** · **b** × **u** = 0), the plane bending does not change the diffracting condition, and the dislocation is invisible. The same field of view can be imaged with another **g** such that **g** · **b** ≠ 0, and the image of the dislocation will be visible. Thus, a Burgers vector analysis can be performed, because **g** is known for each image. Table 3 shows an example of how the value **g** · **b** varies for a

glissile dislocation on (111) in an fcc material when imaged with different **g** reflections. Figure 60 illustrates out-of-contrast and in-contrast images for dislocations in olivine, a magnesium-iron silicate earth mineral.

Large dislocation loops are imaged in the same manner as an isolated dislocation. However, small dislocation loops act like localized strain centers, leading to black-white contrast.

Table 3 Values of g · b for glissile dislocations on (111) in an fcc material

The Burgers vectors, **b**, must be contained in (111), and the **g**'s used must be available in fcc. In this case, all the **g**'s are contained in a [100] diffraction pattern.

g	± ½ [1$\bar{1}$0]	± ½ [10$\bar{1}$]	± ½ [01$\bar{1}$]
(002)	0	±1	±1
(020)	±1	0	±1
(022)	±1	±1	0

Fig. 60 Dislocation/precipitate images in olivine

(a) and (b) Small nonplanar precipitates heterogeneously nucleated on a dislocation. (c) and (d) Coarser heterogeneous precipitates on a dislocation. In (a) and (c), the [001] dislocations are out of contrast, **g** = (100); in (b) and (d), the dislocations are in contrast, **g** = (001).

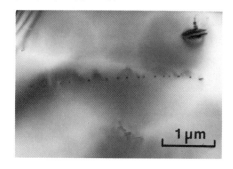

(a)

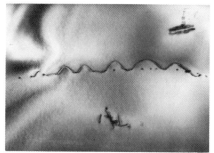

(b)

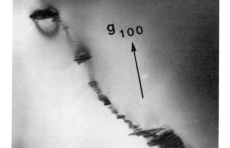

(c)

(d)

Two-Dimensional Defect Analysis

Stacking faults and antiphase, twin, and grain boundaries are planar defects that occur in crystals. As with dislocations, a displacement can be defined for these defects, **R**, which usually does not have an associated long-range component. When the electron beam travels through the inclined interface associated with the displacement, it is as if the thin foil is comprised of two overlapping wedges. When one or both parts of these overlapping wedges are in a strong diffracting condition, fringes are observed running parallel to the intersection of the planar defect with the foil surfaces. Figure 61 shows an example of stacking faults in the fcc phase of a cobalt-base alloy. This figure also presents an example of stacking-fault fringes going in and out of contrast for different operating reflections, **g**. The same area is being viewed in each case.

As in the case of dislocations, the displacement, **R**, can be determined for a stacking fault, thin twin, or antiphase boundary through **g** · **R** experiments. The fringes observed from grain boundaries cannot be analyzed through a **g** · **R** analysis alone, because considerable misorientations and displacements may be present. Although similar fringe effects occur from grain boundaries, stacking faults, antiphase boundaries, and twin boundaries, these features can normally be distinguished by their shapes in the image.

For a stacking fault, the bounding partial dislocations with Burgers vectors $\mathbf{b_p}$ can be analyzed by $\mathbf{g} \cdot \mathbf{b_p}$ experiments as described above for a dislocation; however, the condition $\mathbf{g} \cdot \mathbf{b_p} = \pm \frac{1}{3}$ is, along with $\mathbf{g} \cdot \mathbf{b_p} = 0$, an invisibility criterion.

Three-Dimensional Defect Analysis

When a precipitate forms in a crystalline lattice, the matrix surrounding the precipitate will usually be distorted due to the misfit strain generated in precipitation. As in the cases above, a displacement field around the precipitate, can be defined. Any defect, such as a small dislocation loop (<10 nm), a cluster of vacancies or interstitials, or a small gas bubble that distorts the matrix in a near-spherically symmetric manner, can also be thought of in terms of generating a radially symmetric displacement, **R**.

When such a strain center is viewed under a two-beam imaging condition, a depression in intensity comparable to that seen for a dislocation is observed wherever $\mathbf{g} \cdot \mathbf{R} \neq 0$. Because **R** radiates outward or

Fig. 61 Stacking faults on {111} in an fcc cobalt-base alloy

All images are from the same area in the specimen, but are viewed under three separate ⟨220⟩ diffraction conditions, as seen in the accompanying diffraction patterns.

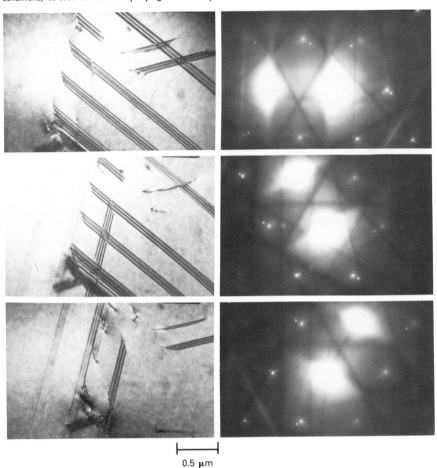

0.5 μm

inward from the strain center and **g** is fixed in space, there will be some conditions under which $\mathbf{g} \cdot \mathbf{R} = 0$, namely, when **g** and **R** are perpendicular. For those positions around the strain center, no contrast will be observed. Because the positions in which **g** and **R** are perpendicular occur diametrically across the strain center, the image appears as if it has a line-of-no-contrast that must be perpendicular to **g**. Such contrast is observed in Fig. 62, which is an image obtained from small precipitates in an aluminum-lithium-titanium alloy. For very small strain centers (≤10 nm) and small dislocation loops, the image will appear as a small bright circle next to a small dark circle, referred to as black-white or double lobe contrast.

Weak-Beam Microscopy

The analysis and results presented above demonstrate that a strain-related defect yields a wide image (approximately 15 to 20 nm) in bright-field microscopy. Wide images are generated from strain-related defects in strong dark-field micrographs as well. For many years, these wide images from defects were considered to be a standard result of TEM, although the consequences of wide images are many. Wide images produce an effective resolution limitation on microstructural observations that is much more severe than the operating restrictions created by the optical resolution of a modern transmission electron microscope. The ability of the microscopist to resolve dense arrays of dislocations, second-phase particles near dislocations, and closely spaced partial dislocations is directly related to the image width of the defects under observation. If two dislocation images overlap significantly, although the separation of the dislocations may be approximately 15 nm, they will not be resolved as two individual dislocations. If wide defect images can be replaced with narrower images, an improvement in practical resolution will result.

Fig. 62 Double arc contrast from spherical Al₃Li(δ′) precipitates in an aluminum-lithium alloy

Careful inspection shows that the precipitate body can be observed. The diffraction vector is **g** = (311).

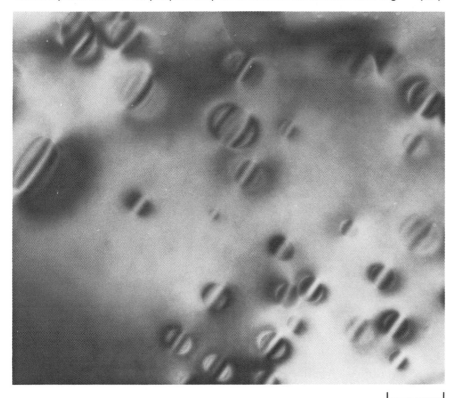

0.1 μm

The high-resolution technique of weak-beam electron microscopy will generate narrow image widths (approximately 1.5 nm) from dislocations and other strain-related defects, producing improved practical resolution. The technique requires use of a weakly diffracted beam to image one or more defects, making this a dark-field technique. Weakly diffracted in this context denotes that the diffracted beam used must be deviated from the exact Bragg condition by a large amount; that is, s must be large for the beam used. However, to view the defect, the $\mathbf{g} \cdot \mathbf{b}$ or $\mathbf{g} \cdot \mathbf{R}$ must still be nonzero for the reasons presented above in this example.

The reason that this technique generates narrow images can be explained with reference to Fig. 58. For a reflection that is far from the Bragg condition, there exists only a small region near the defect at which the atomic plane bending is sufficient to reorient the weak beam into a strong (Bragg) condition, and only for that position near the core of the defect will an image from the defect be generated.

Figure 63 shows a bright-field/weak-beam image pair for a dense array of dislocations in an aluminum alloy. The clusters of dislocations that cannot be resolved in bright field are resolved and interpretable in the weak-beam image. In addition, the geometry of individual dislocations can be established in the weak-beam image.

Fig. 63 Bright-field/weak-beam micrograph pair showing a dislocation tangle in deformed aluminum

Note the improved resolution of the details of the dislocation tangle in the weak-beam image (right side). The diffraction vector is **g** = (220) for each micrograph.

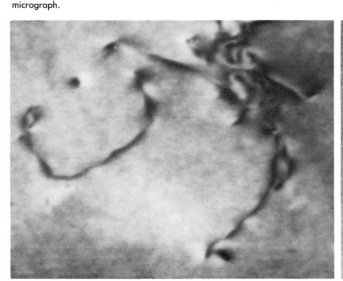
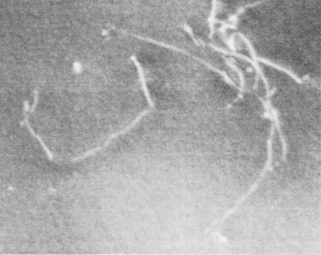

0.1 μm

Example 6: Analysis of Deformation, Recovery, and Recrystallization Structures by TEM

E.L. Brown
Metallurgical Engineering Department
Colorado School of Mines

The deformation of metals and alloys can be a complex process. Of concern are deformation parameters, such as strain, strain rate, temperature, and mode of deformation, and material parameters, such as prior structure, alloying, crystal structure, and stacking-fault energy. Because deformation parameters are interrelated through microstructure, constitutive equations defining these relationships depend on the nature and scale of structure evolved. Structure depends on material parameters; therefore, relationships between deformation and material parameters also depend on structure. Consequently, observations of structure at all levels are necessary to elucidate the fundamental nature of otherwise empirically based correlations. The purpose of this example is to illustrate how AEM analysis helps quantify structural/property relationships.

With a given set of deformation parameters, the evolution of microstructure is basically due to the balance between processes of dislocation production and annihilation and to the rearrangement of dislocations. The interplay between these dislocation processes is manifested by a corresponding interplay between processes of deformation and processes that restore the material to an undeformed low-energy metallurgical state. Restoration processes include recovery and recrystallization and may be further classified as dynamic or static, depending on whether the process occurs with or subsequent to deformation, respectively.

The structures of interest exist over a scale that spans the range of resolution capable using optical (light) and electron microscopy. Thus, correlation of microstructural observations at different levels of resolution must frequently be accomplished to detail structure adequately. Furthermore, much of the fine structure associated with dislocation and precipitate arrangements can be resolved only using TEM of replicas and thin foils.

Fig. 64 Austenite dislocation sources (arrows) in an austenite/ferrite interface during cryogenic tensile deformation

Thin foil TEM specimen

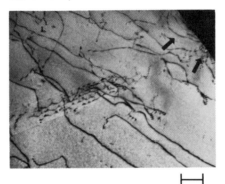

⊢——⊣
0.15 μm

Substructure Due to Cold Deformation

With increasing strain, dislocation sources become activated and the dislocation density of the metal or alloy increases. Dislocation sources are frequently located at interfaces in the prior microstructure. Figure 64 shows a duplex stainless steel casting in which dislocation loops are being emitted into the austenitic stainless steel matrix from sources in the austenite/ferrite interphase interface during cryogenic deformation.

Dislocation movement after production can result in dislocation interaction and the formation of various dislocation distributions. Variation in distribution can be aided by variations in deformation temperature, alloying, and the presence of prior structure. Dislocation interactions in low-alloy, high stacking fault energy metals at low deformation temperatures can result in dislocation tangles that impede further dislocation movement and result in work hardening. Figure 65 shows a relatively homogeneous dislocation tangle in δ-ferrite deformed to fracture in tension at 4 K. The dotted contrast of some dislocations shown in Fig. 65 is due to the diffraction contrast from dislocation lines oriented approximately normal to the foil surface. Diffraction contrast is discussed in the section "Imaging in the Analytical Electron Microscope" in this article.

In contrast to homogeneous dislocation distribution, metals and alloys can exhibit localized deformation. This is especially the case in higher alloy, lower stacking fault energy materials in which planar slip is promoted. Planar slip can result in the formation of slip or deformation bands in which deformation is confined mainly to the region

Fig. 65 Homogeneous dislocation tangle in δ-ferrite deformed to fracture in tension at 4 K

Thin foil TEM specimen

⊢——⊣
0.08 μm

Fig. 66 Slip/deformation bands in cryogenically deformed austenitic stainless steel

Traces of {111} planes parallel to bands are indicated.

⊢——⊣
0.08 μm

of the band. Figure 66 shows intersecting slip bands in an austenitic stainless steel matrix deformed 2% at 4 K. The slip bands lie parallel to {111} planes, as confirmed by SAD observations in association with a habit plane trace analysis. The alternating light and dark fringes parallel to the trace of the slip bands are due to the diffraction contrast from the stacking-fault region separating partial dislocations in the slip band that is lying oblique to the surface of the foil. This is a characteristic of low stacking fault energy alloys in which large separation of partial dislocations is possible.

When dislocations moving on intersecting slip planes interact, dislocation networks can be formed (Fig. 67). These networks are characterized by segments of dislocations emanating from nodes or points of intersection in the network.

Fig. 67 Dislocation interaction to form a network (arrow) during deformation of austenitic stainless steel

Thin foil TEM specimen

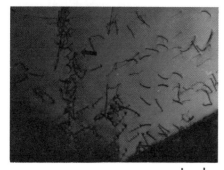

0.40 μm

Fig. 68 Dislocation dipoles and loops in ferrite deformed 0.5% in tension at 4 K

Thin foil TEM specimen

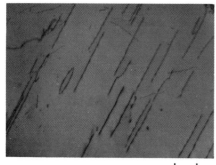

0.15 μm

Dislocation debris is frequently a by-product of deformation. Dislocation dipoles (pairs of parallel segments of dislocation line) and dislocation loops are often the result of dislocation interactions during deformation. Both features are present in the microstructure of ferrite deformed 0.5% in tension at 4 K (Fig. 68).

Prior dislocation substructure in the form of a subgrain boundary can impede the motion of dislocations and cause work hardening. The micrograph of an austenitic stainless steel in Fig. 69 illustrates the interaction between an existing subgrain boundary and dislocations generated during 0.5% tensile deformation at 4 K.

An alternate low-temperature deformation mode is deformation twinning in which the twinning operation shears the matrix while creating a region of different crystallo-

graphic orientation. The change in crystallographic orientation can be monitored using electron diffraction, and the twinned regions identified by centered dark-field microscopy. This type of microscopy uses twin reflections for imaging (see the section "Imaging in the Analytical Electron Microscope" in this article). Figure 70 shows deformation twins in an austenitic stainless steel.

At an advanced stage of cold deformation, a dislocation cell structure may form. This inhomogeneous dislocation distribution is characterized by tangled cell walls with a relatively high dislocation density and cell interiors with a low dislocation density. The crystallographic misorientation across the cell walls is generally small; this may be confirmed using SAD. Figure 71 shows a dislocation cell structure developed in electrolytic tough pitch (ETP) copper by cold rolling. The cell walls are composed of dislocation tangles and partially formed networks produced by numerous dislocation interactions.

Substructure Due to Hot Deformation and Restoration

Thermal activation can aid dislocation movement by climb mechanisms. The enhanced dislocation movement results in more dislocation annihilation and the arrangement of dislocations into equilibrium configurations, such as regular subgrain boundary networks. These are recovered substructures. Subgrain structures formed by recovery of dislocations produced by differential thermal contraction and solid-state phase transformation during solidification and cooling are examples of this type of cell structure.

Static recovery results in larger misorientations between subgrains than in the cell structure discussed above. Figure 72 shows a well-defined statically recovered subgrain structure formed after annealing a warm-worked aluminum-lithium alloy.

Recrystallization requires the formation of a high-angle boundary and a critically sized nucleus of strain-free material. These boundaries sweep out dislocations in the deformed matrix. Figure 73 illustrates a recrystallization nucleus in ferrite formed during the intercritical annealing of a cold-worked low-carbon steel.

Hot working is accompanied by dynamic recovery and sometimes dynamic recrystallization. Dynamic restoration processes are generally aided by high temperature and low strain rate. High stacking fault energy metals, such as aluminum, dynamically recover

Fig. 69 Dislocation interaction with existing subgrain boundary (arrow) during tensile deformation of austenitic stainless steel

Thin foil TEM specimen

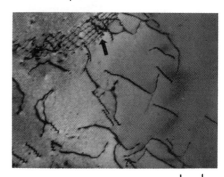

0.15 μm

Fig. 70 Centered dark-field micrograph of deformation twins imaged with 1$\bar{1}$1 twin reflection

Thin foil TEM specimen

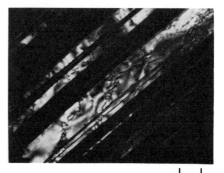

0.10 μm

Fig. 71 Dislocation cell structure developed by cold rolling ETP copper

Thin foil TEM specimen

0.20 μm

Fig. 72 Warm-worked and annealed aluminum-lithium alloy showing statically recovered subgrain structure

Thin foil TEM specimen

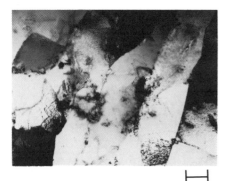

1.0 μm

Fig. 73 Recrystallization nucleus (arrow) in cold-worked ferrite formed during intercritical annealing

Thin foil TEM specimen

0.20 μm

Fig. 74 1100 aluminum dynamically recovered during hot tensile deformation at 400 °C (750 °F) and a strain rate of 0.05 s⁻¹

Thin foil TEM specimen

1.0 μm

energy effects. Another alloying effect on restoration processes, observable using TEM, is manifested by fine precipitate or inclusion dispersions that prevent formation of recrystallization nuclei and the movement of recrystallization fronts by pinning boundaries. Figure 76 shows an example of precipitate pinning. Spheroidized cementite particles pin a static recrystallization front in ferrite during intercritical annealing of a cold-worked low-carbon steel. The recovered dislocation substructure is visible to the left of the front.

ACKNOWLEDGMENT

The author is indebted to J. Cotton, B. Damkroger, R. Nichting, and D. Symons for their invaluable aid in the preparation of this contribution.

Example 7: Analysis of Dislocation Cell Structure by AEM

William A.T. Clark
Department of Metallurgical Engineering
The Ohio State University

In many metallurgical systems, the size of the individual crystallites or precipitates is very small compared to the diameter of the typical electron optical or x-ray probes used to study them, that is, <1 μm in diameter. Some examples include the structures observed in deformation textures, the early stages of recrystallization, systems strengthened by precipitation or dispersions of small second-phase particles, and most rapidly solidified alloys.

The relative crystallographic orientation of contiguous grains or phases often significantly influences the thermomechanical properties of the material, and interest is increasing in experimental techniques capable of determining such relationships accurately, without sacrificing the ability to identify the individual grains or precipitates involved (Ref 58). This contrasts with more traditional x-ray methods used to obtain orientation information from fine-grained polycrystals, which display the information obtained in the form of pole figures describing textures. These suffer from the collective disadvantage that the incident x-ray beam is typically much larger in diameter than the individual crystallites; therefore, although such pole figures will show the development

readily. Figure 74 depicts a dynamically formed subgrain structure superimposed on a prior subgrain structure in 1100 aluminum.

Hot rolling at approximately 1100 °C (2010 °F) results in recrystallization of AISI 304 stainless steel, as evidenced by optical microscopy (Fig. 75a). Examination of this microstructure using TEM reveals the presence of significant residual dislocation density in the equiaxed grains of the microstructure (Fig. 75b). This indicates dynamic recrystallization. Subsequent annealing reduces the residual dislocation density of the dynamically recrystallized microstructure by static recrystallization.

Alloying can hamper dislocation movement and restoration processes through solute drag effects on individual dislocations and boundaries and through stacking fault

Fig. 75 Hot-rolled (50% reduction) AISI 304 stainless steel

(a) Dynamically recrystallized microstructure at approximately 1100 °C (2010 °F); optical micrograph. (b) Residual dislocation substructure in equiaxed grains of Fig. 75(a); thin foil TEM specimen

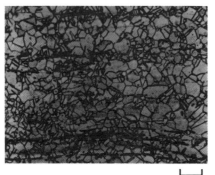

(a)   40 μm

(b)   0.5 μm

Fig. 76 Spheroidized cementite particles pinning a recrystallization front during intercritical annealing of a low-carbon steel

Note the recovered dislocation substructure to the left of the front. Thin foil TEM specimen

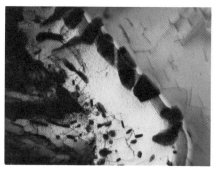

⊢——⊣
0.40 μm

of an overall texture in a polycrystalline material, they cannot provide specific information about the particular orientation relationship between any two crystallites in contact. Recent developments in the understanding of interfacial structures and their role in many metallurgical phenomena focus attention on these individual orientation relationships and the ways in which they relate to the macroscopic textures observed using x-rays (Ref 59). Therefore, considerable attention is being given to those methods that allow this information to be retrieved.

Limitations and Conditions for Orientation Determination

It is important to consider the limitations of the traditional methods for orientation determinations in the transmission electron microscope, then to consider how modern analytical electron microscopes can offer improvements upon them for this particular task. First, the requirements of a system designed to examine orientation relationships in fine-grained structures must be determined. It must be able to obtain sharp diffraction patterns containing sufficient detail for precise analysis from each individual grain. This requires an electron beam that can be focused to a diameter smaller than the diameter of the smallest crystallite to be analyzed so that diffraction information from surrounding crystals does not appear in the diffraction pattern. This must be accomplished without significantly reducing the intensity of the electron beam in order to

retain the fine detail in the diffraction pattern (especially Kikuchi lines) necessary for accurate measurements (to ±0.1°) of crystal orientations.

Second, given that orientation relationships between many crystals are required to develop a texture, the technique must be rapid and easy to use and capable of manipulating the data and displaying them intelligibly. This example will describe such a method (Ref 60) and illustrate its usefulness in characterizing a fine-grained cell structure lying below the surface of a copper block subjected to dry sliding wear (Ref 61).

Computerized Misorientation Determination

The methods of determining orientation relationships from Kikuchi patterns were outlined in the section "Electron Diffraction" in this article. The methods of orientation determination used in this example are standard. The only significant differences are the actual imaging conditions used to obtain the Kikuchi pattern, the method of measuring the relevant parameters from that pattern, and the automation of its solution.

In a conventional transmission electron microscope, diffraction information is obtained from specific areas of a specimen using a selected-area aperture (see the section "Electron Diffraction" in this article). This defines the region of the specimen through which the incident electrons are allowed to pass and therefore determines the area of the specimen that contributes information to a diffraction pattern or image. Theoretically, all that is necessary for obtaining diffraction patterns from small areas of the specimen is to make this aperture as small as is required. However, in practice, attenuation of the intensity of diffraction patterns obtained when using progressively smaller selected-area apertures limits the usefulness of this approach to areas of a few micrometers minimum diameter. In addition, the reduction in size of the selected-area aperture is also accompanied by a corresponding reduction in the precision with which a specific area of the specimen can be selected to provide a diffraction pattern.

Figure 77(a) shows a Kikuchi pattern obtained from a single cell in deformed oxygen-free high-conductivity (OFHC) copper, approximately 0.5 μm in diameter, using conventional SAD in a 100-keV transmission electron microscope; the absence of clear detail is apparent. With more modern electron microscopes capable of producing a small, highly convergent probe, beam diameters much smaller than typical selected-area

Fig. 77 Kikuchi patterns obtained from single cells in deformed OFHC copper

(a) Conventional SAD. (b) CBED. Note the improvement in the clarity of the lines in (b).

(a)

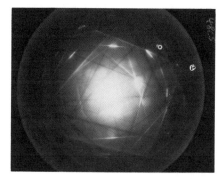

(b)

apertures can be obtained without any reduction in the intensity of the pattern. Figure 77(b) is such a pattern obtained from a single cell, again approximately 0.5 μm in diameter, but formed using the convergent-beam mode of a modern analytical electron microscope. The presence of clear, sharp Kikuchi lines is evident, in contrast with the pattern in Fig. 77(a), and the electron-beam direction normal to this pattern can be solved to an accuracy of a few minutes of arc.

As stated above, standard methods for solving the Kikuchi patterns are used in this example. However, the coordinates of the Kikuchi lines in the pattern are not measured manually, but are entered into a micro- or minicomputer using a standard digitizing pad. This reduces the time required for analysis of a single pattern by a factor of up to 20 and eliminates the need to measure angles on the pattern with a protractor, improving the accuracy of the orientation determination. In addition, the rapidity with which the data from a single pattern can be collected makes overdetermination of the beam direction routine; therefore, average values and estimates of the accuracy of the solution are easily obtained.

The data from each Kikuchi pattern are stored in a file in the computer. The misorientation between any two crystals, which need not necessarily be contiguous, is then obtained by supplying the data from two of these files (one for each crystal taken at exactly the same orientation of the microscope goniometer stage) as input to another computer program that calculates the misorientation. In addition, the program provides all the equivalent crystallographic descriptions of the misorientation (there can be up to 24 in a cubic crystal), so that the most appropriate description for the particular application can be selected. The relative orientation of the two crystals is typically described by the disorientation (Ref 62), which is the misorientation for which the angle is a minimum. Overdetermination of the misorientation, using multiple sets of data for the same two crystals, provides an estimate of the errors involved in the determination.

Misorientation Determination for Small Cells

Although the method outlined above significantly improves the rapidity and accuracy with which misorientations across individual interfaces can be obtained, it is in the study of small cell structures that it has its most important advantages. In this case, the convergent-beam method allows accurate orientation of individual cells to be measured, and use of the computer makes obtaining the relative orientation of many cells (50 or more) manageable. Therefore, the relationship between cell misorientations and a texture can be examined.

In this example, the subsurface structure in OFHC copper was examined after it had been deformed by dry sliding against an AISI 440C stainless steel ring. To produce a TEM foil, the block was plated with copper to protect the wear surface to a thickness of approximately 2 mm (0.08 in.), and slices approximately 0.8 mm (0.03 in.) thick were sectioned parallel to the sliding direction and normal to the wear surface. From these slices, 3-mm (0.12-in.) diam disks suitable for TEM were electrical discharge machined such that the wear track was positioned along the diameter of the disk. Final thinning for TEM observation was carried out using standard electropolishing techniques.

Figure 78 shows a typical cross section. The sliding direction is indicated, as is the interface between the wear surface and the plating. The microstructure consists of a very fine-grained region just below the sur-

face, referred to as the transfer layer, in which material from the block and the ring appear to have been mechanically alloyed during sliding. Below this layer, small cells are apparent that increase in size as a function of depth into the sample. Also visible is a high-angle grain boundary, across which the misorientation is approximately 54°. This boundary has been bent over almost parallel to the sliding surface by the extensive plastic deformation during sliding. Its shape can be well described by a simple exponential function, indicating that the highest strains are close to the sliding surface and decrease rapidly with depth below it.

This region is selected to illustrate the application of the method; Fig. 79 is a schematic diagram on which disorientations across the individual boundaries are marked.

Fig. 78 Typical longitudinal cross-section TEM micrograph of a subsurface region in an OFHC copper wear specimen showing the cells examined in a typical analysis

S.D., sliding direction

This diagram makes clear which interfaces are cell walls of less than approximately 20° misorientation and which are separate crystals of much higher misorientations. A general trend is also apparent for disorientations to increase closer to the surface, as might be anticipated from the increase in plastic deformation in the same direction.

This can be more clearly demonstrated by selecting a reference grain well below the sliding surface and plotting the rotation of all measured grains relative to it as a function of depth below the surface. Figures 80 and 81 show such plots for rotations about the y, x, and z axes. These plots demonstrate that the principal component of the deformation is a rotation about the y-axis, which is perpendicular to the sliding direction but in the sliding surface. This might also be expected, but is revealed so clearly only using this method, which discloses much detail about the rotations of individual grains.

The orientation data can also be analyzed to show that, in contrast to conventional views of texture development during sliding, there is no obvious tendency for the grains to rotate such that their {111} planes align parallel to the sliding surface and that the rotation about the y-axis is by far the most

Fig. 79 Region shown in Fig. 78

The numbers show the disorientation in degrees across individual cell boundaries. Areas with similar shading are associated with the same parent grain.

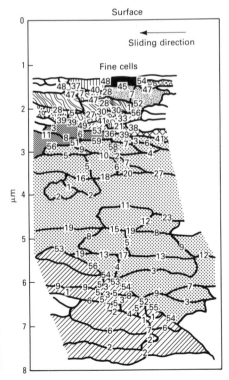

Fig. 80 Rotation of the cells in Fig. 78 and 79 about the *y*-axis (see inset) as a function of depth *z* below the wear surface

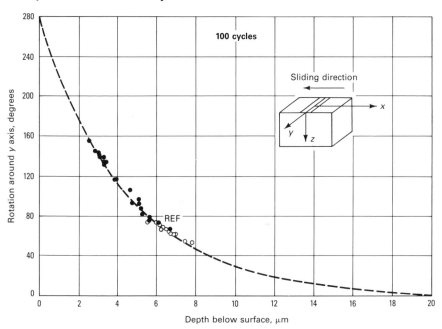

dominant mechanism. The data collected from a cross section come from a region extending from the surface to approximately 20 μm below it; x-ray techniques applied to study the surfaces of bulk specimens pene- trate to a depth of only a few hundred nanometers. The additional insight provided by the cross-sectional view is essential in developing a more complete picture of the deformation accompanying sliding.

Fig. 81 Rotation of the cells in Fig. 78 and 79 about the *x*- and *z*- axes (see inset) as a function of depth *z* below the wear surface

Comparison with Fig. 80 demonstrates that the major component of the deformation is by rotation about the *y*-axis.

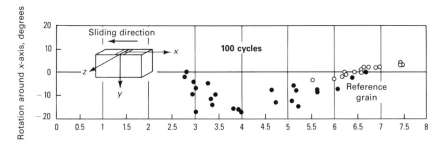

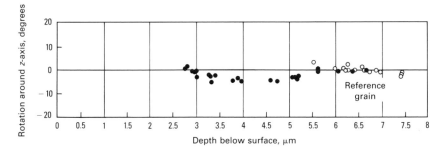

Example 8: Determination of Phase Diagrams by AEM

Raghavan Ayer
Exxon Research and
Engineering Company

Determination of phase diagrams to un- derstand the equilibria among phases in me- tallic and ceramic systems has been of par- amount interest in many areas of materials research. Traditionally, phase diagrams have been determined by selecting several exper- imental compositions to map the region in the system of interest, exposing the alloys to temperature to achieve equilibrium, and characterizing one or more of the physical properties of the bulk material, such as the crystal structure(s), magnetic properties, and materials properties to determine the number and type of phases present in each alloy. Phase boundaries are then determined by delineating the regions of alloy compositions relative to the number and types of phases present.

The traditional methods have several dis- advantages, including the need for numerous samples, difficulties in determining multi- phase regions accurately, assumptions that the bulk samples are macro- and microscop- ically homogeneous, and difficulties in es- tablishing the attainment of equilibrium. The limitations of these traditional methods de- rive mainly from their inherent inability to characterize the crystal structure and compo- sition of the individual phases (Ref 63). More recently, methods have been devel- oped to determine phase boundaries by x-ray microprobe analysis of bulk diffusion cou- ples (Ref 64). Although this approach offers some advantages over conventional meth- ods, it is limited by the poor spatial resolu- tion of x-ray microprobe analysis.

The modern probe-forming transmission electron microscopes can accurately define the crystal structure and chemical composi- tion of the phases at submicrometer levels and can be used to determine the phase boundaries with good accuracy and preci- sion. The method essentially consists of determining the compositions of the individ- ual microscopic phases by x-ray microan- alysis and their crystal structures by CBED in a material that has been equilibrated at the temperature of interest. This approach has several advantages and, in principle, can eliminate all or most of the limitations of the conventional techniques. The method can provide tie-line information and precise determination of invariant phase fields, such as eutectoid transformation in binary systems and three-phase regions in the isothermal section of ternary systems, and it requires fewer samples for the entire study. The approach does not require accurate knowledge of the average bulk composition of the alloy samples, nor does it assume that the composition is uniform throughout the sample. The procedure assumes only that equilibrium among the phases is established at least in local regions of the sample. Furthermore, the attainment of equilibrium can also be verified experimentally.

Experimental Procedure

Alloys for determining phase diagrams are generally prepared by arc melting premixed pure-metal powders in 50-g buttons; each button is remelted several times to minimize segregation. For ceramic powders, conventional compaction and sintering techniques can be used. The buttons are then homogenized at approximately 0.8 to $0.9 \times T_m$ (where T_m is the homologous temperature in degrees Kelvin) in an inert atmosphere for approximately 100 h. The homogenized samples are then exposed to the desired temperature for up to 10 000 h to attain equilibrium. When the equilibrium temperature exceeded $0.6 \times T_m$, exposure time of the order of 1000 h was found to be adequate.

Specimens for electron microscopy are prepared using conventional grinding and electropolishing techniques. In addition, ion milling may be necessary to thin large regions of second phases uniformly, particularly the intermetallics. If the size of the second-phase particles is of the order of, or less than, the foil thickness (approximately 100 to 200 nm), they should be extracted and analyzed after supporting them on carbon-coated grids made of copper or, preferably, beryllium.

Phase-Boundary Determination. The procedure for determining phase diagrams using AEM is illustrated by the schematic isothermal section of the Ni-Cr-Mo system at 1523 K (Fig. 82a). Experimental alloys using the procedure described above are made specifically in the two- and three-phase fields, for example, along the dotted line AB shown in Fig. 82(a). These alloys are exposed to the temperature of interest for an extended period of time, and the chemical composition and crystal structure of all the phases present are

Fig. 82 Determination of phase diagrams using AEM

(a) Isothermal section of the Ni-Cr-Mo system. (b) Bright-field microstructure of alloy composition marked C in (a)

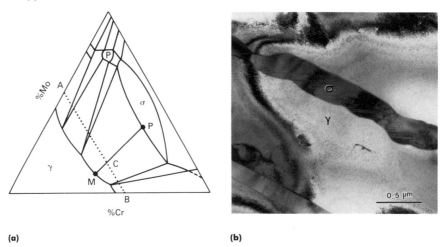

(a)   (b)

Fig. 83 Invariant phase field determination using AEM

(a) Bright-field micrograph of an Ni-Cr-Mo alloy in a three-phase field region showing P, σ, and γ (austenite) phases. (b) The compositions of the three phases define the entire three-phase field triangle.

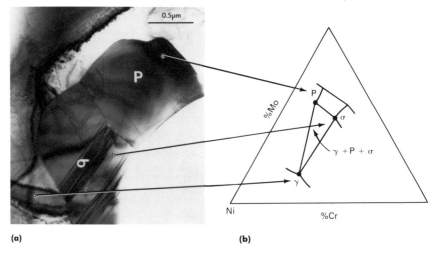

(a)   (b)

determined using x-ray microanalysis and CBED, respectively.

For example, point C in Fig. 82(a) is an alloy composition containing two phases, as shown by the bright-field image (Fig. 82b). The composition of the matrix provides point M, the composition of the intermetallic phase precipitate locates the point P on the diagram, and the line MP represents the tie-line. The intermetallic phase was identified as the tetragonal σ phase by CBED analysis (Ref 63). By selecting several alloys along line AB and measuring the composition and crystal structure of the individual phases, the γ/(γ + intermetallics) and the (γ + intermetallic)/intermetallics phase boundaries can be determined.

This method has the unique advantage of accurately determining invariant phase fields. This is illustrated in Fig. 83, which shows the bright-field image of an alloy in a three-phase γ + P + σ region. The measured compositions of the three phases define the corresponding corners of the triangle of the three-phase field, and the entire triangle was defined from one alloy composition. The isothermal section of the nickel-rich portion of the Ni-Cr-Mo system at 1523 K was determined experimentally using the above-mentioned procedure (Fig. 84). This diagram was obtained by selecting 14 alloy compositions in the two- and three-phase field regions and homogenizing and equilibrating 100 h at 1523 K.

Fig. 84 Isothermal section of the Ni-Cr-Mo system at 1523 K determined using AEM

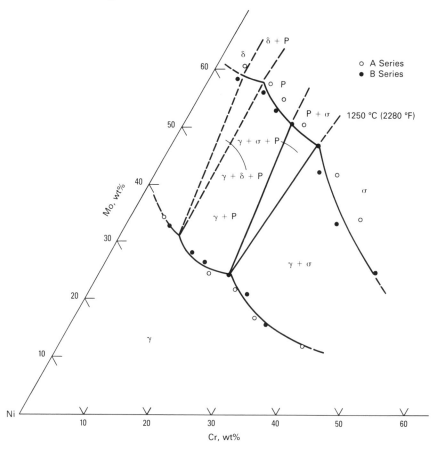

lished, then the average compositions of the phases do not represent their equilibrium concentration. Therefore, the second important consideration is to verify that equilibrium has been achieved among the phases. The attainment of equilibrium can be best verified by carrying out a compositional line profile across the interface of the phases using a small probe, preferably in the STEM mode.

Figure 85(a) shows a concentration profile of molybdenum across an austenite/μ interface obtained using a 1.5-nm probe in a Ni-20Cr-20Mo alloy. The concentration of molybdenum varies monotonically across the interface, indicating that the system is in equilibrium. If the phases are not in equilibrium, the profile will not be monotonic at the interface. An example of nonequilibrium is illustrated in Fig. 85(b), which shows a profile of molybdenum across an austenite/M_6C carbide interface in a Ni-20Cr-20Mo alloy (Ref 69). The molybdenum concentration shows nonmonotonic behavior at the interface (shaded region in Fig. 85b). This indicates that equilibrium between the phases has not been achieved; therefore, the average composition of the phases will not represent the equilibrium concentration. However, even when equilibrium is not reached, it is still possible to determine the equilibrium concentration of the phases by extrapolating the line profiles near the interface (Ref 70).

The procedure described above has also been used effectively to determine the phase boundaries in Fe-Ni-Cr and Fe-Ni-Cr-Mo systems (Ref 71). At the present time, the approach is limited to systems containing heavy elements ($Z \geq 11$), because such techniques as EELS and windowless EDS for analyzing light elements suffer from poor

To determine the phase boundaries with good accuracy, it is necessary to eliminate the major sources of spurious x-rays in the electron microscope and to adopt an acceptable procedure for quantitative x-ray microanalysis. The following experimental conditions must be satisfied for accurate x-ray microanalysis (Ref 65-68):

- A "clean" analytical microscope with minimal spurious x-rays
- Sufficient x-ray counts to obtain favorable statistics; typically, the tallest peak should contain at least 100 000 counts
- Adequate computer software package with acceptable background and absorption (and fluorescence) corrections and peak-fitting procedure
- A reliable method of determining specimen thickness
- k-values determined experimentally for the microscope used

Equilibrium Verification. The approach for determining phase boundaries discussed above assumes that there are no compositional gradients in the phases, which implies that equilibrium has been established. However, if equilibrium is not estab-

Fig. 85 Molybdenum concentration profiles in a Ni-20Cr-20Mo alloy

(a) Profile across an austenite/μ-phase interface in a sample equilibrated 100 h at 1523 K showing a monotonic variation and attainment of equilibrium. (b) Profile across an austenite/M_6C carbide interface in a sample exposed 1 h to 1033 K showing a nonmonotonic behavior at the interface (shadowed region), indicating a nonequilibrium condition

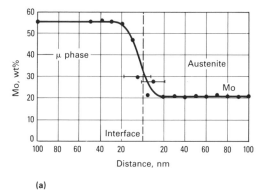

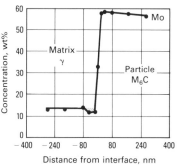

(a)

(b)

sensitivity and accuracy of quantification. Further developments may permit reliable quantitative analysis of light elements, which could expand the horizon of phase diagram determination by AEM.

Example 9: Diffusion Measurements by AEM

J.I. Goldstein and M.R. Notis
Department of Metallurgy
and Materials Engineering
Lehigh University

A.D. Romig, Jr.
Sandia National Laboratories

When two materials are placed in intimate contact, the atoms of each material will migrate into one another. This process of atomic transport is known as interdiffusion. The physical process that occurs on the atomic scale will vary, depending on the specific nature of the materials involved. The transport of atoms can be caused by one of several physical phenomena or forces. In the case of the processing and in-service behavior of engineering materials, diffusion is usually driven by some potential gradient. The most commonly encountered potential gradient is concentration (or, more correctly, activity or chemical potential). Other potential gradients that can drive interdiffusion include stress, temperature, magnetic fields, and electric fields.

To study interdiffusion in a concentration gradient, it is necessary to measure composition as a function of distance in a diffused sample. The analytical electron microscope provides the capability of measuring these gradients at spatial resolutions of 1 μm or less. This capability has permitted the study of diffusion over very short distances, such as those encountered in systems processed at low temperatures or for short times. This example discusses the use of AEM in measuring the chemical composition variation that occurs as a result of diffusion.

Advantages of AEM Analysis

The x-ray spatial resolution obtained by using the analytical electron microscope is at least 50 to 100 times better than that obtained using the electron probe microanalyzer. Such an improvement has several important consequences for diffusion measurements. To perform a diffusion analysis, 10 to 20 unique (spatially resolved) chemical analyses in the chemical concentration gradients are required. For data collected using electron probe microanalysis (EPMA), the diffusion gradient must be approximately 25 μm in length. Conversely, for data collected using AEM, the diffusion gradient must be approximately 250 to 500 nm in length, some 50 to 100 times less than that for the electron probe microanalyzer. Because the diffusion distance, x, is approximately $\sqrt{Dt}$, where D is the diffusion coefficient and t is time, use of the analytical electron microscope allows measurement of diffusivities as much as 10^4 times smaller than those obtained using the electron probe microanalyzer when diffusion experiments are conducted for the same heat treatment time. Conversely, the analytical electron microscope allows one to perform diffusion experiments using heat treatment times that are approximately 10^{-4} times less than EPMA. The analytical electron microscope has another special advantage in that grain boundaries can be observed, and any potential effects of grain-boundary diffusion can be avoided in the composition measurement.

Sample Preparation

The preparation of diffusion couples for the analytical electron microscope may be difficult. Rarely do two different materials, such as those that might be used to make a diffusion couple, thin at equal rates in an electrochemical polishing solution or in an ion beam thinner. Combinations of electrochemical thinning solutions and/or ion beam thinning may be required. Off-center sample positioning and masking may be useful for ion beam thinning. Following electropolishing, it is often advisable to clean the thin foil in an ion beam thinner for a few minutes to remove any potential chemical residue. Because the electron-transparent thin area is often limited, it is usually impossible to measure concentration profiles much more than 1 to 2 μm in length.

A schematic of the TEM-AEM preparation technique is given in Fig. 86 (Ref 72). After the diffusion couple is removed from the furnace and quenched, it is electrical discharged machined with the interface parallel to the brass electrode. The resulting 3-mm (0.12-in.) diam cylinder must be checked carefully for discontinuities, and if present, they must be removed by hand

filing. The cylinder is then glued to a metal support, and disks up to 4 mm thick are sawed off using a diamond blade (Fig. 86). Experience has proven that these precautions are necessary because stresses due to the diamond wheel are sufficient to cause the bond interface to tear apart. This is particularly true when (1) too thin a slice is taken, (2) no support is given to the cylinder, or (3) cracks, or discontinuities, acting as stress concentrators are present at the interface. The 3-mm diam disks are then ground to a thickness of approximately 80 μm using 600-grit paper, using ethanol as the wetting agent. After proper cleaning and drying, the samples are electrojet polished and/or ion milled. In nearly all cases, the thin area will not be located at the bond interface.

The sample is then ion milled until the thin area is present at the diffusion interface. In some cases, specimen preparation must be performed completely by ion milling. The advent of a new generation of ultramicrotomes capable of cutting metal foils thinner than 30 nm may also prove to be important for AEM applications.

The thinning of a heterogeneous multilayer structure is particularly difficult. Electrochemical jet thinning has been used for the preparation of aluminum-silver (Ref 73) and aluminum-zinc (Ref 74) foils where concentration gradients have been measured and diffusion calculations made at grain-boundary solute-depleted regions. A combination of electrochemical jet thinning and ion thinning has been used to prepare edge-on multilayer Ni/Ni₃Al/NiAl foils from bulk diffusion couples (Ref 75). A method for examining layered gold/silver/gold and gold/palladium/silver films edge-on has been documented (Ref 76, 77). This method involves cementing the layered material between two steel hemicylinders and inserting this cylindrical sandwich into a brass tube that is thin sectioned perpendicular to the tube axis and then ion thinned. Edge-on TEM foils of semiconductor devices involving impurity-doped silicon on SiO_2 or Al_2O_3 have also been noted in the recent literature (Ref 78, 79). Finally, ball cratering (Ref 80) and precision ion milling techniques should provide promising approaches for edge-on thinning or multilayer foils, but are just now being developed.

Data Analysis

Once a suitable thin foil has been obtained, certain precautions must be observed during data analysis. The profile must be measured parallel to the diffusion direction, and if the sample is a multiphase couple, the phase interface(s) must be oriented parallel

Fig. 86 Specimen preparation for AEM, beginning with a bonded diffusion couple

Note location of the bond interface during the various stages of specimen preparation. Source: Ref 72

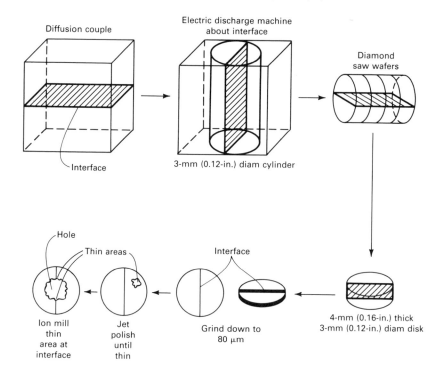

also very important that concentration profiles not be measured in the vicinity of grain boundaries so that only the bulk diffusion contribution is obtained.

Diffusion Couples. The analytical electron microscope has only recently been used for analysis of diffusion couples. Although the advantages of the improved spatial resolution of AEM have been known for some years, the difficulty of specimen preparation has slowed the application of the technique. The first known application of AEM was to the Fe-Ni system (Ref 72, 81). Figure 87 shows a TEM photomicrograph of a typical diffusion zone and a nickel profile over a ≤2-μm diffusion field in a Fe-20Ni versus Fe-25Ni ternary diffusion couple heat treated at 650 °C (1200 °F) for 4 months. The error resulting from the best-fit concentration gradient was estimated at ±2% (Fig. 87b). This small error allowed the diffusion coefficient to be determined to within an error of ±15%.

Figure 88 shows the binary iron-nickel diffusion coefficients measured between 900 °C (1650 °F) and 610 °C (1130 °F) in the austenite phase. The binary diffusion coefficients follow the curves of the Goldstein *et al.* data (Ref 82) extrapolated from high temperatures for varying nickel contents. Figure 89 shows a diffusion profile in another thin area of the sample at which a grain boundary is present. The distortion of the

Fig. 87(a) TEM photomicrograph of a ternary Fe-20Ni versus Fe-25Ni diffusion couple containing approximately 0.25P (F20NP-F25NP)

Diffused at 650 °C (1200 °F) for 121 days. The diffusion couple bond interface is shown along with contamination spots indicating the positions of the point analyses during the measurement of a nickel concentration profile. The smallest step size between points is 50 nm. Source: Ref 72

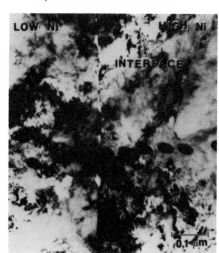

to the incident beam. If x-ray absorption is a concern, the specimen must also be oriented such that the direction of the x-rays from the analysis point to the EDS detector is parallel to the diffusion front, and the foil thickness at each analysis point must be known. It is

Fig. 87(b) Experimental nickel concentration gradient from the F20NP-F25NP ternary γ couple shown in Fig. 87(a)

Error bars for individual points and for the best-fit profile are given. Four traces were obtained from the couple. Source: Ref 72

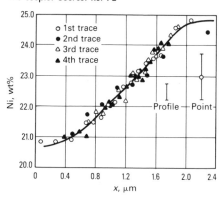

Fig. 88 Experimental results for the binary γ interdiffusion coefficient, $\tilde{D}_\gamma$, as a function of temperature

The error bar on $\tilde{D}_\gamma$ at 610 °C (1130 °F) indicates the possible range of $\tilde{D}_\gamma$ values at that temperature. Source: Ref 72

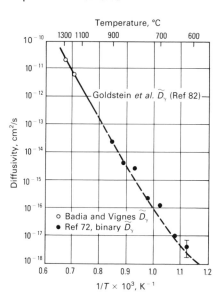

Fig. 89 Example of grain-boundary diffusion compared to volume diffusion

Same 650 °C (1200 °F) ternary austenite specimen as shown in Fig. 87(a) and (b). Source: Ref 72

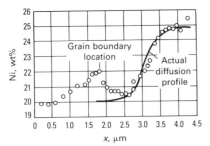

Fig. 90 STEM (a) and thickness profiles (b) for a NiAl/Ni specimen held at 1100 °C (2010 °F) for 15 min

The subscript ss denotes solid solution. Source: Ref 75

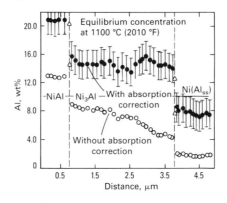

(a)

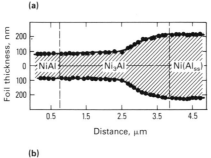

(b)

volume diffusion profile is easily observed, thereby demonstrating that the effect of grain-boundary diffusion can easily be avoided using the AEM technique.

The results of the Dean and Goldstein (Ref 72) AEM study of iron-nickel diffusion can be compared with those of the Goldstein *et al.* EPMA study (Ref 82) of iron-nickel diffusion. The lowest temperatures and the lowest measured diffusivities in these two studies were 650 °C (1200 °F), 1.2×10^{-17} cm^2/s and 1000 °C (1830 °F), 1.0×10^{-12} cm^2/s for the AEM and the EPMA studies, respectively. The respective diffusion times were 121 days versus 9 days. If one compares the products of Dt for the two temperatures, the Dt product for the AEM data is approximately 10^{-4} that of the EPMA data. This decrease in Dt is due to increased spatial resolution, as discussed previously. In this specific case, by using the increased spatial resolution of the analytical electron microscope and a heat treatment 13 times longer, the measured diffusivity was almost five orders of magnitude smaller, and the measurement occurred 350 °C (630 °F) lower than was previously obtained.

The major advantage in using AEM for multiphase couples is not only to measure the diffusivity, but to study the early-stage growth of intermediate phases and the development of concentration gradients at the multiphase interface. One of the earliest multiphase diffusion couple studies deals with the growth kinetics and the intermediate phase microstructure developed during early stage growth of Ni$_3$Al layers in NiAl/Ni diffusion couples (Ref 75).

STEM profiles obtained across the diffusion interfaces, are shown in Fig. 90(a) for a specimen held at 1100 °C (2010 °F) for 15 min. The corresponding thickness profile taken across the thin foil is shown in Fig. 90(b). In order to obtain the final concentration profile (upper data set in Fig. 90a), the data were corrected both for thickness and

absorption effects. The equilibrium concentrations at the appropriate two-phase boundaries at 1100 °C (2010 °F) are shown in Fig. 90(a). Within the error of the present technique, the data obtained at the NiAl/Ni$_3$Al and Ni$_3$Al/Ni interfaces after 1100 °C (2010 °F) for 15 min appear consistent with the interface concentrations predicted from phase equilibria. It has been proposed that nonequilibrium conditions may exist at short times at the interfaces in a diffusing system. Unfortunately, the data obtained from the multiphase couples were not of sufficient quality (see Fig. 90) to obtain the diffusion coefficients. The difficulty of obtaining such high-quality data when the foil thickness is nonuniform and x-ray absorption is a factor cannot be minimized.

Diffusion Coefficients. Interdiffusion and intrinsic diffusion coefficients can be determined using AEM. Both were reported for the Ta-W system in the temperature range of 1300 to 2100 °C (2370 to 3810 °F) in Ref 83. The concentration profiles were measured in the STEM mode on the analytical electron microscope, and the displacement of the inert markers was measured by imaging in the conventional TEM mode.

Diffusivities can also be measured by using second-phase precipitation from homogeneous alloys. Doig and Edington suggested that values of the diffusion coefficient and the activation energy for solute depletion could be obtained from composition profiles taken across grain boundaries (Ref 84). Doig and coworkers used plasmon energy loss analysis in an electron microscope to measure composition profiles in Al-7Mg and Al-4Cu binary alloys (Ref 84) and in Al-6Zn-3Mg ternary alloys (Ref 85), and then calculated solute-diffusion coefficients. The spatial resolution was limited to approximately 50 nm. Because the plasmon loss process is element-specific, the results cannot be generalized. More recently, low-temperature volume-diffusion coefficients of a zinc solute in aluminum-zinc alloys have been measured by monitoring the composition gradient across grain boundaries using AEM. For the situation when precipitates intercede in the matrix, diffusion coefficients may be measured by the motion of the precipitation front, because this front must also be a constant composition plane.

ACKNOWLEDGMENT

Work performed at Sandia National Laboratories supported by the U.S. Department of Energy under Contract No. DE-AC04-76DP00789.

Example 10: Interpretation of Weld Metal Microstructure by AEM

M.J. Cieslak, T.J. Headley, and A.D. Romig, Jr.
Sandia National Laboratories

Weld soundness can often be affected by a small volume fraction of a secondary constituent, such as carbides, nitrides, borides, or intermetallic phases. Understanding the behavior of weld metal during fabrication or service requires a knowledge of the generation of microstructure. Electron optical techniques, including EPMA, SEM, and AEM, have proved effective in determining the physical metallurgy of alloy weld metals.

In this example, the analysis of the microstructure generated during gas tungsten arc welding of Hastelloy Alloy C-22 will be discussed. This analysis will be extended to predict the weld microstructure of Hastelloy

Table 4 Weld metal compositions examined in Example 10

Element	Hastelloy C-22	Hastelloy C-276
Nickel	56.96	55.58
Chromium	21.22	15.83
Molybdenum	13.43	15.56
Iron	3.17	5.44
Tungsten	3.29	3.93
Cobalt	0.84	0.96
Manganese	0.31	0.50
Silicon	<0.02	0.03
Vanadium	0.14	0.18
Carbon	0.006	0.003
Sulfur	<0.002	0.002
Phosphorus	0.010	0.014

Note: All values given in weight percent.

Alloy C-276. The materials under consideration are highly corrosion-resistant nickel alloys based on the Ni-Cr-Mo ternary system. The compositions are given in Table 4. In the mill-annealed condition, they are single-phase austenitic (fcc) alloys not hardenable by aging treatments.

Experimental Method

Gas tungsten arc welds of Alloy C-22 containing solidification hot cracks were studied using various electron microscopy techniques. Weld metal specimens were prepared metallographically and etched using a 10% chromic acid electroetch. These surfaces were subsequently carbon coated and examined in the scanning electron microscope. Figure 91 shows a typical region of the microstructure near a hot crack. A minor solidification constituent is found associated with the crack. Small patches of the same microconstituent are also found scattered throughout the weld in interdendritic regions. These are the last positions in the microstructure to solidify, and the minor constituent is characteristic of the terminal solidification event.

The occurrence of a secondary solidification constituent is a direct result of the nonequilibrium nature of weld solidification. In general, alloys do not solidify at a single temperature, but rather over a temperature range. Segregation of alloying elements during solidification is a natural consequence of this phenomenon and results in the formation of phases not expected under equilibrium conditions.

Figure 92 shows the segregation pattern, as determined using the electron probe microanalyzer, of the major alloying elements found in Alloy C-22 weld metal. The profile begins in the center of an austenite dendrite and traverses the dendrite perpendicular to the growth direction, crosses an interden-

Fig. 91 Secondary solidification constituent associated with weld metal hot crack in Alloy C-22

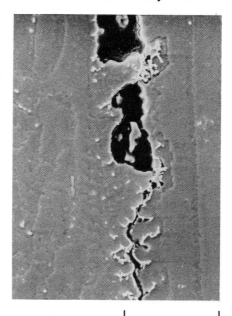

30 μm

dritic (ID) region, and ends in the center of the adjacent dendrite. Care was taken to avoid any interdendritic constituents. The profiles show that nickel depletion (≈10 wt%) and molybdenum (≈9 wt%) and chromium (≈1 wt%) enrichment are associated with the interdendritic regions. Little segregation of the minor elements was noted. These data indicate that the solidification path projected away from higher nickel concentration and toward higher molybdenum (and, to a small extent, chromium) concentrations.

Detailed analysis of the weld metal microstructure was accomplished by thin foil examination in the analytical electron microscope. In addition to phase identification by crystallographic (electron-diffraction) means, chemical analysis of individual phases was accomplished in the analytical electron microscope by EDS microanalysis. In the Alloy C-22 weld metal, three minor phases are observed in addition to the austenite matrix. These are P phase (orthorhombic: $a = 0.907$ nm, $b = 1.698$ nm, $c = 0.475$ nm), σ phase (tetragonal: $a = b = 0.908$ nm, $c = 0.475$ nm), and μ phase (hexagonal: $a = 0.476$ nm, $c = 2.591$ nm). The relative amounts of each of these phases are ≈80% P phase, ≈20% σ phase, and only a trace amount of μ phase. Figure 93 shows transmission electron micrographs, SADPs, and EDS spectra from the intermetallic phases found in the Alloy C-22 weld

Fig. 92 Major element segregation profile obtained by EPMA of Alloy C-22 weld metal

ID, position of interdendritic region

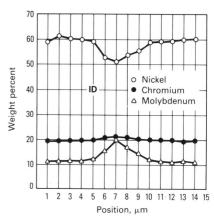

metal. The results clearly show that all phases are enriched in molybdenum and depleted in nickel relative to the bulk chemistry.

The absolute compositions of the intermetallic phases found in the Alloy C-22 weld metal were determined using the standardless ratio technique, where the compositions are related to the measured x-ray intensities by:

$$\frac{C_x}{C_{Ni}} = k_{xNi}\frac{I_x}{I_{Ni}}$$

where x = Mo, Cr, Fe, W, or Co; C is the composition in weight percent; I is the integrated x-ray intensity; and k_{xNi} is the Cliff-Lorimer sensitivity factor. The standardless ratio technique is valid only if the thin film criteria, requiring negligible x-ray absorption and fluorescence in the specimens, is not violated (Ref 24). The values of the sensitivity factors were determined from an annealed sample of Hastelloy Alloy C-276 with a well-known composition. The values of the sensitivity factors used are:

Elemental ratio	k_{xNi}
Cr/Ni	0.83
Mo/Ni	3.41
Fe/Ni	0.95
W(Lβ)/Ni	9.09
Co/Ni	1.62

The compositions of all phases were calculated with the experimental values of k_{xNi} and a standard data-reduction routine (Ref 22). X-ray absorption in these specimens was not significant, and no correction to the standardless ratio technique was used.

Fig. 93 Transmission electron micrographs, SADPs, and EDS spectra from intermetallic phases in Alloy C-22 weld metal

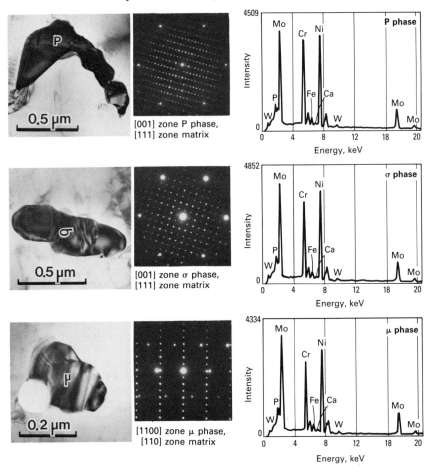

[001] zone P phase,
[111] zone matrix

[001] zone σ phase,
[111] zone matrix

[1100] zone μ phase,
[110] zone matrix

Fig. 94 Three-element (Ni-Cr-Mo) isothermal sections at selected temperatures

(a) 1523 K isothermal section. (b) 1123 K isothermal section. Source: Ref 63

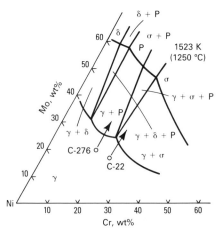

(a)

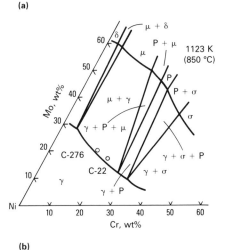

(b)

Table 5 shows the results of this analysis on all phases present in the Alloy C-22 microstructure. Several interesting relationships among the component elements can be observed. All the intermetallic phases are depleted in nickel and iron relative to the matrix. Conversely, all the intermetallic phases are enriched in molybdenum and tungsten relative to the matrix. This suggests an equivalence in chemical behavior relative to the formation of specific phases between nickel and iron, and molybdenum and tungsten, respectively. That is, nickel and iron tend to stabilize the austenite matrix; molybdenum and tungsten tend to stabilize the intermetallic phases. In addition, the behavior of molybdenum and tungsten appears to be even more phase-specific. Among the intermetallic phases, the molybdenum and tungsten contents increase in the following order: σ, P, μ. The similarity in chemical effect should not be surprising. Molybdenum and tungsten are bcc elements whose refrac-

tory nature suggests analogous bonding characteristics. Similarly, nickel and iron are fcc in the temperature range in which transformations (solidification and solid state) occur in this alloy system, and both are found to stabilize the austenite matrix.

Discussion

There are no five-element phase diagrams available from which phase relationships can be determined unambiguously for Alloy

C-22. There are three-element (Ni-Cr-Mo) isothermal sections available at selected temperatures. Two of the most recently determined are shown in Fig. 94. All the phases observed in the Alloy C-22 weld microstructure (γ, P, σ, and μ) are possible in the Ni-Cr-Mo system. Several points of interest are visible: (1) μ phase is not present

Table 5 Phase compositions in the Alloy C-22 microstructure

Phase	Ni	Mo	Cr	W	Fe	Co
μ	33.1 (2.4)	38.7 (0.2)	19.3 (0.7)	6.3 (1.1)	2.1 (0.2)	0.6 (0.2)
P	32.6 (0.8)	37.4 (1.0)	21.7 (0.7)	5.3 (1.1)	2.2 (0.2)	0.9 (0.4)
σ	34.5 (0.6)	34.9 (0.4)	23.4 (1.3)	4.2 (1.2)	2.2 (0.1)	0.9 (0.2)
γ	58.5 (1.2)	12.7 (0.8)	21.6 (0.5)	2.9 (0.7)	3.4 (0.1)	0.9 (0.2)
Nominal	56.96	13.43	21.22	3.29	3.17	0.84

Note: All values are in weight percent; values in parentheses = 1 standard deviation.

in the high-temperature diagram; (2) the region of single-phase μ stability at 1123 K lies in approximately the same compositional space as that occupied by P phase at 1523 K; (3) a similar relationship exists between the γ(austenite) + μ field at 1123 K and the γ + P field at 1523 K, indicating that the transformation P → μ occurs as the temperature falls (weld metal cools) from 1523 K to 1123 K; and (4) the lower chromium regions of σ and σ + γ stability transform to regions of P and P + γ stability as the temperature falls, necessitating the transformation σ → P.

The general conclusions obtained from analyzing these diagrams are: (1) σ phase is stabilized relative to the other two phases by increasing the chromium content and decreasing the molybdenum content, (2) μ phase is stabilized relative to the other two phases by increasing the molybdenum content and decreasing the chromium content, (3) P phase is intermediate in chromium and molybdenum content among the intermetallic phases, and (4) the transformations P → μ and σ → P occur as the temperature falls.

A solidus diagram does not exist for the Ni-Cr-Mo system. The liquidus surface has been determined (Ref 86), but explicit solid/liquid phase relationships were not defined. A provisional series of high-temperature invariant reactions above 1523 K were proposed. In the vicinity of 50 wt% Ni, 30 wt% Mo, and 20 wt% Cr, the possible solidification phases are γ, P, and σ. In all cases, γ is the first phase to crystallize from the liquid, with P phase or σ phase solidifying as a secondary interdendritic constituent. The crossover between σ-phase and P-phase solidification was proposed to occur at 20 wt% Cr. That is, σ would be expected at higher chromium concentrations, and P would be expected at lower chromium concentrations. In no case was μ phase observed as a high-temperature (1523 K) phase in this system or in any similar system.

With this as background, an equivalent concept was proposed to predict the sequence of transformations in Hastelloy C alloys using the available Ni-Cr-Mo ternary diagrams (Ref 87). The molybdenum and tungsten weight fractions are combined to create a molybdenum equivalent, Mo_{eq}. The chromium equivalent, Cr_{eq}, was set equal to the chromium weight fraction because no other alloying element was found to behave similarly to chromium in terms of phase stabilization. The nickel and iron weight fractions (plus the small quantity of the remaining residual elements) are combined to produce a nickel equivalent, Ni_{eq}.

For the Hastelloy C-22 weld under consideration, a new equivalent composition can be calculated as $Ni_{eq} = 62.06$,

$Cr_{eq} = 21.22$, and $Mo_{eq} = 16.72$. This composition is shown plotted on the known ternary diagrams (Fig. 94). The arrow on the 1523-K section (the closest section to the solidus available) shows the solidification path as determined from the microprobe analysis. This indicates that σ phase would be the expected interdendritic solidification phase in Alloy C-22. As the 1123-K section indicates, this weld can be expected to enter into a region of μ-phase stability during cooling to room temperature. To enter a region of μ-phase stability, this alloy would have to pass through a region of P-phase stability at some intermediate temperature. The extent of transformation among these intermetallic phases will depend on the thermal history of the weld metal. In general, the transformations are diffusion controlled and incomplete when the relatively rapid cooling rates associated with arc welding are considered.

In the present case, all three intermetallic phases are present in the Alloy C-22 weld metal. Substantial transformation of σ phase to P phase occurs, but only a very small amount of the P → μ transformation is observed. The P → μ transformation occurs at lower temperatures and would thus be expected to go far less toward completion than the σ → P transformation. The sequence of transformations involved in solidification and cooling of Hastelloy C-22 weld metal according to the proposed model is:

$$L \rightarrow L + \gamma \rightarrow L + \gamma + \sigma \rightarrow \gamma + \sigma \rightarrow$$
$$\gamma + \sigma + P \rightarrow \gamma + \sigma + P + \mu$$

Application of this elemental equivalency model to the Alloy C-276 weld metal of composition given in Table 4 gives an equivalent composition that is also plotted on the ternary diagrams of Fig. 94. The arrow on the 1523-K section indicates the solidification path for this alloy weld metal, as determined using EPMA. The equivalent model predicts that P phase will be the secondary interdendritic solidification constituent in Alloy C-276 weld metal. The 1123-K section indicates that the transformation P → μ will also occur. Analytical electron microscopy of the intermetallic constituents in this weld metal microstructure revealed only the presence of P and μ phases (no σ phase) in approximately equal amounts, which is in qualitative agreement with the model.

ACKNOWLEDGMENT

Work performed at Sandia National Laboratories supported by the U.S. Department of Energy under Contract No. DE-AC04-76DP00789.

Example 11: Analysis of Grain-Boundary Segregation by AEM

Anthony J. Garratt-Reed
Center for Materials Science
and Engineering
Massachusetts Institute of Technology

An important application of AEM is the study of compositional changes at interfaces. Such compositional changes can extend a significant distance away from the interface, as in the case of sensitization of stainless steels or nickel-base alloys, when chromium levels may be depleted over tens of nanometers (or more) from the boundary, or they may be limited essentially to a single atomic plane, as is usually the case when grain-boundary segregation is under investigation. Because x-ray analysis is used almost exclusively in the analytical electron microscope for these studies, this example will be limited to that type of analysis. Electron energy loss spectroscopy is a more specialized mode that is rarely used for interface analysis.

Boundaries are invariably examined in the analytical electron microscope by orienting them parallel to the electron beam, then analyzing a series of points at intervals along a line perpendicular to the boundary, producing a composition profile (Fig. 95). The spacing of the points is selected by considering the extent of the compositional variation and the spatial resolution of the microanalysis.

In an infinitely thin specimen, when there is no beam spreading, the volume of the specimen irradiated by the electron beam is given simply by the area of the beam spot multiplied by the specimen thickness. Therefore, the resolution can be equated to the diameter of the spot. However, in this case, the x-ray signal will be infinitely small (the x-ray signal depends linearly on the product of the beam current and the specimen thickness) and therefore is of no practical value. In practice, the phenomenon of beam broadening and therefore the effect of specimen thickness on the analysis must be considered. Detailed information on the ultimate spatial resolution achievable in AEM can be found in Ref 88.

Fig. 95 Generation of a composition profile

(a) View of specimen with the boundaries oriented parallel to the electron beam. The positions at which the composition is measured are indicated by x. (b) The resulting composition profile

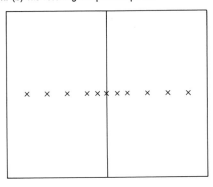

(a)

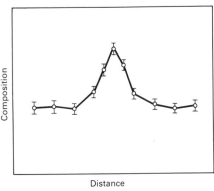

(b)

Fig. 96 Analysis of region whose dimensions are large compared with the beam diameter and the corresponding beam broadening

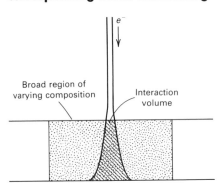

Fig. 97 Analysis of region that is narrow compared with the beam diameter and the corresponding beam broadening

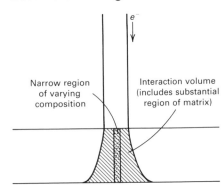

Analysis of Broad Segregant Distributions

As the probe is stepped across the interface, the measured profile will represent a convolution of the real profile, the electron probe diameter, and the beam broadening (Fig. 96). If the compositional variation over the dimensions of the probe diameter and the broadening are small, the measured x-ray profile will represent the actual profile fairly accurately. A useful definition of the spatial resolution in this case is provided by the diameter of the cylinder within which 90% of the x-rays are generated. Given a knowledge of the specimen thickness and the incident probe diameter and using models of beam broadening from the literature, computer calculations readily estimate this parameter.

Analysis of Narrow Interfaces

In principle, when the actual profile is narrower than the beam diameter, the measured profile may be deconvoluted to obtain the actual profile if the specimen thickness, probe diameter, and broadening are precisely known. However, in practice, it is not possible to acquire data with sufficiently accurate statistics and spatial precision to provide useful results. Only by making simplifying assumptions can some semiquantitative conclusions be drawn from the measurements. An often valid assumption is that the solute is segregated in a monolayer at the boundary.

Figure 97 shows the analysis of a narrow interface by a broader beam. Clearly, most of the electrons will interact with material remote from the interface and will contribute only matrix information to the resulting spectrum. Information on the boundary is contributed only by those electrons in the center of the beam. Therefore, for a maximum ratio of boundary-to-matrix signal, the impetus is to minimize the beam diameter

and specimen thickness. The beam diameter and beam current are related; as a result, both courses reduce the x-ray count rate and therefore degrade the statistics of the spectrum. For any choice of conditions, computer modeling will provide an estimate of the ratio of segregant to matrix that will be measured. Comparison of the predictions with the actual results enables conclusions to be drawn about the degree of segregation.

In this example, calculations were performed for microscopes fitted with a field emission source or a W-hairpin for a range of electron accelerating voltages, assuming an x-ray count rate of 2000 cps and ideal operation of the microscope; as such, these represent basic physical limitations of microanalysis. Table 6 lists the computed optimum diameter of the cylinder of 90% x-ray production in iron, the specimen thickness required to achieve this optimum, and the minimum fraction of a monolayer of chromium that would be detectable in iron for electron energies from 100 to 500 keV. The assumptions made in these computations and the sources of the parameters used are described in Ref 88. No account has been taken of experimental difficulties in compiling

Table 6   Optimum specimen thickness, t, and resolutions, d, and estimate of minimum fraction of monolayer of segregation that would be detectable, f, for analyzing chromium in iron using tungsten and field emission microscopes at different voltages

Beam voltage, eV	Field emission			Tungsten		
	t, nm	d, nm	f	t, nm	d, nm	f
100	21.9	1.81	0.005	88	14.4	0.04
200	29.4	1.40	0.003	117	11.1	0.024
300	34.5	1.19	0.002	138	9.5	0.017
400	38.7	1.06	0.0017	154	8.4	0.014

these results; in practice, measurements will only approach these figures.

The result that 0.0015 of a monolayer of chromium is detectable in a field emission microscope at 500 keV in a foil 42 nm thick using a 1.0-nm-diam probe implies the detection of only two atoms of chromium. Because such a microscope has not been built, this prediction is not testable. However, results at lower voltages generally agree with these predictions. Predictions for microscopes fitted with LaB_6 guns will fall between the values for field emission and tungsten gun microscopes. Because the counting statistics of the x-ray signal enter the calculation, the sensitivity of the x-ray detector influences the quality of the analysis. A typical modern high-sensitivity detector was assumed in this calculation.

Applications

Three applications of the use of AEM to study interfaces are provided below. These profiles were obtained in a microscope fitted with a field emission source operating at 100 keV.

Chromium Sensitization in Inconel 600. During high-temperature service, Inconel 600, like many other alloys, exhibits growth of chromium carbides on grain boundaries. The extremely rapid diffusion of chromium along the boundary feeds the growth, lending to a region depleted in chromium on either side of the boundary, which can promote grain-boundary corrosion. Figure 98 illustrates a profile from such a boundary that appears to be approximately 40 nm wide and depleted to a chromium concentration of approximately 10% at the boundary. This specimen was estimated to be 100 nm thick, and computer modeling indicates that the profile closely represented the actual concentration.

Manganese Segregation in Dual-Phase Steels. An investigation of the growth of dual-phase steels has included an investigation of manganese partitioning. A low-resolution profile (Fig. 99a) shows the expected preferential partitioning of the manganese to the austenite (martensite), but a high-resolution profile (Fig. 99b) indicates clearly the presence of substantial manganese segregation at the phase boundary. Because the thickness was not known in this case, a more precise statement about the magnitude of this segregation is not possible.

Yttrium Segregation at Grain Boundaries in Cr_2O_3. Alloy Co-45Cr oxidizes by forming a scale of Cr_2O_3 that grows by outward diffusion of chromium. However, in specimens ion implanted with 2×10^{16} atoms/cm² of yttrium, a dramatic reduction in the thickness of the scale is

observed, and it now grows by inward diffusion of oxygen. The grain boundaries of the scale formed on the implanted material were examined for yttrium segregation (Fig. 100). Strong segregation is visible; the specimen was estimated to be 50 nm thick, and computer modeling indicates that the measured value of 4% Y on the grain boundary corresponds to a substantial fraction, possibly approaching complete coverage, of the boundary by the yttrium. Thus, there is a strong possibility that outward diffusion of chromium along grain boundaries is blocked by the yttrium, leaving the only available oxidation mechanism to be the relatively slow inward diffusion of oxygen.

Limitations

The above discussion has assumed ideal conditions for analysis. However, all microscopes to a greater or lesser degree suffer from contamination, drift, and interference problems. In addition, the orientation of the specimen may not be perfect. These problems lead to degradation of the spatial resolution and sensitivity. The specimens required are very thin, and it may not be possible to locate an area of interest in such a region; degradation of the resolution and sensitivity will again result. It is necessary to ensure that electron diffraction is not contributing to the beam broadening; the material on each side of the boundary of interest should be oriented such that no strong diffraction is occurring.

These problems are most critical when the highest resolution analysis is being undertaken; this is the case in a microscope fitted with an FEG. However, they must be considered in all analyses.

Fig. 98 Depletion of chromium measured at a grain-boundary in Inconel 600

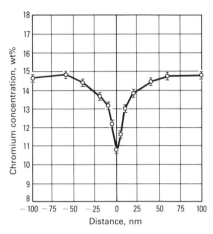

Fig. 99 Composition profiles at manganese segregation in a dual-phase steel

(a) Profile obtained at low resolution showing manganese partitioning between austenite (martensite) and ferrite. (b) A high-resolution profile across the same boundary showing strong manganese segregation. Source: Ref 89

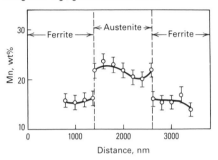

(a)

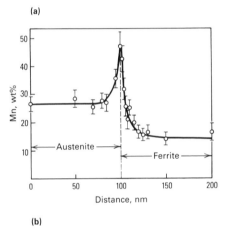

(b)

Fig. 100 Yttrium profile across a grain boundary in Cr_2O_3 scale grown on yttrium-implanted Co-45Cr

The data plotted are simply the ratio of Y-Kα and Cr-Kα x-ray lines measured at each point.

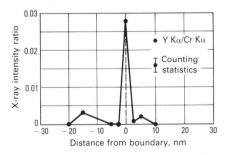

ACKNOWLEDGMENT

Thanks are due to Il-Soon Hwang and Kaz Przybylski for use of their unpublished results. This work was supported by the National Science Foundation block grants No. DMR81-19295 and DMR84-18718.

Example 12: Determination of Microstructures of Ion-Implanted Alloys by AEM

D.M. Follstaedt
Sandia National Laboratories

Ion implantation is a technique for producing a surface alloy with a tailored composition on a substrate material by injecting atoms of the desired alloy addition(s) into the near surface of the material. Virtually any atomic species can be added over penetration depths of approximately 0.01 to 1 μm by accelerating its ions to energies ranging from a few keV to several MeV. Concentrations up to tens of atomic percent can be implanted, but the resulting concentration profile depends on the energy and mass of the implanted species and on the host. Because the alloy is formed independently of many of the thermodynamic constraints that apply to thermal alloying processes, metastable alloys can be produced and studied (Ref 90). In some instances, implanted alloys are examined because of their favorable physical properties, such as reduced friction and enhanced wear (Ref 91).

Fig. 101 Weak-beam dark-field image showing the dislocation network that results from implanting 4.4 at.% Mo into aluminum at room temperature
Source: Ref 97

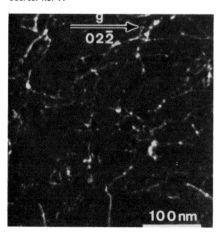

To characterize implanted alloys properly, techniques providing the concentration as a function of depth are used in addition to AEM. The depth-profiling techniques used in metals are most often ion beam analysis techniques (Rutherford backscattering or nuclear reaction analysis), but secondary ion mass spectrometry (SIMS) and Auger analysis are used as well (these techniques are covered in separate articles in this Volume). Ion channeling is also used to probe lattice disorder as a function of depth and to obtain lattice locations for implanted atoms. The alloy thickness is often ≤0.1 μm, which is within the thickness range for examining metals, such as transition elements, using AEM at 100 keV. Microscopy can determine phases and furnish microstructure images as well as provide compositional analysis with lateral resolutions approaching approximately 0.01 μm by such analytical techniques as EDS and EELS. This example examines the use of various AEM techniques for the characterization of ion-implanted alloy microstructures.

Sample Preparation

Because the surface layer is to be examined, a method of removing the substrate is required. Metals are most often thinned for TEM examination by electropolishing, and methods using a single-sided jet thinner to examine surface alloys have been developed (Ref 92, 93). The implantation of high fluences (a measure of time-integrated particle flux expressed in particles per square centimeter) in some cases produces compressive stresses that cause the implanted layer to curl after thinning; its examination is then difficult, but usually not impossible. However, in other cases, the different composition of the alloy layer causes it to resist electropolishing, and it can be observed standing free of the substrate (Ref 91). In favorable alloy systems, a gradual thinning through the alloy layer is achieved, and examination of successively thicker areas can yield the microstructure as a function of depth (Ref 94, 95).

Radiation-Induced Changes

In addition to the changes produced in composition, ion implantation displaces atoms in the host material, creating vacancy/interstitial pairs. In metals, these usually agglomerate to produce dislocation loops. In aluminum, in which interstitials and vacancies are mobile at room temperature, low fluences of nickel ions (2×10^{15} Ni/cm^2)

implanted at 150 keV produced dislocation loops; higher fluences (1×10^{16} Ni/cm^2) produced a mixture of extended dislocations and loops in the fcc matrix (Ref 96). When fluences of approximately 10^{17} ions/cm^2 are used to produce implanted alloys of approximately 10 at.%, dense dislocation tangles are observed. Weak-beam imaging can help resolve such dislocations, as shown for molybdenum-implanted aluminum in Fig. 101.

The atomic displacements can also produce changes in lattice structure, such as disordering of ordered compounds and amorphitization of compounds. Transformations to other crystalline structures can also be induced (Ref 90), as shown for room-temperature implantation of iron into 304 stainless steel in Fig. 102. The material was initially in the metastable fcc phase, and the atomic displacements due to the subsequent implantation induced a transformation to the bcc phase, which is stable at room temperature. As with phase transformations in bulk metallurgy, the two phases have a specific orientation relative to each other (Ref 90).

Fig. 102 AEM analysis of ion-implanted stainless steel

(a) Electron-diffraction pattern from bcc particles (inner reflections) in an fcc matrix (outer reflections) of 304 stainless steel implanted with 3×10^{16} Fe/cm^2 at 160 keV. (b) Dark-field micrograph, showing the bcc particles, that was obtained by imaging with the $(002)_{bcc}$ reflection circled in (a).

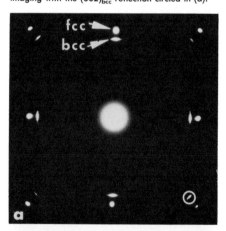

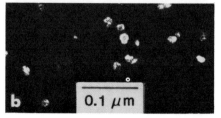

Figure 102(a) shows a [100]$_{fcc}$ zone axis pattern with a superimposed pattern from the parallel [100]$_{bcc}$ zone axis. The bcc reflections are less intense and are positioned immediately inside the fcc reflections. Within the (100) plane shown in Fig. 102(a), the orientation relationship is [010]$_{bcc}$ ‖ [011]$_{fcc}$. Programs are available (which run on the computer systems used for EDS) to generate superimposed electron-diffraction patterns and thus help determine the orientational relationship between the two phases (Ref 46). The dark-field imaging used to illuminate the bcc particles shown in Fig. 102(b) is a useful technique for examining second phases in heavily damaged metals.

Precipitation

Implantation of Metals. Nickel-implanted aluminum has been found to be a model system exhibiting several metastable features. At concentrations of approximately 1 at.% Ni, ion channeling showed 0.2 at.% Ni on substitutional fcc aluminum lattice sites, which exceeds the maximum solid solubility of nickel in aluminum ten times (Ref 98). Similar lattice substitutionality determinations have recently been demonstrated with electron channeling and EDS in the analytical electron microscope (Ref 99). Metastable solid solutions are formed in many pure metals for implanted concentrations generally less than 10 at.% (Ref 100).

At a higher concentration of 20 at.% Ni, an amorphous phase was observed. At 32 at.% Ni, particles of AlNi were also observed at the interface between the metal substrate and the aluminum surface oxide (Ref 90, 94). The bright-field micrograph shown in Fig. 103 shows the approximately 0.2-μm AlNi particles. The darker part of the micrograph is from a thicker area that contains the amorphous phase as identified by the diffuse ring in the electron-diffraction pattern. The superimposed spot reflections identify the particles as AlNi; these are also found suspended on the oxide layer in the lighter areas of the micrograph.

The aluminum-nickel equilibrium phase diagram shows two other phases near these implanted concentrations, Al$_3$Ni and Al$_3$Ni$_2$, that were not observed (Ref 101). A metastable phase diagram with fcc aluminum, amorphous Al(Ni), and AlNi can describe the observed aluminum-rich alloys (Ref 102). In such a diagram, the AlNi phase is expected to extend to lower nickel concentrations than under equilibrium conditions; therefore, the composition of the AlNi particles suspended on the oxide layer shown in Fig. 103 was examined using EDS (Ref 94). After subtracting contributions to the

Fig. 103 Suspended ~0.2-μm AlNi particles on the aluminum oxide surface layer (light area) and with amorphous Al(Ni) in the thicker sample regions (dark area)

Bright-field micrograph obtained by 120 kV. Inset: Electron-diffraction pattern from the thicker area showing the amorphous phase (diffuse rings) and AlNi (isolated spots)

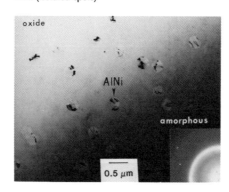

x-ray spectrum from the aluminum oxide, the composition was determined to be 36.5 ± 2.5 at.% Ni. This value can be interpreted as the minimum nickel composition for AlNi in the absence of the other two compounds and is lower than the lowest equilibrium concentration of nickel in AlNi, which is 43 at.% (Ref 101). Such phase diagrams may be useful in predicting phases in other implanted alloy systems.

Implantation of Metalloids. Many engineering alloys have been found to exhibit improved mechanical properties when implanted with nitrogen. Examination of Ti-6Al-4V (wt%) that was implanted with nitrogen to 20 to 30 at.% below 100 °C (212 °F) revealed an improvement in fatigue life with the treatment (Ref 103). Electron diffraction showed that TiN precipitated, and the dark-field image shown in Fig. 104 displays the 10- to 20-nm precipitates. An increase in hardness of the near surface and reduced wear have also been observed with this treatment (Ref 104). Implantation of nitrogen also reduces wear on many steel surfaces, and nitrides have again been found to have formed (Ref 105). The criteria for whether metalloid implantation of metals produces crystalline compounds (TiN, for example) or amorphous phases are discussed in Ref 90 and 106.

Implantation of Inert Elements. Inert gas elements are very insoluble in metals and are not expected to remain in solution when implanted. With helium implantation small bubbles form, as shown in Fig. 105 for iron implanted to a peak concentration of 6

Fig. 104 Dark-field micrograph of TiN precipitates in Ti-6Al-4V implanted with 2 × 10^{17} N/cm^2 at 75 keV

Source: Ref 102

Fig. 105 Bright-field image of helium bubbles in bcc iron after implantation at room temperature of 4 × 10^{16} He/cm^2 at 15 keV

(a) Underfocused. (b) Overfocused. The same pair of bubbles is identified by arrows in each micrograph. Note that the point-to-point resolution achieved with 120 kV is approximately 5 Å.

(a)

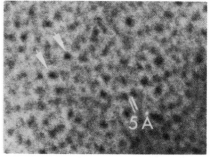

(b)

at.% He (Ref 107, 108). The contrast change observed upon going from underfocus to overfocus (light center → dark center) demonstrates that the features are cavities, with diameters of approximately 1 nm. The resolution required to image such small features

Fig. 106 Bright-field image from the center of a wear track on 304 stainless steel implanted with 2 × 10¹⁷ Ti/cm² (180 to 90 keV) plus 2 × 10¹⁷ C/cm² (30 keV)

The worn surface is amorphous, as shown by the diffuse ring in the inset diffraction pattern.

Fig. 107 EELS spectrum obtained with 120-kV electrons from iron implanted with 2 × 10¹⁷ Ti/cm² (180 keV) plus 2 × 10¹⁷ N/cm² (40 keV)

A plasmon peak at 25 eV follows the zero-loss peak, and carbon, nitrogen, titanium, oxygen, and iron edges are observed on the falling background. Source: Ref 95

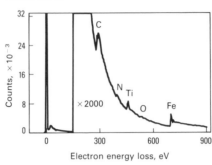

in ferromagnetic iron specimens approximately 50 μm thick was obtained by realigning the microscope controls with the specimen in place. Implantation of helium has been shown to form such bubbles in several metals (Ref 109). For higher implanted helium fluences and concentrations, the bubbles increase in size and eventually rupture, blistering the surface.

Implantation of Two Species: Ternary Alloys

The microstructures of alloys with two or more implanted species have been examined in only a few systems. In the Fe-Ti-C system, an amorphous phase forms at concentrations exceeding 12 at.% of both titanium and carbon (Ref 110). The amorphous ternary alloy is obtained in ferrous alloys even when only titanium is implanted to high fluences, because carbon is incorporated into the near-surface alloy from residual carbonaceous species in the implantation vacuum chamber, in which pressures are typically approximately 10⁻⁶ torr. Such carbon incorporation has been observed to accompany the implantation of a number of carbide-forming elements (Ref 111, 112).

Amorphous Fe-Ti-C is important because of the reduced friction and wear achieved when steels are implanted with titanium and carbon (Ref 113). The surface alloy on 304 stainless steel that was implanted with both titanium and carbon to maximize the amor-

phous layer thickness is shown in Fig. 106 after 1000 cycles of pin-on-disk wear (Ref 91). The amorphous Fe-Ti-C alloys resist electropolishing with nitric acid solution; thus, free-standing areas of the amorphous surface layer remain after the steel substrate is removed. The grooves observed in Fig. 106 show the direction of pin motion. Electron diffraction from the surface layer produces the diffuse ring pattern shown in the inset, indicating that the surface layer being worn is still amorphous as it was initially after implantation. In the wear track shown in Fig. 106, the maximum wear depth was reduced from approximately 1 to 0.15 μm, and the coefficient of (unlubri-

cated) friction from 0.8 to 0.5. The direct observation of such continuous amorphous layers across wear tracks closely links the reductions in friction and wear to the amorphous phase.

Because most EDS detectors have beryllium windows, x-rays from light elements ($Z < 11$) are not detected. Such elements can, however, be detected using EELS. Figure 107 shows a spectrum taken from an amorphous layer on iron implanted with titanium and nitrogen (Ref 95). The spectrum shows characteristic edges from iron, titanium, nitrogen, and carbon, which was incorporated into the alloy as discussed above, as well as from oxygen due to oxide on the surface of the specimen. Thus, EELS is seen to be sufficiently sensitive to detect and quantify the presence of heavy (titanium) and light (carbon, nitrogen) implanted elements at typical concentrations (~10 at.%) in metals.

Thermal Treatments

The increase in temperature during or after implantation to produce increased point defect or implanted species mobility can alter the microstructure of the implanted alloy significantly. The molybdenum-implanted aluminum alloy shown in Fig. 101 was annealed 100 min at 550 °C (1020 °F) to obtain the lamellar-like structure shown in Fig. 108. The composition of the precipitated phase was determined using EDS to be 9.3 ± 1.0 at.% Mo. To identify the phase completely, CBED was used as shown for the ⟨100⟩ pattern in Fig. 108(b). Diffraction spots (such as those shown in Fig. 102) are broadened into disks using CBED because a

Fig. 108 Effects of annealing a molybdenum-implanted aluminum sample at 550 °C (1020 °F) for 100 min

(a) Bright-field micrograph showing pseudolamellar Al₁₂Mo precipitates (dark areas). (b) ⟨001⟩ CBEDP from the precipitates showing two mirror symmetry planes (m). Source: Ref 114

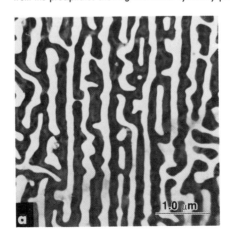
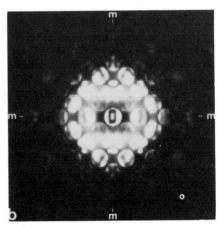

wider range of incident angles is used to form the electron beam. The disk pattern and the structures observed in the disks reflect the symmetry of the lattice. By examination of planar spacings and symmetries in such patterns, the structure was determined to be $Al_{12}Mo$. The composition of $Al_{12}Mo$ can be obtained by implanting molybdenum into aluminum, and when a specimen implanted to a peak concentration of 11 at.% Mo was subsequently annealed at 550 °C (1020 °F), a transformation to a continuous layer of $Al_{12}Mo$ was observed to propagate across the surface (Ref 97).

Thus, thermal treatments offer an additional degree of control over the microstructures produced by ion implantation. In addition, monitoring the evolution of depth profiles of implanted species during annealing has been used to obtain solid solubilities and diffusivities in binary alloys and trapping strengths of solutes at such microstructural features as bubbles and precipitates (Ref 115). Interpretation of such profile evolution requires that the phases present be well characterized using AEM.

ACKNOWLEDGMENT

Work performed by Sandia National Laboratories supported by the U.S. Department of Energy under Contract No. DE-AC04-76DP00789.

REFERENCES

1. L.E. Murr, *Electron Optical Applications in Materials Science*, McGraw-Hill, 1970
2. J.W. Edington, *Practical Electron Microscopy in Materials Science*, Van-Nostrand Reinhold, 1976
3. D.B. Williams, *Practical Analytical Electron Microscopy in Materials Science*, Philips Electronic Instruments, Inc., Mahwah, NJ, 1984
4. D.C. Joy, A.D. Romig, Jr., and J.I. Goldstein, Ed., *Analytical Electron Microscopy*, Plenum Press, 1986
5. P. Hirsch, A. Howie, R.B. Nicholson, D.W. Pashley, and M.J. Whelan, *Electron Microscopy of Thin Crystals*, Butterworths, 1965 (revised edition, Krieger, 1977)
6. K.W. Andrews, D.J. Dyson, and S.R. Keown, *Interpretation of Electron Diffraction Patterns*, Hilger and Watts Ltd., 1967
7. G. Thomas and M.J. Goringe, *Transmission Electron Microscopy of Materials*, John Wiley & Sons, 1979
8. J.I. Goldstein, D.E. Newbury, P. Echlin, D.C. Joy, C.E. Fiori, and E. Lifshin, *Scanning Electron Microscopy and X-ray Microanalysis*, Plenum Press, 1981
9. N.F. Mott and H.S.W. Massey, *The Theory of Atomic Collisions*, Oxford University Press, 1965
10. D.C. Joy, D.E. Newbury, and D.L. Davidson, *J. Appl. Phys.*, Vol 53, 1982, p R81
11. B.D Cullity, *Elements of X-ray Diffraction*, Addison-Wesley, 1978
12. F.D. Bloss, *Crystallography and Crystal Chemistry*, Holt, Rinehart and Winston, 1971
13. Joint Committee on Powder Diffraction Standards, JCPDS International Centre for Diffraction Data, Swarthmore, PA
14. G. Kurdjumov and G. Sachs, *Z. Physik*, Vol 64, 1930, p 325
15. A. Guinier, *Phys. Status Solidi*, Vol 9, 1959, p 293
16. L.E. Tanner, *Philos. Mag.*, Vol 14, 1966, p 111
17. P. Goodman, *Acta Crystallogr.*, Vol A31, 1975, p 804
18. J.W. Steeds, in *Quantitative Microanalysis with High Spatial Resolution*, G.W. Lorimer, M.H. Jacobs, and P. Doig, Ed., The Metals Society, London, 1981, p 210
19. A.V. Crewe, J. Wall, and J. Langmore, *Science*, Vol 168, 1970, p 1338
20. M. Isaacson, M. Ohtsuki, and M. Utlaut, in *Introduction to Analytical Electron Microscopy*, J.J. Hren, J.I. Goldstein, and D.C. Joy, Ed., Plenum Press, 1979, p 343
21. D.E. Newbury, J.E. Goldstein, D.C. Joy, D.B. Williams, E. Lifshin, and C.E. Fiori, *Advanced Topics in Scanning Electron Microscopy and Microanalysis*, Plenum Press, 1986
22. A.D. Romig, Jr., ''X-ray Microanalysis in the Analytical Electron Microscope,'' Report SAND82-2938, Sandia National Laboratories, Albuquerque, 1983
23. G. Cliff and G.W. Lorimer, in *Proceedings of the 5th European Congress on Electron Microscopy*, The Institute of Physics, Bristol and London, 1972, p 141
24. J.I. Goldstein, J.L. Costley, G.W. Lorimer, and S.J.B. Reed, *Scan. Elec. Microsc.*, Vol 1, O. Johari, Ed., 1977, p 315
25. A.D. Romig, Jr., D.E. Newbury, and R.L. Myklebust, in *Microbeam Analysis—1982*, K.F.J. Heinrich, Ed., San Francisco Press, 1982, p 88
26. D.E. Newbury, in *Microbeam Analysis—1982*, K.F.J. Heinrich, Ed., San Francisco Press, 1982, p 79
27. S.J.B. Reed, *Ultramicroscopy*, Vol 7, 1982, p 405
28. G. Cliff and G.W. Lorimer, in *Quantitative Microanalysis with High Spatial Resolution*, G.W. Lorimer, M.H. Jacobs, and P. Doig, Ed., The Metals Society, London, 1981, p 47
29. P. Doig, D. Lonsdale, and P.E.J. Flewitt, in *Quantitative Microanalysis with High Spatial Resolution*, G.W. Lorimer, M.H. Jacobs, and P. Doig, Ed., The Metals Society, London, 1981, p 41
30. J.R. Michael and D.B. Williams, *Metall. Trans.*, Vol 15A, 1984, p 99
31. D.B. Williams and J.W. Edington, *J. Microsc.*, Vol 108, 1976, p 113
32. M. Isaacson, *J. Chem. Phys.*, Vol 56, 1972, p 1813
33. B.K. Teo and D.C. Joy, *EXAFS Spectroscopy: Techniques and Applications*, Plenum Press, 1981
34. D.R. Liu and L.M. Brown, in *Electron Microscopy and Analysis—1981*, M.J. Goringe, Ed., The Institute of Physics, Bristol and London, 1982, p 201
35. K.C. Thompson-Russell and J.W. Edington, *Electron Microscope Specimen Preparation Techniques in Materials Science*, Macmillan Press Ltd., 1977
36. J.T. Armstrong and P.R. Buseck, *Anal. Chem.*, Vol 47, 1975, p 2178
37. P.J. Statham and J.B. Pawley, *Scan. Elec. Microsc.*, Vol 1, O. Johari, Ed., 1978, p 469
38. M.J. Carr, *J. Elec. Microsc. Techn.*, Vol 2, 1985, p 439
39. D. Kay, Ed., *Techniques for Electron Microscopy*, Blackwell Scientific Publications Ltd., 1965
40. R.B. Marcus and T.T. Sheng, *Transmission Electron Microscopy of Silicon VLSI Circuits Structures*, John Wiley & Sons, 1983
41. R. Anderson and G.G. Johnson, Jr., in *37th Annual Proceedings of the Electron Microscopy Society of America*, G.W. Bailey, Ed., 1979, p 444
42. M.J. Carr and W.F. Chambers, in *Powder Diffraction*, Vol 1, in press
43. W.B. Pearson, *A Handbook of Lattice Spacings and Structures of Metals and Alloys*, Pergamon Press, 1967
44. R.W.G. Wyckoff, *Crystal Structures*, Interscience, 1963
45. B.L. Rhoades, ''XIDENT, A Computer Technique for the Direct Indexing of Electron Diffraction Spot Patterns,'' Research Report 70/76, Department of Mechanical Engineering, University of Canterbury, Christchurch, New Zealand, 1976
46. M.J. Carr and W.F. Chambers, *J. Microsc.*, Vol 134, 1984, p 55
47. J.R. Hellmann, W.R. Sorenson, M.J.

Carr, and T.J. Headley, in *Microbeam Analysis—1985*, J.T. Armstrong, Ed., San Francisco Press, 1985, p 189

48. R.C. Ecob, R.A. Ricks, and A.J. Porter, *Scripta Metall.*, Vol 16, 1982, p 51

49. D.A. Smith and A.H. King, *Philos. Mag. A*, Vol 44, 1981, p 333

50. M. Hillert and G.R. Purdy, *Acta Metall.*, Vol 26, 1978, p 330

51. G. Cliff and G.W. Lorimer, *J. Microsc.*, Vol 103, 1975, p 203

52. M.N. Thompson, P. Doig, J.W. Edington, and P.E.J. Flewitt, *Philos. Mag.*, Vol 35, 1977, p 1537

53. J.R. Michael and D.B. Williams, in *Analytical Electron Microscopy—1984*, D.B. Williams and D.C. Joy, Ed., San Francisco Press, 1984, p 61

54. A.J. Porter and R.A. Ricks, in *Electron Microscopy and Analysis—1983*, P. Doig, Ed., The Institute of Physics, London, 1983, p 51

55. P. Angelini and J. Bentley, in *Analytical Electron Microscopy—1984*, D.B. Williams and D.C. Joy, Ed., San Francisco Press, 1984, p 96

56. R.E. Ecob, M.P. Shaw, A.J. Porter, and B. Ralph, *Philos. Mag. A*, Vol 44, 1981, p 1117

57. P.M. Jones, G.M. Rackham, and J.W. Steeds, in *Proceedings of the Royal Society of London, Series A*, Vol 354, 1977, p 197

58. G. Gottstein and K. Lucke, Ed., *Proceedings of the Fifth International Conference on the Textures of Materials*, Vol I and II, Springer-Verlag, 1978

59. R.W. Balluffi, Ed., *Grain Boundary Structure and Kinetics*, American Society for Metals, 1980

60. P. Heilmann, W.A.T. Clark, and D.A. Rigney, *Ultramicroscopy*, Vol 9, 1982, p 365

61. P. Heilmann, W.A.T. Clark, and D.A. Rigney, *Acta Metall.*, Vol 31, 1983, p 1293

62. H. Grimmer, W. Bollmann, and D.H. Warrington, *Acta Crystallogr.*, Vol A30, 1974, p 197

63. M. Raghavan, R.R. Mueller, G.A. Vaughn, and S. Floreen, *Metall. Trans.*, Vol 15A, 1984, p 783

64. M. Haseke and T. Nishizawa, *Applications of Phase Diagrams in Metallurgy and Ceramics*, Vol 2, National Bureau of Standards, Washington, DC, 1977, p 911

65. N.J. Zaluzec, *EMSA Bull.*, Vol 14 (No. 1), 1984, p 67-75

66. N.J. Zaluzec, *EMSA Bull.*, Vol 13 (No. 2), 1985, p 61-72

67. J.I. Goldstein and D.B. Williams, *Scan. Elec. Microsc.*, Vol 1, 1978, p 427-434

68. N.J. Zaluzec, in *Introduction to Analytical Electron Microscopy*, D.C. Joy, J.J. Hren, and J.I. Goldstein, Ed., Plenum Press, 1979

69. M. Raghavan, R.R. Mueller, and C.F. Klein, *Scr. Metall.*, Vol 17, 1983, p 1189

70. A. Romig and J.I. Goldstein, *Metall. Trans.*, Vol 11A, 1980, p 1151

71. R. Ayer, R.R. Mueller, and C.F. Klein, *Analytical Electron Microscopy*, D.B. Williams and D.C. Joy, Ed., San Francisco Press, 1984, p 170

72. D.C. Dean and J.I. Goldstein, *Metall. Trans.*, submitted for publication

73. S.M. Merchant, M.R. Notis, and D.B. Williams, *Metall. Trans.*, Vol 14A, 1983, p 1825-1831

74. A.W. Nicholls and I.P. Jones, *J. Phys. Chem. Solids*, Vol 44 (No. 7), 1983, p 671-676

75. R. Glitz, M. Notis, and J.I. Goldstein, in *Solid → Solid Phase Transformations*, American Institute of Mining, Metallurgical, and Petroleum Engineers, Warrendale, PA, 1982

76. C.S. Baxter, S.B. Newcomb, and W.M. Stobbs, in *Electron Microscopy and Analysis—1983*, Conference Series No. 68, Institute of Physics, London, 1984

77. S.B. Newcomb and W.M. Stobbs, *Mater. Sci. Eng.*, Vol 66, 1983, p 195-204

78. M.C. Roberts, G.R. Booker, S.M. Davidson, and K.J. Yalley, in *Microscopy of Semiconducting Materials—1983*, Conference Series No. 67, Institute of Physics, London, 1983

79. G.R. Booker, in *Electron Microscopy and Analysis—1983*, Conference Series No. 68, Institute of Physics, London, 1984

80. Young Young-An, in *Electron Microscopy and Analysis—1983*, Conference Series No. 68, Institute of Physics, London, 1984

81. C. Narayan and J.I. Goldstein, *Metall. Trans.*, Vol 14A, 1983, p 2437-2439

82. J.I. Goldstein, R.E. Hanneman, and R.E. Ogilvie, *Trans. Met. Soc. AIME*, Vol 233, 1965, p 812-820

83. A.D. Romig, Jr. and M.J. Cieslak, *J. Appl. Phys.*, Vol 58 (No. 9), 1985, p 3425-3429

84. P. Doig and J.W. Edington, *Philos. Mag.*, Vol 28 (No. 5), 1973, p 961-970

85. P. Doig, J.W. Edington, and G. Hibbert, *Philos. Mag.*, Vol 28 (No. 5), 1973, p 971-981

86. D.S. Bloom and N.J. Grant, *Trans.* *AIME*, Oct 1951, p 261

87. M.J. Cieslak, A.D. Romig, Jr., and T.J. Headley, *Microbeam Analysis—1985*, San Francisco Press, 1982, p 179

88. A.J. Garratt-Reed, *Scan. Elec. Microsc.*, Vol 1, 1985, p 21-29

89. Xue-Ling Cai, A.J. Garratt-Reed, and W.S. Owen, *Metall. Trans.*, Vol 16A, 1985, p 543

90. D.M. Follstaedt, *Nucl. Instrum. Meth.*, Vol B7/8, 1985, p 11

91. D.M. Follstaedt, F.G. Yost, L.E. Pope, S.T. Picraux, and J.A. Knapp, *Appl. Phys. Lett.*, Vol 43, 1983, p 358

92. J.M. McDonald, Report SAND-81-0368, Sandia National Laboratories, Albuquerque, April 1981

93. B.J. Kestel, Report ANL-80-120, Argonne National Laboratory, Argonne, IL, July 1981

94. D.M. Follstaedt and A.D. Romig, Jr., in *Microbeam Analysis—1985*, J.T. Armstrong, Ed., San Francisco Press, 1985, p 173

95. D.M. Follstaedt, J.A. Knapp, L.E. Pope, and S.T. Picraux, *Nucl. Instrum. Meth. B*, Vol B12, 1985, p 359

96. S.T. Picraux, D.M. Follstaedt, P. Baeri, S.U. Campisano, G. Fote, and E. Rimini, *Radiat. Eff.*, Vol 49, 1980, p 75

97. J. Bentley, L.D. Stephenson, R.B. Benson, Jr., P.A. Parrish, and J.K. Hirvonen, *Material Research Society Symposium Proceedings*, Vol 27, 1984, p 151

98. S.T. Picraux, D.M. Follstaedt, J.A. Knapp, W.R. Wampler, and E. Rimini, in *Material Research Society Symposium Proceedings*, Vol 1, 1981, p 575

99. S.J. Pennycock and J. Narayan, *Phys. Rev. Lett.*, Vol 54, 1985, p 1543

100. D.K. Sood, *Radiat. Eff.*, Vol 63, 1982, p 141

101. T. Lyman, Ed., *Metallography, Structures and Phase Diagrams*, Vol 8, 8th ed., *Metals Handbook*, American Society for Metals, 1973, p 262

102. D.M. Follstaedt and S.T. Picraux, in *Alloy Phase Diagrams*, L.H. Bennett et al., Ed., Materials Research Society, Pittsburgh, 1984, p 94

103. R.G. Vardiman and R.A. Kant, *J. Appl. Phys.*, Vol 53, 1982, p 690

104. W.C. Oliver, R. Hutchings, J.B. Pethica, E.L. Paradis, and A.J. Shuskus, in *Material Research Society Symposium Proceedings*, Vol 28, 1984, p 705

105. F.G. Yost, S.T. Picraux, D.M. Follstaedt, L.E. Pope, and J.A. Knapp,

Thin Solid Films, Vol 107/108, 1983, p 287

106. B. Rauschenbach and K. Hohmuth, *Phys. Status Solidi (a)*, Vol 72, 1982, p 667; K. Hohmuth, B. Rauschenbach, A. Kolitsch, and E. Richter, *Nucl. Instrum. Meth.*, Vol 209/210, 1983, p 249

107. D.M. Follstaedt and S.M. Myers, in *Proceedings of the 40th Annual Electron Microscopy Society of America Meeting*, G.W. Bailey, Ed., 1982, p 590

108. D.M. Follstaedt, Report SAND-81-2176, Sandia National Laboratories, Albuquerque, Sept 1982

109. P.B. Johnson and D.J. Mazey, *J. Nucl. Mater.*, Vol 93/94, 1980, p 721

110. J.A. Knapp, D.M. Follstaedt, and B.L. Doyle, *Nucl. Instrum. Meth.*, Vol B7/8, 1985, p 38

111. I.L. Singer and T.M. Barlak, *Appl. Phys. Lett.*, Vol 43, 1983, p 457

112. I.L. Singer, *J. Vac. Sci. Technol.*, Vol A1, 1983, p 419

113. D.M. Follstaedt, *Nucl. Instrum. Meth.*, Vol B10/11, 1985, p 549

114. R.B. Benson, Jr., L.D. Stephenson, J. Bentley, G.K. Hubler, and P.A. Parrish, in *Proceedings of the Fifth International Conference on Ion and Plasma Assisted Techniques*, H. Oechsmer, Ed., C.E.P. Consultants, Edinburgh, 1985, p 169

115. S.M. Myers, in *Treatise on Materials Science and Technology*, Vol 18, J.K. Hirronen, Ed., Academic Press, 1980, p 51

Scanning Electron Microscopy

John D. Verhoeven, Department of Metallurgy, Iowa State University

General Uses
- Imaging of surface features at 10 to 100 000×. Resolution of features down to 3 to 100 nm, depending on sample
- When equipped with a backscattered detector, microscope allows (1) observation of grain boundaries on unetched samples, (2) domain observation in ferromagnetic materials, (3) evaluation of the crystallographic orientations of grains with diameters down to 2 to 10 μm, and (4) imaging of a second phase on unetched surfaces when the second phase has a different average atomic number
- When suitably modified, the microscope can be used for defect and quality control of semiconductor devices

Examples of Applications
- Examinations of metallographically prepared samples at magnifications well above the useful magnification of the optical microscope
- Examination of fracture surfaces and deeply etched surfaces requiring depth of field well beyond that possible with the optical microscope
- Evaluation of crystallographic orientation of features on a metallographically prepared surface, for example, individual grains, precipitate phases, and dendrites
- Identification of the chemistry of features down to micron sizes on the surface of bulk samples, for example, inclusions, precipitate phases, and wear debris
- Evaluation of chemical composition gradients on the surface of bulk samples over distances approaching 1 μm
- Examination of semiconductor devices for failure analysis, function control, and design verification

Samples
- *Form*: Any solid or liquid having a low vapor pressure ($\gtrsim 10^{-3}$ torr, or 0.13 Pa)
- *Size*: Limited by the scanning electron microscope available. Generally, samples as large as 15 to 20 cm can be placed in the microscope, but regions on such samples that can be examined without repositioning are limited to approximately 4 to 8 cm
- *Preparation*: Standard metallographic polishing and etching techniques are adequate for electrically conducting materials. Nonconducting materials are generally coated with a thin layer of carbon, gold, or gold alloy. Samples must be electrically grounded to the holder, and fine samples, such as powders, can be dispersed on an electrically conducting film, such as a silver paint that has been thoroughly dried. Samples must be free from high vapor pressure liquids, such as water, organic cleaning solutions, and remnant oil-base films

Limitations
- Image quality on relatively flat samples, such as metallographically polished and etched samples, is generally inferior to the optical microscope below 300 to 400×
- Feature resolution, although much better than the optical microscope, is inferior to the transmission electron microscope and the scanning transmission electron microscope

Capabilities of Related Techniques
- *X-ray diffraction*: Provides bulk crystallographic information
- *Optical microscopy*: Faster, less expensive, and provides superior image quality on relatively flat samples at less than 300 to 400×
- *Scanning transmission electron microscopy, Auger electron microscopy*: See Table 3 for comparison
- *Transmission electron microscopy*: Provides information from within the volume of material, such as dislocation images, small angle boundary distribution, and vacancy clusters. Superior resolution, but requires thin samples

Introduction

The first commercial scanning electron microscope became available in 1965. Significant changes in these instruments have since taken place, including improvements in resolution, dependability, ease of operation, and reduction in size. The cost of the instrument in constant dollars has fallen dramatically, and today it is quite common to have a scanning electron microscope in the materials characterization laboratory. The scanning electron microscope provides two outstanding improvements over the optical microscope: it extends the resolution limits so that picture magnifications can be increased from 1000 to 2000× up to 30 000 to 60 000×, and it improves the depth-of-field resolution more dramatically, by a factor of approximately 300. The first portion of this article explains how the scanning electron microscope functions and how it is able to provide these improvements over the optical microscope.

Commercial scanning transmission electron microscopes became available around 1973, and scanning Auger microscopes, with submicron resolution, in the late 1970s. These two microscopes have much in common with the scanning electron microscope, and a section of this article is devoted to comparing the three types of microscopes.

A primary use of the scanning electron microscope is to produce high-resolution and depth-of-field images of sample surfaces. A second use, perhaps just as important, is to provide chemical analyses of micron-sized areas of the structure revealed on these surfaces. When used in this mode, the scanning electron microscope is termed an electron probe microanalyzer. This function is covered briefly in this article; additional information is provided in the article "Electron Probe X-Ray Microanalysis" in this Volume.

In addition to image formation and microchemical analysis, the scanning electron microscope provides several additional functions that will be discussed briefly. These include (1) the use of channeling patterns to evaluate the crystallographic orientation of micron-sized regions, (2) the use of backscattered detectors to reveal grain boundaries on unetched samples and domain boundaries in ferromagnetic alloys, and (3) the use of voltage contrast, electron beam induced currents, and cathodoluminescence for such purposes as characterization and failure analysis of semiconductor devices.

This article will provide detailed information on the instrumentation and principles of scanning electron microscopy (SEM). The article "Scanning Electron Microscopy" in Volume 9 of the 9th Edition of *Metals Handbook* presents a review of the technique.

The Microscope

Figure 1 shows the basic components of the scanning electron microscope. The various components of the microscope can be categorized as (1) the electron column, (2) the specimen chamber, (3) the vacuum pumping system, and (4) the electronic control and imaging system.

Vacuum Pumping System. The column and specimen chamber must operate under vacuum conditions because the electron beam would be scattered by gas atoms. Therefore, the sample and any mounting compound used to hold it must not have a high vapor pressure. A mechanical valving arrangement (not shown in Fig. 1) is provided that allows the electron column to remain under vacuum when a specimen is inserted into the microscope. This arrangement enables the electron gun to remain activated during specimen change, and it hastens the turnaround time for changing specimens.

The low-pressure vacuum pumps generally consist of standard oil-diffusion pumps that produce vacuum levels of approximately 10^{-6} torr (1.3×10^{-4} Pa). When a high-energy electron beam strikes a surface having a monolayer or less of oil, the oil is cracked, and a carbonaceous deposit is formed at the point of interaction; this degrades high-resolution SEM image quality. Therefore, oil-diffusion pumps are being replaced with turbomolecular pumps (and perhaps soon with cryogenic pumps) to reduce the oil vapor pressure in the specimen chamber.

Even with ion-pumped ultrahigh vacuum (UHV) instruments operating in the 10^{-10} torr (1.3×10^{-8} Pa) range, carbon buildup that originates from hydrocarbon contamination trapped within pores and surface cracks is often a problem on metallic samples. Therefore, for high-resolution investigations, it is important to dry the samples thoroughly, to use white glove techniques to avoid sample and holder contact with the skin, and to avoid introducing plastic mounting materials into the specimen chamber that can have high vapor pressures and trap hydrocarbon films at the mount/sample interface.

The electron gun produces a narrowly divergent beam of electrons directed down the centerline of the column. Figure 2 shows a conventional tungsten gun. The electron source is a 0.25-mm (0.01-in.) diam tungsten filament heated to approximately 2500 °C (4530 °F). The electrons essentially boil off (thermionic emission) the sharply bent tip of the filament and are attracted to the anode, which is maintained at a positive voltage relative to the filament, ranging from 5 to 30 kV in scanning electron microscopes. This voltage, controlled by the operator, is generally held at 20 kV, but proper variation can be useful for x-ray and structure analysis. The Wehnelt cylinder is biased negatively relative to the filament. It acts as a grid that repels the emitted electrons and focuses them

Fig. 1 Basic components of the scanning electron microscope

WDS, wavelength-dispersive spectrometer; EDS, energy-dispersive spectrometer; CRT, cathode-ray tube

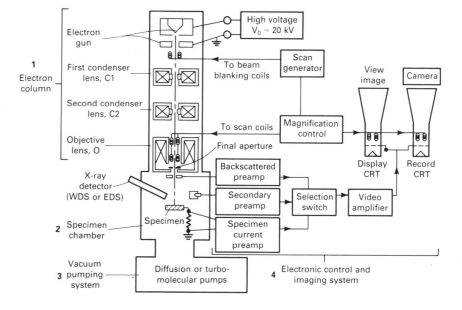

Fig. 2 Conventional tungsten hairpin filament electron gun

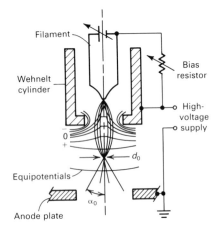

Fig. 3 Ray diagram illustrating lensing action

Magnification, M = S'/ S

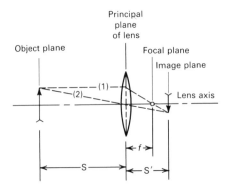

Fig. 4 Lensing action of the three lenses of a scanning electron microscope

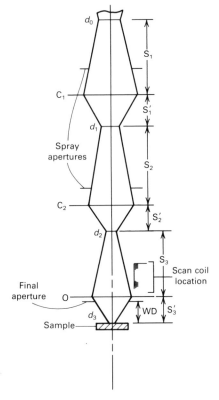

into a spot of diameter d_0 and divergence half angle, α_0. Therefore, the gun is essentially an electrostatic lens that forms an electron beam of diameter d_0 at a point immediately above the hole in the highly polished anode plate.

The most important parameter of the electron gun is its brightness, β:

$$\beta = \frac{\text{Current}}{(\text{Area})(\text{Solid angle})} = \frac{I}{(\pi d_0^2/4)(\pi \alpha_0^2)}$$

where β is a measure of the current I focused on the area $\pi d_0^2/4$ entering and exiting this area through solid angle $\pi \alpha_0^2$. Increasing β improves the performance of the scanning electron microscope. The value of β is a function of the filament material, its operating temperature, and its voltage. Lanthanum hexaboride, LaB_6, is one of the highest β materials available; at 20 kV, experimental β values for LaB_6 can be 10 to 20 times higher that those for tungsten (Ref 1, 2). Many new instruments use an LaB_6 filament as the electron source in place of tungsten. Field emission guns, an even brighter electron source, have been under development since the early 1970s, but have not yet found widespread use in SEM because of technical difficulties. Tungsten filament, LaB_6, and field emission electron sources are discussed further in the article ''Analytical Transmission Electron Microscopy'' in this Volume.

Lenses. Electron microscopes have magnetic lenses that are similar to simple solenoid coils. A coil of copper wire, represented by the X's in Fig. 1, produces a magnetic field that is shaped by the surrounding iron fixture into an optimum geom-

etry to produce the lensing action. As an electron moves through the magnetic field, it experiences a radial force inward, which is proportional to the Lorentz force, $v \times \mathbf{B}$, where v is the electron velocity, and $\mathbf{B}$ is the magnetic flux density. The lensing action is similar to that of an optical lens, in which a ray parallel to the axis of the lens is bent to the lens axis at the focal length, f, of the lens (Fig. 3).

In an optical lens, the focal length is fixed by the curvature of the lens surface and cannot be changed. In the electromagnetic lens, the focal length depends on two factors: the gun voltage (which determines the electron velocity, v) and the amount of current through the coil (which determines the flux density, $\mathbf{B}$). Therefore, the operator controls the focal lengths of the lenses by adjusting the currents supplied to them, an increase in current increases the radial force experienced by the beam and thus reduces the focal length.

The lenses in a scanning electron microscope reduce the diameter of the electron beam to a very small size on the sample surface. Therefore, the lens must demagnify as illustrated in Fig. 3. The arrow in the object plane is reproduced upside down in the image plane, and the arrow tip image can be located by following the two rays (1) and (2). The magnification is $M = S'/S$; as the focal length f is reduced, the value of S' is reduced, and the smaller is M. Therefore, if the length of the arrow is taken as the electron beam diameter produced by the gun, d_0, then the diameter of the beam, d_1, after passing through the first condenser lens is $d_1 = M_1 d_0$, where M_1 is the magnification of the first condenser lens.

Figure 4 shows the coupling of the three lenses; the object for a given lens is the

image from the lens above it. The net result is that the diameter of the electron beam at the sample surface, d_3, is:

$$d_3 = d_0 \cdot M_1 \cdot M_2 \cdot M_3 \qquad \text{(Eq 1)}$$

where M_1, M_2, and M_3 are the demagnification factors for each lens. The actual beam size on the sample surface, d_s, will be somewhat larger than d_3 due to lens aberrations. A typical value of d_0 is 60 μm, and the value of d_3 can range to less than 2 nm, which corresponds to $M_1 \cdot M_2 \cdot M_3 = 30\,000$. In most instruments, the upper two condenser lenses are coupled together so that one knob automatically controls these two lenses simultaneously; this adjustment is used to control the final spot size d_3. The focal length of the objective lens is adjusted to make S_3' fall on the sample surface. The sample may move up and down in the specimen chamber.

The distance of the sample below the bottom of the objective lens is termed the working distance (WD). Whenever the working distance is changed, the objective lens current must be adjusted to have S_3' fall

Fig. 5 Double-deflection scanning system showing a line scan with only the line coil pairs, l_1-l_1 and l_2-l_2, activated

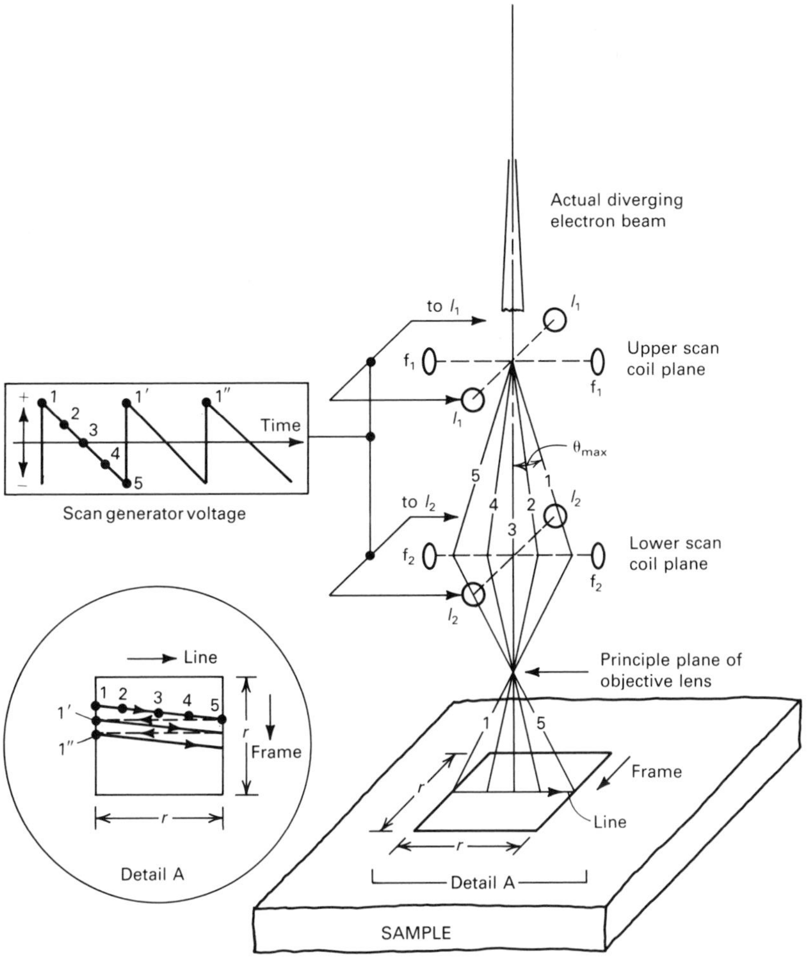

duce a magnetic field at time 1, which provides a Lorentz force on the beam, causing it to deflect to the right through angle θ_{max} as shown. The lower scan coil pairs l_2-l_2 deflect the beam back to the left through angle $2\theta_{max}$ so that it strikes the sample as shown at the left edge of the raster. The scan generator voltage drives both coil pairs. The voltage signal decreases linearly with time, as shown at the upper left of Fig. 5. As it decreases from time 1 to time 5, the beam scans along the line of length r shown on the sample surface in Fig. 5. At time 5, the scan voltage "flies back" quickly to 1', causing the beam to return rapidly to the left side of the raster, shown as position 1' in Detail A of Fig. 5.

The position 1' is slightly lower than position 1 because the two frame coil pairs f_1-f_1 and f_2-f_2 cause the line to deflect in the direction of the arrow labeled frame in Fig. 5 (see Detail A). During the fly-back time from 5 to 1', the beam moves along the dashed line shown in Detail A in Fig. 5. Therefore, the raster area of size $r \times r$ on the sample surface is covered by the beam moving relatively slowly along lines from left to right, then flying back to the left very quickly between lines, with the spacing between lines determined by the frame coil signal. The scan generator controls the frame and line times as well as the raster size, r. The double-deflection system allows the electron beam to pass through the principal plane of the objective lens very close to on-axis, which reduces lens aberrations.

Detectors and Image Formation. Four detector schemes are shown in Fig. 1 that use specimen current, secondary electron, backscattered electron, and x-ray signals. The secondary electron detector is generally used for image formation with the scanning electron microscope. The secondary electron detector has a screen on its outer surface that is biased at approximately 200 V. Electrons that pass through the screen are accelerated by a high voltage into a quartz light pipe coated with a scintillator material. The photons generated by the scintillator pass down the light pipe to a photomultiplier tube outside the vacuum system, in which a significant amplification is achieved having high signal-to-noise characteristics. The secondary electron energies are low (approximately 5 eV); consequently, the 200 V on the screen will pull many of the electrons to the screen even though that is not their initial direction.

Figure 6(a) shows a line scan, with the beam scanning from positions 1 to 5 across a bump on a surface. Possible trajectories of the secondary electron paths are shown for beam positions 2 and 4, and it is apparent that even though the secondary electron

on the sample surface and thus produce the minimum spot size on the sample surface for the prior settings of C_1 and C_2. This adjustment is the focusing operation performed by the operator; it is readily accomplished by adjusting the objective lens current, I_3, until the sharpest image is obtained. Because f_3 and therefore S_3' are functions of I_3, a unique value of the working distance corresponds to each value of I_3 after focusing. Therefore, once the image is focused, the value of the working distance is determined from the objective lens current, I_3. Newer instruments display the working distance directly on the viewing screen. In summary, the two condenser lenses are adjusted to control the beam diameter on the surface, d_3, and because the working distance of the sample will vary, the objective lens is adjusted to minimize the beam size on the sample surface. A minimum d_3 is necessary for maximum magnification. Because most analyses are performed at less than maximum magnification, the optimum value of d_3 will generally exceed its minimum value.

The Scan Coils and Raster Formation. The scanning electron microscope causes the electron beam to scan the sample surface. The two sets of scan coils located in the bore of the objective lens cage shown in Fig. 1 perform the scanning function. These coils (Fig. 5) cause the beam to scan over a square area of size $r \times r$ on the sample surface. This scanned area is generally termed the raster. Although the beam is shown in Fig. 5 as a line, it is actually diverging as it passes through the scan coils (Fig. 4). However, because the divergence half-angle is in the milliradian range, representation as a line is fairly accurate.

A double-deflection system is used, with the beam deflected by the Lorentz force produced from the magnetic fields of coil pairs. The upper scan coil pairs, l_1-l_1, pro-

Fig. 6 Line scan of the beam across a bump (a) and the synchronous locations of the beam on the sample and the beam on the CRT (b)

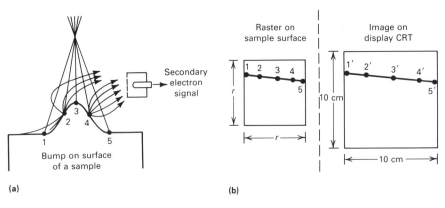

(a)

(b)

Advantages of SEM

As a tool for examining surfaces, the scanning electron microscope offers two major advantages over the optical microscope: improvements in (1) resolution and (2) depth of field. Information on the determination of resolution and depth of field in the optical microscope is provided in the article "Optical Microscopy" in Volume 9 of the 9th Edition of *Metals Handbook*.

Resolution. A pearlite sample will be used to illustrate what controls the resolution limit of a scanning electron microscope. Pearlite consists of alternating plates of Fe_3C in a matrix of α-iron. When etched using nital or picral, the Fe_3C plates stand in relief (Fig. 7a). Because the Fe_3C plates are in relief, the secondary electron yield from them will be very high. Consider a scanning electron beam having a diameter, d_s, much smaller than the Fe_3C spacing, S_α. As the beam scans from positions 1 to 5, the scanning electron signal intensity will exhibit the

paths can curve over to the detector, many electrons from position 2 never reach the secondary electron detector. Consequently, the secondary electron signal will be much higher at position 4 because of its direct line of sight path to the detector.

An image corresponding to the surface under the raster is accumulated point by point on the CRTs shown in Fig. 1. To elucidate, Fig. 6(b) shows the raster on the sample surface on the left and the CRT display on the right. As shown in Fig. 1, the same scan generator signal that drives the scan coils of the electron column drives the scan coils of the CRTs. Therefore, as shown in Fig. 6(b), there is a synchronous positioning of the column beam within the raster on the sample surface and the CRT beam on the CRT surface.

To prepare a picture, the intensity of the CRT beam is modulated proportionally to the magnitude of the signal from the secondary electron detector. When the beam is at position 2 on the sample, the signal will be low; therefore, the point at 2′ on the CRT will be dark. Similarly, the point at position 4′ will be bright because position 4 faces the detector and provides a large secondary electron signal. Therefore, as the beam scans the full raster, a picture accumulates on the CRT; the side of the bump facing the secondary electron detector will appear bright, and the opposite side dark. (During the fly-back shown by the dashed lines in Detail A of Fig. 5, the CRT beams are blanked so that they produce no information.)

A picture can be prepared with the signal from any of the four detectors shown in Fig. 1. The shadowing contrast on the picture when using the secondary electron signal will be similar to the optical case in which the eye is positioned at the detector and a light is shone on the sample surface along the line of the electron beam. That is, the

side of the bump facing the eye would appear bright, and the side behind the bump would be dark. Therefore, shadowing effects with secondary electron images on the scanning electron microscope are similar to the effects of typical optical light images.

Scanning electron microscopes generally have two or more CRTs. The viewing CRTs have a long persistence phosphor that retains the image so that the entire image can be observed without significant fading as the line moves down the screen. The record CRT, which records photographs, must have a very short persistence phosphor because the information contained on one line of the raster must not overlap into the next line. Record CRTs generally have minimum line spacings without overlap of 0.1 mm (1000 lines over 10 cm), which is slightly below the limit of resolution of the eye.

The magnification, M, achieved using the scanning electron microscope can be seen from Fig. 6(b) to be simply $M = 10/r$, where a CRT of 10×10 cm and the raster size r in centimeters have been assumed. As shown in Fig. 5, the size of r is determined by the scan generator voltage. To increase magnification, r is reduced by decreasing this voltage. The lens settings are not changed, and the sample remains in focus as the magnification is altered. Figure 5 also shows that if the working distance is increased, the raster size increases, and M decreases; magnification depends on working distance. Because the objective lens current, I_3, is a known function of working distance for a focused sample, magnification may be evaluated from I_3 after focusing; new machines display the magnification directly on the CRT. These magnifications are generally not highly accurate, and a calibration grid should be used if it is important to be sure of magnification.

Fig. 7 Line scan across the surface of a polished and etched pearlite sample (a) and the effect of beam diameter, d_s, on the secondary electron signal intensity (b)

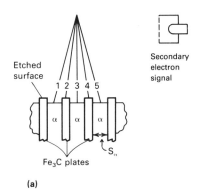

(a)

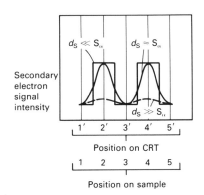

(b)

Fig. 8 Line scan signal across a feature of interest

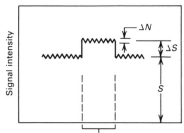

CRT location of feature of interest

sharp square wave form shown in Fig. 7(b), and the Fe_3C plates will appear in sharp contrast on the CRT display. If the beam diameter were increased such that $d_s \approx S_\alpha$, the signal would become more like a sine wave, and the edges of the Fe_3C plates would become very "fuzzy" on the CRT. Finally, for $d_s > S_\alpha$, the Fe_3C plates would no longer be distinguishable on the CRT. In general, to resolve a feature of size S, a beam diameter less than S is required. Additional information on the resolution limits of the scanning electron microscope is provided in Ref 3 to 6.

If a line scan across a feature produces the signal intensity into the CRT shown in Fig. 8, a generally accepted rule for the ability of the eye to discern this feature is that $\Delta S > 5\Delta N$ (see Fig. 8 for an explanation of S, ΔS, and N). Based on this criterion, the secondary electron signal current, i_s, required to see a feature that produces a signal jump of ΔS is:

$$i_s = i_B \epsilon > \frac{4 \times 10^{-12}}{\left(\frac{\Delta S}{S}\right)^2 t_f} \qquad \text{(Eq 2)}$$

where i_B is the beam current in the beam diameter, d_s; ϵ is an efficiency of collection of secondary electrons; and t_f is the time required to prepare the picture, that is, the frame time. As the spot size is made smaller, it contains less current. The current in the beam spot is a function of the brightness of the electron gun, β; the beam voltage, V; and the aberrations of the electron lens.

Spherical aberration is generally considered to be the controlling aberration factor for scanning electron microscope resolution, and it is characterized by a constant, C_s, where the larger the value of C_s, the greater the aberration. For conditions of optimum aperture size selection, beam current, i_B, varies with beam diameter on the sample, d_s:

$$d_s = a \left[b\frac{i_B}{\beta} + \frac{c}{V} \right]^{3/8} C_s^{1/4} \qquad \text{(Eq 3)}$$

where a, b, and c are constants. The value of d_s will be larger than the d_3 value given by Eq 1 due to the lens aberrations. Equations 2 and 3 illustrate the important factors in resolution limits with a scanning electron microscope. Equation 2 shows that resolving a feature with $\Delta S/S$ greater than a certain minimum value necessitates a certain critical minimum beam current, $(i_B)_c$:

$$(i_B)_c = \frac{4 \times 10^{-12}}{\epsilon[\Delta S/S(\text{min})]^2 t_f} \qquad \text{(Eq 4)}$$

By increasing the collector efficiency, ϵ, and by using longer frame times, t_f, the value of $(i_B)_c$ can be reduced. Equation 3 shows that reductions of d_s are limited, because decreasing d_s will decrease i_B, and eventually it will fall below $(i_B)_c$. For the critical value of $(i_B)_c$, Eq 3 shows that smaller beam spot diameters are achieved by increasing β and V and decreasing the spherical aberration coefficient, C_s. Maximum resolution requires a minimum d_s, which requires maximum values of β, V, ϵ, and t_f and minimum C_s values. For reasons discussed in Ref 3 to 6, V is optimized at approximately 20 to 25 kV and t_f at approximately 100 s; ϵ for the secondary electron signal is fixed by the sample detector geometry. Improved resolution is available on commercial instruments by using LaB_6 cathodes to increase β and special objective lenses that decrease C_s. In general, C_s increases as the sample is moved farther below the objective lens, that is, as the working distance increases.

In recent years, manufacturers have provided objective lenses where the sample is placed essentially within the field of the lens, minimizing the working distance and reducing C_s significantly. Figure 9 illustrates the in-lens configuration; the secondary electron detector is located above the objective lens, and the secondary electrons spiral up to it. This configuration was developed originally for scanning transmission electron microscopes. Consequently, the scanning transmission electron microscope can also function as an in-lens scanning electron microscope and provide a high-resolution secondary electron picture of the upper surface of the foil specimen used in the scanning transmission electron microscope. Conventional scanning electron microscopes are also available that allow the sample to be placed in both positions shown in Fig. 9 (Ref 7). The in-lens instruments provide improved resolution, and current scanning elec-

Fig. 9 Two secondary-electron detector sample configurations used for SEM mode operation

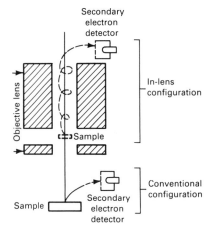

tron microscopes have resolution limits of 1.5 to 2 nm (Ref 8). These in-lens units, however, have two limitations: (1) the sample size must be fairly small (around millimeter heights in the scanning transmission electron microscope and centimeter heights in the conventional scanning electron microscope), and (2) the resolution for ferromagnetic samples, such as α-iron, is generally poorer because its magnetic field interacts with the objective lens field.

Typical resolution values claimed by manufacturers when using LaB_6 cathodes are given in Table 1 and compared with those of a conventional optical microscope (values with a conventional tungsten-filament gun tend to be higher by approximately 20%). The scanning electron microscope offers a distinct improvement over the optical microscope in the high-resolution range. Table 1 also lists the maximum useful magnification; at magnifications above approximately twice these values, an empty magnification is obtained where the image becomes noticeably fuzzy.

Figure 10, which shows a pearlite nodule formed on the surface of a quenched hyper-

Table 1 Resolution limits of currently available scanning electron microscopes compared with the optical microscope

Microscope	Minimum resolution range, nm	Maximum useful magnification
In-lens scanning electron microscope	1.5–3	67 000–130 000×
Conventional scanning electron microscope	4–5	40 000–50 000×
Optical microscope	100–200	1000–2000×

Fig. 10 Comparison of the resolution in an optical microscope and the scanning electron microscope

(a) A pearlite nodule in a martensite matrix taken with a high-quality optical microscope, oil immersion, green filter, original magnification of 1600×, 4% picral etch. (b) Same nodule taken in the scanning electron microscope, secondary electron image, 20-kV beam, 10-mm (0.40-in.) WD, original magnification of 3020×. (c) The center region of (b) with the magnification increased to 10 400×

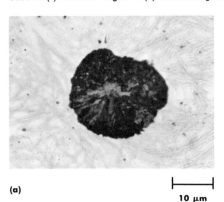 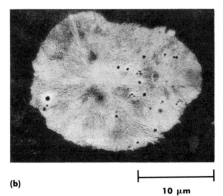 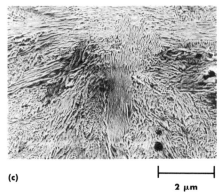

(a) 10 μm   (b) 10 μm   (c) 2 μm

Fig. 11 Line scan across gold particles on resolution sample often used with SEM

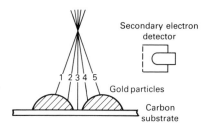

eutectoid steel, illustrates a metallurgical example of the usefulness of the improved resolution of the scanning electron microscope. The optical micrograph (Fig. 10a) was taken at the upper limit of magnification of the optical microscope using optimum resolution conditions. The micrographs shown in Fig. 10(b) and (c) were taken on a scanning electron microscope at higher magnifications; the characteristic pearlite plate structure that was not resolved in the optical microscope is visible. The micrograph shown in Fig. 10(c) was taken at the center region of 10(b); the Fe_3C plate spacing in the nodule measures 38 nm, which means the Fe_3C plate thicknesses must be 7.0 nm (the Fe_3C occupies 18 vol% in this 1.25 wt% C steel). The scanning electron microscope can resolve the pearlite plate spacing because of the favorable contrast produced by the picral etch that removed α-iron from between the Fe_3C plates.

A dark square raster region is visible at the center of Fig. 10(c); this feature can also be found immediately below the pearlite nodule center in Fig. 10(b). It is a contamination mark made when the pictures were taken at 41 000× to evaluate the spacing. This mark appeared even though the sample had been

removed from its plastic mount after polishing and etching, thoroughly dried, and held 48 h in a turbomolecularly pumped machine at 10^{-6} torr (1.3×10^{-4} Pa) before examination. After slight ion sputtering of the surface, the mark vanished.

The numbers presented in Table 1 involve some limitations. The secondary electrons emitted when the beam strikes the sample surface are weakly bound electrons emitted from near the surface (see discussion below). The yield of secondary electrons is increased by increasing the atomic number of the sample and by decreasing the angle the beam makes with the sample surface, which is termed the tilt angle. The numbers in Table 1 are generally determined with optimum samples, such as that shown in Fig. 11.

Small gold particles are evaporated onto a carbon substrate. As the beam moves from points 2 to 3, there is an optimally large change in atomic number and beam surface angle geometry. Consequently, the $\Delta S/S$ between points 2 and 3 will be large, thereby allowing operation with minimum i_B and thus minimum d_s conditions.

The term $\Delta S/S$ is sometimes referred to as contrast, C, which is very sample dependent. The influence of the sample on contrast is illustrated in Fig. 12(a) and (b). Both micrographs were taken on the same in-lens instrument using an LaB_6 cathode. Figure 12(b) shows a sample containing thin niobium filaments that have been put into relief by etching away the copper matrix in which they were formed. The niobium filaments are of the order of 7 nm thick.

The resolution in Fig. 12(b) is at least twice that shown in Fig. 12(a). The reason for this loss of resolution is the reduced contrast of the sample. As the beam moves between the filaments for the sample shown in Fig. 12(b), the variation in $\Delta S/S$ value is

less. This is probably due to the emission of secondary electrons from surfaces of the thin protruding niobium filaments and surroundings (discussed below).

In general, then, the numbers listed in Table 1 should be interpreted carefully. For example, it is well established from TEM studies that lath martensite has a lath substructure consisting of parallel laths, each approximately 100 nm thick. From the data in Table 1, it may appear that these features would be easily resolved using a scanning electron microscope. However, they cannot be seen, because $\Delta S/S$ across the lath boundary is too low. This is because the boundaries are low angle boundaries and an etchant that provides suitable surface relief at the boundaries is unavailable.

Depth of Field. The fracture surface shown in Fig. 13, which depicts a line scan from positions 1 to 5, will be used to illustrate what controls the depth-of-field resolution in a scanning electron microscope. The beam has been focused to the highest point of the sample at 4. Because of the divergence of the beam, the beam size on the sample surface at positions 1 and 2 will be considerably increased because of the local increase in working distance at those two positions. The depth of field is given as follows:

$$\text{Depth of field} = \frac{\text{Constant}}{\alpha \cdot M} \qquad \text{(Eq 5)}$$

where M is the magnification, and α is the divergence of the beam striking the sample. As may be deduced from Fig. 13, the value of α is determined by the working distance and the diameter of the final aperture, d_a:

$$\alpha \approx \frac{d_a/2}{\text{WD}} \qquad \text{(Eq 6)}$$

Fig. 12 Influence of the sample material on resolution

(a) A gold on carbon resolution sample demonstrating 3-nm (30-Å) resolution. (b) A niobium filament sample examined in the same instrument under the same conditions, but having a resolution of only 7 nm (70 Å)

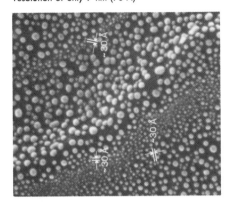

(a)

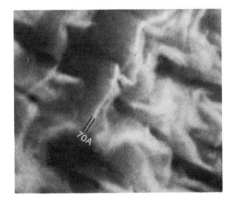

(b)

For a given magnification, then, depth of field is optimized by using a long working distance and selecting a small aperture. For high resolution, the working distance should be short. Therefore, conditions for optimizing resolution are different from those for optimizing depth of field.

The depth of field of a scanning electron microscope is very good in comparison with an optical microscope. The difference in the two microscopes is illustrated by comparison of Fig. 14(a) and (b), which show three different mesh screens lying on top of one another with the microscopes focused on the central screen. In general, the depth of field of the scanning electron microscope exceeds that of the optical microscope by a factor of approximately 300 (Ref 6). Therefore, scanning electron microscopes have found widespread use for examination of fracture surfaces and deeply etched samples.

The scanning electron microscope is generally inferior to the optical microscope for routine examination of samples prepared using standard metallographic techniques when examined at magnifications less than 300 to 400×. Standard metallographic techniques do not produce surface reliefs that are adequate (even after etching) to provide suitable contrast in the scanning electron microscope at the lower magnification ranges. Color variations often produce subtle contrasts visible in the optical microscope that are not present with SEM. Because of the relatively poor contrast of the scanning electron microscope on metallographically polished and etched samples at low magnifications, it is generally useful to use microhardness indentations as fiducial marks. Placing such marks near a point examined in the optical microscope facilitates locating that same point in the scanning electron microscope for examination at higher magnification.

Scanning Electron Beam Instruments

Three types of scanning electron beam instruments are currently available: the scanning electron, scanning transmission electron, and scanning Auger microscopes. These instruments all have in common the feature of obtaining information from the surface (or volume, for the scanning transmission electron microscope) of the sample by scanning an electron beam over a raster and analyzing the various signals generated. The scanning transmission electron microscope is closely related to the conventional transmission electron microscope and is discussed in the article "Analytical Transmission Electron Microscopy" in this Volume. The scanning Auger microscope is designed to optimize information obtained from the Auger electron signal (see the article "Auger

Fig. 13 Line scan across a jagged fracture surface

See text for details.

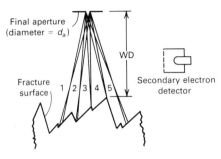

Electron Spectroscopy" in this Volume). The primary detector in a scanning electron microscope that produces the high-resolution images is the secondary electron detector. Generally, scanning transmission electron and scanning Auger microscopes use a secondary electron detector; therefore, they can also operate in the SEM mode.

Signals Generated by the Scanning Electron Beam. A picture of the scanned surface region can be taken using any signal generated by the electron beam. In the scanning Auger microscope, it is possible to use as many as five different signals to generate pictures. To understand the potential utility of these instruments, it is necessary to understand some elementary ideas on the nature of the signal generation when the electron beam interacts with sample surface.

When an electron beam strikes a solid surface, electrons and x-rays are emitted from the surface. The energy distribution of these signals is shown qualitatively in Fig. 15 (electromagnetic radiation of lower energies than x-rays is also emitted, which is termed cathodoluminescence and is discussed later in this article). In addition to the

Fig. 14 Depth-of-field comparison between optical microscopy (a) and SEM (b)

Original magnification, 300×

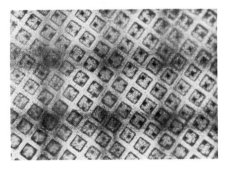

(a)

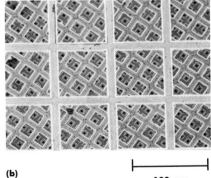

(b)

100 μm

Fig. 15 Energy distribution of signals generated by the electron beam

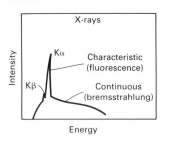 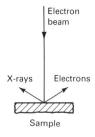 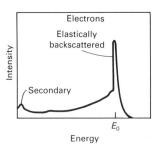

Fig. 16 The energy distribution of emitted electrons at (a) low beam energy (around 1 keV) and (b) a higher beam energy (around 5 keV)

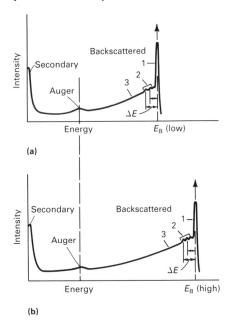

secondary electron detector (which can also be used to detect backscattered electrons), most scanning electron microscopes are equipped with an x-ray detector, and specialized backscattered detectors are available at relatively low cost.

The addition of an x-ray detector allows determination of the energy of the emitted characteristic x-ray shown in Fig. 15. Because each element in the periodic table has a different characteristic energy, the x-ray analyzer enables determination of the chemical analysis from point to point on the sample surface. After obtaining a scanned image of the surface with the secondary electron detector, the saw-tooth signal to the scan coils shown in Fig. 5 is deactivated, and a spot appears on the CRT image where the stationary beam strikes the surface. This spot is then positioned over a particle or region of interest by manual control of the scan coil voltages, and the x-ray spectrum is collected from that point. Addition of an x-ray detector to a scanning electron microscope converts the microscope into an electron probe microanalyzer.

Two types of x-ray detectors are used: wavelength-dispersive spectrometers and energy-dispersive spectrometers. Most scanning electron microscopes are currently being equipped with energy-dispersive detectors. The energy-dispersive detector is limited to analysis of elements with atomic number, Z, above sodium ($Z = 11$); therefore, it cannot detect the important light elements boron, carbon, nitrogen, and oxygen. The wavelength-dispersive detector allows detection of all elements of $Z = 5$ (boron) and above, improves sensitivity (analysis down to approximately 0.01%), and enables analysis of samples in which characteristic x-ray peaks from different elements overlap. The wavelength-dispersive detectors, however, are large and slow. Because of their size, they are not compatible with scanning transmission electron microscopes. Thin window energy-dispersive detectors are available that allow detection of elements with Z down to carbon ($Z = 6$), although their sensitivity below $Z = 8$ (oxy-

gen) is poor. These detectors are compatible with the UHV requirements of scanning Auger microscopes; the detectors are particularly useful because carbon contamination can be eliminated by the combination of UHV and surface sputtering. A detailed discussion of energy-dispersive and wavelength-dispersive spectrometry can be found in the article "Electron Probe X-Ray Microanalysis" in this Volume.

The electrons generated by the electron beam can be partitioned into three types: secondary, Auger, and backscattered (Fig. 16). The intensity scale shown in Fig. 16 has been increased to reveal the details not apparent in Fig. 15. The backscattered electrons may be further partitioned into three types so that the emitted electron distribution becomes:

- Backscattered electrons
  Type 1: Elastically scattered
  Type 2: Plasmon and interband transition scattered
  Type 3: Inelastically scattered
- Auger electrons
- Secondary electrons

Backscattered Electrons (BE). When an electron strikes the sample, it may be scattered back out from the surface. These electrons are termed backscattered, and there are three processes that can scatter an electron back out from the surface, as listed above. Elastically scattered electrons emerge with essentially the same energy as the beam energy, E_B; inelastically scattered electrons generally undergo many scattering interactions and emerge with a spectrum of energies lower than the beam energy. Figure 17(a) shows Monte Carlo calculated trajectories of the inelastically scattered electrons below the surface of iron for a beam energy of 20 keV. Many of the electrons eventually emerge from the surface, and these are the type 3 backscattered electrons. The type 2 electrons are scattered by interactions that produce a plasmon oscillation of the electrons in the sample material or a transition of sample electrons between different energy bands.

The energy to excite these effects has a fixed value shown as ΔE in Fig. 16; therefore, backscattered electrons that emerge after one of these interactions have an energy lower than E_B by the amount ΔE. Two types of plasmon oscillations occur, in which surface electron or bulk electron oscillations are excited, and two small peaks can be observed below E_B. The interband transitions also require a specific ΔE. The ΔEs for all these small peaks differ from element to element, and sometimes they differ according to whether the element is present as a pure element or an oxide, hydride, nitride, and so on. These backscattered electrons are often termed energy loss electrons because they have lost a specific amount of energy. The energy loss electrons may be detected in the scanning transmission electron and scanning Auger microscopes to provide useful information on chemical identity. In the scanning transmission electron microscope, however, scattering is forward through the thin samples. As illustrated in Fig. 1, scanning electron microscopes often contain a backscattered detector. These detectors generally measure an energy average of all three types of backscattered electrons.

Characteristic x-rays and Auger electrons are generated as a result of the incoming electrons knocking out intershell electrons (K, L, and M, depending on atomic number) from atoms near the surface. These knock-

(a) Scattering locations of incoming electrons. (b) Scattering locations that produced K-shell ionization events that provide Kα x-rays or Auger electrons. Source: Ref 3

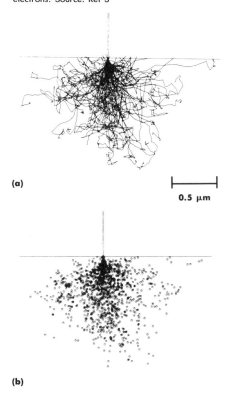

(a)

├──────────┤

0.5 μm

(b)

out events occur within the scatter volume shown in Fig. 17(b). After a K electron is knocked out, the surface atom emits either a characteristic x-ray or an Auger electron. The probability for Auger emission exceeds that for x-ray emission as atomic number decreases. This is one of the reasons why Auger analysis has some advantages for light-element analysis. As with the characteristic x-ray emission, the energy of the Auger electrons is different for each element; therefore, analysis of Auger energies yields information on chemical identity. In addition, as with energy loss electrons, the Auger energy levels sometimes shift when an atom becomes oxidized, nitrided, and so on; therefore, information on the chemical state of the surface atoms may sometimes be obtained from Auger analysis.

Secondary electrons (SE) generally display a peak intensity at approximately only 5 eV (Fig. 16). These electrons are the signal used to generate high-resolution images in the scanning electron microscope. They can be generated by the primary electron beam or

any scattered electron that passes near the surface. Comparison of Fig. 16(a) and (b) illustrates that the energies of the secondary and Auger electrons are fixed, but the backscattered electrons shift their energy values as the primary beam energy is changed.

Sample Volume Contributing to the Various Signals. To interpret correctly the physical significance of the various signals used in the three scanning electron beam instruments, the volume below the surface from which the signal is originating must be known. Based on the Monte Carlo pictures shown in Fig. 17 for 20-keV electrons on iron, the volumes producing Kα x-rays and inelastically backscattered electrons are roughly as shown in Fig. 18. Therefore, although the electron probe size may be less than 10 nm, the x-rays are being generated over a volume with a diameter roughly 100 times larger.

In general, it is not possible to analyze quantitatively particles with diameters less than approximately 1 to 2 μm using the electron probe microanalyzer, although these particles appear to be huge on the scanning electron microscope screen. It is important to realize that the x-ray sample volume and shape vary with the electron beam voltage and the sample atomic number, effects that are discussed in Ref 3 and in the article "Electron Probe X-Ray Microanalysis" in this Volume. In general, higher voltages, lower density, and lower atomic number elements produce larger volumes, which tend to "balloon out" below the beam, as shown by the dashed line in Fig. 18. Thin foil samples can be used to reduce the x-ray generation volume. This is performed using the scanning transmission electron microscope; minimum sampling diameters of 30 nm can generally be achieved, with 5 nm possible in specialized instruments. Similar results can be obtained in a conventional scanning electron microscope simply by using thin foil samples, but the lower voltages of the scanning electron microscope will produce larger volumes than for the scanning transmission electron microscope due to the volume shape change with voltage.

Table 2 lists some estimates of the sample volume for the remaining signals. The inelastic backscattered electrons emerge from a volume roughly one-half the depth of the scattered electron range (Ref 9), as shown in Fig. 18. The Auger electrons are collected from sample depths of 0.5 to 3 nm below the surface, depending on their energy. The Auger electron energies are relatively low, and only those electrons near the sample surface escape without suffering additional energy loss. Figures 4 and 5 in the article "Auger Electron Spectroscopy" in this Vol-

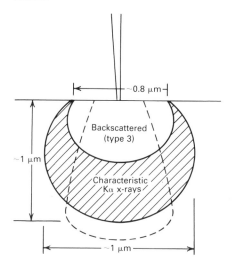

ume demonstrate this point. Therefore, the Auger signal of the scanning Auger microscope is very surface sensitive. This fact is particularly important when considering use of the scanning Auger microscope for metal samples, which generally are covered with a thin oxide layer. The scanning Auger microscope uses UHV vacuum levels in the 10^{-9} torr (1.3×10^{-7} Pa) range, and samples generally must be cleaned in the scanning Auger microscope chamber either by ion sputtering or by fracturing the sample in the chamber and examining the fractured surface.

The energy loss electrons may be used as a signal in the scanning Auger microscope; contrary to the Auger signal, the depth of its sample volume will be a function of the beam energy. By using beam energies from 70 to 100 eV, surface sensitivities of less than half that of the Auger signal can be achieved, that is, down to 0.25 nm, or approximately one monolayer.

The diameters of the Auger and secondary electron volumes listed in Table 2 assume that the inelastically scattered electrons do not produce any Auger or secondary electrons out to the 0.8-μm diameter, where they leave the surface (Fig. 18). This is not true; there is some Auger and secondary electron production out to the 0.8-μm diameter, but the intensity is relatively low (Fig. 19a). The secondary electrons excited by the primary beam are often termed SE(1) electrons; those excited by the backscattered electrons in the area away from the primary beam are termed SE(2) electrons (Fig. 19a). A larger part of

Table 2 Estimation of the volume of the various signals produced in iron by a 20-keV electron beam

Signal		Approximate volume dimensions Diameter	Depth
X-ray		≈1 μm	≈1 μm
Backscattered electrons	inelastic (Type 3)	≈0.8 μm	≈0.5 μm
	energy loss (Type 2)	≈d_B	...
	elastic (Type 1)	≈d_B	...
Auger electrons		≈1.1 d_B	≈0.5–2 nm
Secondary electrons		≈1.2 d_B	≈10 nm

Fig. 19 Secondary or Auger electron signal generation

(a) Estimated intensity distribution of emitted secondary or Auger electrons about the centerline of a 20-keV electron beam on iron. (b) Secondary electron signal to CRT as beam of (a) makes a line scan at 20 000× across an 80-nm feature.

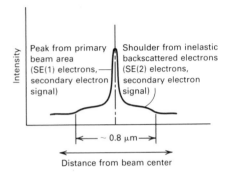

(a)

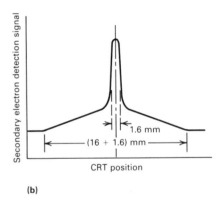

(b)

the secondary electron signal is generated by the SE(2) electrons, with the emission yield ratio of SE(1)/SE(2) varying from 0.4 to 1, depending primarily on atomic number and beam tilt angle (Ref 9). In view of this fact, it is surprising that the SE(2) electron shoulder does not significantly reduce resolution over that expected from the primary beam diameter, but studies show that it does not (Ref 10, 11).

This can be understood by imagining that the beam shown in Fig. 19(a) is swept across an 80-nm feature that increases the signal intensity. A secondary electron line scan signal at 20 000× would look like that shown in Fig. 19(b). At 20 000×, the 0.8-μm shoulder is 16 mm wide, and the 80-nm feature is 1.6 mm wide. The SE(1) electrons from the primary area will produce a peak superimposed on a gradually peaked background due to the shoulder of the SE(2) electrons. The feature will still be apparent, but with a lower signal-to-noise ratio than would occur if the SE(2) electrons were not there.

The Auger signal in the scanning Auger microscope is much lower, and it is difficult to achieve resolutions exceeding 100 nm in the scanning Auger microscope using the Auger signal because the lower Auger signal intensity requires the use of larger beam diameters. The scanning Auger microscope is extremely useful, however, because when equipped with secondary electron and x-ray detectors, it becomes a scanning electron microscope, an electron probe microanalyzer, a scanning Auger microscope, and a scanning electron loss microscope. Its multifunctional use is illustrated in Example 5 in the section "Applications" in this article.

Tables 3 and 4 provide an overview of the three types of scanning electron beam instruments and summarize the source of the signals used. Because this article is concerned with the scanning electron microscope, which examines only the specimen surface, Table 3 compares the scanning transmission electron microscope and scanning Auger microscope with regard to top surface analysis. The scanning transmission

electron microscope enables direct probing through the sample. With the scanning Auger microscope, surface films can be probed through by ion sputtering. In general, these instruments are multifunctional. Additional information is provided in the articles "Analytical Transmission Electron Microscopy" and "Auger Electron Spectroscopy" in this Volume.

Scanning electron microscopes are available that have been designed specifically to optimize chemical analysis with x-ray detectors. These instruments are often termed electron microprobes. Commercial electron microprobes were available before the commercial scanning electron microscope. Recent models of these machines, which provide structural resolution nearly equivalent to the less expensive conventional scanning electron microscope, are generally superior in their function as an electron probe microanalyzer, and they include an optical system that enables viewing of the sample *in situ* at approximately 400X. They are, however, generally more expensive than a scanning electron microscope equipped with equivalent x-ray analyzers.

Image Contrast in the Scanning Electron Microscope

In addition to the secondary electron detector, the scanning electron microscope is often equipped with a backscattered electron detector. The secondary electron detector, often termed the Everhart-Thornley detector, has been the most widely used detector with the scanning electron microscope. In the past eight to ten years, there have been significant developments in backscattered electron detectors that have made them more sensitive and easier to use. These backscattered electron detectors complement the secondary electron detector and provide some information not available in the secondary electron signal. To understand the differences in the images provided by the two detectors and to obtain a better understanding of resolution limitations, it is

useful to consider some general ideas about contrast mechanisms.

The image observed on an SEM micrograph results from variation in the contrast, $\Delta S/S$, as the beam moves from point to point on the sample surface. Contrast can be very sample dependent; therefore, it is important to understand the various factors that control contrast. Variations in the detected signal from two points on a surface can arise from two physically different mechanisms: (1) emission contrast—the number of electrons emitted from the surface varies, or (2) collection contrast—the number of electrons reaching the detector varies.

Consider the secondary electron signal shown in Fig. 6(a). When the beam is at positions 2 and 4, the number of secondary electrons emitted from the surface is roughly the same because the beam/surface tilt angle is the same. However, because point 4 faces the detector and 2 does not, the secondary electron signal is much higher at point 4. Consequently, in this example, the contrast between points 2 and 4 results entirely from collection contrast. Emission contrast with a

Table 3 Comparison summary of scanning electron beam instruments equipped with secondary electron and x-ray detectors

Instrument	Features optimized	Surface pictures	Minimum area Microchemical analysis	Comments
Scanning electron microscope	Surface pictures: above ~500× on polished and etched samples; at all magnifications on high depth-of-field surfaces; accuracy and sensitivity of microchemical analysis	4–5 nm (conventional) scanning electron microscope) 2–3 nm (in-lens)	1–3 μm (EDS and/or WDS)	Can be equipped with a WDS x-ray detector that maximizes sensitivity and light-element analysis. WDS: elements with Z > 4. EDS: elements with Z > 10
Scanning transmission electron microscope	Small area microanalysis of thin films; small area diffraction	2–3 nm (SEM mode, in-lens)	5–30 nm (EDS)	Samples must be thinned; generally also functions as a transmission electron microscope; allows chemical analysis of particles characterized by transmission electron microscope observation
Scanning Auger microscope	Chemical analysis of (1) monolayers on surfaces made by *in situ* fracturing, and (2) low-Z elements on surfaces cleaned by *in situ* ion etching	~100 nm (Auger) 10 nm (SEM mode)	~100 nm (Auger) 1–3 μm (EDS)	Requires UHV and careful surface preparation; can also detect electron loss signal (see Example 5 in the section "Applications" in this article)

Table 4 Comparison summary of signals used in scanning electron beam instruments

Signal type	Type	Energy	Source	Use
X-ray	Characteristic (fluorescent)	Discrete values; different for each element: Cu Kα ~ 8000 eV; Si Kα ~ 1800 eV	Interband transitions: L → K = Kα, M → K = Kβ; Kα: (1) lose K electron, (2) L → K, (3) photon ejects	Chemical analysis from micro areas in SEM, STEM, and SAM
	Continuous	Continuous	Deceleration electron	None (background noise)
Electron ...	Auger	Discrete values; different for each element; range: 100–1500 eV; Si LMM ~ 100 eV; Cu LMM ~ 900 eV	Interband transitions; LMM: (1) lose L electron, (2) M → L, (3) M electron ejects	Monolayer surface analysis in SAM
	Backscattered (elastic)	Essentially same as beam energy	Beam electron scattered back after elastic collision	Atomic number contrast, channeling contrast, channeling patterns, and magnetic contrast in SEM
	Backscattered (inelastic)	Energies less than beam energy	Beam electron scattered back after inelastic collision	
	Backscattered (plasmon and interband transition interactions)	1–1000 eV less than beam energy	Beam electron scattered back after collision producing plasmon oscillations or interband transition	Surface analysis in SAM; light-element analysis in STEM where scattering is in forward direction
	Secondary	~5 eV	Loosely bound electrons scattered from surface	Main signal for image formation in SEM

secondary electron detector is important when the two points have the same line of sight to the detector as for positions 3 and 4 shown in Fig. 6(a); here the contrast results mainly from a variation in secondary electron emission due to changes in the beam/surface tilt angle.

The contrast mechanisms, observable due to secondary and/or backscattered electron emissions, can be subdivided as follows:

• Collection contrast
• Emission contrast
  Type 1: Edge effects
  Type 2: Incident angle of beam with the surface
  Type 3: Atomic number of sample
  Type 4: Electron channeling effects
  Type 5: Magnetic domain effects

Each of these mechanisms is discussed below.

Contrast With the Secondary Electron Detector. Contrast with the secondary electron detector was explained in the section "Image Contrast in the Scanning Electron Microscope" in this article. It results in a shadowing effect that can be adjusted by tilting the sample away from normal incidence; SEM micrographs are often taken with a beam/surface tilt angle of 60 to 80°, rather than at normal incidence where the tilt angle is 90°. Collection efficiency is a strong function of the sample detector geometry. Therefore, the collection contrast for the in-lens detector arrangement will be somewhat different from that for a conventional below-lens arrangement. Referring to Fig. 9, the in-lens arrangement will produce less

dramatic shadowing effects upon tilting because nearly all the secondary electrons are trapped in the bore of the lens, and the variation of collection efficiency from point to point is reduced somewhat.

Collection contrast with the secondary electron detector is influenced significantly by the backscattered electrons. The secondary electron detector will detect any backscattered electron that passes through the front screen of the detector assembly. However, because of their high energies, the backscattered electrons travel in straight lines; consequently, the secondary electron detector measures directly only those backscattered electrons having line-of-sight trajectories into the detector. In the example of Fig. 6(a), the direct backscattered electron contribution to the secondary electron

Fig. 20 Four types of electrons detected by the secondary electron detector

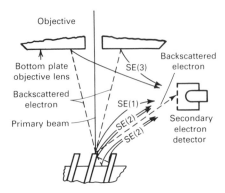

detector signal would be zero at point 2 and a maximum somewhere between points 3 and 4. Therefore, the collection contrast with a conventional below-lens secondary electron detector will result from a combination of secondary and backscattered electrons. Although small, the total contribution of the backscattered electrons comes only from surface areas facing the detector and results in a strong highlighting of these areas.

Emission contrast involves variation in the yield of secondary electrons at two closely spaced points on the sample surface. The yield of secondary electrons is a function of the beam voltage, dropping from a peak value at approximately 0.8 keV as roughly $(1/E)^{0.8}$ (Ref 9). Therefore, the secondary electron signal will increase somewhat at lower voltages, but this effect does not contribute directly to emission contrast.

Before discussing the five types of emission contrast listed above, it is useful to consider the source of the electrons detected by the secondary electron detector. Figure 20 shows the primary sources of the electrons detected by the secondary electron detector for a sample similar to the pearlite and niobium fiber samples discussed above. In addition to SE(1) electrons generated in the primary beam area and the SE(2) electrons from the surrounding area, as discussed above, there are several other sources of electrons. Additional SE(2) electrons are generated by primary electrons that emerge through the protruding fiber phase when these electrons leave the fiber and when they strike the surrounding sample surfaces after emerging. There is a third source of secondary electrons, SE(3). These electrons are generated when the backscattered electrons strike the bottom plate of the objective lens. In addition, there is also the contribution to the secondary electron detector signal from

backscattered electrons mentioned above, which have a line-of-sight trajectory into the detector screen. In total, then, there are three types of secondary electrons plus these backscattered electrons contributing to the secondary electron signal.

Techniques have been developed to separate some of these signals by placing negatively biased screens over the sample and/or lens plate. It is believed that 15 to 20% of the signal derives from SE(3) electrons and approximately 5% from backscattered electrons (Ref 12). The SE(1) and SE(2) electrons cannot be directly separated, but some methods of partial separation by signal addition are under development (Ref 13).

Type 1 emission contrast, edge effects, results from the SE(2) electrons that are generated by effects near the edge of a feature. As seen in Fig. 20, these SE(2) electrons can be generated when a primary or scattered electron emerges from around the corner of an edge and when it again strikes the surface. This effect can become dominant for thin protruding fibers and can play a significant role in the large sample-to-sample variation in contrast found in high-resolution studies.

Type 2 emission contrast is normally the primary source of emission contrast with the secondary electron detector. When the primary beam makes a low angle of tilt with the local sample surface, the interaction volume lies nearer the surface, and this produces increased yields of both secondary and

backscattered electrons (Fig. 21a). Therefore, on a nonflat sample, the beam/surface tilt angle varies from point to point, and this gives rise to a point-to-point variation of secondary and backscattered electron yield that produces this type of emission contrast.

Type 3 emission contrast results from the fact that the yield of both secondary and backscattered electrons increases with atomic number (Fig. 21b). For beam voltages of 20 to 30 keV, a large atomic number difference at two points in a sample, for instance, at a phase boundary, will change the backscattered electron signal more than the secondary electron signal. Because the secondary electron detector detects some backscattered electrons as well as the secondary electrons, some type 3 emission contrast will be obtained at such a phase boundary. It will, however, be quite small, and much less than that obtained using the backscattered detectors to be discussed below.

Type 4 and 5 emission contrast mechanisms are discussed in the sections below devoted to electron channeling and magnetic domains. The signal variation produced by these mechanisms is quite small and occurs primarily for the backscattered electrons; consequently, these contrast mechanisms are again also optimized with the backscattered electron detector, not the secondary electron detector.

Contrast With the Backscattered Electron Detector. The number of backscattered electrons emitted from the sample

Fig. 21 Variation of backscattered and secondary electron yields

(a) Effect of angle of tilt between beam and surface at 30 keV. (b) Effect of the atomic number of the sample at 5 and 30 keV. Source: Ref 12

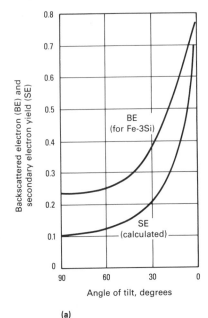

(a)

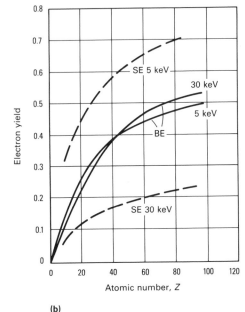

(b)

Fig. 22 Wide and narrow angle backscatter/sample geometric arrangement

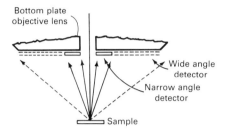

exceeds the number of secondary electrons. However, one of the problems in using backscattered electrons is the development of detectors having a high efficiency, ϵ, of collection and therefore favorable collection contrast. By simply biasing the front screen of the secondary electron detector negatively to repel the low-energy secondary electrons, this detector will collect only backscattered electrons; however, the value of ϵ is very small, and the resulting micrographs are very "noisy." In the past 10 to 15 years, there have been significant advancements in the development of backscattered detectors. At present, there are over six backscattered electron detector systems that use either solid-state detectors or scintillator detectors (Ref 12, 14). These detectors collect all three types of backscattered electrons shown in Fig. 16, and the type 3 electrons make the major contribution. Most scanning electron microscope manufactures offer the option of one or two types of backscattered electron detectors at a relatively modest cost.

As suggested in Fig. 1 and shown more clearly in Fig. 22, the backscattered electron detectors generally have a ring geometry and are placed above the sample immediately below the plate of the objective lens (these detectors may also be placed over the sample inside the lens of the in-lens arrangement of scanning transmission electron microscopes). There are basically two types of detectors, depending on whether they sample a wide or narrow takeoff angle from the sample (Fig. 22). The narrow takeoff angle detectors sample backscattered electrons that are scattered through high angles. Because these electrons are less sensitive to the beam/surface tilt angle, the narrow and wide angle detectors show differences in collection contrast on rough surfaces (Ref 12). Because the backscattered electron ring detectors are looking at the sample surface through a large solid angle, there is less shadowing produced by collection contrast on tilting, and samples are generally observed in an untilted orientation.

The image contrast for the backscattered electron detectors may be divided into the same five types as discussed above for the secondary electron detectors. Type 1 (edge contrast), however, is significantly reduced with the backscattered electron detector. As illustrated in Fig. 20, the electrons that forward scatter through the thin fibers produce SE(2) electrons that contribute to the secondary electron image. This effect occurs at the edge of any surface feature having a sharp edge, and a flaring is sometimes observed at the edges of such features in the secondary electron image. Because the backscattered electron detectors do not detect the forward scattered electrons, the backscattered electron images display a reduced edge contrast.

The type 2 emission contrast for backscattered electron detectors is similar to that for the secondary electron detectors. The backscattered electron yield increases as the beam/surface tilt angle decreases from normal incidence as illustrated in Fig. 21(a); therefore, etching metallographic samples to produce surface relief improves contrast.

A principal advantage of the backscattered electron detector versus the secondary electron detector is that type 3 contrast (atomic number contrast) is stronger; therefore, features that do not have contrast due to surface relief effects are more easily observed. This is important in many polyphase samples prepared using standard metallographic polishing techniques where surface relief is small or not desired.

Figure 23(b) presents a backscattered electron micrograph of an as-polished (not etched) copper-tin diffusion couple sample that was formed at 550 °C (1020 °F). The light phase is δ ($Cu_{31}Sn_8$, 32.5 wt% Sn), and the dark phase is α-bronze of 15.8 wt% Sn. The contrast between the δ and α phases in the backscattered electron image shown in Fig. 23(b) is substantially better than that in the secondary electron image shown in Fig. 23(a) due to the improved atomic number contrast of the backscattered electron detector. The secondary electron contrast between δ and α was so weak that it was visible only on the image CRT at very slow scan rates and required taking a picture to view the phase distribution on the sample. This sample displayed no visible contrast in the optical microscope in the unetched condition. The usefulness of the backscattered electron detector for examination of such an unetched sample is discussed further in Example 2 in the section "Applications" in this article.

Type 4 contrast (electron channeling contrast) and some type 5 contrast (magnetic domain contrast) are significantly better with the backscattered electron detector than the secondary electron detector. Use of these

Fig. 23 As-polished copper-tin diffusion couple sample

(a) Secondary electron detector image.
(b) Backscattered electron detector image taken with a solid-state wide angle detector, 20 keV, and original magnification of 1190×

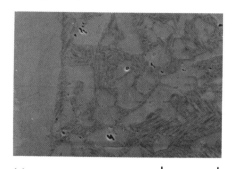

(a)

|———————| 20 μm

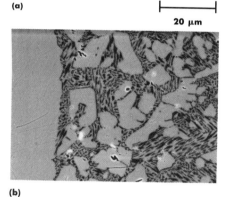

(b)

modes of contrast is discussed further below.

A potentially useful feature of emission contrast formation with backscattered electron detectors not covered by the five contrast types discussed above involves charging effects in nonconducting samples. Generally, nonconducting samples are coated with a thin layer of an electrically conducting metal, such as gold, to avoid charging effects and to provide a high atomic number surface for high backscattered and secondary electron yields. Plating the sample surface is sometimes not desired. For example, nonconducting particles, such as alumina (Al_2O_3) inclusions in steel, tend to collect incoming electrons, which results in very bright secondary electron images of the inclusion, which is a charging artifact. This charging problem is reduced with some of the backscattered electron detectors because the backscattered electrons are less sensitive to the charge buildup.

A potentially useful development is a backscattered electron detector arrangement (Ref 6) that detects the backscattered electrons shown as type 1 and 2 in Fig. 16. As discussed regarding Table 2, these electrons originate from a very small sample area,

Fig. 24 Source of channeling contrast for a line scan

(a) Sample. (b) Backscattered electron signal to CRT. (c) CRT display. W' is the band width on the CRT; D' the CRT screen width. W and D are determined by $2\theta_B$ and γ, respectively.

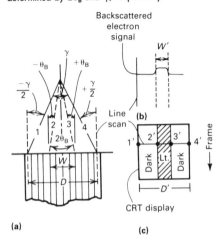

(a)   (c)

approaching the beam diameter, and edge sharpness has been demonstrated down to 1.5 nm. The method is very surface sensitive, but has not found widespread use, apparently because of the relatively low signal-to-noise ratio.

For the conventional scanning electron microscope, wide angle backscattered electron detectors are better than narrow angle detectors for metallographically prepared samples because of their large signal-to-noise ratio. The backscattered electron detector is superior to the secondary electron detector for studies requiring atomic number, channeling, and some magnetic contrast. For high-resolution work, the secondary electron detector is usually better, although recently developed backscattered electron detectors have demonstrated resolution capabilities on some samples of less than 10 nm (Ref 15, 16).

Electron Channeling Patterns and Contrast

The emission contrast mechanism, termed electron channeling contrast, results from a crystallographic effect and therefore has potentially useful applications. A detailed review of electron channeling contrast is provided in Ref 17.

Channeling Patterns. Channeling effects can be understood with the aid of the line scan picture shown in Fig. 24(a). The sample is a single crystal shown with a vertical set of (hkl) planes that are also perpendicular to the page. As the beam scans from positions 1 to 4, it makes an angle θ with this (hkl) plane set, which varies from $-\gamma/2$ to 0 and up to $+\gamma/2$, where γ is the

maximum scan angle shown in Fig. 24(a). If θ_B equals the Bragg angle for diffraction, then:

$$n\lambda = 2d_{hkl} \sin \theta_B \cong 2d_{hkl}\theta_B \qquad \text{(Eq 7)}$$

where λ is the wavelength of the electron beam, which varies inversely with the beam voltage. Because λ is small, θ_B will be small; this allows the approximation in Eq 7. In addition, θ_B will often be less than γ. Therefore, as the beam swings from positions 1 to 4 shown in Fig. 24, it will make an angle of $-\theta_B$, with the (hkl) plane set at position 2, and $+\theta_B$ at position 3.

The physics of electron beam/crystal interactions is related to a channeling of electrons down the (hkl) plane sets, and it demonstrates that the backscattered electron yield becomes higher for $\theta < |\theta_B|$ (Ref 17). Therefore, when the beam lies between positions 2 and 3, the backscattered electron detector signal to the CRT will increase (Fig. 24b). At points between $2'$ and $3'$ on the line scale of the CRT, a bright intensity is expected relative to points between $1'$ to $2'$ and $3'$ to $4'$. If the line scan is allowed to move down the frame direction, it should be apparent that a central light band will appear on the image (Fig. 24c).

If the vertical (hkl) plane set that is perpendicular to the page remained vertical, but slanted out from the page at 30° to the right, the band shown in Fig. 24(c) would lie at 30° down and to the right from the vertical position shown in Fig. 24(c). Each (hkl) plane set that causes diffraction and satisfies Bragg's law will produce a band on the CRT. This is illustrated in Fig. 25, which is an electron channeling pattern (ECP) on a single crystal of vanadium taken under the conditions shown in Fig. 24. There is a band down the center of this pattern similar to that in Fig. 24(c). This band has been produced by the (202) plane set of the crystal. The band is dark rather than light as in Fig. 24(c) because the signal used in Fig. 25 was not from a backscattered electron detector. A specimen current detector was used that inverts the signal. The star at the center of Fig. 25 is a [$\bar{1}11$] direction that clearly displays the threefold symmetry required in the cubic vanadium crystal. Two more dark bands are visible at 60° to either side of the (202) band; these are from the (220) and (0$\bar{2}$2) plane sets.

The pattern shown in Fig. 25 illustrates the above statement: each (hkl) plane set that causes diffraction and satisfies Bragg's law produces a band on the CRT pattern. The center of each band may be thought of as the projection of the responsible (hkl) plane set up to the observer's eye, positioned above the sample surface. The pattern is actually

Fig. 25 Electron channeling pattern of vanadium taken in the ECP mode

Specimen current detector, no differentiation, $\gamma/D' = 1.2°/$cm, 29 kV, magnification control of $20\times$

rotated relative to the (hkl) plane sets of the sample by some angle about the sample normal (Ref 17). This rotation can be determined, and it has been neglected here for ease of presentation. It is evident, therefore, that the crystallographic orientation of the single-crystal region beneath the beam can be evaluated from the ECP.

The channeling patterns are essentially the same as Kikuchi patterns obtained in thin foil samples in transmission electron and scanning transmission microscopes (see Fig. 11 in the article "Analytical Transmission Electron Microscopy" in this Volume). Just as Kikuchi patterns allow evaluation of crystallographic orientation more precisely than is possible with the electron diffraction pattern, the ECP enables more precise orientation evaluation than an x-ray Laue pattern.

Producing the Channeling Pattern. The channeling contrast, $\Delta S/S$, determined by the increase in the backscattered electron signal shown in Fig. 24(b), is a small effect, of the order of only 5% or less. Use of this contrast requires proper control of the electron optics of the scanning electron microscope. A sharp channeling pattern, such as that shown in Fig. 25, is produced only when the divergence of the primary beam, $\alpha \approx d_a/(2 \cdot WD)$ in Fig. 13, is significantly reduced. This causes a majority of the primary beam electrons to satisfy the Bragg condition simultaneously when the beam crosses position 2 in Fig. 24(a), which sharply increases the backscattered electron signal at $2'$ in Fig. 24(b) and thus makes the band edge sharply defined.

The divergence, α, is reduced by lessening the aperture diameter, d_a, but this reduces the signal current, i_s. Because of the small contrast noted above, large i_s values are required to observe the patterns clearly, and it is thus necessary to increase the beam diameter, d_s, as α is reduced. The sharpest patterns require d_s so large that the resolution for surface features is severely reduced. As d_s is decreased, the channeling pattern begins to fade, but the smaller d_s value will show surface features, such as polishing scratches. In normal operation of the scanning electron microscope with small d_s and larger α, the channeling patterns, although present, are too diffuse to be visible.

Channeling patterns and contrast are very surface sensitive. The signal is carried by electrons scattered from depths below the surface of only 10 to 100 nm. Therefore, sample preparation is important. For metals, the worked surface layer produced by standard metallographic techniques will degrade and in some cases eliminate the patterns because of the variation in d_{hkl} produced by the residual strains. With more brittle materials, for example, intermetallic compounds and semiconductors such as germanium and silicon, residual strains are less of a problem.

With metals, electropolishing or chemical polishing is generally necessary as a final step. Even then patterns are not always obtained on metals that are prone to oxidation. For example, in some iron-rare earth magnetic alloys, sharp patterns are not obtainable after electropolishing. However, by switching to a different type of electropolishing solution, sharp patterns can be obtained. The first electropolish solution leaves a film on the surface, probably a rare-earth-rich oxide, which degrades channeling contrast. A convenient way to overcome the problem of oxide films on reactive metals is to ion sputter clean the surface, but ion sputter guns are not usually available on scanning electron microscopes.

Because the effect that produces the channeling contrast involves the backscattered electrons, channeling patterns and channeling contrast are better observed using the backscattered electron detector than the secondary electron detector. The specimen current detector is also useful for channeling work and in some cases has certain advantages.

Channeling Contrast. From the geometry shown in Fig. 24, it is apparent that:

$$\frac{2\theta_B}{\gamma} = \frac{W}{D} = \frac{W'}{D'} \qquad \text{(Eq 8)}$$

Combining Eq 7 and 8 reveals the band width on the CRT:

$$W' = \frac{n\lambda/d_{hkl}}{\gamma/D'} \qquad \text{(Eq 9)}$$

Fig. 26 Grain boundaries revealed by channeling contrast

Images taken in the δ phase at the left side of the sample of Fig. 23. (a) Secondary electron detector. (b) Backscattered electron detector. Original magnification, 700 ×

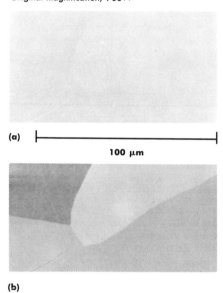

(a)

100 μm

(b)

This result shows that for a given (hkl) plane set, the band width on the CRT, W', is determined by the beam voltage (which sets λ) and the scan angle γ, which is set by the magnification control. As magnification increases, γ decreases and W' expands on the CRT. For example, in Fig. 25 the pattern expands about the center point of the screen as magnification increases. Above a few 100 ×, a featureless uniform pattern is observed whose gray level corresponds to the center point of Fig. 25. Rotating the crystal causes the gray level to change because the different bands of Fig. 25 are moving to the center of the screen. This variation in contrast with crystal orientation, termed channeling contrast, allows observation of grain boundaries.

Figure 26(b) demonstrates the utility of channeling contrast for observation of grain boundaries in the δ phase of the tin bronze sample shown in Fig. 23. The sample is unetched. The grain boundaries are not visible in the optical microscope and are only dimly detected by the secondary electron signal (Fig. 26a). The contrast shown in Fig. 26(b) is due to the different crystallographic orientations of the various grains. This results in different gray levels. As the sample is rotated, the relative brightnesses of the various grains will change. For example, a 20° stage tilt caused inversion of the dark/light contrast of the two grains shown at the top of Fig. 26(b).

The sensitivity of channeling contrast to surface preparation was revealed in an experiment on 6061 aluminum in the scanning Auger microscope. The aluminum matrix was examined in the SEM mode with a secondary electron detector (Ref 18). No grain boundaries were visible after a very light surface sputtering. The sample had been prepared by standard metallographic techniques, with the final polish using a colloidal silica suspension, which is effective for aluminum alloys. After a more severe surface sputtering, the grain boundaries become very distinct in the secondary electron detector image. The channeling contrast had been dramatically increased by sputter removal of surface oxide and surface-worked layers from the 6061 surface; thus, the grain boundaries were visible without the aid of a backscattered electron detector.

Selected-Area Channeling Patterns (SACP). In order to achieve the greatest usefulness of channeling patterns for evaluation of metallurgical microstructure, it is necessary to be able to produce patterns from small regions, such as individual grains. This may be accomplished using the SACP technique. In this mode of operation, the electron beam is held at a fixed point of interest on the sample surface and rocked back and forth about that point. To understand how this is accomplished, note the position on Fig. 5 at which all the rays cross through the same point (at the principal plane of objective lens in normal operation). To obtain an SACP, it is necessary to move this point down onto the sample surface. This results in the situation shown in Fig. 27 for a line scan. Just as in the ECP case shown in Fig. 25, the beam makes angles with the (hkl) set varying from $-\gamma/2$ to $+\gamma/2$ and will pass through the Bragg angles $-\theta_B$ and θ_B. Consequently, a channeling pattern similar to that shown in Fig. 25 is obtained, except the pattern arises only from the limited volume about which the beam is rocking.

To achieve the electron optical arrangement shown in Fig. 27 with a conventional scanning electron microscope, manufacturers provide a double-deflection system or a deflection-focusing system. In both systems, aberrations occur as a result of the deflections and cause the beam to spread out on the sample surface, thereby limiting the minimum diameter particle that can be examined. For a rocking angle $\gamma = 10°$, the minimum area is approximately 50 μm for the double-deflection systems and 5 to 10° for the deflection-focusing system (Ref 17). For the deflection-focusing system, it is possible to extend the minimum area down to 1 to 2 μm. Examples 3 and 4 in the section ''Applications'' in this article illustrate the usefulness of such systems.

In practice, a surface image of the sample is first obtained, and the area of interest located. By suitable adjustments, this area is then made to expand on the CRT into the SACP. The technique allows evaluation of the crystallographic orientation of microstructural features of sizes down to the limit of the system available. With the deflection-focusing system (5- to 10-μm limit), orientations of such individual features as grains, twin bands, dendrites, and precipitate phases can be easily evaluated. Similar information can be obtained on even smaller areas in the transmission electron and scanning transmission electron microscopes; however, the advantage of the SACP technique is that the samples do not have to be thinned, but can be examined following standard metallographic preparation, with the precautions mentioned above. The SACP technique is also available for examining thick samples in the scanning transmission electron microscope.

Applications of Channeling Patterns. Evaluation of crystallographic orientation is a major application of channeling patterns. To carry out such an evaluation, it is helpful to use a channeling map for the crystal system under analysis. These maps are essentially identical to Kikuchi maps. Reference 17 presents example maps for the common crystal structure.

Another application results from the fact that straining a crystal affects the channeling pattern. In the elastic region, the changing d_{hkl} will change the bandwidths (see Eq 9); at higher strains, the crystalline defect structure degrades the sharpness and contrast of the patterns. An interesting application using these effects involves examining SACPs as the crack on a fractured sample is approached (Ref 17). Such studies allow evaluation of the extent of the residual strain away from the crack tip with a resolution of approximately 10 μm.

Special Techniques With SEM

Specimen Current Detectors. As indicated in Fig. 1, it is possible to detect the current flowing from the sample to ground and use this signal to generate CRT images. In the absence of charging effects, the total beam current must equal the sum of all electron currents leaving the sample; therefore, from consideration of Fig. 20:

$$i_B = i_{SE} + i_{BE} + i_{SC}$$

where the three terms on the right are currents due to secondary electrons, backscattered electrons, and the specimen current flowing to ground, respectively. Effects such

Fig. 27 Arrangement for SACP

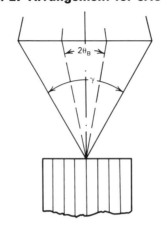

as channeling that alter i_{BE} will in general alter i_{SC} in an opposite sense. Therefore, the i_{SC} signal can be used as an alternative to the backscattered electron signal (a specimen current detector was used for the image shown in Fig. 25).

The bandwidth (frequency range over which amplification is linear) of direct current (dc) amplifiers is relatively small; consequently, it is difficult to use a specimen current detector because scan rates must be kept low. Bandwidth limitations are not a problem with secondary electron detectors; they were originally a problem with solid-state backscattered electron detectors, but that has now been largely overcome. Specimen current detectors have significantly poorer resolution than backscattered and secondary electron detectors. They are useful, however, for SACPs where very small working distance values can be used to reduce spherical aberrations and thus obtain patterns from smaller areas, for example 5 μm rather than 10 μm using the double-deflection focusing technique. This advantage results because the specimen current detector is not positioned between the sample and lens as are the backscattered electron and secondary electron detectors.

Magnetic Contrast. It is possible to obtain images of magnetic domains in the scanning electron microscope. Ferromagnetic materials are composed of small subgrain-sized regions termed domains. In every domain, the magnetic moment of each electron has a common direction along a certain crystallographic axis, which is often termed the easy axis. In certain crystals, such as cobalt, there is only one easy axis; such crystals are termed uniaxial crystals. In these crystals, the magnetic moment at a surface will often have a component normal to the surface, which means that a small magnetic flux **B**, will "leak" out of the surface. A secondary electron ejected from

the surface of a uniaxial crystal with velocity v will thus experience a Lorentz force $v \times \mathbf{B}$. Because the local external flux changes sign over each domain, the change in the Lorentz force will cause the secondary electron detector signal to change when the beam moves over each domain; thus, images of domains can be obtained using the secondary electron signal. This contrast has been termed type I magnetic contrast.

In most ferromagnetic crystals, there is more than one easy axis; for example, in α-iron they are the three cubic directions [100], [010], and [001]. In these crystals, closure domains form at the surface that have their moment lying along the easy axis most closely parallel to the surface, which greatly reduces the magnetic flux leakage outside the surface. In these crystals, domains are revealed by type II magnetic contrast. Inside the metal, there is an abrupt change in the magnetization direction at a domain boundary. This means that the direction of **B** switches from domain to domain inside the metal. Therefore, after entering the sample, a primary electron will experience a Lorentz force in different directions from domain to domain. This gives rise to changes in the backscattering yield as the primary beam sweeps across a domain boundary; therefore, the backscattered electron detector is used to detect type II magnetic contrast.

Domains can be observed in the optical microscope using such techniques as the Bitter method or the Kerr effect, and resolutions of domains of the order of 1 μm are achievable. Type I contrast achieves comparable resolutions (Ref 19). Type II resolution has theoretical limits of approximately the thickness of the domain wall, 0.1 μm. However, the magnetic contrast is very weak, and high beam currents and therefore large beam diameters are required to reveal the domains. Resolution of a few tenths of a micron are possible. The factors controlling magnetic contrast are summarized in Ref 20. Detailed information on techniques used to observe domain structures can be found in the article "Magnetic and Electrical Materials" in Volume 9 of the 9th Edition of *Metals Handbook*.

Voltage Contrast. This contrast mechanism has proved to be quite useful for analysis of semiconductor devices. The secondary electrons emerge from the sample surface with a peak intensity at a voltage of approximately 5 V (Fig. 16). If a screen is placed over the sample and biased with −5 V, it will repel the emitted secondary electrons and act as a retarding voltage. If the sample is an integrated circuit (IC) chip, and a negative voltage is applied to certain elements of the IC, the emitted secondary electrons from those elements will not be stopped by the retarding voltage. They will emerge past the screen and will be detected by the secondary electron detector; the negatively biased elements of the IC will consequently appear bright on the CRT image. By proper analysis, the potential of the IC elements can be evaluated from the magnitude of the secondary electron signal and retarding voltage (Ref 21).

Voltage contrast is a form of pure collection contrast because the voltages applied to the sample and screen do not affect the number of secondary electrons emitted, but only those collected. An introductory explanation of voltage contrast is provided in Ref 20. Scanning electron microscope manufacturers supply instruments that are dedicated to the use of voltage contrast for such purposes as failure analysis, function control, and design verification of ICs. Recent developments are discussed in Ref 21 and 22.

Electron Beam Induced Current (EBIC). This technique is also very useful for semiconductor device characterization and failure analysis. In addition, it allows imaging of defects in semiconducting materials. The electron beam induces a current between two electrodes contacting the semiconductor sample, and this current is used for analysis or to modulate the CRT and produce an image. When the electron beam strikes the sample surface, electron-hole pairs are created within some interaction volume. If the semiconductor contains an internal electric field near these charge carriers due to, for example, a p-n junction, the charge carriers will be swept away, creating a current between the two attached electrodes.

To study crystals that do not contain p-n junctions, a surface Schottky barrier is fabricated on the crystal surface by deposition of a thin metallic layer (Fig. 28). The thickness of material beneath the junction depleted of mobile carriers is shown as Z_D in Fig. 28 and is a function of the applied reverse bias voltage. Crystal defects and composition gradients within this zone that affect the charge dissipation current can be imaged. The current used in the EBIC technique is different from the current flow to ground used with specimen current detectors.

It is possible to obtain images of such localized crystal defects as dislocations and stacking faults. In addition, crystal growth defects, such as dopant inhomogeneities at growth striae and swirl defects, can also be imaged. The lateral resolution is of the order of 0.5 μm, and sample depths may range from a few tens of nanometers to 15 to 20 μm. The factors that control image formation are reviewed in Ref 23.

Fig. 28 Experimental EBIC arrangement using the Schottky barrier technique

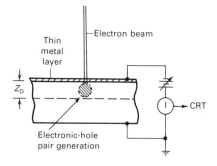

Many electrical parameters of semiconductor devices can be evaluated using quantitative EBIC techniques, for example, doping level, diffusion length and lifetime of minority carriers, mobility and surface recombination velocity, surface potential, electric field, multiplication factor, and ionization coefficients (Ref 24). In addition, the EBIC technique is used for failure analysis and device diagnostics in such ways as locating a defective device in an array, locating a defect in a device or junction, or locating an irregularity in a junction. A recent review is provided in Ref 25.

Cathodoluminescence is the emission of light by a solid under electron beam bombardment and is the same process that occurs at the face of the CRT of the scanning electron microscope. To use cathodoluminescence in the scanning electron microscope, the light given off by the sample must be collected with a special photon collector inside the specimen chamber, which converts the emitted light intensity to an electrical signal for modulating the intensity of the image CRT or for spectral analysis. Introductory reviews are provided in Ref 20 and 26.

The cathodoluminescence technique examines photons of the visible, near-infrared, and ultraviolet regions of the spectrum that are emitted as a result of electron beam induced electron transitions between energy levels much higher than the K and L levels used in the x-ray analysis of the electron probe microanalysis (EPMA) technique. Consequently, the cathodoluminescence spectrum is much broader, and its usefulness as a tool for chemical analysis remains only qualitative. However, it has the advantage that it can be extremely sensitive for strongly luminescent impurities, for which detection limits as low as 10^{-6} have been demonstrated (Ref 27), which compares to 0.01% for EPMA. However, cathodoluminescence is applicable only for luminescent impurities. The cathodoluminescence and EPMA techniques are compared in Ref 28.

Cathodoluminescence is used almost exclusively with nonmetallic materials, organic and inorganic. It has useful applications in examination of materials traditionally associated with materials science, such as certain ceramics, semiconductors, and plastics as well as the materials of mineralogy, inorganic and organic chemistry, biology, and medicine. In the case of semiconductors, electron-hole pairs are generated, and the physical basis of the cathodoluminescence technique in the scanning electron microscope is the same as that for EBIC, being governed by generation, motion, and recombination of excess charge carriers. Therefore, with semiconductors, cathodoluminescence analysis has found use for such applications as imaging dislocations, evaluating minority carrier diffusion length and lifetime, and device analysis. It is often used as a complementary tool along with EBIC. Cathodoluminescence and EBIC analysis can be performed using the scanning transmission electron microscope and scanning Auger microscope as well as the transmission electron microscope. Studies performed on semiconductor materials are reviewed in Ref 27 and 29.

Signal Processing Techniques. The image that appears on the CRT is a result of the point-to-point signal variation as the beam scans across the sample. The signal variation may be observed directly using a wave form monitor, an oscilloscope that displays signal intensity as the beam moves along a line on the sample surface. A line scan can be obtained by stopping the frame scan, and the wave form monitor displays the signal intensity received by the CRT at the line scan position (Fig. 7b).

The contrast of the CRT image may be qualitatively understood from the line scan signal. If the maximum-to-minimum signal variation is large, as for the $d_s \approx S_\alpha$ case, high contrast will be observed; if it is small, as for the $d_s \gg S_\alpha$ case, low contrast is observed. For a given sample, the signal variation will be determined by the contrast mechanisms discussed above. If this natural signal variation is small (as is the usual case for applications involving channeling contrast, magnetic contrast, and voltage contrast), the natural signal can be processed electronically, and its maximum-to-minimum variation increased artificially, enhancing the contrast of the CRT image. For example, desirable image enhancement can often be achieved simply by taking the first derivative of the signal. To illustrate, a channeling pattern showing a {110} pole of a vanadium crystal is shown in Fig. 29. The image using the natural specimen current signal is shown in Fig. 29(b); using the differentiated signal image provides a dra-

Fig. 29 Channeling pattern of vanadium showing a {110} pole

(a) Differentiated specimen current signal.
(b) Natural specimen current signal

(a)   **(b)**

matic improvement in contrast. Second-order bands, barely discernible with the natural signal image, are easily observed using the differentiated specimen current signal.

A rich variety of signal processing techniques are available on commercial scanning electron microscopes. For example, in addition to the capability of increasing contrast, it is also possible to decrease contrast by nonlinear amplification, termed gamma processing. This technique is very useful for preparing micrographs with the secondary electron and backscattered electron detectors where both very bright and dark features are encountered in the same field of view. The signal to the CRT can also be modified by mixing signals from more than one detector. For example, it is sometimes useful to mix a differentiated backscattered electron or specimen current signal with an undifferentiated secondary electron signal. These signal processing techniques are discussed in Ref 3.

Applications*

Example 1: Use of High Resolution in Analysis of a Jominy Bar. AISI 52100 steel is a popular hypereutectoid chromium-bearing steel that is austenitized at approximately 850 °C (1560 °F) to produce spheroidal carbides in the final martensite matrix. High-resolution optical microscopy of this steel is difficult because of effects produced by these carbides. Figure 30 presents data from a Jominy test on 52100. There is an increase in hardness at Jominy distance (J_D) = 10 that is not usually present in Jominy data. Two possible causes of this increase are that (1) cooling conditions in the J_D = 10 range are produc-

*Example 6 was supplied by Ruth E. Whan and David H. Huskisson, Sandia National Laboratories; Example 7 by James A. VanDenAvyle, Sandia National Laboratories; and Example 8 by Nelda A. Creager, Sandia National Laboratories. This work supported by the U.S. Department of Energy under Contract No. DE-AC04-76DP00789.

ing a very finely divided carbide precipitate that leads to the increased strength, or (2) bainite/pearlite microstructural changes are responsible for the increase. Evaluation of the first theory would require cutting up the bar and producing thin foil samples. It should be possible to evaluate the second theory using optical microscopy, but this proved difficult because of the presence of the spheroidal carbides.

After polishing and etching in nital, the final 25 mm (1 in.) of the sample was examined in a scanning electron microscope. Using the Rockwell hardness indentations for reference, the source of the increase became immediately obvious. The carbide distribution was now clearly resolved, and at J_D = 8 (Fig. 31a), the matrix consisted of an upper bainitic microstructure; at J_D = 9 (Fig. 31b), the matrix was a fine pearlite. The micrographs shown in Fig. 31 demonstrate that the carbide spacing was significantly finer in the pearlite, which accounts for the increased hardness at J_D = 10. Similar increases occur on Jominy bar data for many of the chromium-base AISI 5000 steels, and these are also probably due to the increased hardness of fine pearlite versus upper bainite in these steels.

Example 2: Use of Atomic Number Contrast in the Analysis of Two-Phase Alloys. A diffusion couple experiment was performed on copper-tin alloys at 550 °C (1020 °F). Three intermetallic compound layers lying next to the copper in the order of γ, δ, and ε are anticipated (see the Cu-Sn phase diagram on page 299 of Volume 8 of the 8th Edition of *Metals Handbook*). The γ phase decomposes by a eutectoid reaction upon cooling; therefore, room-temperature analysis will reveal a two-phase microstructure in the γ region. The δ phase should also decompose upon cooling, but the kinetics of this reaction are too slow to allow decomposition under normal cooling rates.

As shown in Fig. 23(b), the copper was at the right, and the location of the original δ/γ phase boundary is visible at the left side. To the right of the boundary, the γ phase has decomposed into primary δ plus a δ/bronze pearlite. A tin composition gradient exists from left to right in this two-phase region, and the EPMA capability of the scanning electron microscope can be used to evaluate it. If the surface of the sample is etched, it becomes easy to locate the δ/γ boundary in the optical microscope or scanning electron microscope. However, the surface relief produced by etching makes the quantitative analysis of the x-ray data unreliable because if the etch puts the tin-rich δ phase into relief, the apparent percent tin will increase. Therefore, it is important to conduct the x-ray analysis on

Fig. 30 Jominy test data on AISI 52100 steel austenitized at 850 °C (1560 °F)

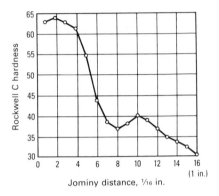

flat, as-polished surfaces. As indicated by the micrographs shown in Fig. 23, by using a backscattered electron detector, phase boundaries can be observed on flat samples, where they are not visible or are seen only dimly with a secondary electron detector in the scanning electron microscope or with the optical microscope.

Example 3: Use of SACP to Understand the Nature of Pearlite Growth. As pearlite grows into austenite, it is generally observed that the growth front passes through the grain boundaries in the austenite. However, approximately 10% of the time the pearlite will be momentarily stopped by an austenite grain boundary, and a layer of ferrite will be deposited at that boundary before pearlite growth is continued.

Figure 32 shows an SEM image of a pearlite growth front with two pearlite colonies, A and B, growing vertically into austenite in a binary Fe-0.8 C alloy. The growth was produced by a directional transformation apparatus, and the sample was quenched so that the quenched austenite is visible as the fuzzy region above the pearlite plates in Fig. 32. A prior austenite grain boundary runs from lower left to upper right. This boundary caused a step to occur at the austenite/pearlite growth front, and it is seen that the dark cementite plates of grain A have been stopped by this boundary.

It appears that the ferrite component of the pearlite in grain A has grown past the austenite grain boundary, and this would be established conclusively if the orientation of the ferrite could be verified as being the same on either side of the prior austenite boundary. Such verification could easily be performed using TEM, but it would be difficult to prepare a thin foil of such a select region as shown in Fig. 32 because these special boundaries appeared only at four or five locations on a 1-cm (0.4-in.)

Fig. 31 SEM micrographs of a 52100 bearing steel Jominy bar

(a) Jominy position 8. (b) Jominy position 10. SE detector, 20 kV, original magnification of 6340 ×

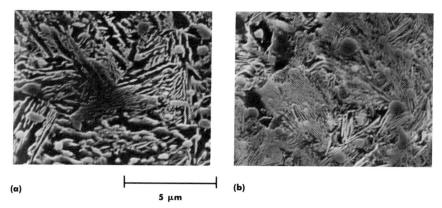

(a)   (b)

5 μm

Fig. 32 SEM micrograph of a longitudinal section at a quenched interface showing two pearlite colonies (A and B) growing into austenite in a Fe-0.8C alloy

Electropolished surface prepared for SACP analysis. Original magnification, 1700 ×

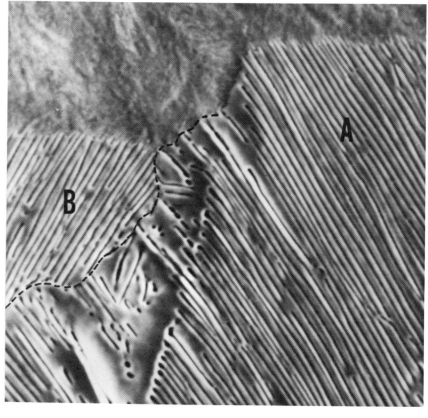

10 μm

sample surface. An SACP technique having a resolution capability of 1 to 2 μm was used to show that the ferrite component had the same orientation in region A all the way over to the dashed line (see Ref 30 for details).

Example 4: Use of SACP to Establish Preferred Crystallographic Growth. Experiments on the directional growth of lead-tin eutectic alloys have shown that the plate eutectic displays two morphologies, regular and degenerate (Fig. 33). In the

regular morphology found at the center of Fig. 33, the plates are flat; in the surrounding degenerate morphology, they curve back and forth with a distinctive wavy appearance.

Directionally grown rods were sectioned transversely, electropolished, and centimeter length sections placed in the scanning electron microscope with their outer surface against a special Faraday cage stage, which allowed alignment of the beam to within 0.1° of the growth axis defined by the outer sample surface. From SACP analysis, it was then possible to examine degenerate and regular grains. Figure 34 presents data from one large regular grain of several experiments. The small circles provide the crystallographic direction in the tin plates, which was parallel to the growth axis, and the line through the circle provides the trace of the interface plane between tin and lead eutectic plates. It is seen that the interface plane lies close to (512), and the tin growth direction clusters within 10° of [$\bar{2}$43]. The degenerate grains tended to have a tin growth direction clustered around [$\bar{1}$6,23,0]. It was also possible to measure the lead growth direction and the crystallographic orientation between the lead and tin plates using the SACP technique (Ref 31).

Use of SACP for these types of studies offers some advantages over the use of TEM and STEM. First, thinning of samples is not required. Second, orientation of the beam with directions of the sample is more accurate. This allows more accurate determination of growth directions, as illustrated above, as well as crystalline interfaces where two surface analyses are required. The transmission electron microscope has the advantage, however, of being able to examine much smaller features.

Example 5: Complementary Contributions of Optical Microscopy, SEM, and SAM. Figure 35(a) shows a secondary electron detector image of the rare earth-Fe_2 alloy known as Terfenol, (0.3Tb-0.7Dy)-Fe_2, which has outstanding magnetostrictive properties. Region A is the Terfenol compound, and B is pure rare-earth metal. This distinction was determined using x-ray analysis in the scanning electron microscope with an energy-dispersive detector. An optical microscope picture of the region of Fig. 35(a) shows a similar image, except that the rare-earth regions B are a distinct blue. It was suspected that this blue phase was a hydride that formed on the rare-earth metal during metallographic preparation. Because hydrogen cannot be detected with x-ray analysis, the sample was examined using SAM.

Figure 35(a) was taken in the scanning Auger microscope using its secondary electron detector; that is, the scanning Auger

Fig. 33 Electropolished section of a lead-tin eutectic alloy

Secondary electron detector image. 630 ×

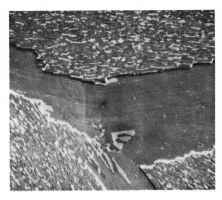

microscope was used in the same manner as a conventional scanning electron microscope. Figure 35(b) was made using the Auger signal from iron, and the iron (light regions) lies only in the regions B, as was already known from x-ray analysis. Auger analyses of regions B revealed no oxide. Hydrogen is not detected directly in the Auger spectrum, but it does produce a shape change in one of the rare-earth peaks, which was found to be quite small. It was discovered, however, using standards, that hydride formation produces a significant change in the plasmon energy loss signal, that is, the ΔE for the type 2 backscattered electrons shown in Fig. 16. This same change was found to occur in regions B, indicating that the blue phase was hydride.

Figure 35(c) is an image generated by use of the hydride energy loss signal, and the hydride overlays positions B. It was confirmed that the hydride formed on metallographic preparation by ion sputtering away

a small amount of surface from the dashed area of Fig. 35(a). Sputtering caused the hydride energy loss signal to disappear. Additional information is provided in Ref 32.

Example 6: Corrosion in Pyrotechnic Actuators. Pyrotechnically driven devices are used in a number of ordnance applications requiring rapid mechanical actuation. Figure 36 shows a typical hermetically sealed pyrotechnic actuator. A fine bridgewire is located in contact with the chemical pyrotechnic, and the charge is ignited by electrical heating of the bridgewire. These actuators are required to have high reliabilities for shelf lives in excess of 20 years. This places stringent materials compatibility requirements on these devices, with corrosion of the bridgewire and pins a primary concern.

Compatibility studies performed during development of one type of actuator suggested that no materials compatibility problems existed. During later production of this device, however, significant problems were encountered. Several actuators were opened to examine the bridgewires, pins, and the adjacent pyrotechnic surfaces. These were examined using a scanning electron microscope equipped with an energy-dispersive x-ray detector.

Examination of the 0.047-mm (0.0018-in.) diam nickel-chromium-iron alloy bridgewire and the nickel-iron alloy pins showed evidence of severe corrosion (Fig. 37 and 38). The electron beam was positioned on the corrosion products of the bridgewire and pins, and x-ray spectra were collected (Fig. 39 and 40). In addition to the metallic elements in the pin or bridgewire, substantial amounts of chlorine were detected. In each case, chlorine was associated with the corrosion product. These alloys are known to be susceptible to corrosion in

Fig. 34 Location of the crystallographic growth axes of tin plates (small circles) and the plate interface plane traces (line through small circles) from large grains of several experiments

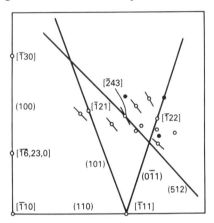

chlorine-containing environments. Examination of the titanium-potassium perchlorate (Ti-KClO$_4$) pyrotechnic also revealed that morphological changes indicative of decomposition and dissolution had occurred in regions of the pyrotechnic that had been in contact with the bridgewire and pin surfaces (Fig. 41).

Additional SEM analyses of the glass surfaces and pins to which the bridgewires were welded revealed the presence of chlorine-containing residue from a post-machining cleaning process. Subsequent analyses by ion-selective electrode confirmed the presence of chloride ion. Parts that had been used for compatibility studies during component development were shown by similar examinations to be free from this chlorine-containing residue. Analyses of

Fig. 35 Analysis of a magnetostrictive alloy by SAM

(a) Secondary electron detector image of a cellular region on a transverse section of directionally solidified Terfenol alloy; original magnification, 500 ×. (b) Iron Auger map of same area, 250 × 250 pixels, $E_P = 46$ eV, $E_B = 70$ eV. (c) Hydride electron energy loss map of same area, 250 × 250 pixels, $E_P = 1988$ eV, $E_B = 1982$ eV

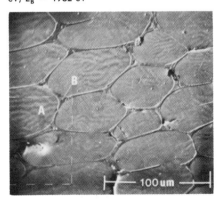

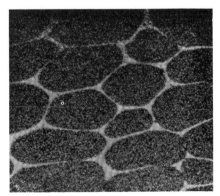

(a)

(b)

(c)

Fig. 36 Cross section of a pyrotechnic actuator

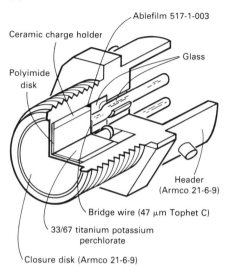

the titanium particles by nuclear magnetic resonance also showed that substantial amounts of water were associated with the surfaces of the titanium particles in the pyrotechnic.

Based on these observations, it was proposed that the chlorine-containing residue be combined with the water from the pyrotechnic to form a thin aqueous film containing a substantial concentration of chloride ions, which began corroding the bridgewire and pins. The $KClO_4$ particles in contact with these surfaces also decomposed, providing sources of additional chloride and oxygen that compounded the problem by creating an oxygen concentration cell. Based on this understanding, a new cleaning procedure was implemented for the glass headers to eliminate the chloride contamination, a vacuum drying procedure was instituted for the pyrotechnic, and it was specified that assembly be carried out in an argon-filled dry box to ensure that moisture was not picked up by the pyrotechnic during assembly. The corrosion problem was thus eliminated.

Example 7: Overload Failure of a Quench-Cracked AISI 4340 Steel Threaded Rod. An AISI 4340 threaded steel connecting rod was part of a connecting linkage used between a parachute and an instrumented drop test assembly. The 31.75-mm (1.25-in.) diam rod fractured under high dynamic loading when the assembly was dropped from an airplane. It was fabricated of aircraft-quality 4340 steel with a quench and temper heat treatment to a hardness of 38 ($\pm$1) HRC, giving an equivalent ultimate strength of approximately 1205 MPa (175 ksi).

A large flaw was visible on the fracture surface (Fig. 42). It originated from the root of a machined thread groove and extended approximately 6.4 mm (0.25 in.) into the diameter and 38 mm (1.5 in.) around its circumference. The surface of most of the flaw was black, indicating heavy oxidation at elevated temperature; the final 0.64 mm (0.025 in.) of flaw growth was light gray.

A length of the bolt was sectioned, and the fracture surface was examined in the scanning electron microscope to determine the fracture mode. Three regions can be distinguished. Heavy oxide growth in the black flaw region obscures most of the metal fracture surface, but fine secondary cracks aligned transverse to the growth direction are common (Fig. 43). The final gray segment of the flaw is intergranular fracture with some oxide visible (Fig. 44). Secondary cracks follow combined transgranular and intergranular paths in this region.

Intergranular cracking and the heavy black oxide in this alloy are commonly associated with quench cracking during heat treating. For this part, because the threads were machined before heat treatment, the thread root served as an effective stress concentration to induce quench cracking. Other thread root cracks were found in the failed part using dye penetrant inspection.

Fracture in the overload region occurred by a ductile void growth and coalescence process. At lower magnifications, lines of ridges (Fig. 45a) are visible that run perpendicular to the growth direction and mark the crack from, zig-zagging above and below the average crack plane. Higher magnifications (Fig. 45b) show a predominantly fine dimple structure that results from void nucleation around very small carbides; larger dimples (~20 μm) are nucleated around bigger inclusions.

Features on the ductile overload region of the fracture are as expected (with one exception discussed below) for 4340 steel of this strength level. Contrast of the ridge structure is improved by tilting the sample approximately 30°, as was done in Fig.

Fig. 37 Scanning electron micrograph of bridgewire showing corrosion and corrosion product

Fig. 38 Scanning electron micrograph of pin showing corrosion and corrosion product

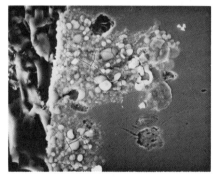

Fig. 39 X-ray spectrum from bridgewire corrosion product

Note the presence of substantial amounts of chlorine.

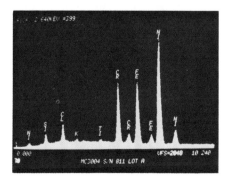

Fig. 40 X-ray spectrum from pin corrosion product

Note the presence of substantial amounts of chlorine.

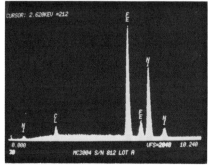

Fig. 41 Scanning electron micrographs of Ti-KClO₄ pyrotechnic

Large particles (area A) are $KClO_4$; small particles (area B) are titanium. (a) Region away from bridgewire. (b) Region adjacent to (in contact with) bridgewire and pins

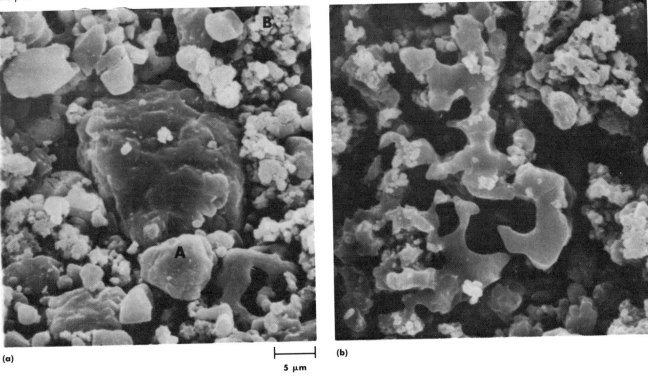

(a)

(b)

5 μm

Fig. 42 Optical micrograph of AISI 4340 steel threaded fracture surface

Arrow points to flaw.

Fig. 43 Oxidized surface of black area in flaw

Crack growth direction is from bottom to top.

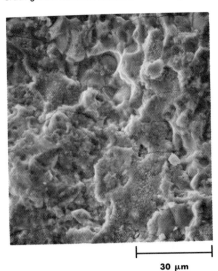

30 μm

Fig. 44 Intergranular fracture mode within gray area of flaw

Crack growth direction is from bottom to top.

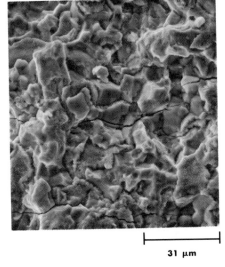

31 μm

45(a). A measurement of the average spacing of the ridges can be used to estimate fracture toughness using established correlations for this alloy. Spacing measurements taken from several micrographs resulted in an average value of 70 ± 8 μm (corrected for tilt). This spacing correlates to a fracture toughness of 150 ± 10 MPa $\sqrt{M}$ (137 ± 9 ksi $\sqrt{}$ in.), which is in the expected range for this strength level of 4340 steel.

The curved feature in the center of the overload region of the fracture (Fig. 42) resulted from axial delamination within the rod during fracture. The main crack front intersected the delamination and formed small shear lips. Delamination of this form would likely increase crack growth resistance by blunting the main crack and absorb-

Fig. 45 Ductile fracture in overload region

(a) Low-magnification view showing ridges, 30° tilt. (b) High-magnification view of ductile dimple fracture. Crack growth direction is from bottom to top.

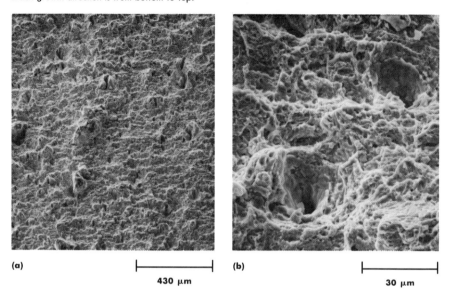

(a)   (b)

430 μm   30 μm

Fig. 46 Cross section of integrated circuit

Arrows points to the LPCVD tungsten layers.

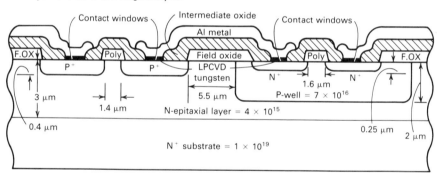

Fig 47 Scanning electron micrographs of an integrated circuit

(a) and (b) Proper aluminum alignment. (c) and (d) Aluminum misalignment. Note the crescent-shaped void on (d) shown by arrow indicating aluminum misalignment.

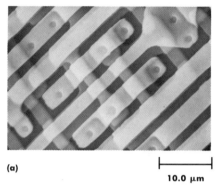

(a)   10.0 μm

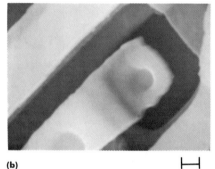

(b)   1.0 μm

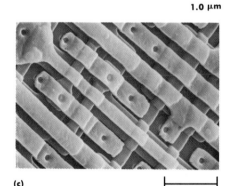

(c)   10.0 μm

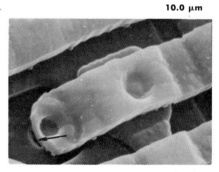

(d)   1.0 μm

ing energy. Based on this fractographic evidence, premature failure of the threaded rod was attributed to the presence of the quench crack flaw caused by an improper machining sequence and heat treatment practice.

Example 8: Use of SEM in Solving Integrated Circuit Problems. Two packaged 16K random access memory (RAM) dice were submitted to the scanning electron microscope laboratory to determine why one die failed electrical testing after an elevated-temperature stress test (that is, burn in). Figure 46 shows a schematic of the cross section. A tungsten layer on the contact windows is under evaluation in this series of devices as an aluminum-silicon diffusion barrier in addition to providing an etch barrier at the aluminum/silicon contact window interface. Sample SN5430, which passed the electrical test, was subjected to a standard hydrofluoric acid bath for 1 min to remove

native silicon oxide on exposed P^+ and N^+ contact windows before the low-pressure chemical vapor deposition (LPCVD) tungsten was selectively deposited in contact windows (Ref 33). To test the importance of the pretungsten clean, the hydrofluoric acid cleaning step was omitted from sample SN5417, which failed the electrical test. It is known that if 2 nm of native oxide exists on the silicon and is not adequately removed, the tungsten deposition is hampered (Ref 34).

Scanning electron microscopy was used to observe alignment of the aluminum deposition on the die. The good sample, SN5430, showed proper aluminum alignment and adequate contact window coverage (Fig. 47a and b). The bad sample, SN5417, showed aluminum misalignment. Apparently, when the blanket aluminum overcoating was plasma etched to define the

Fig 48 Scanning electron micrographs of bad integrated circuit sample

(a) Secondary electron image, showing the nonuniform tungsten deposit. (b) Backscattered electron image, showing the tungsten locations (bright areas). The arrow in (b) points to the crescent-shaped void caused by misalignment at the mask during aluminum etching.

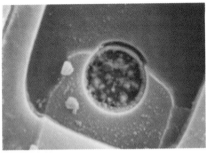
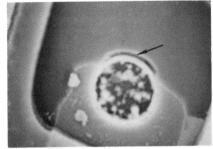

(a)   ⊢———⊣   (b)
1.0 μm

Fig. 49 Analysis of good integrated circuit sample

(a) Secondary (left) and backscattered (right) electron micrographs of the good sample, SN5430, showing the uniform tungsten deposit. (b) Energy-dispersive spectrum that confirms tungsten in the contact windows

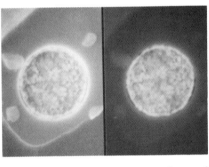
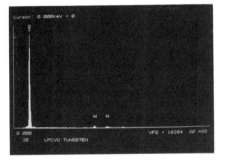

(a)   ⊢———⊣   (b)
1.0 μm

aluminum lines, a misaligned mask caused formation of a crescent-shaped void in the silicon adjacent to the contact window (Fig. 47c and d).

The aluminum was then removed using a wet etch process, allowing inspection of the tungsten on the contact windows. The window of primary interest is P^+ (boron-doped) silicon (Fig. 46). Photomicrographs in secondary and backscattered electron imaging of the bad sample, SN5417, show nonuniform partial coverage of tungsten on the contact window (Fig. 48). Backscattered electron imaging is especially useful in this case because the large difference in atomic number between tungsten ($Z = 74$) and silicon ($Z = 14$) results in good contrast. The crescent shape on the P^+ window was caused by misalignment of the mask during aluminum etching (Fig. 48). The photomicrographs of the good sample, SN5430, show a more complete and uniform coverage of tungsten on the P^+ contact window (Fig.

49a). Energy-dispersive spectral analysis confirmed the presence of tungsten in the contact windows (Fig. 49b).

Comparisons of the photomicrographs show the misalignment of the aluminum on the bad sample and incomplete tungsten coverage because of the omitted hydrofluoric acid cleaning step to remove the native oxide layer. This example illustrates use of the scanning electron microscope in solving process control problems in the development and production of microelectronic integrated circuits.

ACKNOWLEDGMENT

J.D. Verhoeven would like to acknowledge helpful discussions with A.J. Bevolo and A.R. Pelton; the assistance of H.H. Baker, F.C. Laabs, and E.D. Gibson in preparing micrographs, and the financial support of the Basic Energy Science Division of USDOE and Iowa State University.

REFERENCES

1. A.N. Broers, *Scan. Elec. Microsc.*, 1974, p 10-18
2. J.D. Verhoeven and E.D. Gibson, *J. Phys. E*, Vol 9, 1976, p 65-69
3. J.I. Goldstein, D.E. Newbury, P. Echlin, C. Fiori, and E. Lifshin, in *Scanning Electron Microscopy and X-Ray Microanalysis*, Plenum Press, 1981, p 123
4. A.N. Broers, in *Microprobe Analysis*, C.A. Anderson, Ed., John Wiley & Sons, 1973
5. C.W. Oatley, *The Scanning Electron Microscope*, Cambridge Press, 1972
6. O.C. Wells, *Scanning Electron Microscopy*, McGraw Hill, 1974
7. H. Kawamoto, S. Yamazaki, A. Ishikawa, and R. Buchanan, *Scan. Elec. Microsc.*, Vol 1, 1984, p 15-22
8. *JEOL News*, Vol 23E (No. 1), 1985, p 17-18; R. Buchman, *Ind. Res. Dev.*, Vol 24, Aug 1982, p 92-95
9. L. Reimer and M. Riepenhausen, *Scanning*, Vol 7, 1985, p 221-238
10. K.R. Peters, *Scan. Elec. Microsc.*, Vol 4, 1982, p 1359-1372
11. K.R. Peters, *Fortieth Annual Electron Microscopy Society of America Meeting*, G.W. Bailey, Ed., Claitors Publications Division, Baton Rouge, LA, 1982, p 368-369
12. V.N.E. Robinson, in *Electron Optical Systems for Microscopy, Microanalysis and Microlithography*, J. Hern, F. Lenz, E. Munro, and P. Sewell, Ed., Scanning Electron Microscopy Inc., AMF O'Hare, IL, 1984, p 187-195
13. A. Niemietz and L. Reimer, *Ultramicroscopy*, Vol 16, 1985, p 161-174
14. V.N.E. Robinson, *Scanning*, Vol 3, 1980, p 15-26
15. E.P. George and V.N.E. Robinson, *Scan. Elec. Microsc.*, Vol 1, 1977, p 63-70
16. S.H. Moll, F. Healey, B. Sullivan, and W. Johnson, *Scan. Elec. Microsc.*, Vol 1, 1978, p 303-310
17. D.C. Joy, D.E. Newbury, and D.L. Davidson, *J. Appl. Phys.*, Vol 53, 1982, p R81-R122
18. A.J. Bevolo, unpublished research, Ames Laboratory, Iowa State University, Ames, IA, 1984
19. L.J. Balk and J.B. Elsbrock, *Scan. Elec. Microsc.*, Vol 1, 1984, p 141-149
20. D.E. Newbury and H. Yakowitz, in *Practical Scanning Electron Microscopy*, S.I. Goldstein and H. Yakowitz, Ed., Plenum Press, 1975

21. E. Menzel and R. Buchanan, *Solid State Technol.*, Vol 28, Dec 1985, p 63-70

22. B. Gilhooley and A.R. Dinnis, in *Microscopy of Semiconducting Materials*, H.G. Cullis, S.M. Davidson, and G.R. Booker, Ed., Institute of Physics, London, 1983

23. H.J. Leamy, L.C. Kimerling, and S.D. Ferris, *Scan. Elec. Microsc.*, Vol 1, 1978, p 717-725

24. J.F. Bresse, *Scan. Elec. Microsc.*, Vol 4, 1982, p 1487-1500

25. J.D. Shick, *Scan. Elec. Microsc.*, Vol 1, 1985, p 55-66

26. G. Pfefferkorn, W. Bröcker, and M. Hastenrath, *Scan. Elec. Microsc.*, Vol 1, 1980, p 251-258

27. D.B. Holt and F.M. Saba, *Scan. Elec. Microsc.*, Vol 3, 1985, p 1023-1045

28. D.B. Holt and S. Datta, *Scan. Elec. Microsc.*, Vol 1, 1978, p 259-278

29. K. Löhnert and E. Kubalek, in *Microscopy of Semiconducting Materials*, Conference Series 67, A.G. Cullis, S.M. Davidson, and G.R. Booker, Ed., Institute of Physics, London, 1983, p 303-314

30. D.D. Pearson and J.D. Verhoeven, *Metall. Trans. A*, Vol 15, 1984, p 1037-1045

31. J.D. Verhoeven, D.P. Mourer, and E.D. Gibson, *Metall. Trans. A*, Vol 8, 1977, p 1239-1247

32. J.D. Verhoeven, A.J. Bevolo, D.T. Peterson, H.H. Baker, O.D. McMasters, and E.D. Gibson, *Metallography*, Vol 18, 1985, p 277-290

33. R.S. Blewer and V.A. Wells, *J. Electrochem. Soc.*, to be published

34. H.H. Busta and C.H. Tang, *J. Electrochem. Soc.*, to be published

Electron Probe X-Ray Microanalysis

Kurt F.J. Heinrich and Dale E. Newbury, National Bureau of Standards

General Uses

- Qualitative and quantitative elemental analysis of solids for elements with atomic number of 11 (sodium) or greater, detection limits of the order of 100 ppm, and at a lateral spatial resolution of the order of 1 μm
- Qualitative elemental analysis for light elements with atomic numbers from 5 (boron) to 10 (neon)
- Elemental compositional mapping of areas with dimensions as large as millimeters with spatial resolution to 1 μm

Examples of Applications

- Compositional analysis of individual phases at the microstructural level in multiphase samples, for example, analysis of individual inclusions in steels and other alloys
- Analysis of compositional gradients at boundaries
- Determination of compositional homogeneity or heterogeneity at the micrometer scale in single-phase materials
- Compositional mapping of heterogeneous specimens to produce maps of elemental location and concentration

Samples

- *Form*: A bulk solid sample metallographically polished to a mirror finish is ideal for optimum analysis. Other forms include rough surfaces, individual particles, and films on substrates
- *Size*: Typically 25 mm in diameter by 10 mm thick, but can be larger depending on the configuration of the instrument stage

Limitations

- Detects elements with atomic number ≥5 (boron); quantitative analysis is successful for atomic number ≥11 (sodium)

- Sensitivity is 100 ppm with x-ray measurement by wavelength-dispersive spectrometry; 1000 ppm (0.1 wt%) with x-ray measurement by energy-dispersive spectrometry. Poorer sensitivity for light elements in a heavy matrix
- Lateral and depth spatial resolution approximately 1 μm, limited by electron scattering in specimen and not the focused electron beam diameter
- Quantitative analysis limited to flat, polished specimens. Unusual geometries such as fracture surfaces, individual particles, and films on substrates can be analyzed, but with greater uncertainty

Estimated Analysis Time

- 100-s spectrum accumulation time per analysis point; 10 s for on-line computerized data reduction to yield quantitative analysis results

Capabilities of Related Techniques

- *Analytical electron microscopy*: Extends spatial resolution of electron probe analysis down to approximately 10 nm and provides high-resolution imaging and electron diffraction for crystallographic information
- *Secondary ion mass spectrometry, laser microprobe mass analysis*: Provide coverage of the entire periodic table at part per million sensitivity for most elements, but destructively and with larger uncertainties in quantitative analysis
- *Auger microprobe analysis*: Provides elemental analysis of the surface (1 to 5 nm deep) of the sample at the same lateral spatial resolution, and has particular sensitivity to the light elements
- *Raman microprobe analysis*: Provides molecular analysis at the micrometer spatial level

Introduction

Metallurgy has for many years combined chemical analysis on a macroscopic scale with the microscopic investigation of structures by means of metallography. Electron probe microanalysis (EPMA) now enables us to combine structural and compositional analysis in one operation.

The electron probe analyzer was first demonstrated in 1948 by R. Castaing, student of A. Guinier, at the University of Paris. Castaing converted a transmission electron microscope into an optical bench capable of producing a focused electron beam of less than 1 μm in diameter, which on impact on the specimen caused the elements in the specimen to emit characteristic x-ray lines. The x-ray spectrum could be observed by means of a curved crystal spectrometer, while the area of electron beam impact could be viewed in an optical microscope attached to the instrument. In his thesis, Castaing demonstrated the usefulness of the instrument as a tool for diffusion and other metallurgical studies, and he developed a scheme for reducing the observed x-ray intensities to quantitative elemental concentrations (Ref 1).

Duncumb, studying with Cosslett at Cambridge, applied to the electron probe microanalyzer the scanning capabilities of the scanning electron microscope. Thus, an instrument was obtained that permits point-by-point quantitation, analysis along a line, and the representation both of topography and composition over an area of microscopic dimensions (Ref 2).

The development of the solid-state x-ray detector (Ref 3) was a significant advance in microanalysis (Ref 4). It not only serves as an indispensable attachment to the electron probe microanalyzer for rapid qualitative and quantitative analysis, but it converts any scanning electron microscope into an electron probe microanalyzer. The effective application of this tool was made possible by the availability of on-line minicomputers that could be used in deriving quantitative information from the low-resolution x-ray spectra obtainable with such detectors. A schematic of a modern electron probe microanalyzer is shown in Fig. 1.

The electron optics of the electron probe microanalyzer correspond exactly to those of the scanning electron microscope. An electron beam is generated from a heated metal filament and is accelerated through an aperture in the grid cap down the instrument column. The electron beam is focused by two or three magnetic lenses to a small (10-nm- to 1-μm-diam) spot on the sample surface. Scan coils in the final lens can drive the beam across the sample surface in a controlled raster pattern. Secondary signals are emitted from the sample under primary electron bombardment, including backscattered and secondary electrons, characteristic and continuous x-rays, and photons of longer wavelength. A variety of signal detectors surrounds the specimen and makes possible the simultaneous recording of images that convey structural and compositional information. All of the imaging modes of the scanning electron microscope are available in the electron probe microanalyzer, augmented by the analytical capabilities of x-ray microanalysis. The electron optics of the electron probe microanalyzer are often improved beyond that of the scanning electron microscope to provide additional beam stability by incorporating feedback circuitry to adjust the beam current in response to instabilities and drift. Long-term stability with drift less than 0.1% per hour is routinely available in modern instruments. For additional detail on electron optics and scanning electron imaging, see the articles "Scanning Electron Microscopy" and "Analytical Transmission Electron Microscopy" in this Volume.

Basic Microanalytical Concepts

Microanalysis provides information concerning specimen composition on a microscopic scale; hence, microanalytical processes relate to both chemical analysis and microscopy. An analytical procedure is characterized by its specificity, accuracy, and sensitivity. A specific reaction is one that refers uniquely to the element or compound being analyzed.

The electron probe produces highly element-specific signals that can be used for quantitative measurements of high accuracy. The sensitivity of the method reaches into the parts per million region for most elements; in view of the requirements in modern technology, the sensitivity of EPMA is moderate only, being in most cases much poorer than that of secondary ion mass spectrometry (see the article "Secondary Ion Mass Spectroscopy" in this Volume).

In the comparison of the above characteristics with those of chemical microanalytical methods, we would not do justice to electron probe analysis unless we add to the previously mentioned microanalytical criteria one which is related to the microscopy aspect of electron beam analysis: the possibility of local analysis of a small region on the specimen surface. The physical separation of microscopic specimen fragments from their surroundings, which would be impracticable in most instances, is unnecessary since in EPMA the element-specific x-rays are emitted from a small region surrounding the point of impact of the electron beam, and are therefore independent of the composition of the rest of the specimen.

Fig. 1 Schematic diagram of electron probe microanalyzer and associated circuitry

l, Meters; 2, operating potential; 3, gun current; 4, monitor current; 5, vacuum; 6, sample current

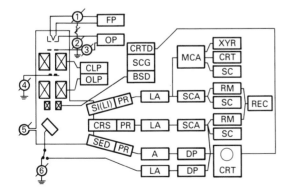

A	amplifier
BSD	beam scan driver
CLP	condenser lens supply
CRS	crystal spectrometer
CRT	cathode-ray tube
CRTD	cathode-ray tube driver
DP	data processor
FP	filament power supply
LA	linear amplifier
MCA	multichannel pulse height analyzer
OLP	objective lens power supply

OP	operating potential
PR	preamplifier
REC	recorder
RM	ratemeter
SC	scaler
SCA	single-channel pulse height analyzer
SCG	scan generator
SED	secondary electron detector
SI(LI)	lithium-doped silicon detector
XYR	x-y recorder

X-ray spectra are characteristic for the emitting elements and simple to interpret. Therefore, at least for major components, EPMA based on such spectra is remarkably specific. Line interferences can arise in energy-dispersive analysis, due to the low resolution of the solid-state detector. However, ingenious techniques for spectral deconvolution have been designed (Ref 5); hence, for all practical purposes, specificity is not a problem.

Physical Bases of the Method (Ref 6)

Electron probe microanalysis is based on the measurement of characteristic x-rays emitted from a microscopic part of a solid specimen bombarded by a beam of accelerated electrons. The electrons are focused into a beam of less than 1 μm in diameter, so that their action can be limited to the chosen microvolume at the surface of the specimen. The impinging electrons are decelerated and scattered; they lose energy and suffer directional changes through collision with the specimen atoms, which limits the maximum depth of penetration to about 1 μm. A graphic representation of these effects can be obtained by use of the Monte Carlo electron trajectory simulation. An example of the determination of the interaction volume by this method is shown in Fig. 2. The depth of

penetration, and hence the resolution in depth of the method, depend on the acceleration imparted to the electron beam; to keep the reactive volume within one or a few micrometers, the energy of the electron beam should not exceed 20 keV.

Most of the energy imparted to the specimen is in the form of heat. However, a small but important fraction of the interactions ionizes the inner shells of the target atoms. The ionized atoms emit x-rays and Auger electrons. The characteristic x-ray lines so formed, which are specific to the atomic number of the emitting atoms, are used in EPMA. Their wavelengths (or photon energies) identify the emitting element (qualitative analysis), and after some corrective calculations, the intensities of the emitted lines permit determination of the concentration of the emitters (quantitative analysis). The x-ray spectrum also contains a continuum of x-ray photons (called bremsstrahlung), due to the electron deceleration in the Coulombic field of the atomic nucleus. The x-ray continuum forms a background to the characteristic peaks and sets a limit on sensitivity.

The ionization leading to the emission of a characteristic x-ray photon requires that the exciting electron possess or exceed a minimum energy that is also characteristic of the element and line involved. The energy required sets a minimum to the usable beam

energy, which typically is between 10 and 20 keV.

The x-rays generated within the specimen suffer attenuation on their way to the specimen surface. When low-energy x-rays are used in EPMA for elements of low atomic number ($Z < 15$), the corresponding signal loss, and the concomitant loss of accuracy, can only be limited by maintaining the beam energy towards the lower end of the range indicated above.

X-ray spectra can be obtained for all elements except hydrogen. The emission from the first ten elements consists of bands in the low-energy region, where the losses of emission by absorption in the specimen are large. Chemical effects, related to binding energies between atoms, can modify the intensity, position, and shape of these lines, thus further complicating their use for quantitative procedures. Therefore, these elements, including such important ones as oxygen, nitrogen, and carbon, are often determined by difference or stoichiometry, and the quantitative analysis for elements of low atomic number is a very specialized field (Ref 8).

Measuring X-Ray Spectra

In modern x-ray microanalysis, the analyst has two possible choices for the x-ray spectrometer: the energy-dispersive spectrometer or the wavelength-dispersive spectrometer. In this section the features of these spectrometers will be compared and contrasted. This discussion will demonstrate that the two different types of spectrometers, rather than being mutually competitive, are in fact highly complementary. The ideal x-ray microanalytical instrument is equipped with both energy-dispersive and wavelength-dispersive systems. However, if resources permit the acquisition of only one spectrometer for the electron beam column, the choice must be made carefully and be based upon the nature of the problems to be solved.

The x-ray photons of interest in x-ray microanalysis will generally be in the energy range from 0.185 keV (Boron K) to about 15 keV. Within this energy range will be found at least one useful analytical x-ray line from the K-, L-, or M-family for all elements in the periodic table with atomic number $Z > 4$. In order to detect a photon, the electromagnetic energy must be converted into an electrical signal.

In both the energy-dispersive spectrometry (EDS) and wavelength-dispersive spectrometry (WDS) detection processes, the photoelectric effect is employed for detection. The x-ray photon is absorbed by an atom with the subsequent ejection of one of

Fig. 2 Monte Carlo electron trajectory calculation of electron interaction volume in an iron target with a beam energy of 20 keV

Source: Ref 7

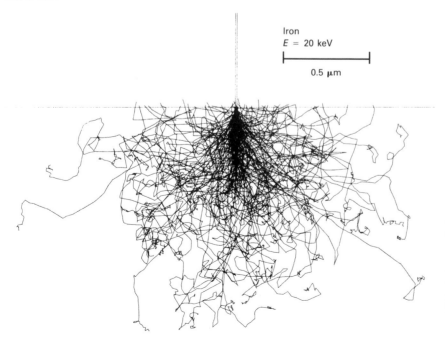

Iron
$E = 20$ keV

0.5 μm

Fig. 3 Schematic diagram of the detector of an energy-dispersive x-ray spectrometer

Source: Ref 9

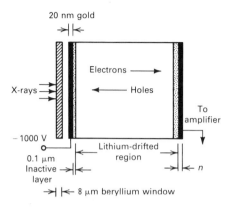

the bound electrons of that atom. This "photoelectron" has a kinetic energy equal to the photon energy minus the binding energy of the electron to the atom, and the atom is left in an excited state equal to the binding energy of the emitted electron. The photoelectron scatters inelastically in the detector, depositing energy and creating charge carriers as a result. These charge carriers are used in different ways in the EDS and WDS detectors. Detailed discussions on the detection process can be found in Ref 6 and 7.

Energy-Dispersive Spectrometry

Figure 3 is a schematic diagram of the detector of an energy-dispersive x-ray spectrometer. The detector consists of a crystal of silicon that is biased by means of electrodes placed on the front and rear surfaces. The photoelectron scattering in the silicon creates free electron-hole pairs in the band structure of the semiconductor. The electrons and holes are separated by the bias applied across the detector, and the charge is collected on the surface electrodes. The detector is maintained at liquid nitrogen temperatures, and is shielded from the vacuum environment of the electron beam system by means of a window.

This window is usually made of 8-μm (nominal) thick beryllium, which will support 1 atm during instrument venting. Unfortunately, this beryllium window is sufficiently thick to absorb virtually all x-rays below 0.750 keV, which precludes any analysis of the light elements with $Z < 10$. As an alternative, the window can be made of an aluminized polymer, which will maintain vacuum integrity around the detector while passing x-rays of energy as low as that of carbon. Such an "ultrathin window" must

be shielded by a gate-valve or a rotating window arrangement must be employed to vent the column to atmosphere.

The basic components of a complete energy-dispersive spectrometer are shown schematically in Fig. 4. The energy-dispersive spectrometer serves to convert an x-ray photon into an electrical pulse with specific characteristics of amplitude and width. The lithium-doped silicon crystal detector is followed by a field effect transistor (FET) preamplifier which is maintained at cryogenic temperatures, a main amplifier, various other signal processing functions, and a multichannel analyzer (MCA). The function of the MCA is to measure the pulse from the amplifier and increment the appropriate "channel" (memory location) in the display, where the channel location (number) is proportional to the energy of the photon. The spectrum that results is thus a histogram of x-ray counts versus channel number, which can be calibrated in energy units (keV) for direct readout by the analyst. Since the detector is sensitive to all x-ray energies that pass through the protective window, the entire spectrum of interest can be measured with no changes in detector parameters.

The measurement of the x-ray spectrum by an EDS system introduces several major artifacts that must be understood for proper interpretation of the spectrum. The artifacts described below include detector resolution, x-ray pulse processing, dead time, sum and escape peaks, and false silicon peaks. Additional information can be found in Ref 9.

Detector Resolution (Peak Broadening).
The measurement of an x-ray photon involves conversion to discrete charge carriers, the number of which is subject to statistical fluctuations. As a result of these fluctuations, the assignment of a channel in the MCA to a given pulse is distributed about a

mean value. A measure of this distribution is the full width in energy units of the peak at half the maximum intensity (FWHM). When an EDS system is operated at the best possible resolution, the peaks have a FWHM value that is about 2.5% of the peak energy, that is, 145 eV FWHM for a Mn Kα peak at 5890 eV. This can be compared to the natural width of the Mn Kα x-ray emission, which is about 2 eV. The substantial degradation of the peak width that is produced in the energy-dispersive spectrometer can lead to significant problems with peak overlap (interference) in many practical analytical applications.

Dead Time.
The EDS system must process x-ray pulses sequentially, although it may appear to an observer watching the output that the entire spectrum is accumulated simultaneously. The time necessary to process a pulse, the dead time, is of the order of 100 μs at the best possible system energy resolution. While the energy-dispersive spectrometer is processing a pulse from a photon, special pulse-inspection circuitry serves to detect the possible entry of a second photon into the detector. A second pulse cannot be accurately measured during the dead time, and so the inspection circuitry serves to eliminate these nearly coincident pulses from the spectrum. The pulse-inspection circuitry has a limit to its time resolution so that pulses that enter within the time resolution are in fact detected as a single pulse that is the sum of the two individual pulses.

The practical effect of dead time in the spectral measurement process is to set a limit to the rate at which pulses can be counted. A dead time of 100 μs results in a count rate limitation of 5000 counts per second (cps) for 50% system dead time. Higher input count rates would actually result in a lower output (recorded) count rate. This counting limita-

Fig. 4 Schematic diagram of a complete energy-dispersive x-ray spectrometer

Various pulse processing functions and the multichannel analyzer are shown. Source: Ref 9

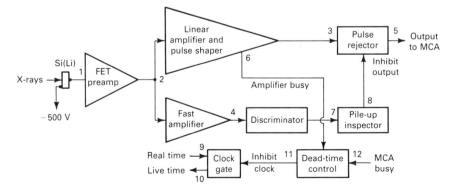

Fig. 5 Examples of sum and escape peaks in energy-dispersive spectra

(a) Escape peaks from Mn Kα and Kβ. (b) Sum peaks in a spectrum of magnesium. Source: Ref 9

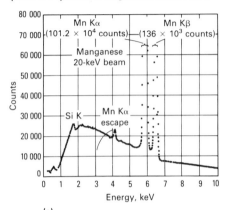

(a)

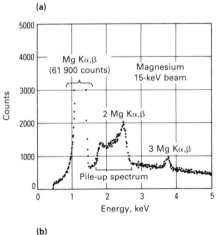

(b)

tion refers to the integrated count rate over the whole x-ray spectrum, not just a single peak of interest, because there is no way to discriminate among incoming photons in advance of the photon-capture process.

Shorter values of the system dead time can be selected, but only at the expense of degradation of the energy resolution. For example, by choosing faster amplifier time constants, a limiting input count rate of 20 000 cps might be possible at 50% dead time, but the energy resolution would degrade to 190 eV. In order to make quantitative measurements of x-ray spectra, it is important to make corrections for dead time, so that the x-ray counts of all lines are recorded on the basis of constant electron dose into the sample. Thus, a low-intensity peak from a minor constituent in a sample may be effectively underreported if the system dead time arises from high-intensity peaks of major constituents. In EDS systems, the dead time is quantitatively and

automatically corrected by pulse-inspection circuitry that adds on extra clock time to compensate for the dead-time losses associated with processing x-ray pulses.

Sum Peaks and Escape Peaks. Two significant spectral artifacts are commonly encountered that must be recognized to avoid misidentification of possible minor constituents in the sample.

Sum peaks arise as a result of coincident photon detection. The pulse-inspection circuitry can exclude coincident events separated by a few microseconds in time. However, there is inevitably a limitation to the time resolution of the inspection circuit, particularly for low-energy photons below 3 keV, which produce pulses just above the fundamental noise of the system, and photons coincident in the detector are detected as a single pulse with the sum of the energies. Sum peaks are observed only from major peaks in the spectrum, particularly in the low-energy region, and the size of the sum peak depends on the input count rate. If a spectrum contains high count-rate peaks for constituents A and B, then sum peaks can occur for A + A, B + B, and A + B.

Escape peaks arise because of an imperfection in the photon-capture process in the detector. The silicon atom that initially captures the x-ray photon and ejects the photoelectron is left in an excited state. If the electron was ejected from the K-shell, the atom can de-excite through the subsequent ejection of either an Auger electron or a K x-ray (Kα = 1.74 keV; the Kβ x-ray has a low probability of formation and can be neglected in this context). The Auger electron will scatter inelastically and deposit all of its energy in the detector. The K x-ray, however, has a significant probability of escaping the detector, which robs the photon pulse being measured by the energy of the Si Kα x-ray photon. Hence, a parasitic peak, the so-called "escape peak," is formed which is located 1.74 keV below the parent peak. The escape peak intensity decreases with increasing energy of the parent peak and is about 1% for a phosphorus K peak. Figure 5 illustrates examples of sum peaks and escape peaks.

False Silicon Peak (Internal Fluorescence Peak). A "dead" or partially active silicon layer approximately 100 nm thick exists on the front of the detector. X-ray photons captured in this layer do not produce a normal pulse, but can excite Si Kα photons that may enter the detector. These Si Kα photons are indistinguishable from x-rays generated in the sample. A false silicon contribution is thus made to the spectrum, as shown in Fig. 5(a) for a manganese spectrum. In a quantitative analysis of an iron alloy, this false silicon peak appears as an

Fig. 6 Schematic diagram of the components of a wavelength-dispersive x-ray spectrometer

Courtesy of Cameca Instruments

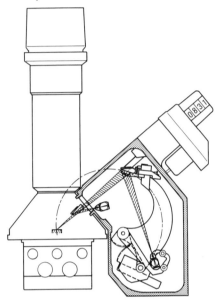

apparent concentration of silicon of about 0.1 wt%.

Wavelength-Dispersive Spectrometry

In the wavelength-dispersive spectrometer, separation of x-rays of various energies is achieved by making use of the wave nature of the photon through the phenomenon of diffraction. For a crystal of interplanar spacing d, Bragg's law gives the relationship between the x-ray wavelength λ and the critical angle θ_B at which constructive interference occurs:

$$n\lambda = 2d \sin \theta_B \qquad \text{(Eq 1)}$$

where n is an integer. X-ray diffraction produces a very sharply defined peak. The typical resolution of a WDS peak in energy terms is 10 eV or less for Mn Kα.

A wavelength-dispersive spectrometer consists of a high-precision mechanical system for establishing the critical Bragg angle between the specimen and the diffracting crystal and between the diffracting crystal and the x-ray detector. A schematic of the spectrometer is shown in Fig. 6. In order to measure x-rays of different energies (wavelengths), the positions of the diffracting crystal and detector must be mechanically changed relative to the fixed specimen to alter the angles. To cover the range of x-ray wavelengths to be measured, for example,

6.8 nm at B Kα (183 eV) to 0.092 nm at U Lα (13.4 keV), several different diffraction crystals must be utilized, and spectrometers often include up to four interchangeable crystals mounted on a turret.

Actual detection of the x-ray in a wavelength-dispersive spectrometer is accomplished in a flow-proportional detector. The x-ray is absorbed by an argon atom in the detector, and the ejected photoelectron ionizes other atoms, producing a cascade of ejected electrons that are accelerated by a bias applied to a wire in the center of the detector. This bias is chosen so that the pulse of charge collected on the wire is proportional to the energy of the x-ray photon, which allows for the possibility of electronic discrimination of x-ray energies in addition to the physical discrimination provided by the diffraction process.

In addition to the excellent spectral resolution of the wavelength-dispersive spectrometer, the dead time of the associated pulse-processing system can be 1 μs or less, which allows limiting count rates of the order of 10^5 cps. Because only x-rays with a narrow energy range—for example, 10 eV—can reach the detector in the wavelength-dispersive spectrometer because of the selectivity of the diffraction process, the full limiting count rate is available from the peak of interest, while other x-rays produced from the specimen usually have no effect on the count rate.

A negative consequence of the sharpness of the diffraction phenomenon coupled with the focusing nature of the wavelength-dispersive spectrometer is the sensitivity of the wavelength-dispersive spectrometer to the vertical position of the specimen relative to the spectrometer and the lateral position of the beam relative to the optic axis of the spectrometer. Because of the need to position the specimen accurately and precisely, an optical microscope with shallow depth of focus is usually incorporated in an electron beam instrument. This provision has the added advantage that the specimen can be viewed in the optical microscope simultaneously with scanning electron microscopy (SEM) imaging, which often simplifies interpretation of morphology. The sensitivity of the spectrometer efficiency to the lateral position of the x-ray source produced by a scanning beam has a major consequence for the preparation of x-ray area scans or maps (described below). Scan excursions in excess of 50 μm produce noticeable drops in x-ray intensity, which can make x-ray maps difficult to interpret.

Artifacts. The principal artifacts in the wavelength-dispersive spectrum are related to the nature of the diffraction process. The integer value *n* in Bragg's law is responsible

for the appearance of different orders of diffraction for a single x-ray wavelength. Hence, a single parent peak can give rise to a series of peaks from diffraction orders that appear at other angular settings of the spectrometer. This multiple occurrence of a single photon energy throughout the wavelength range complicates the qualitative analysis procedure and requires careful bookkeeping to avoid misidentifying low-intensity peaks as minor or trace elements when they are in fact higher order lines related to another parent peak. The multiplicity of diffraction orders can also lead to spectral interference. However, because x-rays of two different energies may be diffracted at the same angular setting, the x-rays can be separated by the different magnitudes of the pulses that they produce in the flow-proportional counter by means of a pulse-height inspection circuit.

The high resolution of the wavelength-dispersive spectrum reveals a great deal more spectral detail than is seen in the energy-dispersive spectrum. In addition to detecting additional members of the family of lines for each element, other spectral effects such as satellite lines can be recognized. For low-energy x-rays (<2 keV), the chemical state of the sample may affect the energy and therefore the wavelength of the x-ray, because the electron states involved in producing the x-ray can be shifted according to the nature of the chemical bonding.

These chemical shifts can be used to study the nature of chemical bonding, but in practical analysis the effect must be recognized for the possibility of shifting the wavelength out of the position at which the spectrometer has been peaked on a standard in which the element of interest is in a different chemical state. Such a shift may lead to erroneous intensity recordings. For very low energy x-rays (<1 keV), the peak shape and the position may change significantly. Special procedures must be instituted to obtain quantitative results in such a case.

Correction for the dead time in a WDS intensity measurement is carried out mathematically after the intensity is determined for a precisely defined counting time. The dead time for a wavelength-dispersive spectrometer is typically set electronically in the pulse-shaping circuitry to a specific value, for example, 1 μs. Formulas for mathematical correction are discussed in standard textbooks (Ref 6, 7).

Comparison of EDS and WDS Systems

Careful comparison of the characteristics of energy-dispersive and wavelength-dispersive spectrometers reveals that these

Fig. 7 Energy-dispersive (a) and wavelength-dispersive (b) x-ray spectra of a multicomponent glass

Courtesy of C. Fiori. Source: Ref 6

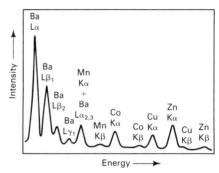

(a)

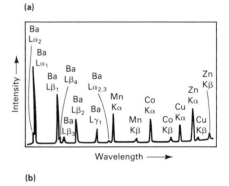

(b)

two systems complement each other in almost every aspect. Figure 7 provides a comparison of EDS and WDS spectra from a complex multicomponent glass. The energy-dispersive spectrometer provides observation of the entire x-ray spectrum of interest in a near simultaneous fashion, which allows for rapid qualitative analysis of major and minor constituents, while the wavelength-dispersive spectrometer must be mechanically scanned through its wavelength range, with several crystal changes to cover the same energy range as the energy-dispersive spectrometer—a time-consuming operation. The energy-dispersive spectrometer thus offers particular advantages over the wavelength-dispersive spectrometer for rapid qualitative analysis, which is especially useful for surveying unknown specimens.

Spectral Resolution. Comparing the relative spectral quality of the EDS and WDS spectra in Fig. 7, it can be seen that the superior resolution of the wavelength-dispersive spectrometer easily separates peaks that are poorly resolved in the energy-dispersive spectrometer, such as the peaks for Zn Kα and Cu Kβ, or completely unresolved, such as those for Mn Kα and Ba L$\alpha_{2,3}$. After an initial qualitative survey of a sample with the energy-dispersive spectrometer, it is often necessary to employ WDS to determine if any peaks of minor or trace constituents of interest are hidden in the vicinity of the major constituent peaks.

A particularly interesting interference problem that is encountered in materials science is the collection of x-ray lines in the vicinity of 2.30 keV. The elemental x-ray lines in this region include S Kα (2.307 keV), Mo Lα (2.293 keV), and Pb Mα (2.346 keV). Although alternative analytical x-ray lines can be found for molybdenum (Mo Kα at 17.48 keV) and lead (Pb Lα at 10.55 keV), the only suitable analytical line for sulfur is the K-line. Thus, the detection and quantitative analysis of minor amounts of sulfur in the presence of high concentrations of lead or molybdenum is extremely difficult with EDS, but straightforward with WDS.

Light-Element Analysis. In the area of light-element analysis ($Z < 10$), both the energy-dispersive spectrometer and the wavelength-dispersive spectrometer can detect x-rays from elements as low in atomic number as boron ($Z = 5$). The superior resolution of the wavelength-dispersive spectrometer often makes it the spectrometer of choice in this region of the periodic table, because the heavier elements in a specimen ($Z > 20$) produce L- or M-family x-rays, which will often be found to interfere with the K-lines of the light elements.

Detection Limits. The long dead time of the energy-dispersive spectrometer combined with its poor peak-to-background ratio results in poor detections limits, typically about 0.1 wt%, while the high peak-to-background ratio and the high counting rates on the peak of interest available in the wavelength-dispersive spectrometer can give detection limits of 0.01 wt% (100 ppm) or lower. For mapping, the energy-dispersive spectrometer does not display defocusing effects, but its poor peak-to-background ratio can lead to poor sensitivity in imaging and artifacts arising from atomic number effects on continuum x-ray production can be encountered. The wavelength-dispersive spectrometer can be used to give much better images in terms of statistics because of the higher peak-to-background ratio, but the defocusing effects limit its application to higher magnifications unless special corrections for defocusing are applied.

Instrument Selection. These points suggest that the ideal analytical electron beam instrument should be equipped with both energy-dispersive and wavelength-dispersive spectrometers. Such an arrangement will provide optimum capabilities for addressing a wide variety of practical problems. If the analyst must make a choice between EDS and WDS systems for an electron probe, that decision should be based upon the specific problems to be solved. If the instrument is to be used for general-purpose work in which the predominant need is qualitative analysis of a wide variety of unknowns with quantitative analysis of major and minor constituents, then the energy-dispersive spectrometer is probably the proper choice. On the other hand, if the predominant problems involve x-ray mapping, the detection of trace or minor constituents, or the separation of serious peak overlaps, then the choice should undoubtedly be the wavelength-dispersive spectrometer.

Qualitative Analysis

The first step in a successful and accurate quantitative analysis is identification of the constituents of the sample. Qualitative analysis is often assumed to be a trivial exercise. Although this may be true for major constituents, the identification of minor and trace constituents is likely to lead to serious errors unless a careful procedure is followed.

The basis for a careful procedure for qualitative analysis has two main aspects: first, an understanding of the nature of characteristic x-ray formation and the spectral artifacts that are encountered in detecting x-rays in the energy-dispersive and wavelength-dispersive spectrometers and, second, a careful system of bookkeeping so that all possible x-ray lines and artifacts associated with each element are located and noted before the next element is attempted (Ref 7, 9).

With regard to the first point, the concept of families of x-ray lines is paramount. Thus, with increasing atomic number the electronic structure of the atom becomes more complicated, and when a vacancy is created in a particular shell, it can be filled by a transition from two or more shells or subshells, which leads to the formation of characteristic x-rays of different energies. These various transitions occur with different probability, so that the different x-ray energies associated with a given shell, for example, the K- or L-family, have different relative intensities.

The multiplicity of lines in a family can be large. For example, the L-family of a heavy element such as gold consists of approximately 35 different lines. Fortunately, not all of these will be seen due to low relative intensities for many and the limitations imposed by the resolution of the spectrometer. The information available on relative intensities is a considerable aid in qualitative analysis. For a major constituent, the identification of an entire family of lines greatly increases the confidence with which the assignment of the presence of that element can be made. By the same token, unless all members of the family of x-ray lines are identified, including those with low relative intensity, then it is very likely that a low relative intensity member will be misidentified as a peak of a minor constituent later in the procedure.

A second related point is that for a given electron beam energy, all x-rays whose critical excitation energy is exceeded may be found in the spectrum. Thus, if a K-family is identified for an element, the analyst should also locate the possible L- and M-family at lower energy in the spectrum. Certain spectral artifacts result in parasitic peaks, such as escape peaks or sum peaks, generally from the high-intensity peaks in the spectrum. These artifact peaks also must be identified when a major constituent is recognized in the spectrum, to prevent their subsequent misidentification later in the procedure. The qualitative analysis procedure thus consists of a methodical recognition and labeling process. Because of the differences in energy-dispersive and wavelength-dispersive spectra, different qualitative analysis procedures are followed for each.

Qualitative Energy-Dispersive Spectrometry

An x-ray energy database is the first requirement for qualitative analysis. Figure 8 shows a plot of the x-ray lines and the escape peak energy associated with the principal line in each family as observed in energy-dispersive x-ray spectra. All modern computer-based multichannel analyzers have such a database incorporated into the software for convenient display on the spectrum under study.

The procedure for systematically identifying the peaks in an energy-dispersive spectrum is based on the characteristics of the x-ray families as seen in Fig. 8. As the x-ray energy increases, the separation in energy of the members of a family increases, making it more likely that the peaks will be resolved, thus providing a multiplicity of x-ray lines to increase the confidence in an identification. A suitable procedure consists of the steps described below.

First, the spectrum should be viewed at a scale expansion such that the highest intensity peak in the spectrum is on scale. Second, the high-energy region of the spectrum (>5 keV) is examined for a peak, its energy determined, and the closest match for a Kα or Lα x-ray found. Because of the separation of family members, the corresponding Kβ or Lβ and Lγ lines must also be present. All members of the family must be located, adjusting the intensity of the scale appropriately. The possible lower energy family associated with the element (L- or M-family) should be identified. Third, possible escape peaks and sum peaks associated with the major intensity peaks should be located and marked. Fourth, working to lower energies, the next peak is located and the process is repeated until all high-intensity peaks in the spectrum are identified.

Once the major constituents are identified, remaining minor intensity peaks can be examined, again starting with the high-energy end of the spectrum. It should be noted that the confidence with which minor and trace constituents can be identified is usually poorer than that for major constituents, because the number of lines that can be identified is generally smaller because of reduced intensity, and often there may only be one line on which to base an identification.

The final step the analyst should perform is to make a list of the possible elements that may be hidden under the major peaks. Figure 8 is a valuable aid in this task because the lines of all elements that can appear at a particular energy can be quickly noted by reading along a vertical line. If it is important to check for these elements, then either a wavelength-dispersive spectrometer should be used, or the spectrum should be examined for other possible lines for identification. This may necessitate operation at a higher beam energy, for example, 30 or 40 keV if the instrument has this acceleration capability, to excite a more energetic x-ray family from the element of interest. Such a procedure will also require adjusting the gain of the energy-dispersive spectrometer so as to examine a wider energy range, for example, 1 to 20 keV or 1 to 40 keV. The analyst should also be aware that x-ray peaks above 15 keV may be at very low intensity because the overvoltage, the ratio of the incident-beam energy to the critical x-ray excitation energy, will be low for such lines, and the efficiency of the detector will decrease due to penetration of x-rays through the detector.

Qualitative Wavelength-Dispersive Spectrometry

Qualitative analysis for major constituents is relatively straightforward using WDS. The identification of minor and trace constituents, however, is considerably complicated by the multiplicity of lines that can be observed from heavy elements that form major constituents in the sample, generally exceeding that observed in EDS. A major consideration is the database to be used for analysis. The database supplied with most computer-based EDS systems is not adequate for WDS analysis. Reference 10 is a comprehensive source of x-ray energies suitable for WDS analysis.

Fig. 8 Plot of all the x-ray lines in the energy range from 1 to 10 keV observed in practical EDS

The escape peak associated with the highest intensity line in each family is also plotted. The approximate peak width (FWHM) produced at each keV unit of energy across the spectrum is plotted at the top. Source: Ref 9

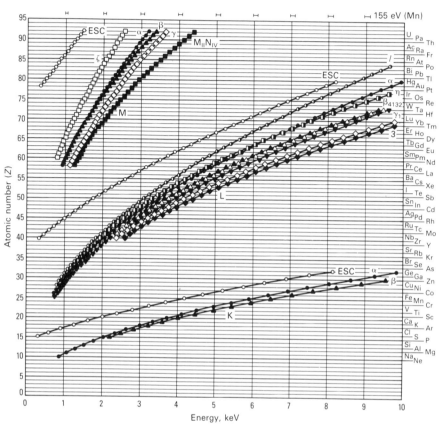

In addition to the problem of identifying a large family of x-ray lines, WDS is complicated by the nature of the diffraction measurement process. The presence of the integer multiplier in Eq 1 results in several orders appearing in a spectrum from a single parent peak; the higher order lines may appear on a crystal other than that of the parent peak. Another complication is the possible appearance of satellite lines that arise as a result of bonding effects.

WDS Qualitative Analysis. A practical procedure for WDS qualitative analysis can be based upon using information initially obtained from an EDS spectrum to identify the major constituents in the sample (Ref 7). From this information, the family of lines (K and L or L and M) of the major constituents should be identified in the set of wavelength scans made for all of the different diffraction crystals available in the spectrometer(s). Next, higher order (n = 2, 3, 4, and so on) reflections of each of these principal lines should be located in the scans.

For low-energy lines of principal constituents, satellite lines should be located.

After all lines associated with major constituents are located, then remaining peaks can be assigned to possible minor constituents. The principal source of ambiguity in qualitative analysis of minor and trace constituents is the possibility that a low-intensity peak is actually a high-order reflection of a peak that is produced by a major constituent. Thus, bookkeeping during the process of identifying the major constituents is critical to accurate peak assignments to minor and trace constituents. Starting with the shortest wavelengths (highest x-ray energies), candidate peaks should be checked against an x-ray data compilation to determine possible elements.

Following the same procedure described above for major constituents, when a possible assignment of a minor constituent is made to a peak, this assignment should be confirmed by locating the other members of its family of lines. Because of the superior resolution of the wavelength-dispersive spectrometer, it should be possible to obtain more than one x-ray line to identify minor constituents. For trace constituents near the limit of detectability (about 100 ppm), it will probably be possible to locate only one peak per element, particularly for K-lines, where the intensity of the $K\beta$ peak is reduced by a factor of ten or more below that of the $K\alpha$ peak. With only one peak to identify a trace constituent, the confidence with which an identification can be made is necessarily poorer than the confidence with which a major or minor constituent can be identified.

With wavelength-dispersive spectrometers, even under computer control, it is not practical to carry out a complete qualitative analysis at each location on the sample. However, the energy-dispersive spectrometer inevitably accumulates the entire spectrum each time a measurement is made, so that the possibility exists of performing a complete qualitative analysis at all analysis locations, at least for major and minor constituents. This capability is especially valuable when unexpected changes in composition may occur.

A useful procedure when examining an unknown for the first time is to accumulate an EDS spectrum while scanning a large area on the sample. Although such a spectrum is not useful for quantitative analysis, it can serve to provide a useful starting point for determining the elements that may be encountered in the sample. The analyst should recognize that minor constituents in a minor phase may not be detected in such an overscan spectrum except at very long spectrum accumulation times.

Quantitative Analysis

Early experiments in microanalysis by Castaing (Ref 1) and others (Ref 11) indicated that the observed x-ray intensities from the elements in the specimen were roughly proportional to the weight fractions (usually referred to as "concentrations") of the emitting elements. It was also observed that the ratios of intensities from different specimens can be measured repeatably with good accuracy. These two observations set a solid basis for the use of EPMA as a quantitative tool. Further experience showed, however, that the observed ratios of intensities from the specimen and a standard of known composition do not reflect the concentration ratios with sufficient accuracy, without the use of corrective factors. Many years of intensive work were spent relating these factors to the physical processes underlying electron-excited x-ray emission.

The deceleration of the electron in the target and the probability of x-ray generation in the process is a function of the overall composition of the target; it depends mainly on the atomic number of the target components. Castaing proposed that an "atomic number correction" must be applied to take into account its effects on the x-ray emission (Ref 12). The scattering of electrons out of the target (backscattering) also exerts a significant effect, because it removes energy from the target that otherwise would contribute to the production of x-ray photons. The fraction of primary electrons that are backscattered also depends strongly on the average atomic number of the specimen; therefore, both backscatter and deceleration can be treated together in an atomic number correction.

The absorption of x-ray emission within the specimen is similarly compensated by an absorption correction. The loss depends on the average exit path length of the x-ray photons, and thus on the angle over which the x-ray spectrometer subtends the specimen and on the distribution in depth of the x-ray generation. This distribution, in turn, is a function of the electron beam energy and the composition of the specimen. In addition, the absorption varies strongly with the x-ray absorption coefficient of the specimen for the radiation of interest, which also is composition dependent. The correction is usually performed by means of semiempirical expressions (Ref 6).

Finally, it must be taken into account that x-rays can also be produced by the fluorescence mechanism, that is, excited by other x-rays. These exciting x-rays can be either characteristic or part of the continuous background. Fluorescence effects due to characteristic lines are particularly strong in high-alloy steels. A fluorescence correction is included in the correction procedures to compensate for this effect. The combination of the three corrections (atomic number, Z; absorption, A; and fluorescence, F) in the form of multiplicative factors is known as the ZAF procedure (Ref 13), which is embedded in the programs of data reduction used in modern electron probes.

Standards. Although semiquantitative and even quantitative results are sometimes obtained without the use of standards (Ref 14), the usual procedure consists of deriving concentrations from ratios of x-ray intensities from the specimen and from an appropriate standard. When the composition of the standard is close to that of the specimen, the matrix effects on x-ray intensities become insignificant, and the analysis reduces to a comparison of observed intensities, perhaps with the use of a linear calibration curve.

In practice, such standards are seldom available; a microanalytical standard must be carefully analyzed with respect to its overall composition, and must be proven to be microscopically homogeneous (Ref 15), a condition difficult to attain in alloy systems. When the standard differs significantly in composition from the analyzed region, mathematical "corrections" must be applied to determine the specimen composition. Although empirical correction methods have been proposed and are widely used in mineral analysis, the investigation of alloys is usually based on the ZAF correction procedures, which rely at least partially on theoretical considerations (Ref 16-18). The usefulness of such a procedure depends on:

- The correctness and completeness of the theoretical assumptions implicit in the procedure
- The accuracy of physical parameters used in the procedure
- The adequacy of simplifications often introduced to increase the speed of execution
- A careful scrutiny of the program to exclude mistakes that are frequently resident in widely used schemes

The stringent requirements as to the homogeneity and compositional characterization of standards have led to the use of pure elements as standards for routine analysis, because in this case homogeneity is easier to achieve and the specimen composition can be known precisely. In such a case, however, the accuracy of the analysis depends strongly on the correction model, because large matrix effects may have to be taken into account. It should be noted that neither the use of elementary standards nor any other procedure eliminates the need for composite standards for the purpose of testing the viability of the data-reduction scheme.

Accuracy and Precision. The accuracy of quantitative EPMA is the capability of estimating the true composition of the specimen with small error. This accuracy depends on a series of factors such as (1) the precision of the measurement of characteristic x-ray intensities, (2) the degree to which the selected and prepared specimen surface approaches in composition and structure the bulk material it supposedly represents, (3) the quality of the standards and/or standardization procedures used in the analysis, and (4) the nature of the data-reduction procedures used to deduce the specimen composition from the relative x-ray intensities measured from the specimen and standard(s).

The measurement of the characteristic x-ray intensities should include corrections for background, line interferences, count coincidence losses (dead-time correction), and consideration of the uncertainties inherent in counting statistics, instrumental drift, and other sources of random errors. Formulas derived from the Poisson distribution that applies to counting statistics are frequently used to estimate overall accuracy and related parameters such as the limit of detection. Such formulas are optimistic limits of accuracy valid only when all sources of error except counting statistics are negligible. These sources of error cannot be neglected, however, particularly in the use of EDS, where considerable corrections for background and line overlaps must often be applied. The representativeness of the analyzed volume must be considered both from a macroscopic and a microscopic point of view. As far as microscopic conservation of element distribution and the analytical process are concerned, the following points must be considered:

- The artifacts introduced by smearing and extraction of phases in the polishing process are well known to the preparative metallurgist. In analysis, however, he must concern himself also with the possibilities of transport or removal of elements by etching
- Some elements may be eliminated under the impact of the electron beam or, if the vacuum is poor, introduced as surface contamination. Deposition of silica and sulfur as a consequence of decomposition of diffusion pump oil residue in the vacuum has been observed. Diffusion of elements can occur if the specimen is strongly heated, or spontaneously in unstable systems such as some that are obtained by rapid quenching from the liquid state
- In the observation of steep concentration gradients in grain boundaries and inclusions, the analyst must be aware of the limited spatial resolution of the electron probe technique, which can be significantly poorer than that of the SEM image

The large list of factors contributing to the inaccuracy of the calculated result indicates that many aspects must be taken into account if good accuracy is to be achieved. Accuracy must not be confused with precision, which is the ability to obtain repeatable results. Repeatability also depends on various factors, including drifts in beam intensity and energy, as well as in spectrometer alignment. The so-called statistical precision that can be predicted from the number of photon counts collected in every measurement is based on the optimistic assumption that all random errors except those due to Poissonian counting statistics were eliminated from the procedure.

But even if the repeatability has been experimentally documented, the probability of systematic errors always implies that the error of analysis will be larger than the statistical fluctuations of the calculated result.

The effectiveness of microanalytical data-reduction procedures is often tested by applying them to a large number of analyses of materials of presumably known chemical composition, and constructing error-distribution diagrams. Such procedures usually show a disappointingly wide distribution of errors. To judge them, it must be taken into account that the reported errors include not only the inaccuracies of data reduction procedures, but also errors in the chemical analysis of the specimens, inhomogeneity, and instrumental errors. Such distribution diagrams are therefore often not effective in showing the effects of a single correction aspect of the data-reduction procedure.

Limits of Detection. Besides the characteristic lines, the x-ray emission of a target bombarded by electrons emits a background or continuous spectrum, produced in inelastic collisions of electrons with the target atoms. This ever-present background limits the detection of weak characteristic x-ray signals, and consequently the sensitivity (the ability to determine low concentrations of elements in the specimen) is low. The definition of limits of detection is a somewhat controversial matter, because it is based on the interpretation of statistical parameters to produce estimates of confidence limits. But for elements with $Z > 10$, under typical analytical conditions, the smallest amount that can be detected of an element varies between 10 and 100 ppm with WDS. The actual formulation of the limit of detection has never been universally defined; this matter is not serious as long as the calculation of the limit of detection is used to compare techniques and procedures, and provided that the prediction from counting statistics (Ref 19) is not confused wth a realistic estimation from measurements which should include an estimation of systematic as well as statistical errors.

The efficiency of the energy-dispersive spectrometer (detected photons per electron) is about 10 to 100 times that of the crystal spectrometer. This would increase the capability for the detection of low concentrations of elements. However, the reduced spectral resolution of the system causes the background contribution from the continuum to be considerably higher. The two effects roughly compensate, but the sensitivity of the crystal system (WDS system) is higher than that of the EDS system, provided that no line interference is present. When a weak line emission is close to an intense x-ray line produced by another element, the crystal

spectrometer is usually the only effective recourse.

Spatial Resolution. Microanalysis could not be properly interpreted if the dimensions of the volume that emits x-rays could not be estimated. The distance from the specimen surface to the level at which the electrons cease to excite the x-ray photons of interest depends on the operation voltage, V_o, and on the critical excitation voltage for the emitted x-ray line, V_q, as well as on the density of the material, ρ. A useful approximation for the maximum depth of emission is:

$$z = 0.035 \ (V_o^{1.65} - V_q^{1.65})\left(\frac{1}{\rho}\right)\mu m \quad (Eq\ 2)$$

Because the beam electrons are scattered while penetrating the target, they also diffuse sidewise, and the width of the emitting region of the target is roughly of the same dimension as the depth of x-ray emission.

Elemental Mapping

Analog Mapping. A powerful aspect of EPMA is the preparation of elemental-distribution maps, which can provide qualitative and quantitative information on the spatial distribution of the constituents of a sample (for a review, see Ref 2). The method of preparing such maps employs the same scanning image concepts as those used in conventional SEM imaging with electron detector signals. The beam on the display/record cathode ray tubes (CRTs) is scanned in synchronism with the beam on the specimen in a well-defined scan. The x-ray signal derived from an energy-dispersive or wavelength-dispersive spectrometer is used to modulate the brightness of the CRT to produce the image, which is known as an x-ray map or area scan. By obtaining a series of maps for different elemental constituents, the spatial distribution of the composition of the sample can be directly visualized, at least on a qualitative basis. Electron images, particularly those derived from the backscattered electron and specimen current signals, can be used in conjunction with x-ray area scans to examine complex structures. An example of such a series of images for a dental alloy is shown in Fig. 9.

A significant departure from scanning imaging with electron signals occurs because of the special nature of the x-ray signal. Whereas 10 to 50% of the incident electrons will produce usable, information-carrying backscattered or secondary electrons, only about 0.01% of the incident electrons will generate a characteristic x-ray. When the solid angle of the detector is considered, the

Fig. 9 Examples of x-ray scans of a dental alloy

(a) Specimen current image. (b) Ag Lα. (c) Hg Mα. (d) Sn Lα. Source: Ref 6

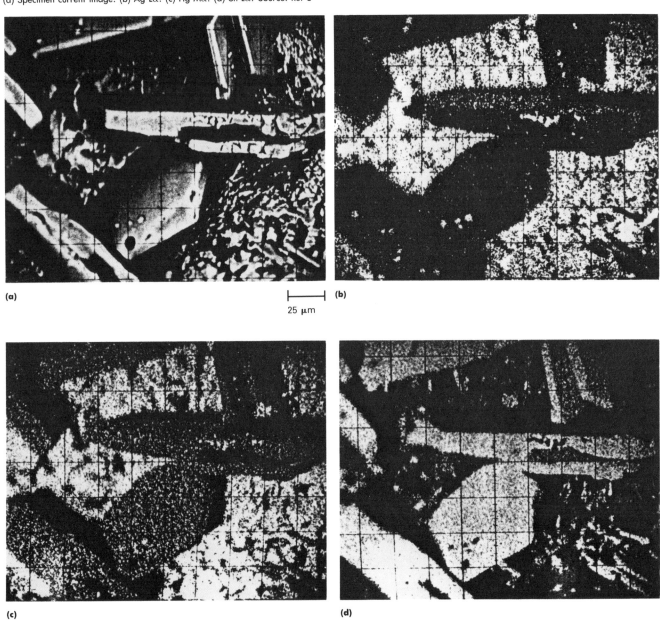

(a)

(b)

25 μm

(c)

(d)

useful portion of the signal will be lower still.

Electron signals are for all practical intent continuous in nature and can thus be used to produce a continuous gray scale in the final image. The high useful yield of electron signals allows "flicker-free" imaging at frame rates as high as television rates. The characteristic x-ray events are so infrequent at the beam currents used for practical EPMA that the signal is discontinuous in nature. The x-ray signal rate is so slow that x-ray images cannot normally be viewed

directly but must be recorded photographically. Under typical image-recording conditions with a 1-ms dwell time per picture point, most pixels (picture elements) would be black, a characteristic x-ray of interest not having been detected during the beam dwell time. Because x-ray signals are so infrequent, the possibility of forming a gray-scale image is lost.

The most widely used technique employed for practical x-ray area scanning is dot mapping. The detection of an x-ray photon is used to trigger the beam intensity on the

record CRT to full brightness, which produces a dot at the pixel location where the x-ray was recorded. An example of such a dot map is shown in Fig. 10. Concentration variations in dot maps are suggested by the area density of dots. Figure 10 demonstrates that careful adjustment of the final brightness of the record CRT must be made to gain the maximum sensitivity of the dot map to concentration differences. Heinrich (Ref 6) has demonstrated that the CRT brightness should be adjusted so that recording a single photon exposes the emulsion to the threshold of

Fig. 10 Dot maps recorded on photographic film

(a) Poor statistics, large dots. (b) Good statistics, large dots. (c) Poor statistics, small dots. (d) Good statistics, small dots. Source: Ref 6

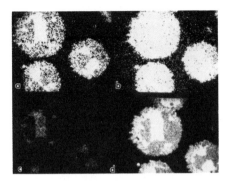

Fig. 11 Dot map for zinc at the grain boundaries of copper showing diffusion-induced grain-boundary migration

The concentration levels mapped extend down to approximately 0.5% Zn, with a maximum concentration of 10% in the field. Source: Ref 20

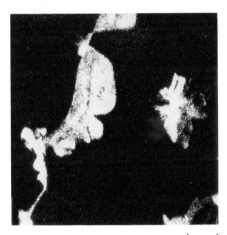

20 μm

visibility. Two events must be recorded to produce full brightness. Such adjustments lead to a diminution of the contribution of noise to such an image, because two random noise events are unlikely to coincide at a pixel where the element of interest does not actually exist. As shown in Fig. 10, the dots thus written do not tend to "bloom" or expose the adjacent pixels, which gives finer resolution in the final image.

Generally, a minimum of 10^5 x-ray photons must be accumulated to produce a useful dot map, and 10^6 photons are needed to give good definition at the boundaries of structures. For constituents present at the 10 wt% level, scan times of approximately 10

min are needed to satisfy the stricter of these conditions with a high beam current (100 nA) and the x-ray signal derived from a wavelength-dispersive spectrometer with a count rate of 25 000 cps on a pure-element standard. When a minor constituent at the 1% concentration level must be mapped, scan times in excess of 3 h must be used. Figure 11 shows an example of a WDS dot map for a minor constituent. This map, which took 6 h to accumulate, reveals concentration levels down to approximately 0.5 wt%.

The limit of spatial resolution of x-ray area scans is determined by the spatial extent of the excitation volume for the characteristic x-ray of interest. The lateral dimension is approximately the same as the value of the x-ray range calculated with Eq 2. In general, if the beam energy is chosen to give an overvoltage of 2, the lateral dimension will be of the order of a micrometer for most useful analytical lines. The practical effect of this excitation volume dimension is to set the upper limit of useful magnification in x-ray area scans at 2000×, beyond which the overlap of pixels becomes objectionable. The lower limit of magnification depends upon the choice of the x-ray spectrometer.

Choice of Spectrometer. Wavelength-dispersive and energy-dispersive spectrometers have strengths and weaknesses when applied to the technique of x-ray mapping. Fortunately, these strengths and weaknesses are generally complementary, so that an instrument equipped with both EDS and WDS can attack a variety of mapping problems.

The strengths of the wavelength-dispersive spectrometer for mapping are mainly derived from two characteristics: first, the high limiting count rates that can be accommodated by the WDS detector, coupled with the extremely narrow photon energy range that actually reaches the detector, and, second, the inherently high peak-to-background ratio. The first factor allows the wavelength-dispersive spectrometer to operate with extremely high beam currents. In the case of major and minor constituents, the use of high beam current allows the analyst to accumulate the necessary x-ray counts in a shorter time. In the case of trace constituents, the combination of both factors makes possible mapping at levels as low as 0.1 wt% if long scan times (>5 h) can be employed.

When the energy-dispersive spectrometer is used for mapping, an energy window for the element of interest is first defined in the multichannel analyzer. When a count occurs within that window, a pulse is generated that can be used to modulate the CRT. As a general observation regarding mapping, the energy-dispersive spectrometer is inferior to

Fig. 12 Direct map of the defocusing of a wavelength-dispersive spectrometer during an x-ray area scan across a pure-element standard

The bands represent successive differences of 6% in signal intensity. Source: Ref 21

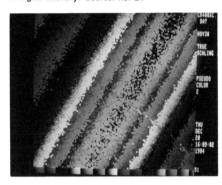

the wavelength-dispersive spectrometer for most mapping applications. The only significant advantage in mapping with the energy-dispersive spectrometer compared to the wavelength-dispersive spectrometer arises when spectrometer defocusing is considered. The wavelength-dispersive spectrometer is a focusing device, which has the consequence that photons generated off the axis of the spectrometer suffer losses in transmission through the spectrometer. This effect is illustrated graphically in Fig. 12, which shows the relative intensity in an image of a standard from a wavelength-dispersive spectrometer. For scans made at a magnification of 800× or less, defocusing will become objectionable, and below 400× the loss in transmission may exceed a factor of two at the edge of the scanned field relative to the center. The energy-dispersive spectrometer, which is not a focusing instrument, does not suffer this loss of transmission and can be used effectively at low magnifications. Defocusing in the wavelength-dispersive spectrometer can be reduced by rocking the diffracting crystal in synchronism with the scan so that the effective line of focus of the spectrometer is placed along the scan line axis.

The energy-dispersive spectrometer has several important disadvantages compared to the wavelength-dispersive spectrometer. The principal disadvantage arises from the long time constant in EDS pulse processing, approximately two orders of magnitude longer than that for WDS. Limiting count rates are necessarily lower in EDS. A second complication arises from the fact that the energy-dispersive spectrometer is sensitive to the entire range of x-ray energies that are excited. Thus, the limiting count rate in EDS cannot be restricted to a single peak of interest for mapping as it can in WDS. This limitation becomes particularly severe for minor constituents, where the peak count rate may be only a few percent or less of the total count rate. Mapping using an energy-dispersive spectrometer is generally impractical below 5 wt%. Special care must be taken to avoid operating at too high a dead time at any location within the image. Unless dynamic dead time corrections are made during an EDS x-ray area scan, it is possible to encounter pulse processing saturation effects in which the signal from a high concentration area may actually be less than the signal from an area with lower concentration, which can lead to an inversion in the apparent compositional contrast.

The contribution of the continuous bremsstrahlung background at a given x-ray energy can also be important. Because the continuum intensity increases proportionally to the atomic number, the intensity in a given energy window may rise due to changes in composition through effects on the continuum. Such intensity changes may be misinterpreted as changes in intensity of a characteristic peak of a minor constituent located at the same energy. Because the peak-to-background ratio of the energy-dispersive spectrometer is at least ten times poorer than that for the wavelength-dispersive spectrometer, the energy-dispersive spectrometer is more susceptible to continuum effects. Fortunately, because the energy-dispersive spectrometer constantly measures the entire spectrum, an energy window that corresponds to true bremsstrahlung can be used to normalize the signal from the characteristic window of interest for variations in the bremsstrahlung intensity with composition.

In WDS mapping, the effect of the bremsstrahlung sensitivity to atomic number is less significant, but when minor or trace levels of an element are to be mapped, the problem can be very significant. Because the wavelength-dispersive spectrometer measures a single narrow energy band, no normalizing bremsstrahlung signal is available from a single spectrometer operating with analog recording of the x-ray map.

Digital Compositional Mapping. Although analog dot mapping is a powerful technique, there are significant limitations on its practical use. Because the dots written on the film are at full brightness, no gray scale retaining any concentration information can be obtained from the individual dots. Strictly speaking, the dot map is qualitative and gives only position information. Thus, a minor constituent and a major constituent will both produce the same intensity dot on the CRT. In practice, concentration

Fig. 13 Digital composition map of a zinc-containing copper specimen

(a) Digital compositional map of a portion of the grain boundary shown in Fig. 11. Note the continuous gray scale presentation. The gray scale corresponds to a concentration scale of 0 to 10 wt% Zn. (b) Same data set processed with eight gray scale bands (1.25% wide) to show concentration contours. (Original in color thermal scale: red-orange-yellow-white). (c) Data set plotted with digital threshold set at 0.2 wt% Zn to emphasize narrow, low-concentration boundary. (d) Plot of concentrations along selected vector. Sample courtesy of D.B. Butrymowicz, National Bureau of Standards

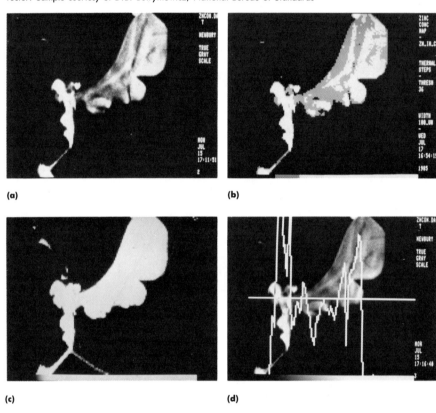

differences are suggested by differences in the area density of dots.

The greatest limitation of the dot mapping procedure is the limited flexibility with which the photographically recorded data can be manipulated at a later time. All knowledge of the x-ray count rates on the sample, which form the basis of any quantitation procedure, is lost in a photographic recording.

An important use of dot maps is to determine spatial relationships among the constituents in a sample. Although the x-ray information in several maps can be superimposed via photographic procedures, registration of separately recorded images can be difficult.

These limitations of the conventional analog dot mapping procedure have stimulated the development of digital mapping techniques in which a computer memory instead of film is used to store the x-ray data (Ref 21, 22). The beam is addressed to a particular point x,y on the sample and the number, n, of x-ray counts accumulated at that location with

a wavelength-dispersive spectrometer or from a window set in the multichannel analyzer of an energy-dispersive spectrometer is stored in an array in a computer memory as (x,y,n). If several wavelength-dispersive spectrometers are available or if multiple windows are set in the EDS spectrum, then several x-ray count arrays can be accumulated simultaneously. The great advantage of such a procedure is that the true x-ray count data are retained for subsequent image processing.

After the array(s) of x-ray counts has been accumulated, the computer memory can be read out at flicker-free rates directly onto a television monitor. A gray scale can be assigned that is proportional to the count in each pixel of the image. The resulting x-ray image has a range of intensities which have a direct relationship to the amount of a constituent that is present (Fig. 13).

Because the true x-ray counts have been retained in the image, the possibility exists that a complete quantitative analysis can be performed at each location in the image. All of the same steps that are applied in the case of a quantitative analysis at a static point beam location must be applied at every point within the array. In the case of EDS mapping, dead time and background corrections must first be applied, with background correction usually made by simultaneously accumulating background intensity arrays that correspond to the characteristic intensity arrays. Background correction is followed by the calculation of the k-ratio (sample/standard) against the intensity measured on a known standard.

For EDS mapping, one set of background-corrected standard intensities for all elements of interest is needed. A series of k-ratio images for all elements in the sample is thus assembled. By taking the k-ratios for all elements at a given location x,y in the scan, matrix-correction procedures such as ZAF can be used to calculate true concentrations, forming as a final product a series of concentration arrays, one for each constituent. These concentration arrays can be read out on a monitor, now encoding true concentrations as a continuous gray scale.

In the case of WDS mapping, an additional important step must be taken in the quantitative mapping procedure to account for the effect of spectrometer defocusing. This correction can be accomplished by recording digital arrays on pure element or compound standards at the same magnification as that used for the sample. The standard intensity shows the same defocusing effects as that of the sample. The "standard map," corrected for dead time and background, is used to provide the appropriate standard intensity at each pixel in the array in order to calculate the k-value map for submission to the matrix-correction procedure which completes the calculation of concentrations (Ref 21).

Digital compositional maps offer many advantages to the analyst. These advantages are principally derived from the flexibility provided by the digital form of that data. The data may be processed in a variety of ways to produce images that enhance the visibility of features to the observer (Fig. 13b and c). Quantitative analysis results can be directly superimposed on x-ray maps to relate specific composition to structure (Fig. 13d). Information can be combined from multiple sources, such as maps for different elements or from different imaging systems. Because complete compositional data are permanently stored for each pixel, the quantitative relationships among selected features in an image field can be determined at any time in the future; the analyst is not compelled to complete all aspects of the analysis during the actual instrument time. This feature is especially valuable when data must be re-

viewed by several researchers over an extended time period so that additional analytical information may be required long after the specimen has been removed from the electron probe microanalyzer.

Strategy for Applying Microbeam Analysis

In order to apply EPMA to problems in materials science, it is useful to follow a strategy that recognizes the strengths and weaknesses of the technique. A suitable strategy consists of the following six stages: determination of applicability, sample preparation, development of a sample strategy, qualitative analysis, quantitative analysis, and statistical evaluation of results.

Determination of Applicability. Electron probe microanalysis is a powerful technique with many possible applications in the study of materials science. In determining the applicability of EPMA to a particular problem, it must be recognized that it is first and foremost a spatially resolved analysis technique that excites and samples a micrometer-sized volume of the specimen. As a general rule, the analyst should not attempt to apply a microanalysis technique to solve a bulk analysis problem. A fundamental requirement in the physical basis for quantitative analysis is that the composition must be constant within the excited volume.

This requirement for homogeneity places strict bounds on the ways in which EPMA can be applied to inhomogeneous samples, which are typical of most actual samples encountered in practice. It is generally this inhomogeneity which one wishes to characterize. Thus, a multicomponent sample may contain two or more chemically distinct phases with dimensions on a micrometer scale; a compositional gradient may exist within a single phase; or an artificial multiphase structure can be fabricated, such as a layered coating. The forte of microanalysis is revealing such inhomogeneous compositional structures, either by a series of point analyses that are located on the sample in an appropriate pattern, or by applying a scanning method to produce a compositional map. Inhomogeneous samples can be accurately characterized providing the scale of the inhomogeneity is larger than the sample volume that is excited.

Unfortunately, there exists a considerable temptation to apply EPMA to inhomogeneous samples by overscanning a large area to obtain an "average" compositional value for the sample as a whole, that is, to use a microanalysis technique to try to solve a bulk analysis problem. Because of the violation of the requirement of homogeneity within the electron-excited volume, such a procedure is

Table 1 Errors observed in quantitative analysis by overscanning a field of mixed phases

Element	Known mass concentration	Analyzed mass concentration	Relative error, %
Aluminum	0.0138	0.0337	144
Silicon	0.110	0.126	14
Calcium	0.0186	0.0438	135
Iron	0.0182	0.039	114
Barium	0.0232	0.0529	128
Lead	0.614	0.469	−24

Source: Ref 23

susceptible to very large and unpredictable errors, as shown in Table 1. These errors can arise, for example, when an element A is partitioned between two phases, including one in which it is strongly absorbed. The presence in the analysis of the strongly absorbing elements will cause the matrix-correction procedure to correct all of the intensity for element A for the apparent strong absorption of the other elements because of the assumption of homogeneity within the excited volume. Because absorption follows an exponential law, such an overcorrection can lead to enormous, unpredictable, and completely unacceptable errors.

The only acceptable way to characterize large, inhomogeneous samples is to sample at many discrete points. If the weight fraction of each phase can be determined by means of methods of quantitative stereology and the compositions of the individual phases determined by EPMA, then the overall composition can be calculated. It must be pointed out that even in this procedure, special attention must be paid to sampling. A single section through the sample may not be adequately representative of an inhomogeneous sample, depending on the scale of the inhomogeneity.

Sample Preparation. The physical basis for EPMA is the interaction of electrons with matter to generate characteristic x-rays. An ideal situation is one in which the x-ray intensities emitted from the sample are only a function of the composition and not of any other sample variable. Unfortunately, the interaction of electrons with a sample is also a strong function of the shape, size, and local surface angle relative to the beam, the so-called "geometric factors." If these variables are not controlled and defined, the accuracy of the final result can be severely compromised. In order to fix the geometric factors to known, constant values, the specimen should be prepared by conventional metallographic grinding and polishing techniques to produce a flat, scratch-free surface that can be set to known angles relative to the incident beam and the x-ray detector axis.

It is also important to examine the specimen in the mechanically polished condition; chemical or electrochemical etching should not be used, because such chemical attack can severely alter the chemical composition of the near-surface layer that is to be analyzed. If it is necessary to etch the polished surface in order to use optical metallography to locate structures of interest, then a procedure should be employed in which fiducial marks such as hardness indentations are pressed into the etched sample and photomicrographs are recorded. The sample can then be lightly repolished to remove the chemically perturbed layer without polishing away the hardness indentations, which serve as reference points to locate the points of interest on the sample.

A suitable sampling strategy for characterizing an inhomogeneous specimen depends on the exact nature of the sample and the form of its inhomogeneity. Each case may require special consideration, which may involve a modification to a previously developed technique or a completely novel approach. Several general cases can be considered as the basis for further development.

Multiphase Samples. Samples in which two or more chemically distinct phases co-exist generally lend themselves readily to analysis by EPMA. Often the individual phases can be recognized in a backscattered electron or specimen current image, which makes working with polished samples considerably more tractable. Providing that regions of each phase can be found with lateral and depth dimensions at least the size of the x-ray generation range, then good-quality EPMA analyses can be performed. An important exception to this size criterion occurs in the case of significant fluorescence excitation, which has a range at least an order of magnitude greater than the electron range.

Each phase should be sampled in several different locations to examine the phase homogeneity. Care should be taken to note the proximity of other phase particles to the analysis location if it is important to determine the partitioning of elements among the phases. If an element of interest is a major constituent in one phase, it may be difficult or impossible to determine that element as a minor or trace constituent in an adjacent phase particle due to fluorescence or pathological electron scattering effects from the high-concentration region. The possible effects of stray electrons from scattering on the final aperture or within the sample chamber can only be assessed by a series of careful experiments. A multicomponent Faraday cup can be used to determine the portion of the electron flux not contained within the focused beam by determining x-ray spectra with the beam alternately placed in the Far-

aday cup and on the materials of the cup assembly (Ref 9). Bimetallic couples of pure metals pressed together can be used to assess the effects of electron scattering off the specimen with subsequent rescattering off the polepiece of the final lens or chamber walls and thence back to the specimen.

Compositional gradients within a single phase can be examined by employing a linear beam scan or stepping of the stage. The spatial resolution of the profile is limited by the dimensions of the x-ray generation volume, and may be degraded by long-range fluorescence effects. The spacing of beam locations for analysis should be selected on the basis of the dimensions of the x-ray generation volume. The maximum spatial resolution cannot exceed about one-half of the x-ray range in cases where fluorescence is negligible.

Applications*

The National Bureau of Standards has developed a series of special Standard Reference Materials (SRM) specifically for use in microprobe analysis. These materials can be used directly as multielement standards in quantitative analysis procedures for certain unknowns that contain members of the specific set of elements represented in these standards. Their principal utility, however,

*Examples 4 and 5 supplied by Paul F. Hlava, Sandia National Laboratories. This work was performed at Sandia National Laboratories and supported by the U.S. Department of Energy under Contract No. DE-AC04-76DP00789.

is to serve as useful tests for the accuracy of microanalysis procedures in establishing a quality-assurance program prior to analysis of actual unknowns. In the following analyses, these homogeneous alloys have been used to compare quantitative analysis by WDS and EDS.

Example 1: Analysis With Well-Resolved Peaks and High Concentrations for Gold-Copper Alloys. The gold-copper SRM 482 alloy series provides a first-level test of quantitative analysis procedures. For these alloys the constituents are all present at concentration levels of 20 wt% or more, and the analytical lines are well separated with no significant overlaps in the EDS or WDS cases. The results from WDS and EDS analyses listed in Table 2 reveal that in this simple case, similar accuracy can be achieved with the different quantitative analysis procedures appropriate to WDS and EDS.

Example 2: Analysis of Major Constituents With Peak Overlap. The second level of testing involves the problem of peak overlap for EDS analysis, with both constituents present as major constituents. The analysis of brass (represented in the SRM set as SRM 478, Cartridge Brass) provides a test of peak overlap corrections in EDS analysis, because the Cu Kβ interferes with the high-energy side of the Zn Kα peak. These peaks are easily resolved by WDS. Table 3 contains EDS and WDS results which again show small relative errors in both bases, with the WDS analyses slightly superior.

Table 2 Analysis of binary gold-copper alloys (SRM 482)
Beam energy: 20 keV

Alloy	wt% Cu certified	wt% Cu, WDS(a)	Relative error, %	wt% Cu EDS(b)	Relative error, %
20Cu80Au	19.8	19.8	0.0	19.8	0.0
40Cu60Au	39.6	39.7	0.3	39.9	0.8
60Cu40Au	59.9	59.7	−0.3	60.5	1.0
80Cu20Au	79.8	79.8	0.0	79.7	−0.1

	wt% Au certified	wt% Au, WDS(a)	Relative error, %	wt% Au EDS(b)	Relative error, %
20Cu80Au	80.1	79.9	−0.3	79.0	−1.4
40Cu60Au	60.3	60.6	0.5	59.4	−1.6
60Cu40Au	40.1	40.2	0.1	40.2	0.1
80Cu20Au	20.1	20.0	−0.5	19.9	−1.0

(a) WDS: Analyses given in Ref 24. Data reduction by NBS theoretical matrix-correction procedure COR. Source: Ref 17. (b) EDS: Analyses given in Ref 25. Data reduction by NBS EDS theoretical matrix-correction procedure FRAME C. Source: Ref 5

Table 3 Results of EDS and WDS analysis of cartridge brass
Beam energy: 20 keV

Element	Certified wt%	EDS wt%	Relative error, %	WDS wt%	Relative error, %
Copper	76.75	77.7	1.2	76.9	0.2
Zinc	23.26	23.6	1.5	23.5	1.0

Source: Ref 5

Fig. 14 Optical micrographs of the cross section of an aluminum wire, iron screw, and brass plate in a conventional household electrical outlet assembly

(a) Overall view. (b) Wire/screw interface. (c) Wire/brass plate interface. See also Fig. 15 and 16.

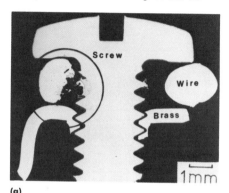

(a)

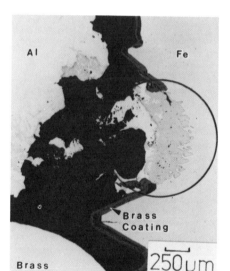

(b)

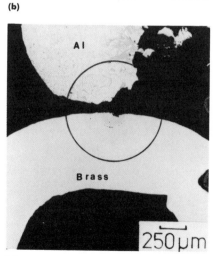

(c)

Fig. 15(a) Scanning electron micrograph of the iron/aluminum interface showing atomic number contrast

Analysis of numbered regions given in Table 4. See also Fig. 15(b) and (c).

Fig. 15(b) X-ray dot map for aluminum at the iron/aluminum interface shown in Fig. 15(a)

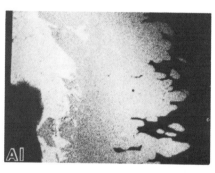

Fig. 15(c) X-ray dot map for iron at the iron/aluminum interface shown in Fig. 15(a)

Source: Ref 27

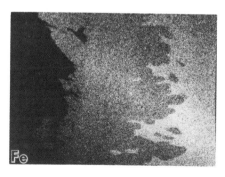

Table 4   X-ray microanalysis of reaction zone at the aluminum wire/steel screw interface shown in Fig. 15(a)

Location	Element, wt%		
	Al	Fe	Cu
1	62.5	38.1	0.5
2	57.5	43.3	0.0
3	57.3	43.3	0.0
4	55.5	44.4	0.0

observed to undergo severe heating, which could lead to failure of the electrical outlet, under certain circumstances of operation in service. Attacking this problem by EPMA necessitated the use of careful metallographic sectioning to expose the regions of electrical contact between the aluminum wire, iron screw, and brass plate in a household electrical plug box that had undergone severe degradation due to the heating.

Optical and scanning electron microscopy of the contacts revealed perturbed regions in which the composition apparently underwent a change during the failure, as suggested by compositional (atomic number) contrast in the SEM images. The SEM images, which were obtained in the electron probe microanalyzer, in fact served as a guide for the location of point beam microanalyses. The optical microscope of the electron beam microanalyzer further aided in locating the regions of interst that had been initially found by optical metallography. Figure 14 shows micrographs of a section showing regions of interest at both the aluminum/iron interface and the aluminum/brass interface. Figures 15(a) and 16(a) illustrate SEM images that correspond to these regions.

The aluminum/iron region (Fig. 15a) contains a structure with two distinct layers. Conventional analog dot maps of these regions are shown in Fig. 15(b) and (c). Analyses of these layers are given in Table 4, which reveals a sequence of iron-aluminum compositions that shift from the pure aluminum of the wire to the nearly pure iron of the screw. The iron-aluminum compositions are homogeneous within each layer, but change sharply from one layer to the next. The compositions correspond to specific intermetallic compounds that are found in the aluminum-iron phase diagram.

Similar compositional variations are noted at the aluminum/brass interface (Fig. 16a). Corresponding x-ray dot maps of this region for aluminum, zinc, and copper are shown in Fig. 16(b), (c), and (d), respectively. A radially symmetric structure is observed from the point of contact. The composition is found to vary along the radius with the values determined by microanalysis given in

Example 3: Failure of Aluminum Wire Connections. The electron probe microanalyzer has been applied to the study of service failures of aluminum wire connections in residential electrical circuits (Ref 26, 27). These aluminum wire connections were

Fig. 16(a) Scanning electron micrograph of the aluminum/brass interface showing atomic number contrast

Analysis of numbered regions given in Table 5. See also Fig. 16(b) to (d).

20 μm

Fig. 16(b) X-ray dot map for aluminum at the aluminum/brass interface shown in Fig. 16(a)

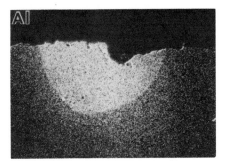

Fig. 16(c) X-ray dot map for zinc at the aluminum/brass interface shown in Fig. 16(a)

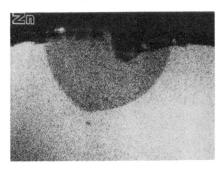

Fig. 16(d) X-ray dot map for copper at the aluminum/brass interface shown in Fig. 16(a)

Source: Ref 27

Table 5   X-ray microanalysis of reaction zone at the aluminum wire/brass plate Interface shown in Fig. 16(a)

Location	Element, wt%		
	Al	Cu	Zn
1	5.2	65.0	29.7
2	16.4	72.4	10.2
3	18.4	74.2	7.3
4	18.7	74.6	6.8
5	0.0	69.4	31.1

Table 5. The principal change appears to be a nearly direct replacement of zinc by aluminum, with the copper content remaining similar.

The failure of the electrical junction due to extreme heating is related to the formation of intermetallic compounds at the current carrying interfaces, as revealed by EPMA (Ref 27). Such intermetallic compounds have substantially higher resistivity than the aluminum, iron, or brass conductors of the junction. The typical resistivity of iron-aluminum intermetallic compounds is 100 $\Omega \cdot$ cm or higher, similar to that of Nichrome. These pads of high-resistivity material through which all of the electrical current must flow provide sufficient resistance to cause significant resistive heating. The reaction causes positive feedback, with increased temperature stimulating formation of more intermetallic compound, initially by solid-state reaction but eventually in liquid phase reaction. Electron probe microanalysis provided in this case the necessary link between understanding events on a micrometer scale with those on a macroscopic scale.

Example 4: Elemental Mapping of a High-Temperature Solder. In a service facility, it is often necessary to verify that a particular item was produced by a third party according to definite specifications. When the item is a piece of homogeneous alloy or ceramic, the strategy is simple; a few quantitative analyses verify the composition. Assemblies of materials require several different sets of quantitative analyses. Some items are so complicated that the distribution of various materials must be known before analysis can proceed. Elemental distribution maps can be invaluable in such cases, as is shown by this example.

The solder joint was under examination to verify that the materials used in its manufacture were compatible during long-term storage and operation at high temperature. The requestor was particularly concerned about the appropriateness of the composition of the solder for the expected operating temperature. Energy-dispersive spectroscopy of the solder revealed the presence of silver, gold, and copper, in addition to the tin and lead, and much more heterogeneity than usual. Instead of proceeding directly to quantitative analyses of the solder, a set of maps was prepared to help decipher the history of the sample and guide further analyses.

Element maps were taken over an area chosen to include a terminal pin, the wires wrapped around it, and the solder joining them. Beam current and exposure time were automatically adjusted for each map so that a chosen concentration of the element would produce a pixel density equivalent to a known reference, allowing semiquantitative estimates of element concentrations to be made.

Inspection of the maps (Fig. 17) reveals the materials present and much about the processing history. Terminal pins are made of Kovar (an iron-nickel-cobalt alloy) plated with nickel, then gold, then nickel again. Wires are silver-plated copper. The solder is a high-tin low-lead alloy. In addition, irregular particles of silver- and gold-rich phases are unevenly distributed throughout the solder, indicating that soldering conditions were vigorous enough to disrupt some of the gold plating on an unseen adjacent part and some of the gold plating and copper from the wires.

Knowing the distribution of the various elements, the solder could then be analyzed quantitatively. More importantly, the client could be informed that the noble metal platings, used as diffusion barriers, had been compromised during soldering and that the storage life of the part would require reevaluation.

Example 5: Study of a Ceramic Nuclear Waste Form Simulant. Ceramic nuclear waste forms are designed to incorporate nuclear waste products in a stable, easily handled solid that has excellent properties for long-term containment of a wide range of elements. One family of such forms is produced by adding calcium and titanium oxides to the waste to force the formation of various titanates. Natural titanate minerals contain many of the same

Fig. 17 Photographs of the SEM image (a) and seven element maps taken over an area chosen to include a terminal pin, the wires wrapped around it, and the solder joining them

(b) Iron, 55 wt%. (c) Nickel, 27 wt%. (d) Copper, 97 wt%. (e) Silver, 10 wt%. (f) Tin, 84 wt%. (g) Gold, 20 wt%. (h) Lead, 10 wt%

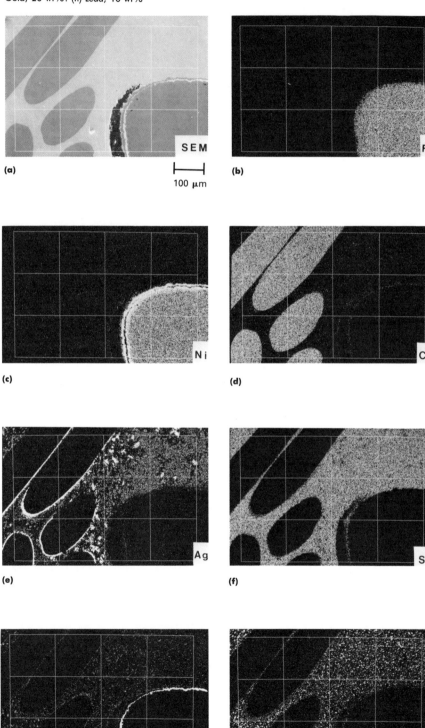

elements as the waste, yet are known to exhibit excellent resistance to weathering and leaching even after becoming metamict (loss of crystallinity due to radiation damage). If the waste elements form only a small portion (<5 wt%) of the mixture, the phases that form could be easily predicted and controlled by the additives. Such low waste loadings are impractical because the additives are costly, and the waste form must be encapsulated in expensive metal containers, moved by remote handling equipment, transported to a disposal site, and widely spaced at the site. One solution is waste forms with high waste loadings, which would reduce the overall bulk per volume of waste.

Samples were hot-pressed from a calcined nonradioactive simulant of the waste form with sufficient calcium and titanium added to produce pellets with 25 wt% waste element oxides for feasibility and characterization studies. Electron microprobe analyses were essential to the characterization of the chemistry and microstructure of the resultant fine-grained mixture of phases. With average grain sizes of less than 5 μm, intimate contact between phases, and encapsulation of phases by one another, characterization by many other means is impossible. Electron microprobe studies determined the variety and chemistry of the phases, their morphology, the texture of the composite, and, in conjunction with TEM studies, the identity of the phases.

Photographs (Fig. 18) taken of a cross-sectioned pellet at 1000× reveal a layered fabric of alternating high average atomic number and low average atomic number phases overlaid by randomly oriented poikiloblastic grains (larger grains that grow around and include earlier materials) of intermediate average atomic number. Samples were prepared by imbedding a cross section of a hot-pressed pellet in epoxy, then grinding and highly polishing a flat surface. The range of gray levels in the SEM image (with significant backscattered electron contribution) indicates at least four major phases. More phases can be discerned by adjusting brightness and contrast. Mapping the identical area for elements of interest made it possible to define eight phases.

Element maps identify four major titanate phases, each characterized by a distinctive set of elements, plus a silicate and three metallic phases. A map of silicon delineates the silicate; maps of the more noble elements (palladium, ruthenium, silver, cadmium, tellurium, molybdenum, nickel, and iron) locate two alloys and an intermetallic compound. Different elements from the nuclear waste concentrate in each of these titanate phases. One titanate is enriched in gadolin-

Fig. 18 Photographs of a ceramic nuclear waste form simulant

(a) SEM image shows the fine-grained layered fabric of the material, the poikiloblastic grains of the hollandite, and the location of rutile (darkest areas). (b) The silicon (5 wt%) map shows the location of the silicate. (c) The iron (5 wt%) map reveals the metallic alloys. (d) The palladium (10 wt%) map indicates the intermetallic compound. The remaining titanate phases can be distinguished as pyrochlore by the uranium (10 wt%) map (e), hollandite by the cesium (10 wt%) map (f), and perovskite by the strontium (2 wt%) map (g).

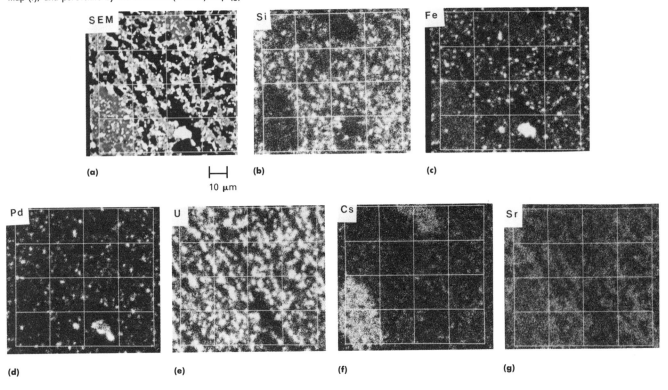

Table 6 Selected quantitative analyses of the four titanate phases in the waste form simulant

Values are listed in terms of the weight percent of the oxide and in terms of the number of cations needed to satisfy the number of oxygens in one formula unit of each phase. N/A, not analyzed

Compound	Pyrochlore wt%	Number of cations per 7 O	Perovskite wt%	Number of cations per 3 O	Hollandite wt%	Number of cations per 16 O	Rutile wt%	Number of cations per 2 O
Na$_2$O	0.04	0.0049	0.21	0.0105	0.08	0.0189	N/A	N/A
SiO$_2$	0.11	0.0074	0.00	0.0000	0.00	0.0000	0.00	0.0000
P$_2$O$_5$	0.36	0.0212	0.74	0.0157	0.00	0.0000	N/A	N/A
K$_2$O	0.13	0.0111	N/A	N/A	2.02	0.3269	N/A	N/A
CaO	9.13	0.6810	25.70	0.6965	0.75	0.1012	0.25	0.0036
TiO$_2$	38.50	2.0157	51.34	0.9767	77.13	7.3531	97.06	0.9801
Cr$_2$O$_3$	0.11	0.0063	0.07	0.0013	0.71	0.0707	N/A	N/A
Fe$_2$O$_3$	0.87	0.0456	0.23	0.0043	0.53	0.0506	N/A	N/A
Rb$_2$O	0.06	0.0029	N/A	N/A	1.30	0.1061	N/A	N/A
SrO	0.00	0.0000	0.92	0.0134	0.00	0.0000	N/A	N/A
Y$_2$O$_3$	0.99	0.0367	0.16	0.0021	0.00	0.0000	0.00	0.00
ZrO$_2$	5.16	0.1753	0.31	0.0038	0.53	0.0330	2.67	0.0174
Cs$_2$O	0.21	0.0061	0.08	0.0008	6.64	0.3588	N/A	N/A
BaO	0.00	0.0000	0.16	0.0016	7.88	0.3912	N/A	N/A
La$_2$O$_3$	0.00	0.0000	1.89	0.0176	0.41	0.0193	0.00	0.0000
CeO$_2$	1.33	0.0322	2.97	0.0262	0.84	0.0372	0.02	0.0001
Pr$_2$O$_3$	0.73	0.0185	1.52	0.0140	0.00	0.0000	N/A	N/A
Nd$_2$O$_3$	3.04	0.0756	5.01	0.0452	0.00	0.0000	0.05	0.0002
Gd$_2$O$_3$	12.31	0.2842	6.18	0.0518	0.12	0.0051	0.00	0.0000
U$_3$O$_8$	27.46	0.4092	1.52	0.0082	0.49	0.0134	0.06	0.0001
Total	100.53		99.00		99.44		100.12	

ium and contains almost all the uranium, another contains all the barium and cesium, a third carries all the strontium, and the last one is almost pure titanium dioxide, TiO$_2$ (lacking heavy elements, it is the darkest in the scanning electron micrograph).

Once the phases have been defined by the elements, quantitative analyses can be performed to determine the exact chemistry and to identify the phase. Quantitative analyses are usually somewhat complicated procedures of measuring count rates on standards and unknowns, storing the raw data, comparing the numbers and applying correction factors, and so on. Because most of the details of operating the machine and number storing and calculating are now handled by computer, it is necessary only to check the standards and perform spot analyses on the unknowns if a good strategy, including detailed checking of line interferences and overlaps, has been designed (rare-earth elements are exceedingly difficult in this respect). If all the work has been done well, and the machine is operating correctly, a set of analyses can be generated that may look like those in Table 6 (where the compositions of each phase total very nearly to 100%).

Based on the stoichiometries found, the phases expected from previous work, and TEM verification, the four titanates were identified as being similar to the minerals pyrochlore, perovskite, hollandite, and rutile. These phases are not those minerals; they are synthetic analogs with similar stoichiometries and structures. The names are used for convenience only. Rutile was the easiest to identify because it is essentially pure TiO_2 and has a tetragonal crystal structure as shown by TEM. Hollandite $(Ba,Cs)(Ti_2^{3+},Ti_6^{4+})O_{16}$ analog of natural $Ba(Mn_2^{2+}Mn_6^{4+})O_{16}$ was expected to form in response to the presence of large ions, such as cesium and barium. Structural and stoichiometric conditions dictate that some of the titanium has to be 3+ valent to stabilize this TEM confirmed phase. Perovskite $(CaTiO_3)$ was also expected, and its chemistry is reasonably close to some natural, analyzed rare earth bearing samples. The fourth titanate was expected to be something like zirconolite $(CaZrTi_2O_7)$ or pyrochlore $(Ca_2Nb_2O_7$ or $RE_2Ti_2O_7)$; because the substitutions are so extreme, TEM studies were required to identify this phase positively as pyrochlore. The silicate and metallic phases were defined and identified similarly.

Using the characterization information on this material, experiments can be designed to test the stability of the phases, compare the forms with natural analogs, and assess the effects of self-encapsulation by the inert rutile component. In addition, each of the phases can be synthesized in bulk for various studies, the phase(s) least stable during leaching studies can be determined, and additive elements to modify phases or force other phases to form can be targeted. Thus, the properties of the material can be tailored because the phases that will form and how the elements will be distributed are known.

REFERENCES

1. R. Castaing, Thesis, University of Paris, France, 1951
2. K.F.J. Heinrich, *Adv. Opt. Elec. Microsc.*, Vol 6, 1981, p 275-301
3. R. Fitzgerald, K. Keil, and K.F.J. Heinrich, *Science*, Vol 159, 1968, p 528
4. K.F.J. Heinrich, D.E. Newbury, and R.L. Myklebust, "Energy Dispersive X-ray Spectrometry," NBS Special Publication 604, National Bureau of Standards, Gaithersburg, MD, 1981
5. R.L. Myklebust, C.E. Fiori, and K.F.J. Heinrich, "FRAME C: A Compact Procedure for Quantitative Energy-Dispersive Electron Probe X-ray Analysis," NBS Technical Note 1106, National Bureau of Standards, Gaithersburg, MD, 1979
6. K.F.J. Heinrich, *Electron Beam X-ray Microanalysis*, Van Nostrand Reinhold, 1981
7. J.I. Goldstein, D.E. Newbury, P. Echlin, D.C. Joy, C. Fiori, and E. Lifshin, *Scanning Electron Microscopy and X-ray Microanalysis*, Plenum Press, 1981
8. G.F. Bastin and H.G.M. Heigliers, *Microbeam Analysis—1985*, San Francisco Press, 1985, p 1
9. C.E. Fiori and D.E. Newbury, *Scan. Elec. Microsc.*, No. 1, 1978, p 401
10. J.A. Bearden, "X-ray Wavelengths and X-ray Atomic Energy Levels," NSRDS-NBS 14, National Bureau of Standards, National Standard Reference Data Series, Washington, DC, 1967
11. J.D. Brown, *Adv. X-Ray Anal.*, Vol 7, 1964, p 340
12. R. Castaing, *Adv. Electr. Elec. Phys.*, Vol 13, 1960, p 317
13. J. Philibert and R. Tixier, in "Quantitative Electron Probe Microanalysis," NBS Special Publication 298, National Bureau of Standards, Gaithersburg, MD, 1968
14. J.C. Russ, *Proceedings of the 9th Annual Conference of the Electron Probe Society of America* (now the Microbeam Analysis Society), Ottawa, Canada, 1974, p 22
15. R.B. Marinenko, K.F.J. Heinrich, and F.C. Ruegg, "Micro-Homogeneity Studies of NBS Standard Reference Materials, NBS Research Materials, and Other Related Samples," NBS Special Publication 260-65, National Bureau of Standards, Gaithersburg, MD, 1979
16. J.W. Colby, *Adv. X-ray Anal.*, Vol 11, 1968, p 287
17. J. Henoc, K.F.J. Heinrich, and R.L. Myklebust, "A Rigorous Correction Procedure for Quantitative Electron Probe Microanalysis (COR 2)," NBS Technical Note 769, National Bureau of Standards, Gaithersburg, MD, 1973
18. H. Yakowitz, R.L. Myklebust, and K.F.J. Heinrich, "FRAME: An Online Correction Procedure for Quantitative Electron Probe Microanalysis," NBS Technical Note 796, National Bureau of Standards, Gaithersburg, MD, 1973
19. K.F.J. Heinrich, *Electron Beam X-ray Microanalysis*, Van Nostrand Reinhold, 1981, p 196-201
20. T.J. Piccone, D.B. Butrymowicz, D.E. Newbury, J.R. Manning, and J.W. Cahn, *Scr. Metall.*, Vol 16, 1982, p 839-843
21. R.B. Marinenko, R.L. Myklebust, D.S. Bright, and D.E. Newbury, *Microbeam Analysis—1985*, San Francisco Press, 1985, p 159-162
22. D.E. Newbury, D.C. Joy, P. Echlin, C.E. Fiori, and J.I. Goldstein, *Advanced Topics in Scanning Electron Microscopy and X-ray Microanalysis*, Plenum Press, 1986
23. R.L. Myklebust, J.A. Small, and D.E. Newbury, *Scan. Elec. Microsc.*, No. 1, 1981, p 477-481
24. K.F.J. Heinrich, R.L. Myklebust, S.D. Rasberry, and R.E. Michaelis, "Standard Reference Materials: Preparation and Evaluation of SRM's 481 and 482 Gold-Silver and Gold-Copper Alloys for Microanalysis," NBS Special Publication 260-28, National Bureau of Standards, Washington, DC, 1971
25. R.L. Myklebust and D.E. Newbury, *Microbeam Analysis—1979*, San Francisco Press, 1979, p 231-237
26. D.E. Newbury, *Anal. Chem.*, Vol 54, 1982, p 1059A-1064A
27. D.E. Newbury and S. Greenwald, *J. Res. Natl. Bur. Stand.*, Vol 85, 1980, p 429-440

Low-Energy Electron Diffraction

Max G. Lagally, Department of Metallurgical and Mineral Engineering, University of Wisconsin

General Uses
- Surface crystallography and microstructure
- Surface phase identification (adsorption, segregation, reconstruction)
- Analysis of surface dynamic processes (growth kinetics, thermal vibration)
- Determination of surface atom positions to 0.1 Å

Examples of Applications
- Reconstruction of semiconductor, metal, and alloy surfaces
- Analysis of chemical reactions at surfaces (chemisorbed layers)
- Influence of surface structure on catalytic processes
- Evolution of crystal structure in epitaxial growth
- Grain size determination in thin oriented films

Samples
- *Form*: Solids (metals and semiconductors; insulators in special cases). Single crystals or oriented films; polycrystalline samples with large grain size can be analyzed under special circumstances
- *Size*: 1 mm^2 to 25 cm^2 (0.0015 to 3.9 in.^{2})
- *Preparation*: Samples must be polished carefully to expose the appropriate surface orientation. Surface contaminants must be removed by annealing in vacuum, annealing in a low-pressure ($\leq 10^{-6}$ torr) oxidizing or reducing atmosphere to clean the surface chemically, or ion beam etching and annealing *in situ*. Some samples can be cleaved on appropriate crystallographic planes *in situ*; in this case, no further preparation is required

Limitations
- Samples must be at least slightly electrically conductive. Electrical charging of nonconductors is a problem
- Ultrahigh vacuum is required
- Determination of sizes of ordered regions (grains, islands, terraces, and so on) is limited by instrumental parameters to sizes less than approximately 500 nm
- Surface preparation is extensive and can be difficult

Estimated Analysis Time
- 10 min to 3 months, depending on information desired and initial condition of sample

Capabilities of Related Techniques
- *Reflection high-energy electron diffraction*: High-energy (~10 keV) analog of low-energy electron diffraction. Provides basically the same information as low-energy electron diffraction. However, some measurements—for example, atom positions—are more difficult than with low-energy electron diffraction; others—for example, three-dimensional crystal growth on surfaces—are facilitated
- *Glancing-angle x-ray diffraction*: More limited than low-energy electron diffraction, unless synchrotron radiation is used. Interpretation of atom positions is simpler. The structure of internal interfaces can be determined in special cases. Flat surfaces and large sample areas are required
- *Transmission electron microscopy, scanning transmission electron microscopy*: Many transmission electron or scanning transmission electron microscopes allow reflection diffraction. This is analogous to reflection high-energy electron diffraction, but the use of higher-energy electron beams (of the order of 100 keV) requires very shallow angles of incidence for surface sensitivity. Standard transmission electron and scanning transmission electron microscopes do not operate under ultrahigh vacuum conditions

Introduction

Low-energy electron diffraction (LEED) is a technique for investigating the crystallography of surfaces and overlayers adsorbed on surfaces. It is the surface analog of x-ray diffraction, which is sensitive to bulk crystallography. Low-energy electron diffraction is generally performed with electrons from 30 to several hundred electron volts. The limited penetration of electrons in this energy range provides the sensitivity to the surface.

Low-energy electron diffraction measurements are conducted using a monoenergetic beam of electrons that impinges on the crystal surface. Diffraction of electrons occurs because of the periodic arrangement of atoms in the surface. This periodic arrangement can be conceptualized as parallel rows of atoms analogous to grating lines in a diffraction grating. Thus, the diffraction in LEED occurs from rows, unlike x-ray diffraction, which can be considered as occurring from planes. The diffracted beams emanate from the crystal surface in directions satisfying interference conditions from these rows of atoms. The diffraction pattern and the intensity distribution in the diffracted beams can provide information on the positions of atoms in the surface and on the existence of various crystallographic defects in the periodic arrangement of surface atoms. In its most elementary form, LEED can be used to test for the existence of overlayer phases having a two-dimensional crystal structure different from the surface on which they are adsorbed and to test whether a surface phase is ordered or disordered.

Although LEED is the best known and most widely used surface crystallographic technique, other diffraction techniques can provide information on the surface structure. Reflection high-energy electron diffraction (RHEED) is applied widely to the epitaxial growth of films. X-ray diffraction can also be used for surface crystallography under appropriate conditions.

Surface Crystallography Vocabulary

If an imaginary plane is drawn somewhere through a perfectly periodic three-dimensional crystal, and the two halves of the crystal are separated along this plane, ideal surfaces are formed. If the imaginary plane corresponds to an (hkl) plane in the bulk crystal, the surface is defined as an (hkl) surface, using the usual Miller indices. Bonds between atoms must be broken to create a surface. The coordination number defines the number of nearest neighbors of

Fig. 1 Singular (a) and vicinal (b) surfaces of a cubic lattice

The solid circles represent atoms having missing nearest-neighbor bonds. The dashed line defines the surface orientation (hkl) with surface normal [hkl].

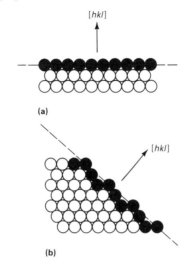

any atom in the crystal structure. The necessity of breaking bonds to create a surface implies a coordination number for surface atoms that is lower than that of atoms in the bulk. Surfaces can be singular or vicinal (Fig. 1). A singular surface is one in which only atoms in the outermost layer have broken nearest-neighbor bonds (reduced coordination number). It corresponds to a low Miller index plane. For example, (111) and (100) surfaces of face-centered cubic (fcc) crystals and the (110) surface of body-centered cubic (bcc) crystals are singular. Most surfaces are vicinal; that is, some atoms in deeper layers also have broken nearest-neighbor bonds. Such surfaces can be pictured as rougher and more open, with lower atomic density as well as a reduced average coordination number per unit surface area than singular surfaces. The average coordination number is also generally a measure of surface reactivity. Vicinal surfaces have a higher surface energy and are less stable than singular surfaces because of the larger number of broken bonds per unit area.

The periodic arrangement of atoms in the surface can be viewed as a two-dimensional lattice; that is, every point in this arrangement can be reached by a translation vector. The smallest translation vectors define the unit mesh, the two-dimensional analog of the unit cell. Primitive unit meshes contain one lattice point per mesh; nonprimitive, more than one lattice point per mesh. Figure 2(a) shows the five two-dimensional Bravais nets. The unit mesh vectors are conventionally defined, as shown, with the angle be-

Fig. 2 Unit meshes and two-dimensional Miller indices

(a) The five two-dimensional Bravais nets. (b) Examples of families of rows with Miller indices referenced to the unit mesh vectors. (11) and (31) families of rows are shown.

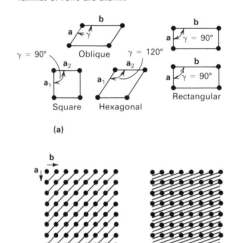

tween the unit vectors $\geq 90°$, **a** denoting the shorter unit vector, and **b** (aligned horizontally) the longer one. A two-dimensional lattice may also have a basis. The lattice is defined by those points that can be reached by a translation vector. The basis is the conformation of atoms around each of these points.

The arrangement of lattice points in a two-dimensional lattice can be visualized as sets of parallel rows. The orientation of these rows can be defined by two-dimensional Miller indices (hk) (Fig. 2b). Interrow distances can then be expressed in terms of two-dimensional Miller indices, just as they are for three-dimensional crystals. For example, for square or rectangular primitive unit meshes, the interrow distance d_{hk} is:

$$d_{hk} = \left[\frac{h^2}{\mathbf{a}^2} + \frac{k^2}{\mathbf{b}^2} \right]^{-1/2} \quad \text{(Eq 1)}$$

where **a** and **b** are the unit mesh vectors.

In the discussion so far, an ideal termination of the bulk crystal has been assumed at the surface; that is, the positions of atoms in the surface have been assumed to be the same as those they would have in the bulk before the surface was created. This need not be true. Reconstruction, a rearrangement of atoms in the surface and near-surface layers, occurs frequently. It is caused by an attempt of the surface to lower its free energy by eliminating broken bonds. The atomic layers participating in this reconstruction can then

Fig. 3 Examples of overlayer structures with appropriate notation

(a) fcc (100)p(2 × 2). (b) fcc (100)c(2 × 2). (c) fcc (111)p($\sqrt{3}$ × $\sqrt{3}$)R30°. (d) bcc (110)p(2 × 1) and bcc (110)p(1 × 2). The two orientations for the unit mesh in (d) are both possible because of the symmetry of the substrate; they have the same free energy and are termed degenerate.

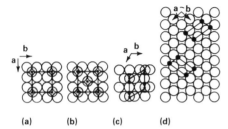

(a) (b) (c) (d)

be considered a different phase having a different periodic arrangement of atoms. This region is sometimes referred to as a selvedge.

Even when no reconstruction occurs, adsorption of a foreign species onto the substrate surface from the ambient gas, from a deliberately created beam of atoms, or as a consequence of segregation of an impurity out of the bulk creates a surface phase termed an overlayer. An overlayer can be a fraction of a single atomic layer or several atomic layers. Thicker overlayers are referred to as thin films. The overlayer phase has its own crystal structure, which may or may not be related in a simple manner to that of the substrate surface.

An overlayer may be commensurate or incommensurate with the substrate. Commensurate overlayers have unit meshes that are related by simple rational numbers to those of the substrates on which they are adsorbed. This is not true for incommensurate layers. The unit mesh of overlayers is defined as a multiple of that unit mesh of the substrate surface that would be produced by the ideal termination of the bulk lattice. Thus, (100) and (111) surfaces of an fcc crystal have square and parallelogram-shaped primitive unit meshes, respectively (Fig. 2a), both of which would be considered (1 × 1) unit meshes. Commensurate overlayer unit meshes are then p(m × n) or c(m × n), where p and c refer to primitive and centered overlayer unit meshes relative to the primitive substrate unit mesh, and m and n are constants. An example of a complete unit mesh description of an overlayer on a particular substrate is W(110) p(2 × 1)−O, which describes an oxygen overlayer adsorbed on the (110) surface of tungsten having a unit mesh twice that of the primitive W(110) unit mesh in the **a** direc-

tion and the same as the W(110) unit mesh in the **b** direction.

The overlayer unit mesh is sometimes rotated relative to that of the substrate (Fig. 3). An example of such a notation is Ni(111) ($\sqrt{3}$ × $\sqrt{3}$) R30°−O. The symmetry of the substrate is often such that it permits formation of energetically equivalent structures rotated relative to each other by some specific amount. Domains having such symmetry-related structure are called rotational antiphase domains and are degenerate; that is, they have the same free energy, and there is no preference for formation of one over the other. Overlayers with (m × n) meshes generally also form (n × m) meshes; for example, p(2 × 1) → p(1 × 2) and c(2 × 4) → c(4 × 2) (Fig. 3d).

Principles of Diffraction From Surfaces

Diffraction from surfaces can be viewed most simply as the scattering of waves from families of lattice rows that connect scattering centers lying in a single plane (Fig. 4). If a wave with wavelength λ is permitted to fall at an angle of incidence θ_0 onto a family of rows, each separated by a distance d_{hk}, the two-dimensional Laue condition can be calculated for constructive interference between incoming and outgoing waves by considering the difference in paths traveled by the rays striking two adjacent rows of atoms.

One can see that:

$$\lambda = d_{hk} (\sin \theta_{hk} - \sin \theta_0) \quad \text{(Eq 2)}$$

where the difference in paths traveled by two adjacent rays is one wavelength. For higher order reflections ($m > 1$):

$$m\lambda = d_{hk} (\sin \theta_{mh,mk} - \sin \theta_0) \quad \text{(Eq 3)}$$

where the path difference is m wavelengths. The wavelength λ of electrons (in angstroms) is related to their energy E (given in electron volts) by:

$$\lambda(\mathring{A}) = \sqrt{\frac{150}{E(eV)}} \quad \text{(Eq 4)}$$

For a fixed incident-beam energy, that is, a fixed wavelength, and a fixed angle of incidence, each family of (hk) rows diffracts radiation at the appropriate exit angle, θ_{hk}. If a fluorescent screen or other detector is positioned to intercept these scattered beams, a diffraction pattern having the symmetry of the surface or overlayer unit mesh will be observed (Fig. 5). At the center of the pattern will be the (00) beam, which has a path difference of zero and is therefore not

Fig. 4 Diffraction from a family of rows spaced d_{hk} apart and its dependence on wavelength

Each solid circle represents a row of atoms into the plane of the paper. Rays with wavelength λ fall on this family of rows at an angle θ_0. Interference maxima occur at angles θ_{hk} that satisfy Eq 2. Only the first-order reflection is shown. (a) Longer wavelength. (b) Shorter wavelength

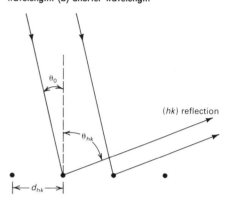

sensitive to d_{hk}, that is, to the relative lateral positions of the surface atoms. Around it will be the first-order diffracted beams from each family of possible rows that can be drawn through the surface atoms, for example, (10), (01), (11), (21), and so on. In addition, there will be higher-order reflections at larger angles. For example, the (20) and (30) reflections will fall on the extension of a line connecting the (00) and (10) beams; the (00), (11), (22), (33), . . . beams will be colinear; and so forth.

If the energy of the incident beam or the angle of incidence is changed, the diffraction angles θ_{hk} adjust to continue to satisfy the Laue conditions. For example, if the energy is increased, the entire pattern will appear to shrink around the (00) beam because θ_{hk} becomes smaller.

The diffraction conditions can be depicted most easily using a reciprocal lattice and Ewald construction (Fig. 6). The Ewald

Fig. 5 Interference pattern created when regularly spaced atoms scatter a plane wave incident on them

A spherical wave emanates from each atom; diffracted beams form at the directions of constructive interference between these waves. The mirror reflection [(00) beam] and the first- and second-order diffracted beams are shown.

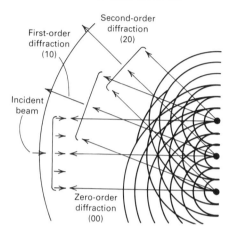

sphere provides a schematic description of the conservation of energy; that is, because diffraction involves elastic scattering, the incident and exiting beams have the same energy. Its radius is inversely proportional to the wavelength λ. The reciprocal lattice for a single layer of atoms consisting of families of rows is a set of rods (hk) normal to the crystal surface with spacing $2\pi/d_{hk}$. The intersection of the Ewald sphere and the reciprocal-lattice rods is a graphical solution of the Laue equation and therefore yields the diffraction pattern. As the energy of the incident beam or the angle of incidence is varied, the radius of the Ewald sphere or its orientation relative to the rods changes, consequently also changing the points of intersection with the rods. The directions of the outgoing vectors define the directions of the diffracted beams.

The discussion of diffraction so far has made no reference to the size of the two-dimensional "grating." It has been assumed that the grating is infinite. As in three dimensions, finite sizes of the ordered regions on the surface (finite-size gratings) broaden the diffraction features. This can be confirmed by calculating the amplitude, $A(S)$, scattered from a grating consisting of N rows spaced a distance d_{hk} apart:

$$A(S) = \sum_{n=1}^{N} f_n \, e^{iS \cdot r_n} \qquad \text{(Eq 5)}$$

where S is the momentum transfer vector $S = k - k_0$, $|S| = 2\pi/\lambda - 2\pi/\lambda_0$, f_n is the

atomic scattering factor of the nth atom, and r_n is the position of the nth atom. The exponent represents the phase factor in summing up waves scattered from different atoms at positions r_n. The scattered intensity I_{hk} from the (hk) family of rows is:

$$I_{hk} = AA^* = \frac{\sin^2 \frac{1}{2} N \, S_{hk} d_{hk}}{\sin^2 \frac{1}{2} S_{hk} d_{hk}} \qquad \text{(Eq 6)}$$

where A^* is the complex conjugate of A. For $N = \infty$, I_{hk} is a δ function, but for finite N, it is a function having a width proportional to $1/Nd_{hk}$. Thus, the smaller N is, the broader is the diffraction peak. A measurement of the angular profile of the diffracted beams provides information on two-dimensional particle (island) size effects and other finite-size effects in the surface or overlayer. In terms of the unit mesh vectors a and b:

$$I(S) = \frac{\sin^2 \frac{1}{2} S \cdot N_1 a}{\sin^2 \frac{1}{2} S \cdot a} \frac{\sin^2 \frac{1}{2} S \cdot N_2 b}{\sin^2 \frac{1}{2} S \cdot b} \text{(Eq 7)}$$

where $N_1 a$, $N_2 b$ are the average dimensions of the islands or domains of the surface layer. The width of the angular profile is correspondingly $1/N_1 a$ and $1/N_2 b$ in the a and b directions.

If an overlayer with a superlattice exists, additional diffracted beams appear that correspond to the periodicity of the superlattice. A larger unit mesh yields diffracted beams that are nearer each other (Eq 2) (Fig. 7).

Diffraction Measurements

Figure 8 is a schematic of a typical LEED system. The electron gun can produce a monoenergetic beam having energies from approximately 10 to 1000 eV, with beam sizes typically a fraction of a millimeter, but ranging in newer instruments to submicron sizes (additional information on electron guns is provided in the article "Analytical Transmission Electron Microscopy" in this Volume). The goniometer generally allows two sample motions: a rocking about an axis in the plane of the crystal surface and a rotation about an axis normal to the crystal surface. In addition, the goniometer generally permits heating and sometimes cooling of the sample as well as temperature measurement. Most LEED systems have a detector consisting of concentric grids and a fluorescent screen (Fig. 8). The grids filter inelastically scattered electrons that also emanate from the crystal surface. In addition, a Faraday cup detector for accurate measure-

Fig. 6 Reciprocal lattice and Ewald construction corresponding to LEED and comparison to real-space picture

(a) Real-space schematic diagram of diffraction from a surface. The electron beam is incident on the sample along the direction given by e^-. The five diffracted beams represent the $(\overline{2h}\ \overline{2k})$, $(\overline{h}\overline{k})$, (00), (hk), and $(2h\ 2k)$ beams from a family of rows (hk) with spacing d_{hk}. (b) The corresponding cut through the reciprocal lattice and Ewald construction. The reciprocal-lattice rods are normal to the crystal surface, given by the nearly horizontal line. They represent the same set of beams as above. The Ewald sphere always intersects the origin of the reciprocal lattice at the point of incidence of the incoming ray. Directions of the diffracted beams depend on the radius of the Ewald sphere ($2\pi/\lambda$). Similarly, as the orientation of the crystal surface is changed in relation to the incident beam, the reciprocal lattice rotates about its origin.

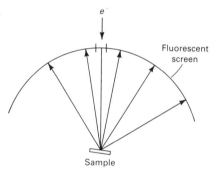

(a)

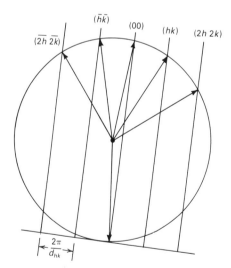

(b)

ment of beam currents and beam profiles can be used. The Faraday cup is biased to exclude inelastically scattered electrons. A RHEED system is similar, except the beam energy is higher, and the diffraction geometry is arranged to provide grazing incidence and exit (Fig. 9).

Fig. 7 Diffraction pattern from a superlattice

(a) Rectangular substrate lattice and corresponding diffraction pattern showing fundamental reflections. (b) Substrate plus $p(2 \times 1)$ overlayer and corresponding diffraction pattern showing fundamental and superlattice reflections. The overlayer atoms (x's) are arbitrarily shown to sit on top of the substrate atoms.

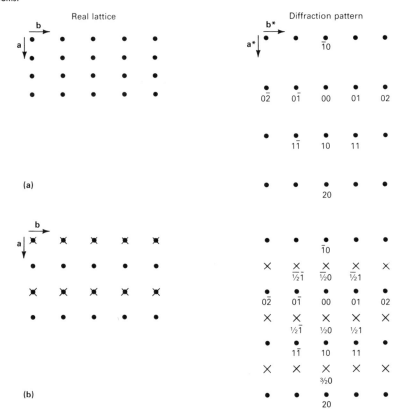

Fig. 8 LEED diffractometer

The vidicon camera can be interfaced with a computer to record the diffraction pattern displayed on the fluorescent screen.

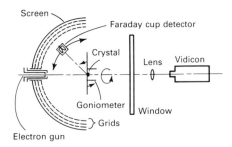

Fig. 9 RHEED system that uses a fluorescent screen to display and a photomultiplier to record the diffraction pattern

A heater is shown behind the sample. The incident beam (top) strikes the surface at grazing angles.

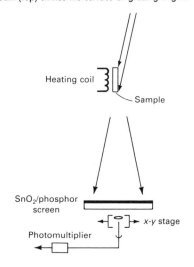

Fig. 10 Mean free path for inelastic scattering of electrons as a function of energy

Electrons in the LEED energy range travel only of the order of 4 to 20 Å in the crystal before losing energy and thus becoming lost for diffraction. Surface sensitivity is a consequence of this behavior.

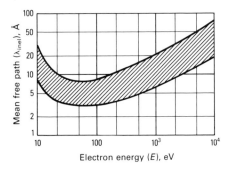

The surface sensitivity in LEED is provided by the limited mean free path for inelastic scattering of slow electrons. This mean free path is the distance traveled by an electron in the solid before it collides inelastically, loses energy, and thus becomes lost for diffraction. The mean free path in the energy range of LEED is from 4 to 20 Å. Because a layer spacing is of the order of 3 Å, these slow electrons probe only a few atomic layers. Although in the section "Principles of Diffraction From Surfaces" in this article it was assumed that only one layer contributed, the basic principles still apply. In RHEED, the same effect is obtained by grazing incidence, maintaining the beam near the surface in this manner. Figure 10 shows a mean free path versus energy curve.

The simplest diffraction measurement is determination of the surface or overlayer unit mesh size and shape. This can be performed by inspection of the diffraction pattern at any energy of the incident beam. The determination is simplest if the electron beam is incident normal to the surface, because the symmetry of the pattern is then preserved.

Diffracted beams are indexed with the (hk) notation of the families of rows from which they are diffracted. Thus, the (10) beam is scattered from (10) rows in the direction perpendicular to these rows. The distance of the (hk) reflection from the mirror reflection, the (00) beam, is inversely related to the (hk) interrow distance (Fig. 7). Figure 11 shows diffraction patterns obtained from GaAs (110) cleaved in ultrahigh vacuum (UHV).

In the analysis of a diffraction pattern, it first must be determined which diffracted beams belong to the substrate pattern and which are due to the superperiodicity of the overlayer. This can be accomplished experimentally by observing diffraction from the substrate surface without the overlayer adsorbed (Fig. 7a), then adsorbing the overlayer (Fig. 7b). Alternatively, the diffraction pattern of the ideal surface can be calculated from knowing the crystal structure of the bulk sample and the orientation at which it was cut and assuming that the surface is the ideal termination of the bulk lattice.

For example, the unit mesh of an fcc (110) surface appears rectangular (Fig. 7a). The

Fig. 11 Diffraction patterns from GaAs (110)

(a) LEED pattern near normal incidence, E_p = 100 eV. (b) RHEED pattern, incident beam along [100] azimuth at grazing angle of incidence of 4.5°, E_p = 10 keV. The lowest arc of spots corresponds to the $(\bar{2}0)$, $(\bar{1}0)$, (00), (10), and (20) beams.

(a)

(b)

Fig. 12 Possible placements of overlayer atoms on an fcc (100) substrate that produce a $c(2 \times 2)$ overlayer unit mesh

The diffraction pattern from these structures differs in the intensities of the diffracted beams, but not in the symmetry of the pattern.

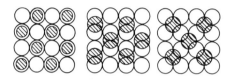

Fig. 13 Measured intensity versus energy curve for the (00) beam from W (110) at an incident angle θ_0 = 7°

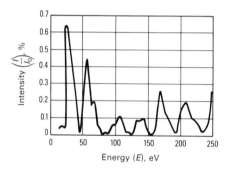

diffraction pattern from a rectangle can be calculated to be a rectangle rotated by 90° relative to the real lattice (Fig. 7b). The unit distances, a^*, b^*, in the diffraction pattern are related to the real-space unit mesh by $a^* = 2\pi/a$ and $b^* = 2\pi/b$. Once the substrate diffraction pattern is known, the unit mesh for the overlayer can be determined by constructing reciprocal-space unit distance $a^*_{overlayer}$ and $b^*_{overlayer}$. If the patterns are aligned relative to orientation:

$$a^*_{overlayer} = \frac{1}{m} a^*_{substrate} \qquad (Eq\ 8)$$

$$b^*_{overlayer} = \frac{1}{n} b^*_{substrate} \qquad (Eq\ 9)$$

From the relationship between reciprocal and real-space vectors, the unit mesh of the overlayer is (m, n) times that of the substrate. In the general case, the patterns may not be aligned:

$$a^*_{overlayer} = \frac{1}{m_1} a^*_{substrate}$$
$$+ \frac{1}{m_2} b^*_{substrate} \qquad (Eq\ 10)$$

$$b^*_{overlayer} = \frac{1}{n_1} a^*_{substrate}$$
$$+ \frac{1}{n_2} b^*_{substrate} \qquad (Eq\ 11)$$

The unit mesh of the overlayer can be determined directly by solving Eq 10 and 11 in terms of the relationships $a^* = 2\pi/a$ and $b^* = 2\pi/b$.

The diffraction pattern determines only the size and shape of the unit mesh. The positions of overlayer atoms relative to substrate atoms, that is, the arrangement of

atoms within the unit mesh, cannot be determined from visual inspection of the diffraction pattern, but must be obtained from an analysis of the intensities of the diffracted beams as a function of diffraction parameters, particularly the energy and the angles at which the diffracted beams emerge relative to the surface normal.

Figure 12 shows three fcc $(100)c(2 \times 2)$ overlayer structures. All yield the same diffraction pattern, but the intensities of the beams differ. An analogy is provided by the missing reflections in x-ray diffraction from particular three-dimensional structures, in which the intensity of certain beams is zero. In two dimensions, the intensity of some beams may also be zero, but different positions of overlayer atoms generally make some beams weaker than others at particular diffraction conditions. This can be visualized as an interference between the substrate atoms and the overlayer atoms that differs for different positions of overlayer atoms. A calculation of the geometric structure factor for each of the overlayer unit meshes will demonstrate these differences in diffracted-beam intensities.

To determine lateral and vertical positions of overlayer atoms relative to those of the substrate atoms, the intensity in a diffracted beam is measured as a function of the incident-beam energy. These intensity versus energy curves are then compared to model calculations of the geometric structure factor. The existence of an intensity contribution in diffracted beams due to the multiple scattering of electrons off surface rows and between substrate and overlayer makes this determination more complicated than this discussion suggests. Figure 13 shows a measured intensity versus energy profile.

If the overlayer or surface structure is not perfect, that is, does not have long-range

periodicity, the diffracted beams show a change in shape. A common occurrence in LEED or RHEED is the existence of streaks, large spots, and additional diffuse intensity in the pattern, indicating the presence of structural disorder. A measurement of the angular profile of diffracted beams provides information on disorder and finite-size effects in surfaces analogous to x-ray diffraction measurements of three-dimensional particle sizes or strains. The measurement of angular profiles as a function of diffraction parameters, such as energy, angles, and beam order, makes it possible to distinguish among various defects, such as finite island sizes, strain, crystal mosaic, monatomic and multiatomic steps at the surface, and regular or irregular domain or antiphase boundaries. To measure a profile, a detector with a narrow slit or a point aperture must be used to minimize the influence of instrumental broadening. Figure 14 shows an example of a two-dimensional angular profile (intensity versus θ_x and θ_y) using a surface-sensitive diffractometer.

Sample Preparation

All surface-sensitive diffraction must occur in a vacuum system, and in most cases,

Fig. 14 Two-dimensional angular profile of a diffracted beam

The (00) beam from a slightly misoriented silicon surface is shown; $E = 235$ eV and $\theta_0 = 8°$. Such a surface can be conceptualized as a staircase with wide terraces and monatomic risers. The splitting of the diffracted beam reflects the terrace size.

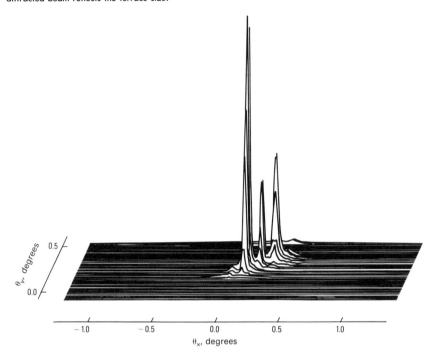

measured independently using, for example, Auger electron spectroscopy (additional information is provided in the article "Auger Electron Spectroscopy" in this Volume).

Limitations of Surface-Sensitive Electron Diffraction

Surface-sensitive diffraction is in general limited to analysis of surfaces of single crystals and overlayers and films on such surfaces. If a polycrystalline sample is illuminated using a beam of low-energy electrons, each crystallite surface exposed will create its own diffraction pattern, all of which will be superimposed on the fluorescent screen. If more than a few orientations are illuminated by the beam, the pattern becomes too complicated to analyze. However, non-single-crystal films having preferred crystalline orientation in the surface plane can be analyzed. For example, a silver thin film, grown on mica, that has a (111) orientation and twin boundaries as its major defect appears in the LEED pattern as a (111) surface of a single crystal of silver, except the spots are broader, and their behavior with diffraction parameters reveals the existence of twin boundaries. If the film had (111) orientation, but with a random azimuthal orientation (random rotations around the surface normal), diffraction would still be possible, but the spots would turn into rings.

Any two-dimensional disorder is observable. Analysis of some three-dimensional disorder—for example, the random orientation of surface normals in a polycrystalline sample—is limited essentially by the instrument, particularly the size of the incident beam. As this size is reduced to typical grain sizes (≤ 1000 Å), surface-sensitive diffraction can be used to investigate the surface crystallography of polycrystalline samples by analyzing individual grains of a polished sample sequentially.

Similarly, analysis of the surfaces of liquids and amorphous solids is not meaningful. In this case, however, the problem is fundamental and not simply instrumental. Diffraction is useful whenever there is a distinct phase relationship between scattering units. The greater the degree of this phase relationship, the better defined are the diffraction features. Three-dimensional crystals give diffraction spots. If disorder is introduced, the spots broaden and weaken. Two-dimensional structures give diffraction rods. Disorder in the plane broadens the rods, and in the case of complete in-plane randomness, converts them into cylinders observed as diffraction rings. Disorder out of

this must be a UHV system. A high vacuum is necessary because surface contamination rates from ambient gases are rapid. A useful criterion is that formation of one monolayer of contamination, such as hydrogen, oxygen, or carbon monoxide, on the surface requires of the order of 1 s at 10^{-6} torr (1.3×10^{-4} Pa). Even a fraction of a monolayer is sufficient to prevent meaningful surface crystallography measurements. Thus, except for the most unreactive surfaces, a vacuum exceeding 10^{-10} torr (1.3×10^{-8} Pa) is essential.

Contaminated surfaces generally do not provide diffraction patterns. Because the beam penetration is so small, even a few layers of adsorbed gas or oxide can mask the underlying pattern. In some cases, the oxide (or other surface phase) is crystalline and exhibits its own, generally very complicated, diffraction pattern. Therefore, the surface must be cleaned.

The ideal surface preparation method is cleavage in vacuum. Cleavage exposes an internal interface that has not been subjected to ambient atmospheric contamination. The diffraction patterns shown in Fig. 11 are from cleaved GaAs, producing a (110) surface. However, cleavage is limited to a few crystals and a few surfaces.

Samples not cleaved in vacuum must be cut from a single crystal, polished, and oriented carefully to the desired surface us-

ing a Laue diffraction camera. Standard polishing procedures are used. These samples must then be chemically or ion-bombardment cleaned *in situ*. Chemical cleaning generally consists of oxidation-reduction cycles in oxygen and hydrogen combined with annealing cycles. In a few cases, simple annealing cycles in vacuum produce clean surfaces. The most prevalent approach is a combination of inert-gas ion bombardment (sputter etching) of the surface with subsequent annealing to reorder the lattice. Ion bombardment cleans the surface effectively, but leaves it so disordered that no diffraction pattern is generally observable. Subsequent annealing restores most of the order, but the reordering is never complete. Sputter etching is not advisable in some applications, notably where structural defects influence such properties as thin film growth or chemical interactions at surfaces.

Overlayer deposition for volatile species is accomplished using a gas-handling system consisting of a gas bottle or other source of vapor and a set of control valves. For non-volatile species, an evaporation source is used that consists of a container for the source material inside an apertured can, a heater, and a cooled shroud that acts as a cryopump to prevent increase of the vacuum system pressure during deposition. Many materials can be deposited easily in this manner. The coverage in both cases can be

Fig. 15 Diffraction patterns from oriented pyrolytic graphite
(a) Freshly cleaved sample. (b to d) Increasing surface damage caused by ion beam etching

(a)

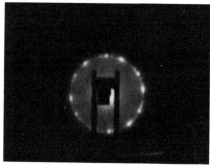

(b)

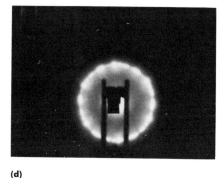

(c)

(d)

the plane, as in an amorphous solid or a fine-grained polycrystalline solid with random orientations, moves these rods over all space, creating only diffuse intensity and no pattern.

Because electrons are charged, only materials having reasonable conductivity can be investigated. Insulators and ceramics pose difficulties because a charge accumulates on the sample that eventually prevents the incident beam from striking the surface. The usual approach of coating insulators to make them conductive is ineffective because the coating, although only a few atomic layers thick, prevents diffraction from the substrate surface. Most insulators can be investigated with special techniques, such as providing surface conduction paths near the analysis area or using very thin samples mounted on a conducting plate.

Applications

Example 1: Wettability of Graphite.
The wettability of a material is often an important consideration. In some applications, a wettable surface is desired, for example, the flow of ink in a fountain pen; in others, a nonwettable surface is needed,

such as polymer film or foil. Surface wettability can be determined by contact angle measurements.

One possible influence on surface wettability is roughness on an atomic scale. Such roughness is too small to observe in optical or scanning electron microscopes. Using these techniques, an atomically rough surface may appear featureless, yet it may have a considerably different wettability than one that is atomically smooth. Graphite is a useful material with which to conduct roughness-wettability correlations, because it is chemically fairly inert. Thus, it is possible to separate chemical changes that may influence wettability from structural ones. Graphite also illustrates the capabilities of LEED for analysis of materials that are not single crystals.

A high-purity commercially available pyrolytic graphite called oriented graphite was used. This material has the basal [(0001)] plane oriented parallel to the surface. The sample was cleaved in air and mounted in a LEED vacuum chamber.

After degassing the chamber, Auger electron spectroscopy (AES) was used to determine that the sample surface was clean. The vacuum chamber also has capabilities for ion

beam etching of the surface and for contact angle measurements *in situ*. The experiment consisted of ion beam etching the surface to make it atomically rough, observing the changes in the diffraction pattern, and correlating the changes in contact angle to the LEED results.

Figure 15 shows the LEED results. The freshly cleaved sample (Fig. 15a) exhibits a hexagonal diffraction pattern that reflects the symmetry of the graphite unit mesh. It also shows other weaker spots, which indicate that the arrangement of atoms on the surface is not perfect, but that some in-plane rotational randomness exists. Therefore, the graphite sample is oriented in terms of having only (0001) planes in the surface, but crystallites can be rotated relative to each other.

Figures 15(b) to (d) show LEED patterns from the graphite sample, with increasing surface crystallographic damage caused by ion beam etching. Two effects are evident. At first, the sample becomes more rotationally random, that is, planes with various rotations become evident, but all still with a (0001) orientation in the plane. Analysis of the intensity of the various diffraction spots can determine the percentage of crystallites having a given orientation. In Fig. 15(c), the sample begins to approach the randomness that would be evident in a two-dimensional liquid, in which a bright ring would be observed.

Figure 15(d) shows a new effect. The diffraction spots begin to broaden. This is evidence of a decrease in the size of the individual graphite grains. A measurement of the increase in the width of the reflection relative to the width of reflection in the initial surface (Fig. 15a) can be interpreted in terms of the decrease in size of the crystallites. The crystallites shown in Fig. 15(a) are approximately 10 nm in diameter; those shown in Fig. 15(d) are approximately half that. In this experiment, a direct correlation between wettability and surface roughness was observed: the rougher the surface, the greater its wettability.

Example 2: Grain Size in a Silver Film Grown on Mica.
Vacuum evaporation is a common technique for preparing thin film coatings that have application in various technologies.

In vacuum evaporation, a crucible containing the source material is heated to temperatures high enough to create a significant evaporation rate. The surfaces to be coated are then placed into the evaporant stream, and the source atoms adhere to this surface. Because of the directionality of the flux and the generally low temperatures at the substrate, a columnar microstructure with a preferred orientation frequently forms. In

Fig. 16 Schematic diagram of a thin film with columnar growth morphology

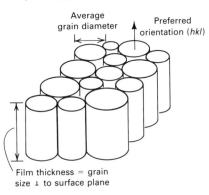

Average grain diameter

Preferred orientation (*hkl*)

Film thickness = grain size ⊥ to surface plane

many cases, this preference for some orientation can be beneficial.

Two aspects of the microstructure are significant: the preferred orientation and the size of the columnar grains. The preferred orientation of a film can be ascertained using a standard x-ray diffractometer by comparing a θ-2θ scan to one from a powder of the same material. This type of measurement also provides the grain size in the vertical direction (the average height of the columns), but does not easily provide information about the average diameter of the columns.

Figure 16 illustrates the desired parameters. With LEED, the preferred orientation and the grain size in the surface plane (but not in the vertical direction) can be measured. Low-energy electron diffraction (or more commonly RHEED) can also be combined with the evaporator to study the microstructure of the growing film in real time.

In this instance, a 100-nm-thick silver film was grown on a clean mica substrate using an electron beam evaporation source. The film was grown at a rate of 10 nm/min. The sample was then inserted into a LEED vacuum chamber, and surface contaminants were removed by heating the sample to approximately 500 °C (930 °F) in a partial pressure of 1×10^{-5} torr of oxygen. This removed all contaminants except for a trace of carbon.

A LEED diffraction pattern of the surface was then formed by illuminating the film surface with an electron beam of approximately 100 eV at normal incidence. If a preferred orientation is present, a diffraction pattern corresponding to the symmetry of the exposed surface plane will be observed. It was found that the silver film had a very strong preferential (111) orientation; that is, the growth direction was [111]. It was possible to determine that the average misori-

entation from (111) was less than 0.25°. However, extensive twinning was found in the crystal.

Twinning in this type of crystal structure is caused by stacking faults. The normal sequence of planes in an fcc (111) stacking is ABCABC. That is, every third plane is alike. A stacking fault occurs if the stacking is ABCABABC, a common occurrence in the growth of such structures. The result is crystal structures that have a 60° rotational relationship to each other. These are termed twins. Twins can be identified in the LEED pattern because they make the diffraction pattern sixfold symmetric instead of threefold symmetric, as would be expected for an fcc (111) surface.

The average grain size in the plane of the surface, that is, the average column diameter, of the oriented silver film was determined by analysis of the diffracted beam shape in the LEED pattern. The width of diffracted beams is inversely related to the average column diameter. By measuring the beam shape at various diffraction parameters, the average in-plane grain size was determined to be 7.5 ± 1.5 nm. Thus, the film consisted of oriented (111) columns of approximately 7.5 nm diameter that were rotationally very well aligned (unlike Example 1), but contained a significant concentration of twins.

Any possible strain in the surface plane was also investigated by examining the diffraction profiles of higher order reflections. The results indicate that no strain was present in the surface plane; this was expected in light of the small column size.

Other Applications. The unit mesh size and shape of an overlayer adsorbed on a single crystal can be determined by observing the diffraction pattern. The positions of overlayer atoms relative to the substrate atoms can be determined from model calculations to fit intensity versus energy measurements of several diffracted beams.

The density of steps on a single-crystal surface can be determined by varying the diffraction conditions such that the amplitudes of electrons scattered from terraces separated by a step interfere destructively. The angular profile of the diffracted beams then reflects the average terrace size, and from this the step density is readily obtained. For the example shown in Fig. 14, the average terrace size is 300 Å, with a distribution of terrace sizes of ±100 Å about this average value.

Order-disorder and order-order transitions in two-dimensional overlayers can be studied in the same manner that x-ray diffraction is used for three-dimensional phase transformations. The intensity of a superlattice reflection is monitored as a function of the

temperature at constant coverage or as a function of the coverage at constant temperature. When a phase boundary is crossed, the superlattice beam intensity vanishes. The transition type (first or second order) and the critical exponents can be determined from the mechanics of this process. Order-disorder phenomena in surface phases of binary alloys and in reconstructed surfaces can also be investigated in this manner. The enthalpies of interaction of overlayer atoms can be modeled from the transition temperatures.

The kinetics of overlayer growth at the submonolayer level and above can be investigated by following the development of reflections belonging to the overlayer structure. Nucleation and growth of an ordered phase, α, proceeds out of a two-phase coexistence region, α + β, in which the component of interest (A) has a supersaturation. The α phase forms to eliminate this supersaturation. The existence of the overlayer phase can be ascertained from the existence of diffracted beams corresponding to it. The size distribution of ordered two-dimensional islands (analogous to a three-dimensional precipitate of α in β) can be determined from the angular profiles of the relevant diffracted beams. As the islands grow, the profiles become narrower. The kinetics of growth can be investigated by measuring the average island size as a function of time for a given temperature. Activation energies for the process can be extracted. Domain growth (recrystallization) in an oriented film or a monolayer can be investigated in this manner.

The thermodynamics of surface or grain-boundary segregation of a binary or ternary trace element in a solid can be investigated by monitoring the absence or presence of a surface phase ascribable to this element as a function of temperature. Free energies for segregation and solution can be established from the behavior with temperature.

ACKNOWLEDGMENT

Preparation of this article was supported by the Office of Naval Research.

SELECTED REFERENCES

- G. Ertl and J. Küppers, *Low-Energy Electrons and Surface Chemistry*, Verlag Chemie, 1974, Chapters 9, 10
- P.J. Estrup, in *Modern Diffraction and Imaging Techniques in Materials Science*, S. Amelinckx, R. Gevers, G. Remaut, and J. Van Landuyt, Ed., North-Holland, 1970
- P.J. Estrup and E.G. McRae, *Surf. Sci.*, Vol 25, 1971, p 1
- M. Henzler, *Top. Curr. Phys.*, Vol 4, 1977, p 117

- M. Henzler, *Appl. Surf. Sci.*, Vol 11/12, 1982, p 450
- M.G. Lagally, *Appl. Surf. Sci.*, Vol 13, 1982, p 260
- M.G. Lagally, *Springer Ser. Chem. Phys.*, Vol 20, 1982, p 281
- J.J. Lander, *Prog. Solid State Chem.*, Vol 2, 1965, p 26
- J.W. May, *Adv. Catal.*, Vol 21, 1970, p 152
- R.L. Park and M.G. Lagally, Ed., *Methods of Experimental Physics—Surfaces*, Vol 22, Academic Press, 1985, Chapter 5
- J.B. Pendry, *Low-Energy Electron Diffraction*, Academic Press, 1974
- G.A. Somorjai and H.H. Farrell, *Adv. Chem. Phys.*, Vol 20, 1972, p 215
- G.A. Somorjai, *Surf. Sci.*, Vol 34, 1973, p 156
- M.B. Webb and M.G. Lagally, *Solid State Phys.*, Vol 28, 1973, p 301

Electron or X-Ray Spectroscopic Methods

Auger Electron Spectroscopy

A. Joshi, Lockheed Palo Alto Research Laboratory

General Uses

- Compositional analysis of the 0- to 3-nm region near the surface for all elements except H and He
- Depth-compositional profiling and thin film analysis
- High lateral resolution surface chemical analysis and inhomogeneity studies to determine compositional variations in areas $\geq$100 nm
- Grain-boundary and other interface analyses facilitated by fracture
- Identification of phases in cross sections

Examples of Applications

- Analysis of surface contamination of materials to investigate its role in such properties as corrosion, wear, secondary electron emission, and catalysis
- Identification of chemical-reaction products, for example, in oxidation and corrosion
- In-depth compositional evaluation of surface films, coatings, and thin films used for various metallurgical surface modifications and microelectronic applications
- Analysis of grain-boundary chemistry to evaluate the role of boundary precipitation and solute segregation on mechanical properties, corrosion, and stress corrosion cracking phenomena

Samples

- *Form:* Solids (metals, ceramics, and organic materials) with relatively low vapor pressures ($<10^{-8}$ torr at room temperature). Higher vapor pressure materials can be handled by sample cooling. Similarly, many liquid samples can be handled by sample cooling or by applying a thin film onto a conductive substrate
- *Size:* Individual powder particles as small as 1 μm in diameter can be analyzed. The maximum sample size depends on the specific instrument; 1.5 cm (0.6 in.) in diameter by 0.5 cm (0.2 in.) high is not uncommon
- *Surface topography:* Flat surfaces are preferable, but rough surfaces can be analyzed in selected small areas ($\sim$ 1 μm) or averaged over large areas (0.5 mm in diameter)
- *Preparation:* Frequently none. Samples must be free of fingerprints, oils, and other high vapor pressure materials

Limitations

- Insensitivity to hydrogen and helium
- The accuracy of quantitative analysis is limited to $\pm$30% of the element present when calculated using published elemental sensitivity factors (Ref 1). Better quantification ($\pm$10%) is possible by using standards that closely resemble the sample
- Electron beam damage can severely limit useful analysis of organic and biological materials and occasionally ceramic materials
- Electron beam charging may limit analysis when examining highly insulating materials
- Quantitative detection sensitivity for most elements is from 0.1 to 1.0 at.%

Estimated Analysis Time

- Usually under 5 min for a complete survey spectrum from 0 to 2000 eV. Selected peak analyses for studying chemical effects, Auger elemental imaging, and depth profiling generally take much longer

Capabilities of Related Techniques

- *X-ray photoelectron spectroscopy:* Provides compositional and chemical binding state information, relatively nondestructive
- *Ion scattering spectroscopy:* Provides superb top atomic layer information, specificity of surface atomic bonding in selected cases, and surface composition and depth profiling information
- *Secondary ion mass spectroscopy:* High elemental detection sensitivity from part per million to part per billion levels; surface compositional information; depth profiling capability; sensitivity for all elements, including hydrogen and helium
- *Electron probe:* Analysis to 1-μm depth in conventional operation, quantitative and nondestructive
- *Analytical electron microscopy:* Chemical analysis in conjunction with high-resolution microscopy

Introduction

Auger electron spectroscopy (AES), x-ray photoelectron spectroscopy (XPS), secondary ion mass spectroscopy (SIMS), and low-energy ion-scattering spectroscopy (LEISS), discussed in articles so named in this Volume, are among the most widely used surface-sensitive analytical techniques capable of providing elemental composition of the outermost atomic layer of a solid. These techniques are used to investigate the surface chemistry and interactions of solid surfaces of metals, ceramics, organic materials, and biological materials. The techniques use electrons, x-rays, or ions as the probing sources, and the surface chemical information is derived from analysis of electrons or ions emitted from the surface.

Auger electron spectroscopy and XPS involve precise measurements of the number of emitted secondary electrons as a function of kinetic energy. Auger and photoelectron electrons, characteristic of the specific element emitting them, are useful in qualitative analysis. Auger electrons were discovered in 1925 (Ref 2), and the utility of the technique for surface analysis was demonstrated in 1968 (Ref 3). Numerous advances in the experimental methods (Ref 4, 5), spectral interpretations, data-manipulation techniques, and various application fields have made AES an effective surface analytical technique. Detailed descriptions of the principles and applications of AES are available in Ref 6-10.

Principles of Auger Electron Spectroscopy

Auger electrons are produced whenever incident radiation—photons, electrons, ions, or neutral atoms—interacts with an atom with an energy exceeding that necessary to remove an inner-shell electron (K, L, M, . . .) from the atom. This interaction, or scattering process, leaves the atom in an excited state with a core hole, that is, a missing inner-shell electron. These excited atoms are unstable, and de-excitation occurs immediately, resulting in the emission of an x-ray or an electron termed an Auger electron. Figure 1 illustrates this process with incident x-rays. When the x-ray is absorbed by an inner-shell electron (K electron in Fig. 1a), the electron is emitted from the atom and is termed a photoelectron. The resulting atom with a K electron missing is unstable, and de-excitation occurs immediately, resulting in emission of an x-ray or Auger electron. The emission of an x-ray would occur with a characteristic energy of $E_K - E_{L_{2,3}}$ for the transition shown in Fig.

1(b). Alternatively, an Auger electron may be emitted, and probable transition is also shown in Fig. 1(b).

The kinetic energy of this Auger electron E_{ke} is:

$$E_{ke} = E_K - 2E_{L_{2,3}} - \phi \qquad \text{(Eq 1)}$$

where ϕ, the work function of the sample, represents the kinetic energy of the electron lost in escaping the sample surface (Fermi energy) into the vacuum. In practice, when measurements are conducted using an electron spectrometer, the work function of the analyzer is significant rather than that of the sample (Ref 11). The typical work function of an analyzer is from 3 to 5 eV and is a constant. Thus, the E_{ke} of an Auger electron is characteristic of the three electron binding levels of the atom from which it originates. Generation of an Auger electron also requires participation of at least three electrons, which excludes hydrogen and helium from being detected by AES.

Auger Emissions and Light-Element Sensitivity. An excited atom with a core level (electron) hole can decay to a lower energy state in several ways, of which the Auger and x-ray emission processes are the most probable. Auger de-excitation is a common mode for orbitals involving low energies; x-ray emission is equally probable or dominant for strongly bound orbitals. Therefore, x-ray emission is equally or more probable from the inner orbitals of heavy elements. All elements (except hydrogen and helium) produce high Auger yields, making AES highly sensitive for light-element detection.

Auger Emission Probabilities and Qualitative Analysis. The example shown in Fig. 1 describes emission of a specific Auger electron via a $KL_{2,3}$, $L_{2,3}$ transition. Because most atoms have several electron shells and subshells, emission of various other electrons becomes probable. The series of transitions from various levels, often represented by the series KLL, LMM, MNN, and so on, are shown in the chart of principal Auger electron energies (Fig. 2). The chart shows the energies at which principal Auger electrons appear for each element and their relative intensities. A closed circle represents a higher Auger yield transition relative to others for the same element. This and similar charts are often used as references to identify spectral features in Auger spectra.

Mode of Primary Excitation. Primary excitation can be achieved by various energetic particles, resulting in a final state culminating in Auger electron emission. Many of the conventional investigations un-

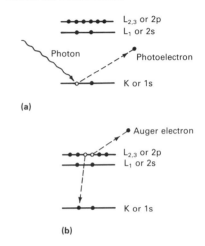

dertaken involve primary electron excitation using 1- to 30-keV electrons. The ease of electron generation using high primary electron currents from 0.05 to 5 μA and the ability to focus and deflect electrons electrically are among the chief advantages of using electron beams for primary excitation. In this respect, secondary electron images are often used to locate precise positions of interest on a sample surface and to complement Auger elemental images.

In XPS, bombardment of the sample surface with x-rays results in photoelectron and Auger electron emission. Thus, an XPS spectrum contains both sets of peaks representing sample surface and provides much information (see the article "X-Ray Photoelectron Spectroscopy" in this Volume). Auger electron emission is also caused by energetic ions, such as those used for ion beam sputtering of solid surfaces, in conjunction with most surface analysis techniques. However, ion-induced Auger yields are pronounced only for some elements, for example, aluminum, and generally from 0 to 100 eV in the spectrum. This phenomenon has been used to align ion guns such that the ion gun and electron spectrometer axes coincide precisely at the sample surface.

Electron Energy Distribution. Figure 3 shows the typical modes of display of the Auger electron spectra. The electron energy distribution $N(E)$ was obtained by excitation of a pure silver specimen with a 1-keV primary electron beam. The large peak at 1000 eV represents the elastically backscattered electrons. The intensity at lower energies corresponds to electrons that are backscattered and have undergone nondiscrete energy losses. The peak in the very low

Fig. 2 Chart of principal Auger electron energies

Open circles indicate the electron energies of the principal Auger peaks from each element. Closed circles represent predominant peaks for each element. Source: Ref 1

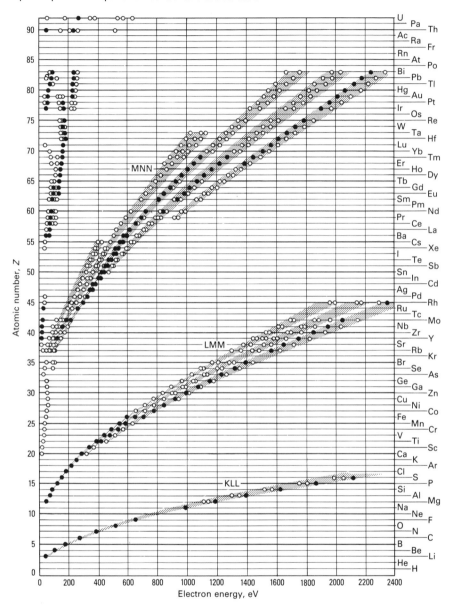

Fig. 3 AES spectrum of pure silver

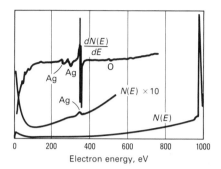

tions. Only those electrons from the near-surface region can escape without losing a significant portion of their energy and thus be identified as Auger electrons. This average depth, from which electrons escape the solid without losing energy, is often referred to as the escape depth, λ, and is a function of the kinetic energy of the electrons.

Figure 4 shows the functional dependence of the escape depth on the kinetic energy of the electrons in various elements. In the energy range of interest, the escape depth varies in the 2 to 10 monolayers regime. The spectral information contained in the Auger spectra are thus to a greater extent representative of the top 0.5 to 3 nm of the surface. The atoms present at depth, t, greater than λ also contribute to the total signal. Such a contribution to the signal can be significant and is proportional to $(1 - e^{-t/\lambda})$.

Escape depth is independent of the primary electron energy used. The unique dependence of λ on Auger electron energy also distinguishes top monolayer chemistry from the layers below. The scattering of electrons depends on the electron density of the solid

Fig. 4 Experimental measurements of electron escape depths in various elements

Source: Ref 12

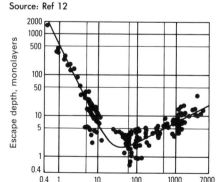

energy region (0 to 50 eV) corresponds to the true secondary electrons.

Auger electron peaks are readily visible in the amplified $N(E) \times 10$ spectrum. The peaks are relatively small because only 0.1% of the total current is typically contained in Auger peaks. The problem of a small signal over a large background is usually solved by taking the derivative $dN(E)/dE$ of the spectrum (Fig. 3). The peak-to-peak heights (measured from the most positive to the most negative excursion) in the dN/dE spectra and the peak areas under the $N(E)$ curve were

shown to be proportional to the number of atoms originating the Auger electrons. These measurements are commonly used to quantify Auger spectra.

Electron Escape Depths. The most useful kinetic energy range of Auger electrons is from 20 to 2500 eV and corresponds to electrons with high scattering cross sections in solids. As these low-energy electrons emanate from the solid, they undergo additional scattering events and lose their (characteristic) energy through plasmon losses, core excitation, or interband transi-

material and on kinetic energy. Therefore, the curve shown in Fig. 4, although not universal, is a close approximation for many solids.

The escape depth of Auger electrons is small compared with that of characteristic x-rays used in x-ray microprobe analysis. The x-ray analysis volume (Fig. 5) is typically approximately 1 μm^3 and can complement AES information of the top 0.5 to 3 nm.

Chemical Effects in Auger Electron Spectroscopy.

Changes in the chemical environment of atoms in the surface region of a solid can affect the measured Auger spectrum variously, for example, in the kinetic energy at which an Auger transition occurs, the energy distribution of the Auger electrons, or the loss structure associated with Auger transitions. Precise measurements to determine energy shifts and lineshape changes are useful in identifying the chemical states of surface atoms.

Energy shifts are expected whenever there is charge transfer from one atom to another. In ionic bonding, the net electron transfer causes core-level electrons of electronegative elements to shift to lower binding energies and those of electropositive elements to shift to higher binding energies. The result is often a shift of several electron volts in the Auger peaks compared with their zero-valence states.

Changes in composition of metallic components in metal alloys would not be expected to produce measurable changes in the Auger energies (for core levels) of the components. However, submonolayer quantities of oxygen adsorbed on clean metal surfaces can produce measurable changes in the metal Auger peaks, the shift increasing with oxy-

gen coverage. For most metals such shifts are typically 1 eV or less. When bulk sulfides, carbides, or oxides are formed at the surface, the shifts usually exceed 1 eV, for example, 6 eV for tantalum in tantalum oxide (Ta_2O_5). The observed shifts typically increase with differences in electronegativities, but the oxidation number and relaxation effects will also affect the magnitude of a shift. The size of the Auger chemical shift is usually larger than the photoelectron chemical shift.

Figure 6 shows Auger chemical shifts observed in alumina compared with metallic aluminum. Large shifts of the order 17 to 18 eV are evident in the low-energy (68 eV) LVV transition and the high-energy (1396 eV) KLL transition. Lineshape changes can also occur when only core levels are in-

volved in the Auger process due to changes in the electron energy loss mechanism; for example, aluminum KLL Auger electrons suffer strong plasmon losses escaping from the pure metal (Fig. 6), but not from its oxide.

Several changes in the lineshapes of Auger spectra have been observed due to changes in bonding, particularly when one or two valence electrons are involved in the process. Although the lineshape could be related to the energy distribution of electrons in the valence band, this relationship is not simple because some materials exhibit quasiatomic Auger spectra rather than bandlike spectra. Experimentally observed changes in Auger lineshapes have proved useful in identifying chemical states of elements at surfaces, for example, in carbon,

Fig. 5 Comparison of Auger electron escape depths with emission depths of backscattered electrons and x-rays

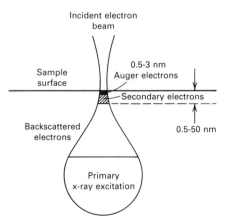

Fig. 6 AES spectra from alumina and aluminum showing peakshifts and plasmon loss peak structures

Source: Ref 1

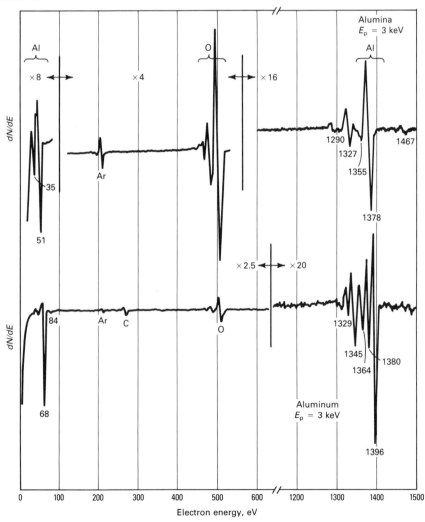

sulfur, nitrogen, and oxygen. Figure 7 illustrates changes in carbon KVV lineshapes.

Energy shifts and changes in lineshape can affect quantitative analysis significantly. Methods used to implement these effects and improve quantitative accuracies include fitting and subtracting backgrounds from measured spectra and then appropriately integrating the results, dynamic background subtraction, and tailored modulation techniques. When more than one component is present in a spectrum, they can be separated using, for example, factor analysis.

Quantitative analysis can be conducted using calculated Auger yields from first principles (electron energy distribution, escape depths, chemical effects, and so on) by comparison with standards or by using experimentally derived elemental sensitivity factors. The Auger yield calculations from first principles require knowledge of various material, primary electron beam, and analyzer characteristics. With some assumptions (Ref 6), the detected Auger current I_α for a WXY Auger transition is:

$$I_\alpha \, (WXY) = I_p \, TN_\alpha \, x_\alpha \, \gamma_\alpha \, (WXY) \, R\sigma_\alpha$$

$$(E_{p'} \, E_W) \, \lambda \, (1 + R_B) \qquad \text{(Eq 2)}$$

where I_p is the primary electron current; T is the analyzer response function; N_α is the atomic density of element α; x_α is the atom fraction; $\gamma_\alpha(WXY)$ is the WXY Auger transition probability factor; $\sigma_\alpha(E_{p'}, E_W)$ is the ionization cross section of the core level W, which is a function of the primary electron energy E_p; λ is the escape depth of Auger electrons in the material; R is the surface-roughness factor; and R_B is the electron backscattering factor.

For a given Auger transition and primary energy, σ decreases smoothly with the atomic number of the element. The cross section goes through a maximum as a function of E_p, as exemplified by the AES peak height measurements in Fig. 8. The maximum in E_p is observed commonly from four to eight times E_W and indicates the importance of selecting an appropriate value of E_p for a given experiment. The backscattering factor and the Auger transition probability for the major transitions change little with atomic number, and they can be taken into account in the calculations. The value of the surface-roughness factor, R, is generally not as readily obtained as some others, such as N, T, and λ, and leaves a major uncertainty in the calculation. By making some assumptions, relative Auger yields I_α/I_p for $x_\alpha = 1$ have been calculated for elements with atomic numbers from 3 to 83, and can be used to calculate the atomic concentrations of surface species, x_α (Ref 14). The accuracy of measurements achievable using this approach has not been evaluated.

Quantitative analysis using elemental sensitivity factors is based on measuring relative Auger intensities, I_x (peak-to-peak heights in the dN/dE data or peak areas in the $N(E)$ data), of element x and calculating the atomic concentrations, C_x, using:

$$C_x = \frac{(I_x/S_x)}{\sum\limits_\infty (I_\alpha/S_\alpha)} \qquad \text{(Eq 3)}$$

where S_x is the relative sensitivity factor of element x. The elemental sensitivity factors are relative values derived from pure elements. Use of these matrix-independent sensitivity factors normally ignores the chemical effects, backscattering factor, and escape depth variations in the material under investigation and is therefore only semiquantitative. A principal advantage of the method is the elimination of standards. The calculations are also insensitive to surface roughness because all Auger peaks are uniformly affected by surface topography to a first approximation.

Performing a quantitative analysis necessitates measuring the peak-to-peak heights of selected elements (one peak per element) in the dN/dE data, using the available S_x values for those peaks, and calculating the concentrations, C_x, using Eq 3. Relative Auger yields calculated for common Auger transitions are available (Ref 1). The accuracies of concentration values thus obtained depend on the nature of the material and the accuracies of Auger intensity measurements and S_x used in the calculation. Materials with little or no strong chemical effects will produce accurate quantitative determinations, typically within ± 10% of actual concentrations. In ionic compounds, the errors could be large; ± 200% is not inconceivable. In such instances and whenever more favorable accuracies are required, a more effective approach would involve use of standards of composition close to the material under investigation.

Auger intensities derived from $N(E)$ data (peak areas) can provide a more accurate quantitative analysis. The peak areas inherently contain complete Auger emission cur-

Fig. 7 Carbon KVV Auger spectra from molybdenum carbide (Mo₂C), silicon carbide (SiC), and graphite
Source: Ref 13

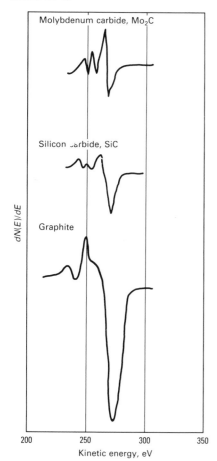

Fig. 8 AES peak-to-peak amplitudes as a function of primary beam energy for gold 2024 eV and 69 eV peaks

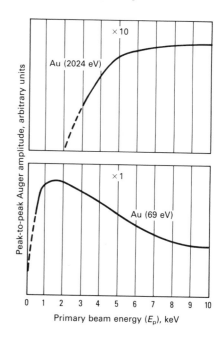

rents and are not influenced by most chemical effects. A primary disadvantage of this technique is the difficulty of measuring peak areas accurately, which involves achieving accurate background subtraction.

Experimental Methods

The instrumentation typically used in AES includes an electron gun for primary electron excitation of the sample, an electron spectrometer for energy analysis of secondary electrons, a secondary electron detector for secondary electron imaging, a stage for sample manipulation, and an ion gun for sputter removal of atoms from the sample surface. The stage and the electron and ion optical components are housed in an ultra high vacuum (UHV) system capable of ultimate vacuum to 10^{-10} torr. The vacuum system may also be equipped with special-purpose auxiliary equipment such as a fracture attachment for *in situ* fracture studies, an evaporation unit for thin film deposition, and a hot/cold stage to conduct elevated-temperature studies or to maintain a low vapor pressure for the sample. Some systems combine other techniques, such as XPS, SIMS, LEISS, low-energy electron diffraction (LEED), and reflection high-energy electron diffraction (RHEED), to obtain complementary information. Modern systems use sophisticated electronics to operate the various components and computers for data acquisition and manipulation.

The electron spectrometer is usually the central component of an AES system. Various types of analyzers are in use and include sector analyzers, retarding field analyzers, hemispherical analyzers, and cylindrical mirror analyzers. Retarding field analyzers are used commonly in conjunction with LEED, and hemispherical analyzers are more often used in conjunction with XPS. For electron-excited AES, the cylindrical mirror analyzer generally offers superior signal-to-noise performance, which is associated with its high point transmission. Consequently, it remains the most prevalent spectrometer.

Operation of a cylindrical mirror analyzer to obtain Auger spectra is illustrated in Fig. 9. An electron gun, commonly located coaxially to the cylindrical mirror analyzer, provides primary electrons. A portion of the electrons scattered from the sample surface enter the inlet aperture of the cylindrical mirror analyzer and traverse the space between the inner and outer cylinders of the cylindrical mirror analyzer. A negative bias applied to the outer cylinder directs electrons with specific energy toward the cylindrical mirror analyzer axis and permits collection at the electron multiplier of electrons exiting

Fig. 9 Operation of a cylindrical mirror analyzer in an Auger spectrometer

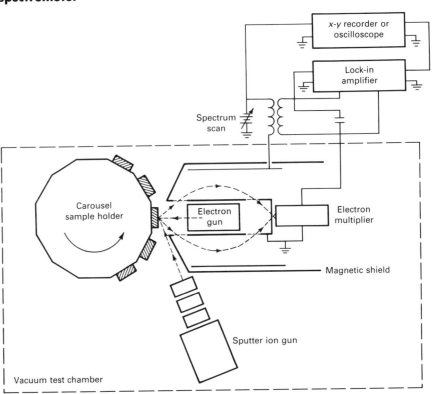

the apertures. The pass energy of the cylindrical mirror analyzer and the kinetic energy of detected electrons (E) are proportional to the bias applied to the outer cylinder. The spread, ΔE, in the energy of the transmitted electrons is determined by the resolution $R = (\Delta E/E)$ of the analyzer. Most commercial spectrometers have R values of approximately 0.5%, which is adequate for routine analysis. Electronmultipliers typically provide a gain factor of 10 to 10^6, allowing direct measurement of electron current. In practice, the collected electron intensity is measured as a function of bias on the outer cylinder (proportional to E).

Data Acquisition. The electron energy distribution, $N(E)$, plots (Fig. 3) contain direct information of Auger transitions. The $dN(E)/dE$ function, which reduces the effect of high background, can be generated by electronic or digital conversion methods. The electronic method of generating dN/dE involves superimposition of a small alternating current (ac) voltage on the outer cylinder and synchronous detection of the in-phase component of the analyzer output using a lock-in amplifier. Common practice entails direct accumulation of $N(E)$ data by pulse counting (for small primary electron currents

of approximately 10^{-9} A) or voltage to frequency conversion and detection (for high primary electron currents of approximately 10^{-6} A).

The data can be displayed directly in the $N(E)$ form or differentiated digitally to obtain the dN/dE format. Although $N(E)$ data contain the most complete information, the dN/dE form of display has become common practice.

The electron beams used in AES offer various choices in examining a given surface. They can be used to obtain secondary electron images to complement AES information, Auger spectra (from large areas or from small areas defined approximately by the finely focused electron beam size), Auger line scans, and Auger elemental images. In addition, Auger elemental depth profiles can be obtained in conjunction with ion sputtering.

Auger electron spectra from large areas can be obtained by using defocused electron beams or by rastering a selected area. Rastering is often preferred because it permits a clear definition of the area under investigation and limits edge effects. The acceptance area of the analyzer often places a maximum limit on the area of analysis. Most cylindrical mirror analyzers can examine an area no larger than approximately 0.5 mm (0.02 in.) in diameter. When using the electron beam in the spot mode, the electron beam size usually determines the area of analysis. Backscattering effects become significant only when using very small beams (<100 nm) and high electron beam voltages. In such cases, the AES signal arises from a slightly larger area than that represented by the beam size.

A commonly used technique for obtaining compositional-depth information is AES profiling (Ref 6, 15-17). Energetic inert gas ions, for example, argon, from 1 to 5 keV are used to sputter the surface, followed by AES. Sputtering is often performed continuously; AES is conducted in cycles on a set of selected elemental peaks. This type of data acquisition permits analysis at the surface (before activating the ion sputter gun) and compositional evaluation at any depth within the film and at any thin film interface.

Figure 10 shows such a profile. The abscissa (etching time) can be converted to depth scale by suitable calibration and conversion of the ordinate to atomic concentrations using appropriate sensitivity factors. The data indicate layering of surface oxides. The approximately 10-nm-thick top oxide layer is enriched in iron and followed by a 5-nm region of chromium-rich oxides. Nickel was found to be depleted in the entire surface oxide. These and similar results enhanced understanding of the complex oxidation behavior of stainless steels (Ref 18).

The data presented in Fig. 10 were obtained during continuous sputtering. Profiling data can also be obtained using alternate sputtering and data acquisition. Such independent control of sputtering and data acquisition permits profiling with improved depth resolution. Auger electron spectroscopy profiles can be obtained in applications relating

Fig. 10 Depth-composition profiles for 304 stainless steel that was oxidized 75 min in air at 500 °C (930 °F)
Source: Ref 18, 19

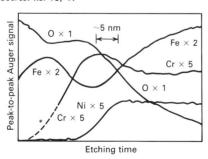

Fig. 11 Secondary electron micrograph of crystalline structure on an integrated circuit
Source: Ref 20

to deposited thin films, coatings, and various surface/interface phenomena, such as segregation, corrosion, and gas reactions. Although AES profiling is often used for thin films, analysis of relatively thick films may require alternate approaches.

Auger images and line scans are used to define surface chemical inhomogeneities uniquely. Auger imaging is performed sim-

ilarly to x-ray imaging in an electron microprobe. A selected area of a sample surface is scanned by the electron beam as the AES elemental signal generated by the electron beam and detected by the analyzer is used to intensity modulate (z-axis) an oscilloscope display. The x and y axes of the display correspond to the selected area of the sample and may be used to display the secondary electron image.

An example of an etch residue on an integrated circuit demonstrates the imaging capability of AES (Ref 20). Figure 11 illustrates a secondary electron image of the unexpected crystalline-like residue observed on silicon between two aluminum metallization interconnect lines. An Auger spectrum obtained from a selected area of the residue suggested that it is SiO_2. Several Auger images were then obtained using AES peaks at 72 eV (corresponding to silicon in SiO_2), 89 eV (elemental silicon), 505 eV (oxygen), and 65 eV (elemental aluminum). These images show that the residue (crystalline structure), except a few localized areas, contains SiO_2 (Fig. 12). Figure 12 also illustrates chemical state mapping ability in addition to the Auger elemental imaging capability.

Fig. 12 Auger images from the area of the integrated circuit shown in Fig. 11
(a) Silicon oxide. (b) Elemental silicon. (c) Oxygen. (d) Aluminum. Source: Ref 20

Experimental Limitations

Elemental Detection Sensitivity. Limitations of the technique include its insensitivity to hydrogen and helium and its relatively low detection sensitivity for all elements. Because the Auger process involves three electrons in a given atom, hydrogen and helium cannot be detected. However, hydrogen effects on the valence-electron distribution of selected metals have been obtained using AES. The AES detection sensitivity for most elements is from 0.01 to 0.1 at.%. The sampling volume and associated number of atoms examined using AES are often small compared with x-ray and other bulk-analysis techniques, and this limits the sensitivity of the technique. Use of high currents and longer time signal averaging often improves the detection level, but overall detection is limited by time and shot noise associated with the background current upon which the Auger peaks are superimposed.

Electron Beam Artifacts. Another limitation involves the primary electron beam used in Auger electron excitation. Electrons interact with matter more readily than x-rays and may cause electron beam artifacts. Electron beams can change the surface by promoting migration of atoms into or out of the area of analysis. Poor thermal conductivity of the sample also causes localized heating and associated artifacts. Such effects include decomposition of surface materials (prominent with organic, biological, and selected inorganic compounds) and polymerization. Many oxides, although relatively strong compounds, can be reduced to a lower oxidation state. These artifacts can be minimized by using low primary current densities (associated with some sacrifice of detection sensitivity), low primary beam voltages, and electron beam rastering of large areas.

Sample charging due to electron beams is another common problem with AES applied to insulating materials. Charging causes peak shifts in the spectrum and in severe cases prevents obtaining useful data. The high surface sensitivity of the technique generally precludes metal coating of the analysis surface, a common practice in scanning electron microscopy (SEM) (see the article "Scanning Electron Microscopy" in this Volume). Grazing angle electron incidence, which induces high secondary electron emission and therefore minimizes surface charge buildup, is used to minimize charging effects. Use of low electron beam currents, optimizing voltages, and large-area rastering often helps to minimize surface charging. Another practice involves masking the surface with a conductive metal grid, which acts as a local sink to the electron charge.

As a result of these limitations, most AES applications involve good conductors, such as metals, their alloys, and semiconductors. Oxides, other insulators, and organic materials have been examined, but often with limited success. Most common glasses and other insulating compounds are sufficiently impure and permit reasonable analysis using AES.

Spectral peak overlap is a problem in relatively few situations in AES. This occurs when one of the elements is present in a small concentration and its primary peaks are overlapped by peaks of a major constituent in the sample. Often the effect is significant degradation of sensitivity. For example, titanium and nitrogen, iron and manganese, and sodium and zinc are frequently encountered combinations in which peak overlap is of concern. This problem is the most severe when one of the elements has only one peak, such as nitrogen. In most cases, one or both of the elements have several peaks, and the analysis can be performed using one of the nonoverlapping peaks, although it may be a minor peak in the spectrum. Peak overlap problems may also be solved by acquiring the data in the $N(E)$ mode, followed by spectral stripping to separate the peaks.

High vapor pressure samples pose another limitation for AES analysis. A sample is vacuum compatible if its vapor pressure is low enough not to degrade or ruin the vacuum in the spectrometer—normally less than 10^{-8} torr. If the sample outgasses at a high rate, the surface chemistry may change upon introduction into the vacuum chamber, and the vacuum may be degraded. By using an appropriate sample cold-stage, it may be possible to cool the sample to liquid nitrogen temperature, thereby reducing the outgassing. This procedure helps to maintain the appropriate vacuum in the spectrometer and the original surface chemistry. Use of suitable techniques enables handling for AES of most solids and many liquids.

Sputtering Artifacts. Another limitation/artifact arises from use of surface atom removal techniques, such as sputter etching. Many of the surface layers sputtered consist of a mixture of compounds and elements. Because the sputter rates for such layers are unknown, only an estimation of the layer thickness is possible. This is often sufficient to help solve problems. In addition, sputtering artifacts, such as ion beam mixing, differential sputtering, and cone formation, can confuse the data. Artifacts can become severe if the depth profile is for relatively thick films (>1 μm). Mechanical wedging techniques, such as ball cratering, can be used for thick layers to avoid sputtering problems. The variation of composition across the layer can be obtained by stepping the electron beam across the wedge. Techniques for thick film analysis are discussed in Example 5 in the section "Applications" in this article.

Applications*

Example 1: Corrosion Resistance of Cold-Rolled Steel. The corrosion resistance of painted cold-rolled steel is a problem in the automobile industry. Concern over cosmetic corrosion and the full corrosion penetration of body panels has increased because the trend toward lighter automobiles has resulted in reduced gage thickness of the cold-rolled steel used. The corrosion resistance of painted cold-rolled steel has been shown to be a function of surface carbon contamination before phosphate conversion coating and painting.

Two series of samples were selected for this study on the basis of performance in a salt fog corrosion test (Ref 21, 22). One set each was selected from materials exhibiting satisfactory and unsatisfactory corrosion performance and will be designated as favorable and poor samples, respectively. The samples were examined in the as-cold-rolled condition and also after being alkaline washed and zinc phosphate coated.

Figure 13 is a secondary electron micrograph of a typical poor material in the as-cold-rolled condition. The material exhibits some surface topography as well as dark (arrow A) and light (arrow B) patches on the surface. Auger point analysis on these areas showed that the primary chemical constituents on the surface are carbon, oxygen, and iron and that the dark patch contains considerably higher concentrations of carbon than the light areas (Fig. 14). Auger chemical maps for carbon (Fig. 13b), iron (Fig. 13c), and oxygen (Fig. 13d) confirmed that the dark patches are high in surface carbon concentration. Auger analysis of favorable samples indicated lower carbon concentrations similar to that shown for point B in Fig. 13(a). Analysis of multiple samples provided excellent correlation between surface carbon contamination and unsatisfactory corrosion test results.

After zinc-phosphate coating, substantial differences were observed in images taken

*Examples in this section were provided by Stephen P. Clough, Perkin-Elmer Corporation; Stephen W. Gaarenstroom, General Motors Research Laboratory; John T. Grant, University of Dayton Research Institute; Michael B. Hintz, Michigan Technological University; A. Joshi, Lockheed Palo Alto Research Laboratory; and M.T. Thomas, Battelle Pacific Northwest Laboratory.

Fig. 13 Surface of an as-cold-rolled steel sample exhibiting poor corrosion performance

(a) Secondary electron image. (b) Auger image for carbon. (c) Auger image for iron. (d) Auger image for oxygen. Source: Ref 20

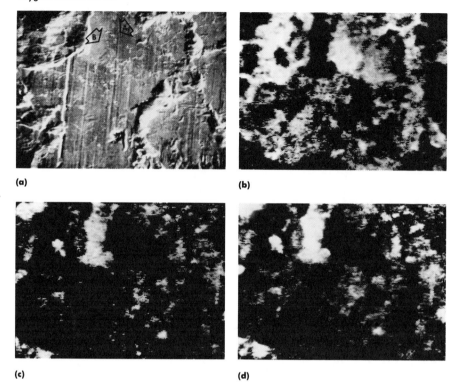

(a)　(b)

(c)　(d)

Fig. 14 AES point analysis from points A and B on the steel surface shown in Fig. 13(a)

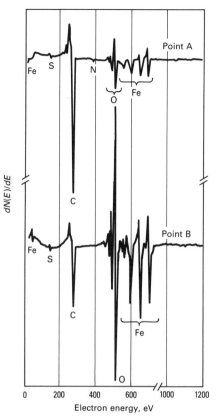

for favorable and poor samples (Fig. 15). The coating of the favorable sample (Fig. 15a) consists of finely dispersed lenticular crystals that cover the surface completely. The poor sample (Fig. 15b) is covered by coarser crystals separated by large planar areas. Figure 16 illustrates Auger point analysis from the crystalline (arrow A) and planar (arrow B) areas of the poor sample. In addition to a higher carbon concentration, the planar area exhibits substantially different ratios of iron, zinc, and phosphorus than the crystalline region. The AES results obtained from the surface of the favorable sample were similar to the crystalline region of the poor sample.

These results indicate that the poor material contains higher surface carbon concentrations, and the carbon is present in patches on its surface. During zinc-phosphate application, carbon is incorporated into the coating and modifies its morphology and stoichiometry. These effects are believed to degrade seriously the corrosion performance of the cold-rolled steel.

Example 2: AES Study of Thin Passive Films. Many chemical environments require use of corrosion-resistant materials. The acceptable rate of corrosion depends on the particular environment, the length of

exposure to the environment, the criticality of the part, and the cost factors involved. Many applications necessitate selection of a passive material, that is, one having little or no reaction with the environment. Passivity often results from the formation of a thin protective surface film capable of slowing the reaction rate of the material with the environment. This example will be limited to the details of the formation and detection of the passive film without recourse to the exact mechanism affecting the corrosion kinetics. The ability of AES to analyze thin surface layers is well suited to these studies.

For this study, a commercial nickel-base alloy, Inconel 625, was exposed to a dilute acid environment (Ref 23). Figure 17 shows a potentiostatic polarization curve for the material that illustrates the current density (corrosion rate) as a function of the applied potential between the sample and a silver/silver chloride (Ag/AgCl) reference electrode, beginning at the free corrosion potential.

As the potential is increased, an exponential increase in the current density is noted. At a potential of approximately 0.3 V, a plateau is reached at which further increases in potential have little effect on increasing the corrosion rate. This is the passive region.

Above the 0.6-V potential in the transpassive region, the corrosion current again increases rapidly.

Auger thin film analyses were performed on samples that were polarized at potentials of 0.3, 0.6, and 0.9 V, corresponding to the beginning and end of the passive region and the transpassive region of the polarization curve. The results (Fig. 18) provide the chemical composition of the samples as a function of sputter etching time (or depth into the sample). The surface films formed at 0.3 and 0.6 V in the passive region are observed to be very thin and rich in chromium oxides. The film formed at 0.9 V is much thicker and is a mixed metal oxide. This is consistent with the theory that passivity results from a thin chromium oxide film that covers the sample surface and acts as a barrier to further corrosion. At the higher potentials, this thin film is dissolved, and the sample again begins to corrode rapidly.

The passive film on this material is estimated to be only approximately 5 to 10 nm thick and thus is easily detected using Auger thin film analysis. In selected instances,

Fig. 15 Secondary electron images of phosphated steel surfaces

(a) A favorable steel sample. (b) A poor steel sample. See text for explanation.

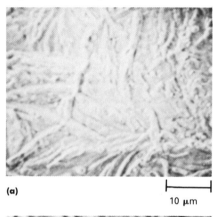

(a)

10 μm

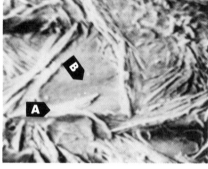

(b)

AES peak shift information may also be available, which is of significant interest in the thorough characterization of passive films.

Fig. 16 AES point analysis from points A and B on the phosphated steel surface shown in Fig. 15(b)

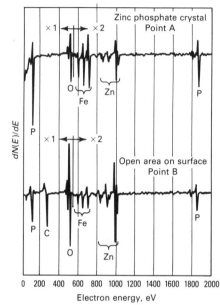

Example 3: Metallographic Identification of Light Elements. Metallographic examination of polished cross sections is perhaps one of the most common means of evaluating material metallurgically. The addition of microanalytical examination of polished cross sections allows evaluation of morphology and chemical composition on a microscopic scale. The most common methods of microchemical

Fig. 17 Potentiostatic polarization curve for Inconel 625 in a pH 3.7 acidic solution at 313 K

Source: Ref 23

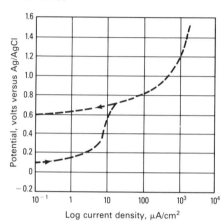

examination involve use of energy-dispersive or wavelength-dispersive x-ray analysis using a scanning electron microscope or an electron microprobe. Both techniques are limited in that the analysis volume for the x-ray techniques is large, of the order of 0.5 to 10 μm in depth and diameter, and the sensitivity to elements with atomic number less than approximately 11 is small.

In this example, Auger analysis was used with metallographic examination to characterize precipitates in a beryllium copper alloy (Ref 24). Metallographic examination of this cast alloy indicated a diversity of precipitate morphology. Figure 19 shows a secondary electron micrograph of the sample. X-ray microanalysis of the material failed to iden-

Fig. 18 Concentration versus sputter etching time for Inconel 625 polarized 30 min in pH 3.7 nitric acid

(a) 0.3 V versus Ag/AgCl. (b) 0.6 V versus Ag/AgCl. (c) 0.9 V versus Ag/AgCl

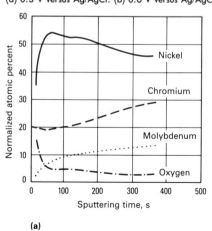

(a)

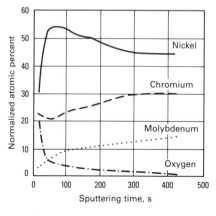

(b)

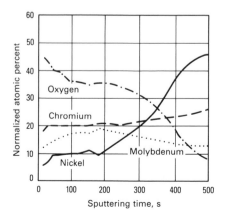

(c)

Fig. 19 Secondary electron micrograph of a beryllium copper alloy

See also Fig. 20.

Fig. 20 Auger point analysis of the six selected points shown in Fig. 19

(a) Point 1: the long rod-shaped precipitate is a beryllium sulfide. (b) Point 2: this small round precipitate is a titanium carbide. (c) Point 3: this small irregular precipitate is also a titanium carbide. (d) Point 4: the large blocky angular precipitate is a beryllium carbide. (e) Point 5: this is the primary copper-rich phase of the base alloy. (f) Point 6: the copper-rich phase of the alloy that also contains alloyed beryllium

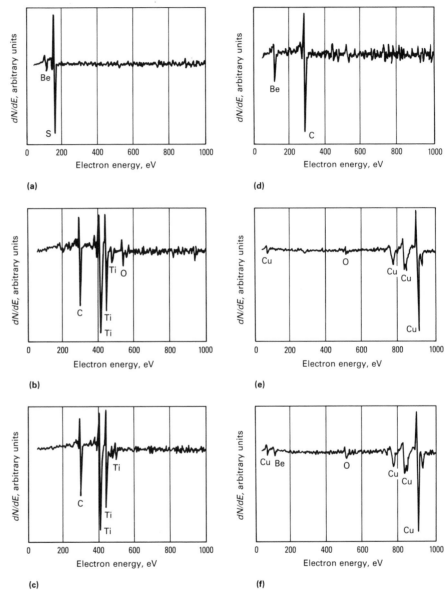

tify fully the chemical constituents of the various precipitates. Six selected points were analyzed using AES to investigate the phase distributions in this material. Before analysis, the sample was ion sputter etched to a depth approximately 10 nm to remove contamination from sample preparation. Figure 20 shows the Auger point analysis data used in the determination of chemical composition of the precipitate and bulk alloy phases.

The ability of AES to distinguish hydrocarbons and other forms of carbon from carbide was useful in determining titanium and beryllium carbides. Its ability to detect low atomic number constituents, such as oxygen, carbon, and beryllium, and to examine microscopic constituents was particularly valuable in this study.

Example 4: Thin Film Characterization. Many modern technological applications require thin film coatings for decoration, corrosion protection, or other selected property improvements. These films (thin films are categorically defined to be less than 1 μm thick) often require determination of physical and mechanical properties coupled with chemical characterization for product development, quality assurance, or failure analysis. Auger electron spectroscopy can be applied to obtain compositional information at selected areas of the surface, with high lateral resolution at any depth within the film and at interfaces, and to evaluate diffusion and reactions occurring between thin film layers and substrate.

A gold-nickel-copper metallization system is widely used in electronics for such applications as connectors, external leads for hybrid microcircuits, and thin films on ceramic substrates. A thin nickel layer typically serves as the diffusion barrier between gold and copper. The outer gold layer protects the surface from environmental attack,

helps to ensure bondability, and provides low contact resistance. In this example, the sample was a copper-coated ceramic substrate electroplated with approximately 0.1-μm nickel and 2.0-μm gold (Ref 25). This gold-nickel-copper-ceramic substrate system was heat treated 4 h in air at 300 °C (570 °F) to simulate typical processing for evaluation of the poor bondability.

Evaluation of the surfaces using AES provided information that could explain poor

bondability. An AES spectrum (Fig. 21) from a 25- × 25-μm area (averaging several grains of surface gold) indicated the presence of carbon, oxygen, and nickel at the surface in addition to gold. Detailed Auger elemental mapping of the surface (not shown) indicated nickel and oxygen to be present in some areas and complemented by gold and carbon in the others. A composition-depth profile from a nickel-rich region (Fig. 22) further indicated that nickel

Fig. 21 Auger spectrum from a large surface area of a gold-nickel-copper metallization sample that was heated 4 h in air at 300 °C (570 °F)

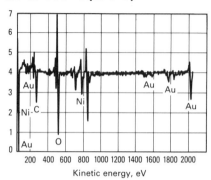

Fig. 22 Depth-composition profile obtained from a nickel-rich area of a gold-nickel-copper metallization surface

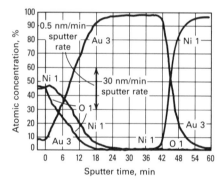

Fig. 23 Results of a scanning Auger microprobe study performed on a gold-plated stainless steel lead frame

(a) Secondary electron image. (b) Iron Auger image. (c) Oxygen Auger image. (d) Gold Auger image. (e) Nickel Auger image

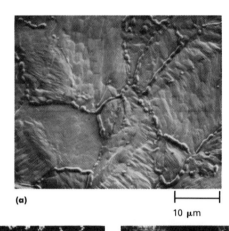

(a)

10 μm

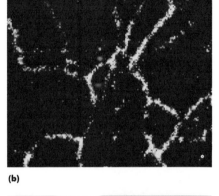

(b)

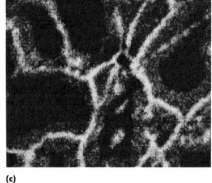

(c)

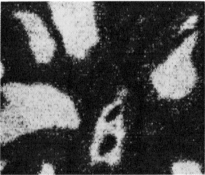

(d)

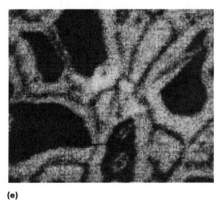

(e)

and oxygen are highly localized near the surface within the top 5 nm. Only a small amount of nickel was observed within the gold film, and the nickel distribution profile indicates its diffusion through grain boundaries of gold. The surface enrichment probably results from surface diffusion coupled with simultaneous oxidation at high temperature. These measurements suggest that nickel in the form of nickel oxide (NiO) covering most of the gold surface is responsible for its poor bondability.

These observations reflecting the problems of surface and grain-boundary diffusion are not uncommon in many applications. The surface and grain-boundary diffusional aspects are further illustrated by another example of stainless steel lead frame also used for microelectronic packaging applications (Ref 26). Figure 23 shows the results of a scanning Auger microprobe study performed on a gold-plated stainless steel lead frame. The grain structure of the substrate is evident in the secondary electron micrograph. An Auger spectrum obtained while averaging over a large surface area disclosed the presence of iron, nickel, oxyen, silicon, gold, and carbon at the surface. Nickel and oxygen are present at the surface in appreciable quantities and are distributed alike, as indicated by their Auger images (Fig. 23).

These images and depth profiling data indicated that nickel migrates rapidly to the surfaces along substrate grain boundaries and spreads on the gold surface by surface diffusion. Iron oxides are localized also in a narrow region near the substrate boundaries. The grain size of the gold film is small compared with that of the substrate and is not resolved in these images. The observed elemental distributions suggest that the substrate grain size is important in the kinetics of surface coverage by substrate components. Surface coverage by NiO (a transparent oxide) to a thickness of 5 nm was concluded to have a direct adverse influence on the bondability of the surface.

Example 5: Thick Film Analysis. The analysis of thick films using such surface analysis techniques as AES can be approached in several different ways.

One common method involves use of ion sputter etching in combination with Auger analysis to collect Auger sputter depth profiles. The principal disadvantage of this approach is that nonuniform sputter etching and surface roughening due to sputter etching can reduce the depth resolution drastically. These effects can be minimized through the use of dual ion guns, reactive ion sputter etching, and sample rotation. In addition, the time required to profile thick films may be prohibitive. A second method entails chemical etching of a thick film to reduce the thickness to the point at which Auger sputter depth profiling is effective.

A third method consists of preparing metallographic cross sections of the thick film sample, then using line scan Auger analysis. The thickness of the film and the required depth resolution will help determine the angle at which the metallographic polishing is performed. By using very shallow angles, it is possible to expand interfacial regions by factors of 250 or more.

Ball cratering of the sample surface using a rotating hemisphere is another method to produce a lapped surface. If the layer thickness is small compared to the hemisphere radius, this variation will closely approximate planar angle lapping and can be very efficient.

The example selected for demonstration is the examination of a multilayer carbide-coated cutting tool. The tool was produced through sequential chemical vapor deposition of tantalum carbide (TaC), titanium carbide (TiC), alumina (Al_2O_3), and titanium nitride (TiN) layers over a tungsten carbide-cobalt (WC-Co) substrate. The study was designed to investigate interdiffusion of the various layers as a function of deposition conditions.

Figure 24 represents the layered structure and relative thickness of the tool layers. The

Fig. 24 Vapor deposited multilayer structure on a WC-Co tool substrate

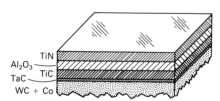

sample was metallographically polished at an angle of 20° to the surface. The resultant surface was solvent cleaned, rinsed with deionized water, then lightly ion sputter etched before Auger line scan analysis.

Figure 25 shows the Auger line scans obtained at the TiC/WC-Co interface. The data indicate cobalt enrichment at the interface. Auger analysis of an uncoated substrate showed no indication of cobalt enrichment; therefore, the cobalt must have segregated to the interface during the deposition processing. Analysis of the other interfaces provided further insight into interfacial reactions and interdiffusion.

Example 6: Application of AES to the Study of Grain-Boundary Chemistry. Much of the evidence accumulated over the past few years shows a relationship between grain-boundary chemistry and various grain-boundary phenomena that include grain-boundary embrittlement, intergranular corrosion, some forms of hydrogen embrittlement, and stress corrosion cracking of metals and alloys. Much attention was drawn to the enrichment of certain metalloid impurity elements, such as sulfur, phosphorus, antimony, and tin, at grain boundaries that have been found to induce intergranular failure in iron and nickel and several of their alloys (Ref 27-29). Temper embrittlement of low-alloy steels is one such problem area that has been investigated extensively.

Scanning AES is ideally suited to grain-boundary studies in metals and alloys because of its inherent high spatial resolution coupled with high surface sensitivity. Modern intruments have spatial resolution exceeding 50 nm. For most alloys and typical average grain sizes, this resolution is suffi-

Fig. 25 AES line scans obtained from the 20° angle lapped surface of the vapor deposited WC-Co tool substrate shown in Fig. 24

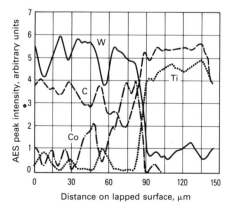

cient to distinguish between the intergranular features from cleavage and ductile rupture features on mixed mode fracture surfaces. In addition, the impurity segregants are often present on the grain boundaries in concentrations as low as 0.1 at.% in a layer less than 1 nm thick. Auger electron spectroscopy is currently the only technique capable of measuring such layers with the required spatial resolution.

Avoiding surface contamination often necessitates fracturing samples in the vacuum chamber of the spectrometer. A freshly exposed surface, such as that obtainable from a fracture, is chemically very active and will adsorb active gases quickly. Even in a good vacuum, it is possible to observe the adsorption of oxygen and carbon from the residual carbon monoxide and water in the vacuum chamber. The most frequent method used for *in situ* fracture is impact fracture or a combination of sample cooling and impact fracture. For many metals and alloys that exhibit a ductile-to-brittle transition temperature, sample cooling is effective. However, many other metals and alloys will not fracture intergranularly in this manner. For such materials, it may be possible to expose enough grain boundaries by hydrogen charging the sample and/or using an *in situ* slow strain rate fracture apparatus.

Grain-boundary surface coverages for segregated elements can be estimated from the Auger peak signal amplitude (Ref 30). The coverage C_x of element x on a substrate composed primarily of element y is approximated using:

$$C_x = \frac{I_x (S_y) (\lambda_x)}{(S_x) (I_y)}$$

where I_x and I_y are the observed peak-to-peak Auger signal amplitudes for the elements x and y, S_x and S_y are the relative sensitivities for elements x and y for the Auger system being used, and λ_x is the electron escape depth for the electrons of energy corresponding to that of the I_x Auger transition. The λ_x values are proportional to $E_x^{1/2}$ and the proportionality factor can be deduced using the formulas provided in Ref 31. The more common technique of calculating atomic concentrations from Auger data and normalizing to 100% will not yield accurate results because it assumes that the component x is uniformly present rather than segregated in a shallow region near the surface.

An excellent example of the application of AES to study the influence of segregation to sulfur on the intergranular hydrogen embrittlement of nickel is given in Ref 32. Because

Fig. 26 Histograms indicating the coverage and distribution of sulfur on intergranular fracture surfaces of vacuum-melted nickel for two heat treatments

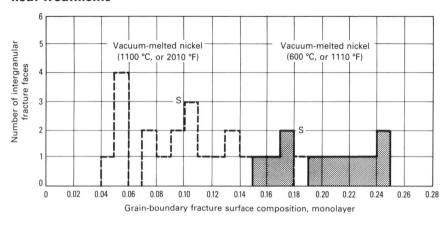

Table 1 Bulk composition of nickel alloys

Material	S	P	Sb	C	N	O
			Element, at. ppm			
ZR nickel ..	0.5	...	0.3	670	5	45
VM nickel..	≤5	<40	<50	45	5	180

Table 2 Grain-boundary compositions of nickel alloys

Nickel alloy	Final heat temperature °C	°F	Average grain-boundary fracture surface coverage, fraction of a monolayer of sulfur	Number of intergranular surfaces analyzed
ZR ...	1100	2010	0.05	8
	600	1110	0.10	10
VM ..	1100	2010	0.10	18
	600	1110	0.20	11

Fig. 27 Typical Auger spectra for fracture surfaces of nickel heat treated at 600 °C (1110 °F) for 240 h

A, VM nickel; B, ZR nickel

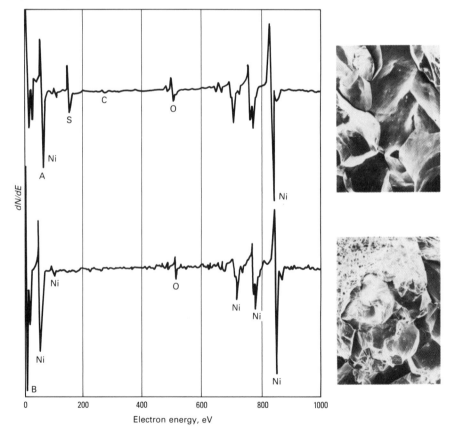

the vacuum-melted nickel used for this study had sufficient sulfur, additions of sulfur were unnecessary. The low-sulfur case was studied using a zone-refined (ZR) rod of nickel. Table 1 lists the bulk chemistry of each of the alloys. Table 2 provides the final heat treatments and the average grain-boundary chemistry for the various alloys. The grain-boundary chemistry varied greatly from grain to grain (Fig. 26). The shaded portion of the histogram corresponds to data taken from the 600 °C (1110 °F) heat-treated vacuum-melted (VM) sample.

It is necessary to calculate the average sulfur composition for each sample analyzed to obtain grain-boundary compositions that can be compared. Figure 27(a) shows a typical Auger spectrum and fracture micrograph for a VM sample that had an average grain-boundary composition of approximately 0.2 of a monolayer of sulfur and exhibited 100% intergranular failure. When the average grain-boundary composition of sulfur was 0.1 of a monolayer, a mixed mode fracture was found (Fig. 27b). An Auger spectrum taken from ductile rupture areas showed only the peaks expected from nickel. Figure 28 shows that the ductility and fracture mode of the nickel alloys depended on the grain-boundary chemistry.

The interrelationship between grain-boundary sulfur coverage and intergranular fracture illustrates the important effect of impurity segregation in alloys. When combined with other types of mechanical tests, AES experiments to measure grain-boundary composition are useful for investigating the mechanisms of embrittlement and for helping develop models or distinguishing between models of embrittlement. Thus, AES has been used to study failure mechanisms in materials containing many solid-solid interfaces, such as composites, mechanically alloyed materials, bonded or joined materials, and materials containing interphase boundaries (Ref 33, 34).

Example 7: Application of AES to Stress Corrosion Crack Fracture Surfaces. Most proposed stress corrosion cracking (SCC) models are based on the occurrence of one or more specific chemical

Fig. 28 Effect of sulfur grain-boundary coverage on the fracture mode and ductility

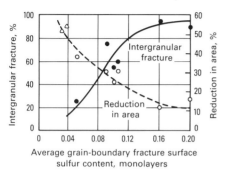

Fig. 30 Representative Auger survey spectra from an α-brass sample cracked in a nontarnishing ammonia solution

(a) Ductile region. (b) Transgranular SCC facet

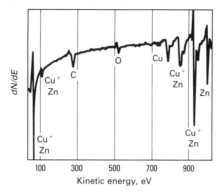 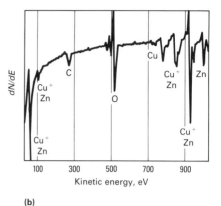

(a)   (b)

reactions at the crack tip. Thus, experimental information about the operative near-crack-tip chemical reactions should be helpful in elucidating SCC mechanisms. Such information can be obtained by locally sampling a small volume of the crack-tip solution or by chemical analysis of the resultant fracture surfaces. For the latter approach, AES has been used, and the experimental techniques implemented have ranged from broad-beam (1-mm electron beam diameter) analysis of free surfaces exposed to an SCC environment to high-resolution (1-μm beam diameter) analysis of SCC fracture surfaces near the crack tip. These inves-

Fig. 29 Tensile sample geometry discussed in Example 7

The sample is gripped in conventional tensile grips by the ends (A) during SCC testing. After SCC testing, the ends are cut off at the reduced cross section regions (B). The remaining shoulders (C) facilitate holding the central portion of the sample for final fracture of the gage section (D) inside the Auger spectrometer

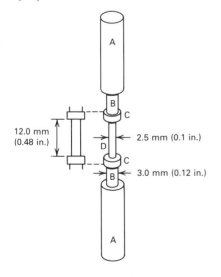

tigations have contributed to understanding of the chemical processes responsible for SCC. In the following, a recent application of AES to the study of SCC near-crack-tip surface chemistry is summarized (Ref 35).

Three brass alloy-SCC environment combinations were investigated: an α-phase alloy tested in nontarnishing ammonia solution, an admiralty alloy in aqueous copper sulfate, and an α-β alloy in distilled water. Only the α-brass/nontarnishing ammonia result will be presented (see Ref 35 for details). Similar experimental techniques were used for all alloy environment combinations. Axisymmetric samples of the configuration shown in Fig. 29 were prepared by lathe turning and electropolishing; the somewhat unusual sample configuration facilitated gripping the sample for final tensile failure in the Auger

spectrometer. The experimental technique for each sample involved slow strain rate ($\sim 5 \times 10^{-6}$ s^{-1}) SCC testing in a selected environment that was interrupted before sample failure. The final fracture was accomplished by uniaxial tension inside the UHV chamber of the Auger spectrometer, and the crack tip was subjected to AES analysis.

The Auger analyses were accomplished using a primary electron beam energy of 5 keV and 0.1 to 0.2 μA of beam current; these conditions corresponded to an electron beam diameter of approximately 1.2 μm. Care was taken to select regions of analysis having little apparent surface roughness to minimize the effects of surface inclination on the measured Auger signals. Particular attention was devoted to transition zones between SCC fracture surfaces and the central ductile

Fig. 31 Auger data from a series of points near the crack tip on an α-brass sample cracked in a nontarnishing ammonia solution

(a) Oxygen concentration versus distance from the transition zone. (b) Copper/zinc ratio versus distance from the transition zone

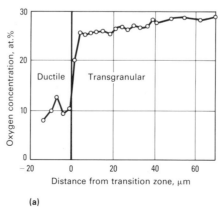 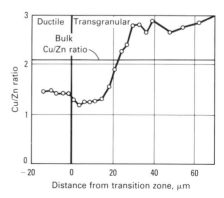

(a)   (b)

Fig. 32 Variation of surface composition during heating of a 304 stainless steel foil sample in a vacuum
(a) Heated to 350 °C (660 °F). (b) Heated to 535 °C (995 °F). (c) Heated to 745 °C (1375 °F)

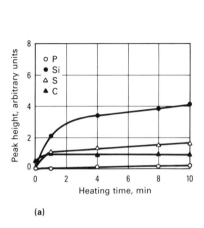

(a)

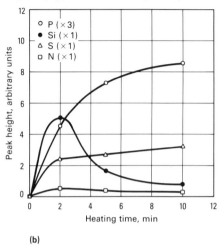

(b)

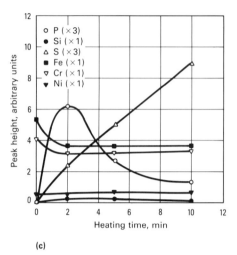

(c)

ligament because these zones correspond to positions of the SCC crack tips at the time of tensile test interruption.

Figure 30 shows typical Auger survey data from the transgranular (TG) SCC and ductile rupture regions of an α-brass sample cracked in nontarnishing ammonia. Upon initial inspection, the most obvious differences are the increased level of oxygen and an apparent increase in the ratio of copper to zinc on the TG facet regarding the ductile failure region. Figure 31 shows some of the most significant analytical results. The rapid increase in oxygen concentration (Fig. 31a) and the transition in fracture surface appearance (ductile to transgranular) delineate the position of the transgranular SCC crack tip. Examination of the copper/zinc ratio as a

Fig. 33 Surface distribution of sulfur and phosphorus after heating a 304 stainless steel sample at 750 °C (1380 °F)

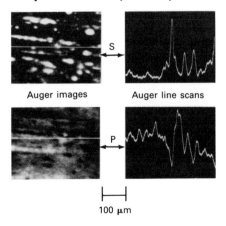

Auger images   Auger line scans

⊢——⊣
100 μm

function of distance from the transition zone reveals no significant increase in the copper/zinc ratio until positions 15 to 20 μm behind the crack tip are reached (Fig. 31b). Similar behavior was observed on several TG-SCC facets in this alloy-environment system.

The above observations indicate that selective dissolution (in this case, dezincification) can occur on transgranular SCC crack walls, but does not occur at the tip of the SCC crack. It was therefore suggested that selective dealloying at the crack tip is not crucial to crack propagation (Ref 35). Thus, although the above findings have been subject to alternative interpretations, they demonstrate that Auger spectrometry can provide important information about the local chemical reactions responsible for stress corrosion cracking.

Example 8: Surface Segregation. Many alloying elements and impurity elements present in small amounts (even in the part per million range) within an alloy can alter the surface chemistry substantially by diffusing and segregating at the surface. Reversal of such segregation could also occur under suitable conditions, for example, due to certain heat treatments. Because most engineering materials are binary or more complex alloys, segregation can play a major role in surface chemistry and has received significant attention. Further, the surface segregation behavior can sometimes be used as a guideline to understand grain-boundary segregation. This information is particularly helpful when it is difficult to obtain grain-boundary fracture, which is necessary to permit grain-boundary composition studies by surface analysis methods. The correlation of surface segregation to grain-boundary

segregation in materials examined has been qualitatively similar (Ref 36, 37).

The segregation behavior in multicomponent alloys can be complex. The complexity arises from such aspects as surface activity of the components, the diffusion rates, site competition, and interaction effects between segregating species. Typically, highly surface active solutes readily reduce the surface energy by segregation. Site competition and interaction effects may exist between segre-

Fig. 34 Depth-composition profile of a 304 stainless steel sample that has been heated at 750 °C (1380 °F)

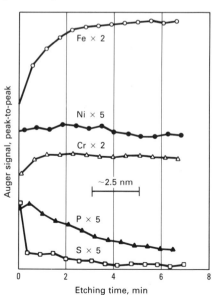

Fig. 35 Scanning electron micrographs of a cam lobe at approximately the center of the nose of the lobe

(a) Image taken before a sputter etch. Numbered locations correspond to Auger depth profiles in Fig 36. (b) Image taken after a 50-nm ion sputter etch

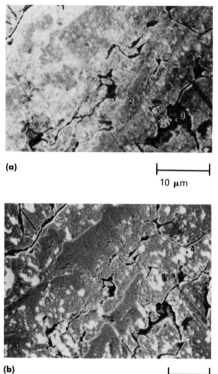

(a)

⊢————⊣
10 μm

(b)

⊢————⊣
10 μm

Fig. 36 Auger depth profiles of three selected locations on the cam lobe shown in Fig. 35(a)

Etch rate was 4 nm/min for the first 4 min and 8 nm/min thereafter. Right-hand profiles are expansions of the vertical axes to give detail on minor elements.

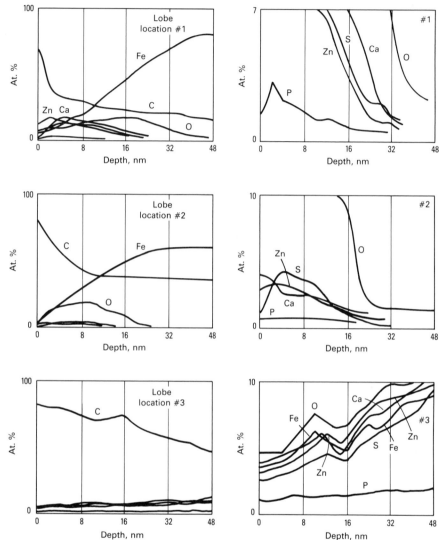

gating species. Solute interaction can enhance or reduce segregation of the interacting components, depending on whether the interaction is attractive or repulsive, respectively (Ref 38).

This example of segregation of such elements as phosphorus, sulfur, silicon, and nitrogen to the surface of a 304 stainless steel will detail the many aspects and the complexity of segregation (Ref 39). A commercial 304 steel taken in the form of a ribbon was sputter cleaned and heated in vacuum in front of an Auger spectrometer as the surface observations were conducted. Figure 32(a) shows the variations in peak heights (proportional to atomic concentration) of elements phosphorus, silicon, sulfur, and carbon as a function of heating time at 350 °C (660 °F). Rapid segregation of silicon is evident at this temperature. The segregation at 535 °C (995 °F) is more complex (Fig. 32b).

The surface concentration of silicon, which increased rapidly in the initial stages of heating, diminished with increasing

times, but the phosphorus continued to accumulate at the surface. Nitrogen exhibits similar behavior. Sulfur continued to segregate to the surface at a low rate. At 745 °C (1375 °F), the surface segregation did not include much silicon or nitrogen. Figure 32(c) illustrates the segregation behavior of sulfur and phosphorus as well as variations of silicon, iron, chromium, and nickel as a function of time. These data indicate that silicon segregates rapidly to surfaces at temperatures as low as 350 °C (660 °F); phosphorus dominates the surface at approximately 535 °C (995 °F). Site competition between silicon and phosphorus is believed

to be the major reason for reversal of segregation of silicon. Similar competition between phosphorus and sulfur is believed to occur at higher temperatures, such as 745 °C (1375 °F).

The high spatial resolution capabilities of the scanning Auger microprobe, with an electron beam diameter of approximately 3 μm, have been used to investigate uniformity of surface coverage by the various elements. Figure 33 shows the phosphorus and sulfur elemental distributions and Auger line scans from the surface of a sample that was heated 10 min at 750 °C (1380 °F). The data obtained at room temperature indicate a nearly uniform distribution of phosphorus and a highly localized distribution of sulfur on the surface. Ion sputtering studies in conjunction with AES (Fig. 34) have demonstrated that the extent of segregation from the surface for sulfur and phosphorus is very small (approximately 3 nm).

In this example, detection of the surface-segregated species was possible only due to the high surface sensitivity of AES. In addition to the surface sensitivity, its ability to provide rapid and real time data acquisition during segregation and high lateral resolution coupled with elemental imaging and light-element sensitivity were instrumental in achieving the wealth of information.

Segregation to surfaces is of primary significance in many material properties, including adhesion, oxidation, catalysis, corrosion, and sintering; interfacial segregation influences such properties as grain-boundary fracture, intergranular corrosion, creep rupture, hydrogen embrittlement, and recrystallization behavior. Various factors controlling segregation and the role of segregation on material properties are discussed in Ref 40.

Example 9: Application of AES to Tribology. Tribology, the study of friction, wear, and lubrication, has benefited greatly from the introduction of surface spectroscopies, such as AES. Investigations have been of fundamental and applied natures. The most widely studied problems include the adhesion theory of friction, material transfer during sliding, surface modification of frictional surfaces, and the interaction of lubricants with surfaces. Application of surface analysis techniques, including AES, to tribological problems has been reviewed (Ref 41).

An example of an AES study in tribology is the characterization of the antiwear film formed on a camshaft lobe during engine operation (Ref 42). Figure 35 shows a scanning electron photomicrograph of a cam-lobe region. The lobe is composed of a hardenable cast iron alloy with three phases present: iron carbide, martensite, and graphite. The phases can be distinguished on a worn surface and probed individually with a high-spatial-resolution Auger electron microprobe. In this way, the interaction of lubricant additives (primarily zinc dialkyldithiophosphate, an antiwear-extreme pressure additive, and calcium sulfonate, a detergent-inhibitor) with the worn surface can be compared with locations having different compositions, load histories, or degrees of wear.

Figure 36 shows Auger depth profiles from three cam-lobe locations. The martensite matrix surface (lobe location #1) has

ten times the amount of additives present compared with an iron carbide location (lobe location #2) that carried higher load. A void location (lobe location #3) that was graphite is now filled with lubricant derivatives. Following the sputter-etch depth profiles, the photomicrograph shown in Fig. 35(b) reveals many patchy regions across the cam-lobe surface that Auger analysis identified as sulfides of iron, zinc, and calcium. These investigations demonstrate the ability of AES with high spatial resolution to characterize extremely heterogeneous surface films rapidly.

REFERENCES

1. L.E. Davis, N.C. MacDonald, P.W. Palmberg, G.E. Riach, and R.E. Weber, *Handbook of Auger Electron Spectroscopy*, Perkin-Elmer Corporation, Physical Electronics Division, Eden Prairie, MN, 1976
2. P. Auger, *J. Phys. Radium*, Vol 6, 1925, p 205
3. L.A. Harris, *J. Appl. Phys.*, Vol 39, 1968, p 1419
4. R.E. Weber and W.T. Peria, *J. Appl. Phys.*, Vol 38, 1967, p 4355
5. P.W. Palmberg, G.K. Bohn, and J.C. Tracy, *Appl. Phys. Lett.*, Vol 15, 1969, p 254
6. A. Joshi, L.E. Davis, and P.W. Palmberg, in *Methods of Surface Analysis*, A.W. Czanderna, Ed., Elsevier, 1975
7. D. Briggs and M.P. Seah, Ed., *Practical Surface Analysis by Auger and X-Ray Photoelectron Spectroscopy*, John Wiley & Sons, 1983
8. C.C. Chang, *Surf. Sci.*, Vol 25, 1971, p 53
9. D.F. Stein and A. Joshi, *Annu. Rev. Mater. Sci.*, Vol 11, 1981, p 485
10. G.E. McGuire and P.H. Holloway, in *Electron Spectroscopy: Theory, Techniques and Applications*, Vol 4, C.R. Brundle and A.D. Baker, Ed., Academic Press, 1981
11. R.S. Swingle II and W.M. Riggs, *CRC Crit. Rev. Anal. Chem.*, Vol 5 (No. 3), 1975, p 267
12. M.P. Seah and W.A. Dench, *Surf. Interface Anal.*, Vol 1, 1979, p 4
13. T.W. Haas, J.T. Grant, and G.J. Dooley, *J. Appl. Phys.*, Vol 43, 1972, p 1853
14. S. Mroczkowski and D. Lichtman, *J. Vac. Sci. Technol.*, Vol A3, 1985, p 1860
15. H.L. Marcus and P.W. Palmberg, *Trans. Met. Soc. AIME*, Vol 245, 1969, p 1664
16. P.W. Palmberg, *J. Vac. Sci. Technol.*,

Vol 9, 1972, p 160
17. N.C. McDonald and G.E. Riach, *Elec. Pack. Prod.*, Apr 1973, p 50
18. G. Betz, G.K. Wehner, L.E. Toth, and A. Joshi, *J. Appl. Phys.*, Vol 45, 1974, p 5312
19. A. Joshi, *Rev. Coatings Corros.*, Vol 3 (No. 243), 1979, p 51-77
20. "Auger Chemical State Mapping," 8101, Perkin-Elmer Corporation, Physical Electronics Division, Norwalk, CT, 1982
21. J.A. Slane, S.P. Clough, and J.R. Nappier, *Met. Trans.*, Vol 9A, 1978, p 1839-1842
22. S.P. Clough, in *Modern Surface Analysis, Metallurgical Applications of AES and XPS*, American Institute of Mining, Metallurgical, and Petroleum Engineers, Warrendale, PA, 1979
23. C.E. Locke, J.H. Peavy, O. Rincon, and M. Afzal, *Symposium on Advances of Metal and Polymer Surfaces*, Academic Press, 1977
24. S.P. Clough, personal communication, Perkin-Elmer Corporation, Physical Electronics Division, Norwalk, CT
25. "Au-Ni-Cu Metallization System," 8005, Perkin-Elmer Corporation, Physical Electronics Division, Norwalk, CT, 1980
26. S. Thomas and A. Joshi, in *Materials and Processes—Continuing Innovations*, Vol 28, Society for the Advancement of Materials and Process Engineering, Azusa, CA, 1983, p 752
27. A. Joshi and D.F. Stein, *J. Test. Eval.*, Vol 1, 1973, p 202
28. C.J. McMahon, Jr., and L. Marchut, *J. Vac. Sci. Technol.*, Vol 15, 1978, p 450
29. R.A. Mulford, C.L. Briant, and R.G. Rowe, *Scan. Elec. Microsc.*, Vol 1, 1980, p 487
30. E.D. Hondros and M.P. Seah, *Int. Met. Rev.*, Vol 222, 1977, p 262
31. M.P. Seah, *J. Vac. Sci. Technol.*, Vol 17, 1980, p 16
32. S.M. Bruemmer, R.H. Jones, M.T. Thomas, and D.R. Baer, *Metall. Trans. A*, Vol 14A, 1983, p 223
33. A. Joshi, in *Role of Interface Chemistry in Failure of Materials*, STP 645, B.M. Strauss and W.H. Cullen, Jr., Ed., ASTM, Philadelphia, 1978, p 275
34. W.C. Johnson and J.M. Blakely, Ed., *Interfacial Segregation*, American Society for Metals, 1979
35. M.B. Hintz, L.A. Heldt, and D.A. Koss, *Embrittlement by the Localized Crack Environment*, R.P. Gangloff, Ed., American Institute of Mining, Metallurgical, and Petroleum Engi-

neers, Warrendale, PA, 1984, p 229
36. C. Lea and M.P. Seah, *Scr. Metall.*, Vol 9, 1975, p 583
37. A. Joshi, unpublished research, Lockheed, Research and Development Division, Palo Alto, CA
38. M. Guttmann and D. McLean, in *Inter-*

facial Segregation, American Society for Metals, 1977
39. A. Joshi, in *Modern Surface Analysis, Metallurgical Applications of AES and XPS*, American Institute of Mining, Metallurgical, and Petroleum Engineers, Warrendale, PA, 1979

40. S. Hoffmann, *Scan. Elec. Microsc.*, Vol 3, 1985, p 1071
41. D.R. Wheeler, *Scan. Elec. Microsc.*, Vol 2, O.M. Jahari, Ed., 1984, p 589-599
42. S.W. Gaarenstroom and F. Caracciolo, *J. Vac. Sci. Technol.*, in press

X-Ray Photoelectron Spectroscopy

J.B. Lumsden, Rockwell International Science Center

General Uses

- Elemental analysis of surfaces of all elements except hydrogen
- Chemical state identification of surface species
- In-depth composition profiles of elemental distribution in thin films
- Composition analysis of samples when destructive effects of electron beam techniques must be avoided

Examples of Applications

- Determination of oxidation states of metal atoms in metal oxide surface films
- Identification of surface carbon as graphitic or carbide

Samples

- *Form*: Solids (metals, glasses, semiconductors, low vapor pressure ceramics)
- *Size*: ≤ 6.25 cm^3 (≤ 0.4 in.^{3})
- *Preparation*: Must be free of fingerprints, oils, or other surface contamination

Limitations

- Data collection is slow compared with other surface analysis techniques, but analysis time can be decreased substantially when high resolution or chemical state identification is not needed
- Poor lateral resolution
- Surface sensitivity comparable to other surface analysis techniques

- Charging effects may be a problem with insulating samples. Some instruments are equipped with charge-compensation devices
- The accuracy of quantitative analysis is limited

Estimated Analysis Time

- Requires an overnight vacuum pumpdown before analysis
- Qualitative analysis can be performed in 5 to 10 min
- Quantitative analysis requires 1 h to several hours, depending on information desired

Capabilities of Related Techniques

- *Auger electron spectroscopy*: Compositional analysis of surfaces. Faster, with better lateral resolution than XPS. Has depth-profiling capabilities. Electron beam can be very damaging; bonding and other chemical state information are not easily interpreted
- *Low-energy ion-scattering spectroscopy*: Sensitive to the top atom layer of the surface and has profiling capabilities. Quantitative analysis requires use of standards; no chemical state information; poor mass resolution for high-Z elements
- *Secondary ion mass spectroscopy*: The most sensitive of all surface analysis techniques. Can detect hydrogen, and depth profiling is possible. Has pronounced matrix effects that can cause orders of magnitude variations in elemental sensitivity and make quantitative analysis difficult

Introduction

X-ray photoelectron spectroscopy (XPS) has two associated phenomena whose physical basis has been known for years. The photoelectric effect (Ref 1) was described in 1905, and the radiationless transition (Ref 2) was discovered in 1923 during an investigation of radioactive decay. However, these phenomena attracted only limited attention for many years following their discovery.

Interest in these effects was revived soon after World War II. High-resolution spectrometers, which had been developed to measure the energy of β-rays, were applied to study electrons ejected by x-rays. An x-ray photoelectron spectrometer was constructed, and use of the technique was proposed for chemical analysis of surfaces (Ref 3).

Developments that led to current XPS date from 1954, when a discrete XPS line was

obtained. This was followed by the systematic measurement of the atomic binding energies of many elements with improved accuracy. The chemical environment was observed to affect core-level binding energies, originating the term electron spectroscopy for chemical analysis (ESCA) (Ref 4).

Commercial x-ray photoelectron spectrometers appeared in 1969. Reliable ultra-high vacuum (UHV) systems were developed and combined with x-ray photoelectron spec-

Fig. 1 Energy-level diagrams showing the electron transitions that form the basis for three techniques
(a) XPS. (b) X-ray analysis. (c) AES (Auger electron spectroscopy). ϕ, spectrometer work function

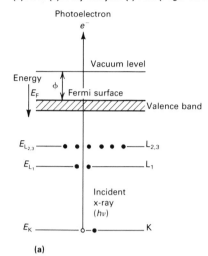

(a)

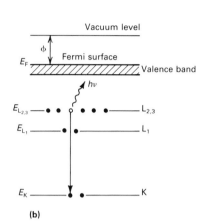

(b)

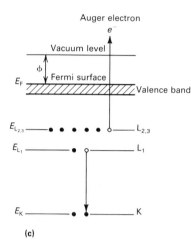

(c)

trometers in commercial instruments during the early 1970s. Today, XPS has advanced from the atomic physics laboratory to routine use for chemical analysis of surfaces.

Principles

Figure 1 illustrates the electronic transitions involved in XPS. The initial event is the ejection of an electron from one of the core electronic levels by an incident x-ray photon. The kinetic energy KE of the photoemitted core electron is:

$$KE = h\nu - BE + \phi \qquad \text{(Eq 1)}$$

where $h\nu$ is the energy of the exciting radiation, BE is the binding energy of the emitted electron in the solid, and ϕ is the spectrometer work function.

After a core hole is produced, it is filled by an outer electron. When this electronic transition occurs, energy is conserved by the emission of a photon (Fig. 1b) or by the emission of a secondary electron through radiationless transition (Fig. 1c). If the atom returns to the ground state by the emission of a characteristic x-ray, the energy E_X of the emitted photon is the difference in energy of the two levels involved in the transition with the addition of the work function, or if the transition is between the K and L energy levels (Fig. 1), then:

$$E_X = E_K - E_{L_{2,3}} + \phi \qquad \text{(Eq 2)}$$

This transition, in which a photon is emitted, enables energy-dispersive x-ray analysis and electron probe microanalysis (EPMA). In the radiationless transition, the secondary electron emitted is the Auger electron. One of the

outer electrons fills the core hole as another is ejected from the atom with a discrete amount of energy equal the difference between the initial and final states. The energy E_A of the Auger electron (Fig. 1c) is:

$$E_A = E_K - E_{L_1} - E_{L_{2,3}} + \phi \qquad \text{(Eq 3)}$$

As discussed below, $E_{L_1} + E_{L_{2,3}}$ does not describe the final state correctly, but is often a suitable approximation.

The transitions in which Auger emission and photon emission occur are mutually exclusive processes; the total probability for their occurrence must add to one. Auger emission is the more probable transition for low atomic number elements. This explains why x-ray spectroscopy is not more sensitive to these elements, and why the reverse is true for AES.

Nomenclature

The binding energy of an electron in a core level is the difference between the total energies of the initial and final states of the atom following photoemission. The final state is that in which an electron has been removed from the given energy level. The energy levels of an atom involved in photoemission can be represented conveniently in terms of an energy-level diagram that provides the energy of the atom when one electron of the indicated quantum numbers n, l, j is missing. Figure 2 shows such a diagram for uranium. Also shown are the x-ray and spectroscopic notations corresponding to the n, l, j quantum numbers.

Spectroscopic notation is customary in XPS, but an Auger transition is usually described using x-ray notation. An XYZ

transition is an Auger transition in which a core hole in level X is filled by an electron in level Y and an electron is ejected from level Z. Thus, the Auger transition shown in Fig. 1(c) is a $KL_1L_{2,3}$ transition. X-ray notation cannot be used to describe the final state following an Auger transition, because the atom is doubly ionized. Interactions between the two holes can sometimes lead to additional energy states. In such cases, a spectroscopic term must be added, and an Auger transition is described by XYZ (spectroscopic term). These additional Auger transitions can usually be observed only using high-resolution spectrometers designed for the detection of these lines. In spectra obtained from commercial instruments designed for chemical analysis, x-ray notation is usually adequate.

Surface Sensitivity

The Auger and photoemitted electrons of interest have relatively low kinetic energies ranging from approximately 50 to 2000 eV. These low-velocity electrons have a high probability of undergoing an inelastic collision with an atom in the matrix if they travel very far before leaving the surface. After a single collision, the Auger or photoemitted electrons will lose sufficient energy to be removed from the flux of electrons having energies given by Eq 1 and 3. Thus, only those electrons originating from the surface or a few atomic layers below the surface will contribute to an XPS peak. This is illustrated in Fig. 3, which provides experimental values obtained for the inelastic mean free path for electrons having the range of energies important in XPS. The inelastic mean free path is:

$$dN = N_0 e^{-x/\lambda}\, dx \qquad \text{(Eq 4)}$$

where dN is the number of electrons that do not undergo an inelastic scattering event while moving a distance x in the matrix, and N_0 is the number of photoelectrons emitted per unit area for the given shell. Defining θ as the angle between the surface normal and the direction of the emitted electron, $\lambda \cos \theta$ is sometimes termed the escape depth.

An empirical value for the inelastic mean free path obtained from the data in Fig. 3 for electrons having energies above 50 eV is:

$$\lambda = 0.41 a^{1.5}\, E^{0.5} \qquad \text{(Eq 5)}$$

where E is the electron energy in electron volts, and a is the atom size defined in terms of the density ρ, Avogadro's number N, and the mean atomic weight A, by:

$$1000\rho N a^3 = A \qquad \text{(Eq 6)}$$

Instrumentation

Because the electronic structure of each element is unique, determining the energy of one or more of the photoemitted electrons permits identification of the element from which it originated. Thus, an x-ray photoelectron spectrometer consists of an x-ray source, an energy analyzer, an electron detector, and instrumentation for data acquisition.

X-ray Source. X-rays are produced whenever fast electrons strike a target. An x-ray source consists of a hot filament and a target anode. The electrons are accelerated from the filament to the anode by a potential maintained between them. Figure 4 shows a typical x-ray spectrum, which consists of a sharp line spectrum superposed on a continuous background. The continuous background, termed bremsstrahlung, is caused by the accelerations experienced by the electrons in the target material during scattering of the incident high-energy electrons. The sharp lines are a result of transitions of the bound electrons between energy levels in the target material and are termed the characteristic x-rays of the element.

The kinetic energy of the photoelectrons depends on the energy of the incident radiation (Eq 1); therefore, a monochromatic x-ray source is necessary for high resolution in an XPS spectrum. In most commercial electron spectrometers, the characteristic Kα aluminum or magnesium x-ray lines are used with an aluminum foil window to filter some of the bremsstrahlung radiation. Some spectrometers are equipped with dual anodes, one of magnesium and one of aluminum; either can be used by simply changing an

Fig. 2 Energy-level diagram of an atom

The energy of the atom with one electron of the indicated quantum number (n, l, or j) missing

n	l	j		
4	3	7/2	N_7	$4f_{7/2}$
4	3	5/2	N_6	$4f_{5/2}$
4	2	5/2	N_5	$4d_{5/2}$
4	2	3/2	N_4	$4d_{3/2}$
4	1	3/2	N_3	$4p_{3/2}$
4	1	1/2	N_2	$4p_{1/2}$
4	0	1/2	N_1	$4s$
3	2	5/2	M_5	$3d_{5/2}$
3	2	3/2	M_4	$3d_{3/2}$
3	1	3/2	M_3	$3p_{3/2}$
3	1	1/2	M_2	$3p_{1/2}$
3	0	1/2	M_1	$3s$
2	1	3/2	L_3	$2p_{3/2}$
2	1	1/2	L_2	$2p_{1/2}$
2	0	1/2	L_1	$2s$
1	0	1/2	K_1	$1s$

external switch. This arrangement is convenient when a sample contains Auger electrons having the same energy as the photoemitted electrons. Changing the energy of the incident radiation will alter the kinetic energy of the photoemitted electrons, but not that of the Auger electrons (Eq 1 and 3).

The Kα aluminum and magnesium lines are unresolved doublets. The Kα doublet of magnesium has an energy of 1253.6 eV with a composite linewidth of 0.7 eV full width at half maximum (FWHM). The Kα doublet of aluminum has an energy of 1486.6 eV with a composite linewidth of 0.85 eV FWHM. For high resolution, x-ray sources are also avail-

able that have monochromators (Ref 7). These instruments can achieve a linewidth of approximately 0.5 eV by removing the bremsstrahlung and selecting one of the doublet lines; however, the photon flux in a monochromatized source is considerably less than that of an unmonochromatized source in which all the Kα emission is available. This makes the analysis more time-consuming using a monochromatized source.

Analyzer. An electron energy analyzer is more correctly a velocity analyzer. Most commercial instruments use the cylindrical mirror analyzer or the concentric hemispherical analyzer. Figure 5 shows the cylin-

Fig. 3 The energy dependence of the mean free path of an electron

Source: Ref 5

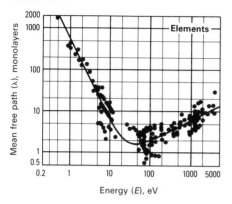

Fig. 6 A 0- to 1000-eV scan of the photoelectrons emitted from a clean iron surface using the Mg Kα line as the source

The inset is a narrow sweep width range on the iron 2p lines (resolution = 0.5 eV). The symbol V indicates that the final vacancies are in valence levels.

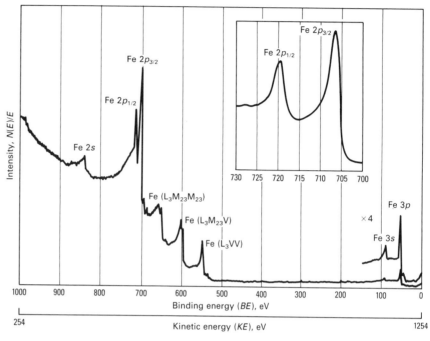

Fig. 4 The x-ray intensity from aluminum and magnesium anodes at 10 kV showing the bremsstrahlung radiation and characteristic Kα peaks

Source: Ref 6

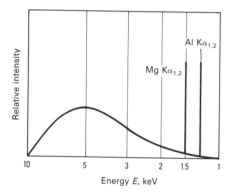

Fig. 5 Double-pass cylindrical mirror analyzer used for XPS

Source: Ref 8

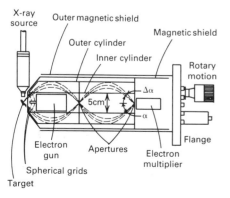

drical mirror analyzer, which consists of two coaxial cylinders. For the high resolution needed for XPS, two cylindrical mirror analyzers are placed in series, termed a double-pass cylindrical mirror analyzer (Ref 8). Cylindrical mirror and concentric hemispherical analyzers are electrostatic dispersive units.

A negative potential (relative to that applied on the inner surface) is applied to the outer cylinder or sphere. Thus, for a given potential difference between the two cylinders or hemispheres, only electrons within a very narrow velocity range will follow a trajectory that takes them from the entrance slit through the analyzer and through the exit aperture to the detector. The energy range of the photoemitted electrons can be swept by varying the potential across the analyzer. However, the usual procedure is to retard the incoming electrons using a lens or grids so that the kinetic energy of the electrons in the analyzer remains fixed at a preselected value, the pass energy, as the retarding field is scanned. In this procedure, the applied potential across the analyzer is constant. Decelerating the incoming electrons before they enter the analyzer increases the energy resolution of the analyzer (Ref 8). Maintaining a constant pass energy as the energy range is swept fixes the resolution for all lines in the spectrum (Ref 9).

The detector is an electron multiplier or a channel plate multiplier. In most cases, the data acquisition system includes a multichannel analyzer or a computer that permits repetitive scans to be made. Multiple scans over the same energy region improve the signal-to-noise ratio, enhancing weak signals.

The vacuum requirement for the electron optics is a pressure less than 10^{-5} torr. This pressure will minimize electron scattering through collisions with gas molecules. If the surface under analysis is active and subject to contamination, a pressure of approximately 10^{-9} torr is necessary.

Qualitative Analysis

Figure 6 shows an example of the general appearance of a spectrum obtained from an x-ray photoelectron spectrometer. The incident radiation was Mg Kα x-rays, and the pass energy of the analyzer was 100 eV with a 2-eV resolution. The spectrum includes several peaks superimposed on a background that increases with binding energy (kinetic energy decreases). The peaks are identified on the spectrum, showing the core level from which the photoemission occurred. The Mg Kα photons are not sufficiently energetic to probe core levels below the 2s shell. The peaks have variable intensities, and the core 2p level is split into a doublet. The LMM

Auger lines are also present in the spectrum. Photoemission caused by bremsstrahlung radiation and primary and secondary electrons that have undergone inelastic collisions cause the sloping background. The number of secondary electrons increases sharply in the low kinetic energy region.

In a typical analysis, a broad survey scan is conducted over a wide energy range. The most intense lines, usually including the carbon 1s and oxygen 1s, are first identified. Other less intense lines of the identified elements are then found. Portions of the spectrum often must be examined in more detail over a narrower energy range; such a scan of the iron 2p lines is also shown in Fig. 6. When a qualitative analysis of a spectrum is performed, it is very helpful to have spectra from pure elements for comparison. One source is provided in Ref 10.

Energy Calibration. It is often essential to be able to measure binding energies to ±0.1 eV for proper interpretation of spectra. Accomplishing this necessitates adjusting the instrument parameters to attain the desired resolution. An accurate calibration of the energy scale is also necessary. A survey of the literature shows that general agreement on accurate values of binding energies does not exist. The report of an ASTM round-robin to survey values of binding energies of standard materials highlighted some of the errors encountered (Ref 11). Procedures of calibration and standard line positions are found in Ref 10 and 12.

Chemical Shifts. One of the most important capabilities of XPS is its ability to measure shifts in the binding energy of core electrons resulting from a change in the chemical environment. Such changes in binding energy, termed chemical shifts, can result from a change in the nearest neighbor, the oxidation state, compound, or the crystal structure.

The simple model of chemical shifts is that alterations in the valence (outer) shell electrons change the nuclear attractive force on the core electrons. This effect arises because the valence-shell electrons exert a repulsive force on the core electrons that screens these electrons from the nuclear charge, reducing the nuclear attractive force. The addition of valence electrons, to change the oxidation state, increases the screening effect, which reduces the binding energy. If valence electrons are removed, the effective positive charge of the nucleus is increased, and the binding energy increases. Screening effects can vary for the same ion in different compounds. Covalent bonds can exert similar effects, in which case the electronegativity of neighboring atoms is important. An example is shown in Fig. 7, which is an XPS spectrum of carbon in ethyl trifluoroacetate;

each of the four different chemical environments of carbon is distinguishable.

Identification of the chemical state of an element by its chemical shift is sometimes not possible. This is frequently the case for transition metals that have broad lines. For example, it is extremely difficult to resolve the ferric and ferrous lines separately in the iron 2p spectrum of magnetite. Many of the commercial instruments have software packages that will deconvolute a line. However, these involve approximations and must be used with extreme care. In most cases, a unique deconvolution of a line cannot be obtained; the more component lines used to fit a spectrum, the more ambiguous the solution. Thus, it is useful to obtain "fingerprint" spectra for compound identification. Multiplet splitting and shake-up phenomena sometimes introduce features into a spectrum that aid interpretation.

Multiplet splitting can occur when there are one or more electrons in the valence shell with unpaired spins and photoionization occurs in another shell. This situation typically arises for the transition and rare-earth metals that have unfilled d and f levels, respectively. When a hole is created in a filled level by photoionization, two orbitals will exist with uncoupled spins. These two orbitals will couple, leading to a splitting in the energy levels.

Multiplet splitting is usually most pronounced when the unpaired electrons are in orbitals with the same principal quantum number. For example, the iron 3s line in Fe_2O_3 becomes a doublet with a 7.3-eV separation (Ref 13). However, the component lines (Fig. 8) in the iron $2p_{3/2}$ spectrum are close in energy and are not separately resolvable (Ref 14). Multiplet splitting causes asymmetry and changes in the separation of the 2p lines in compounds of first-row transition metals. The separation of the 3s doublet of a first-row transition metal depends on its chemical environment (Ref 13). Thus, multiplet splitting sometimes can be used for compound identification.

Shake-up Satellites. When photoionization occurs in a core level, there is a sudden change in the effective nuclear charge due to the loss of a shielding electron. This reorganizes the valence electrons, which may result in the excitation of one of these electrons into an unfilled higher energy level. This transition causes a quantum loss in energy of the photoemitted electron and will result in a discrete satellite photoelectron line at higher binding energy (lower kinetic energy) to the primary line. The intensity of satellite lines is much higher in paramagnetic compounds (unpaired spins) than in diamagnetic compounds (Ref 15).

The Auger Parameter. Auger lines,

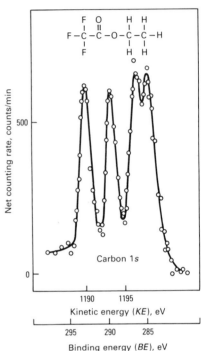

Fig. 7 XPS spectrum of the carbon 1s lines in ethyl trifluoracetate
Source: Ref 4

which are produced by transitions of core electrons (electrons below the valence level), frequently undergo chemical shifts larger than the core-level photoelectron lines. These shifts are caused by the relaxation of the electron cloud resulting from an increase in the effective nuclear charge, as in the case of shake-up lines. Because the final state following an Auger transition is a two-hole configuration versus a one-hole configuration for photoelectron emission, relaxation energy is larger for an Auger transition, causing a larger energy shift.

The Auger parameter (Ref 15, 16) is the difference in kinetic energy between the Auger electron and the photoemitted electrons:

$$\alpha = KE_A - KE_p = BE_p - BE_A \quad \text{(Eq 7)}$$

This quantity is unique to each compound. It is defined as the difference between two line energies in the same element in the same sample, obviating the need for corrections for charging of the sample and work function corrections.

Quantitative Analysis

There are two approaches to performing quantitative analysis. Fundamental physical principles can be used, or a more empirical

Fig. 8 The iron $2p_{3/2}$ spectrum showing a model calculation of the deconvolution into component lines whose intensity and energy were rationalized on the basis of multiplet splitting

CG, center of gravity. Source: Ref 14

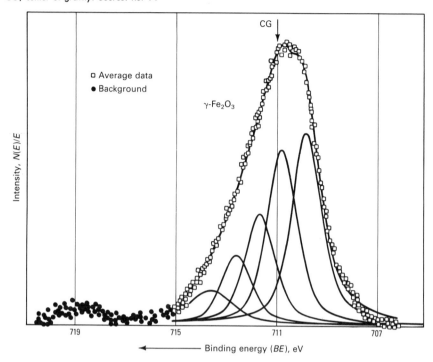

approach can be implemented in which standards are used as reference materials or to obtain elemental sensitivity factors. In arriving at an expression (Ref 17, 18) describing the intensity of an XPS line, an x-ray beam having an intensity I_0 and characteristic energy $h\nu$ is considered to be incident on a homogeneous smooth surface sample. It is assumed that reflection and refraction effects of the x-ray beam can be ignored. While penetrating the sample, the characteristic x-rays ionize the core level, x, in atoms of element i. It is assumed that the x-ray flux does not undergo any loss in intensity over the depth from which the photoexcited electrons can effectively escape from the sample. The ejected electrons have kinetic energy, $KE_{i,x}$. The measured current of photoemitted electrons from this event, $I_{i,x}$, is proportional to the density of i atoms in the analysis volume, N_i, and to instrumental and basic material properties of the sample. The complete expression is:

$$I_{i,x} = I_0 N_{i,x} A \sigma_{i,x} \theta_{i,x} \lambda_{i,x} T \qquad \text{(Eq 8)}$$

where $\sigma_{i,x}$ is the photoionization cross section for the level x, which depends on the energy of the incident x-ray flux; $\lambda_{i,x}$ is the mean free path of photoexcited electrons; A is the area of the sample from which photo-

electrons are detected; $\theta_{i,x}$ is an asymmetry factor for photoemitted electrons that provides the angular dependence of photoemission in terms of the angle between the photon path and the emitted photoelectrons; and T is the detection efficiency of the analyzer. The detection efficiency depends on the acceptance solid angle of the spectrometer, intensity loss due to retarding the electrons, and the efficiency of the electron detector. Equation 8 is seldom used for quantitative analysis because the data needed for its application is unavailable or not known to sufficient accuracy using theoretical calculations.

For a given photoemission process in element i, an atomic sensitivity factor, S_i, can be defined:

$$S_i = I_0 A \sigma_i \theta_i \lambda_i T \qquad \text{(Eq 9)}$$

The XPS intensities for elements 1 and 2 in the same matrix can be compared according to:

$$\frac{N_1}{N_2} = \frac{I_1/S_1}{I_2/S_2} \qquad \text{(Eq 10)}$$

Thus, by using a given photoemission transition in a reference atom, a set of empiri-

cally derived sensitivity factors can be obtained for a given spectrometer. This has been accomplished for the double-pass and hemispherical analyzers with retarding fields using compounds of fluorine and potassium (Ref 19). Table 1 lists the set of sensitivity factors obtained in which the fluorine $1s$ line is the reference and is arbitrarily given a sensitivity factor of 1. In most cases, the strongest line is used.

Equation 10 can be written in a more general form so that the atom fraction, C_i, of any constituent in a sample can be obtained:

$$C_i = \frac{N_i}{\sum_j n_j} = \frac{I_i/S_i}{\sum_j I_j/S_j} \qquad \text{(Eq 11)}$$

where $\sum\limits_j$ is summed over all of elements

observed in the spectrum from the sample. In using this expression, the area under the appropriate line is taken as the intensity I.

In applying Eq 11, the area under the curves is integrated. This is accomplished by defining the baseline as the straight line drawn tangent to the base at both sides of the peak (Ref 19). The appropriate sensitivity factors from Table 1 are then inserted in the equation. Shake-up lines, if present, should be included in the measured areas. If the sensitivity factors in Table 1 are used in spectra from instruments other than double-pass and hemispherical analyzers (Ref 19), it may be necessary to correct for differences in detection efficiency.

Depth Analysis

Using the concentric hemispherical analyzer, the surface sensitivity of XPS can be enhanced by tilting the sample so that the angle θ between the surface tangent and the direction of the ejected electron approaches zero. The double-pass cylindrical mirror analyzer has an aperture between the two units to accomplish this. As θ approaches zero, the path that photoelectrons emitted below the surface must traverse before they can exit the sample increases as $z/\sin\theta$, where z is the depth below the surface at which the electron was emitted. Thus, the probability of escape decreases as $\exp\{-z/\lambda\sin\theta\}$. Figure 9 shows how the surface sensitivity changes when the takeoff angle is varied (Ref 20). Thus, by tilting a sample having a thin film relative to the entrance slit of the spectrometer, it is possible to separate surface composition from that near the substrate.

A second method of obtaining a depth-composition profile is to bombard the sample with a beam of inert gas ions, usually argon or xenon. Sputtering rates can be varied from

Table 1 Empirical atomic sensitivity factors relative to fluorine $1s = 1$ for some instruments(a)

	Strong line		Secondary line(c)	
	Area, 1s	Height(b), 1s	Area, 2s	Height, 2s
Lithium	0.020	0.020	...	...
Beryllium	0.059	0.059	...	...
Boron	0.13	0.13	...	...
Carbon	0.25	0.25	...	...
Nitrogen	0.42	0.42	...	...
Oxygen	0.66	0.66	0.025	0.025
Fluorine	1.00	1.00	0.04	0.04
Neon	1.5	1.5	0.07	0.07
Sodium	2.3	2.3	0.13	0.12
Magnesium	3.5*(d)	3.3	0.20	0.15

	$2p_{3/2}$	$2p$	$2p_{3/2}$	$2s$	$2s$
Magnesium	...	0.12	0.12	0.20	0.15
Aluminum	...	0.185	0.18	0.23	0.17
Silicon	...	0.27	0.25	0.26	0.19
Phosphorus	...	0.39	0.36	0.29	0.21
Sulfur	...	0.54	0.49	0.33	0.24
Chlorine	...	0.73	0.61	0.37	0.25
Argon	...	0.96	0.75	0.40	0.26
Potassium	0.83	1.24	0.83	0.43	0.26
Calcium	1.05	1.58	1.05	0.47	0.26
Scandium	(1.1)	(1.65)	(1.1)	0.50	0.26
Titanium	(1.2)	(1.8)	(1.2)	0.54	0.26

	$2p_{3/2}$	$2p$	$2p_{3/2}$	$3p$	$3p$
Titanium	(1.2)(e)	(1.8)	(1.2)	0.21	0.15
Vanadium	(1.3)	(1.95)	(1.3)	0.21	0.16
Chromium	(1.5)	(2.3)	(1.5)	(0.21)	(0.17)
Manganese	(1.7)	(2.6)	(1.7)	(0.22)	(0.19)
Iron	(2.0)	(3.0)	(2.0)	(0.26)	(0.21)
Cobalt	(2.5)	(3.8)	(2.5)	(0.35)	(0.25)
Nickel	(3.0)	(4.5)	(3.0)	(0.5)	(0.3)
Copper	(4.2)	(6.3)	(4.2)	(0.65)	(0.4)
Zinc	4.8	...	4.8	0.75	0.40
Gallium	5.4	...	5.4	0.84	0.40
Germanium	6.1*	...	6.0	0.92	0.40
Arsenic	6.8	...	6.8	1.00	0.43

	Area		Height,	Area		Height,
	$3d_{5/2}$	$3d$	$3d_{5/2}$	$3p_{3/2}$	$3p$	$3p_{3/2}$
Gallium	...	0.31	0.31	...	0.84	0.40
Germanium	...	0.38	0.37	...	0.91	0.40
Arsenic	...	0.53	0.51	...	0.97	0.42
Selenium	...	0.67	0.64	...	1.05	0.48
Bromine	...	0.83	0.77	...	1.14	0.54
Krypton	...	1.02	0.91	0.82	1.23(f)	0.60
Rubidium	...	1.23	1.07	0.87	1.30	0.67
Strontium	...	1.48	1.24	0.92	1.38	0.69
Yttrium	...	1.76	1.37	0.98	1.47	0.71
Zirconium	...	2.1	1.5	1.04	1.56	0.72
Niobium	1.44	2.4	1.57	1.10	...	0.72
Molybdenum	1.66	2.75	1.74	1.17	...	0.73
Technetium	1.89	3.15	1.92	1.24	...	0.73
Ruthenium	2.15	3.6	2.15	1.30	...	0.73
Rhodium	2.4	4.1	2.4	1.38	...	0.74
Palladium	2.7	4.6	2.7	1.43	...	0.74
Silver	3.1	5.2	3.1	1.52	...	0.75
Cadmium	3.5	...	3.5	1.60	...	0.75
Indium	3.9	...	3.9	1.68	...	0.75
Tin	4.3	...	4.3	1.77	...	0.75

(continued)

(a) In the instrument used, AT (see Eq 8) varies as $E^{-0.34}$. (b) Height sensitivity factors based on linewidths for strong lines of 3.1 eV, typical of lines obtained in survey spectra on insulating samples. When spin doublets are unresolved, data are for the convoluted peak heights. (c) Factors for the strong lines are insensitive to the radiation source (aluminum or magnesium). Factors for the secondary lines ($2s$, $3p$, $4d$, and $5d$) are dependent to an extent upon the photon energy. Values shown are average for aluminum and magnesium. For more accurate results, multiply the factors by 0.9 when magnesium radiation is used and by 1.1 when aluminum radiation is used. (d) Starred data are for peaks obtained only by using aluminum x-rays. (e) Data in parentheses indicate great variability with chemical state, because of the prevalence of multielectron processes. Data shown for the series titanium-copper are for diamagnetic forms; data for paramagnetic forms will be lower in general. Data for the rare earths are based on few experimental points and should be regarded only as a rough approximation. (f) Many of the area data are supplied for spin doublets for $3p$ and $4d$ because of the considerable width of many of those lines. Data for combined spin doublets in the $2p$ series for transition metals and the $3d$ for the rare earths are supplied because of the prevalence of shakeup lines, which makes it desirable to deal with the doublet as a whole. Source: Ref 19

Fig. 9 Dependence of surface sensitivity on takeoff angle

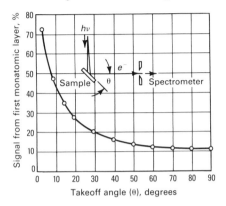

a few angstroms per minute to several hundred angstroms per minute by changing the ion current and accelerating potential. However, ion bombardment can introduce uncertainties into the results. In some cases, differential sputtering (Ref 21) can occur, in which some elements are sputtered from the surface at a faster rate than others, changing the surface composition. The knock-on effect (Ref 22) can occur, in which the ion beam drives surface species into the matrix. The incident ion beam can cause valence changes in surface species. Observations have been made in which metal ions in surface oxides have been reduced to the metal (Ref 23). Although in-depth profiling using ion bombardment has potential problems, many published accounts report successful use of this technique.

A base pressure of approximately 10^{-9} torr or less is highly desirable for depth profiling to remove the possibility of residual gases in the vacuum system contaminating the surface. To put this in perspective, at a pressure of 10^{-6} torr a monolayer of contamination is produced each second if it is assumed that every molecule that strikes the surface remains; that is, the surface has a sticking constant of 1. Thus, 10^{-10} torr gives a minimum of 10^4 s of observation time. This estimate is conservative because not all of the residual gas in the vacuum chamber is active, and many surfaces have a sticking constant one or two orders of magnitude less than 1. Only very reactive surfaces, such as the clean surface of some metals, have a sticking constant approaching 1.

Preparing and Mounting Samples (Ref 10)

In most XPS applications, sample preparation and mounting are not critical. The

Table 1 (continued)

	Strong line			Secondary line(c)		
	Area, 3d_{5/2}	3d	Height(b), 3d_{5/2}	Area	4d	Height, 4d
Antimony 4.8	4.8	...	4.8	...	1.00	0.86
Tellurium.......... 5.4	5.4	...	5.4	...	1.23	0.97
Iodine 6.0	6.0	...	6.0	...	1.44	1.08
Xenon 6.6	6.6	...	6.6	...	1.72	1.16
Cesium 7.2	7.2	...	7.0	...	2.0	1.25
Barium 7.9	7.9	...	7.5	...	2.35	1.35
Lanthanum......... ...		(10)(e)	...	...	(2)	...
Cerium		(10)	...	...	(2)	...
Praseodymium		(9)	...	...	(2)	...
Neodymium......... ...		(7)	...	...	(2)	...
Promethium......... ...		(6)	...	...	(2)	...
Samarium		(5)	...	...	(2)	...
Europium.......... ...		(5)	...	...	(2)	...
Gadolinium .... (3)*		...	...	...	(2)	...
Terbium .... (3)*		...	...	...	(2)	...

		4d		4p3/2		
Dysprosium		(2)(e)	...	(0.6)(e)	...	...
Holmium		(2)	...	(0.6)	...	...
Erbium		(2)	...	(0.6)	...	...
Thulium............. ...		(2)	...	(0.6)	...	...
Ytterbium		(2)	...	(0.6)	...	...
Lutetium		(2)	...	(0.6)	...	...

	Area		Height,		Area	Height,
	4f_{7/2}	4f	4f_{7/2}	4d_{5/2}	4d	4d_{5/2}
Hafnium		2.05	1.70	1.42	2.35	0.90
Tantalum.............. ...		2.4	1.89	1.50	2.50	0.90
Tungsten		2.75	2.0	1.57	2.6	0.90
Rhenium		3.1	2.1	1.66	2.75	0.90
Osmium		3.5	2.2	1.75	2.9	0.90
Iridium 2.25		3.95	2.4	1.84	...	0.90
Platinum 2.55		4.4	2.55	1.92	...	0.90
Gold 2.8		4.95	2.8	2.05	...	0.90
Mercury 3.15		5.5	3.15	2.15	...	0.95

	Area		Height,	Area,	Height,	Area		Height,
	4f_{7/2}	4f	4f_{7/2}	4d_{5/2}	4d_{5/2}	5d_{5/2}	5d	5d_{5/2}
Thallium 3.5	3.5	6.15	3.5	2.25	0.95	...	0.9	0.55
Lead 3.85	3.85	6.7	3.82	2.35	1.00	...	1.0	0.6
Bismuth...... 4.25	4.25	7.4	4.25	2.5	1.00	...	1.1	0.65
Thorium 7.8	7.8	...	7.8	3.5	1.2	0.9	1.5	0.9
Uranium 9.0	9.0	...	9.0	3.85	1.3	1.0	1.6	1.0

(a) In the instrument used, AT (see Eq 8) varies as $E^{-0.34}$. (b) Height sensitivity factors based on linewidths for strong lines of 3.1 eV, typical of lines obtained in survey spectra on insulating samples. When spin doublets are unresolved, data are for the convoluted peak heights. (c) Factors for the strong lines are insensitive to the radiation source (aluminum or magnesium). Factors for the secondary lines (2s, 3p, 4d, and 5d) are dependent to an extent upon the photon energy. Values shown are average for aluminum and magnesium. For more accurate results, multiply the factors by 0.9 when magnesium radiation is used and by 1.1 when aluminum radiation is used. (d) Starred data are for peaks obtained only by using aluminum x-rays. (e) Data in parentheses indicate great variability with chemical state, because of the prevalence of multielectron processes. Data shown for the series titanium-copper are for diamagnetic forms; data for paramagnetic forms will be lower in general. Data for the rare earths are based on few experimental points and should be regarded only as a rough approximation. (f) Many of the area data are supplied for spin doublets for 3p and 4d because of the considerable width of many of those lines. Data for combined spin doublets in the 2p series for transition metals and the 3d for the rare earths are supplied because of the prevalence of shakeup lines, which makes it desirable to deal with the doublet as a whole. Source: Ref 19

sample can often be attached mechanically to the sample mount, and the analysis can be performed with the sample in the as-received condition. Sample preparation is discouraged in many cases especially when the natural surface is of interest, because almost any procedure will tend to modify surface composition. The following techniques can be used for samples that require special preparation or mounting procedures.

Removal of Volatile Material. Any volatile material usually must be removed from the sample before analysis; in exceptional cases, when the volatile layer is of interest, the sample may be cooled for analysis. Volatile materials can be removed by long-term pumping in a separate vacuum system or by washing with a suitable solvent. Choice of the solvent can be critical. Hexane or other light hydrocarbon solvents are probably least likely to transform the surface, providing the solvent properties are satisfactory. However, the solvents themselves can also adsorb on the surface, causing problems in the interpretation of the spectra. If the sample is likely to be sensitive to oxygen, extraction under a nitrogen atmosphere is preferred.

Removal of Nonvolatile Organic Contaminants. When the nature of an organic contaminant is not of interest, or when a contaminant obscures underlying inorganic material that is of interest, it must be removed. Freshly distilled solvent should be used to avoid the possibility of contamination by high boiling impurities within the solvent.

Surface Etching. Ion sputter etching or other erosion techniques can also be used to remove surface contaminants. Argon ion etching is also commonly used to obtain information on composition as a function of depth into the sample. However, use of these methods for surface removal will probably change the chemical nature of the surface. Thus, identification of the remaining chemical states may not reflect initial composition accurately.

Abrasion of a surface can be accomplished without significant contamination by using 600-grit silicon carbide paper. Because this causes local heating, reaction with environmental gases may occur. The roughness produced by abrasion will increase the XPS signal intensity relative to that of a smooth sample. Use of this technique usually provides intense spectra of metals along with a contribution from the oxides and/or nitrides that form on the surface. Alkali and alkaline earth metals cannot be prepared satisfactorily in this manner. Spectra of such samples can be obtained only with rigorous UHV preparation and measurement conditions. Abrasion should only be used when the bulk material is of interest and not the surface properties.

Fracture and Scraping. With proper equipment, many materials can be fractured or scraped within the test chamber under UHV conditions. Although this obviates contamination by reaction with atmospheric gases, attention must be given to unexpected results that can occur. When fracturing, for example, the fracture may occur along grain boundaries. Scraping a multiphase sample can cover hard material with soft material.

Grinding to Powder. Spectra reasonably characteristic of bulk composition are most frequently obtained on samples ground to a powder in an alumina mortar. Again, protection of the fresh surfaces from the atmosphere is required. When grinding samples, localized high temperatures can also be produced; therefore, grinding should proceed slowly to minimize chemical changes at the newly created surfaces. The mortar should be well cleaned before each use, preferably ending with a concentrated nitric acid cleaning, followed by rinsing with distilled water and thorough drying.

Mounting Powders for Analysis. Several methods can be used to mount powders for analysis. Perhaps the most widely used method involves dusting the powder on polymer film based adhesive tape carefully and lightly with a camel's hair brush. The powder must be dusted on lightly, with no wiping strokes across the powder surface. Although organic tape is often avoided for UHV experiments, certain types have been used successfully in the 10^{-9}-torr range.

Alternate methods for mounting powders include pressing the powder into an indium foil, supporting the powder on a metallic mesh, pressing the powder into pellets, and simply depositing the powder by gravity. With the indium foil method, the powder is pressed between two pieces of pure foil. The pieces are then separated, and one of them mounted for analysis. Success with this technique has been varied. Bare indium sometimes remains exposed, and if the sample is an insulator, portions of the powder can charge differently. Differential charging can also be a problem when a metallic mesh is used to support the powder. If a press is used to form the powder into a pellet of workable dimensions, a press with hard and extremely clean working surfaces should be used. If a sample holder with a horizontal sample surface is used, the powder can simply be deposited by gravity in a uniform layer. With this method, care must be taken in pumpdown to ensure that gas evolution does not disturb the powder.

Considerations of Mounting Angle. In XPS, the sample mounting angle, although not critical, affects the results. The use of a shallow electron takeoff angle accentuates the spectrum of any layer segregated on the surface (Fig. 9); a sample mounting angle normal to the analyzer axis minimizes the contribution from such a layer. This effect can be used to estimate the depth of atoms contributing to the spectrum. It is not limited to planar surfaces, but is observed with powders, although the effects are muted.

Applications*

Example 1: Investigation of Diffusion Phenomena. The machining performance of cemented carbide cutting tools can be improved significantly by chemical vapor deposition (CVD) of carbide and oxide coatings. These coatings protect the cemented carbide material from high temperatures and severe frictional forces inherent in machining.

*Examples 1 and 2 were provided by Richard L. Moore, Perkin-Elmer Corporation, Physical Electronics Division. Example 3 was provided by M.B. Chamberlain, Sandia National Laboratories; this work was performed under U.S. Department of Energy Contract No. DE-AC04-76DP00789.

Fig. 10 Coating system of the type characterized in Example 1 in the section "Applications" in this article

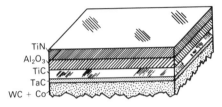

One problem associated with cemented carbide cutting tools is the diffusion of cobalt out of the bulk. Thermal cycling during CVD accelerates this diffusion, leaving the bulk depleted in cobalt and ultimately weakening the tool. In multilayered systems, a diffusion barrier is desirable to slow depletion of cobalt during thermal cycling and to maintain suitable adhesion properties.

The work described here was part of a larger effort to characterize interfacial regions in multilayered systems (Fig. 10) using surface analysis techniques. X-ray photoelectron spectroscopy was used for the isolated study. It was selected for the relatively high sensitivity to cobalt and the large area of analysis.

Uncoated WC-Co tool inserts have been shown to exhibit no cobalt enrichment at the surface (Ref 24). To prove that the cobalt diffusion is a result of thermal cycling and the mobility of cobalt in such matrices as TaC, a 1-µm coating of TaC was applied under normal conditions to a WC-Co tool insert (normal conditions entail heating the substrate to 1000 °C, or 1830 °F). X-ray photoelectron spectroscopy was first performed on the as-received surface of the single-layer TaC-coated insert. These spectra are shown in Fig. 11.

The broad energy scan (Fig. 11a) indicates a composition of predominantly tantalum and carbon with some oxygen species. However, a multiplexed spectra of higher energy resolutions (Fig. 11b) shows cobalt to be present, with the two peaks being the metallic and oxide species. It must be assumed that this is cobalt diffusing through the TaC and not a nonuniform coating due to the lack of indication of any substrate constituents in the surface spectrum.

To characterize the near-surface composition further, the sample was ion sputtered for 20 min, removing approximately 40 nm of material. X-ray photoelectron spectroscopy was again performed on the sputtered surface, and these spectra are shown in Fig. 12. The most significant difference is the increase in the intensity of the cobalt lines in

Fig. 11 XPS surveys for a heavily TaC-coated WC + cobalt substrate

(a) Broad scan. (b) Multiplexed cobalt "window." Note the presence of cobalt on the surface of the as-received sample.

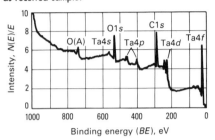

(a)

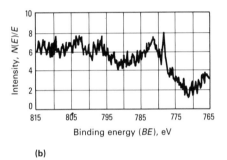

(b)

Fig. 12 XPS surveys for a heavily TaC-coated sample after 20 min of argon ion-sputtering

(a) Broad scan. (b) Multiplexed cobalt "window." Note the significant increase in cobalt intensity, yet no detectable tungsten. A indicates an Auger transition.

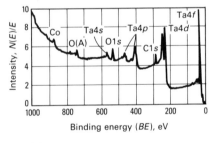

(a)

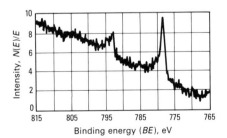

(b)

the spectra. There was still no indication of detectable tungsten to substantiate the cobalt diffusion theory.

Cobalt diffusion out of the bulk of the WC-Co substrate has been shown to be thermally driven. The effect appears to be rapid and not constrained by thick layers of TaC. The TaC coating on the single-layer insert examined was thicker than the typical coating used in the multilayer coatings (Fig. 10) by a factor of ten, yet the diffusion proceeded through to the surface. The formation of a TaC-Co phase due to the diffusion was postulated using the XPS compositional studies. The existence of such a phase and its effect on layer adhesion remains in question.

Example 2: Shear Fracture Studies of Kovar-Glass Seals. Kovar-borosilicate glass seals are frequently used in electronic and vacuum applications due to the excellent thermal expansion match and bond strength. This study was conducted to examine shear fracture behavior as a function of firing atmosphere (oxygen, nitrogen, or air). X-ray photoelectron spectroscopy was the most suitable technique for characterizing the fracture surfaces due to the insulating properties of the glass and the chemical state information that can be obtained.

Kovar and glass shear fracture assemblies were prepared as shown in Fig. 13. All assemblies were prepared identically. These assemblies were placed in a furnace, heated in a gas flow of oxygen, nitrogen, or air, then allowed to cool. Samples of similarly prepared Kovar without glass bonding were also heated with the same firing schedules as the bonded assemblies.

Shear strength measurements were conducted on the fired assemblies. Table 2 lists the results as a function of firing atmosphere. The shear strength appears to scale with the partial pressure of oxygen in the firing atmosphere.

Scanning electron microscopy (SEM) was used to characterize the fracture surfaces. The nitrogen-fired surfaces fractured through the glass. Numerous bubbles were visible in the micrograph and may have contributed to the low shear strength of that assembly. The oxygen-fired surface displayed a surface that was predominantly metallic, indicating the

Fig. 13 Glass-Kovar shear fracture assembly

The Kovar was sized, polished, cleaned, and decarburized before bonding.

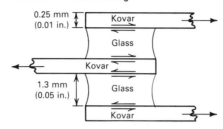

fracture was through the metal oxide layer. This was the strongest of the bonds tested. The air-fired assemblies showed a mixed mode of fracture, with varying amounts of glass and metal oxide. Bubbles were present on the glass surfaces as observed in the nitrogen-fired samples. X-ray photoelectron spectroscopy was performed on the fractured surfaces and on the fired Kovar coupons to determine their compositions. This information may suggest the mechanism for shear failure.

Figure 14 illustrates an XPS survey (broad scan) of a typical unfired Kovar surface. The labeled peaks indicate the expected constituents with contaminants. Table 3 lists the XPS atomic composition of the fired Kovar samples as obtained in narrow scan spectra using area integration. The most significant points of this table are the lack of any detectable nickel and the increase of iron/cobalt ratios as a function of shear strength (Table 2).

The preferential diffusion of cobalt in the oxygen-firing atmosphere enriches the adhesion oxide layer with cobalt oxide. Cobalt oxide is known to improve bond quality in enameling and other sealing glass applications. The cobalt spectrum obtained in the

Fig. 14 XPS survey of as-received Kovar

Note the presence of nickel on the surface.

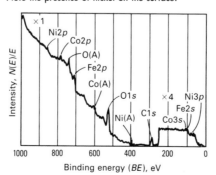

Fig. 15 XPS survey of the nitrogen-fired fracture surface

No detectable nickel on this surface

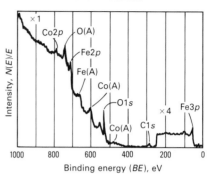

Fig. 16 XPS survey of air-fired fracture surface

Note the presence of glass species.

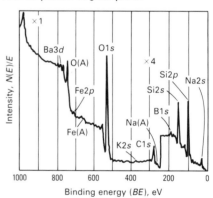

Fig. 17 XPS survey of oxygen-fired fracture surface

The mixed mode of fracture accounts for the metallic and glass peaks. Note the nickel peaks at approximately 850 eV.

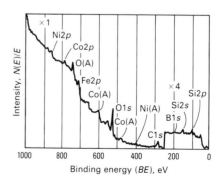

Table 2 Average fracture strength versus firing atmosphere

Firing atmosphere	Average fracture stress	
	MPa	psi
Nitrogen	3.6 ± 0.4	522 ± 58
Air	4.5 ± 0.3	652 ± 44
Oxygen	6.3 ± 0.4	914 ± 58

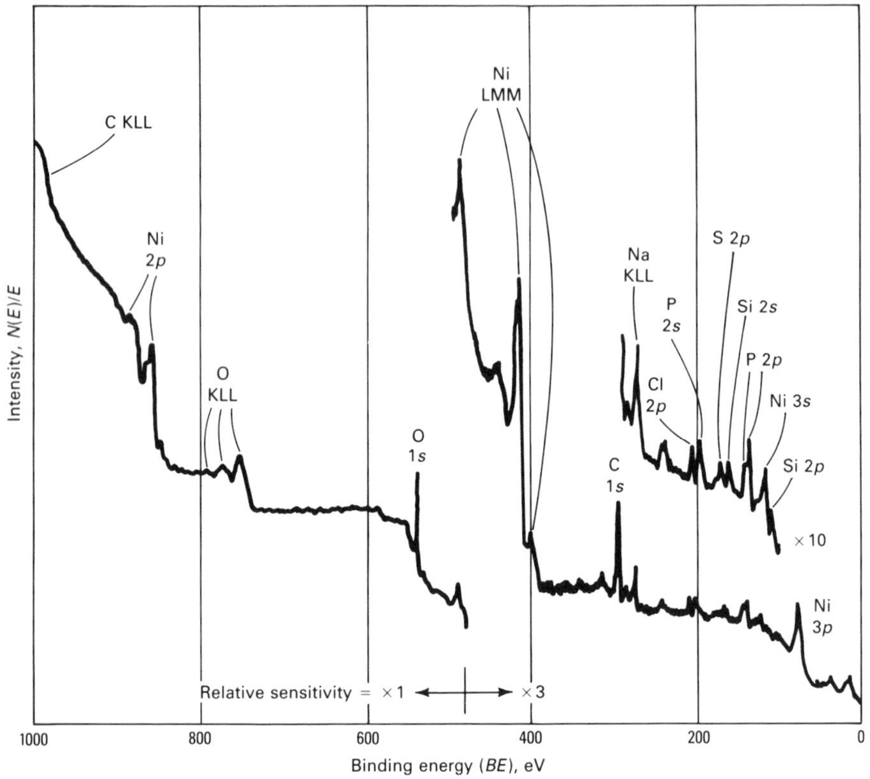

Fig. 18 XPS spectrum showing elements present in electrode surfaces

Fig. 19 XPS spectra of the nickel $2p_{3/2}$ line

A, Pins freshly coated with electroless nickel; B, coated pins after ten-day exposure to factory air; C, sputtered pins; D, sputtered pins after exposure to 100% relative humidity air at 60 °C (140 °F) for 1 h

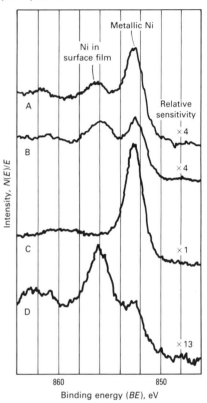

narrow scan multiplex routine speciated as CoO. X-ray photoelectron spectroscopy surveys of the fractured surfaces supported the SEM observations.

Figures 15 to 17 depict the spectra with peaks labeled. As expected, the nitrogen-fired fracture surface (through the glass) shows mostly glass constituents. The air- and oxygen-fired surfaces display varying amounts of metal and glass species. Nickel was detected on the oxygen-fired surface. This suggests segregation with the adhesive oxide layers, making the less enriched mixed oxide layer the fracture plane.

X-ray photoelectron spectroscopy of oxidized Kovar samples fired in nitrogen, oxygen, or air showed the alloy surfaces to be depleted in nickel and enriched in cobalt. The cobalt oxidized during bonding and improved the bond quality of the assembly, the improvement being a function of the amount of cobalt enrichment.

Example 3: Analysis of Surface Films on Electrical Contacts in a Mercury Switch. The switch analyzed consisted of a sealed cavity containing a mercury drop that contacted two electrodes to close an electrical circuit. The electrodes proposed for this switch consisted of Niron 52 (Ni-49.5Fe) pins coated with an approximately 2-μm-thick layer of electroless

nickel (Ni-8P). Mercury wetted these electrodes when initially fabricated; however, it did not after they were exposed to humid air for ten days at room temperature. To establish whether the surfaces of these exposed pins would remain unwetted in the hydrogen atmosphere of the switch cavity, the compositions and thicknesses of the surface films on the pins were determined using XPS.

The elements present on pin surfaces were established from survey spectra, such as that shown in Fig. 18. The concentrations in atomic percent calculated for the elements in this spectrum are Ni(7), O(36), C(36), P(9), Si(4), Na(3), Cl(2) and S(2). Thus, compounds in the pin surfaces can contain only these elements plus possibly hydrogen, which is not detected by XPS. Changes in the chemical states of nickel caused by the humid-air exposure were revealed by high-resolution spectra of the nickel $2p_{3/2}$ photoelectron lines. Figure 19 shows spectra recorded before (spectrum A) and after (spectrum B) the ten-day exposure. Each spectrum has two major lines. As revealed in the following analysis, the 856.0-eV line is attributed to photoelectrons ejected from an ultrathin surface film, and the 852.5-eV line is produced by the metallic nickel beneath this film. Because the intensity of the 856.0-

eV line increased as that of the 852.5-eV line simultaneously decreased, the average thickness of the thin surface film increased during the exposure.

To identify the nickel compound in the film, the pins shown in spectrum B in Fig. 19 were sputtered using a 500-eV argon ion beam; the cleaned surfaces were then exposed to 100% relative humidity air at 60 °C (140 °F) for 1 h. Spectra recorded before and after the exposure (spectra C and D, respectively) reveal that the intensity of the metallic nickel line decreased and a new line at 856.0 eV appeared. A sputter-cleaned 99.999% Ni sample also was exposed to 100% relative humidity air at 60 °C (140 °F) for 1 h. The latter exposure produced the same changes in the nickel $2p$ spectrum as those in spectra C and D for the Ni-8P alloy. Based on published spectra of thin compound films on pure nickel (Ref 25) and on the results of these two exposures, the peak at 856.0 eV was assigned to the chemical state of $Ni(OH)_2$ present in an ultrathin surface film. Thus, the surface film is predominantly $Ni(OH)_2$; however, spectra A

Table 3 Surface atomic values of Kovar alloy

In relative atomic percent

Processing	Fe	Co	Ni	C	O	Fe/Co
			Element			
Nitrogen-fired	19.3	6.1	...	5.1	49.5	3.2
Air-fired	10.3	3.8	...	31.1	54.8	2.7
Oxygen-fired	16.9	7.2	...	26.1	49.8	2.3

and B may also contain some nickel in the NiO state, suggesting that a small amount of this film is NiO. To further corroborate this assignment of the chemical composition of the film, the oxygen photoelectron spectra were investigated. Because oxygen was also chemically combined with the silicon and phosphorus in the surface, the analysis of its spectra was used only to establish whether the nickel was present primarily in $Ni(OH)_2$ or NiO.

The spectra shown in Fig. 20 were recorded from factory-exposed pins before (spectrum A) and after (spectrum B) they were sputter cleaned and exposed to 100% relative humidity air at 60 °C (140 °F) for 1 h. Both spectra contain one dominant line. Spectrum C contains two lines, and it was recorded from the sputter-cleaned pure nickel sample after exposure to 99.998% oxygen at 20 °C (70 °F) in the analytical chamber, then exposed to 100% relative humidity air at 60 °C (140 °F) for 1 h. The line at 529.5 eV was assigned to NiO, and that at 531.3 eV, the dominant line in spectra A and B, is attributed to $Ni(OH)_2$. These assignments are consistent with published results (Ref 25). Because the 531.3-eV line dominates oxygen spectra A and B (Fig. 20), this result supports the above conclusion from the nickel 2p spectra (Fig. 19), showing that $Ni(OH)_2$ is the principal nickel compound in the exposed pin surfaces.

The thickness of the ultrathin hydroxide surface film can be estimated from such spectra as those shown in Fig. 19. Sputter cleaning changed the nickel 2p spectrum shown in Fig. 19 from spectrum B to spectrum D. The intensities of the 852.5-eV line in these two spectra were used to determine film thickness. Assuming that the surface is flat, and the thickness of the film is uniform, the film thickness can be calculated (Ref 26) using:

$$I(t) = I_0 \exp\left(\frac{-d}{\lambda}\right) \quad \text{(Eq 12)}$$

where $I(t)$ is the area under the 852.5-eV metallic nickel line when the film thickness is d, I_0 is the area under this line when $d = 0$, and λ is the inelastic mean free path of the nickel 2p photoelectrons ($\lambda = 0.8$

nm). The thicknesses for the hydroxide surface films on the samples shown in Fig. 19—spectra A, B, and C, respectively—were estimated at 1.4, 1.8, and 2.6 nm.

The effect of a hydrogen exposure on the thickness of the hydroxide surface film was investigated. Pins that had been exposed to factory air for ten days and to the laboratory atmosphere for six weeks were characterized using XPS, then exposed to 1.2 atm hydrogen at 110 °C (230 °F) for 10 min and analyzed a second time. The spectra of the nickel 2p lines before and after this exposure are shown in Fig. 21. This experiment reveals that the line for the $Ni(OH)_2$ surface film is reduced in intensity by this exposure and is consistent with thermodynamic calculations. The change in free energy for the reduction of $Ni(OH)_2$ at 25 °C (75 °F) is −27 kcal/mol, given by:

$$Ni(OH)_2 + H_2(g) \rightarrow Ni + 2H_2O(g) \quad \text{(Eq 13)}$$

Therefore, this reduction reaction is favorable in the switch. Thus, disregarding possible electrochemical reactions or effects of mercury, which may also alter the ultrathin surface films, these results reveal that the pin surfaces would be reduced to metallic nickel, which mercury would wet, causing the switch to remain closed, an unacceptable condition.

REFERENCES

1. A. Einstein, *Ann. Physik*, Vol 17, 1905, p 132
2. P. Auger, *Compt. Rend.*, Vol 177, 1923, p 169
3. R.G. Steinhardt, Jr. and E.J. Serfass, *Anal. Chem.*, Vol 23, 1951, p 1585
4. K. Seigbahn, C. Nordling, A. Fahlman, R. Nordberg, K. Hamrin, J. Hedman, G. Johansson, T. Bergmark, S. Karlsson, I. Lindgren, and B. Lindberg, *Electron Spectroscopy for Chemical Analysis—Atomic, Molecular, and Solid State Structure Studies by Means of Electron Spectroscopy*, Almqvist and Wiksells, Stockholm, 1967
5. M.P. Seah and W.A. Dench, *Surf. Interface Anal.*, Vol 1, 1979, p 2
6. W.M. Riggs and M.J. Parker, in *Methods of Surface Analysis*, A.W. Czanderna, Ed., Elsevier, 1975
7. K. Siegbahn, G. Hammond, H. Fellner-Feldegg, and E.F. Barnett, *Science*, Vol 176, 1972, p 245
8. P.W. Palmberg, *J. Electron Spectrosc.*, Vol 5, 1974, p 691

Fig. 20 XPS spectra of the oxygen 1s line

A, Coated pins after ten-day exposure at the factory; B, pins sputtered and exposed to 100% relative humidity air at 60 °C (140 °F) for 1 h; C, 99.999% Ni sputtered and exposed to 99.998% oxygen and humid air

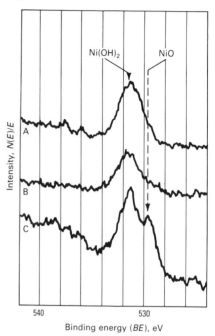

Fig. 21 XPS spectra of the nickel 2p line

Before, A, and after, B, exposure to 1.2-atm hydrogen at 110 °C (230 °F) for 10 min

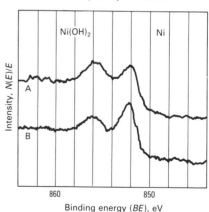

9. D. Roy and J.D. Carette, *Topics in Current Physics*, Vol 4, *Electron Spectroscopy for Chemical Analysis*, Springer-Verlag, 1972, p 13-58
10. C.D. Wagner, W.M. Riggs, L.E. Davis, J.F. Moulder, and G.E. Muilenberg, *Handbook of X-Ray Photoelectron Spectroscopy*, Perkin-Elmer Corporation, Physical Electronics Division, Norwalk, CT, 1979
11. C.J. Powell, N.E. Erickson, and J.E. Madey, *J. Electron Spectrosc.*, Vol 25, 1982, p 87
12. M.T. Anthony and M.P. Seah, *Surf. Interface Anal.*, Vol 6, 1984, p 107
13. J.C. Carver, G.K. Schweitzer, and T.A. Carlson, *J. Chem. Phys.*, Vol 57, 1972, p 973
14. N.S. McIntyre and D.G. Zetaruk, *Anal. Chem.*, Vol 49, 1977, p 1521
15. C.D. Wagner, *Farad. Discuss. Chem. Soc.*, Vol 60, 1975, p 291
16. C.D. Wagner, L.H. Gale, and R.H. Raymond, *Anal. Chem.*, Vol 51, 1979, p 466
17. C.S. Farley, *J. Electron Spectrosc.*, Vol 5, 1974, p 725
18. C.J. Powell, in *Quantitative Surface Analysis of Materials*, N.S. McIntyre, Ed., STP 643, ASTM, Philadelphia, 1978, p 5
19. C.D. Wagner, L.E. Davis, M.V. Zeller, J.A. Taylor, R.H. Raymond, and L.H. Gale, *Surf. Interface Anal.*, Vol 3, 1981, p 211
20. T.A. Carlson, *Photoelectron and Auger Spectroscopy*, Plenum Press, 1975, p 265
21. M. Tarng and G.K. Wehner, *J. Appl. Phys.*, Vol 42, 1971, p 2449
22. H.H. Anderson, *Appl. Phys.*, Vol 18, 1979, p 131
23. H.J. Mathieu and D. Landolt, *Appl. Surf. Sci.*, Vol 10, 1982, p 100
24. R.L. Moore, L. Salvati, Jr., G. Sundberg, and V. Greenhut, *J. Vac. Sci. Technol.*, Vol A3, 1985, p 2426
25. N.S. McIntyre and M.G. Cook, *Anal. Chem.*, Vol 47, 1975, p 2208
26. P.H. Holloway, *J. Vac. Sci. Technol.*, Vol 12, 1975, p 1418

Methods Based on Sputtering or Scattering Phenomena

Field Ion Microscopy and Atom Probe Microanalysis

G.D.W. Smith, Department of Metallurgy and Science of Materials, University of Oxford

General Uses

- Observation of the microstructure of materials in atomic detail
- Chemical microanalysis of materials at the atomic level, with equal sensitivity to all chemical elements

Examples of Applications

- Study of point defects in radiation damage, dislocations, stacking faults, grain boundaries, and interphase interfaces in metals and alloys
- Study of the nucleation, growth, and coarsening of precipitates in age-hardening materials, including aluminum, iron, and nickel-base alloys
- Study of alloying element partitioning, phase stability, and phase transformation phenomena, for example, in steels and turbine alloys
- Study of order-disorder reactions and of spinodal decomposition in magnetic materials
- Study of segregation of alloy elements and impurities to dislocations and interfaces
- Study of metal surfaces, including surface diffusion and reconstruction, surface segregation, surface reactions, adsorption, heterogeneous catalysis, oxidation, nucleation and growth of thin films, and depth profiling through surface layers
- Study of semiconductor materials, including oxidation and metallization, interdiffusion, and investigation of local composition variations in thin films

Samples

- *Form*: Solids (metals or semiconductors)
- *Size*: Needlelike, end radius below 100 nm, overall length to 10 mm (0.4 in.)
- *Preparation*: Chemical or electropolishing, or ion milling, from round or square cross-section sample blanks

Limitations

- Samples must possess some degree of electrical conductivity
- Samples must have appreciable mechanical strength
- Field of view is restricted to areas of approximately 200 nm in diameter
- Needlelike geometry restricts sample types that can be studied
- Method of analysis is destructive; material is removed from surface

Estimated Analysis Time

- 3 to 30 h per sample

Capabilities of Related Techniques

- *Transmission electron microscopy, scanning transmission electron microscopy, x-ray analytical electron microscopy, electron energy loss spectroscopy*: Microscopy and microanalysis of solids with larger field of view. Faster analysis, but with lower spatial resolution, and sensitivity to different chemical elements varies
- *Low-energy electron diffraction, Auger electron spectroscopy, x-ray photoelectron spectroscopy*: Determination of structure and chemistry of surfaces, providing more crystallographic data and information on chemical state
- *Secondary ion mass spectroscopy, Rutherford backscattering spectroscopy*: Depth profiling through surface layers, with lower spatial and depth resolution. Analytical sensitivity to different chemical elements varies widely in secondary ion mass spectroscopy
- *Laser microprobe mass analysis*: Time-of-flight mass spectrometric analysis of solids. Relatively fast, suitable for a wide range of materials, and sensitive to all chemical elements, but much lower spatial resolution and less quantitative than the atom probe

Introduction

Field ion microscopy (FIM) can be used to resolve the individual atoms on the surface of a solid. It can also be used to study the three-dimensional structure of a material because successive atom layers can be ionized and removed from the surface by field evaporation. The ions removed from the surface by field evaporation can be analyzed chemically by coupling to the microscope a time-of-flight mass spectrometer of single-particle sensitivity, known as an atom probe (AP). The range of applications of the FIM/AP technique has extended rapidly, and virtually all metals and semiconductors can now be studied. Whenever atomic-scale information on the structure or composition of a material is necessary, this approach should be considered.

Field Ion Microscopy

Principles of Field Ion Microscopy.
Figure 1 shows the essential features of the field ion microscope. The microscope consists of a vacuum tube, across the end of which is a fluorescent screen. The needlelike sample, mounted on a test-tube-size "cold finger" with a high-voltage lead, points toward the screen. A small amount of an inert gas, typically 10^{-3} Pa (10^{-5} mbar) of helium or neon, is admitted to the microscope chamber, and a high positive potential of 5 to 30 kV is applied to the sample. Figure 2 illustrates the overall process of image formation. The strong electric field on the sample tip polarizes nearby gas atoms and draws them in toward the surface. When the gas atoms strike the sample, they lose part of their energy by thermal accommodation and become trapped in the high-field region. The gas atoms then execute a hopping motion across the tip surface until they become ionized by a quantum mechanical tunneling process termed field ionization.

In this process, electrons pass through the potential barrier from the gas atoms to the solid, leaving positively charged gas ions above the metal surface. These ions are then repelled from the sample toward the fluorescent screen, where they form an enlarged, projected image of the surface from which they originate. Field ionization occurs preferentially above the most prominent surface atoms, and narrow cones of ions from these regions give rise to individual bright spots on the image screen. A microchannel plate-image converter, usually interposed between the tip and screen, converts the incident ion beam to a more intense secondary electron beam. This produces a bright picture on the microscope screen, usually approximately 70 mm (2¾ in.) in diameter.

Fig. 1 Field ion microscope

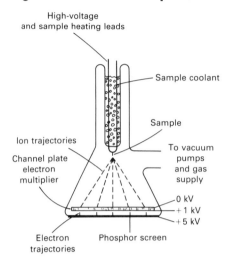

Fig. 2 Principles of FIM image formation

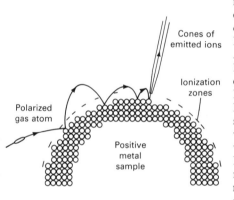

Figure 3 shows a typical field ion microscope image. The overall pattern resembles a stereographic projection of a cubic crystal of the same orientation (Fig. 4). Because the image consists of several sets of intersecting, concentric systems of rings, its details are complex; a ball model (Fig. 5) provides clarification. The tip of the sample, which is smoothed by field evaporation, is approximately hemispherical. The intersection of each atomic layer with the surface of the sample has the form of a ring. The most prominent atoms on the surface, shown in white on the model, lie on the ring edges and image brightly in the field ion microscope.

The successive atomic layers lying parallel to any one crystallographic plane produce a set of concentric rings in the image, and the different planes exposed on the curved suface of the sample tip yield the pattern of intersecting ring systems comprising the final projected image. Nearest-neighbor atoms are often not fully resolved, and atoms in the interior of low-index atomic plans are par-

ticularly difficult to observe. The best separation of individual atoms is found in high-index regions, where it is often possible to view the complete two-dimensional arrangement of atoms on the planes.

Sample Preparation

The needlelike samples required for FIM can be prepared by electropolishing, chemical polishing, or ion milling, depending on the nature and form of the material. It is convenient to begin with materials of round cross section, such as wires or whiskers, if available. Samples can also be prepared from much larger objects, such as a turbine blade, a steel forging, or a semiconductor single crystal, by sectioning a sample blank of square cross section approximately 0.5 mm (0.02 in.) across and 10 to 15 mm (0.4 to 0.6 in.) long.

Electropolishing is the most commonly used final preparation technique, and a floating thin-layer, or two-layer, polishing method is often used (Fig. 6). A layer of electrolyte approximately 5 mm (0.2 in.) deep is floated on top of a heavier inert liquid, such as carbon tetrachloride (CCl_4). As material is removed in the electrolyte layer, a waist develops on the sample, which eventually fractures under its own weight. Brief further polishing to remove the irregular fractured region usually yields a sharp sample. Another method of producing a waist on the sample is to coat the bottom end with a protective lacquer before polishing. Blunted samples can be resharpened using a micropolishing technique in which the apex region of the needle is immersed in a drop of electrolyte and suspended on a small platinum loop (1 to 2 mm, or 0.04 to 0.08 in., in diameter). This process is observed using a low-power optical microscope (10 to $100 \times$).

Chemical polishing is required for many poorly conducting materials, such as intrinsic semiconductors, for which electropolishing cannot be used. A sharp point can be obtained by a repeated dipping method, or a waist can be formed by suspending the sample from one end, then the other.

Ion milling, a versatile and controllable method of FIM sample preparation, can be carried out in a commercial transmission electron microscopy (TEM) sample preparation unit, with only slight modification to the holder to accommodate the differently shaped sample blank. Although extremely slow, this method generally produces a smooth surface, without preferential etching at grain boundaries or second-phase particles, which can be a problem with other techniques.

Fig. 3 Typical field ion micrograph of a tungsten sample

Courtesy of T.J. Godfrey, University of Oxford

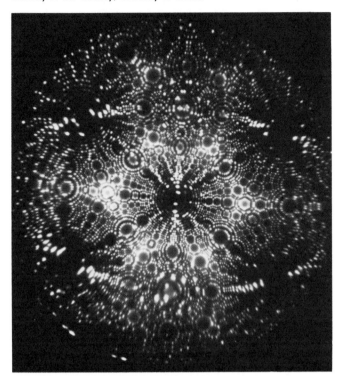

Fig. 4 Stereographic projection of a cubic crystal of [011] orientation corresponding to the field ion micrograph of tungsten in Fig. 3

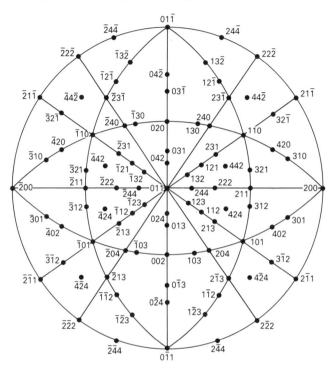

A compromise approach useful in some circumstances is to prepolish using a chemical or electrolytic method, then to conduct the final sharpening by ion milling. Table 1 lists recommended preparation techniques for different materials.

Field Ionization

Figure 7 shows a simplified one-dimensional potential-energy diagram that illustrates field ionization near a metal surface. The potential well of the gas atom is distorted by the externally applied electric field and is affected by the image potential near the sample surface. Therefore, an electron from the gas atom can tunnel through a narrow barrier into a vacant electronic state in the metal. Field ionization cannot occur appreciably within a critical distance from the surface, because the energy of the electron in the gas atom falls below that of most of the vacant levels in the sample. The critical distance for field ionization, x_c, is:

$$x_c = \frac{I - \phi}{eF} \qquad \text{(Eq 1)}$$

where I is the ionization potential of the gas atom, ϕ is the work function of the metal, e

is the electronic charge, and F is the electric field gradient at the surface. The rate of electron tunneling is extremely sensitive to the width of the potential barrier, and x_c must be reduced to approximately 0.5 nm to obtain a significant ion current. Electric fields of the order of tens of volts per nanometer or hundreds of millions of volts per centimeter are required. Such fields are obtained conveniently only in the region of sharp points, which explains the needlelike geometry of FIM samples. The electric field strength, F, is related to the end radius of the needle, r, and the applied voltage, V, by:

$$F = \frac{V}{kr} \qquad \text{(Eq 2)}$$

where k is a constant related to the cone angle of the needle and is usually of the order of 5. To obtain FIM images using helium image gas from 5 to 30 kV, end radii must range from 20 to 120 nm. This restricts severely the field of view in the microscope, a principal disadvantage of FIM. Use of a gas of lower ionization potential to produce the image provides some extension; but the ionization potentials of the inert gases vary

Fig. 5 Ball model of sample tip with imaging sites highlighted

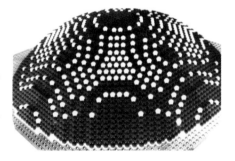

only by a factor of 2 (Table 2), and maximum extension in the field of view is therefore limited. A greater advantage of using image gases of lower ionization potential is that the tendency of the sample to field evaporate during imaging is greatly reduced.

Field Evaporation

Figure 8 shows a one-dimensional potential-energy diagram. In the absence of an applied electric field, the removal of an atom from the sample surface in the form of a

Fig. 6 Setup for the floating thin-layer electropolishing technique for FIM sample preparation

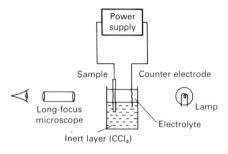

Fig. 7 Potential energy of an outer electron in an image gas atom near the sample surface in the presence of a high field

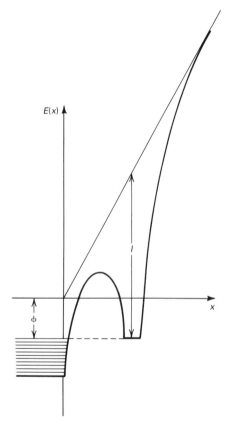

Table 1 Sample preparation techniques for selected materials

Material	Recommended preparation technique
Steels	First-stage electropolish by two-layer method to form thin waist on sample: 25% perchloric acid in glacial acetic acid, 20–25 V dc, 0–10 °C (32–50 °F). Final-stage electropolish in a single bath of electrolyte: 2% perchloric acid in 2-butoxy-ethanol, 20–25 V dc, 0–10 °C (32–50 °F)
Nickel alloys	First-stage electropolish by two-layer method to form thin waist on sample: 10% perchloric acid + 20% glycerol + 70% ethanol, 22 V dc. Final-stage electropolish in a single bath of electrolyte: 2% perchloric acid in 2-butoxy-ethanol 25 V dc
Copper alloys	Electropolish in concentrated orthophosphoric acid, 16 V dc
Aluminum alloys	Procedures vary from alloy to alloy; one versatile method is to electropolish with 2–10% perchloric acid in methanol, 5–10 V ac at −10 °C (14 °F)
Titanium alloys	Procedures vary from alloy to alloy; one method is to electropolish in 6% perchloric acid + 34% n-butyl alcohol + 60% methanol
Molybdenum alloys	First-stage electropolish by two-layer method to form thin waist on sample: 5 N aqueous sodium hydroxide solution, 6 V ac. Final-stage electropolish in a single bath of 12% concentrated sulfuric acid in methanol, 6 V dc
Platinum alloys	Electropolish in molten salt mixture of 80% sodium nitrate + 20% sodium chloride at 440–460 °C (825–860 °F) using a repeated-dipping technique. Begin at 5 V dc, reducing to 3 V
Tungsten	Electropolish using two-layer method in 5% aqueous sodium hydroxide solution (by weight), 5–6 V ac
Silicon	Polish chemically in a solution of 15% concentrated nitric acid, 80% hydrofluoric acid (40% solution), and 5% glacial acetic acid. Finish by ion milling if required
Gallium arsenide	Polish chemically in a solution of 44% concentrated sulphuric acid, 28% hydrogen peroxide (30% weight per unit volume of solution), and 28% water at approximately 60 °C (140 °F)

Note: Perchloric acid refers to a 60% by-weight solution having a specific gravity of 1.54 at 20 °C (68 °F). Use of more concentrated forms of this acid is dangerous, and all solutions containing perchloric acid and organic chemicals should be prepared and handled with extreme care. Unless otherwise stated, the proportions of all polishing mixtures listed above are expressed in percentages by volume. Unless otherwise stated, polishing may be carried out satisfactorily at room temperature.

ne, and ϕ is the work function of the substrate.

In the presence of a positive field, this energy requirement for desorption is reduced, because the potential of the ion is lowered progressively as it moves away from the surface. Neglecting polarization energy terms, for a given field strength F, the maximum energy barrier Q to be overcome is:

$$Q = Q_0 - (n^3 e^3 F)^{1/2} \qquad (Eq\ 4)$$

If the field strength is increased sufficiently, the energy barrier will approach zero, permitting field evaporation to occur even at cryogenic temperatures. The fields required to produce this effect are of the same order as those required to produce field ionization. Table 3 lists calculated and observed evaporation fields for different metals. Equations 3 and 4 demonstrate that sublimation energy principally determines the evaporation field for a given element. Thus, refractory materials, such as tungsten and iridium, are most resistant to field evaporation; low melting point materials, such as aluminum and gold, field evaporate most easily. The field dependence of evaporation rate is strong. For example, in the case of tungsten at 20 K, the evaporation rate changes by more than an order of magnitude for a 1% change in field strength.

Field evaporation is important because, first, it provides a means of cleaning and smoothing the apex region of the sample on an atomic scale. When a sample is inserted into the microscope immediately after preparation, its surface is somewhat irregular and is contaminated by prior exposure to the atmosphere. As the voltage is increased, contaminant layers are progressively stripped off, and any protrusions or roughness on the surface is also removed, because these are the areas in which the local field will be highest. A smoothly rounded, atomically clean, field-evaporated end-form eventually develops in the apex region. The images are usually recorded at this stage.

Second, field evaporation provides a method of investigating the three-dimensional structure of the sample. Unlike the transmission electron microscope, the

Table 2 Ionization potentials and imaging fields for selected gases

Gas	Ionization potential, eV	Best imaging field, V/nm
Helium	24.6	45.0
Neon	21.6	37.0
Hydrogen	15.6	22.8
Argon	15.7	23.0
Krypton	14.0	19.4
Xenon	12.1	15.6

Source: Ref 1

positive ion requires an amount of energy, Q_0:

$$Q_0 = \Lambda + \Sigma I_n - n\phi \qquad (Eq\ 3)$$

where Λ is the sublimation energy, ΣI_n is the sum of the ionization potentials to a charge

Fig. 8 Potential-energy diagram illustrating field evaporation

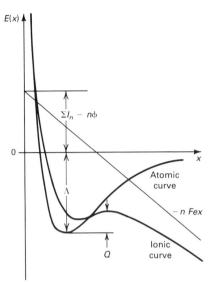

Fig. 9 Working range of the field ion microscope

The working range can be defined as the regime of operating conditions where stable micrographs may be obtained.

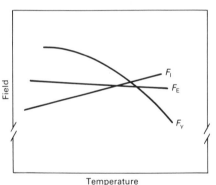

Table 3 Calculated and experimental evaporation fields

Material	Calculated field for most easily evaporated species, V/nm			Observed field, V/nm	Main observed species
	M^+	M^{2+}	M^{3+}		
Be	...	46	...	34	Be^+, Be^{2+}
Al	19	...	...	33	Al^+, Al^{2+}
Si	...	32	...	30	Si^{2+}
Ti	...	26	...	25	Ti^{2+}
V	...	30	...	...	V^{2+}
Cr	27	29	...	...	Cr^{2+}
Mn	30	30	...	...	Mn^{2+}
Fe	...	33	...	35	Fe^{2+}
Co	...	37	...	36	Co^{2+}
Ni	35	36	...	35	Ni^{2+}
Cu	30	...	...	30	Cu^+
Zn	33	...	...	...	Zn^{2+}
Ga	15	...	...	...	...
As	...	42	...	...	...
Zr	...	28	...	35	Zr^{2+}
Nb	...	37	...	35	Nb^{2+}
Mo	...	41	...	46	Mo^{2+}, Mo^{3+}
Ru	...	41	...	45	...
Rh	...	41	...	46	Rh^{2+}, Rh^{3+}
Pd	37	...	...	...	Pd^+
Ag	24	...	...	...	Ag^+
In	13	...	...	...	...
Sn	...	23	...	...	...
Hf	...	39	...	...	Hf^{3+}
Ta	...	...	44	...	Ta^{3+}
W	...	...	52	57	W^{3+}
Re	...	45	...	48	Re^{3+}
Ir	...	44	...	53	Ir^{2+}, Ir^{3+}
Pt	...	45	...	48	Pt^{2+}
Au	53	54	...	35	Au^+, Au^{2+}

Source: Ref 2, 3

field ion microscope shows only the surface atom layer of the sample. However, if, after recording one image, the voltage is raised carefully so that a small amount of material is removed (this can be observed on the microscope screen), another micrograph can be recorded showing the atomic arrangement slightly further down in the sample, and so on. Repetition of this procedure enables reconstruction of an entire three-dimensional structure of the sample. This is particularly important in the study of grain boundaries and other interfaces and in the measurement of the size and distribution of second-phase particles.

Third, field evaporation provides a controllable means of removing atoms from the surface in the form of charged particles, which can be identified chemically using mass spectrometric methods. This is the basis of AP microanalysis.

Electric Field and Stress

The mechanical force between the plates of a charged parallel plate capacitor tends to draw the two plates together. A similar force exists in the field ion microscope; however, one of the electrodes (the sample) is small, and highly localized stresses develop in the region of the sample apex. These stresses vary with the square of the applied electric field and are large under imaging conditions, approaching the theoretical strength of the sample material. One corollary is that FIM samples must possess substantial mechanical strength to survive imaging. Notches and grooves formed by irregular electropolishing during sample preparation may lead to brittle fracture. Internal defects, such as voids and inclusions, may also cause problems. In addition, field-induced stresses produce extensive rearrangement of dislocation configurations within the samples. If initiated in the high-field region of the sample, slip often propagates catastrophically, leading to disintegration of the sample. Such an event is known as a flash, because a bright flash of light appears on the image screen as the sample ruptures.

Working Range

A set of stable operating conditions can be defined for FIM (Fig. 9). Stable images are obtained when the evaporation field of the sample material, F_E, is significantly above the ionization field of the image gas, F_I, and the stress required to produce mechanical failure, F_Y, exceeds each of these. Because field evaporation is thermally assisted, working at the lowest possible temperatures is advantageous if condensation of the image gas can be avoided.

The use of image gases of low ionization potential extends the range of material that can be studied in the field ion microscope, but the types of gases that can be used are restricted. First, the gas must not react chemically with the sample surface, or the stability of the image will be destroyed. Enhanced reactivity is often observed in the presence of an electric field (field corrosion); therefore, the possible imaging species are effectively limited to the inert gases and (for some materials) hydrogen. Second, use of a lower field means that background gases in the vacuum system, such as water vapor and carbon monoxide, may be able to reach the sample surface without field ionization and thus cause corrosion. Therefore, the microscope vacuum must be improved, ideally to the 10^{-8} to 10^{-9} Pa (10^{-10} to 10^{-11} mbar) range. In general, optimum results are obtained using helium or neon image gases, with sample temperatures from 10 to 50 K.

Magnification, Resolution, and Image Contrast

Magnification. The field ion microscope is a simple device that has no internal lenses. The ion trajectories are initially normal to the sample surface, then curve in the direction of the microscope screen. The magnification, M, is:

$$M = \frac{R}{\beta} r \qquad \text{(Eq 5)}$$

where R is the sample tip-to-screen distance, r is the tip radius, and β is a constant (approximately 1.5). For typical values of $R = 10$ cm (4 in.) and $r = 65$ nm, M is therefore approximately 1 million.

The resolution of the microscope, δ, is defined in terms of the minimum size of the image spot of a single atom on the field ion microscope screen at a given magnification. The value of δ depends on several factors, including the area over which ionization occurs above a given surface atom, the uncertainty in the tangential momentum of the gas ions, and the lateral thermal velocity of the imaging ions. An approximate expression for δ is:

$$\delta = \frac{(6 \times 10^{-4} \, Tr)^{1/2}}{F} \qquad \text{(Eq 6)}$$

where T is the absolute temperature of the sample. The major factor limiting the resolution is the lateral thermal velocity of the gas ions. For a 50-nm radius sample imaged in helium, the effective resolution at 20 K is approximately 0.2 nm; at 80 K, it is only approximately 0.35 nm. Therefore, efficient sample cooling is important in practical microscopy.

Image Contrast. Another important concept in field ion microscopy is the best image voltage (BIV). This is the voltage at which the best overall image contrast is obtained for a sample of a given radius in a given image gas. If the applied voltage is too low, the field will not produce an adequate ion current from the sample; if too high, ionization occurs uniformly over the sample tip surface, and the image blurs. Image contrast is due to variation in the overall rate of field ionization at different points on the sample surface. Whether this is mainly associated with variations in the local concentration of image-gas atoms on the surface or with variations in tunneling probability is unclear. Both effects would be expected to

vary with local field strength and surface charge.

An additional complication arises due to field adsorption. Gas atoms that penetrate beneath the critical ionization distance x_c cannot be field ionized, but may bind to the surface by field-induced dipolar interactions. These bound atoms will be most stable in the highest field regions, that is, over the apex of the most prominent surface atoms. Thus, field ionization may take place by tunneling through an adsorbed gas atom, rather than through a vacuum barrier.

Although a full theory of this process has not been developed, the magnitude of field adsorption binding energies is of the order of 10 to 20 kJ/mole; therefore, coverage of the surface with adsorbed-gas atoms will be almost complete at the lowest imaging temperatures. The presence of the adsorbed gas layer does not seem to affect determination of atom position in the field ion microscope, because the adsorbed atoms are located directly over the tops of the substrate atoms. However, if neon or argon is adsorbed on the surface, the brightness of the image is increased and BIV is lowered because the rate of tunneling through these atoms is greater than that through helium atoms or a vacuum barrier. Small additions of hydrogen are particularly effective in lowering BIV when helium or neon is used as the primary image gas. This effect is sometimes useful in the FIM examination of nonrefractory materials. However, addition of hydrogen often leads to formation of metal hydride species during field evaporation, and this causes

complications when conducting AP microanalysis.

Images of Defects in Pure Metals

Point defects can be seen clearly only in regions in which all the surface atoms are resolved. Vacancies can be identified from missing bright spots in the image (Fig. 10a), but interstitial atoms are associated with additional bright spots (Fig. 10b). Such features must be interpreted carefully. Irregularities in field-evaporation behavior or field corrosion by active gases may generate surface artifact vacancies or add bright spots due to the displacement of surface atoms from their normal lattice sites. In addition, contrast from self-interstitial atoms is complicated by their rapid migration at all but the lowest imaging temperatures and by surface-relaxation effects during field evaporation. Despite these difficulties, FIM has been used extensively to study radiation-damage phenomena, especially in refractory metals, and has yielded unique information on the nature of the damage "spikes" produced by single irradiation events.

The contrast from dislocations depends on the orientation of the Burgers vector relative to the crystal surface at the point of emergence of the defect. If the vector lies parallel to the surface, the dislocation will be virtually invisible. If the vector has a component normal to the surface, a spiral will be produced in the image (Fig. 11). Perfect dislocations produce smooth spirals, but the stacking-fault region between partial disloca-

Fig. 10 Point defects observed using FIM

(a) Vacancies in iridium. Courtesy of J.A. Hudson, UKAEA Harwell Laboratory. (b) Self-interstitial atoms in tungsten. Source: Ref 4

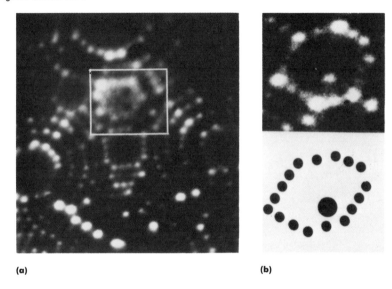

(a)

(b)

Fig. 11 Influence of Burgers vector orientation on the FIM contrast from dislocations

(a) Dislocations in tungsten. The Burgers vector in this material has a component normal to the surface, producing the spiral images shown. Courtesy of T.J. Godfrey, University of Oxford. (b) Origin of image contrast. 1, one pole of a field ion tip when perfect; 2, same as 1, but after cutting and displacing an amount b, introducing a dislocation at point A; 3, same as 2, but after field evaporation

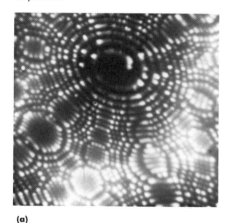

(a)

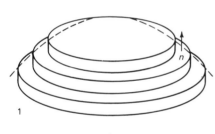

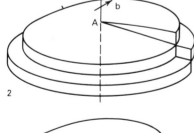

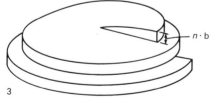

(b)

tions gives rise to a serrated or stepped spiral, in which the atomic rings are no longer continuous across the fault.

Figure 12 shows grain-boundary contrast. A high-angle boundary appears as a line of

Fig. 12 Grain boundary in tungsten

See text for discussion. Courtesy of T.J. Godfrey, University of Oxford

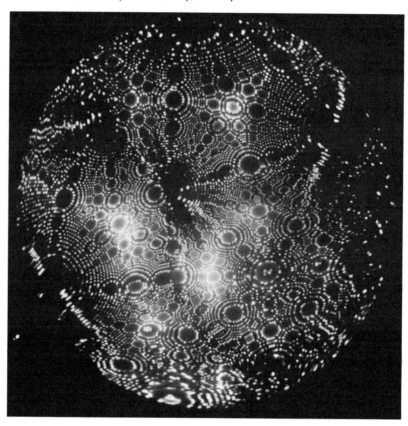

discontinuity running across the ring pattern. The images of the crystals on either side of the boundary appear regular up to the plane of the interface, indicating that the disordered region at a grain boundary is narrow.

Images of Alloys and Semiconductors

The FIM images of disordered solid solutions are less regular than those of pure metals because, first, the field-evaporation behavior varies due to variations in the local environment of different surface atoms. Therefore, the end-form of the sample becomes less uniform on an atomic scale. Second, chemical differences between alloy species result in formation of local surface dipoles, which in turn affect the extent of field adsorption and the local tunneling probability for field ionization. Micrographs of disordered solid solutions are provided in Examples 1 and 2 in the section "Applications" in this article. For ordered alloys, the images appear more regular, but on super-

lattice planes the brightness of successive atom layers will vary systematically for the reasons outlined above. Stacking-fault and grain-boundary-like contrast are also found in ordered alloys because of the presence of antiphase boundaries. Figure 13 shows an FIM image of an ordered nickel-molybdenum alloy containing several domain boundaries.

In two-phase materials, one phase usually images substantially more brightly than the other because differences in binding energies lead to variations in evaporation field and consequently to variations in local radius of curvature between the two phases. Therefore, the magnification of the two phases in the FIM image may differ, leading to errors in, for example, the determination of precipitate particle sizes. Figure 14, which illustrates the information obtainable on second-phase particles, shows a sequence of micrographs of a Guinier-Preston zone in an aluminum-copper alloy, demonstrating that the zone consists of two parallel atomic layers. Other examples of FIM images of two-phase materials are in the section "Applications" in this article.

Fig. 13 Domain boundaries in an ordered Ni₄Mo alloy

Courtesy of R.W. Newman, University of Florida

Fig. 14 Sequence of FIM images of a Guinier-Preston zone in an Al-1.7Cu alloy aged 5 h at 100 °C (212 °F)

Source: Ref 5

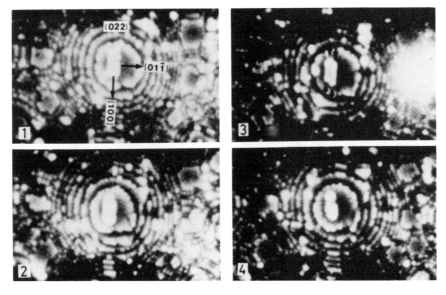

A hard-sphere representation of the sample surface can be assumed to be valid for metals and alloys, which have closely packed crystal structures, but is not valid for semiconductors, which generally have lower coordination numbers and a more covalent bonding. Field evaporation of semiconductors produces an irregular image in which only the low-index crystal planes can be discerned. A spontaneous surface rearrangement occurs whenever an atom is field evaporated to minimize the number of dangling bonds. The type of image produced is shown in Fig. 39 in this article.

Quantitative Analysis of Field Ion Microscopy Images

The FIM image is a projection of the complex three-dimensional shape of the sample surface. To a first approximation, this projection may be taken as stereographic. Major poles may be indexed from the symmetry of the pattern; the main crystallographic zones can then be constructed, and the indices of minor poles determined from the zone-addition rule. Once indexing has been carried out, the magnification of a given region of the image can be calculated from a direct measurement of the micrograph if the two-dimensional array of atoms on a given plane is fully resolved and the lattice parameter and crystal structure of the material are known.

Alternatively (and more generally), if the number of image rings N between a reference crystallographic pole (hkl) and another pole separated from it by an angle θ are counted, the radius of the sample in this region is:

$$r(1 - \cos \theta) = N \cdot d(hkl) \qquad \text{(Eq 7)}$$

where $d(hkl)$ is the interplanar spacing for the (hkl) pole. The magnification can then be obtained from a calculation of the curvilinear distance $r\theta$ between the two poles and comparison with the corresponding distance on the micrograph.

Complete three-dimensional reconstruction of the sample is hindered by the fact that the end-form is never truly hemispherical. The main reason is that the work function and hence the evaporation field vary with crystallographic orientation. Therefore, accurate measurement of curvilinear distances across the sample surface is extremely difficult, except in localized areas, and extensive computer calculation is often involved. Distance may be measured more simply along the axis of the sample, especially if this coincides with a major crystallographic pole, because the step height of the atomic ledges provides an accurate unit of distance. Field-evaporation sequences may be analyzed in this manner by recording the number of atom layers evaporated between successive micrographs.

One application is measurement of the persistence depth of precipitate particles, which is a more reliable estimate of their linear extent than a lateral measurement based on an individual micrograph. Another important application is reconstruction of the topography of grain boundaries and interphase interfaces. The accurate measurement of angles and distances from FIM micrographs is complicated; specialist monographs treat this subject fully.

Atom Probe Microanalysis

The principle of the atom probe is outlined in Fig. 15. It consists of a modified field ion microscope connected to a time-of-flight mass spectrometer by means of an aperture hole approximately 2 mm (0.08 in.) in diameter located in the center of the microscope screen. The spectrometer consists of an evacuated flight tube, at the end of which is a particle detector of single-ion sensitivity. The FIM sample is mounted on a turntable and can be tilted to position any portion of the image over the aperture hole. Ions are field evaporated from the surface at well-defined instants in time by applying to the sample a succession of brief high-voltage pulses superimposed on the direct current imaging voltage. The field-evaporated ions are accelerated toward the screen, following trajectories similar to those of the gas ions that formed the original FIM image. Consequently, although most of the ions will be stopped by the screen, those from the selected region of the sample will pass through the aperture hole into the spectrometer.

The ions are identified from their overall times-of-flight to the particle detector. The potential energy lost by an ion during acceleration is converted into kinetic energy. Thus, its final velocity, v, is:

$$\frac{1}{2} mv^2 = neV \qquad \text{(Eq 8)}$$

where m is the mass of the ion, ne is its electronic charge, and V is the potential through which it has been accelerated. If the ion is assumed to reach its final velocity near the sample surface (a reasonable first approximation because the electric field is strongly concentrated in this region), then the final velocity is:

$$v = \frac{L}{t} \qquad \text{(Eq 9)}$$

where L is the distance from sample to detector, and t is the overall time that elapses between application of the high-voltage pulse to the sample and arrival of the ion at the detector. The mass-to-charge ratio of the ion (m/n) is then:

$$\frac{m}{n} = \frac{2eVt^2}{L^2} \qquad \text{(Eq 10)}$$

where

$$V = V_{dc} + \alpha V_{pulse} \qquad \text{(Eq 11)}$$

and α is a constant that allows for distortion of the high-voltage pulse during transmission

Fig. 15 Principles of the AP

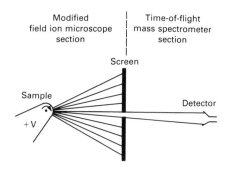

Fig. 16 Progressive field evaporation in the AP

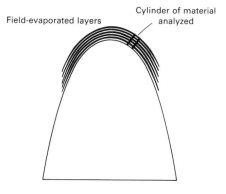

to the sample and for incomplete acceleration of the ions. Numerically:

$$\frac{m}{n} = \frac{0.19297 Vt^2}{L^2} \qquad \text{(Eq 12)}$$

where V is in kilovolts, t is in microseconds, and L is in meters.

Progressive field evaporation leads to the collection of ions at the detector from a small cylinder of material, typically approximately 2 nm in diameter, extending into the sample (Fig. 16). This permits determination of the chemical composition of the selected region and allows investigation of a wide range of metallurgical and surface chemical phenomena on a uniquely fine scale.

Instrument Design and Operation

The AP system (Fig. 17) requires ultrahigh vacuum with a base pressure of 10^{-8} to 10^{-9} Pa (10^{-10} to 10^{-11} mbar). A fast-entry airlock (not shown) permits rapid exchange of samples without breaking the vacuum. The high-voltage pulse generator typically delivers pulses to 5 kV amplitude, with a 1-ns rise time and a 10-ns duration at a repetition rate of 60 Hz. The particle detector consists of two microchannel plates arranged

in series. Each input ion produces a nanosecond-wide output pulse containing 10^6 to 10^7 electrons. The flight tube is approximately 1 m (3⅓ ft) long; therefore, experimental flight times are 1 to 10 μs. Digital timing systems are available that measure such time intervals to an accuracy of 1 part in 1000. Therefore, in principle, precise determination of ion species is possible. However, a practical complication arises because the rapidly time-varying potential of the high-voltage pulse introduces a spread of energies into the field-evaporated ions that limits the mass resolution to approximately 1 part in 150.

Data from the timing system are entered into a computer, which also records the voltages applied to the sample, calculates the mass-to-charge ratio of each ion, and stores and displays the information. The overall rate of removal of ions from the sample can be controlled by adjusting the dc and pulse voltages. As the sample field evaporates, the apex region slowly becomes blunter, necessitating application of progressively higher voltages to continue field evaporation. The number of ions collected fluctuates from pulse to pulse, depending on whether or not a step edge on the sample is aligned exactly over the aperture hole. Consequently, the timing system usually includes several channels, with arrangements to shift from one to the next as successive ions reach the detector. However, because ions of the same mass-to-charge ratio evaporated on the same pulse may not be resolved by the detection system even with a multichannel timing system, the average rate of evaporation is usually maintained below one ion per pulse. Thus, overall collection rates are of the order of 10^3 to 10^4 ions/h.

If the analysis is performed with the image gas present in the chamber, some background noise is evident in the spectra due to the random arrival of image-gas ions at the detector during the analysis. The noise can be eliminated by removing the image gas and conducting the analysis in ultrahigh vacuum, although the feature of interest cannot be observed as it field evaporates. However, the image-gas ions can be deflected electrostatically from the detector because these ions have lower energies than the ions evaporated from the surface during application of the high-voltage pulse. This deflection occurs automatically in the energy-compensated atom probe (ECAP).

Mass Spectra and Their Interpretation

Figure 18 shows a complex mass spectrum taken from a carbide precipitate in a commercial chromium-molybdenum steel. The

Fig. 17 Complete AP system

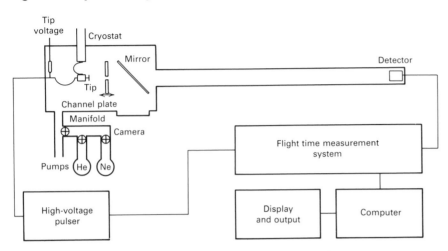

Table 4 Atom probe analysis of chromium-molybdenum

Element	Wet chemical analysis, at.%	Steel carbide analysis, at.%	Ferrite analysis, at.%
Chromium	2.46	12.2	1.5
Molybdenum . . .	0.58	48.6	0.8
Manganese.	0.57	0.7	0.9
Carbon	0.37	34.8	ND
Silicon.	0.38	0.4	0.6
Nickel	0.24	0.4	0.3
Copper	0.18	ND	0.07
Vanadium	0.033	0.3	0.07
Iron.	bal	2.6	bal

Note: ND, not determined

horizontal axis of the spectrum represents mass-to-charge ratio (m/n), which is plotted in atomic mass units. The vertical axis shows the abundance of ions at any mass number and is plotted logarithmically in this example to emphasize minor peaks.

Accurate calibration of the mass scale involves determination of the factor α in Eq 11 and may be performed with reference to known mass peaks, of which there are often several in any one spectrum. Many elements have several isotopes, and more than one charge state may form. For example, molybdenum has seven main isotopes and is evaporated in the two-, three-, and fourfold charge states. Although useful for calibration, this multiplicity may complicate interpretation of the spectra. For example, because iron and chromium have isotopes at mass number 54 and occur predominantly in the doubly charged state, a peak occurring at

m/n 27 cannot immediately be assigned. In most such cases, at least one isotope of each pair of elements will be free from such coincidences. Therefore, using tables of natural abundances and the number of ions determined for each distinguishable isotope, the number of atoms of each element in the coinciding peak can be estimated.

An additional complication is that adjacent isotopes are not always fully resolved in the spectra, especially for the heavier elements. The limited resolution is due to the energy spread of the ions, as mentioned above. Various procedures have been developed to aid deconvolution of overlapping mass peaks, mainly based on the trailing edge of each peak having an approximately exponential form. However, these procedures are difficult because of statistical limitations when the individual peaks contain only small numbers of ions. Particular diffi-

culties arise in some important, useful systems. For example, in steels, the manganese peak lies between two closely adjacent iron isotopes, and in nickel-base superalloys, the cobalt peak lies between two of the main isotopes of nickel. In such cases, the optimum solution is use of a high-resolution ECAP.

Table 4 lists the overall analyses for the carbide in Fig. 18 and for the surrounding ferrite matrix. The following factors merit consideration:

- Once the problems of coincident or overlapping peaks have been dealt with, further complicated correction procedures, such as those often required in x-ray microanalysis, are unnecessary. The chemical composition is obtained by directly counting the numbers of ions of each species that have been collected
- Because of the low background noise, minor additions and impurities can be detected and measured easily, the sensi-

Fig. 18 AP mass spectrum of a carbide particle in a tempered 2.25Cr-1Mo steel

Source: Ref 6

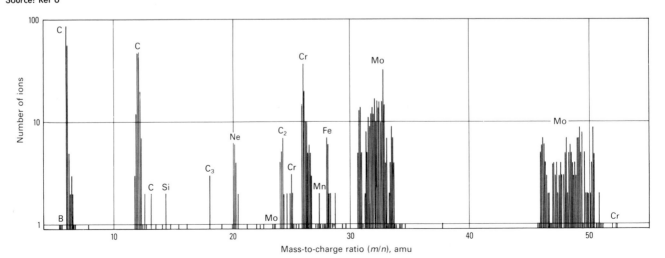

Fig. 19 Possible orientations of an interface BB with the sample surface SS

(a) Precisely parallel. (b) Precisely perpendicular. (c) General case. The distance *d* indicates one atomic spacing. Source: Ref 6

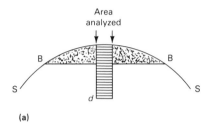

(a)

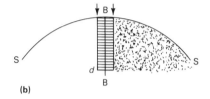

(b)

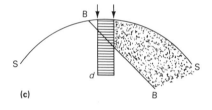

(c)

An absolute depth scale may be established by monitoring the FIM image and recording the number of atom layers evaporated during the analysis. If the analysis is conducted without the image gas present, an effective aperture size at the sample can be estimated and an approximate depth scale can be obtained from a record of the total number of ions collected during the experiment. However, differences in local magnification between phases having different evaporation fields can lead to significant errors.

Composition profiles are useful in the study of such phenomena as surface and interface segregation, ordering, clustering, precipitation, and spinodal decomposition. However, their interpretation necessitates care because of the three-dimensionality of the sample. This is illustrated in Fig. 19, with reference to analysis across an interphase interface. If the plane of the interface lies exactly at right angles to the direction of analysis, an abrupt change in composition will be recorded in the profile. However, if the interface is oblique to the sampling direction, the apparent variation in overall composition will be more gradual, because the aperture will cover both phases simultaneously during part of the analysis. The interface will appear diffuse because it has been sampled at an inappropriate angle. Another problem with an oblique profile is that a difference in local curvature between the phases can lead to aberrations in ion trajectories, which result in some of the evaporated ions from one phase appearing to derive from the other.

The construction of a composition profile inevitably involves some smoothing of the data because each point on the curve represents an analysis averaged over a certain number of ions. If the number selected is too small, the profile will exhibit excessive statistical fluctuations; if too large, excessive smoothing may obscure features of interest. Plotting a family of profiles from one experiment, using different numbers of ions per

Fig. 20 AP composition profile across a cementite/ferrite interface in a pearlitic steel (Fe-0.6C-0.85Cr-0.66Mn-0.26Si)

Source: Ref 7

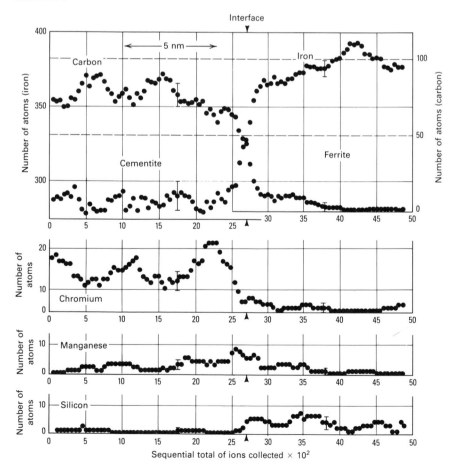

tivity being limited mainly by counting statistics and sample size

- The small aperture size means that overlap between the signals from the two phases is minimized; therefore, the concentration of matrix elements in the precipitate can be determined with a high degree of confidence
- Because the ion detector is sensitive to charged particles of all mass-to-charge ratios, light elements, such as carbon, can be analyzed with the same accuracy as the heavier metallic elements; in the example given, the carbon content indicates that the precipitate was of the M_2C type

Composition Profiles

Mass spectra, which provide the average compositions of the cylinders of material that have been sampled, represent only a small portion of the information potentially available using AP analysis. Because the ions are removed layer by layer from the sample (Fig. 16), with 50 to 60 ions being recorded for each atomic terrace evaporated, the sequence of data contains information on local variations of composition within the analyzed region. Thus, a composition depth-profile can be plotted for the sample.

data point, is often advisable to obtain the maximum amount of useful information from the analysis.

Figure 20 shows a composition profile taken transversely across the cementite-ferrite interface in a microalloyed pearlitic steel. Each data point is averaged over 400 ions. Chromium is partitioned strongly to the carbide phase, silicon is rejected into the ferrite phase, and the concentration of manganese is highest at the interface. Information of this kind is important in understanding the heat-treatment response of various alloy steels. Composition profiles are also discussed in Example 2 in the section "Applications" in this article (Fig. 34).

Alternate Forms of Data Representation

An alternative that overcomes the averaging problem inherent in normal composition profiles is the ladder diagram. This is a vector chart, in which two axes are selected to represent two elements (or groups of elements) present in the material. When an ion of one of the selected species is recorded, a step of unit length is drawn on the diagram in the appropriate direction. When the next ion is caught, a further step is added, and so on. This method is useful for detecting small composition fluctuations that can easily be overlooked in normal concentration profiles. Ladder diagrams are also used to study ordered alloys because analysis perpendicular to a superlattice plane may permit direct determination of an order parameter. Another use is for identifying the location of impurity atoms at interfaces. Ladder diagrams are also discussed in Example 1 in the section "Applications" in this article (Fig. 31 and 32).

Periodic composition fluctuations in a spinodally decomposing alloy may be analyzed using a Fourier transformation of the data. In principle, this provides information on the spectrum of wavelengths present. However, AP data sequences are rarely long enough to exploit this approach fully. A more useful method of processing such information is autocorrelation analysis. This is designed to identify regular periodic features from complex waveforms. Only the main frequency component is identifiable, but much additional information is generated regarding the volume fraction of second-phase particles and the distribution of interparticle spacings. The autocorrelation coefficient $R(k)$ is:

$$R(k) = \frac{n\sum_{i=1}^{n-k}(c_i - c_0)(c_{i+k} - c_0)}{(n-k)\sum_{i=1}^{n}(c_i - c_0)^2} \quad \text{(Eq 13)}$$

Fig. 21 Variation of the field-evaporation rate with temperature

V_{dc} is the direct current standing voltage, and V_p is the voltage-pulse amplitude.

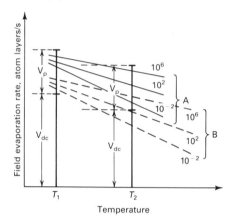

where c_i and c_{i+k} are the solute concentrations in the ith and $(i+k)$th field-evaporated plane, respectively; c_0 is the mean solute concentration; n is the total number of field-evaporated planes; and k is the correlation distance. If the correlation between the solute contents of the ith and $(i+k)$th planes is positive, the value of $R(k)$ will be positive, and conversely. A regular periodic structure will generate a curve having a regular oscillatory form, with an initial peak corresponding to correlations of solute content within an individual solute-rich region, and subsequent peaks corresponding to correlations between a series of such regions. Autocorrelograms are also discussed in Example 2 in the section "Applications" in this article (Fig. 35) for a spinodally decomposing iron-chromium-cobalt permanent-magnet alloy. The k-value corresponding to the first minimum in the curve is a measure of the width of an individual solute-rich region, and the k-value of the next peak is a measure of the mean distance between adjacent regions of this type. Longer-range periodicities will appear in the form of a succession of such peaks.

Requirements for Quantitative Analysis

The principal requirement for quantitative analysis is collection of a statistically significant number of ions. The quantity necessary for obtaining any desired degree of accuracy can be estimated from the standard deviation of the normal distribution function. If the total number of ions collected is N, and the number of ions of a particular species x is n_x, the standard deviation σ associated with the measurement of n_x is:

$$\sigma = \left(\frac{n_x(N - n_x)}{N}\right)^{1/2} \quad \text{(Eq 14)}$$

Thus, measuring an alloy element concentration of 10% to an accuracy of $10 \pm 1\%$ necessitates collecting at least 1000 ions from the sample, but measuring a trace addition at the 0.1% level to an accuracy of $0.1 \pm 0.01\%$ requires a sample size of 100 000 ions.

Some experimental precautions are necessary to obtain accurate quantitative analyses. The background vacuum in the system must be very good to eliminate any possibility of field corrosion during the experiment. Hydrogen image gas should be excluded from the system because it tends to form hydrides with such metals as copper, iron, and aluminum. Analysis at the centers of low-index poles on the sample should be avoided because surface migration under the influence of the applied field may affect the results. The sample temperature should also be kept low, and the pulse fraction (the ratio of the voltage pulse amplitude to the dc standing voltage) should be maintained high to minimize slow field evaporation between pulses.

Figure 21 provides clarification; it shows the field dependence of the evaporation rate for the two components of a binary alloy as a function of sample temperature. In general, the field dependence is strongest at the lowest sample temperatures. Thus, to suppress slow dc field evaporation in the time intervals between successive high-voltage pulses, a higher pulse fraction must be used at higher sample temperatures. Slow field evaporation is unlikely to affect the two components equally. For example, Fig. 21 shows component A as having a higher evaporation field than component B. Analysis can be conducted safely with the pulse fraction indicated at temperature T_1. However, if the temperature is raised to T_2 while the pulse fraction is maintained at a constant value, selective loss of B ions will begin at the dc holding voltage, and consequently the AP analysis at T_2 will appear anomalously rich in component A ions. This effect is strongest if the sample material contains elements of widely different evaporation fields.

Analysis of standard samples of known homogeneous composition is desirable to check analysis conditions for a given class of material. The standard samples should be used to establish a pulse-fraction curve, a plot of apparent sample composition against the pulse fraction used in the analysis. Figure 22 shows such curves for alloys typical of the γ and γ' phases in nickel-base superalloys. If the pulse fraction is high enough, a plateau region is attained, in which the real and measured composition agree closely

Fig. 22 Pulse-fraction curves to establish correct operating conditions for analysis of nickel-base superalloys

(a) Nickel-cobalt-chromium alloy. (b) Nickel-aluminum-titanium alloy. Source: Ref 8

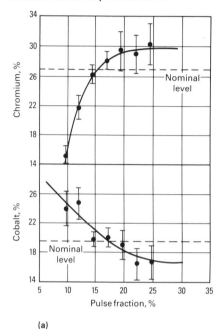

(a)

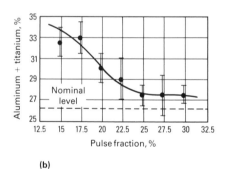

(b)

with one another. The sample temperature in Fig. 22 was 100 K, and pulse fractions of 25% or more were found to be necessary to obtain the correct analysis. At lower sample temperatures, smaller pulse fractions will suffice. For example, at 50 K, pulse fractions of 15 to 20% are adequate for the quantitative analysis of diverse materials.

Table 5 summarizes an example of accurate quantitative analysis of a high-purity 18Cr-12Ni austenitic stainless steel containing a small addition of titanium. The analysis was obtained from a spectrum containing 2400 ions using the procedures outlined earlier for separating ^{54}Cr and ^{54}Fe, and ^{58}Fe and ^{58}Ni isotopes. The agreement is excellent for

the major elements, although substantially more data would be required for adequate analysis of minor and trace additions.

Factors Limiting Spatial Resolution

The depth resolution and lateral resolution of the analysis must be differentiated. From the layer-by-layer nature of evaporation, the depth resolution is approximately one atom layer, or approximately 0.2 nm. Slight complications arise if more than one atomic ledge overlaps the aperture hole at any one time, but this can usually be avoided by positioning the aperture over a region of the sample where adjacent ledges are well separated. Convincing evidence of the single-layer depth resolution derives from analyses of ordered alloys, where ladder diagrams from superlattice planes show a well-defined staircase structure reflecting the alternating composition of successive atom layers. Such an analysis is discussed in Example 1 in the section "Applications" in this article (Fig. 31).

The lateral resolution of the AP varies somewhat with surface topography and with location on the sample. It is approximately the same as the effective aperture size, which

Table 5 Analysis of high-purity 18Cr-12Ni austenitic stainless steel

Element	Bulk analysis, at.%	Atom probe analysis, at.%
Chromium	18.9	18.8 ± 0.80
Nickel	11.5	12.1 ± 0.7
Titanium	0.37	0.6 ± 0.15
Iron	bal	bal

depends directly on the physical size of the hole in the microscope screen and inversely on the sample radius and sample-to-screen distance. To compensate for the progressive increase in radius during field evaporation, many instruments incorporate a facility for varying sample-to-screen distance. The effective aperture size is usually maintained at approximately 2 nm.

If the local radius of curvature of the sample varies sharply, for example, in the region of a phase boundary, ion optical aberrations may be introduced and the flight paths of the evaporated ions from the two phases may overlap. In extreme cases, the resolution may be no better than 3 to 4 nm. Smaller aberrations occur in the trajectories of ions exiting the step edges of

Fig. 23 Imaging atom probe

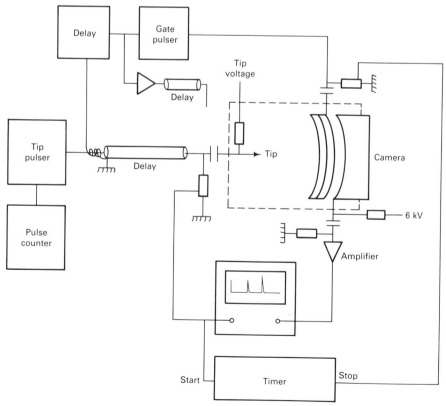

Fig. 24 IAP study of Nimonic 90 showing (clockwise from bottom left): mass spectrum, FIM image, and time-gated images for nickel + cobalt, chromium, titanium, and aluminum

Courtesy of K.M. Delargy, University of Oxford

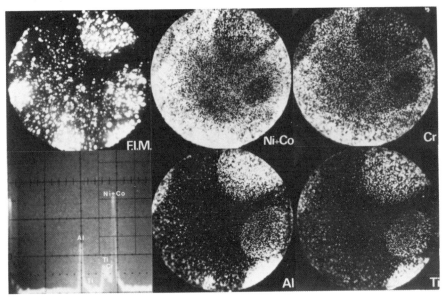

Fig. 25 Energy-compensated atom probe

Source: Ref 9

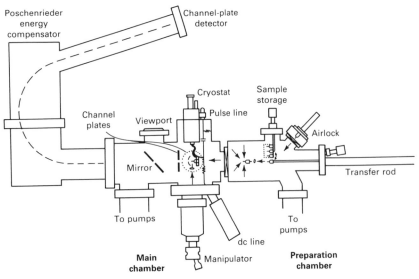

The Imaging Atom Probe (IAP)

The aperture hole in the screen of the conventional AP prevents most of the ions exiting the sample from reaching the detector. This provides favorable lateral spatial resolution, but results in inefficient sampling of the material. The IAP overcomes this problem by using a large double-curved channel-plate screen assembly as the FIM image screen and the ion detector for time-of-flight measurements (Fig. 23). The sample is located at the center of curvature of the channel-plate assembly so that the time-of-flight of ions to any part of the detector is the same. Because the system has no aperture, all ions impinging on the detector contribute to the spectrum. Thus, a single high-voltage pulse is usually sufficient to produce a meaningful spectrum, which is displayed on an oscilloscope or fast-transient recorder. The shorter flight path, typically approximately 12 cm (4.7 in.) compared to the 1.0 m (3⅓ ft) in the conventional AP, provides an adequate field of view of the image together with a mass resolution in the spectrum of approximately 1 part in 25.

The particular advantage of this instrument is its capability for displaying the spatial distribution of a single element over the entire imaging region. The mass spectrum is first used to identify the field-evaporated species, then the detector is switched to a time-gated mode, in which the instrument resembles a high-speed stroboscope. The dc voltage applied to the channel plates is lowered to a value at which the light output from the screen is negligible. A high-voltage pulse is then applied to the sample to produce further field evaporation, and after a delay time corresponding to the time-of-flight of a species of interest, a nanosecond-wide pulse is applied to the detector to reactivate it momentarily. The ions of the selected species will generate a light output from the detector, which can be recorded photographically; ions of other species will not register.

By pulsing the sample repeatedly, a spatially resolved atomic map of the distribution of a selected element over the whole of the imaged region can be constructed. Varying the delay time extends the procedure to accumulate maps for several elements. Figure 24 shows the results of an IAP investigation of the distribution of major elements in Nimonic 90, a nickel-base superalloy. Another application, showing a study of grain-boundary segregation, is provided in Example 3 in the section "Applications" in this article (Fig. 37).

The information obtained using the IAP is essentially complementary to that obtained from the conventional time-of-flight AP with an aperture hole. Because obtaining both

low-index poles, but here the deviations in paths are rarely more than approximately 1 nm. More aberrations are introduced if the region under analysis lies far from the apex of the tip, especially if a high pulse fraction is used. The reason is that the pulse voltage decays before the ions are fully accelerated, and thus the curvature of their trajectories decreases slightly as the potential drops. This produces a net deflection of the ions outward from the axis of the instrument. In practice, this effect is small at angles less than approximately 35° from the apex of the sample.

Fig. 26 High-resolution spectrum of tungsten obtained using the ECAP shown in Fig. 25

Source: Ref 9

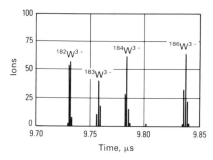

Fig. 27 Comparison of the principles of voltage-pulsed and laser-pulsed APs

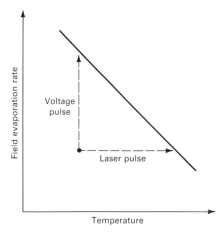

kinds of information from the same sample is useful, it has become common practice to build combined instruments with the two kinds of screen and detector assemblies mounted at right angles to each other and with a sample-rotation device to permit operation in either orientation.

The High-Resolution Energy-Compensated Atom Probe (ECAP)

The main limitation on the mass resolution of the conventional straight-flight-tube AP is due to the energy spread of the ions, caused by the rapidly time varying potential of the high-voltage pulse. This difficulty can be overcome by using an instrument having a curved flight path (Fig. 25). The curvature is introduced using a toroidal-sector electrostatic lens and deflector system, known as a Poschenrieder analyzer, and the instrument is termed an ECAP.

The ions are deflected through a total angle of 163° and are focused onto a detector the same distance from the output side of the analyzer as the sample is from the input side. Higher-energy ions, which travel faster, swing wide on the bend in the analyzer and thus travel on longer paths than lower-energy ions. They also undergo some retardation in the analyzer. If the voltages on the deflector plates are adjusted correctly, the analyzer becomes time focusing. That is, ions of the same mass-to-charge ratio but different energies have the same overall times-of-flight to the detector. The resultant increase in mass resolution is more than a factor of ten (Fig. 26). The problem of resolving adjacent isotopes is completely overcome, and the

analysis of many important classes of materials, such as steels and nickel-base superalloys, is greatly simplified.

However, with higher mass resolution the possibility of separately detecting the arrival of two ions of the same mass-to-charge ratio following application of a single high-voltage pulse is much less. Consequently, additional care is necessary to control evaporation rates to minimize pile-up of ions at the detector, or statistical correction procedures must be used to allow for the "missing" ions.

The Pulsed Laser Atom Probe (PLAP)

The PLAP, another recent development, is particularly important in the study of semiconducting materials. In a conventional AP, the sample is maintained at a constant temperature and the voltage is momentarily increased to produce evaporation. Because the field required for evaporation is a function of temperature, it is equally possible to hold the voltage constant and momentarily increase the temperature. This sudden temperature increase may be induced by focusing onto the tip of the sample a nanosecond time-width laser pulse, for example, from a nitrogen gas laser or a neodymium-YAG (yttrium-aluminum-garnet) solid-state laser. The temperature increase necessary to produce evaporation is modest, for example, from 50 to approximately 300 K; therefore, danger of modifying the nature of the sample is minimal. Figure 27 compares the principles of voltage-pulsed and laser-pulsed APs.

With the pulsed laser method, materials of lower electrical conductivity, such as semiconductors, which do not respond properly to application of kilovolt-amplitude high-voltage pulses, can be analyzed. In addition, the intense mechanical shock associated with the high-voltage pulse is eliminated; therefore, relatively brittle materials, such as oxides, can be studied with less risk of fracture during analysis. Further, because the potential applied to the sample remains constant during pulsing, the energy spread of the ions is much reduced and high-resolution mass spectra can be obtained without an energy-compensating spectrometer. Disadvantages of the method are the difficulties of working with pulsed lasers and the possibility that the temperature increase may induce surface migration on the sample, which could affect analysis results. Surface diffusion occurs particularly easily on metals, and because these can be studied equally well using conventional voltage-pulsed techniques, the laser-pulse method is generally

Fig. 28 Pulsed-laser atom probe

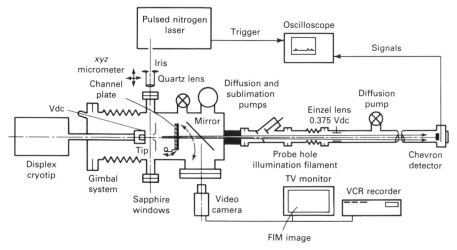

regarded primarily as a tool for semiconductor research.

Figure 28 shows a high-resolution PLAP, which resembles a conventional time-of-flight AP. An alternate design approach is to incorporate laser-pulsing facilities into an ECAP. The energy-compensating sector is redundant when used in the PLAP mode, but the overall instrument is useful for metallurgical and semiconductor applications. Use of this technique to study a compound semiconductor is discussed in Example 4 in the section "Applications" in this article (Fig. 39 and 40).

Applications

Example 1: Phase Chemistry and Phase Stability of a Nickel-Base Superalloy (Ref 8, 10). Alloy IN 939 is a high-chromium, nickel-base superalloy intended primarily for marine and industrial use. The composition of alloy IN 939 is:

Element	Concentration, at.%
Nickel	46.47
Cobalt	18.23
Chromium	24.47
Aluminum	3.98
Titanium	4.37
Tungsten	0.62
Tantalum	0.44
Niobium	0.61
Carbon	0.71
Boron	0.05
Zirconium	0.06

Table 6 outlines the four-stage heat treatment used to obtain optimum properties. As part of a broader investigation of the structure and properties of this alloy, FIM and AP measurements were carried out. The objectives were (1) to establish the role of the final (700 °C, or 1290 °F) stage of heat treatment, which produced no obvious changes in the transmission electron microscopy (TEM) images of the microstructure, but was important in attaining the desired creep properties, (2) to measure accurately the compositions of the major phases present to predict the phase stability of the alloy, and (3) to determine whether or not segregation of refractory elements occurred at the interphase interfaces, as this had been suggested as a possible creep-strengthening mechanism.

Sample blanks were sectioned from heat-treated bars of the material using a low-speed diamond saw. Electropolishing was conducted in two stages using the technique described in Table 1. Imaging and analysis were performed in neon at 100 K. Analysis was executed with the image gas removed to reduce background noise in the spectra.

Table 6 Four-stage heat treatment of alloy IN 939

Temperature		Time,	Cooling
°C	°F	h	procedure
1160	2120	4	Air cool
1100	1830	6	Air cool
900	1650	24	Air cool
700	1290	16	Air cool

Table 7 Analyses of γ and γ' phases in IN 939

Element	γ, at.%	γ', at.%
Nickel	40.9	61.4
Cobalt	22.4	9.8
Chromium	32.9	1.5
Aluminium	1.3	11.7
Titanium	0.8	13.8
Tungsten + tantalum	1.6	1.7
Boron	0.02	0.03
Carbon	0.04	0.04

Table 8 Secondary γ' precipitate compositions in IN 939

Element	Analysis 1 at.%	Analysis 2 at.%	Analysis 3 at.%	Average, at.%
Nickel	67.5	66.5	70.3	68.1
Cobalt	3.7	2.9	3.1	3.2
Chromium	2.1	1.4	0.8	1.4
Aluminium	16.8	14.6	10.1	13.8
Titanium	7.8	13.2	13.3	11.4
Tungsten	0.5	1.4	0.8	0.9
Tantalum	1.6	...	1.6	1.2

Fig. 29 Comparison of FIM and TEM images of alloy IN 939 after the (a) third and (b) fourth stages of heat treatment

Source: Ref 10

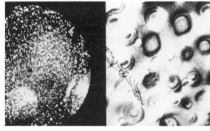

(a)

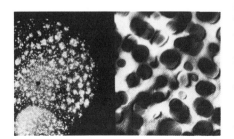

(b)

Pulse-fraction curves similar to those shown in Fig. 22 were plotted, and a pulse fraction of 25% was selected to obtain reliable quantitative analyses of each phase.

Figure 29 shows FIM and TEM images of the alloy after the third and fourth stages of heat treatment. The primary γ' precipitates, approximately 100 nm in diameter, are visible in the TEM images and appear as large bright areas on the FIM images. However, an additional feature in the FIM image of the four-stage heat-treated material is visible as a dense distribution of small bright regions approximately 3 to 5 nm in diameter. This feature is absent in the FIM image obtained after the third stage of heat treatment and is also not well resolved in the TEM images of the four-stage heat-treated material. Therefore, the final heat treatment stage produces an ultrafine secondary precipitate, which is not clearly visible except in the field ion microscope.

Figure 30 illustrates AP mass spectra of the γ matrix and the primary γ' precipitates, and Table 7 lists the corresponding analyses. Some chromium, a matrix-segregating element, is in the γ' precipitates, and some of the aluminum and titanium, the main γ' forming elements, remain in solution in the γ matrix. However, the overall extent of partitioning of these elements to their preferred phases is strong. Analysis of the data using a standard computer program for the calculation of phase stability shows that the alloy lies in a stable range and should not be prone to σ-phase formation.

Table 8 summarizes chemical analyses of the ultrafine secondary precipitates. They are of the γ' type, although with a lower cobalt content that the primary precipitates. This would appear to be due to their lower temperature of formation (700 °C, or 1290 °F, as opposed to 900 to 1000 °C, or 1650 to 1830 °F, for the larger particles).

Ladder diagrams were recorded to show the distribution of minor elements between the successive atomic layers of the ordered γ' structure and to check for segregation at the γ/γ' interfaces. Figures 31 and 32 show examples of the results. In the γ' phase, chromium atoms were found in the (nickel + cobalt)-rich layers and the (aluminum + titanium)-rich layers in proportions indicating that this element can occupy either type of atomic site. No clear indication could be found for the presence of refractory metal species at the interfaces, suggesting that segregation is not a significant mechanism of creep strengthening, at least in this particular alloy.

Example 2: Spinodal Decomposition of an Iron-Base Magnet Alloy (Ref 11, 12). The ternary iron-cobalt-chromium alloys form the basis of the Chromindur

Fig. 30 AP mass spectra of IN 939

(a) γ-phase matrix. (b) γ' phase. Source: Ref 10

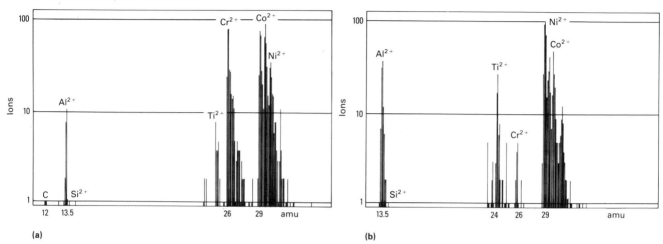

(a)

(b)

series of ductile permanent magnets. Their hard magnetic properties are developed through exploitation of a precipitation reaction that occurs in the low-temperature miscibility gap in this alloy system. Attempts to investigate the relationship between microstructure and magnetic properties using TEM and x-ray diffraction techniques met with limited success. This was partly because of the similar sizes and scattering factors of the elements involved and the extremely fine scale of the microstructures produced using low-temperature heat treatment. Investigation using FIM and AP techniques was more productive and allowed complete characterization of the morphology of the two-phase microstructure and the nature of the decomposition reaction.

The results may be illustrated by reference to the alloy Fe-28.5Cr-10.6Co and the heat-treatment temperature 560 °C (1040 °F). Samples were prepared from heat-treated material using the electropolishing techniques described in Table 1. Field ion micrographs were recorded at 80 K using neon as the imaging gas. Images at lower temper-

ature yielded improved atomic resolution, but the contrast between the phases was reduced, making characterization of the microstructure less certain. In the AP analyses, pulse fractions exceeding 12% and sample temperatures of 80 K were used. Composition profiles were obtained in the presence of a small trace of image gas to allow visual monitoring of the amount of material removed and its correlation with the atoms captured in the mass spectrometer.

Figure 33 illustrates field ion micrographs of material aged for various lengths of time that indicate the progressive development of a dark-imaging phase as the aging time is increased. Careful reconstruction from field-evaporation sequences reveals that the dark regions are not isolated particles, but form a fully interconnected three-dimensional network.

Figure 34 shows the corresponding AP composition profiles. Each data point represents the average concentration of chromium in a volume of material two atom planes (0.4 nm) thick, and less than 2 nm in diameter. The onset of phase separation is revealed clearly even at the earliest aging time of 10 min. The dark-imaging regions are found to be rich in chromium. The peak concentration of chromium increases with increasing aging time, consistent with the occurrence of a spinodal decomposition reaction. Autocorrelograms reveal a transition from statistically random composition fluctuations in the as-quenched condition to a regular periodic waveform within an aging time of 20 min (Fig. 35).

Figure 36 illustrates frequency-distribution curves that show the composition of successive blocks of equal numbers of field-evaporated ions. These curves exhibit a pro-

gressive broadening during aging and eventually develop into a bimodal distribution as the compositions of the two phases approach their equilibrium values. The scale of the microstructure is extremely fine. After a 1-h aging, the characteristic spacing between adjacent branches of the chromium-rich phase is approximately 3 nm; after 100 h, it increases only to 5 nm.

Example 3: Interfacial Segregation Studies in Molybdenum (Ref 13-15). Impurity elements, such as oxygen, are potential sources of grain-boundary embrittlement in refractory metals, but the characterization of the atomic distribution of such species has proved extremely difficult. Some recent experiments with molybdenum using the IAP have shed new light on this problem.

Fig. 31 Location of elements in successive superlattice planes in alloy IN 939

Evaporation sequence from (110)$_{γ'}$ planes

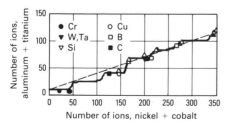

Fig. 32 Ladder diagram showing the composition change across a γ/γ' interface in alloy IN 939

Source: Ref 8

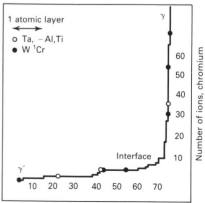

Number of ions, aluminum + titanium

Fig. 33 FIM images of an Fe-Cr-Co permanent-magnet alloy showing the progress of the spinodal decomposition reaction

Aged at 560 °C (1040 °F) for (a) 10 min, (b) 1 h, (c) 8 h, and (d) 100 h. Source: Ref 11

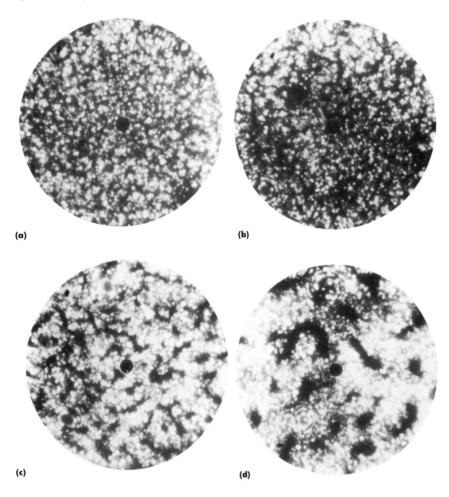

(a)

(b)

(c)

(d)

Fig. 34 Composition profiles of an Fe-Cr-Co alloy

Aged at 560 °C (1040 °F). See also Fig. 33. Source: Ref 11

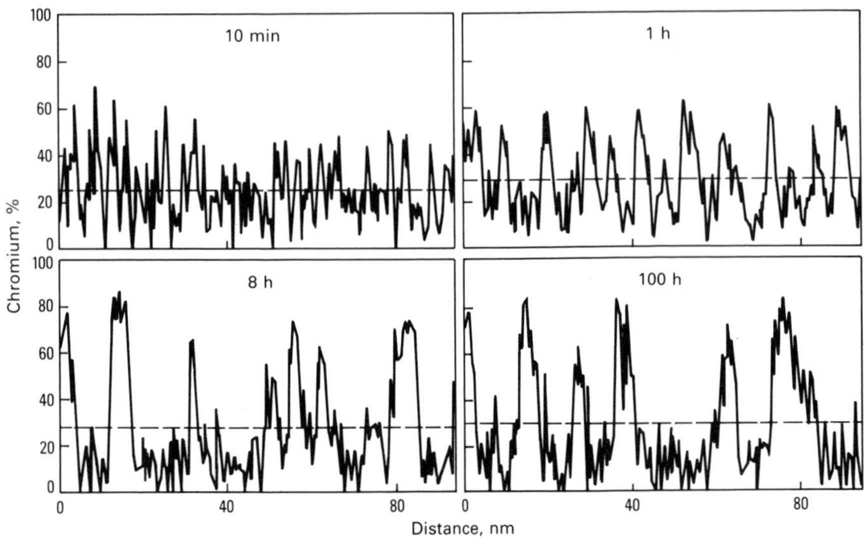

Samples were prepared from as-received commercial molybdenum wire using the electropolishing procedure described in Table 1. The samples were imaged in helium at 60 K. Gated desorption images were obtained using 1-min exposures, during which some 1800 pulses were applied to the sample, and an estimated 15 atoms layer of material were field evaporated. Figure 37 shows a FIM image of a sample containing a grain boundary and the corresponding gated desorption images for Mo^{3+} and O^+ ions. The O^+ image shows clear evidence for segregation at the boundary. The segregant concentration at the boundary can be established by counting the number of segregant atoms detected in the unit length of the boundary when a known thickness of material is field evaporated. In the case shown, the concentration is approximately 1×10^{14} atoms/cm^2. The segregant profile across the boundary can also be measured. In this example, most of the impurity (oxygen) atoms are located within a 1-nm-wide band along the boundary.

One puzzling feature of the IAP results was that the oxygen content of the grain boundaries seemed to be inconsistent. Further investigation using a conventional probe-hole time-of-flight AP provided an explanation. It appears that the form in which oxygen is desorbed from the surface depends on the evaporation rate (Fig. 38). At

Fig. 35 Autocorrelograms for an Fe-Cr-Co alloy

(a) As-quenched. (b) After aging 20 min at 560 °C (1040 °F). Source: Ref 11

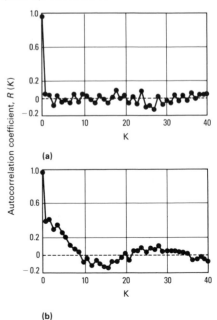

(a)

(b)

Fig. 36 Frequency-distribution curves for Cr in an Fe-Cr-Co alloy
Source: Ref 11

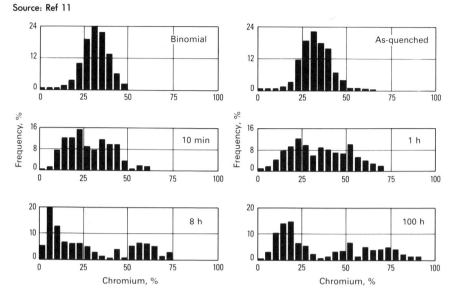

Fig. 37 Field-ion Mo³⁺ and O⁺ images from a molybdenum sample containing a grain boundary (arrows) at which segregation of oxygen has occurred

Ten net planes were field-evaporated for the Mo³⁺ image, and thirty for the O⁺ image. Source: Ref 13

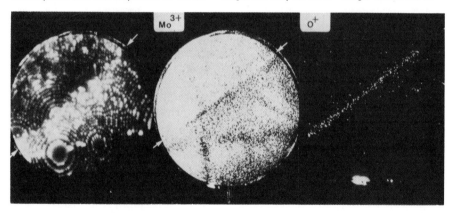

Fig. 38 AP analyses of a grain boundary in molybdenum

Oxygen appears as O^+ at relatively high field-evaporation rates (a) and as molecular ions (MoO^{3+} and so on) at relatively low rates (b). The neon ions are from field-adsorbed imaging gas (helium was also present). Source: Ref 15

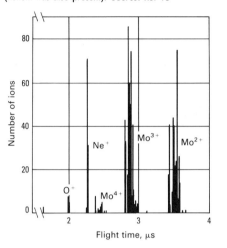

(a)

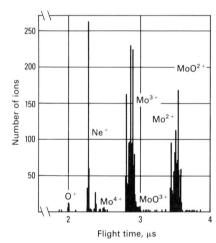

(b)

relatively high rates, desorption occurs predominantly as the species O^+, but at lower rates, a significant proportion of molybdenum oxide molecular ions is formed. This illustrates the necessity of combining different types of information available from AP analysis to obtain a complete picture of the phenomena.

Example 4: Local Composition Fluctuations in a Ternary 3:5 Semiconductor (Ref 16, 17). Vapor-deposition methods are widely used in the manufacture of multilayer thin-film semiconductors. One application is the fabrication of single and multiple quantum wells and superlattices composed of gallium arsenide (GaAs) and gallium aluminum arsenide (GaAlAs) for

optoelectronic devices. The composition of each successive deposited layer must be controlled accurately. Because these layers may be only a few nanometers thick, chemical microanalysis is extremely difficult. The PLAP characterizes such materials accurately.

A 50-μm-thick layer of $Ga_{(1-x)}Al_xAs$ having a nominal x-value of 0.1 was grown using metallo-organic chemical-vapor deposition (MOCVD), implementing a fast growth rate. Field ion microscopy sample blanks of square cross section were sectioned using a fine diamond saw. Subsequent polishing was carried out chemically, as described in Table 1. Field ion microscopy images were obtained using neon image gas

at 100 K. Figure 39 shows an example. Pulsed laser atom probe analyses were conducted at the base temperature of 100 K using 10-Hz, 5-ns-wide neodymium-YAG laser pulses to produce field evaporation. Figure 40 shows a typical PLAP spectrum of this material, and Table 9 lists chemical analyses of some selected areas. Wide fluctuations occur in the aluminum:gallium ratio. The effect is thought to be due to the high growth rate used in the formation of the layer, which may lead to instabilities in the flow of the reactive gas mixture across the substrate surface.

Fig. 39 Neon FIM image of GaAs
Courtesy of A. Cerezo, University of Oxford

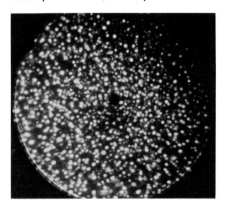

Fig. 40 PLAP analysis of a ternary 3:5 semiconductor
Source: Ref 16

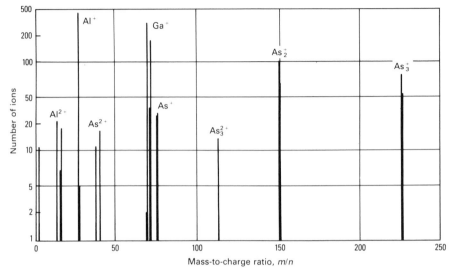

REFERENCES

1. E.W. Muller, *Science*, Vol 149, 1965, p 591-601
2. E.W. Muller and T.T. Tsong, *Field Ion Microscopy, Principles and Applications*, Elsevier, 1969, p 211-233
3. T.T. Tsong, *Surf. Sci.*, Vol 70, 1978, p 211-233
4. D.N. Seidman, *J. Phys. F. (Met. Phys.)*, Vol 3, 1973, p 393
5. K. Hirano *et al.*, *Philos. Mag.*, in press, 1986
6. M.K. Miller, P.A. Beaven, and G.D.W. Smith, in *Surface and Interface Analysis*, Vol 1, Heyden and Sons, 1979, p 149
7. P.R. Williams, M.K. Miller, P.A. Beaven, and G.D.W. Smith, in *Proceedings of Phase Transformations Conference*, Vol 2 (No. 3), Conference Series 3, York, U.K., Institution of Metallurgists, London, 1979, p 98
8. K.M. Delargy and G.D.W. Smith, *Metall. Trans. A*, Vol 14A, 1983, p 1771-1783
9. A. Cerezo, A.R. Waugh, and G.D.W. Smith, *J. Phys. (Orsay)*, Colloque C9, supplement to Vol 45 (No. 12), 1984, p 329
10. P.A. Beaven, M.K. Miller, and G.D.W. Smith, in *Electron Microscopy and Analysis 1977*, Institute of Physics, London, 1977, p 199-203
11. S.S. Brenner, P.P. Camus, M.K. Miller, and W.A. Soffa, *Acta Metall.*, Vol 32, 1984, p 1217-1227
12. F. Zhu, H. Wendt, and P. Haasen, *Scr. Metall.*, Vol 16, 1982, p 1175-1180
13. A.R. Waugh and M.J. Southon, *Surf. Sci.*, Vol 68, 1977, p 79-85
14. A.R. Waugh, *J. Phys. E (Sci. Instrum.)*, Vol 11, 1978, p 49-52
15. A.R. Waugh and M.J. Southon, *Surf. Sci.*, Vol 89, 1979, p 718-724
16. A. Cerezo, C.R.M. Grovenor, and G.D.W. Smith, in *Proceedings of the 32nd International Field Emission Symposium*, Wheeling, WV, 1985; also to be published in *J. Phys.*, 1986
17. A. Cerezo, C.R.M. Grovenor, and G.D.W. Smith, *Appl. Phys. Lett.*, Vol 46, 1985, p 567-569

Table 9 Local composition variations in a metallo-organic chemical-vapor-deposited GaAlAs layer

Ratios	Nominal	Region 1	Region 2	Region 3
Aluminum:gallium	0.1	0.2 ± 0.01	0.10 ± 0.01	0.70 ± 0.05
(Gallium + aluminum):arsenide	1.00	1.08 ± 0.03	1.03 ± 0.04	1.14 ± 0.04

SELECTED REFERENCES

- K.M. Bowkett and D.A. Smith, *Field Ion Microscopy*, North-Holland, 1970
- R. Gomer, *Field Emission and Field Ionization*, Harvard University Press, 1961
- J.J. Hren and S. Ranganathan, Ed., *Field Ion Microscopy—A Short Course*, Plenum Press, 1968
- E.W. Muller, in *Methods of Surface Analysis*, A.W. Czanderna, Ed., Elsevier, 1975, p 329
- E.W. Muller and T.T. Tsong, *Field Ion Microscopy, Principles and Applications*, Elsevier, 1969
- E.W. Muller and T.T. Tsong, *Prog. Surf. Sci.*, Vol 4, 1973, p 1
- J.A. Panitz, *J. Phys. E (Sci. Instrum.)*, Vol 15, 1982, p 1281
- J.A. Panitz, *Prog. Surf. Sci.*, Vol 8, 1978, p 261
- R.E. Thurstans and J.M. Walls, Ed., *A Bibliography of Field Ion Microscopy and Related Techniques, 1951-1978*, Warwick Publishing, 1980
- R. Wagner, *Field Ion Microscopy in Materials Science*, Springer, 1982

Low-Energy Ion-Scattering Spectroscopy

G.C. Nelson, Sandia National Laboratories

General Uses

- Identification of elements present on solid surfaces
- Semiquantitative determination of the atomic concentration of the elements present on the surface

Examples of Applications

- Identification of surface stains and corrosion products
- Determination of composition depth profiles and film thicknesses when combined with inert gas ion sputtering
- Study of the segregation of alloy and compound constituents to the surface
- Study of oxidation using ^{18}O
- Determination of the extent of coverage of ultrathin films
- Study of desorption of adsorbed layers
- Identification of the faces of polar crystals

Samples

- *Form*: Solids (metals, ceramics, ores, corrosion products, thin films, and so on) as powders or flat solid surfaces
- *Size*: Flat surface or distributed powders—2 × 1 × 0.5 cm (0.8 × 0.4 × 0.2 in.) maximum. Minimum size is determined by the probing beam size (0.05 cm, or 0.02 in. typical)

- *Preparation*: None; samples must be handled with clean instruments to avoid contamination

Limitations

- For high atomic number materials, elements must be present at a level of >0.1 at.% of a monolayer. For low atomic number materials, elements must be present at a level of >10 at.% of a monolayer
- Samples must be vacuum worthy
- For high atomic number materials, adjacent elements cannot be separated due to insufficient mass resolution
- Minimum beam size is 150 μm

Estimated Analysis Time

- 10 min for a single surface scan
- Several hours for depth profiles up to several thousand angstroms

Capabilities of Related Techniques

- *Auger electron spectroscopy*: Identification of elements present in the first 1 to 10 nm (10 to 100 Å)
- *X-ray photoelectron spectroscopy*: Identification of elements present in the first 1 to 10 nm (10 to 100 Å) over a 3- to 10-mm (0.12- to 0.40-in.) area
- *Secondary ion mass spectroscopy*: Mass/charge identification of elements present in the first 0.2 to 2 nm (2 to 20 Å)

Introduction

Low-energy ion-scattering spectroscopy (LEISS) is used extensively to analyze solid surfaces. Also used are Auger electron spectroscopy (AES), x-ray photoelectron spectroscopy (XPS), and secondary ion mass spectroscopy (SIMS), which are discussed in articles elsewhere in this Volume. The primary advantages of LEISS are its sampling depth of only 1 to 2 monolayers (0.2 to 0.4 nm, or 2 to 4 Å), its ability to analyze insulators, its ability to depth profile ultrathin films, and its ability to use isotopes to study reactions, particularly oxidation.

Use of low-energy backscattered ions to determine the surface composition of solids originated in a series of experiments conducted in 1967 (Ref 1). Helium, neon, and argon ions were used to study molybdenum and nickel targets. The reason for the low-energy tail when hydrogen ions were used and why this tail was absent when noble gases were used was interpreted correctly. Use of helium ions allowed peaks corresponding to the surface atoms of a molybdenum substrate and from adsorbed oxygen and carbon to be obtained. In later experiments, the cadmium and sulfur faces of a CdS single crystal were determined by ana-

Fig. 1 LEISS spectra obtained from a ZnO sample using a 2-keV ³He ion beam

Note the low background under the bismuth and zinc peaks and the moderate background under the oxygen peak.

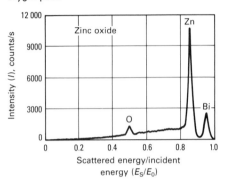

Fig. 2 LEISS spectra obtained from a copper sample

Note the large tail when hydrogen ions are used and the absence of the tail when helium ions are used.

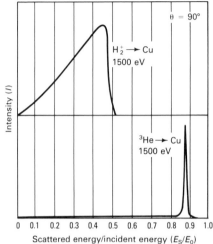

Fig. 3 LEISS spectra obtained from an aluminum sample using helium ions

Note the large tail when 4-keV ions are used and the absence of the tail when 1 keV is used.

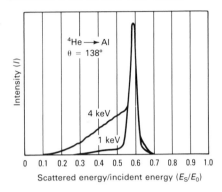

lyzing the relative peak heights (Ref 2). The quantitative nature of LEISS was demonstrated by analyzing the oxygen and aluminum peak heights from Al_2O_3 and pure aluminum. Thus, in a classic set of experiments, LEISS was proven to be surface sensitive, able to detect multiple elements present on a surface, able to yield quantitative information, and able to determine crystal structure.

Scattering Principles

Binary Collisions. Low-energy ion-scattering spectroscopy relies on binary elastic collisions between an incident ion beam and the atoms in the sample to obtain information (in this case, the mass) on the surface atoms. These collisions are analogous to those in the game of billiards; the colored balls would have different masses just as the target atoms have different masses. Measuring the velocity of the cue ball enables determination of the mass of the ball that is struck. Similarly, the velocity of the scattered ion can be used to determine the mass of the atom that is struck.

The equations used to calculate the mass of the target atoms derive from two fundamental laws of physics: the conservation of energy and the conservation of momentum. When combined and reformed in a useful format, these equations provide:

$$\frac{E_S}{E_0} = \left(\frac{M_0}{M_0 + M_T}\right)^2 \left\{\cos\theta + \left[\left(\frac{M_T}{M_0}\right)^2 - \sin^2\theta\right]^{1/2}\right\}^2 \quad \text{(Eq 1)}$$

where E_S is the energy of the scattered ion (related to the velocity by $E_S = \frac{1}{2}M_0 V_S^2$), E_0 is the energy of the incident ion, M_0 is the mass of the incident ion, θ is the angle through which the ion has scattered, and M_T is the mass of the target atom (the number under determination). If $\theta = 90°$, which is one of two common scattering angles used in commercial equipment, then:

$$\frac{E_S}{E_0} = \frac{M_T - M_0}{M_T + M_0} \quad \text{(Eq 2)}$$

Because the incident ion beam is produced using instrumentation, M_0 and E_0 are known. The equipment is also used to measure the number of scattered ions as a function of E_S. When a peak occurs in the spectra, Eq 1 can be used to calculate the target mass. In practice, the target mass for a given E_S, E_0, and M_0 for a fixed θ is usually obtained from a calculated table.

Contributions to Scattered Intensities.
The rate at which scattered ions arrive at the detector depends on several parameters including the number of atoms of a particular mass present on the surface. Determining the relationship between this number and the detected signal for each species enables conducting a quantitative analysis for the surface constituents. Other factors that contribute to the scattered ion signal include:

- The probability that an ion will scatter when it encounters an atom; this is the scattering cross section, σ

- The number of incident ions that strike the sample surface; this factor is the current in the incident beam
- The probability P that a scattered ion remains an ion and does not become a neutral atom; this term is necessary because most analyzers used in LEISS can detect only charged particles
- A parameter that is a function of how well the analyzer of the instrument can detect the scattered ions, ω; usually termed the transmission function of the analyzer, this parameter also includes the detection efficiency of the detector

Equation 3 relates the detected ion intensity I_i to the number of atoms of a particular kind on the surface, N_i:

$$I_i = K\, I_0\, N_i \sigma_i P_i \omega_i \quad \text{(Eq 3)}$$

The constant K is added to account for other, perhaps unknown, factors, such as shadowing. Although some information is known about each of these parameters, Eq 3 is usually not used for quantitative analysis. Tabulated sensitivity factors or standards to measure sensitivity factors are typically used.

LEISS Spectra in Qualitative Analysis

General Spectral Features. In LEISS, spectra are usually obtained using noble gas ion beams from 0.5 to 5 keV (Fig. 1). This spectrum was obtained by scattering a 2-keV ³He ion beam from a ZnO sample that contained a small amount of bismuth. Sharp individual peaks for oxygen, zinc, and bis-

Fig. 4 LEISS spectra showing anomalies

(a) Presence of peaks due to doubly charged ions.
(b) Presence of peaks due to multiple scattering

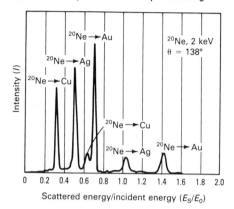

(a)

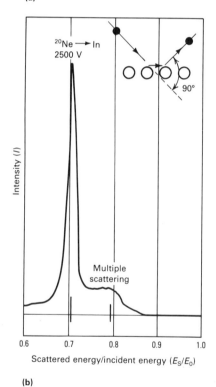

(b)

Fig. 5 LEISS spectra showing the improved mass resolution when a heavier mass ion is used

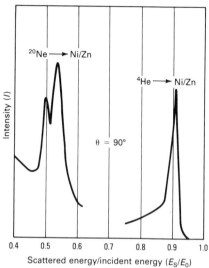

muth are visible. Little background exists under the bismuth and zinc peaks. Somewhat more background is found under the oxygen peak. When active gases, such as hydrogen or nitrogen, or higher energies are used, the measured spectra are considerably different (Fig. 2 and 3).

The top of Fig. 2 shows a plot of hydrogen scattering off of copper. The sharp edge at high energy is due to binary elastic scattering from the copper atoms. The long intense tail is due to inelastically scattered ions that have

remained charged, that enter the analyzer, and are added to the spectrum. This large tail complicates identification of small peaks that may be present on top of this background. Noble gas ion scattering, such as that shown at the bottom of Fig. 2, has a much higher probability that the inelastically scattered ions will be neutralized and thus lost from the spectrum. This neutralization contributes significantly to the sharp peaks observed in LEISS.

Figure 3 shows LEISS spectra obtained using ^{4}He at two different energies. At the higher energy, the tail is more pronounced, primarily because few inelastically scattered ions are neutralized. At low energies, the inelastically scattered ions travel more slowly and spend more time near the surface. Thus the probability that they will be neutralized is greater. High scattering cross sections also contribute to the sharp peaks. For low-energy ions, the scattering cross sections are of such a magnitude that relatively few penetrate past the first one or two monolayers; thus, only these ions are available for inelastic scattering (Ref 3).

Unexpected features can appear in LEISS spectra. Figures 4(a) and (b) show the two most commonly observed. Figure 4(a) illustrates scattering of singly and doubly charged ions. The doubly charged peak falls at twice the energy of the singly charged peak. The doubly charged ions are formed in the ion gun, and if the ion beam is not mass/charge analyzed (as is the case with most commercial instruments), they scatter along with the singly charged ions. Lower-

ing the ionization voltage in the ion source reduces the number of doubly charged ions.

Figure 4(b) shows a peak at an energy higher than that from a single binary elastic collision. This is due to the ion undergoing two or more elastic collisions, and the sum of the scattering angles equals that for the single event. This peak is somewhat washed out due to the various combinations of scattering events that can add up to the final scattering angle. For total scattering angles of 90° or greater, the peak is small compared to the major peak. At low scattering angles (approximately 10°), this peak can dominate the single scattering peak.

Surface Sensitivity. The sensitivity of LEISS to only the outer one or two monolayers is a major advantage. This is especially important for studies of such phenomena as catalysis or surface passivation, in which the outer monolayer governs surface activity. The extreme surface sensitivity is due to the large probability of subsurface neutralization of the incident ion beam and the large surface atom-incident ion scattering cross sections noted above. For sulfur adsorbed on nickel, the nickel signal disappears when one monolayer has been adsorbed (Ref 4). Surface sensitivity has also been demonstrated in studies of the polar faces of noncentrosymmetric crystals, such as CdS, CdSe, and ZnS.

Mass Resolution. For a mass-sensitive technique, mass resolution determines whether neighboring elements (elements with similar masses) can be separated from each other. Equation 1 shows that E_S/E_0 is not a linear function of target mass and that differences in E_S/E_0 for adjacent masses become progressively smaller as the target mass increases. Thus, for a given energy analyzer (with a given $E_S/\Delta E_S$), separation of elements with large Z values and nearly equal masses becomes more difficult. Optimum mass resolution is obtained if the ion and target masses are nearly equal. This is demonstrated in Fig. 5, which shows spectra from a nickel-zinc alloy using helium and neon ions, respectively. The increase in resolution for the higher mass ion is evident. However, as the mass of the probe gas is increased, the ability to detect low-mass elements is lost (Eq 1). The poor mass resolution for high-mass elements (above 40 with helium, 60 with neon, and 80 with argon) is the major limitation of a low-energy scattering technique.

Quantitative Analysis

Elemental Sensitivity. Equation 3 demonstrated that scattered intensity is related to the scattering cross section and the

Fig. 6 Relative sensitivity as a function of atomic number for 2-keV helium and neon ions

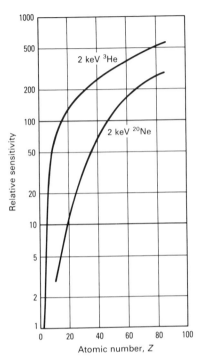

Fig. 7 Spectra showing the improved sensitivity for carbon when ³He is used instead of ⁴He

This improvement is attributed to an increase in ion velocity.

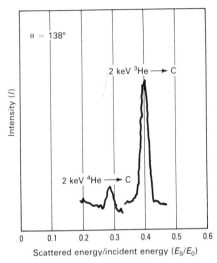

Fig. 8 Plot of the copper-gold ratio as determined using LEISS as a function of the bulk copper-gold ratio

Note the linearity of the plot.

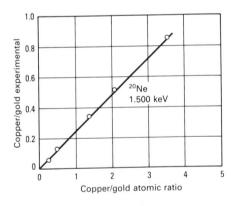

neutralization probability. Both of these factors favor the detection of high atomic number elements; that is, the cross section increases with Z, and the neutralization probability decreases with Z. Figure 6 shows elemental sensitivity curves for helium and neon ions at 2 keV. These curves indicate that for helium the elemental sensitivity varies by nearly three orders of magnitude across the periodic table. Absolute elemental sensitivity is a function of several other parameters, including scattering geometry and ion velocity. The increase in signal and thus elemental sensitivity obtained using a cylindrical mirror analyzer over the 127° sector analyzer exemplifies optimizing the scattering geometry. Figure 7 illustrates the dependence on ion velocity for ³He and ⁴He scattered from carbon. The increased signal strength for ³He for a given energy results from the higher velocity of the ³He ion; the ion spends less time near the surface, reducing the probability of neutralization. The absolute sensitivities vary by approximately 0.3×10^4 in going from lithium to gold (Ref 5).

Standards. The unknown magnitudes of scattering cross sections and neutralization probabilities necessitate calibrating the technique using standard samples and comparison with other techniques to obtain quantitative information. Linear dependence of the

scattered yield on the target atom density is desirable; the sulfur on nickel mentioned above is an example (for submonolayer coverage). Pure-element standards can be used as sensitivity standards for compounds when neon but not helium or argon is used as the probe gas (Ref 6). For binary alloys, linear relationships are found for helium and neon (Ref 7) (Fig. 8).

Calculated Correction Factors. In principle, a relative sensitivity factor may be calculated for a specific instrument using Eq 1. However, factors other than those included in the equation must be considered,

such as surface roughness. In addition, selective sputtering (alteration of the surface due to higher sputtering rates for a given element) can influence results.

The usual approach to quantitative measurements is to express Eq 1 for two elements and divide them to eliminate constant terms:

$$\frac{I_1}{I_2} = \frac{(NP\sigma\omega)_1}{(NP\sigma\omega)_2} \qquad (Eq\ 4)$$

The unknown terms for scattering cross sections, neutralization, and geometry are usually grouped into a sensitivity factor S, and Eq 4 becomes:

$$\frac{I_1}{I_2} = \frac{(NS)_1}{(NS)_2} \qquad (Eq\ 5)$$

The sensitivity factors are obtained from standards using pure elements. In this, N_i is replaced with A_i, where the A_i are atom sizes:

$$\frac{S_1}{S_2} = \left(\frac{I_{01}}{I_{02}}\right)\left(\frac{A_1}{A_2}\right) \qquad (Eq\ 6)$$

where I_{01} and I_{02} are the measured intensities from pure elements. However, changes in neutralization probability with the chemical state necessitate care when using this approach to quantify LEISS results.

Instrumentation

The experimental apparatus for LEISS varies with the type of experiment, but is simple for most activities. Figure 9 shows an ion-scattering spectrometer that consists primarily of an ion beam, a target, an energy analyzer, and the electronics necessary for energy analysis and signal detection. Because of the ion beam requirement and the necessity of maintaining a clean surface, the experiment must be conducted in an ultrahigh vacuum.

Ion Beam. In commercial instruments, electron bombardment in an ion source at a pressure of 10^{-5} to 10^{-4} torr produces the noble gas ions. Source pressure is achieved by backfilling the entire vacuum chamber or by admitting the gas into the ion source and pumping the ion source and/or chamber dynamically. The latter method is more desirable and minimizes the unwanted effects of outgassing from the vacuum system or sample.

The ions are extracted electrostatically from the source and focused onto the target. Beam diameters in commercial instruments

Fig. 9 Basic elements of a LEISS system

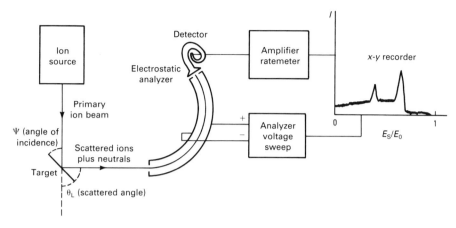

Fig. 10 Four types of electrostatic analyzers commonly used for LEISS

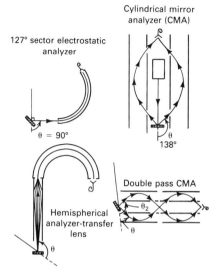

Fig. 11 LEISS spectrum from a stained connector

The connector surface consists primarily of sulfur, copper, and silver.

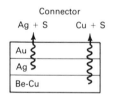

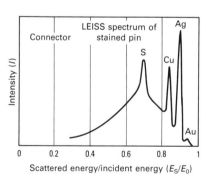

range from 150 μm to 2 mm. Total beam currents vary from a few nanoamperes to several microamperes. The maximum current density available from commercial ion guns is of the order of 600 μA/cm^2 (3.9 mA/in.^{2}).

Most ion guns incorporate deflection plates used to position the ion beam or raster it over an area on the sample. Rastering minimizes the surface damage caused by the beam and, when sputter depth profiling, enables electronic acceptance (gating) of only that portion of the signal arising from the center portion of the sputter area.

Energy Analyzer. Electrostatic analyzers are most frequently used to obtain the energy spectra of the scattered ions. As the voltage between the analyzer plates is changed, the energy of the scattered ions transmitted to the detector varies. Various analyzers and scattering geometries have been used in low-energy ion-scattering spectroscopes. Figure 10 shows the four configurations used in commercial instruments. The system in which the ion gun is mounted coaxially offers the best overall performance.

Spectral Display. The most prevalent method for recording data is to route the pulses from the detector in the analyzer through a preamplifier, amplifier, and into a count rate meter, whose output is then fed into an x-y recorder. This technique has several disadvantages, and automatic data collection using a multichannel analyzer or a computer is becoming the standard method of data collection. This method has many advantages, including background subtraction, peak fitting, spectral expansion, and smoothing.

Vacuum System. Due to the large mean free paths necessary for LEISS and the necessity of keeping the surface free of contamination during the measurements, base pressures of 10^{-9} torr or lower should

be achieved in the scattering chamber. Dry systems are most common, consisting of sorption pumps for roughing and sputter-ion pumping along with titanium sublimation and liquid nitrogen cryopumping to achieve ultrahigh vacuum. The titanium sublimation and liquid nitrogen trap are also used to remove active gases if the ion gun is operated in the backfill mode.

Applications

Identification of Surface Stains and Corrosion Products on a Connector. The formation of high contact resistance layers on electrical contact surfaces in electromechanical switches and connectors can cause failure of the component. The identification of the constituents of these layers and the mechanisms by which they are produced can lead to their elimination.

A connector experienced a gross blackening of the connector pins during accelerated aging at 70 °C (160 °F) for 6 months in its operating environment. It was thought that the change in color was due to compound formation and could lead to contact resistance problems. The LEISS spectrum shown in Fig. 11 indicates that gold, sulfur, copper, and silver were present on the surface. Cross sectioning and analysis of the pins indicated that the pin base material was beryllium-copper followed by silver and gold layers. Sputter depth profiling of the pin indicated considerable silver was present in the gold layer. This amount of silver was unexpected because bulk diffusion could be eliminated at the low temperature of the aging. Grain boundary diffusion could be ruled out because the ratio of the boundary width to grain size would have to be extremely high to account for the amount of silver found in the gold. Surface diffusion along holes or cracks in the gold plating was suspected. Scanning

electron microscopy (SEM) of the surface confirmed this assumption. The defects in the gold were large and numerous. These connectors have been improved by replacing the silver layer with a nickel layer and enhancing the quality of the gold plating.

Study of the Segregation of Lead to the Surface of a Tin-Lead Solder. Thermodynamic effects can result in the surface composition of an alloy differing significantly from its bulk composition. Tin-lead

Fig. 12 Low-energy ion-scattering spectra from a Sn-0.2Pb (at.%) sample

(a) Representative of the bulk. (b) The same surface after annealing 15 h in vacuum at 23 °C (73 °F)

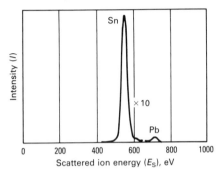

(a)

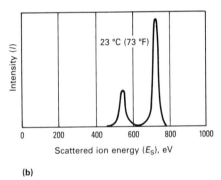

(b)

Fig. 13 Depth profiles of the oxidized surface of the tin-lead alloy

(a) Sample was oxidized at 10^{-5} torr of oxygen. (b) Sample was oxidized in air.

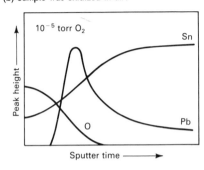

(a)

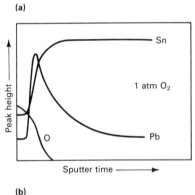

(b)

alloys are ideal for the study of this effect because their low melting point implies that the segregation should be significant at room temperature. Low-energy ion-scattering spectroscopy was used to determine the surface and near-surface composition of a single phase tin-lead alloy whose bulk composition was 99.83% Sn and 0.17 at.% Pb.

Measurements were conducted as a function of temperature in vacuum and in an oxidizing ambient. Pure tin and lead samples were used as standards, and the method outlined above was used to quantify the LEISS results. In vacuum, lead was found to segregate to the surface at all temperatures used in the study. The data indicated that the greatest surface enrichment of lead was obtained at 23 °C (73 °F); above this temperature, enrichment decreased. Figure 12 shows a plot of the LEISS spectra representative of the bulk alloy and the same alloy annealed 15 h at 23 °C (73 °F). From these data, the lead enrichment factor was found to be 325. The temperature dependence of the surface composition was used to calculate the heat of segregation, which was found to be 4.7 kcal/mole.

In an oxidizing environment, measurements were conducted as a function of time

and temperature and as a function of partial pressure of oxygen. The near-surface depth profile showed that the outermost layer consisted of tin oxide under which there was a layer with enhanced lead concentration followed by the bulk composition. The tin oxide region may or may not contain lead oxide, depending on the oxidation temperature and oxygen partial pressure. Figure 13(a) shows a profile for the case in which the partial pressure oxygen was 10^{-5} torr at room temperature. The surface consists of tin and oxygen but no lead. As this layer is removed, the lead concentration increases, reaches a maximum, then decreases to bulk value. The profile shown in Fig. 13(b) was obtained at atmospheric pressure and room temperature; the same effect is observed, except lead is present in the oxide layer near the surface.

The results obtained in vacuum agree qualitatively with theoretical predictions. This theory predicts, for an oxidizing environment, that the surface would consist of tin oxide. This conclusion agrees with that found experimentally for a low partial pressure of oxygen.

The difference in oxidation behavior between the low oxygen pressure and the high

oxygen pressure environments can be explained in terms of kinetics. At the higher pressures, the rate of oxidation is sufficiently fast that the available tin is rapidly consumed, and oxidation of lead follows. At sufficiently low partial pressures of oxygen, the rate of oxidation is slower than the rate of tin diffusion from the bulk to the surface; thus, a supply of tin is always sufficient for the oxidation reaction, and the lead remains in the metallic state.

Determination of the Extent of Coverage of a Nickel-Phosphorus Film on a Platinum Substrate. Metallic glasses are under investigation for their corrosion resistance properties. Of particular interest are nickel-phosphorus alloys with a composition of 80% Ni and 20% P. One method of depositing these materials is chemical vapor deposition (CVD). The corrosion properties of these films are being investigated and compared with those of bulk materials of similar composition. Ascertaining that the observed effects are due to the nickel-phosphorus film and not the substrate material (in this case platinum) necessitates determining if any platinum is exposed before and after the study. Low-energy ion-scattering spectroscopy, having a sample depth of 1 to 2 monolayers, is ideally suited to this determination. Figures 14(a) and (b) show the LEISS spectra from the as-deposited nickel-phosphorus film and after electrochemical exposure. Figure 14(a) indicates that the starting material had no exposed platinum and that the major constituents were nickel and phosphorus, with a small amount of oxygen and carbon. The results obtained after exposure indicate that a considerable amount of platinum is exposed and that the electrochemical results are dominated by the platinum substrate and are not representative of the film. These data have led to a redesign of the experiments such that the nickel-phosphorus film is not penetrated during the experiments.

Composition Versus Depth of a Passive Film on a Tin-Nickel Substrate. The surface passivity of an equiatomic tin-nickel alloy has been studied using AES (Ref 7). The air-formed surface layer was concluded to be tin rich. However, due to the escape depth of the Auger electrons used for the analysis, it was not possible to state clearly whether the layer is devoid of nickel. Therefore, the surface composition of equiatomic electrodeposited tin-nickel alloy has been determined using LEISS. A 2-keV helium ion beam was used to obtain the LEISS data and to sputter the near-surface region. The ion beam was rastered over a 4-mm² (0.006-in.²) area, with only the signal originating in the center 1 mm² (0.0015 in.²) accepted in the detector system. Rutherford backscattering spectroscopy (RBS)

Fig. 14 LEISS spectra from a nickel-phosphorus film on a platinum substrate

(a) From the as-deposited film. (b) From a treated film; the film has been penetrated, and the platinum substrate is exposed.

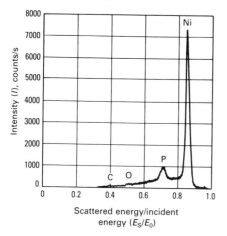

(a)

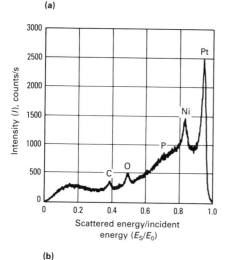

(b)

was used to determine the composition of the films at a depth of 100 nm (1000 Å). This composition was considered to represent that of the bulk.

These data indicated that the sample consisted of 55 at.% Ni and 45 at.% Sn. By

Fig. 15 Depth profile of a nickel-tin alloy showing that the surface does not contain nickel

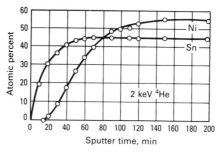

using these bulk composition values and the relative nickel-tin peak height obtained from the sputter profiles, sensitivity factors for nickel and tin were obtained. With the sensitivity factors, the depth profile data were converted to a concentration profile (Fig. 15). The initial rise in the tin signal is due to the removal of carbonaceous material and the tin oxide layer. The delay in the nickel signal indicates clearly that the nickel is absent in the surface region. By measuring the current density and estimating the sputtering yield, the depleted surface layer was found to be 0.5 to 1 nm (5 to 10 Å) thick. These results are consistent with the principle that a tin oxide will form on the surface because tin is more readily oxidized than nickel.

Study of the Oxidation of Copper Using ^{18}O. The oxidation of copper films in $^{16}O_2$ and $^{18}O_2$ has been studied (Ref 8). The $^{18}O/^{16}O$ ratio of oxides grown in varying concentrations of $^{16}O_2$ and $^{18}O_2$ was measured. Within experimental error, the sum of the peak heights of ^{18}O and ^{16}O were found to equal that for pure $Cu^{16}O_{0.67}$. Figure 16 shows an example of the spectra obtained from these types of measurements. The separation between the ^{16}O and ^{18}O is favorable.

This technique has been used to study the degradation in an $^{16}O_2$ environment of polypropylene films that had been coated onto $Cu^{18}O_{0.67}$ (Ref 8). The results agree with a model of reduction of the oxide by the

Fig. 16 LEISS spectrum of a copper surface oxidized in a ^{16}O-^{18}O mixture

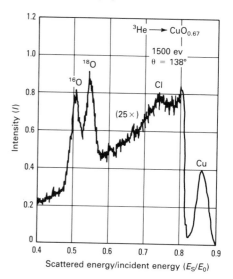

polymer and partial reoxidation of the copper by the $^{16}O_2$.

REFERENCES

1. D.P. Smith, *J. Appl. Phys.*, Vol 38, 1967, p 340
2. W.H. Strehlow and D.P. Smith, *Appl. Phys. Lett.*, Vol 13, 1968, p 34
3. T.M. Buck, Y.S. Chen, G.H. Wheatley, and W.F. van der Weg, *Surf. Sci.*, Vol 47, 1975, p 244
4. E. Taglauer and W. Heiland, *Appl. Phys. Lett.*, Vol 24, 1974, p 437
5. J.A. Leys, *Proceedings of the 1973 Pittsburgh Conference on Analytical Chemistry and Applied Spectroscopy*, Cleveland, March 1973
6. G.C. Nelson, *Surf. Sci.*, Vol 59, 1976, p 310
7. H.G. Tompkins and J.E. Bennett, *J. Electrochem. Soc.*, Vol 123, 1976, p 1003
8. A.W. Czanderna, A.C. Miller, H.H.G. Jellinek, and H. Kachi, *J. Vac. Sci. Technol.*, Vol 14, 1977, p 227

Secondary Ion Mass Spectroscopy

Carlo G. Pantano, Department of Materials Science and Engineering, The Pennsylvania State University

General Uses

- Surface compositional analysis with approximately 5- to 10-nm depth resolution
- Elemental in-depth concentration profiling
- Trace element analysis at the parts per billion to parts per million range
- Isotope abundances
- Hydrogen analysis
- Spatial distribution of elemental species

Examples of Applications

- Identification of inorganic or organic surface layers on metals, glasses, ceramics, thin films, or powders
- In-depth composition profiles of oxide surface layers, corrosion films, leached layers, and diffusion profiles
- In-depth concentration profiles of low-level dopants (≤1000 ppm) diffused or ion implanted in semiconductor materials
- Hydrogen concentration and in-depth profiles in embrittled metal alloys, vapor-deposited thin films, hydrated glasses, and minerals
- Quantitative analysis of trace elements in solids
- Isotopic abundances in geological and lunar samples
- Tracer studies (for example, diffusion and oxidation) using isotope-enriched source materials
- Phase distribution in geologic minerals, multiphase ceramics, and metals
- Second-phase distribution due to grain-boundary segregation, internal oxidation, or precipitation

Samples

- *Form*: Crystalline or noncrystalline solids, solids with modified surfaces, or substrates with deposited thin films or coatings; flat, smooth surfaces are desired; powders must be pressed into a soft metal foil (for example, indium) or compacted into a pellet
- *Size*: Variable, but typically 1 cm × 1 cm × 1 mm
- *Preparation*: None for surface or in-depth analysis; polishing for microstructural or trace element analysis

Limitations

- Analysis is destructive
- Qualitative and quantitative analyses are complicated by wide variation in detection sensitivity from element to element and from sample matrix to sample matrix
- The quality of the analysis (precision, accuracy, sensitivity, and so on) is a strong function of the instrument design and the operating parameters for each analysis

Estimated Analysis Time

- One to a few hours per sample

Capabilities of Related Techniques

- *Auger electron spectroscopy*: Qualitative and quantitative elemental surface and in-depth analysis is straightforward, but the detection sensitivity is limited to >1000 ppm; microchemical analysis with spatial resolution to <100 nm
- *Rutherford backscattering spectroscopy*: Nondestructive elemental in-depth profiling; quantitative determination of film thickness and stoichiometry
- *Electron microprobe analysis*: Quantitative elemental analysis and imaging with depth resolution ≥1 μm

Introduction

In secondary ion mass spectroscopy (SIMS), an energetic beam of focused ions is directed at the sample surface in a high or ultrahigh vacuum (UHV) environment. The transfer of momentum from the impinging primary ions to the sample surface causes sputtering of surface atoms and molecules. Some of the sputtered species are ejected with positive or negative charges; these are termed secondary ions. The secondary ions are then mass analyzed using a double-focusing mass spectrometer or an energy-filtered quadrupole mass spectrometer. The principles of SIMS are represented schematically in Fig. 1.

This method can be used to acquire a variety of information about the surface, near-surface, or bulk composition of the sample, depending on the instrumental parameters. If the rate of sputtering is relatively low, a complete mass spectrum can be recorded to provide a surface analysis of the outermost 5 nm of the sample. This is often termed static SIMS. Although a useful mode of operation, it is not yet a routine analytical technique. Alternatively, the intensity of one or more of the peaks in the mass spectrum can be continuously recorded at a higher sputtering rate to provide an in-depth concentration profile of the near-surface region. At very high sputtering rates, trace element or impurity analysis in the bulk is possible. Finally, a secondary ion image of the surface can be generated to provide a spatially resolved analysis of the surface, near surface, or bulk of the solid. This article will focus on the principles and applications of high sputter rate dynamic SIMS for depth profiling and bulk impurity analysis.

In general, secondary ion mass spectroscopy can provide characterization of solid samples with high spatial and in-depth resolution; due to the inherent sensitivity of mass spectroscopy, this is usually attained with high detection sensitivity as well. The extent to which these capabilities can be realized, especially in a quantitative fashion, depends on the nature of the specimen, the instrument design, and the particular instrumental parameters and methods used in the analysis. The interpretation of SIMS spectra and depth profiles can be difficult; thus, SIMS is not yet applicable for chemical analysis of unknowns in the true sense of the word. Rather, SIMS has unique capabilities for answering specific questions about specimens whose stoichiometry and matrix structure are already characterized.

Sputtering

The bombardment of a solid surface with a flux of energetic particles can cause the ejection of atomic species. This process is termed sputtering (Ref 1-3), and in a more macroscopic sense, it causes erosion or etching of the solid. The incident projectiles are often ions, because this facilitates production of an intense flux of energetic particles that can be focused into a directed beam; therefore, these techniques are referred to as ion sputtering and ion beam sputtering. However, in principle, sputtering (and secondary ion emission) will also occur under neutral beam bombardment. Secondary ion mass spectroscopy is typically based on ion beam sputtering of the sample surface, although new approaches to SIMS based on fast atom bombardment are being developed.

The interaction between the energetic primary ions and the solid surface is complex. At incident ion energies from 1 to 20 keV, the most important interaction is momentum transfer from the incident ion to the target atoms. This occurs because the primary ion penetrates the solid surface, travels some distance (termed the mean free path), then collides with a target atom. Figure 2 shows schematically that this collision displaces the target atom from its lattice site, where it collides with a neighboring atom that in turn collides with its neighbor. This succession of binary collisions, termed a collision cascade, continues until the energy transfer is insufficient to displace target atoms from their lattice positions.

The sputtering, or ejection, of target atoms and molecules occurs because much of the momentum transfer is redirected toward the surface by the recoil of the target atoms within the collision cascade. Because the lifetime of the collision cascade produced by a single primary ion is much smaller than the frequency of primary ion impingements (even at the highest primary ion beam current densities), this process can be viewed as an isolated, albeit dynamic, event. The ejection of target atoms due to a single binary collision between the primary ion and a surface atom occurs infrequently.

The primary ion undergoes a continuous energy loss due to momentum transfer, and to the electronic excitation of target atoms. Thus, the primary ion is eventually implanted tens to hundreds of angstroms below the surface. In general, then, the ion bombardment of a solid surface leads not only to sputtering, but also to electronic excitation, ion implantation, and lattice damage. Figure 3 summarizes the effects of ion bombardment and indicates that the sputtered species may be monatomic species or molecular clusters. The effects of ion implantation and electronic excitation on the charge of the sputtered species are discussed in the section "Secondary Ion Emission" in this article.

The sputtering yield, S, is the average number of atoms sputtered per incident pri-

Fig. 1 Schematic representation of the principles of SIMS

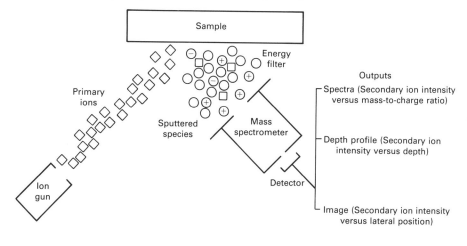

Fig. 2 The physical effects of primary ion bombardment: implantation and sputtering

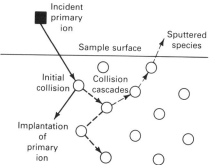

Fig. 3 Schematic diagram of the sputtered species ejected during primary ion bombardment of a compound $i_x j_y$

These sputtered species may be monatomic, molecular, and/or incorporate implanted primary ions. $i = \circ$, $j = \bullet$

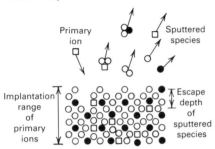

mary ion. This number depends on the target material and on the nature, energy, and angle of incidence of the primary ion beam. The sputtering yield is directly proportional to the stopping power of the target (because this determines the extent of momentum transfer near the surface), and it is inversely proportional to the binding energy of the surface atoms. Therefore, the sputtering yield also exhibits a dependence upon the crystallographic orientation of the material being sputtered. The sputter yield is usually assumed to be proportional to the square root of the incident ion energy, but there is not universal agreement with experiments in the energy range from 1 to 20 keV. In most SIMS experiments, Cs^+, O_2^+, O^-, and Ar^+ primary ion species are used in the energy range from 2 to 20 keV at angles of incidence between $45°$ and $90°$. Under these conditions, the sputtering yields for most materials range from 1 to 20. Information on the effects of the primary ion beam and the target material on sputtering yields is provided in Ref 4.

Selective sputtering, or preferential sputtering, can occur in multicomponent, multiphase, or polycrystalline materials. Thus, it is possible for the composition of alloy surfaces to become modified during sputtering where the species with the lowest sputtering yield become enriched in the outermost monolayer, while the species with the highest yield are depleted. In the case of multiphase materials, those phases with the higher yield will be preferentially etched; this alters the phase composition at the surface, and introduces microtopography and roughness. For polycrystalline materials, the variation in sputter yield with crystallographic orientation can also lead to the generation of surface roughness during sputtering. All of these effects can influence the quality and interpretation of a SIMS analysis.

Secondary Ion Emission

The species ejected from a surface during sputtering may be monatomic, polyatomic, or multicomponent, and each of these may be positively charged $(+)$, negatively charged $(-)$, multiply charged $(+p, -p)$, or neutral (0). Thus, the sputtering yield S for a compound of composition $i_x j_y$ can be expanded to:

$$
\begin{aligned}
S = \{&(i^+) + (j^+) + (i^-) + (j^-) + (i_2^+) \\
&+ (j_2^+) + (i_2^-) + (j_2^-) + (i^{2+}) \\
&+ (j^{2+}) \dots (i_n^{\pm P}) + (j_n^{\pm P}) \\
&+ (i_2 j^+) + (i_2 j^-) \dots + (i_n j_m^{\pm P}) \\
&+ (i^0) + (j^0) + (ij^0) \dots \\
&+ (i_n^0)\,(j_n^0)\,(i_n j_m^0)\} \div I_p
\end{aligned}
$$

(Eq 1)

where ( ) represent the fluxes of secondary ions and neutrals, and I_p represents the primary ion (or neutral) beam flux.

Whereas the sputter yield, S, defines the total number of species ejected per incident ion, the secondary ion yield, $S_{i_n}^{\pm P}$ defines the number of positive ions i^+, i^{+2}, i_2^+, i_n^{+P}, or negative ions, i^-, i^{-2}, i_2^-, i_n^{-P}, and in the case of multicomponent systems, molecular ions $i_n j_m^{+P}$ ejected per incident primary ion. It is related to the sputter yield, S, through a factor termed the ionization probability $\gamma_{i_n}^{+P}$; for example, in the case of material $i_x j_y$, one can define the secondary ion yield for i^+ as:

$$S_i^+ = \gamma_i^+ S(i_x j_y)$$

(Eq 2)

where γ_i^+ is the number of i^+ ions ejected divided by the total number of species ejected that contain i, and $S(i_x j_y)$ is the sputter yield for material $i_x j_y$.

The secondary ion yield is an important parameter because it determines the relative intensities of the various SIMS signals. The secondary ion yield depends on the same factors as the sputter yield, but it also depends on the ionization probability. Although a complete and unbiased theory of secondary ion emission, particularly the ionization probability, has not yet been reported, most models emphasize the importance of chemical and electronic effects (see the Selected References in this article). Accordingly, the presence of reactive species at the surface is believed to modify the work function, the electronic structure, and the chemical bonding, and all of these can influence the probability that a sputtered species will be ejected in a neutral or charged state.

The details of these various models are not important to this discussion. Rather, it is necessary to recognize that the secondary ion emission phenomenon is sensitive to the presence of electropositive or electronegative species at the sample surface. Thus, the sputtering of surfaces in the presence of oxygen enhances the production of many positive metal ions, because the electronegative oxygen increases the probability that the sputtered atom or molecule can release an electron. The oxygen may be a constituent of the sample (for example, a metal oxide), it may adsorb onto a metallic or semiconductor surface during the sputtering (for example, from an oxygen gas jet or a high residual oxygen pressure in the vacuum environment), or it may be implanted in the surface during the sputtering (for example, by using an oxygen primary ion beam). In all these cases, the production of positive ions is enhanced relative to that observed in the absence of the oxygen (or any other electronegative species); Table 1 shows the effect of oxygen on the absolute secondary ion yields of various metals. Similarly, the sputtering of surfaces in the presence of electropositive species (e.g., the use of Cs^+ primary ion beams) leads to an enhanced production of negative secondary ions.

There is an alternative to this chemical secondary ion emission mechanism. That is, in the case of very clean surfaces under inert ion bombardment in a UHV environment, intrinsic secondary ion emission may be observed. Under these conditions, the production of secondary ions is greatly reduced (Table 1, clean surfaces). However, this situation is seldom achieved in typical SIMS analyses because of the presence of reactive

Table 1 The effect of oxygen on positive secondary ion yields in metals

Element, M	Sputtering yield S_{M^+} (clean surface)	Sputtering yield S_{M^+} (oxygen-covered surface)
Magnesium	0.01	0.9
Aluminum	0.007	0.7
Titanium	0.0013	0.4
Vanadium	0.001	0.3
Chromium	0.0012	1.2
Manganese	0.0006	0.3
Iron	0.0015	0.35
Nickel	0.0006	0.045
Copper	0.0003	0.007
Strontium	0.0002	0.16
Niobium	0.0006	0.05
Molybdenum	0.00065	0.4
Barium	0.0002	0.03
Tantalum	0.00007	0.02
Tungsten	0.00009	0.035
Silicon	0.0084	0.58
Germanium	0.0044	0.02

Source: Ref 5

species in the specimen or vacuum environment, nor is it desirable, due to the need to enhance secondary ion production for detection sensitivity. Thus, intrinsic ion emission is of little concern here, because it contributes very little to the overall emission mechanism in conventional SIMS.

The secondary ion yield, which determines the measured SIMS signal, is a very sensitive function of the chemical and electronic properties of the surface under bombardment. Thus, it exhibits a dependence upon the element, its matrix, and the bombarding species being implanted in the surface during the analysis; moreover, it is influenced by residual gas pressure and composition during the analysis because adsorbates can modify the chemical and electronic state of the surface monolayer.

The matrix dependence of the secondary ion yield is the characteristic of secondary ion emission that has received perhaps the most attention. In the case of inert primary beam bombardment, for example, Ar^+ on aluminum versus aluminum oxide, the positive metal ion yield is recognized to be three to four orders of magnitude higher in metal oxides than in their pure metal counterparts. This ion yield dependence is due to the ionization probability, γ_{Al}^+, which is approximately 100 times greater for Al_2O_3 than for aluminum metal, not to the sputtering yield, which is approximately two times greater for the metal than for the metal oxide.

Similarly, Ar^+ bombardment of a pure aluminum metal sample is known to produce a larger Al^+ signal in a dirty vacuum or in the presence of an intentional oxygen leak than in a nonreactive UHV environment. Therefore, most modern approaches to SIMS analysis—at least when quantitative elemental analysis is of interest—use reactive primary ion beams rather than inert ion beams; an oxygen beam (O_2^+ or O^-) or a cesium (Cs^+) beam is typically used. Thus, the surface is always saturated with a reactive species (due to the primary ion implantation) that enhances the ion yield and makes the elemental analysis less sensitive to matrix effects and/or to the residual vacuum environment during analysis.

Crystallographic orientation further compounds the matrix dependence of the secondary ion yield. This is due primarily to the difference in electronic properties (for example, work function or band structure) from one crystal face to another and to the difference in adsorptivity or implantation range from one face to another (and much less so due to variation in sputtering yield). In the case of polycrystalline and/or multiphase materials, the emission intensity can vary considerably from one grain to another. This can be an important source of contrast in

secondary ion emission imaging of polycrystalline materials.

Regarding the energy and angular distribution of the ejected species, the secondary ions are ejected with a wide distribution of energies. The distribution is usually peaked in the range from 1 to 10 eV, but depending on the identity, mass, and charge of the particular secondary ion, the form of the distribution will vary. In general, the monatomic species (for example, i^+ or j^+) have the widest distribution, often extending to 300 eV under typical conditions; the molecular species (such as i_2^+ or i_2j^+) cut off at lower energies. The energy distribution of the ejected secondary ions is relevant to the design of the SIMS instrument (because it must be energy filtered before mass analysis) and to the mode of operation (because i^+ can often be resolved, for example, from i_2^+ or j_2^+ on the basis of energy).

Instrumentation

There is a wide variety of instrument designs for SIMS, and the quality and applicability of the analysis depends strongly on the details of the instrumentation. Secondary ion mass spectroscopy instruments can be categorized into three broad classifications in which the distinctions refer to versatility, mass resolution, primary beam characteristics, and, in particular, imaging capability.

The simplest SIMS instrument, sometimes called an add-on, macro-, or broad-beam instrument, is intended primarily for surface analysis and qualitative depth profiling and less so for quantitative elemental analysis, microanalysis, or imaging. This is seldom a dedicated unit, but rather a set of components often used in conjunction with an Auger or x-ray photoelectron spectrometer. Figure 1 shows a simple SIMS system. The instrument uses a standard electron-impact inert ion gun that is often the same sputter gun used for sample cleaning or Auger sputter-profiling. The mass spectrometer is usually a quadrupole type, but to select a portion of the wide energy distribution of sputtered secondary ions, it requires an energy prefilter. Other than the addition of the energy prefilter, the quadrupole mass spectrometer and the ion detector are very standard.

A dedicated SIMS instrument often incorporates a more intense, finely focused primary ion beam suitable for probe imaging. Because it is unnecessary to provide the flexibility for performing analyses by Auger electron spectroscopy (AES) or x-ray photoelectron spectroscopy (XPS) in this type of instrument, the sample orientation and the ion collection system can also be optimized.

These instruments, often called ion microprobes, are designed primarily for quantitative in-depth profiling and microanalysis and less so for surface analysis. Figure 4 shows a typical ion microprobe that uses a duoplasmatron ion source to generate inert, as well as reactive, primary ion beams. The instrument shown in Fig. 4 and most commercially available units use an energy-filtered quadrupole mass spectrometer, but in principle, a magnetic analyzer could also be used.

A direct-imaging SIMS instrument, usually called an ion microscope, creates a secondary beam with the ejected secondary ions. The secondary beam is mass analyzed in a double-focusing electrostatic/magnetic sector; the transmitted secondary ions can then be counted or used to create a direct image of the sample surface on a microchannel plate. Figure 5 shows a schematic diagram of a direct-imaging ion microscope in which the primary ion beam and secondary ion beam are clearly distinguished. This instrument is designed primarily for microstructural analysis and imaging, quantitative in-depth profiling, and trace element analysis. It is not suitable for true surface analysis, and due to the precise ion collection optics, the ability to treat or manipulate the specimen in situ is essentially lost.

System Components. The design and operation of the various instrumental components will not be discussed in detail, because many excellent treatments are available (Ref 6-8). However, there are several components and features of the instruments whose specific design and/or availability can influence the quality of the analysis. These are summarized below.

The quality of the vacuum environment during SIMS analysis is important for two reasons. First, any variations in the vacuum pressure can influence the secondary ion intensity due to the effects of reactive species on ionization probability and, to a lesser extent, on sputtering rate. Thus, day-to-day reproducibility and the quality of the depth profile, which must be acquired under constant vacuum pressure, will be affected. Second, the pressure and composition of the vacuum environment will influence the background levels and therefore the detection limits for some species. This is usually due to their adsorption onto the surface and their subsequent ejection as secondary ions. The background species of most concern are hydrogen, oxygen, and water, because these are readily adsorbed and quite prevalent in most vacuum systems. Ideally, pressure of the order of 10^{-9} to 10^{-10} torr should be maintained at the specimen surface, especially for hydrogen (Ref 9), oxygen, or carbon analysis.

Fig. 4 Schematic diagram of the layout and components used in an ion microprobe

Courtesy of ISA Inc., Riber Division

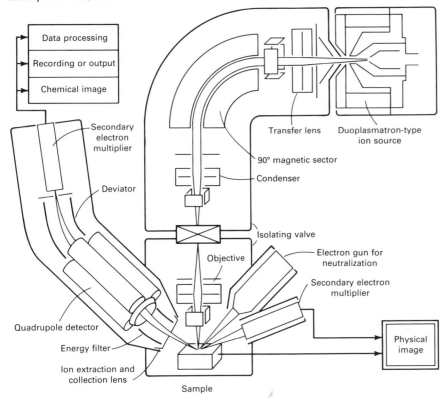

Fig. 5 Schematic diagram of the layout and components used in an ion microscope

Courtesy of Surface Science Western

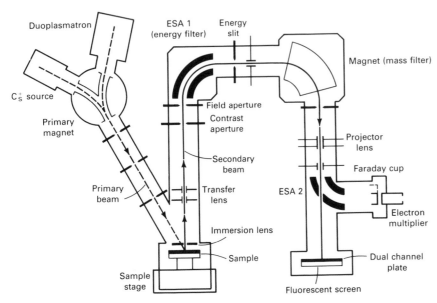

In the case of the primary ion beam, several features are of interest. First, the ability to generate reactive primary ions, for example, O_2^+ O^-, and Cs^+, requires a duoplasmatron or liquid metal source; the more conventional electron-impact ion guns typically used in surface analysis are limited to inert species (He^+, Ne^+, or Ar^+). The negative oxygen species can be of great benefit for the analysis of insulators. Second, the beam diameter and maximum current density characteristics will vary with the type and design of the gun. Simple ion guns usually provide beam diameters (spot sizes) of the order of 25 to 250 μm; dedicated ion microprobes and ion microscopes can produce spot sizes as small as 1 to 2 μm. Third, the background levels that can influence detection limits are controlled to some degree by the ion source. This refers not only to residual gases, but also to metallic species that can become incorporated in the beam, implanted in the sample, and then ultimately appear in the analysis of the sample.

The ability to pump the ion source differentially (relative to the sample chamber) can greatly alleviate the background due to residual gases and other contaminants produced in the ion source. However, the metallic and other impurities that become ionized and thus incorporated in the primary ion beam are most effectively eliminated using a primary beam mass filter, essentially a mass spectrometer that filters the primary ions before they strike the specimens. A primary beam mass filter will also reject any neutral species in the beam. The use of a primary beam mass filter is almost a necessity for trace element and low-level dopant analyses. Finally, rastering of the primary ion beam over the specimen surface is a requirement in SIMS depth profiling and secondary ion imaging; thus, incorporation of raster plates is now fairly standard in most ion guns and SIMS systems.

The secondary ion collection optics represent the feature that is perhaps most variable among commercial and laboratory-built SIMS systems. Ideally, the secondary ions are extracted electrostatically from the center of the crater (over the maximum solid angle), instead of simply collecting that portion of the ejected flux of secondary ions that intersects the entrance aperture of the analyzer. Many dedicated SIMS instruments include an extraction lens over the sample, but this limits the sample geometry that the instrument can tolerate and the capability for a multitechnique apparatus. The extracted secondary ions are then energy analyzed to select the optimum portion of the energy distribution for subsequent mass filtering; if this is not done, mass resolution is severely degraded. This is an absolute necessity for quadrupole spectrometers and single-focusing magnetic sectors, whereas an electrostatic energy filter is an inherent component of higher resolution double-focusing magnetic mass spectrometers. Various electrostatic energy filters are available for use with quadrupoles, including grids, apertures, Bessel boxes, and spherical or hemispherical plates (Ref 10); the collection efficiency, selectivity, resolution, and transmission of these filters vary and will influence the overall sensitivity of the SIMS instrument.

The instrumental features required for secondary ion imaging are presented in the section "Ion Imaging" in this article, while the differences between quadrupole and high-resolution magnetic mass filters are described in the next section of this article. Data acquisition for spectral and depth-profiling analyses simply requires an ion detector and an automated control for scanning the mass spectrum or, in the case of depth profiling, for sequential acquisition of selected peak intensities in the spectrum. The ion detector should be electronically gated in all instruments except the ion microscope, in which apertures can be used to eliminate crater-edge effects. The instrumental features for computerized data acquisition, data manipulation, and output vary considerably, depending on the versatility of the mass spectrometer.

Secondary Ion Mass Spectra

Figure 6 shows the positive SIMS spectrum for a very high purity silicon sample (Ref 11). This bar graph was obtained in an ion microscope using an O_2^+ primary ion beam and a double-focusing mass spectrom-

eter. The spectrum shows the presence of silicon isotopes $^{28}Si^+$, $^{29}Si^+$, and $^{30}Si^+$ and thus demonstrates the isotopic sensitivity of SIMS. Also shown are the polyatomic species Si_2^+ and Si_3^+ and the molecular species SiO^+, SiO_2^+, Si_2O^+, $Si_2O_2^+$, Si_3O^+, $Si_3O_2^+$, $Si_3O_3^+$ and so on. In this case, the oxide species are not representative of the silicon sample, but are due to the use of the oxygen primary beam. The oxygen ions are implanted in the surface, and these charged molecular secondary ion clusters are subsequently sputter-ejected. In addition, of course, the $^{16}O^+$ and $^{32}O_2^+$ secondary ions are also generated.

The use of an oxygen primary ion beam has enhanced the positive secondary ion yields; therefore, the measured secondary ion signals are quite strong. If this specimen had been analyzed using an inert primary ion beam (for example, argon), the positive secondary ion signal intensities would be 100 to 1000 times less intense, and the presence of the aluminum impurity ($^{27}Al^+$) probably would not have been detected. In some instances, it may be considered a disadvantage to use an oxygen primary beam for enhancing the secondary ion yields, because it precludes an oxygen analysis in the specimen. However, it is common to use an ^{18}O primary ion beam when ^{16}O analyses are of interest or to use a Cs^+ beam (if available), because it enhances the secondary ion yield for electronegative species such as oxygen.

The other peaks in the spectrum shown in Fig. 6 that have not been identified are due primarily to the molecular species that form between the silicon sample and implanted primary ions as well as between the Si_n, O_n, Si_nO_m species and ^1H, ^{12}C, and ^{14}N in the

residual vacuum. The SIMS spectrum is clearly very complex due to this multitude of molecular secondary ion matrix species. Although it may not be evident in this bar graph (Fig. 6), the presence of the molecular species further complicates the analysis due to mass interferences. For example, Si_2^+ ($m/e = 55.9539$) will interfere with Fe^+ ($m/e = 55.9349$) unless the spectrometer is optimized for and capable of high resolution (m/e is the mass-to-charge ratio).

The interference problem and spectral complexity become even more evident in multicomponent specimens. Figure 7 shows portions of the SIMS spectra for a stainless steel. The molecular secondary ions from the matrix species (Fig. 7a) represent a background that precludes identification of minor or trace elements in this material. Figure 7(b) shows that much of this background can be eliminated by energy-filtering the secondary ions; here, only the higher energy secondary ions, dominated by the monatomic species, are permitted to enter the mass analyzer.

The advantages of a selective energy filter and a high mass resolution spectrometer are further demonstrated in Fig. 8. This CuTi specimen produced a doublet at mass number 63 that could be resolved to show the presence of both Cu^+ ($m/e = 62.9296$) and TiO^+ ($m/e = 62.9467$) secondary ions. The spectra shown in Fig. 8 demonstrate the detection sensitivity and resolution that can be achieved in a double-focusing magnetic spectrometer by energy filtering and high-resolution mass filtering; this is 10 to 100 times the resolution obtainable with a quadrupole spectrometer.

The spectra shown in Fig. 6 to 8 really represent the bulk composition of these samples. This is due in part to the nature of the specimens, which were not subjected to any surface treatment, but it is also a result of the analysis mode. The use of an oxygen (or any reactive) primary ion beam requires the attainment of a steady state in the surface and the detected signal. During this transient time period, the reactive primary ions are implanted in the surface up to a steady-state concentration determined by the primary beam energy and flux, the target material, and the total sputtering rate. The ion yields are changing during this period; therefore, the SIMS spectra generated during the first few minutes of sputtering (in the outermost 10 to 20 nm) are of little analytical value. Moreover, the ability to detect very low concentration levels requires the use of high sputtering rates when data acquisition in the surface would be difficult even in the absence of the transient effect. Clearly, then, the data in Fig. 6 to 8 represent trace element analyses in the near surface or bulk, not true surface analyses.

Fig. 6 Positive SIMS spectra (in the form of a bar graph) for high-purity silicon under oxygen bombardment in an ion microscope

Source: Ref 10

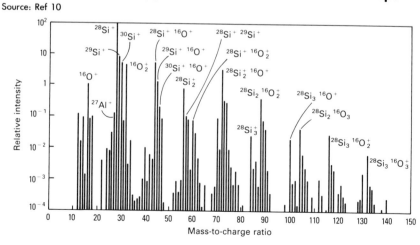

Fig. 7 Positive SIMS spectra for an NBS reference steel under oxygen bombardment in an ion microscope

(a) Recorded without a voltage offset. (b) Recorded with a voltage offset to reject low-energy molecular secondary ions

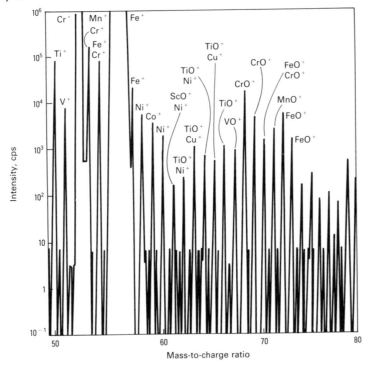

(a)

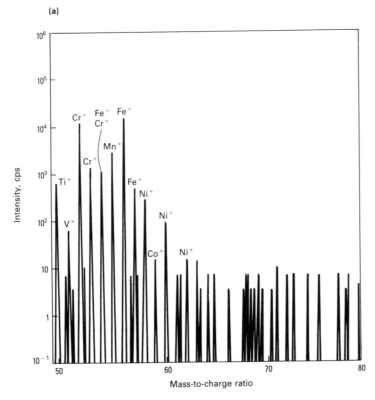

(b)

Fig. 8 High-resolution mass scan over the region of *m/e* = 63 for a CuTi specimen

Obtained using an ion microscope

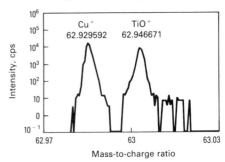

Figure 9 presents the positive SIMS spectrum for a silicon substrate upon which an organometallic silicate film (~100 nm thick) has been deposited. In contrast to the spectra shown in Fig. 6 to 8, this spectrum was obtained in an ion microprobe using an argon primary ion beam and an energy-filtered quadrupole mass spectrometer. Due to the oxide nature of the film, the ion yields are more than sufficient to produce measurable intensities, even though an inert argon primary ion beam is used. Because the spectrum is presented on a linear scale, much of the background due to the molecular secondary ions has been eliminated.

The spectrum indicates the presence of hydrogen and hydroxylated molecular oxide species, but the quadrupole analyzer has insufficient resolution to separate the interferences. Although some of these molecular species may be due to hydrogen background in the vacuum system, they are primarily indicative of the hydrated nature of the film. There also appear to be boron, carbon, sodium, and potassium impurities in the film. These impurities were undetected in a corresponding Auger analysis; thus, the high sensitivity of SIMS is further exemplified. This spectrum demonstrates the use of SIMS for a thin film analysis, in this case using an inert primary ion beam. In the next section in this article, a depth profile will be presented for this film that demonstrates the effects of the matrix change (at the oxide film/semiconductor substrate interface). The in-depth analysis of oxide and other nonmetallic films and coatings on metallic or semiconducting substrates is a common objective of SIMS analyses in metallurgy and materials science.

Due to the high detection sensitivity in SIMS, almost any constituent can be found in the SIMS spectrum. The analyst must determine (1) whether or not these constituents are inherent to the sample or to the instrument background and (2) what concen-

Fig. 9 Positive SIMS spectra for an organometallic silicate film deposited on a silicon substrate

Obtained using a scanning ion microprobe under inert argon bombardment

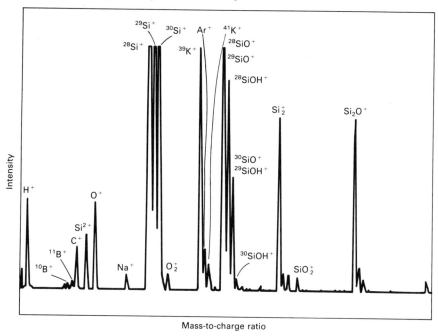

Fig. 10 Depth profiles for the organometallic silicate film shown in Fig. 9

Note the matrix effects at the film/silicon substrate interface due to the use of an inert argon ion beam. Obtained using raster gating in a scanning ion microprobe

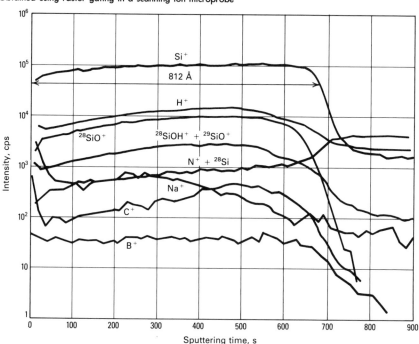

tration levels the peak intensity represents. Thus, even qualitative analysis with SIMS is a nontrivial matter, because the presence of certain species in the spectra may be independent of the sample and/or may be at levels that are negligible relative to the problem.

Depth Profiles

As noted above, with the exception of static SIMS, most analytical applications of SIMS do not emphasize true surface compositional analysis. Rather, in-depth profiling (from 20 to 2000 nm), bulk impurity analysis, and imaging of microstructural features are more common applications of SIMS. Of these, quantitative depth profiling with high detection sensitivity and depth resolution is unquestionably the forte of SIMS. In a depth-profiling analysis, one or more of the secondary ion signals are monitored as a function of sputtering time (or depth) into the surface or bulk of the specimen or through an adherent thin film or coating.

The profiles shown in Fig. 10 illustrate several important points about matrix effects and the use of reactive primary ion beams in thin film profiling. These profiles were obtained for the film whose spectrum is shown in Fig. 9. The interface between the silicate film and silicon substrate is evident. This is due to the change in secondary ion yield between the oxide thin film and the silicon substrate. Although the substrate is pure silicon, the $^{28}Si^+$ signal falls by nearly two orders of magnitude between the film and substrate. In contrast, although the effects are fundamentally related, the $^{28}Si^{2+}$ signal increases by a factor of ten upon sputtering through to the substrate. These are matrix effects upon the secondary ion yields (or, more specifically, the ionization probability), not indications of any concentration or chemical structure change at the interface. If an oxygen primary ion were used in this analysis, the changes in secondary ion signal for $^{28}Si^+$ and $^{28}S^{2+}$ would not occur (at least under ideal conditions), although a transient would be observed in the signals at the interface (during which time the oxygen primary ion implantation would reach a steady state). Clearly, the use of an inert primary beam enhanced location of the film/substrate interface.

There are advantages to be gained in using an oxygen primary ion beam for a depth-profiling analysis of this type. They have little to do with the silicon species as such, but rather concern the interpretation of the other signals. For example, the $^1H^+$, $^{12}C^+$, $^{23}Na^+$, and $^{11}B^+$ signals also drop at the interface. However, the extent to which the signal drop is due to the matrix effect versus any real change in concentration is unknown. Due to the large variation in ionization between the oxide film and semiconducting substrate, the concentrations of hydrogen, carbon, sodium, and boron could increase, even though their signals decrease. The use of a reactive primary ion beam would be of great benefit in this situation. The oxygen implantation would in this case provide a constant matrix from which the secondary emission could occur throughout the depth-profiling analysis. Therefore, any changes in these signals would be due to real concentration gradients. Thus, it would be possible to follow the B^+, Na^+, or H^+ across the interface to follow, for example, diffusion effects.

In addition to the minimization of matrix effects, the use of a reactive oxygen primary ion beam would also enhance the sensitivity (or detectability) for positive ions in the silicon substrate. This effect is perhaps best exemplified in Fig. 11, which shows a depth profile for boron in silicon (the quantitative analysis of which will be discussed in the next section of this article). The boron is a dopant that was intentionally put into the surface of this sample by ion implantation. The profile was obtained using an oxygen primary ion beam. These levels of boron could not be detected under argon bombardment (nor with AES or XPS); the yield enhancement due to the use of a reactive primary ion beam is critical to this analysis. In addition, the $^{30}S^{2+}$ matrix signal did not

vary over the profile; that is, the observed variation in the boron signal is due to a real change in concentration.

The factors that determine or influence the depth and interface resolution of the measured profiles must now be considered. This complex subject has received considerable attention because it is depth profiling with high resolution for which SIMS is most applicable and unique. Discussions of SIMS depth profiling more detailed than that presented below are provided in the Selected References.

A depth-profiling analysis aims to define the concentration or concentration gradient of selected elements at finite depths below the original surface. Thus, the detected secondary ion signal must originate from well-defined planes below and parallel to the original surface. Ideally, these planes would be of atomic dimensions (in which case the in-depth resolution would be atomic or monomolecular), but Fig. 3 illustrates that the ejected secondary ions originate from a layer with a finite thickness termed the escape depth.

The escape depth varies to some extent with the energy and mass of the primary ions as well as with the material, but it is typically 3 to 5 atomic layers. In practice, though, this theoretical limit on depth resolution is not achieved. At the very least, each composition or concentration data point defined in the depth profile requires the erosion of sufficient material to collect a measurable and statistically significant secondary ion signal; this effective layer thickness depends

on the sputtering rate and the secondary ion yield.

Perhaps of greater concern are a number of other phenomena, including crater-edge effects, halo effects, knock-on, atomic mixing, diffusion, preferential sputtering, and roughening, which are essentially artifacts that distort the true profile. Some of these effects are instrumental and can be alleviated to some extent through the design of the apparatus, but others are intrinsic to the sputtering process. Altogether, these effects can limit the depth resolution in a typical SIMS depth-profiling analysis from the theoretical limit of approximately 1 nm to as much as 5 to 10 nm. Thus, special attention should be paid to the effects described below when the highest possible depth resolution is required.

Figure 12 shows a schematic cross section through a sample that has a distinct surface layer. For the purposes of this discussion, it will be assumed that the layer is approximately 1 μm thick and that the interface between the layer and substrate is atomically sharp (the latter is unlikely in practice, but the assumption allows defining the extent to which the SIMS measurement itself broadens the true interface). Again, this schematic sample design represents a common situation that can arise in practice by oxidation, nitridation, or other surface treatment of a metal or semiconductor, or by deposition of thin films and coatings by one of a multitude of techniques. Although a SIMS analysis could be used to determine the composition or compositional uniformity of the layer, it would more likely be applied to answer the following questions:

- What impurities are present in the layer, and what are their concentration and depth distribution?
- What are the thickness of the film and the width of the interface?
- What is the diffusion profile for selected surface or interfacial reactants?
- Has segregation or compound formation occurred at the interface?

The effects to be described below can influence any depth-profiling analysis, regardless of the presence or absence of a distinct surface layer, but consideration of a surface film of finite thickness with a subsurface interface best illustrates the points.

A situation that can be most detrimental to depth resolution is shown in Fig. 12(b). This crater-edge effect is the result of nonuniform erosion of the specimen caused by nonuniform distribution of ions in the primary beam. The detection system will simultaneously filter and count secondary ions

Fig. 11(a) Raw $^{11}B^+$ and $^{30}Si^{2+}$ secondary ion signals versus sputtering time for a boron-implanted silicon substrate

Obtained using oxygen beam bombardment in an ion microscope

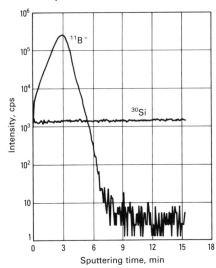

Fig. 11(b) Boron profile (see Fig. 11a) after quantitative analysis of the sputtering rate and secondary ion intensity

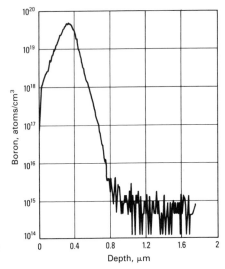

Fig. 12 Schematic representations of the artifacts that can distort a SIMS depth-profiling analysis

See text for details.

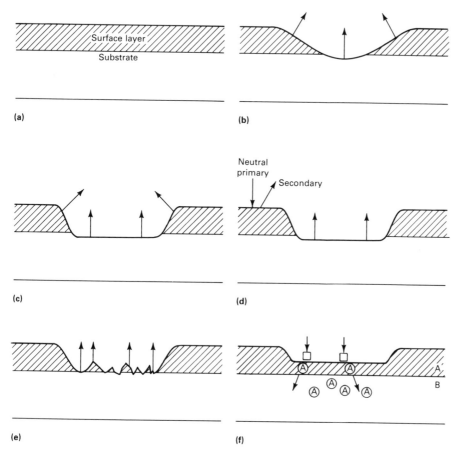

(a)

(b)

(c)

(d)

(e)

(f)

over a range of depths in the sample, and the depth resolution will be severely degraded. The practical consequence of this in the measured depth profile is a gross broadening of interfaces, diffusion profiles, or surface layer thicknesses. The most common remedy is to produce a flat-bottomed crater (Fig. 12c) by rastering a focused ion beam in a square pattern over the specimen. In this case, most of the secondary ions originate from a well-defined depth, but there are still contributions from the side walls.

There are several approaches to eliminating side-wall contributions, which may seem negligible but which nonetheless can limit depth resolution. In simple SIMS systems and ion microprobes, electronic raster gating is used. In this method, the scanning primary ion beam and the detector are synchronized so that whenever the ion beam is near the periphery of the crater, the collected secondary ions are not counted. Under optimal conditions, secondary ions would be detected only from the central 10 to 20% of the crater; obviously, the electronic rejection of

80 to 90% of the secondary ions reduces the signal and thus the detection limits. However, this is an absolute requirement for the acquisition of meaningful depth profiles. In the ion microscope, the direct-imaging optics preclude the need for electronic gating, because the extraction lens and field aperture combine to gate off the side-wall contributions mechanically.

The mechanical aperture used in the ion microscope has an additional advantage over electronic raster gating because it can reject secondary ions produced by neutral primary species bombarding the specimen. That is, the primary ion beam will contain a neutral component of energetic species (unless the primary beam is electrostatically deflected before striking the specimen) that does not respond to the raster plates. Thus, as shown in Fig. 12(d), there can be secondary ion ejection and detection from the original surface (and side walls) regardless of the position of the primary ion beam. The analysis will show species that may be present only near the original surface even when the

erosion has proceeded to great depths; in this situation, species present only at the original surface or in the overlayer can be mistakenly believed to have migrated or diffused deep into the specimen. A useful remedy for this (when direct-imaging ion microscopy is not available or is ineffective) is to coat the specimen with a thin film of gold or other material that is not expected to be found in the specimen during analysis.

Figure 12(e) describes another effect that must be recognized in the interpretation of depth profiles. The ion beam erosion of even atomically smooth, single-crystal materials can generate roughness, but in polycrystalline or multiphase materials, this roughening can be especially severe due to differential sputtering rates (from grain to grain or phase to phase). This too will broaden the appearance of interface or diffusion profiles. The scale of the roughness increases with sputtering time and is usually assumed to be approximately 10% of the etch depth plus the original roughness. For example, after sputtering a smooth single crystal to a depth of 1 μm, the scale of the roughness is approximately 100 nm, and even an atomically sharp interface encountered at that depth will appear to be approximately 100 nm in width.

Figure 12(f) depicts a phenomenon termed atomic mixing or knock-on. Here, the primary ions displace atoms, for example, across an interface, and thus distort their original distribution. This effect can be minimized to some extent by using primary ions with lower energy and higher mass. Another related source of distortion is beam-induced diffusion or migration of solute species due to heating, radiation damage, chemical interaction with implanted primary ions, and electrostatic charging of the surface. In some cases, these effects cannot be avoided, and caution is advised.

There is at least one other source of distortion in a depth profile. It occurs only in multicomponent materials due to a phenomenon termed preferential sputtering. This is a transient effect that occurs at the beginning of a depth profile (or at internal interfaces) due to differences in sputtering yield among the various constituents.

This preferential sputtering effect in, for example, alloy AB changes the relative concentration of AB in the sputtered surface region so that the concentration of the high-yield species is reduced, and the concentration of the low-yield species is enhanced. Thus, once the transient is complete, the steady-state sputtered surface composition yields a relative flux of secondary ions A and B that is proportional to their true concentration ratio in the material. That is, in a sample where $S_A \neq S_B$, the relative fluxes of A and B

do not represent their true concentration ratio until preferential sputtering has occurred.

In a SIMS analysis, then, the relative secondary ion signals can change even in the absence of a true concentration gradient in the material. This transient will persist only over a short range (of the order of 1 to 10 nm) and thus is another reason to ignore the first portion of the depth profile. Nonetheless, it can be a severe limitation for the surface analysis of metal alloys or for the analysis of interfaces between alloy films.

An important parameter required for the interpretation of depth profiles is the sputtering rate. These rates typically range from 0.5 to 50 nm/min and are fundamentally related to the incident ion current density at the sample surface and the sputter yield of the material for the type and energy of the primary ions being used. In practice, the sputter rate is determined for a given set of operating conditions and the material of interest by measuring the depth of the sputtered crater. The crater depth can be measured using optical interferometry or profilometry. When appropriate, the sputter rate can also be obtained by depth profiling films of known thicknesses; that is, thin films whose thicknesses have been measured independently using optical techniques or Rutherford backscattering spectrometry (RBS). In this case, it must be assumed that the sputtering rate of the film will be the same as that of the specimen. Therefore, the use of oxide or metallic films for the determination of sputtering rates of bulk materials—even if the film and the bulk are of identical composition—is not recommended.

In general, it is not necessary to measure the sputter rate for each analysis of the same material if the primary ion beam current can be accurately measured or reproduced. In some cases, it is possible to translate the sputtering rate measured for one material into a rate appropriate for another material using tabulated values of the sputter yield. However, the sputtering rate can vary through a depth profile where large concentration changes occur; that is, it is an assumption to apply a constant sputtering rate to a depth profile if the concentration or composition changes are severe.

Quantitative Analysis

The relationship between the secondary ion current I_i^+ (that is, the positive secondary ion count rate for a monoisotopic element i) and the concentration of i in the specimen is:

$$I_i^+ = I_p \cdot S \cdot \gamma_i^+ \cdot C_i \cdot \eta \qquad \text{(Eq 3)}$$

where I_p is the primary ion beam current, S is the sputter yield, γ_i^+ is the ionization effi-

ciency for i^+, C_i is the atomic fraction of i, and η is an instrumental factor that characterizes the collection, transmission, and detection efficiency of the instrument, that is, the ratio of ions i^+ emitted to ions i^+ detected. Clearly, the problem in quantitative SIMS analysis is that the measured signal I_i^+ depends not only on the concentration of i in the specimen, but also on the specimen matrix (S, γ_i^+) and the electronic properties of the surface (γ_i^+).

Many attempts have been made to develop a routine approach for quantitative SIMS analysis, but none has been successful. Currently, SIMS—at least in a practical sense—is limited to the quantitative analysis of the impurities, dopants, or minor elements detected in a depth profile or bulk impurity analysis; SIMS is not used extensively for quantitative analysis of the surface or bulk stoichiometry of unknowns. Because SIMS supersedes other techniques primarily in the analysis of dopants and trace impurities, this apparent limitation should not be viewed as a disadvantage.

A quantitative SIMS analysis requires independent knowledge of the sputtering rate (see the previous section in this article) and a calibration of the secondary ion signal using standards whose matrix and surface electronic properties match those of the specimen. The use of reactive primary ion beams facilitates reproduction of the surface electronic properties between the specimens and the standards. The methods for preparation and calibration of standards with matrices identical to the specimens are varied, but the ion implantation of known doses of the element of interest into the matrix of interest is unquestionably the most convenient (Ref 12). This approach is described below.

The use of ion-implanted standards for quantitative SIMS analysis assumes a linear relationship between the SIMS signal and the elemental concentration. That is, the product of I_p, S, γ_i^+, and η (see Eq 3) is assumed to be a constant for the specimen and the standard (at least during analysis). This is true only at low concentrations (that is, dopants and impurities in the sub-ppm to 1000-ppm range); at higher concentrations, the electronic and chemical properties of the matrix can become a function of this concentration. The basic concept behind the use of ion-implant standards is that the implant fluence F determines the total number of atoms implanted per unit area; F (atoms or ions per square centimeter) can be measured and controlled to within approximately 5%. Thus, the secondary ion signal, when integrated over the entire profile measured for the implant standard (Fig. 11a), can be related to the total number of implanted atoms contained in the specimen:

$$\int_0^z I_i^+(z)dz = K \int_0^z C_i(z)(dz) \qquad \text{(Eq 4)}$$

where z is the depth of the analysis, and K is a constant that accounts for the terms in Eq 3; that is, K is the calibration factor used to convert the secondary ion signal (I_i^+ in counts per second) measured over the range dz into an average concentration (C_i in atoms per cubic centimeter). If z exceeds or equals the maximum extent of implantation in the standard, all the implanted atoms per unit area will have been analyzed, and:

$$\int_0^z C_i(z)(dz) = F \text{ (atoms or ions/cm}^2) \qquad \text{(Eq 5)}$$

Thus, the calibration factor can be obtained by integrating the secondary ion signal over the depth z:

$$K = \frac{\int_0^z I_i^+(z)dz}{F} \qquad \text{(Eq 6)}$$

Because the secondary ion signal is measured over a time interval dt, it is apparent that an independent measure of the sputtering rate, $\dot{z}$, is required; then:

$$K = \frac{\dot{z}}{F} \int_0^t I_i^+(t)dt \qquad \text{(Eq 7)}$$

where t is the total time over which the profile is integrated.

The calibration constant K can now be used to convert the measured secondary ion signal into absolute concentration in atoms per cubic centimeter:

$$C_i = \frac{1}{K} I_i^+ \qquad \text{(Eq 8)}$$

The secondary ion signal is usually measured in counts per second (averaged over a time interval dt); therefore, the units of K are essentially (atoms/cm^3)/cps. This constant is valid only for element i in a matrix that is identical to that of the standard. Moreover, the concentration C_i in the unknown must be in the dilute range, and the instrumental parameters used during analysis of the unknown must be the same as those used to obtain K from the unknown. Ideally, the standard is analyzed along with the unknowns. However, when the specimens and instruments are well characterized and controlled, or it is impractical to examine the implanted standard repeatedly, a normalized calibration constant, K_n, can be determined.

It is assumed that the ratio of the terms in Eq 3 for the element i (I_i^+) and some matrix species $M(I_M^+)$ is constant, that is:

$$K_n = \frac{\dot{z}}{F} \int_0^t \frac{I_i^+(t)}{I_M^+(t)} \, dt \qquad \text{(Eq 9)}$$

and then:

$$C_i = \frac{1}{K_n} \cdot \frac{I_i^+(z)}{I_M^+(z)} \qquad \text{(Eq 10)}$$

Perhaps the most obvious use of the calibration factor K is for quantitative analysis of the ion-implantation profile itself (Fig. 11a). The quantitative analysis of ion-implantation profiles is an important application of SIMS in the microelectronics industry. In this case, the implanted specimens (assuming the implanted fluence is known) are self-standardizing; that is, the integrated profile provides the calibration factor that can be used to convert the instantaneous secondary ion signals to concentration units. This conversion is shown in Fig. 11(b) for the raw data plotted in Fig. 11(a). More common, though, is the use of K or K_n (obtained using the implanted standard) to convert the secondary ion signals from another sample.

Fig. 13 The relationship between the $^{120}Sn^+$ secondary ion signal (normalized to the $^{16}O^+$ signal) and the relative tin content of various tin-oxide-doped silicate glasses

This calibration curve has been used for quantitative analysis of tin-oxide profiles in glass surfaces obtained in a scanning ion microprobe.

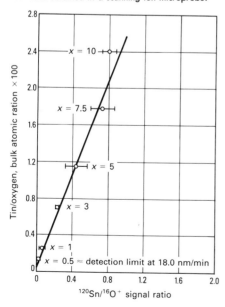

It is often desirable to use SIMS for quantitative analysis when concentrations from 0.1 to 10 at.% are of interest. In this case, it is necessary to verify the existence of a linear relationship between the secondary ion signal and the concentration. Thus, it is common to prepare a set of standards that bracket the concentration range of interest. The calibration curves shown in Fig. 13 and 14 illustrate these relationships for a glass matrix (where the analysis of tin is of interest) and a steel matrix (where the analysis of nickel is of interest). Once again, normalization of the secondary ion signal to a matrix species facilitates the definition of a practical calibration constant.

Ion Imaging

The acquisition of secondary ion images can be accomplished in one of two ways, depending on the instrument design (Fig. 15). In the case of the ion microprobe (Fig. 4 and 15a), the incident primary ion beam is focused to a small spot, then rastered over the sample surface. The analysis is carried out point by point, and the image is constructed by synchronizing the cathode ray tube (CRT) and the detector with the primary ion beam. That is, a particular secondary ion (for example, $^{27}Al^+$, FeO^+, and so on) is selected at the mass spectrometer, and its intensity variation from point to point is displayed on the CRT. This approach is analogous to that used for x-ray imaging in

Fig. 14 The relationship between the Ni^+ secondary ion signal and the nickel content of NBS standard reference steels 661, 662, 663, 664, and 665

This calibration curve can be used for quantitative analysis of nickel in comparable low-alloy steels using an ion microprobe. Source: Ref 13

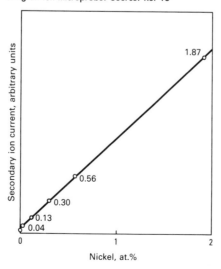

the electron microprobe. The resolution is determined by the diameter of the primary ion beam, typically 2 to 5 μm. In contrast, the ion microscope is a direct-imaging system in which the secondary ions are simultaneously collected over the entire imaged area (Fig. 5 and 15b). A strong electrostatic field between the specimen and the immersion lens preserves the spatial distribution of the emitted secondary ions. This secondary ion beam is then mass analyzed (only a double-focusing magnetic mass spectrometer is applicable for direct imaging), and in essence, the spatial distribution of the secondary ions is transmitted through the mass spectrometer. The transmitted secondary ions (for example, $^{27}Al^+$, FeO^+, and so on) then strike a microchannel plate, where the image is formed. The direct-imaging ion microscope can be compared to the transmission electron microscope or emission microscope. The resolution is determined by the optics of the system, for which the size of the imaged area on the specimen, that is, the field aperture, and the contrast aperture are major factors; however, the resolution is typically of the order of 0.5 to 1 μm.

The interpretation of secondary ion images must be approached with caution. Because the secondary ion intensity depends not only on the concentration of the imaged species, but also on the chemical and electronic properties of the matrix, the image contrast from point to point may have many origins. In polycrystalline materials, for example, the differences in crystallographic orientation between grains can influence the adsorption of oxygen from the residual vacuum, the implantation of oxygen from the primary beam, or the sputtering rate. Any one of these can lead to contrast in the secondary ion image for one grain relative to the other, even though no concentration difference exists. This sensitivity to subtle differences in secondary ion yield between various microstructural features can be the major source of image contrast and is in fact the basis of the ion emission microscope. This microscope is used primarily for microstructural imaging and not necessarily for the microchemical analysis of interest in SIMS.

Nonmetallic Samples

The analysis of insulators (glasses, ceramics, geological materials, and polymers) presents "charging" problems in SIMS, and in general, special procedures and additional effort are required (Ref 14, 15). The charging problem associated with these materials is due to the high incident primary ion current relative to the much lower emitted secondary ion current; secondary electron

Fig. 15 Schematic diagrams of secondary ion imaging
(a) In a direct-imaging ion microscope. (b) In a scanning ion microprobe

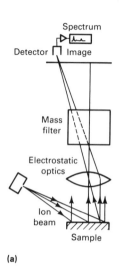

(a)

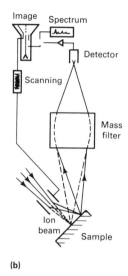

(b)

emission during ion bombardment further enhances the charge imbalance. All of this leads to a net positive charge at the surface (if positive primary ions are used), and the associated surface potential will influence the energy distribution of the emitted secondary ions. In general, the surface potential is unstable and thereby precludes the acquisition of meaningful spectra or depth profiles.

Several procedures have been established for the analysis of insulators, but the optimum method will depend on the specifics of the instrument and the materials. The most common approaches are (1) the deposition of metal coatings on the sample that are sputtered through to provide a path for local charge neutralization at the periphery of the ion beam crater, (2) use of metal grids or metal plates with apertures, which are placed over the sample for local charge neutralization, (3) auxiliary charge neutralization with an electron beam or flood gun, (4) use of a negative oxygen primary beam (O^-) that leads to a finite but stable surface potential after a few moments of bombardment, and (5) bombardment with a neutral beam (Ref 16). There is probably no substitute for experience in the analysis of insulators.

Another problem associated with the analysis of insulators, especially insulating thin films and coatings, is the migration of mobile ions due to the electric field generated by the ion-bombardment-induced surface potential. This migration can severely distort the in-depth profile of, for example, sodium, potassium, chlorine, fluorine, and so on, in oxide materials and films. The proper charge neutralization will greatly alleviate this ef-

fect, but its presence should always be considered.

Finally, the analysis of organic, biological, and other materials with volatile constituents also requires special approaches. It is common to freeze the specimen with liquid nitrogen using a cold stage. The mass spectra of organic and biological materials are exceedingly complex. The use of SIMS for the analysis of these materials must be carefully warranted, such as for trace metal detection in biological specimens, organic polymers, or films.

Detection Limits

It has been emphasized that one of the unique characteristics of SIMS is its high detection sensitivity relative to other surface microanalytical techniques. Nonetheless, it is important to recognize that the detection limit varies with the element, the sample matrix, and the operating procedures of the instrument (primary ion, sputter rate, instrument transmission, and background). For example, the detection limit in metallic, semiconducting, and other nonoxide matrices will be maximized only when reactive oxygen or cesium beams are used. When high spatial resolution, high depth resolution, or high mass resolution is also required, there will be some loss in detection sensitivity. There are at least two reasons for this.

One of these concerns the rate of material consumption, because this ultimately determines the total secondary ion count rate. If high spatial resolution is required in a microanalysis problem, for example, a reduction in the beam diameter will be necessary.

This is often accompanied by a decrease in the beam current and therefore a decrease in the rate of material consumption, even though the sputtering rate $\dot{z}$ may increase. Similarly, a loss in sensitivity occurs when $\dot{z}$ is reduced at a constant spot size to enhance the resolution of in-depth profiles.

The other reason for a less than optimum detection sensitivity concerns the collection and transmission of the secondary ions. Any electronic or mechanical gating of the sputtered crater, such as that required for high-resolution in-depth profiling, will reduce the detected signal. Similarly, the need for high mass resolution will reduce the ion transmission in the mass spectrometer and again result in a loss in detection sensitivity. In addition, any background due to residual gas or primary ion beam contamination will further limit the detection sensitivity.

Because of the element and matrix dependence and the instrumental interdependences noted above, it is not possible to quote a unique detection sensitivity for SIMS. The detection limits will be maximized in a bulk impurity analysis in which the highest beam current can be used because neither depth nor spatial resolution are of concern; this assumes that low mass resolution can be tolerated. Under these conditions, the detection limits for most elements can be expected to be in the parts per billion to parts per million range, assuming an oxide matrix and/or a reactive-ion primary beam.

Applications*

Example 1: Surface Composition Effects During Laser Treatment of AISI Stainless Steel. Although lasers are used for processing many materials, laser welding is not an acceptable procedure for certain metal alloys. If an alloy contains one or more volatile components, selective vaporization of the more volatile components during laser welding may lead to inadequate control of the weld composition and poor mechanical properties of the fabricated product. The loss of alloying elements and the eventual properties of the weld zone are influenced by fluid flow in the weld pool, heat transfer, and the thermodynamics and kinetics of the vaporization of various components from the molten pool.

In this study, SIMS was used to examine the surface region of an AISI 202 stainless steel before and after various treatments with a CO_2 laser. Of particular interest were the effects on hydrogen and oxygen, because

*Example 5 was provided by G.C. Nelson, Sandia National Laboratories. This work supported by the U.S. Department of Energy under Contract No. DE-AC04-76DP00789.

Fig. 16 Negative SIMS depth profiles of oxygen and hydrogen as a function of the laser irradiation of an AISI 202 steel

Obtained using $^{133}Cs^+$ primary ion bombardment in an ion microscope

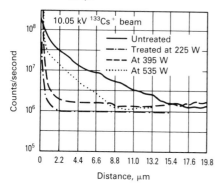

(a)

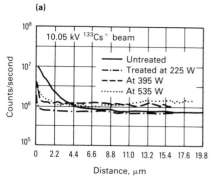

Fig. 17 High-resolution SIMS spectra for a phosphorus-doped silicon substrate

Obtained using $^{32}O_2^+$ primary ion bombardment in an ion microscope

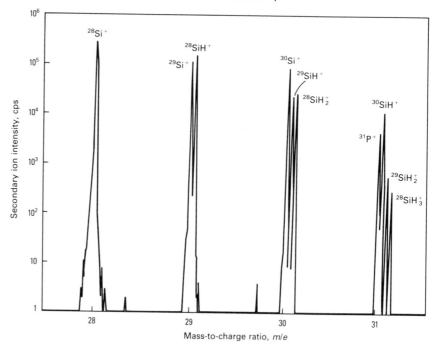

these species can profoundly influence mechanical and chemical properties. Figure 16 shows the oxygen and hydrogen depth profiles for selected samples analyzed using an ion microscope. A $^{133}Cs^+$ primary ion beam was used to enhance sensitivity to the $^{16}O^-$ and $^1H^-$ secondary ions.

It is apparent that the initial untreated surface is oxidized to a depth of the order of 10 μm; the surface also shows hydrogen penetration to approximately 5 μm. After the laser surface treatment, the oxygen and hydrogen contents of the irradiated surfaces have been reduced. A more careful inspection reveals, however, that the extent of this selective vaporization of oxygen and hydrogen is reduced with increasing power levels. These observations are being correlated with independent calculations and measurements of the depth of penetration of the laser treatment, the liquid pool temperature, and the corresponding change in concentration profile for the nickel, chromium, and manganese alloying agents. Although not shown, the latter are also measured with SIMS, but in that case, a $^{32}O_2^+$ primary ion beam is

used to enhance the sensitivity and to attenuate the matrix effects for analysis of the Ni^+, Cr^+, and Mn^+ secondary ions. It has been found that the observed changes in concentration of the alloying elements are due to differences in their solubility in the ferrite and other nonequilibrium phases, which form after laser irradiation of the original austenitic steel. A quantitative analysis has not yet been attempted in this work, but could be conveniently accomplished by ion implantation of hydrogen, oxygen, nickel, chromium, manganese, and so on, in a specimen of AISI 202.

Example 2: Quantitative Analysis of a Phosphorus Ion-Implantation Profile in Silicon. Ion implantation is an important process for low-level, shallow doping of silicon microelectronic devices. Secondary ion mass spectroscopy is uniquely qualified to verify these implantation profiles for process development, quality control, and failure analysis. In this example, the use of SIMS is demonstrated for the analysis of phosphorus (an n-type dopant) after ion implantation into silicon. Due to the presence of hydrogen in the silicon matrix and in the residual vacuum, however, a spectral interference occurs at $m/e \approx 31$ between P^+ ($m/e = 30.9738$), $^{30}SiH^+$ ($m/e = 30.9816$), $^{29}SiH_2^+$ ($m/e = 30.9921$), and $^{28}SiH_3^+$ ($m/e = 31.0004$). Thus, a high-resolution

mass spectrometer is necessary to separate the desired analyte species (P^+) from the molecular matrix ion interference (SiH^+, SiH_2^+, and SiH_3^+).

Figure 17 shows a high-resolution SIMS spectrum for the region $m/e = 28$ to 31, where the separation of the isotopic silicon and silicon-hydride species is demonstrated. It would not be possible to verify unequivocally the presence or concentration of phosphorus in this semiconductor without the high-resolution capability. This level of resolution cannot be attained using a quadrupole, where resolution is typically 1 atomic mass unit (amu). The mass resolution of this double-focusing magnetic sector is 10 to 100 times better; therefore, species whose mass-to-charge ratios differ by fractions of 1 amu can be separated.

Because the instrument has in this case been optimized for mass resolution, a loss in the detection sensitivity for phosphorus must be tolerated. However, the profile in Fig. 18(a) reveals that the sensitivity using a reactive $^{32}O_2^+$ primary ion beam is sufficient to measure the implantation profile over a dynamic range of 10^4 cps. It can also be seen that although the $^{31}P^+$ signal varied over four orders of magnitude through the profile, the $^{28}S^{2+}$ matrix signal ($m/e = 13.9885$) was constant (due to the use of an oxygen primary ion beam). After the profiling anal-

Fig. 18 Phosphorus depth profiles for an ion-implanted silicon substrate

(a) Before quantitative analysis of the positive SIMS data. (b) After quantitative analysis. Obtained using $^{32}O_2^+$ bombardment in an ion microscope. Obtained using $^{133}Cs^+$ beam bombardment in an ion microscope

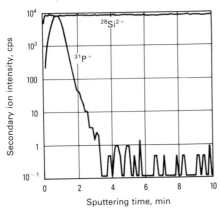

(a)

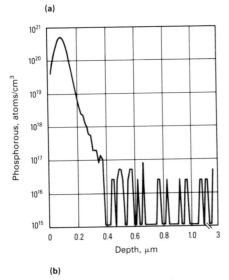

(b)

Fig. 19 Negative SIMS depth profiles for LPCVD SiO$_x$N$_y$ thin films on silicon

(a) NH$_3$/N$_2$O = 3 during deposition. (b) NH$_3$/N$_2$O = 0.33 during deposition. Obtained using $^{133}Cs^+$ beam bombardment in an ion microscope

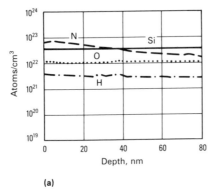

(a)

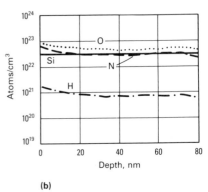

(b)

ration of thin films. In this example, the relationship between the reactive and residual gases in the chemical vapor deposition (CVD) reactor is of interest, as are the composition and hydrogen impurity content of silicon-oxynitride films. Figures 19(a) and (b) present two quantified profiles for SiO$_x$N$_y$ films deposited on silicon with different process parameters. In both cases, the films were deposited at 910 °C (1670 °F) with a total gas pressure of 0.4 torr, and the silicon source was Si$_2$H$_2$Cl$_2$ gas. The film shown in Fig. 19(a) used an ammonia (NH$_3$) to nitrous oxide (N$_2$O) ratio of 3; the film shown in Fig. 19(b) was deposited with an NH$_3$/N$_2$O ratio of 1/3. The average silicon/ nitrogen ratio of the films was not significantly affected by the NH$_3$/N$_2$O ratio, but the relative concentrations of oxygen and hydrogen were influenced. The analysis of many SiO$_x$N$_y$ films processed under different conditions has revealed that NH$_3$ is a more efficient source of nitrogen than is N$_2$O and that the NH$_3$ activity determines the hydrogen level in the film.

The quantitative analyses represented in Fig. 19(a) and (b) were performed using selected silicon-oxynitride thin films whose absolute hydrogen, nitrogen, and oxygen concentrations were independently calibrated using RBS and nuclear reaction analyses. These standards were then used to calibrate the secondary ion signals for the other specimens. The sputtering rate was determined by independently measuring the film thickness with ellipsometry, then observing the time necessary to sputter through the film to the SiO$_x$N$_y$/Si interface.

Example 4: Glass Surface Layer Analyses. The use of SIMS for depth-profiling three (unrelated) glass specimens after surface treatment or corrosion is described in this example. Figure 20 shows the

Fig. 20 Positive SIMS depth profiles

(a) Various constituents. (b) Hydrogen in a calcium-boroaluminosilicate glass ribbon after acid-etching 16 h in H$_2$SO$_4$. Obtained using Ar$^+$ primary ion bombardment in a scanning ion microprobe and an electron beam for charge neutralization

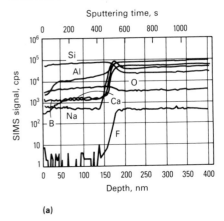

(a)

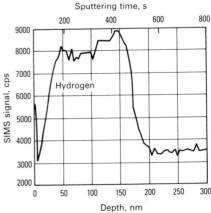

(b)

ysis was complete (approximately 10 min of sputtering), the depth of the sputtered crater was measured independently using a profilometer; the depth was found to be approximately 0.11 μm to yield a sputtering rate of 110 nm/min. The fluence used to prepare this implant was known; therefore, a quantitative analysis could be performed without an external standard. That is, the quantified profile shown in Fig. 18(b) was obtained using Eq 7 and 8. The background concentration represents less than 1 ppm P.

Example 3: Quantitative Impurity Analysis in LPCVD Thin Films. Low-pressure chemical vapor deposition (LPCVD) is used extensively for the prepa-

profiles for a multicomponent calcium-boroaluminosilicate glass ribbon after an acid-etching treatment. The presence of a surface film approximately 200 nm in thickness is evident after 16 h in concentrated sulfuric acid. The surface layer forms due to preferential leaching of the acid-soluble aluminum, boron, calcium, and sodium oxides and fluorides. The insoluble silica remains intact on the glass surface as a hydrated surface layer; the corresponding hydrogen profile is shown in Fig. 20(b). In this application, the kinetics and chemical mechanisms of this leaching process could be followed without the need for a quantitative compositional analysis. These profiles were obtained in an ion microprobe using an inert argon ion beam and raster gating; the charge neutralization was accomplished using an electron beam.

Figure 21(a) shows the profiles for an alkali-lead-silicate glass (commonly termed crystal) that exhibited a haze due to weathering in a humid atmosphere. The haze is essentially a surface film that can be easily removed by rinsing in cold water. Thus, the profiles shown in Fig. 21(b) represent a piece of the same glass specimen shown in Fig. 21(a) after rinsing in deionized water. The secondary ion signals for the various elements in this alkali-lead-silicate glass were normalized to the $^{29}Si^{4+}$ signal to facilitate comparison of the profiles for the hazed and cleaned surfaces.

It is evident that the haze is rich in sodium and potassium (probably hydroxides), which were leached to the surface from depths of the order of 200 to 300 nm; that is, regions depleted of sodium and potassium are apparent in the subsurface. The corresponding penetration of hydrogen to depths of the order of 200 to 300 nm indicates that water in the ambient atmosphere is probably responsible for this corrosion reaction. This glass surface, even after the cleaning, is permanently hydrated and depleted of sodium and potassium. Thus, subsequent exposure to a moist atmosphere requires a greater length of time to regenerate visible haze.

These profiles were obtained in an ion microscope using a $^{18}O^-$ primary ion beam; the negative primary ions were used to eliminate unstable charging of the surface. Although an electron beam could also have been used for charge neutralization, this often leads to electron-stimulated desorption and decomposition of weakly absorbed surface species, such as alkali hydroxides. The $^{18}O^-$ isotope was used to permit analysis of the $^{16}O^+$ that is intrinsic to the specimen.

Figures 22(a) and (b) compare the in-depth profiles of an alkali-lead-silicate glass before and after a hydrogen reduction treat-

ment. This treatment produces a thin black semiconducting layer at the glass surface that is critical to the fabrication of microchannel plates and other charged particle detectors. The kinetics of the hydrogen diffusion and reduction reaction are easily followed using the $^1H^+$ secondary ion profile. It is also noteworthy that sodium has been depleted to

some extent during the hydrogen reduction (probably due to vaporization); this alkali depletion can influence the work function and secondary electron yield of the devices.

Example 5: Determining Isotopes of Oxygen in an Explosive Actuator. Secondary ion mass spectroscopy is unique among surface analytical techniques for its

Fig. 21 Positive SIMS depth profiles for alkali-lead-silicate crystal glass

(a) Hazed surface. (b) Cleaned surface. Obtained using $^{18}O^-$ primary beam bombardment in an ion microscope

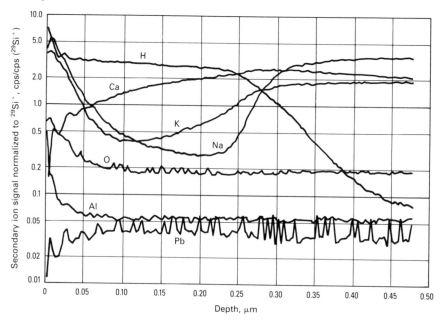

(a)

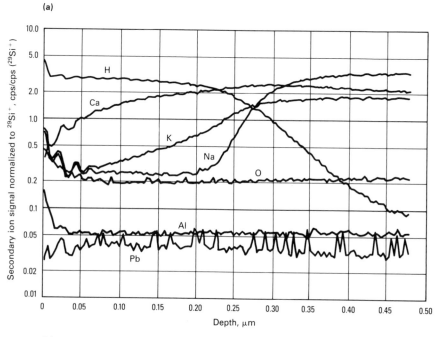

(b)

Fig. 22 Positive SIMS depth profiles for a lead-silicate glass

(a) Before and (b) after hydrogen reduction to produce a semiconducting surface layer. Obtained using $^{32}O_2^+$ primary beam bombardment and electron beam charge neutralization in an ion microscope

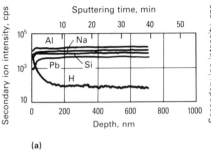

(a)

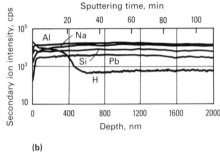

(b)

Table 2 Results of SIMS analysis of an explosive actuator

Component	Intensity, I
Ti	5659
TiH	79.5
TiH$_2$	−3
Ti^{16}O	512
Ti^{16}OH	14
Ti^{16}OH$_2$ + Ti^{18}O	−0.6 ± 0.6
Ti^{18}OH	1.1 ± 1.8
Ti^{18}OH$_2$	−0.2 ± 0.3

ability to detect hydrogen and to distinguish among the various isotopes of an element. This latter capability is very useful when studying the oxidation process in that ^{18}O can be used to differentiate between the oxidation that occurs during the experiment and any oxide (from ^{16}O) that may have been present before the experiment. An example of the use of SIMS to help determine the cause of enhanced output of an explosive actuator will be discussed.

The explosive actuator of interest consists of TiH$_x$ powder mixed with KClO$_4$ powder. The powders are ignited by an electrically heated bridgewire. After extended periods of storage, these actuators experienced outputs of explosive energy that were considerably greater than their nominal value. One of the possible explanations for this occurrence was that the natural TiO$_2$ layer that exists on the surface of the TiH$_x$ powder was reduced during shelf life, allowing a faster reaction with the KClO$_4$. Due to the high free energy for the oxidation of titanium, it was thought to be impossible to open the actuators and transport them to a surface analysis apparatus to locate reduced titanium. Instead, it was decided to open the actuators in an ^{18}O

Fig. 23 Spectra obtained from a TiH$_x$/KClO$_4$ sample exposed to ^{18}O

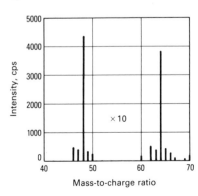

environment so that the elemental titanium, if present, would react with the ^{18}O, forming Ti$^{18}O_2$. Secondary ion mass spectroscopy would then be used to locate the Ti$^{18}O_2$.

Five sample materials were analyzed. Two of the samples, TiH$_x$ and TiH$_x$/KClO$_4$, were used to obtain baseline data in terms of which molecular ion species were present. The other three samples, all of which were TiH$_x$/KClO$_4$, were exposed to ^{18}O. The positive SIMS spectra in the mass-to-charge region of 45 to 70 amu were recorded for each of the above samples. This region contains the lines of the elemental titanium isotopes and the various molecular ions associated with titanium, ^{16}O, ^{18}O, and hydrogen.

Figure 23 shows an example of the spectra obtained from an ^{18}O-exposed sample. The peaks due to the various molecular ions are indicated. Because there is considerable peak overlap among the possible molecular ion species, a linear least squares analysis was used to separate the ^{18}O contribution. In this method, standard spectra for each elemental and molecular ion are linearly combined to obtain the best least squares fit to the experimental data. The result of the fit provides the contribution of each component to the experimental spectra. To determine the absolute concentration of each component, a sensitivity factor for each component must be known. These were not known for the current case, and absolute quantification was not attempted. However, because molecular ions due to Ti^{16}O were easily observed, it was assumed that ions due to Ti^{18}O, if present, would be observed with the same sensitivity.

The standard spectra for each molecular species used in the least squares fitting were calculated from tables of isotopic abundances. Standard spectra were calculated for titanium, Ti^{16}O, Ti^{18}O, TiH, TiH$_2$, Ti^{16}OH, Ti^{18}OH, Ti$^{16}OH_2$, and Ti$^{18}OH_2$. Table 2 shows the results from one of the samples. In all three cases analyzed, the ^{18}O contribution

was zero within experimental error. These results indicate that for the samples used in these experiments the surface Ti$^{16}O_2$ layer had not been reduced and thus was not the source of the enhanced output of the explosive actuator.

REFERENCES

1. G. Garter and J.S. Colligon, *Ion Bombardment of Solids*, Heinemann, 1968
2. M. Kamisky, *Atomic and Ionic Impact Phenomena on Metal Surfaces*, Springer-Verlag, 1965
3. O. Auciello and R. Kelly, Ed., *Ion Bombardment Modification of Surfaces*, Elsevier, 1984
4. G.K. Wehner, in *Methods of Surface Analysis*, A.W. Czanderna, Ed., Elsevier, 1975, p 5-38
5. A. Benninghoven, *Crit. Rev. Solid State Sci.*, Vol 6, 1976, p 291
6. K. Wittmack, in *Ion Beam Surface Layer Analysis*, Vol 2, O. Meyer *et al.*, Ed., Plenum Press, 1976, p 649-658
7. C.W. Magee, W.L. Harrington, and R.E. Honig, *Rev. Sci. Instrum.*, Vol 49, 1978, p 477
8. J.M. Ruberol, M. Lepareur, B. Autier, and J.M. Gourgout, in *8th International Conference on X-Ray Optics and Microanalysis*, D.R. Beaman, Ed., Pendell Publishing, 1979, p 322-328
9. C.W. Magee and E.M. Botnick, *J. Vac. Sci. Technol.*, Vol 19 (No. 1), 1981, p 47
10. W.L. Fite and M.W. Siegel, "Energy Filters for Secondary Ion Mass Spectrometry," Extranuclear Laboratories, Pittsburgh, 1977
11. R.J. Blattner and C.A. Evans, Jr., *Scan. Elec. Microsc.*, Vol IV, 1980, p 55
12. D.P. Leta and G.H. Morrison, *Anal. Chem.*, Vol 52 (No. 3), 1980, p 514
13. D.E. Newbury *et al.*, in *Surface Analysis Techniques for Metallurgical Applications*, STP 596, ASTM, Philadelphia, 1976, p 101-113
14. H.W. Werner and A.E. Morgan, *J. Appl. Phys.*, Vol 47, 1976, p 1232

15. K. Wittmack, *J. Appl. Phys.*, Vol 50, 1979, p 493
16. D.J. Surman and J.C. Vickerman, *Appl. Surf. Sci.*, Vol 9, 1981, p 108

SELECTED REFERENCES

* A. Benninghoven *et al.*, Ed., *Secondary Ion Mass Spectrometry—SIMS II*, Springer-Verlag, 1979
* G. Blaise, in *Materials Characterization Using Ion Beams*, J.P. Thomas and A. Cachard, Ed., Plenum Press, 1978, p 143-238
* J.W. Colbrun and E. Kay, in *CRC Crit. Rev. Solid State Sci.*, Vol 4 (No. 4), 1974, p 561
* R.J. Colton, *J. Vac. Sci. Technol.*, Vol 18 (No. 3), 1981, p 737
* K.F.J. Heinrich and D.E. Newbury, Ed., *Secondary Ion Mass Spectrometry*, NBS 427, National Bureau of Standards, Gaithersburg, MD, Oct 1975
* H. Liebl, *Anal. Chem.*, Vol 46 (No. 1), 1974, p 22A
* J.A.McHugh, in *Methods of Surface Analysis*, A.W. Czanderna, Ed., Elsevier, 1975, p 223-278
* G.H. Morrison and G. Slodzian, *Anal. Chem.*, Vol 47 (No. 11), 1975, p 932A
* N. Shimizu and S.R. Hart, in *Annual Review of Earth and Planetary Sciences*, Vol 10, Annual Reviews, 1981
* N. Winograd, in *Progress in Solid State Chemistry*, Vol 13, Pergamon Press, 1982, p 285-375
* E. Zinner, *Scanning*, Vol 3, 1980, p 57

Rutherford Backscattering Spectrometry

Wei-Kan Chu, Department of Physics and Astronomy, University of North Carolina

General Uses

- Quantitative compositional analysis of thin films, layered structures, or bulks
- Quantitative measurements of surface impurities of heavy elements on substrates of lighter elements
- Defect distribution depth profile in single-crystal sample
- Surface atom relaxation in single crystal
- Interfacial studies on heteroepitaxy layers
- Lattice location of impurities in single crystal

Examples of Applications

- Analysis of silicide or alloy formation; identification of reaction products; obtaining reaction kinetics, activation energy, and moving species
- Composition analysis of bulk garnets
- Depth distribution of heavy ion implantation and/or diffusion in a light substrate
- Surface damage and contamination on reactive ion etched samples
- Providing calibration samples for other instrumentation, such as secondary ion mass spectroscopy and Auger electron spectroscopy
- Defect depth distribution due to ion implantation damage or residue damage from improper annealing
- Lattice location of impurities in single crystal
- Surface atom relaxation of single crystal
- Lattice strain measurement of heteroepitaxy layers or superlattices

Samples

- *Form*: Solid samples with smooth surfaces, thin films on smooth substrates, self-supporting thin foils, and so on
- *Size*: Typically 1 cm × 1 cm × 1 mm; can accept sample as small as 2 × 2 mm
- *Preparation*: No special preparation required other than the surface must be smooth

Limitations

- Composition information may be obtained, but not chemical bonding information
- Poor lateral resolution. Typical beam spot is 1 × 1 mm. With attachment, beam spot may be reduced to 1 × 1 μm
- Poor mass resolution for heavy (high-Z) elements, cannot distinguish surface impurities of gold from platinum, tantalum, tungsten, and so on; mass resolution is better for low- and mid-Z elements, for example, can distinguish ^{37}Cl from ^{35}Cl
- Poor sensitivity for low-Z elements on substrates with elements heavier than the impurity
- Depth resolution is generally approximately 20 nm. Glancing angle Rutherford backscattering spectrometry provides 1 to 2 nm

Estimated Analysis Time

- For routine Rutherford backscattering spectrometry, up to four samples per hour; for channeling Rutherford backscattering spectrometry, about 1 h per sample

Capabilities of Related Techniques

- *Particle-induced x-ray emission*: Mass distinction
- *Nuclear reaction*: Low-Z element sensitivity
- *Low-energy ion-scattering spectroscopy*: Low-energy Rutherford backscattering spectrometry using keV ions rather than typical Rutherford backscattering spectrometry, which uses MeV ions
- *Cross-section transmission electron microscopy*: Depth and types of defect

Introduction

Rutherford backscattering spectrometry (RBS) has evolved in the past few years into a major materials characterization technique primarily due to its versatility and the amount of information it can provide in a short analysis time. Because quantitative information may be obtained without standard samples, RBS analyses often serve as standards for other techniques that are much more sensitive but require calibration. Detailed information on RBS is available in Ref 1 and 2.

Rutherford's first scattering experiment established the analytical utility of the ion beam. Scattering techniques are often used in atomic and nuclear physics to check targets for impurities, thickness, and composition, but only since the late 1960s has ion beam analysis taken hold. This has been due to the need for rapid growth of planar technology in semiconductors and the availability of compatible data processing systems. In the mid-1960s, the discovery of channeling phenomena and recognition of ion implantation in material doping and alteration provided additional motivation for RBS.

Backscattering is a two-body elastic collision process. The first basic concept of backscattering spectrometry is that in an elastic collision, such as backscattering, energy transfer from a projectile to a target atom can be calculated from collision kinematics. The mass of the target atom can be determined by measuring the energy transfer due to collision or by measuring the scattered energy of the backscattered particle. The second basic concept is that the probability of elastic collision between the projectile and target atoms is highly predictable, and the scattering probability or scattering cross section enables quantitative analysis of atomic composition. Lastly, slowing of the projectile in a medium through inelastic energy loss may be treated as a continuous process, leading to the perception of depth. The combination and interplay of these three

concepts allows RBS analysis to perceive depth distribution of masses.

Principles of the Technique

Collision Kinematics. An ion backscattered from a relatively heavy target atom carries a higher backscattered energy and provides smaller energy to the target atom than an ion backscattered from a lighter target atom. Figure 1 defines a backscattering situation. The projectile of atomic mass m and energy E_0 collides with a stationary target atom of atomic mass M_2 ($M_2 > m$). The projectile then backscatters with a scattering angle θ, and its energy becomes E_1. The target atom recoils forward.

A scattering kinematic factor (K) that is defined as the ratio of E_1 to E_0 can be derived from conservation of energy and conservation of momentum along a longitudinal direction and an incident direction for cases before and after scattering:

$$K \equiv \frac{E_1}{E_0} =$$

$$\left[\frac{(M_2^2 - m^2 \sin^2 \theta)^{1/2} + m \cos \theta}{M_2 + m} \right]^2$$

(Eq 1)

Equation 1 reduces to $(M_2 - m)/(M_2 + m)$ at $\theta = 90°$ and to $(M_2 - m/M_2 + m)^2$ at $\theta = 180°$. The kinematic energy loss from a collision is greatest for full backward scattering (180°). Because this type of scattering yields optimum mass resolution, the detector should be placed at the most backward angle possible.

According to Eq 1, when the incident energy E_0 is known, a measurement of the scattered energy E_1 is a measurement of the mass of the target atom at which scattering occurs. That is, the energy scale for a given

Fig. 2 The energy E of a ^{4}He atom scattered elastically at an angle θ upon collision with an atom of mass M is given by the length of the arrow at that angle

The incident energy E_0 is given by the radius of the outer semicircle.

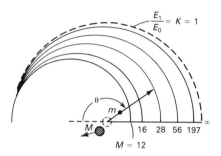

backscattering spectrum can be translated into a mass scale. Such a translation is expressed in Fig. 2 when ^{4}He is used as the probing beam for RBS. The mass resolution for RBS is directly related to the energy resolution of the detecting system. Helium ion scattering of 2 MeV typically has energy resolution of approximately 15 keV (Fig. 2). This is adequate to distinguish scattering from different chlorine isotopes, but not sufficient to separate tantalum from gold and platinum.

Scattering Cross Section. Scattering events occur rarely. Most of the projectiles are moving forward and eventually stop inside the solid, as in ion implantation. Only a small portion of the ion beam is backscattered and detected for RBS. The total number of detected particles, A, is:

$$A = \sigma \Omega Q (Nt)$$

(Eq 2)

where σ has the dimension of area (cm^2) and is termed scattering cross section, Ω is the solid detection angle, Q is the total number of incident projectiles, and Nt is the number of target atoms per unit area of the sample.

The scattering cross section for an elastic collision where Coulomb repulsion is the force between the two nuclei can be calculated using:

$$\sigma = \left(\frac{Z_1 Z_2 e^2}{4E} \right)^2 \frac{4}{\sin^4 \theta}$$

$$\frac{\{[1 - ((m/M_2) \sin \theta)^2]^{1/2} + \cos \theta\}^2}{[1 - ((m/M_2) \sin \theta)^2]^{1/2}}$$

(Eq 3)

Fig. 1 Collision kinematics between a projectile atom m and a target atom M_2

(a) Before collision. (b) After collision

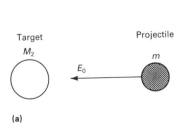

(a)

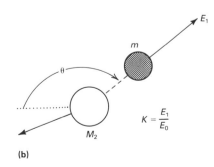

(b)

Fig. 3 The sensitivity of RBS to the various elements is proportional to the backscattering cross section σ, which varies as the square of the charge Z_m contained in the nucleus of an atom of mass m (Eq 4)

The ordinate provides Z_1^2 for a selection of elements. The kinetic energy left in a projectile of mass m after an elastic backscattering collision with an atom of mass m is a fraction k_m of the incident energy (Eq 1 and 2). The abscissa yields K_m for a selection of elements, assuming that the projectiles are helium ions ($m = 4$). Source: Ref 4

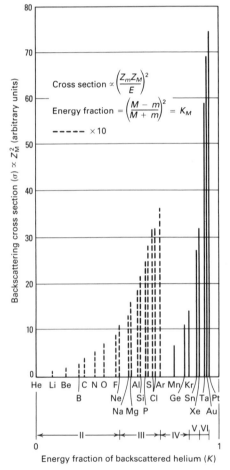

than light elements), and E^{-2} (scattering yield increases with decreasing ion beam energy). In thin film analysis, ratios of scattering cross sections between two elements Z_2 and Z_2' are often used to determine stoichiometry, and σ/σ' reduces to $Z_2^2/Z_2'^2$ as an approximation because Eq 3 is not sensitive to the change of m_2.

Equation 2 demonstrates that calculation of σ and the measurement of the number of detected particles provide a direct measure of the number of target atoms per unit area, (Nt), where N is the number of target atoms per unit volume, and t is the thickness of the target. The concept of scattering cross section leads to the capability of quantitative analysis of atomic composition. Figure 3 shows the approximated scattering cross section and approximated K scale for helium backscattering.

Rutherford scattering cross section is based on the assumption that projectile and target are point charged and their interaction follows the Coulomb law. The factor involving mass ratio in Eq 3 derives from the laboratory/center-of-mass correction. Correction due to electron screening, more pronounced for high-Z target atoms, has been confirmed (Ref 5), revealing that the empirical cross-section formula:

$$\sigma(\text{corrected}) = \sigma\left(1 - \frac{0.049 Z_1 Z_2^{4/3}}{E}\right)$$

(Eq 4)

agrees with a measurement of helium ion 150 to 180° scattering within 1 to 2% throughout the energy range 0.6 to 2.3 MeV for various Z_2. At a scattering angle within a few tenths of a degree from 180°, an unusual enhancement of scattering yield has been observed (Ref 6). This enhancement has a factor of 2 to 3, a consequence of a correlation between the incoming and outgoing paths of the backscattered ions (Ref 7).

Energy Loss. An energetic ion impinging on a target penetrates it, but large angle scattering from a target atom is highly unlikely. The Coulomb interaction between the moving ions and electrons in the target material largely determines the fate of all the incident ions. The moving ions lose their energies by ionization and excitation of target electrons. The numerous discrete interactions with electrons slow the moving ions by transferring the ion energy to the target electrons in an almost continuous frictionlike manner. This type of interaction does not alter significantly the direction of the ion beam. The energy loss per unit path length (dE/dx) can be measured experimentally by

passing the ion beam through a thin foil of thickness Δx and measuring the energy loss ΔE; it can also be calculated theoretically. Energy loss produces the depth perception for RBS.

The value of dE/dx is a function of projectile, target, their atomic numbers, mass, and projectile energy. Another definition, used more frequently in RBS, is stopping cross section (ϵ), which is:

$$\epsilon \equiv \left[\frac{1}{N}\frac{dE}{dx}\right]$$

where N is the atomic density of the target material, that is, the number of target atoms per cubic centimeter. The stopping cross section ϵ carries the unit of electron volts times square centimeters (eV · cm^2), hence the term cross section. This is similar in name but different in meaning from the scattering cross section, which carries the unit of square centimeters. The term ϵ is understandable as the energy loss on the atomic level. For example, if a thin layer contains $N\Delta x$ atoms per square centimeter, the energy loss of the ion beam passing through this thin layer becomes ΔE(eV) and:

$$\Delta E = \epsilon(N\Delta x)$$

where ϵ is the stopping cross section of the given ion in the given elements. The concept of stopping cross section can be generalized for a molecule or for a mixture by the principle of additivity of stopping cross sections:

$$\epsilon^{A_m B_n} = m\epsilon^A + n\epsilon^B$$

where ϵ^A and ϵ^B are stopping cross sections of elements A and B, constituents of molecule $A_m B_n$ (a mixture of A and B with atomic ratio of m to n). For RBS using MeV helium ions, tabulations of ϵ for all elements are given in Ref 8 and 9.

The Channeling Effect

Charged particles that penetrate a single crystal along or near a major axis experience a collective string potential produced by the rows of atoms along that axis. If the incident direction of the ion beam is nearly parallel with the string of atoms, the string potential steers (channels) the charged particle forward. A critical angle is defined as the largest angle between the incident direction of the ion beam and the row of atoms such that the steering effect exists. When charged particles are incident in a direction exceeding the critical angle, those particles have trans-

where Z_1 is the atomic number of the projectile of mass m, Z_2 is the atomic number of the target atom of mass M_2, and e is the electron charge; the other terms are defined in Eq 1. Equation 3 (Ref 3) reveals that the significant functional dependence of Rutherford differential scattering cross section is proportional to Z_1^2 (the heavier the projectile, the larger the scattering cross section; for helium ions $Z_1 = 2$), Z_2^2 (for a given projectile, it is more sensitive to heavy elements

Fig. 4 System for backscattering analysis and signal processing

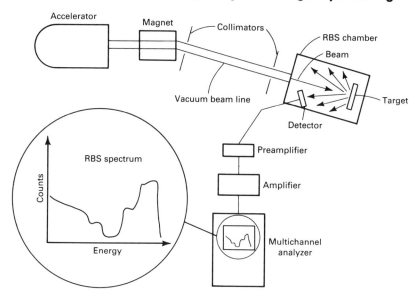

The spectrum consists of a series of steps, each generated by one of the elements in the material. The position of the step indicates the mass of the element (arrows) as obtained from Eq 1. The height of each step is proportional to the elemental concentration and to σ. Because this bubble material is an insulator, a thin film of aluminum was deposited on top before analysis to provide a return path for the beam current. Therefore, the backscattering signal of each element was shifted toward lower energies by an amount corresponding to the aluminum film energy attenuation.

The bubble material was known to contain iron, gadolinium, yttrium, and europium in nominal amounts; the overall composition was known to be that of a garnet, that is, X_8O_{12}. From the step height of the various metal signals in the spectrum, the corresponding relative concentrations can be calculated by dividing through the respective cross sections (Eq 3). The measured composition agrees favorably with nominal composition. The errors for such determinations of composition are of the order of 5% in average cases and 1 or 2% in the optimum cases.

Thin film composition and layer thickness can be obtained routinely using RBS, which has become a powerful technique in thin film analysis. Figure 6 illustrates an example of thin film study, showing the changes in a nickel film on silicon as deposited and after heat treatment at 250 °C (480 °F) for 1 and 4 h, respectively. A new phase develops at the interface with an atomic composition that may be identified as two nickel atoms for one silicon atom from

verse kinetic energy exceeding the collective string potential; the collective steering effect subsequently disappears.

Ion channeling has been used extensively in conjunction with ion backscattering measurements to study single crystals near the surface. One such application of RBS will be discussed in the section "Applications" in this article. Information on the theory of channeling and the experimental study of channeling effects, with emphasis on materials analysis, is given in Ref 10 to 12.

RBS Equipment

A basic piece of equipment in RBS analysis is a small accelerator capable of generating 2-MeV helium ions. Such units, which may be housed in a 6 × 9 m (20 × 30 ft) lab and are dedicated to RBS analyses, have been available since 1980. Because of the fast turnaround of RBS analyses, accelerator time and availability of small accelerators are not a major problem in RBS.

The accelerator generates ions and accelerates them to the desired energy. After passing through a short drift tube, the ion enters an analyzing magnet that selects the ion species and energy for a given experiment. After passing the magnet, the ion beam is collimated and directed onto the sample. In addition to an ion accelerator to produce the analyzing beam, electronics for signal handling are also required. Figure 4 shows the equipment involved and the sequence for signal collecting and processing.

Ions backscattered from the sample are detected and analyzed using a solid-state detector. A silicon surface barrier detector approximately 2 cm (0.8 in.) in diameter is commonly used to collect the particles backscattered into a small solid angle at a fixed backscattering angle. This detector in combination with a preamplifier and linear amplifier generates a voltage signal proportional to the energy of the particle entering the detector.

A multichannel analyzer digitizes the analog input voltage signal and sorts all signals during an experiment. Therefore, at the conclusion of a measurement, the surface barrier detectors receive approximately 10^6 particles with various energies. A measurement typically takes 10 to 30 min. The multichannel analyzer plots backscattering energy spectrum counts versus channel number. That is, it provides the number of scattering events per unit energy interval as a function of energy of the backscattered particles. The RBS spectrum carries information of the sample where scattering events happen.

Applications

Composition of Bulk Samples. An example of the composition analysis of bulk material is shown in Fig. 5. The sample consists of a magnetic bubble material grown on a gadolinium gallium garnet (GGG). Although the bubble material is actually a film, its thickness is much greater than the measurable depth; thus, the film appears as a bulk material.

Fig. 5 Backscattering spectrum of a thick target consisting of magnetic bubble material

The material was known to have the garnet composition X_8O_{12}. The spectrum yields a similar composition ratio. The measured composition was $Y_{2.57}Eu_{0.48}Ga_{1.2}Fe_{3.75}O_{12}$; the nominal composition, $Y_{2.45}Eu_{0.55}Ga_{1.2}Fe_{3.8}O_{12}$.

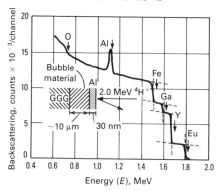

Fig. 6 Energy spectra of 2.0-MeV ^{4}He$^+$ ions backscattered from a sample of 200-nm nickel on a surface of silicon before and after annealing at 250 °C (480 °F) for 1 and 4 h

Ni$_2$Si formation is visible for the RBS spectra on the two annealed samples. Source: Ref 13

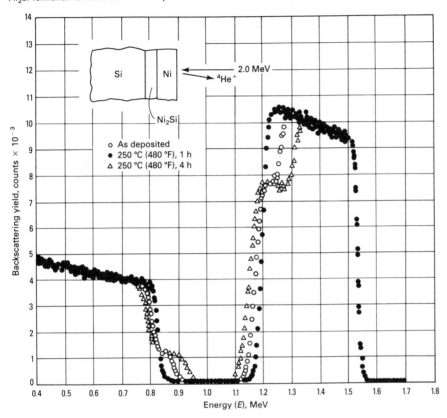

Fig. 7 2.0-MeV ^{4}He RBS spectra of arsenic-implanted silicon samples

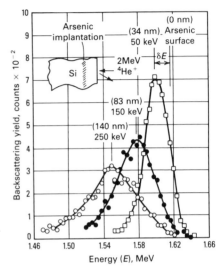

straightforward analysis of this spectrum. The rate of formation of the new phase can be measured from a sequence of such spectra taken after various annealing times.

The growth rate was found to be parabolic with time, suggesting a diffusion-limited process. Upon repeating such measurements at different temperatures, the reaction was found to have an activation energy of 1.5 ± 0.1 eV (3.4 ± 2.3 kcal/mol). Following the signal of heavy inert atoms, for example, xenon, implanted at the silicon-nickel interface enabled identification of the diffusing species as nickel (Ref 14). Once the nickel is fully consumed, a second reaction can be initiated by further annealing, which terminates in the total transformation of the layer to a new atomic composition of one silicon atom for one nickel atom (not shown). At approximately 750 °C (1380 °F), this layer is in turn transformed, and the silicon-to-nickel ratio increases 2:1. This last layer grows epitaxially, that is, under preservation of the crystalline orientation of the substrate—a fact established using RBS by channeling, which is present only when the target is a single crystal.

Impurity Profiles. Depth profiles of heavy element impurities in a light substrate can be obtained easily using RBS. Figure 7 depicts RBS profiles of arsenic in silicon on three ion-implanted silicon samples, showing the energy spectrum of 2.0-MeV ^{4}He ions backscattered from a silicon sample implanted with 2×10^{15} As/cm$_2$ at 50, 150, and 250 keV. The peak positions are below the surface by an energy ΔE that corresponds to the projected range R_p of the arsenic distribution. The surface position of arsenic is defined by calculation from Eq 1 or by scattering from a GaAs calibration sample. The full width at half maximum (FWHM) of the arsenic spectrum corresponds to a FWHM of a depth distribution after subtraction from detector resolution and energy straggling. A detailed analysis of this example is given in Ref 15. A substitutional portion of arsenic can be obtained by channeling. Peak concentration can be obtained from the scattering cross-section ratio of arsenic to silicon and from comparing peak highs of arsenic to silicon.

Damage Depth Profile. Ion channeling in conjunction with ion backscattering

measurements has been used extensively to study near-surface defects in single crystals. Most defect studies by channeling involve backscattering of light particles, such as protons or helium ions, with energies of a few hundred keV to a few MeV. A goniometer is required for target manipulation and crystal alignment.

Figure 8 illustrates conversion from channeling spectrum to depth distribution of defect, representing channeled backscattering spectra of 2.4-MeV He$^+$ ions from single-crystal silicon prebombarded with high dose H$^+$ at various energies. Figure 9 shows a direct translation from energy spectra to the buried defect distribution. The defect concentration given in Fig. 9 is on a relative scale. Assuming the peaks in Fig. 8 are produced by the scattering of silicon atoms randomly distributed in the defect region, the relative concentration scale may be considered to be the percentage of silicon atoms randomly displaced from lattice sites. Unless there is clear evidence that the irradiation has produced a totally amorphous surface layer, the term displaced atoms should be replaced by scattering and dechanneling to describe the degree of disordered atoms or defects in the crystal (Ref 17). Scattering and dechanneling should not be used to measure the number of disordered atoms or defects in the crystal; rather, they are useful indicators of these quantities.

Backscattering is useful for determining the depth distribution of the disorder, but transmission electron microscopy (TEM) is better for defining the nature of the defect. The energy dependence of dechanneling can

Fig. 8 Channeled backscattering spectra of 2.4-MeV ^{4}He ions from silicon bombarded with 4×10^{16} protons/cm^2 at various energies

Channeled and random spectra for unbombarded silicon are shown as the background. Source: Ref 16

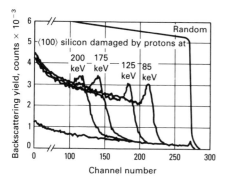

Fig. 9 Defect distribution extracted from Fig. 8

Source: Ref 16

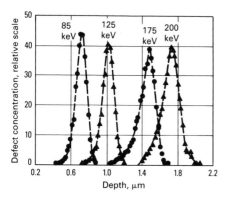

Fig. 10 Angular yield profiles of 1.2-MeV ^{4}He ions backscattering from gold and copper atoms in single-crystal copper containing 2 at.% Au

Source: Ref 20

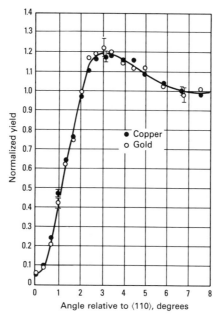

be observed to obtain information on the nature of the defects. Additional information is given in Ref 10 to 12.

Surface Peak. Use of ion scattering to study surface structure by channeling and by blocking is a well-developed technique. Detailed methods and examples are available in Ref 10 to 12. Rutherford backscattering spectrometry channeling of silicon sputtered by low-energy noble gas can provide information on sputter-induced crystal damage. The quantitative number of displaced silicon atoms is obtained by subtracting the surface peak contributions from the native oxide and the normal surface peak for crystalline silicon. Noble gas atoms heavier than silicon, such as argon, krypton, and xenon, can also be incorporated. Similar studies have been extended to reactive ion etching (RIE) involving fluor- or chlorine-containing gases in combination with argon (Ref 18).

Another example using channeling on surfaces is the study of melting of single-crystal lead (Ref 19). This example shows that a simple analysis of surface peaks yields fundamental knowledge of melting phenomena.

Lattice Location of Dopant Atoms. Channeling can reveal the lattice location of the solute atoms in single-crystal solid solutions. In general, a foreign atom species dissolved in a single crystal could take the position of a substitutional site, a well-defined interstitial site, a well-defined displacement from a substitutional site, or a random distribution within the lattice.

Channeling can show the foreign atom location in a lighter matrix. Foreign atoms may sometimes take more than one of these positions. Superposition of the different locations produces superposition of various channeling results, making it difficult to provide a unique answer on the lattice locations.

Substitutional Case. From the analytical point of view, detectable foreign atoms located at the substitutional site are the simplest case in channeling characterization. The yield attenuation of the foreign atoms along all axial and planar channeling directions should be identical to that of the host lattice.

Gold atoms in single-crystal copper assume the substitutional site perfectly (Ref 20). Figure 10 shows the angular yield profiles of the normalized backscattering yield of 1.2-MeV helium ions from gold and from copper atoms in a single-crystal copper sample containing 2% gold. The identical half angle on the angular scan for impurity and first atoms indicates that the gold is substitutional and that the gold atoms are completely shadowed by the copper atoms. This 100% substitutional case is rarely observed. A small percentage of impurity usually occupies a nonsubstitutional site, producing a higher minimum yield for the backscattering signals from the impurity atoms.

Angular scan along more than one channeling direction is often required to deduce the lattice location. Planar and axial channeling are useful in the triangulation analysis, especially when foreign atoms take interstitial locations.

Interstitial Case. For a single cubic crystal, an interstitial site is located at the center of the cube. Body-centered cubic (bcc), face-centered cubic (fcc), or diamond structures have more than one type of interstitial site. Figure 11 illustrates the tetrahedral interstitial and octahedral interstitial site of an fcc single crystal. For the (100) planar direction, the tetrahedral interstitials are located between the (100) planes, and the angular scans indicate a peak for the foreign atom at the well-channeled direction. This is not the case for octahedral interstitials, which are hidden behind the host atoms in (100) and (110) directions.

For planar channeling cases, the ion beam is incident parallel to the lattice planes, which are defined by the atoms on the plane. For axial channeling cases, the ion beam is incident parallel to the major axial direction. Flux peak is shown in ⟨100⟩ tetrahedral sites and ⟨110⟩ octahedral sites, and good shadowing in ⟨110⟩ tetrahedral interstitials. The foreign atoms are off-center of the channel at a well-defined distance, not on center. A double peak can be expected. Through careful triangulation in various channeling directions, a well-defined lattice location can be determined. Examples of hydrogen locations in an fcc crystal (Ref 21) and a bcc crystal (Ref 22, 23) are the classic demonstrations of this type.

Small Displacement From Substitutional Site. Many cases indicate that favorable channeling conditions for impurity atoms are observed. However, the width of the angular scan from the impurities is sometimes much narrower than that of the host atoms. Angular width narrowing indicates small displacement from a substitutional site. Foreign atoms displace from a lattice site for many

Fig. 11 Impurity atom taking tetrahedral and octahedral interstitial sites for fcc crystals

The schematic of the lattice planes and strings and their corresponding form of the angular yield profiles. Source: Ref 21

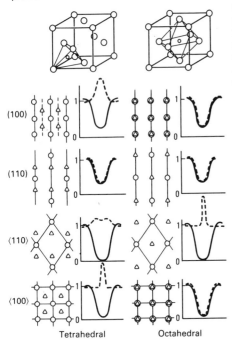

sized in the materials selection for superlattice layers. However, high-quality superlattices can also be grown from lattice-mismatched materials; these are termed strained-layer superlattices (SLS).

In SLS structures, the lattice mismatch is accommodated by uniform layer strains to prevent generation of misfit defects for sufficiently thin layers (Ref 26, 27). This built-in strain provides additional flexibility in tailoring superlattice properties, including the band gap and transport parameters. These both depend strongly on the amount of strain in the SLS. Therefore, strain measurements in SLSs are important for the characterization of these materials. Relative to channeling, strain can be measured in SLSs by the dechanneling method, by angular scan, and by a resonance effect.

Lattice Strain Measurement by Dechanneling. Early studies of InAs/GaSb superlattices found anomalously large dechanneling

along the inclined [110] axis relative to the [100] growth direction. These results were interpreted in terms of a change in lattice spacing at the interfaces. However, computer simulation calculations show that the expected lattice spacing differences provide significantly less dechanneling than was observed, but the dechanneling is consistent with that expected due to the strain in the layers.

Recent studies have shown that dechanneling provides a depth-sensitive monitor of the strain in SLS structures. For a given layer thickness, this technique can be used to determine the maximum amount of strain that could be incorporated into SLS structures through different growth techniques. Quantitative analysis of the magnitude of the strain is more difficult. The only general quantitative analysis available is use of computer simulation calculations for comparison to experiment. More such calculations are

reasons. For example, foreign atom and vacancy pairs could move the foreign atom off the lattice site (toward the vacancy). Small foreign atom clusters could have slightly different bond lengths between them that force the foreign atom clusters to exit the lattice site. The cause of the displacement is unimportant. The amount of the displacement can be measured by observing the amount of half-angle narrowing versus that of the angular scan of the host atoms.

This concept can be illustrated by noting that when silicon crystals are heavily doped with arsenic, arsenic atoms tend to form small clusters and are displaced from the lattice by approximately 0.015 nm. When the sample is subjected to laser irradiation, arsenic clusters dissolve in the silicon solution, and arsenic atoms take an exact substitutional site. The channeling study of atom displacement has been discussed above (Ref 24, 25).

Superlattice/Interface Studies. Channeling can be applied to interfacial problems, especially the investigation of strained layered superlattices. Superlattices are alternating layered structures of fundamental interest and importance for potential application in electronic and optical devices. Lattice matching of heteroepitaxy has been empha-

Fig. 12 Energy spectra of 1.76-MeV He$^+$ ions backscattered from [100] GaSb/AlSb superlattices

Depth scales based on antimony and gallium signals are marked in units of the number of layers (30 nm per layer). [100]- and [110]-aligned spectra, a random spectrum taken at an angle of 3° relative to the [110] direction, and three more spectra between the [110] and random spectra are given. Source: Ref 27

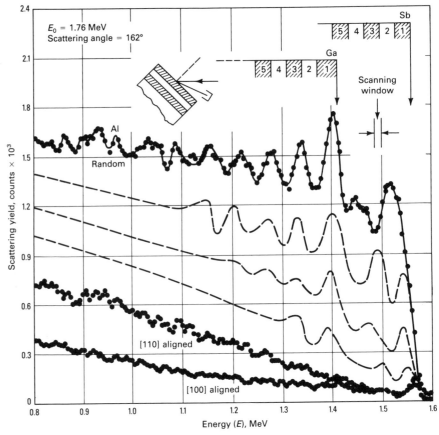

Fig. 13 Angular scan performed by setting an energy interval (window) from the first to fourth layer from 52 spectra run at 52 different angles

The center position of the angular scan changes from layer to layer, indicating that the ⟨110⟩ direction varies. The vertical dashed line is the limiting center position for layers much deeper in the sample. Source: Ref 27

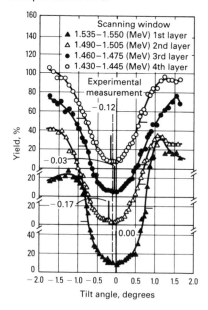

Fig. 14 The resonance effect (oscillations of the ion beam) in RBS channeling

(a) Focusing and defocusing that produces oscillations. (b) Backscattering spectrum of 1.2-MeV ^{4}He ions along the {110} plane in a single GaP crystal. The oscillations in the planar-channeled spectrum provides a measure of wavelength. Source: Ref 30

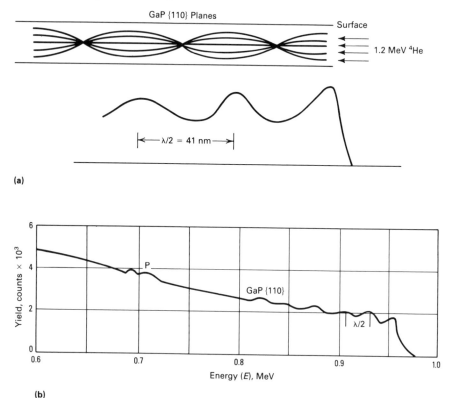

needed to establish general scaling rules for the tilt and thickness dependence of the dechanneling.

Lattice Strain Measurement by Channeling Angular Scan. A second approach to the measurement of strain in SLS structures is to examine the channeling angular scans along inclined directions where the crystal rows are tilted. Figures 12 and 13 show an example.

Studies (Ref 28) indicate that backscattering and channeling measurements of the relative changes in the channel direction in combination with computer simulation are sensitive to relative changes in the channel direction; the strains result in various crystal distortions that alter symmetry directions slightly. Angular scan measurements along ⟨110⟩ and ⟨100⟩ directions with an error of ±0.03° allow bond angle distortion as small as 0.1° to be measured in superlattices. In a two-layered system, pseudomorphic growth of Ge_xSi_{1-x} on silicon by molecular beam epitaxy has been studied by the ion channeling technique (Ref 29); channeling studies indicated that for thin epitaxial layers, lattice mismatch may be accommodated by strain rather than dislocation formation. This pseudomorphic growth condition may be maintained at alloy compositions or layer

thicknesses substantially greater than those predicted by equilibrium theory.

Resonance Effect. When an ion beam enters a single crystal in a direction parallel to a set of planes, the collective atomic potential steers the ions back and forth between the planes. This oscillation during channeling can be observed through the oscillations in the backscattering spectra (Fig. 14). A resonance effect in planar dechanneling when the wavelength of the channeled-particle oscillations is matched to the period of an SLS has been observed (Fig. 15). A simple phase-rotation model is developed to calculate the dechanneling on each layer. The angular dependence of resonance channeling has been studied; its utility in superlattice studies has been extended using more sophisticated potential and detail treatment (Ref 31). This type of analysis provides a means of measuring small lattice strain and establishes a basis for using planar-channeled focusing for the structural study of interface phenomena, such as impurity location, interface reconstruction, and other structural effects.

REFERENCES

1. W.K. Chu, J.W. Mayer, M-A. Nicolet, T.M. Buck, G. Amsel, and F. Eisen, *Thin Solid Films*, Vol 17, 1973, p 1; Vol 19, 1973, p 423
2. W.K. Chu, J.W. Mayer, and M-A. Nicolet, *Backscattering Spectrometry*, Academic Press, 1978
3. J.F. Ziegler and R.F. Lever, *Thin Solid Films*, Vol 19, 1983, p 291
4. J.R. Macdonald, J.A. Davies, T.E. Jackman, and L.C. Feldman, *J. Appl. Phys.*, Vol 54, 1983, p 1800
5. P.P. Pronko, B.R. Appleton, O.W. Holland, and S.R. Wilson, *Phys. Rev. Lett.*, Vol 43, 1979, p 779
6. J.H. Barrett, B.R. Appleton, and O.W. Holland, *Phys. Rev. B*, Vol 22, 1980, p 4180
7. J.F. Ziegler and W.K. Chu, *At. Data Nucl. Data Tables*, Vol 13, 1974, p 463
8. J.F. Ziegler, *Helium: Stopping Powers and Ranges in All Elemental Matter*, Pergamon Press, 1978
9. L.C. Feldman, J.W. Mayer, and S.T.

Fig. 15 The resonance effect in planar dechanneling, with the wavelength of the channeled-particle oscillations matched to the period of an SLS

(a) Catastrophic planar dechanneling condition for matching the wavelength of the beam (82 nm) to the effective pair layer thickness of an SLS. Tracing of the position and direction of the beam is based on the phase rotation analysis. (b) Aligned {110} yield versus depth for 1.2-MeV ^{4}He backscattering from a GaP crystal (background) and from an SLS with a GaAs$_{0.12}$P$_{0.88}$/GaP path length per layer of 41 nm. Source: Ref 30

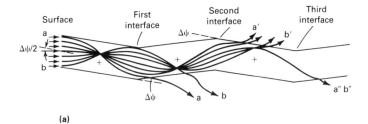

(a)

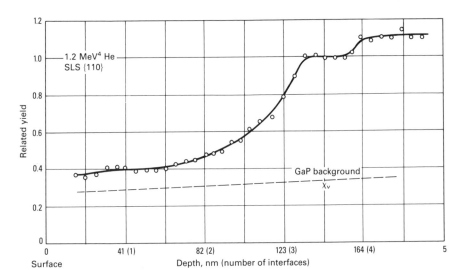

(b)

Picraux, *Materials Analysis by Ion Channeling*, Academic Press, 1982
10. F.W. Saris, *Nucl. Inst. Methods*, Vol 194, 1982, p 625
11. R.M. Tromp, *J. Vac. Sci. Technol.*, Vol A1, 1983, p 1047
12. M-A. Nicolet and W.K. Chu, *Am. Labs.*, March 1978, p 22
13. K.N. Tu, W.K. Chu, and J.W. Mayer, *Thin Solid Films*, Vol 25, 1975, p 403
14. W.K. Chu, H. Krautle, J.W. Mayer, H. Muller, M-A. Nicolet, and K.N. Tu, *Appl. Phys. Lett.*, Vol 25, 1974, p 454
15. T.W. Sigmon, W.K. Chu, H. Muller, and J.W. Mayer, *Appl. Phys.*, Vol 5, 1975, p 347
16. W.K. Chu, R.H. Kastl, R.F. Lever, S. Mader, and B.J. Masters, *Phys. Rev.*, Vol B16, 1977, p 3851
17. Y. Quēré, *Phys. Stat. Sol.*, Vol 30, 1968, p 713
18. T. Mizutani, C.J. Dale, W.K. Chu, and T.M. Mayer, *Nucl. Inst. Methods B*, Vol 7/8, 1985, p 825
19. J.W.M. Frenken and J.F. van der Veen, *Phys. Rev. Lett.*, Vol 54, 1985, p 134
20. R.B. Alexander and J.M. Poate, *Radiat. Eff.*, Vol 12, 1972, p 211
21. J.P. Bugeat, A.C. Chami, and E. Ligeon, *Phys. Lett.*, Vol 58A, 1976, p 127
22. H.D. Carstangen and R. Sizmann, *Phys. Lett.*, Vol 40A, 1972, p 93
23. S.T. Picraux and F.L. Vook, *Phys. Rev. Lett.*, Vol 33, 1974, p 1216
24. S.T. Picraux, W.L. Brown, and W.M. Gibson, *Phys. Rev.*, Vol B6, 1972, p 1382
25. W.K. Chu and B.J. Masters, in *Laser-Solid Interactions and Laser Processing—1978*, Vol 50, S.D. Ferris, J.H. Leamy, and J.M. Poate, Ed., AIP Conference Proceedings, American Institute of Physics, New York, 1979, p 305
26. J.W. Matthews and A.E. Blakeslee, *J. Vac. Sci. Technol.*, Vol 44, 1977, p 98
27. G.C. Osbourn, R.M. Biefeld, and P.L. Gourley, *Appl. Phys. Lett.*, Vol 41, 1982, p 172
28. C.K. Pan, D.C. Zheng, T.G. Finstad, W.K. Chu, V.S. Speriosu, M-A. Nicolet, and J.H. Barrett, *Phys. Rev.*, Vol B31, 1985, p 1270
29. J.C. Bean, T.T. Sheng, L.C. Feldman, A.T. Fiory, and R.T. Lynch, *Appl. Phys. Lett.*, Vol 44, 1984, p 102
30. W.K. Chu, J.A. Ellison, S.T. Picraux, R.M. Biefeld, and G.C. Osbourn, *Phys. Rev. Lett.*, Vol 52, 1984, p 125
31. S.T. Picraux, W.R. Allen, R.M. Biefeld, J.A. Ellison, and W.K. Chu, *Phys. Rev. Lett.*, Vol 54, 1985, p 2355

Chromatography

Gas Chromatography/ Mass Spectrometry

Leo A. Raphaelian, Chemical Technology Division, Argonne National Laboratory

General Uses

- Analysis of complex mixtures of volatile compounds
- In mass spectrometry/mass spectrometry, analysis of nonvolatile compounds
- In pyrolysis gas chromatography/mass spectrometry, analysis and quality control of polymers
- In liquid chromatography/mass spectrometry, analysis of heat-sensitive and degradable compounds, such as biological materials

Examples of Applications

- *Gas chromatography/mass spectrometry*: Mixtures of volatile compounds in petroleum oil, coal gasification and liquefaction products, oil shale, and tar sands; pollutants in air, waste water, and solid waste; drugs and metabolites; pesticides; and additives, such as antioxidants and plasticizers in plastics
- *Liquid chromatography/mass spectrometry*: Mixtures of nonvolatile and heat-sensitive compounds
- *Mass spectrometry/mass spectrometry*: Mixtures of nonvolatile and high molecular weight solids
- *Pyrolysis gas chromatography/mass spectrometry*: Analysis of polymers and their additives

Samples

- *Form*: Solids, liquids, and gases; all organics and some inorganics
- *Size*: For gas chromatography/mass spectrometry, a 1- to 5-μL injection in which each compound of interest is in the 20- to 200-ng range or, when split in the injection port, is in that range. For selected ion monitoring gas chromatography/mass spectrometry, 1.5 μL in which each compound of interest is in the 100- to 500-pg range; in some cases, down to 0.5 pg. For liquid chromatography/mass spectrometry and mass spectrometry/mass spectrometry, sample sizes are 20 to 500 ng per compound of interest and 10 to 500 ng per compound of interest, respectively
- *Preparation*: Samples should be prepared to conform to the sample size restrictions given above

Limitations

- Compound(s) must be ionizable
- Detection limit is from 5 to 20 ng, depending on the compound. In selected ion monitoring gas chromatography/mass spectrometry, the detection limit can be as low as 0.5 pg

Estimated Analysis Time

- When analyzing one compound, direct introduction of sample takes 10 to 20 min per analysis. For gas chromatography/mass spectrometry, analysis of 1 to 2 compounds takes approximately 15 min, while analysis of 20 or more compounds takes 180 min or more
- *Analysis and interpretation of data*: Variable (15 min to days depending on the number of compounds analyzed)

Capabilities of Related Techniques

- *Gas chromatography/Fourier-transform infrared spectroscopy*: Functional group analysis, but at least an order of magnitude less sensitive
- *Nuclear magnetic resonance*: Only single compounds and at least two orders of magnitude less sensitive
- *Secondary ion mass spectroscopy*: A mass spectrometry method for looking only at surfaces of materials

Introduction

The gas chromatograph/mass spectrometer is the coupling of two analytical instruments, the gas chromatograph and the mass spectrometer; it is particularly useful in analyzing mixtures of organic compounds. The mass spectrometer portion of the instrument is a powerful tool for determining the structure of a compound. With it, information on the molecular weight and the pieces that constitute the molecules in a sample can be obtained. However, the mass spectrometer is useless if two or more compounds are introduced into it at a time, because the spectra become unduly complex and difficult to interpret. All products, natural or manmade, occur in mixtures, although in certain cases one compound may predominate. However, even in cases in which one compound is predominant, there is often interest in the impurities and their effect on the product and/or the additives or decomposition products within the sample.

To make the mass spectrometer useful for the analysis of mixtures of compounds, a device is needed that will separate mixtures and supply each compound to the mass spectrometer, preferably, one at a time. When coupled to a mass spectrometer, the gas chromatograph acts as a good separating device for the mass spectrometer.

Gas chromatography/mass spectrometry (GC/MS) has been used in such diverse fields as the analysis of additives in polymers and the analysis of drugs in the urine of athletes participating in the olympics. It is commonly used in the analysis of petroleum oil, coal gasification and liquefaction products, drugs, metabolites, food products, perfumes and other cosmetics, plasticizers, pesticides, pollutants in air, waste water and solid waste, products and by-products of manufacturing processes, and solvents used in manufacturing processes.

Principles of Mass Spectrometry

When a molecule(s) passes through an electron beam having an energy of approximately 10 eV, an electron is removed from the molecule, and a positively charged ion (molecular ion) is formed; that is, the molecule is ionized. If a beam with a higher energy is used, the molecule will not only lose an electron but will also break apart into pieces to form fragment ions. Typically, in GC/MS systems, the electron beam energy is set at 70 eV, and depending upon the compound or molecule, a variety of ions are produced. For example, with ethyl alcohol, some of the ions that are formed are shown

Table 1   Ions produced in ethyl alcohol during GC/MS analysis

$CH_3CH_2OH \xrightarrow{-e} (CH_3CH_2OH)^+$	Mass 46		Molecular or parent ion
$CH_3CH_2OH \xrightarrow{-H} CH_3CH_2O^+$	Mass 45		
$CH_3CH_2OH \xrightarrow{-H} CH_2CH_2OH^+$	Mass 45		
$CH_3CH_2OH \xrightarrow{-CH_3} CH_2OH^+$	Mass 31	}	Fragment ions
$CH_3CH_2OH \xrightarrow{-OH} CH_3CH_2^+$	Mass 29		
$CH_3CH_2OH \xrightarrow{-CH_2OH} CH_3^+$	Mass 15		

in Table 1. Once the ions are formed, a means of detection and identification is needed. One technique is to send the ions down a long tube and see how long it takes each ion to reach the end of the tube where the detector is located. The light low-mass ions arrive first, and the heavy high-mass ions arrive last. Such a mass spectrometer is called a time-of-flight mass spectrometer.

Another technique is to send the ions down a tube that is placed in a magnetic field. The magnetic field will bend the ions, making them travel in approximately a circular path. However, a stronger magnetic field is required to bend the heavier ions than the lighter ones. Thus, ions of varying mass can be successively focused on the end of a tube where the detector is located and the magnetic field is varied. This is a magnetic sector mass spectrometer.

A third technique for analyzing the ions that are produced is to send them down a tube in which four rods are placed. Oscillating electric fields are placed on the rods to force the ions to undergo stable oscillations. Based on a radio frequency (RF) alternating current (ac) voltage superimposed on a ramped direct current (dc) voltage, ions of increasing mass are focused successively on the detector at the end of the tube. This type of mass spectrometer, which is widely used in GC/MS, is called a quadrupole mass spectrometer. Each of the mass spectrometers discussed above has a means of ionizing or fragmenting molecules (in the source), differentiating or separating ions of different mass (in the analyzer), and detecting ions (in the detector). The graphical representation, a mass spectrum, of ethyl alcohol is shown in Fig. 1.

In this mass spectrum, as is typically done in mass spectrometry, all peak intensities are normalized to the highest peak, in this case the 31 peak. The 46 mass peak that is formed with only the loss of an electron is called the molecular or parent ion and provides information on the molecular weight of the compound. All other peaks are fragment ions, that is, pieces of the original molecule. The mass spectroscopist recognizes masses of fragments that occur frequently and is often

Fig. 1 Mass spectrum (major peaks only) of ethyl alcohol (CH_3CH_2OH, molecular weight = 46)

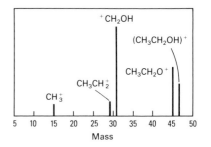

able to deduce the structure of an unknown from knowledge of the molecular ion and the fragment ions. If there is difficulty in identifying a compound, the mass spectroscopist can consult libraries of mass spectra of over 50 000 compounds not only tabulated in books (Ref 1) but also searchable by data systems (Ref 2).

Principles of Gas Chromatography

A gas chromatograph is an instrument in which mixtures of compounds can be separated into their components. In initial experiments in chromatography, several colored compounds in a mixture were placed at the head of a column packed with absorbent. When solvent was added to the column, the compounds moved down the column at different speeds and separated into colored bands, which could be observed visually, hence the term chromatograph, from chroma, which means color. The technique is of course applicable to all compounds, colored or not.

The chromatographic process is the partitioning of compound between two phases, a stationary phase and a mobile phase. The amount of compound in each phase depends upon its relative affinity for the two phases. The proportion to which a compound distributes itself between two phases, which is termed the partition coefficient, is different for different compounds.

A gas chromatographic column can be visualized as basically a series of tiny units in which partitioning takes place many times between a mobile phase and a stationary phase. This partitioning process is demonstrated in Table 2, which shows that the compound partitions equally between the mobile phase and the stationary phase. After stage 1, all of the compound is distributed equally between the mobile and stationary phases in the first partition unit. The mobile phase then carries the amount that is in the mobile phase onto the next partition unit. In this case, that would be 0.5, which now is distributed equally between the mobile and stationary phase, or 0.25 of the original material goes in the stationary phase and 0.25 remains in the mobile phase in the second partition unit. In the first partition

unit, 0.5 of the original material remains in the stationary phase. This is then distributed equally between the two phases, and 0.25 therefore goes from the stationary phase to the mobile phase.

After five such partitioning processes, the compound is distributed as shown in stage 5. The highest concentration is in the third partitioning unit. Table 3 shows that at the end of five partitioning steps on three compounds with 0.3, 0.5, and 0.7 partition coefficients the three compounds have been separated to a certain extent. After eleven steps (Table 4), the compounds have been separated slightly more. After several thousand steps, the separation is appreciable. By this process, a mixture of compounds having different partition coefficients can be separated.

In gas chromatography, the stationary phase is typically a high molecular weight

silicone coated on the inner walls of the column (open tubular wall-coated column, commonly known as a capillary column) or coated on a support, such as Chromsorb, and packed in a column (packed column). The mobile phase is typically helium, nitrogen, hydrogen, or some other inert gas. The gas moves the compounds that are not dissolved in the stationary phase down the column. Detection takes place at the end of the column where the compounds exit the column along with the mobile phase.

In gas chromatography with a flame ionization detector, the compounds reaching the end of the column are ionized in a flame and the number of ions measured. Other detectors used in gas chromatography include the thermal conductivity detector, in which heat-conducting properties or the specific heat changes are measured, and the electron capture detector, in which compounds with a high electron affinity change a standardized electrical current in the detector. With each of these detectors, a change in response of the detector is recorded when a compound exits the column and is present in the detector. The chromatogram is a plot of the change in response of the detector (y-axis) as a function of time (x-axis). With GC/MS, the mass spectrometer is also used as the detector for the gas chromatograph; however, it differs from the flame ionization, thermal conductivity, or electron capture detectors because not only intensity data but also information about the structure of the compound is generated.

Interpreting Mass Spectrum

Isotope Abundances. In determining the structure of a compound from its mass spectrum, the analyst typically uses not only the molecular ion data from which the molecular weight is obtained but also the masses of fragments from which pieces that make up the molecules can be deduced. There is, however, other information in mass spectra that can be useful for determining

Table 2   Representation of the partitioning process between a mobile phase and a stationary phase in a gas chromatograph column

See text for explanation of the process. Tables 2 and 3 show compound separations after 5 and 11 partitioning steps, respectively.

	Phase	1	2	3	4	5
Stage 1	Mobile	0.5	...	...	...	...
	Stationary	0.5	...	...	...	...
Stage 2	Mobile	0.25	0.25	...	...	...
	Stationary	0.25	0.25	...	...	...
Stage 3	Mobile	0.125	0.250	0.125	...	...
	Stationary	0.125	0.250	0.125	...	...
Stage 4	Mobile	0.0625	0.1875	0.1875	0.0625	...
	Stationary	0.0625	0.1875	0.1875	0.0625	...
Stage 5	Mobile	0.03125	0.12500	0.18750	0.12500	0.03125
	Stationary	0.03125	0.12500	0.18750	0.12500	0.03125

Table 3   Separation of three compounds after 5 partitioning steps

See text for details.

Phase	Partition coefficients	1	2	3	4	5
Mobile	0.3	0.07203	0.12348	0.07938	0.02268	0.00243
Stationary	0.7	0.16807	0.28812	0.18522	0.05292	0.00567
Mobile	0.5	0.03125	0.12500	0.18750	0.12500	0.03125
Stationary	0.5	0.03125	0.12500	0.18750	0.12500	0.03125
Mobile	0.7	0.00567	0.05292	0.18522	0.28812	0.16807
Stationary	0.3	0.00243	0.02268	0.07938	0.12348	0.07203

Table 4   Separation of three compounds after 11 partitioning steps

Note the enhanced separation as compared to Tables 1 and 2.

Phase	Partition coefficients	1	2	3	4	5	6	7	8	9	10	11
Mobile	0.3	0.008474	0.036318	0.070042	0.080048	0.060036	0.031366	0.011027	0.002701	0.000434	0.000041	0.000002
Stationary	0.7	0.019773	0.084743	0.163432	0.186780	0.140085	0.073187	0.025730	0.006301	0.001013	0.000096	0.000004
Mobile	0.5	0.000488	0.004883	0.021973	0.058594	0.10254	0.125000	0.10254	0.058594	0.021973	0.004883	0.000488
Stationary	0.5	0.000488	0.004883	0.021973	0.058594	0.10254	0.125000	0.10254	0.058594	0.021973	0.004883	0.000488
Mobile	0.7	0.000004	0.000096	0.001013	0.006301	0.025730	0.073187	0.140085	0.186780	0.163432	0.084734	0.019773
Stationary	0.3	0.000002	0.000041	0.000434	0.002701	0.011027	0.031366	0.060036	0.080048	0.070042	0.036318	0.008474

the structure of a compound from its mass spectrum.

Since many atoms are present naturally in more than one isotopic form, each ion can have those isotopic forms. For example, chlorine occurs naturally as chlorine-35 and chlorine-37 in the ratio of 3:1. Thus, a mass spectrum of hydrochloric acid (HCl) would show those masses associated with the two isotopes:

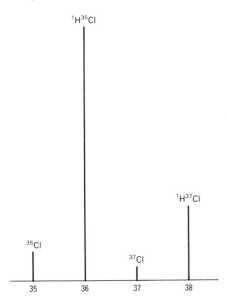

The biggest peak (at 36) is due to HCl with chlorine-35; the second largest peak (at 38) is due to HCl with chlorine-37, and it is one-third as great as the peak of HCl with chlorine-35 because chlorine-35 and chlorine-37 occur naturally in approximately a ratio of 3:1, respectively. If there are two chlorine atoms in a molecule, the relative size of the peaks can be predicted: the probability of finding a ^{35}Cl with another ^{35}Cl is $3/4 \times 3/4$ or $9/16$ because, statistically, three out of every four molecules is ^{35}Cl and one out of every four is ^{37}Cl. Similarly, the probability of finding a ^{37}Cl with another ^{37}Cl is $1/4 \times 1/4$ or $1/16$. The probability of finding a ^{35}Cl with a ^{37}Cl is $3/4 \times 1/4$ or $3/16$ and a ^{37}Cl with a ^{35}Cl is $1/4 \times 3/4$ or $3/16$. Thus, the following is obtained:

Mass	Molecule	Probability	Total probability
70	^{35}Cl^{35}Cl	$3/4 \times 3/4$	$9/16$
72	^{35}Cl^{37}Cl ^{37}Cl^{35}Cl	$3/4 \times 1/4$ $1/4 \times 3/4$	$6/16$
74	^{37}Cl^{37}Cl	$1/4 \times 1/4$	$1/16$

Thus, the peak intensity of the 70, 72, and 74 masses in a spectrum of chlorine gas (Cl$_2$) would be in a ratio of 9:6:1:

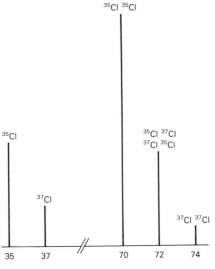

With more chlorines in a molecule, the patterns change and can be used to identify how many chlorines are present:

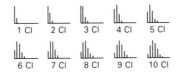

Such patterns are very useful in identifying polychlorinated biphenyls (PCB). Figure 2 shows an example of a spectrum of a pentachlorobiphenyl.

The pattern in the 320 to 340 mass range is similar to the pattern for five chlorines, and the pattern in the 250 and 260 mass range is similar to the pattern for three chlorines.

Table 5 lists naturally occurring isotopes. The ratio for naturally occurring hydrogen isotopes (^{1}H:^{2}H) is 99.985:0.015. Since ^{2}H occurs naturally in small amounts, it is difficult to see this isotope. However, with carbon, the ratio for ^{12}C:^{13}C is 98.892:1.108. Thus, approximately 1% of all naturally occurring carbon is present in the carbon-13 form. In naphthalene, where there are ten carbons per molecule, statistically, approximately one in every ten molecules would have a carbon-13. A mass spectrum of naphthalene is shown in Fig.

3. The largest peak has a mass of 128. It represents the molecular ion, ^{12}C$_{10}$H$_8$. At mass 129, the peak representing ^{12}C$_9$^{13}C$_1$H$_8$ is approximately 10% of the 128 peak. Thus, if a peak is seen at one mass higher than the molecular peak, that is, 15% of the molecular peak, it can be assumed that there are 15 carbons in the molecule (it should be noted that the abundances are not always exact, because impurities are often present). This can be very useful information in determining what the molecule is.

Exact Mass Measurements. With the exception of carbon, which by convention has a mass of exactly 12, all other atoms do not have integral masses (Table 5). For example, hydrogen has a mass of 1.0078246, nitrogen 14.0030738, and oxygen 15.9949141. The mass of a C$_{30}$ hydrocarbon, triacotane, C$_{30}$H$_{62}$, is $(30)(12) + (62)(1.0078246)$ or 422.485128 or almost half a mass unit higher than 422, the nominal mass. In high-resolution mass spectrometry, the mass can be measured out to two or more decimal places. This is useful for differentiating between compounds that have the same nominal mass, such as nitrogen, carbon monoxide, and ethylene:

Nitrogen N$_2$	Carbon monoxide CO	Ethylene C$_2$H$_4$
28.006	27.995	28.033

In a high-resolution instrument, the exact masses of not only the molecular ion but also all fragment ions are recorded. In modern data systems, the exact mass of the ion can be listed, and empirical formulas that would fit best can be tabulated. A tabulated output of one mass spectrum in a GC/MS analysis obtained using a high-resolution mass spectrometer is shown in Table 6. The left-hand column in Table 6 has the nominal mass under m/e, which represents the mass-to-charge ratio. Thus, this particular compound has fragment ions of 41, 42, 53, 55, 56, 82, 84, 97, and 112. The 113 peak is probably the molecular ion, and the 114 peak is probably the molecular ion with one carbon-13. In this tabulation, the data system calculates empirical formulas based on C, H, N, S, and O and compares them to the observed

Fig. 2 Mass spectrum of pentachlorobiphenyl showing five chlorine and three chlorine patterns

Source: Ref 1

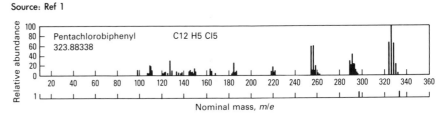

Fig. 3 Spectrum of naphthalene with a peak at 129 for $^{12}C_9\,^{13}C_1H_8$, that is, approximately 10% of the 128 peak

Source: Ref 1

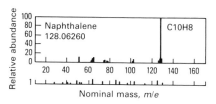

Table 5 Some naturally occurring isotopes and their percent natural abundance and atomic mass

Isotope	Atomic mass	Abundance, %
^1H	1.00782	99.985
^2H	2.014	0.015
^3He	3.0160	0.00013
^4He	4.00260	100.00
^6Li	6.01512	7.42
^7Li	7.01600	92.58
^9Be	9.01218	100.00
^{10}B	10.0129	19.78
^{11}B	11.00931	80.22
^{12}C	12.0000	98.89
^{13}C	13.00335	1.11
^{14}N	14.00307	99.63
^{15}N	15.00011	0.37
^{16}O	15.99491	99.759
^{17}O	...	0.037
^{18}O	...	0.204
^{19}F	18.99840	100.00
^{20}Ne	19.99244	90.92
^{21}Ne	20.99395	0.257
^{22}Ne	21.99138	8.82
^{23}Na	22.9898	100.00
^{24}Mg	23.98504	78.70
^{25}Mg	24.98584	10.13
^{26}Mg	25.98259	11.17
^{27}Al	26.98153	100.00
^{28}Si	27.97693	92.21
^{29}Si	28.97649	4.70
^{30}Si	29.97376	3.09
^{31}P	30.97376	100.00
^{32}S	31.97207	95.00
^{33}S	32.97146	0.76
^{34}S	33.96786	4.22
^{36}S	35.96709	0.014
^{35}Cl	34.96885	75.53
^{37}Cl	...	24.47

Source: Ref 3

Table 6 Tabulated output of one mass spectrum during a GC/MS analysis of extracted shale oil

m/e	C	H	N 14	S 32	O 16	mmu	Observed mass	% height of base peak B
41	3	5	0	0	0	1.9	41.0372	76.93
42	2	4	1	0	0	−2.0	42.0364	35.39
53	4	5	0	0	0	5.9	53.0332	5.90
	3	3	1	0	0	−6.7		
	1	9	0	1	0	9.3		
	0	7	1	1	0	−3.3		
55	3	5	1	0	0	9.6	55.0326	20.02
	2	3	2	0	0	−3.0	55.0326	20.02
56	2	4	2	0	0	4.0	56.0334	86.60
	1	2	3	0	0	−8.6		
	3	4	0	0	1	−7.2		
82	3	2	2	0	1	−1.2	82.0179	7.24
	0	6	2	1	1	2.1		
	1	6	0	1	2	−9.1		
84	4	6	1	0	1	−0.1	84.0450	9.16
	1	10	1	1	1	3.3		
	0	8	2	1	1	−9.3		
97	7	13	0	0	0	−5.9	97.1077	6.78
98	4	8	3	0	0	7.7	98.0641	11.59
	6	10	0	0	1	9.1		
	5	8	1	0	1	−3.5		
	2	12	1	1	1	−0.1		
112	5	10	3	0	0	7.9	112.0796	53.29
	7	12	0	0	1	9.2		
	6	10	1	0	1	−3.4		
	3	14	1	1	1	0.0		
113	5	11	3	0	0	7.5	113.0878	100.00 B
	7	13	0	0	1	8.9		
	6	11	1	0	1	−3.7		
114							114.0929	8.95
							127.9143	18.99

Note: m/e is the mass-to-charge ratio, or nominal mass; mmu is millimass units (see text for discussion)

the molecular ion and fragments, the molecular structure of the compound can be deduced.

With the above techniques, the mass spectroscopist has available a variety of pieces of information from which the molecular structure of an unknown can be determined. These include the molecular ion representing the molecular weight and the masses of fragments of the molecule representing pieces of the molecule from which the whole molecule can be reconstructed. Many atoms, such as chlorine, bromine, sulfur, and mercury, can be recognized due to the uniqueness of their ion patterns arising from various isotopes. When dealing with organic compounds, the number of carbon atoms in the molecule can often be approximated by looking at the ion mass above the molecular ion that is due to carbon-13 occurring naturally approximately 1% of the time. Finally, since atoms, except carbon-12, do not have integral masses, each compound has a unique mass. Therefore, if exact mass measurements with a high-resolution mass spectrometer are conducted, compounds with the same integral mass can be differentiated.

mass. For example, for mass 113, the system found three formulas to be a fairly close fit to the observed mass, 113.0878. They are $C_5H_{11}N_3$, which is 7.5 millimass units high (expected for $C_5H_{11}N_3$ 113.0953, found 113.0878, difference 0.075); $C_7H_{13}O_1$, which is 8.9 millimass units high; and $C_6H_{11}N_1O_1$, which is 3.7 millimass units low. With this exact mass data for

Methodology in GC/MS

In a typical GC/MS experiment, a sample, dissolved in a solvent such as methylene chloride, is injected with a syringe into the injection port of a gas chromatograph. The sample is immediately vaporized onto the column, and the chromatographic process begins. The gas chromatograph oven can be set to operate at one temperature (isothermal) throughout the entire experiment, or can be programmed from, for example, 20 to 280 °C (70 to 535 °F) at a rate of 4 °C/min (7 °F/min). In isothermal operation, the low-boiling compounds tend to bunch up at the beginning of the chromatogram, and the high-boiling compounds tend to spread out. Generally, those compounds that boil somewhat above the temperature of the oven separate satisfactorily. If a programmed run is used, compounds with a wide range of boiling points are separated.

The compounds emerge, it is hoped, one at a time from the end of the column and go directly (or through a separator, which removes carrier gas) to the mass spectrometer source. During the experiment, the mass spectrometer scans continuously; that is, it scans, for example, from 50 to 500 mass units in 1 s, then spends 0.2 s to put the data on the disk. After each scan, the mass spectrometer starts another. Thus, in a 1-h experiment of 3600 s, 3000 mass spectra (3600 ÷ 1.2) are collected and put on disk; a total mass spectrum is taken every 1.2 s during the run.

After the experiment has been completed, data reduction can be initiated (in most GC/MS systems, data reduction can be done while the experiment is in progress). During an experiment, the ion intensity in the mass spectrometer will be low when no compound is entering the mass spectrometer and high when there is compound exiting the gas chromatograph and entering the mass spectrometer. A plot of the ion intensity as a function of time (total ion chromatogram) is useful to identify when, in terms of time or mass spectrum number, compounds emerged from the gas chromatograph and entered the mass spectrometer (Fig. 4). If the analyst is interested in a peak at 30.35 min, the data system can be asked to display the mass spectrum taken at that time during the run (Fig. 5). Once the mass spectrum has been obtained, it can be compared to a spectra tabulated in a library of mass spectra published in a book (Fig. 6) or a library of mass spectra stored in the data system on disk; alternatively, the structure of the compound may be deduced by looking at the molecular ion and the fragment ions.

Selected ion monitoring is often used in cases in which the analyst is not interested in identifying all the compounds in a mixture but only in whether a few (perhaps one or two) specific compounds are present. It is particularly useful when a specific compound is to be analyzed and the amount of that compound within a mixture to be analyzed is exceedingly small.

In selected ion monitoring, the mass spectrometer is set up to allow only those ions associated with the compound(s) of interest to pass through the analyzer and reach the detector throughout the GC/MS analysis. For example, if butylated hydroxy toluene (BHT) were the compound of interest, only ions 220 and 205 would be monitored throughout the GC/MS analysis (see the mass spectrum in Fig. 6). All other ions would be rejected, and data on the other ions would not be collected. The enhancement in sensitivity arises from spending more time collecting data of the ions that the BHT has, rather than scanning the whole mass range. After the GC/MS analysis, chromatograms of each of the ions, 220 and 205, are plotted (Fig. 7). If BHT were present in the mixture, the chromatograms of each of the ions would have a peak at the same time (the retention time of BHT), and the relative area or height

Fig. 4 Typical total ion chromatogram

A plot of the total ion intensity versus time

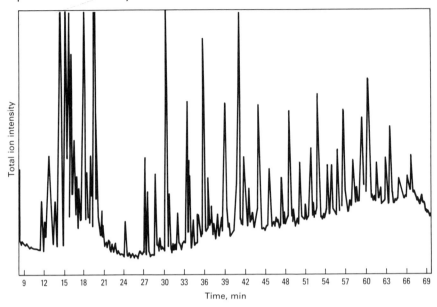

Fig. 5 Mass spectrum of peak at 30.35 min of the 2019th spectrum taken during the analysis

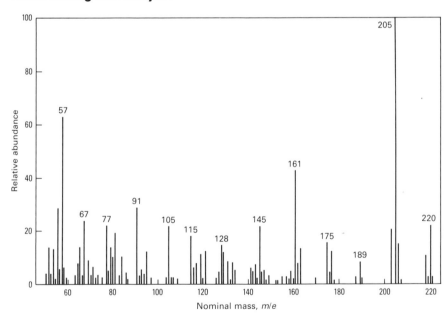

of the 220 and 205 ions would be related to the mass spectrum of BHT (Fig. 6); that is, they should be approximately in the ratio of 1:4. To verify that the peak is BHT, a standard can be run and the retention time determined. If that retention time is identical to the retention time of the peaks in the ion chromatogram and the relative abundances are approximately the same as the standard, the presence of BHT is proven sufficiently that such evidence can be used in a court of law.

Sample Preparation. Gas chromatograph/mass spectrometers can comfortably handle samples that have 20 to 100 ng per component within the mixture. Samples with

Fig. 6 Mass spectrum from Ref 1 that matches the spectrum in Fig. 5

It should be noted that some peaks in the mass spectrum of Fig. 5 are due to background.

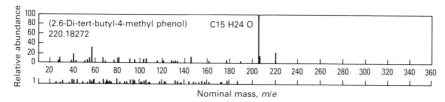

Fig. 7 Single-ion chromatograms of ions 205 and 220 generated from single-ion monitoring GC/MS

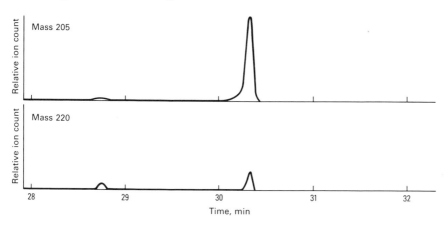

more than 200 ng of a specific compound tend to overload the gas chromatograph column, particularly narrow-bore high-resolution capillary columns. With 5 to 20 ng of compound, the mass spectrum tends to be weak, and it becomes difficult to make an assignment of the structure of the molecule. Unfortunately, the analyst is often interested in identifying the compounds that are present in a wide range of concentrations in a sample. In these cases, it is best to perform two experiments: one at high concentration and one with the sample diluted.

Having established the 20 to 100 ng per component in a mixture as the best concentration for analysis, there are several ways in which this can be achieved. Most gas chromatographs are set up to receive a 1- to 10-μL sample using a 10-μL syringe. The analysis of a gasoline sample will serve as an example. Gasoline has approximately 20 major compounds, 100 minor compounds, and perhaps thousands of compounds in trace quantities. Assume the major compounds represent 50% and the minor components 45% of the gasoline. If $^{1}/_{200}$ μL of gasoline were injected, an average of 125 ng per major component (1 000 000 ng × $^{50}/_{100}$ × $^{1}/_{200}$ × $^{1}/_{20}$) and an average of 22.5 ng per minor component (1 000 000 ng × $^{45}/_{100}$ × $^{1}/_{200}$ × $^{1}/_{100}$) would be obtained. With most gas chromatographs, the

sample can be split in the injection port so that only $^{1}/_{200}$ of a 1-μL injection, or some other fraction, goes on the column. Thus, with a 1-μL injection split 1 to 200, the major and minor components of gasoline can be analyzed. The trace ingredients, however, require a different approach because they tend to be hidden or overwhelmed by the major and minor components. To analyze the trace components, a preliminary separation of the gasoline mixture into simpler mixtures is required before analysis by GC/MS.

Keeping in mind the 20 to 100 ng per component in a mixture as the best concentration for GC/MS analysis, consider the analysis of pollutants that may be present in very small quantities in a waste water stream. The compounds of interest are extracted from the waste water with a solvent, such as methylene chloride, and the solution is concentrated to give the desired concentration range. For example, a 1-L sample of waste water can be extracted three times with 30 mL of methylene chloride, the extracts concentrated to 1 mL, and 1 μL injected into the gas chromatograph. Since 1 μL represents one-thousandth of the total extracts or one-thousandth of the extractables of the original 1 L of waste water and since approximately 20 ppm per component in the extract can be analyzed, concentrations as low as 20

ppb per component in the original waste water can be analyzed. Thus, in samples in which the compounds of interest are present in very small concentrations, the sample can be extracted with a solvent, and the solvent concentrated to give a solution that can be analyzed by GC/MS.

Detection Limits. As mentioned in the previous section, the detection limits (on gas chromatograph column) for most compounds are in the 10- to 20-ng range, but can go as low as 5 ng or less. With the selected ion monitor mode of operation, the detection limit is typically 100 picograms (pg), or 0.1 ng, but with care can go as low as 10 pg and even lower under ideal conditions where the samples are relatively clean (no interferences). These are of course on-column figures, that is, the actual amount of compound that goes on the column.

Complementary Techniques

For many years, mass spectrometry was performed with samples that were introduced directly into the mass spectrometer. Such samples included gases; solids, which were introduced with a probe; and liquids, which were introduced either in the gas inlet system or with a probe, depending upon their vapor pressure.

When GC/MS was introduced in the late 1960s, mixtures of compounds and impurities could be analyzed. However, GC/MS is applicable only to those compounds that are vaporizable, which include compounds that have exceedingly low vapor pressures, such as hydrocarbons with 50 or more carbons. Nevertheless, there is a large body of compounds that simply will not go through a gas chromatograph column.

Since the late 1970s, several techniques have been introduced to broaden the classes of compounds that can be analyzed by mass spectrometry. These include high-performance liquid chromatography/mass spectrometry (HPLC/MS) and mass spectrometry/mass spectrometry (MS/MS), both of which are discussed briefly below. Additional information can be found in the articles "Liquid Chromatography," "Spark Source Mass Spectrometry," and "Gas Analysis by Mass Spectrometry" in this Volume.

High-Performance Liquid Chromatography/Mass Spectrometry. As opposed to the partitioning in the gas phase in gas chromatography, high-performance liquid chromatography (HPLC) is performed in the liquid phase. Since many different liquids can be used as the mobile phase along with various stationary phases, the method is considerably more versatile than gas chromatography. However, there are technical problems in interfacing high-performance liquid chromatographs with mass spectrometers, and the resolution of columns for HPLC is an order of magnitude less than that of gas chromatography columns. Nevertheless, the high-performance liquid chromatograph has proved useful for separating mixtures of compounds that cannot be chromatographed on a gas chromatograph column.

Of the many HPLC techniques that are available, three are noteworthy. First, there is the normal type by which compounds are separated based on their polarity or their affinity or adsorption onto the stationary phase of the column. In a typical separation, the sample is dissolved in a nonpolar solvent, such as benzene, and injected onto the beginning of the high-performance liquid chromatograph column. The column is flushed with additional benzene, and each of the compounds eventually reaches the end of the column. Alternatively, the solvent can be progressively altered, for example, from benzene to methanol, such that the polarity of the solvent is continuously increased (gradient elution); this helps the more polar compounds to go through the column. By this method, nonpolar compounds elute initially, and, progressively, more polar compounds elute during the course of the experiment.

In the second HPLC technique, which is basically the reverse of the normal type (reverse-phase HPLC), a stationary phase is relatively nonpolar, and the sample is dissolved in a polar solvent and injected onto the column. Those compounds that are very polar pass through the column relatively unimpeded, and, progressively, compounds of weaker and weaker polarity go through the column.

Finally, a third HPLC technique, commonly called gel permeation chromatography, is useful for the separation of a mixture of compounds according to their size. The packing material in the column is a polymeric material that is porous. As a mixture of compound passes through the column containing this material, the smaller molecules get trapped in the holes of the packing material, and their travel through the column is therefore impeded or slowed. Large molecules travel through the column rapidly, while smaller molecules take more time traveling through the column, according to their size.

Generally, normal-phase HPLC is used for the separation of mixtures of compounds that are nonpolar or weakly polar, reverse-phase HPLC for the separation of very polar and weakly polar compounds, and gel permeation chromatography for the separation of

Fig. 8 Block diagram of a mass spectrometer/mass spectrometer system

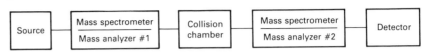

compounds according to their size. Whenever possible, a gas chromatograph is used as an inlet for a mass spectrometer in preference to HPLC because of its higher resolution and relative ease of operation with a mass spectrometer.

Mass Spectrometry/Mass Spectrometry. An MS/MS instrument is basically two mass spectrometers with a collision chamber (to fragment ions) in between (Fig. 8). Three types of experiments can be performed with this arrangement: daughter ion scans, parent ion scans, and neutral loss scans.

In daughter ion scans, the sample is ionized in the source, and ions of only one mass (selected by the mass spectroscopist) are allowed to pass through the first mass analyzer. The first analyzer, in effect, filters out all ions having masses other than the desired mass, which would normally be the parent ion of the compound of interest. When the ions having the desired mass reach the collision chamber, they collide with gas molecules in the collision chamber, fragmenting to ions that are analyzed in the second mass analyzer, which produces a mass spectrum. Essentially, the first mass analyzer behaves like a separation device, based on mass, allowing only molecular ions associated with the compound of interest to pass through it.

Since an electron beam tends to form too many fragment ions at the expense of molecular ions, soft ionization techniques, such as chemical ionization and fast atom bombardment, that give predominantly molecular ions with little or no fragmentation are typically used in MS/MS. When the first mass spectrometer is set up to pass only one ion, a trace impurity in a sample can be detected even at very low levels. With a high-resolution mass analyzer in the first mass spectrometer, the exact mass of the trace impurity can be set for the first mass analyzer so that other compounds with the same nominal integral mass are rejected. With this arrangement, the signal-to-noise ratio can be very high for detecting a specific trace impurity.

In parent ion scans, the second mass analyzer is set to pass only one mass, while the first analyzer is scanned in a normal manner. This type of experiment is useful in identifying compounds within a class of compounds that give a unique fragment ion. For example, all phthalate esters, which are

used as plasticizers, give a fragment ion of mass 149:

O
||
C—OR   Chemical
        Ionization
        →
C—OR
||
O

Phthalate ester
R = Me, Et, Pr, etc.

$^+$OH
||
C—OR   Cyclization
        →
C—OR
||
O

$^+$OH
||
C
    O
C
||
O

Mass 149

To observe phthalate esters in a sample, the second analyzer is tuned to mass 149, while the first analyzer is scanned normally. As the first analyzer is scanned, the molecular ion of each compound within the sample is successively allowed to pass through the first analyzer. After fragmentation in the collision cell, if ions with mass 149 are produced in the collision cell, they will pass through the second analyzer to the detector. Thus, a response in the detector will occur only when molecular ions pass through the first analyzer and, upon fragmentation in the collision cell, produce fragments of mass 149 that can pass through the second analyzer. Thus, the masses of those molecular ions that produce fragment ions of mass 149 are recorded. However, no fragment-ion information (other than the one ion that the second analyzer is tuned to) is produced.

In neutral loss scans, the two mass analyzers are scanned simultaneously, with a constant mass difference maintained between the two analyzers during the scans. When the analyzers are scanned in this way, the molecular weight of compounds within a class that lose a specific ion can be identified. For example, alkyl thiols lose the SH group during fragmentation:

$$RSH \rightarrow R^+ + \underset{\text{Mass 33}}{SH}$$

If the first analyzer scans at a constant 33 atomic mass units (amu) higher than the second analyzer, only molecules that form molecular ions that pass through the first chamber and lose 33 amu in the collision chamber can pass through the second analyzer to reach the detector. Thus, the molecular weight of molecular ions that lose 33 amu is recorded (Fig. 9).

Applications

Example 1: Analysis of Polymers by Pyrolysis GC/MS. The analysis of polymers by conventional GC/MS techniques is normally not possible because polymers are typically high molecular weight materials that do not vaporize. Such additives as antioxidants and lubricants can be analyzed by grinding the polymer material, extracting the additives with a solvent, and, after removing most of the solvent, injecting the extract into a gas chromatograph/mass spectrometer. However, this method is cumbersome and time-consuming.

Another method, pyrolysis GC/MS, is not only more direct and less time-consuming for analyzing the additives but also is useful for identifying the polymer. It is particularly useful for quality control of polymeric materials and for detecting impurities that could lead to undesirable properties in the material.

In pyrolysis GC/MS, the sample is heated very rapidly in a chamber to high temperatures, for example, 600 to 1000 °C (1110 to 1830 °F), in less than 1 s. The high molecular weight molecules break apart into pieces, and the pieces (smaller molecules) are swept by carrier gas (the mobile phase) from the pyrolysis chamber onto the gas chromatograph column and analyzed by GC/MS. With the identification of the small pieces, the structure of original polymeric material can be inferred. Alternatively, the pattern of gas chromatography peaks serves as a fingerprint for the polymer and is very useful for quality control.

The experiment can also be done in three steps. First, the low molecular weight compounds, such as additives and lubricants, are

Fig. 9 Collision-activated dissociation mass spectra obtained in the 33 amu neutral loss mode on (M + 1) ions from organosulfur compounds

Samples include (a) South Swan Hills, (b) Prudhoe Bay, and (c) Gack Saran crude oils. Signals at *m/e* 134, 152, and 216 are due in part to residual ion current from a mixture of compounds 3, 7, and 6 used to set up the instrument for 33 amu neutral loss scans.

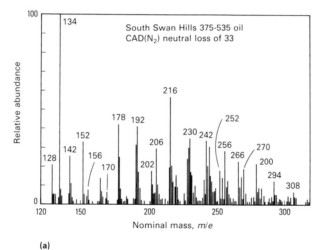

(a)

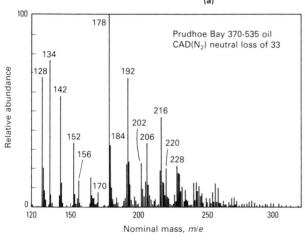

(b)

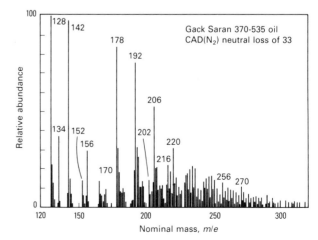

(c)

Fig. 10 New silicone cavity seal (a) versus used one (b)

Thermal desorption curves are shown on the left; pyrolysis gas chromatography spectrum on the right.

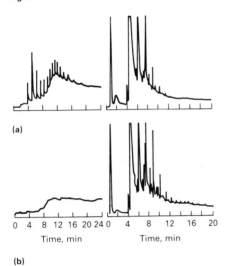

(a)

(b)

0   4   8   12 16 20 24   0   4   8   12   16   20
         Time, min   Time, min

Fig. 11(a) Chromatopyrogram of failed nitrile sheath

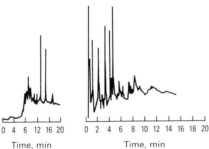

0 4 6 12 16 20   0 2 4 6 8 10 12 14 16 18 20
     Time, min   Time, min

Fig. 11(b) Chromatopyrogram of intact neoprene sheath

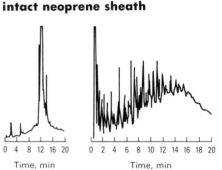

0 4 8 12 16 20   0 2 4 6 8 10 12 14 16 18 20
     Time, min   Time, min

thermally desorbed from the polymeric material by slowly heating the sample in the chamber to approximately 300 °C (570 °F), with subsequent GC/MS analysis. Second, the nonvolatile portion of the sample that remains is pyrolyzed by heating raidly to 600 to 1000 °C (1110 to 1830 °F) in less than 1 s to give pyrolysis products, which are analyzed by GC/MS. Finally, elemental analysis can be performed on the residue.

In a comparison of a new silicone cavity seal and one that had cracks, it was found by pyrolysis gas chromatography that the silicone was unchanged (Fig. 10), while the volatile components had been lost in the used sample (Ref 4). Although the identity of the lost components has not been reported, it is presumed that these materials were identified by GC/MS and more satisfactory additives developed to prevent cracking of the seal.

Example 2: Analysis of Rubber Sheaths by Pyrolysis Gas Chromatography. During a routine inspection of high-

voltage electric cables in a prototype AWACS aircraft, it was found that some of the rubber sheaths showed signs of crazing (Ref 5). Samples of the failed and good rubber sheaths were analyzed by pyrolysis gas chromatography and found to be entirely different rubbers. The chromatopyrograms in Fig. 11(a) and (b) proved that the failed rubber was a nitrile rubber, while the intact rubber was a neoprene rubber. In such instances, pyrolysis gas chromatography can be useful for quick screening of materials for quality control and for identifying the source of problems in materials.

ACKNOWLEDGMENT

Work supported by the U.S. Department of Energy under Contract No. W-31-109-Eng-38.

REFERENCES

1. E. Stenhagen, S. Abrahansson, and F.W. McLafferty, *Registry of Mass Spectral Data*, John Wiley & Sons, 1974
2. AWRE Aldermaston Library on disk in the Hewlett Packard 5933 Data System
3. Table of the Isotopes, in *Handbook of Chemistry and Physics*, 56th ed., CRC Press, 1975
4. J. Chih-An Hu, *Anal. Chem.*, Vol 49 (No. 4), 1977, p 537-540
5. J. Chih-An Hu, *Anal. Chem.*, Vol 53 (No. 2), 1981, p 311A

SELECTED REFERENCES

• J.H. Begyon and A.E. Williams, *Mass and Abundance Tables for Use in Mass Spectrometry*, Elsevier, 1963
• A. Fugerio, *Essential Aspects of Mass Spectrometry*, Spectrum Publications, 1974
• M.C. Hamming and N.G. Foster, *Interpretation of Mass Spectra of Organic Compounds*, Academic Press, 1972
• S.R. Heller and G.W.A. Milne, *EPA/NIH Mass Spectral Data Base*, U.S. Government Printing Office, Washington, 1978
• M.L. Lee, F.J. Yang, and K.D. Bartle, *Open Tubular Column Chromatography, Theory and Practice*, John Wiley & Sons, 1984
• W. McFadden, *Techniques of Combined Gas Chromatography/Mass Spectrometry*, John Wiley & Sons, 1973
• F.W. McLafferty, in *Advances in Chemistry*, Series No. 40, American Chemical Society, Washington, 1963
• F.W. McLafferty, *Mass Spectrometry of Organic Ions*, Academic Press, 1963

Liquid Chromatography

Michael J. Kelly, Sandia National Laboratories

General Uses

- Separation and quantitative analysis of components in organic, inorganic, pharmaceutical, and biochemical mixtures
- Analysis of organic and inorganic compounds for impurities
- Isolation of pure compounds from mixtures

Examples of Applications

- Analysis of solvents for low-level organic contaminants
- Monitoring the stability of polymers during aging tests
- Analysis of foods and natural products for high molecular weight sugars
- Analysis of thermally unstable pesticides
- Isolation of microgram amounts of material for identification purposes
- Isolation of large quantities (1 to 10 g) of purified compounds for synthetic purposes

Samples

- *Form*: Solids (dissolved in a suitable solvent) or liquids
- *Size*: 0.1 to 1 g generally required for quantitative work; however, as little as 10^{-5} g may be analyzed. Larger quantities may be required for preparative work
- *Preparation*: Sample must be dissolved in a suitable solvent at concentrations of 0.1 to 100 mg/mL (although neat liquids may be analyzed). Filtration or extraction of the solution may be necessary. Injection volume ≤ 0.1 mL is typical

Limitations

- Solids must be freely soluble in carrier solvent, and liquids must be miscible with it
- Difficult to make unambiguous identification of a particular component; subsequent analysis by infrared spectroscopy or mass spectrometry may be necessary

Estimated Analysis Time

- Requires 15 to 60 min for an analysis; several replicate analyses are usually performed
- May require one-half day to change column, solvents, or detector for a particular analysis
- Lengthy development may be required if method is not available

Capabilities of Related Techniques

- *Gas chromatography*: Restricted to volatile or pyrolyzable samples
- *Mass spectrometry, infrared spectroscopy, nuclear magnetic resonance*: Used to identify components isolated by liquid chromatography
- *Ion chromatography*: A type of liquid chromatography restricted to the analysis of ionic species

Introduction

In 1903, the Russian botanist M.S. Tswett devised a separation method called liquid column chromatography. Tswett separated structurally similar yellow and green chloroplast pigments obtained from leaf extracts by placing extract onto the top of a column of calcium carbonate particles and then washing the column with carbon disulfide (by gravity flow of the solvent). The colored pigments formed visible bands that separated as they moved down the column; thus, Tswett coined the term chromatography (from Greek, meaning"color writing"), although he realized the method was applicable to colorless compounds. Within a few years, liquid column chromatography had become a widely utilized technique. Significant achievements in biochemistry and the chemistry of complex natural organic compounds were made possible by this method.

In a classic paper published in 1941, Martin and Synge predicted that high-speed liquid column chromatography would require very small column particles and high pressure differences across the length of the column. The theoretical studies of Giddings

Fig. 1 Essential components of a liquid chromatograph

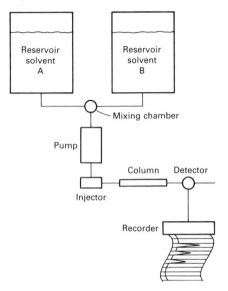

and Hamilton in the 1960s verified the earlier predictions and defined the conditions necessary for high-speed analysis. Modern liquid column chromatography, now called high-performance liquid chromatography (HPLC) or simply liquid chromatography (LC), was made possible by technical advances in equipment, columns, and column packing materials. As a result of these advances, LC is one of the fastest growing techniques in analytical chemistry. It enables the user to perform rapid, efficient separations of complex mixtures of organic, inorganic, pharmaceutical, and biochemical compounds.

Today, there are several modes of LC (bonded-phase, liquid-liquid partition, liquid-solid adsorption, ion-exchange, ion-pair, and size-exclusion), which can be employed with a single apparatus. The wide variety of available LC solvents adds to the selectivity that can be attained. Therefore, modern LC instrumentation (the liquid chromatograph) offers diversified approaches to separation problems.

Liquid Chromatographs

Liquid chromatographs, first constructed in the late 1960s, have since undergone rapid development. The essential components of a liquid chromatograph are shown in Fig. 1 and are characterized by the features listed below.

Dissolved gases in LC solvents can be detrimental to the performance of the system; therefore, they are removed by helium sparging or by a combination of vacuum,

stirring, and gentle heating. Solvent proportioning valves deliver precisely controlled volumes of solvent from the reservoirs to the mixing chamber. Some liquid chromatographs have four reservoirs, enabling complex solvent mixtures to be employed as the mobile phase.

High-pressure pumping systems transfer the solvent mixture from the mixing chamber to the injector valve and are usually capable of outputs of up to 34.5 MPa (5000 psi) and pulseless, reproducible flow deliveries of 0.1 to 10 mL/min. In modern liquid chromatographs, the solvent proportioning valves and the high-pressure pump are microprocessor-controlled. This enables the analyst to employ gradient elution (a stepwise or continuous change in the mobile phase composition) and/or flow programming (a stepwise or continuous change in the mobile phase flow rate) to increase the efficiency of the separation.

Injector valves are designed to accommodate sample introduction from microliter or milliliter syringes. These valves are equipped with sample loops that can be completely filled with sample solution while the mobile phase is flowing through a different channel. When the valve to the loop is opened, the mobile phase washes the solution out of the loop and carries it to the column. In this manner, a precise amount of sample is effectively placed on top of the chromatographic column with only slight perturbations in the mobile phase flow rate.

High-performance columns that provide minimum broadening of separated sample bands are the heart of the liquid chromatograph. Columns are made from 3- to 25-cm (1.2- to 10-in.) lengths of stainless steel tubing with inner diameters of 1 to 20 mm (0.04 to 0.8 in.). Columns are packed with small (3 to 50 μm) particles, which constitute the stationary phase. Porous frits or screens are placed at the ends of the columns to retain the packing. Stationary phases with a variety of chemical and physical properties are available. The choice of a stationary phase/mobile phase combination is determined by the nature of the separation problem.

None of the improvements in columns, stationary phases, or pump systems has facilitated the application of the liquid chromatograph as much as the introduction of the continuous flow-through detector. The immediate visual display on a recorder of the progress of a separation (the chromatogram) has freed the analyst from the tedium of fraction collection and examination. Consequently, it has been possible to devote much creative effort to the improvement and optimization of separation parameters and the screening of potential applications.

An ideal LC detector would (1) have universal response to all compounds, (2) have no response to the mobile phase, (3) have good sensitivity, (4) have response independent of column parameters, (5) have low dead volume, (6) provide structural information, (7) have linear response to sample concentration, and (8) be nondestructive, so that fractions can be collected. No single detector has all of these attributes. However, there are several detectors that meet some of the specifications.

The refractive index (RI) detector is unique among commonly used LC detectors in its close approach to being a universal detector. For the RI detector to be universal, it is necessary only that the mobile phase refractive index be different from that of the sample. With the large number of available LC solvents, this criterion is easily met. However, because this detector responds to changes in a bulk property of the eluent rather than to only a sample property, everything that effects the eluent will cause a response. Thus, eluent temperature and pressure (and those factors that influence them, such as flow rate, heat from columns, and composition) must be carefully controlled to attain the highest sensitivity. Typically, 10^{-6} g of a component in the injected sample is the detection limit with RI detectors.

The most sensitive and versatile detectors are those that measure some property of the sample that is weak or absent in the mobile phase. The ultraviolet/visible (UV/VIS) absorbance detector is currently the most popular detector of this type because most compounds absorb 190- to 700-nm wavelength radiation, and many other compounds that have no absorption can be chemically reacted to form an absorbing species. There are three types of UV/VIS detectors: (1) fixed-wavelength detectors, which operate only at one wavelength (usually 254 or 280 nm, where a large number of organic compounds exhibit at least some absorbance), (2) variable-wavelength detectors, which operate at any wavelength between 190 and 700 nm, and (3) scanning spectrophotometric and photodiode array detectors, which monitor wavelength regions of interest so that qualitative identification by the spectrum is possible. Ultraviolet/visible detectors are nondestructive, and for a highly absorbing species, the lower limit of detection is about 10^{-9} g of a component in the injected sample.

Special problems in trace organic analysis led to the search for detectors with lower limits of detection. With fluorescence detectors, 10^{-10}-g quantities can be detected, provided the compounds or their derivatives emit light (fluoresce) upon excitation. Fluo-

Fig. 2 Parameters for defining retention, peak width, and resolution

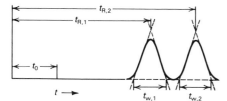

rescence detectors are more specific than UV/VIS detectors because all compounds that absorb light do not subsequently fluoresce. However, high specificity can be a problem when several compounds with different spectral characteristics must be analyzed in a single chromatographic experiment. This problem can be alleviated with detectors that simultaneously monitor absorbance and fluorescence. The choice of mobile phase is restricted to those that do not fluoresce, and minute traces of fluorescent materials commonly present in solvents can cause significant problems.

Unlike the detectors discussed to this point, the electrochemical (EC) detector involves a chemical transformation at a surface; therefore, it is a destructive detector. The eluent from the column passes a working electrode (one of three electrodes in the detector cell), which is set at a specific potential. If a species in the eluent is electroactive at this potential, an oxidation-reduction (redox) reaction takes place. This reaction involves a transfer of electrons and can therefore be followed by measuring current as a function of time. The main advantages of the EC detector are selectivity and sensitivity (10^{-11}-g quantities can be detected). Recently, these devices have found wide applicability in the analysis of biochemical compounds.

Recently, liquid chromatography/mass spectrometry (LC/MS) systems have been developed, combining the excellent separation capabilities of LC with the powerful structural identification capabilities of MS. However, these systems are expensive, and more developmental work is required to optimize the performance of the LC/MS interface.

Many detectors based on other solute properties (for example, infrared absorbance, conductivity, and radioactivity) have been reported for use in LC. Detectors based on bulk properties of the eluent (for example, dielectric constant, density, and viscosity) also have been reported, but they have limited sensitivity because of their high sus-

ceptibility to temperature and pressure changes. It should be noted that the eluent leaving a nondestructive detector can be collected (in fractions corresponding to separated components) and analyzed by other analytical techniques, such as mass spectrometry, infrared spectroscopy, and nuclear magnetic resonance. In this manner, it may be possible to make an unambiguous identification of the compound.

The various components of the liquid chromatograph flow system are connected by tubing and fittings that are inert to sample and mobile phase, have low dead volume, and are able to withstand high pressures without leaking. In modern liquid chromatographs, strip-chart recorders have been replaced by computers, which facilitate acquisition, display, and qualitative and quantitative analysis of the chromatogram.

Fundamental Concepts

The theoretical, chemical, and physical aspects of LC are quite complex. However, the technique is easy to understand from a practical standpoint. The objective is to move different materials through a column at different velocities so that they exit the column at different times. This is known as differential migration.

The hypothetical chromatogram in Fig. 2 displays the response of a detector as a function of time, t. The sample (composed of species 1 and 2 dissolved in a solvent) is applied to the top of the column as a narrow band. Often, the solvent is completely miscible with the mobile phase (or the mobile phase itself is used). In these instances, the solvent molecules have little or no interaction with the stationary phase and elute from the column when the total volume of mobile phase used equals the void volume (V_0) of the column. The time for elution of unretained solvent is t_0. The molecules of species 1 and 2 are also swept along at the velocity of the mobile phase, and they would all exit the column at the same time were it not for the stationary phase. It is the time each molecule spends in the stationary phase that determines when it will exit the column. Species 1 spends less time in the stationary phase and therefore has a shorter retention time (t_R) than species 2. The time each species actually spends in the stationary phase is called the adjusted retention time (t'_R):

$$t'_R = t_R - t_0$$

The sample is applied to the top of the column as a narrow band. While the components in the sample are being separated and

eluted, the bands broaden. This is primarily the result of longitudinal diffusion and slow equilibration between the mobile and stationary phases. As a result of this band spreading, the components are observed as Gaussian peaks rather than as sharp bands. The degree of spreading is indicated by the magnitude of the peak width (t_w), which is usually expressed in terms of the number of theoretical plates (N):

$$N = 16 \left(\frac{t_R}{t_w} \right)^2$$

For a given set of chromatographic conditions, N is approximately constant for all the peaks in a chromatogram. Thus, N is a good measure of column efficiency because it is related to the ability of the column to provide narrow bands (small t_w) and improved separations. The analyst frequently calculates values of N from chromatograms because it is a good indication of the performance level of the liquid chromatograph.

The separation of individual components is of prime importance in LC. The degree of separation depends on the difference in retention times and the sharpness of the peaks in question. Resolution (R) is a measure of the degree of separation:

$$R = \frac{t_{R,2} - t_{R,1}}{0.5(t_{w,2} + t_{w,1})}$$

Narrow peaks with very different retention times are said to be well resolved because they are separated with high resolution. A well-resolved peak arising from a pure substance is very desirable from both an analytical and a preparative viewpoint.

Modes of Liquid Chromatography

For the reasons stated above, the analyst is interested in controlling the equilibrium distribution of materials between the mobile and stationary phases. This is accomplished by the proper choice of mobile and stationary phases for the separation problem at hand.

Liquid-solid chromatography (LSC), also termed adsorption chromatography, is the oldest of the various LC modes. It combines a polar stationary phase (silica or alumina) with a nonpolar mobile phase (for example, heptane, hexane, or pentane, possibly mixed with a small volume of methylene chloride, chloroform, tetrahydrofuran, or isopropanol). Liquid-solid chromatography has been used to separate components in almost every type of sample; however, it is particularly suited to certain sample types.

Liquid-solid chromatography will be discussed further in a later section in this article.

Liquid-liquid chromatography (LLC), also known as liquid-partition chromatography, was first described in 1941. In LLC, a molecule is partitioned (or distributed) between two immiscible liquids according to its relative solubility in the liquids. One liquid is the mobile phase; the other liquid (the stationary phase) is dispersed onto an inert particulate supporting material. Some representative LLC systems employ β,β'-oxydipropionitrile or triethylene glycol as stationary phases with a nonpolar mobile phase (for example, heptane, hexane, or pentane, possibly mixed with a small amount of methylene chloride, chloroform, tetrahydrofuran, or acetonitrile). These systems are useful for relatively polar, water-soluble samples. Liquid-liquid chromatography systems utilized for nonpolar, water-insoluble samples may employ heptane or hydrocarbon polymers as the stationary phase and methanol/water or acetonitrile/water mixtures as the mobile phase.

Liquid-liquid chromatography has been successfully used in the separation of phenols, aromatic alcohols, organometallic compounds, steroids, drugs, and food products. However, there are special problems that severely restrict its use except for special cases. First, because the two phases have to be immiscible, the polarity range of sample that can be separated by any column is quite small. Second, the mobile phase must be presaturated with stationary phase in order to prevent the loss of the stationary phase from the column. This may require that a precolumn be placed between the pump and injector to ensure that the two phases are in equilibrium before the sample is introduced into the stream. Finally, gradient elution generally cannot be used in LLC, because the stationary liquid can be dissolved by some of the stronger solvents used in mixed mobile phases. This would obviously result in a decrease in column performance.

Bonded-Phase Chromatography (BPC), or LC on chemically bonded stationary phases, accounts for the vast majority of all separations performed today. The advantages of BPC compared to LLC are: (1) polar and ionic molecules can be efficiently separated; (2) the stationary phase is very stable, so that a wide variety of solvents can be used (with the exception of oxidizing agents and buffers that are highly basic or acidic); and (3) gradient elution can be employed.

The most useful and widely available BPC stationary phases (Table 1) are those based on siloxanes. Synthetic techniques for the preparation of these materials have advanced to the stage where very few hydroxyl groups

Table 1 BPC stationary phases

Designation	Formula
Silica (Si)	$Si-OH$
Amino (NH_2)	$Si-O-Si(OH)_2-(CH_2)_3-NH_2$
Cyano (CN)	$Si-O-Si(CH_3)_2-(CH_2)_n-CN$
Methyl (C_1)	$Si-O-Si-(CH_3)_3$
Phenyl (C_6)	$Si-O-Si(CH_3)_2-C_6H_5$
Octyl (C_8)	$Si-O-Si(CH_3)_2-(CH_2)_7-CH_3$
Octadecyl (C_{18}) . . .	$Si-O-Si(CH_3)_2-(CH_2)_{17}-CH_3$

on the silica particles are left untreated. This can significantly reduce band spreading. It should be noted that silica, even though it has not been modified with a bonded phase, is usually considered along with polar bonded phases because it is employed in a similar manner.

Normal-phase chromatography (NPC) refers to either LSC or BPC with a polar stationary phase and a nonpolar mobile phase. Figure 3 depicts normal-phase chromatograms of a mixture of organic compounds. On silica, the polar alcohol molecules are strongly adsorbed; therefore, they are the last to elute from the column. In contrast, the relatively nonpolar compounds (toluene, acetophenone, dimethyl phthalate, and benzanilide) adsorb more weakly on silica and therefore elute first.

Unlike the mechanism of adsorption on silica, the mechanism of retention on bonded phases is not well understood. However, it is convenient to consider the bonded phase as an equivalent, mechanically held liquid phase. This can lead to reasonable predictions of retention as a function of sample chemistry and mobile phase composition. However, it does not always allow the analyst to accurately predict the order of elution of components in a mixture. In Fig. 3, benzanilide elutes before the alcohols from the silica and phenyl columns. In contrast, it elutes after the alcohols from the amino and cyano columns. From an operational standpoint, it would not be necessary for the analyst to predict this behavior in advance. It is only necessary that he be able to make the correct peak assignments by (1) comparison with a literature chromatogram, (2) comparison with a chromatogram obtained with an injection of a solution containing individual components of the mixture, or (3) fraction collection and subsequent identification by other techniques. Normal-phase chromatography is particularly suited to nonpolar or moderately polar compounds that are not water soluble. However, it is not restricted to these cases. Normal-phase columns and some materials that are readily analyzed on them include:

- *Phenyl*: Aromatic and unsaturated hydrocarbons, amines, hydroxy compounds

Fig. 3 Normal-phase chromatograms

(a) Using a silica column. (b) Using an amino column. (c) Using a phenyl-NP column. (d) Using a cyano column. Source: Ref 2

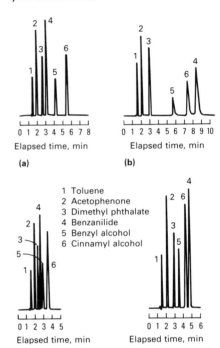

1 Toluene
2 Acetophenone
3 Dimethyl phthalate
4 Benzanilide
5 Benzyl alcohol
6 Cinnamyl alcohol

- *Cyano*: Ketones, aldehydes, halides, esters, surfactants
- *Amino*: Amines, phenols, alcohols, and others that also exhibit hydrogen bonding
- *Silica*: Polar molecules differing in number and types of functional groups, aflatoxins, phospholipids

Reversed-phase chromatography (RPC) is complementary to NPC. The term reversed-phase refers to the use of a nonpolar stationary phase with a polar mobile phase. Typically, a hydrocarbon-bonded support (such as methyl-, octyl-, or octadecyl-siloxane) is used with a methanol/water or acetonitrile/water mobile phase. In this technique, the more polar materials have greater affinities for the mobile phase and so elute first. For example, consider the reversed-phase chromatograms in Fig. 4. Toluene has a longer retention time than acetophenone, which is a more polar molecule. This order of elution is inverted from the normal phase behavior (see Fig. 3). Also note the differences in resolution and retention attained with different RPC columns. Although RPC is suited to the separation of polar molecules, nonpolar molecules can also be successfully separated by using a mobile phase that is sufficiently rich in the organic solvent (for

Fig. 4 Reversed-phase chromatograms of an organic mixture

(a) Using a methyl column. (b) Using an octyl column. (c) Using an octadecyl column. Source: Ref 2

1 Uracil
2 Phenol
3 Acetophenone
4 Nitrobenzene
5 Methyl benzoate
6 Toluene

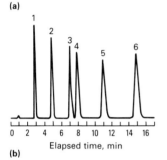

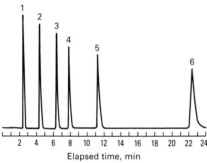

Fig. 5 Ion-exchange chromatogram of radioactive alkali metals

The apparatus used included a polymeric cation exchange column and radiometric detection. Source: Ref 3

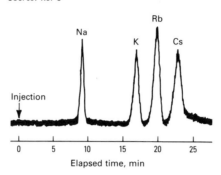

Fig. 6 Ion-pair chromatogram of napthylamine sulfonic acids

A reversed-phase column and UV absorbance detection at 244 nm were used. Source: Ref 4

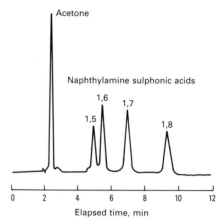

- *Phenyl*: Aromatic and unsaturated hydrocarbons, PCBs, amines, hydroxy compounds
- *Cyano*: Amino acids
- *Amino*: Carbohydrates, polysaccharides, sugars

Ion-exchange chromatography (IEC) is performed on stationary phases that possess charged functional groups. Separation is based on ion-exchange of samples ions (X) and mobile phase ions (Y) with the charged groups (R) of the stationary phase:

$$X^- + R^+Y^- \rightleftharpoons$$
$$Y^- + R^+X^- \text{ (anion exchange)}$$
$$X^+ + R^-Y^+ \rightleftharpoons$$
$$Y^+ + R^-X^+ \text{ (cation exchange)}$$

In IEC, sample ions are in competition with mobile phase ions for ionic sites on the ion-exchange resin. Sample ions that interact weakly with the ion-exchange resin will elute early in the chromatogram. Sample ions that interact more strongly will be retained for longer times. Stationary phases are high molecular weight polymers or silica supports to which ionic groups are chemically bonded. Cation-exchangers contain either sulfonate (SO_3^-) or carboxylate (COO^-) groups, while anion-exchangers have quaternary ammonium groups (NH_4^+) bonded to the support. Amino bonded-phase columns are also used as cation-exchangers. Mobile phases are aqueous buffers that are sometimes mixed with methanol or acetonitrile. By carefully controlling the pH and ionic strength of the mobile phase, good separations can be realized. Figure 5 shows the

separation of alkali metals by cation-exchange chromatography and is representative of the resolution that can be achieved with mixtures of simple ions. Ion-exchange chromatography has also been used in the analysis of amino acids, nucleotides, vitamins, food preservatives, and active ingredients in medicines. A form of IEC called ion chromatography (IC) has been used in analyses of several hundred ions (see the article "Ion Chromatography" in this Volume).

Ion-pair chromatography (IPC) allows the separation of materials that are difficult to analyze by other LC methods. In IPC, the mobile phase contains an ion that will combine with the sample ions, thereby creating a neutral ion pair. The ion pair then undergoes the normal distribution process between the stationary and mobile phases. Ion-pair chromatography is performed in either a normal-phase or reversed-phase mode, and the stationary phases in Table 1 have been used extensively. Ion-pair chromatography is often preferred to IEC because the columns tend to be more efficient, more stable, and more reproducible from lot to lot. The ion-pair chromatogram of a mixture of naphthylamine sulfonic acids is shown in Fig. 6. These highly ionic, very polar compounds have been difficult to separate by other LC methods, including IEC. Ion-pair chromatography of these acids with cetyltrimethylammonium ion in the mobile phase provides excellent resolutions of the isomers. Ion-pair chromatography has been used to analyze very polar compounds, strong bases, multiply ionized compounds, tetracyclines, dyes, and sulfates of steroids.

Size-exclusion chromatography (SEC), also known as gel-permeation chro-

example, methanol) to cause the molecules to elute in a reasonable time. This approach may be useful for separating compounds that are poorly resolved by NPC. Reversed-phase columns and some materials that are analyzed on them include:

- *Octadecyl*: Amino acid derivatives, analgesics, vitamins, triglycerides
- *Octyl*: Lipids, nucleic acid bases, nucleosides, peptides, proteins, steroids, antidepressants, antihistamines, diuretics, expectorants, vitamins, soft drinks, antioxidants, phenols, plasticizers, photoreactive chemicals, herbicides, pesticides
- *Methyl*: Peptides, anticonvulsants, penicillin, sulfa antibiotics, food additives

Fig. 7 Size-exclusion chromatogram

Mixture of (in order of elution) polystyrene (MW = 20 400 amu), polystyrene (MW = 2100 amu), dioctyl phthalate (390.6), dibutyl phthalate (278.3), diethyl phthalate (222.2), dimethyl phthalate (194.2), and benzene (78.12). Source: Ref 5

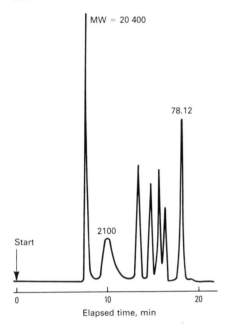

matography (GPC), separates sample molecules on the basis of their physical size. The stationary phase is a gel with pores of a particular average size. Molecules that are too large to permeate the pores move directly through the column and appear first in the chromatogram. Small molecules permeate the pores and follow a long path through the pore matrix; therefore, they have longer retention times. Chromatographic conditions are usually arranged to ensure that retention of molecules by other mechanisms (for example, adsorption) is negligible. Stationary phases used in SEC include cross-linked, semirigid polystyrene gels and small, rigid silica particles. In contrast to other LC modes, the mobile phase is not chosen to control resolution, but instead for its ability to dissolve the sample and for its low viscosity. Tetrahydrofuran is frequently used for organic-soluble compounds, while aqueous mobile phases are used for water-soluble compounds. The size-exclusion chromatogram of a mixture containing polystyrenes is shown in Fig. 7. It can be seen that the components elute in order of decreasing molecular weight. Size-exclusion chromatography is the preferred method for separating components with high molecular weights (2000 to 2 000 000 amu), particularly those

that are nonionic. It has been used in the analysis of epoxies, polyesters, polyolefins, polystyrenes, polyurethanes, polyvinyl alcohol, polyvinyl chloride, proteins, and carboxymethylcellulose.

Fast, efficient separations can often be achieved by selecting an appropriate LC mode for the separation problem at hand. Figure 8 shows a general scheme for choosing an LC mode based on certain sample properties, including molecular weight, solubility, polarity, and ionic character. This scheme does not account for any special reactivity or functionality of the sample which would dictate that a certain method be chosen. However, it does provide a systematic approach to separation problems that is often applicable.

Mobile Phase Programming

This discussion has included only examples of isocratic elution, wherein the mobile phase is unchanged throughout the chromatographic process. Isocratic separations of some samples exhibit poor resolution of early-eluting peaks, significant bandspreading of late-eluting peaks, and unnecessarily long separation times. The solution to these problems is a change in mobile phase composition during the course of the separation. In Fig. 4, toluene could have been eluted from the octadecyl column more quickly had the 50/50 methanol/water mixture been changed to pure methanol. This could have been done (with no detrimental effects on resolution) following the elution of methyl benzoate by linearly changing the mobile phase composition with time. This is known as gradient elution, and it can be used to speed the elution of highly retained compounds or to retard the elution of early-eluting compounds. For optimum resolution and efficiency, it is necessary to begin with a mobile phase just strong enough to dissolve the most soluble species in the sample, and finish with a mobile phase just strong enough to remove the most insoluble species from the column. Alternatively, toluene could have been eluted earlier by simply increasing the mobile phase flow rate following the elution of methyl benzoate. This is called flow programming, and it also is an important tool for optimizing the resolution and speed of LC analyses.

Qualitative and Quantitative Analysis

Qualitative analysis refers to the identification of the components in a sample mixture. On the simplest level, this is ac-

complished when the sample chromatogram matches that of a known mixture obtained under identical conditions. A match is indicated by the peaks having the same retention times and shapes. Next, a portion of the sample mixture can be altered by successive additions of pure substances that are suspected to be components of the sample. Upon an addition, observation of an increase in the size of a peak (with no distortion of the peak shape, such as a shoulder) is taken as evidence for the presence of the substance in the sample. These preliminary identifications are confirmed if the sample chromatogram matches that of the known mixture when the two are obtained under a different set of chromatographic conditions. Unambiguous identification involves the collection of eluent fractions (corresponding to individual peaks) followed by investigation with analytical techniques such as infrared spectroscopy, nuclear magnetic resonance, and mass spectrometry.

Quantitative analysis of the components in a sample is performed by comparison of the height or area of the component peak with those of standards. This can be done with a standard calibration curve or by the method of standard additions. In both approaches, differences in the response of the detector to different sample components are taken into account. The principles of quantitative analysis in LC are the same as those in any other analytical technique.

Preparative Liquid Chromatography

Liquid chromatography is an excellent method for obtaining purified compounds. The amount of purified material to be isolated by LC depends on the objective. If the purpose is to identify the material by instrumental or chemical methods, 0.01 to 100 mg may be needed. If the material is needed as an analytical standard, as a testing material, or for synthetic purposes, as much as several grams may be needed. A standard liquid chromatograph, equipped with a 4- to 10-mm (0.16- to 0.4-in.) inside diameter column, will often suffice if only milligram quantities are desired. Isolation of large amounts (>100 mg) usually requires operating conditions different from those used for analysis. Preparative liquid chromatographs are especially designed for these large-scale separations. They have large mobile phase reservoirs, large flow rate capabilities, large capacity columns, and automated fraction collection systems.

Fig. 8 Selection of a liquid chromatography mode

RPC, reversed-phase; NPC, normal-phase; IPC, ion-pair; IEC, ion-exchange; SEC, size-exclusion

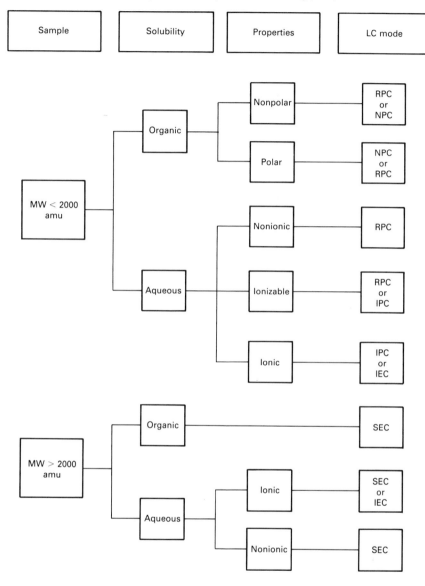

Fig. 9 Parabens commonly used as antimicrobial agents

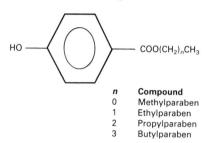

n	Compound
0	Methylparaben
1	Ethylparaben
2	Propylparaben
3	Butylparaben

Fig. 10 Reversed-phase chromatograms of a mixture of parabens and baby lotion extract

(a) Paraben standard. (b) Baby lotion

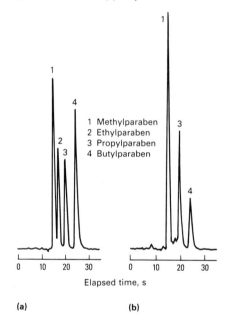

1 Methylparaben
2 Ethylparaben
3 Propylparaben
4 Butylparaben

(a)   (b)

Applications*

Example 1: Analysis of Parabens in Baby Lotion (Ref 1).

Alkyl esters of para-hydroxybenzoic acids, or parabens (Fig. 9), are used as antimicrobial agents in cosmetics, toiletries, and pharmaceuticals. For example, they are found in baby lotions, face creams, antiperspirants, eye shadows, lipsticks, and anticholinergic antidotes. Quantitative analysis of these additives is essential in ensuring the quality of a commercial product. Liquid chromatography is a fast,

*Examples in this section were written by Michael J. Kelly and Philip J. Rodacy, Sandia National Laboratories.

precise, and accurate technique for this purpose. This example describes qualitative and quantitative analysis of parabens in baby lotion.

The baby lotion sample was analyzed by comparison of its chromatogram with that of mixtures of paraben standards. The standards were prepared by dissolving weighed amounts of methyl-, ethyl-, propyl-, and butylparaben in 95/5 ethanol/water. Concentrations of the standards were 18 to 202 ng/μL. Baby lotion extract was obtained by emulsifying 932 mg of baby lotion in 5 mL of tetrahydrofuran. Next, 15 mL of 95/5 ethanol/water was added and the solution was acidified with two drops of 10% sulfuric acid. Finally, the solution was

filtered through 2-μm filters to remove particulates which could clog the chromatographic flow system.

Parabens are amenable to reversed-phase LC because they are low molecular weight compounds that are soluble in polar solvents. Figure 10 shows the chromatogram of a mixture of parabens. The components elute in order of increasing molecular weight (MW = 152.2, 166.2, 180.2, and 194.2 amu), and reasonable separation is achieved on a very short time scale. Also shown is a chromatogram of the baby lotion extract. It is immediately apparent that ethylparaben is not present in the extract. A calibration curve for determining the concentrations of the other three parabens is shown in Fig. 11. The curve plots the area of the chromatographic peaks (in arbitrary units) as a function of

Fig. 11 Calibration curve for quantitative analysis of paraben concentrations in baby lotion

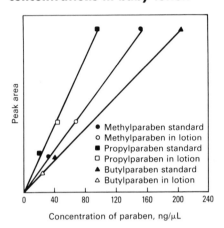

Fig. 12 Chemical synthesis of a light stabilizer

IEM, isocyanatoethylmethacrylate

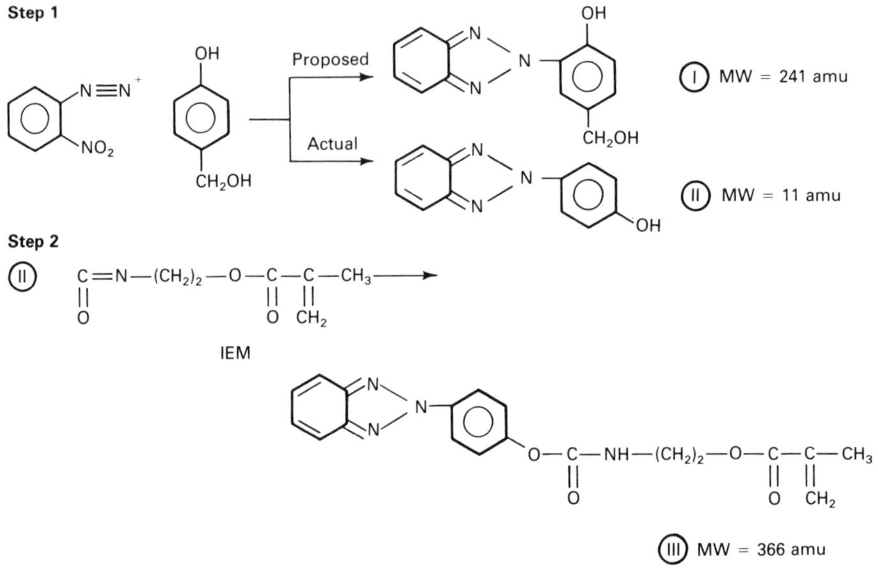

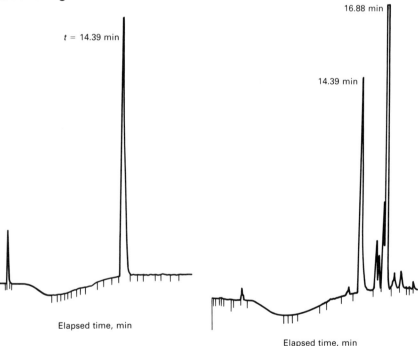

concentration. From this curve, the baby lotion extract is found to have 69.5, 43, and 25 ng/μL of methyl-, propyl-, and butylparaben, respectively. This corresponds to concentrations of 0.149, 0.092, and 0.054 wt%, respectively, in the baby lotion. These values are quite consistent with values reported in the literature for products of this type.

Liquid chromatography is used extensively for other problems of this type in industrial, pharmaceutical, and clinical chemistry. Sample preparation is much simpler than for many other analytical methods. It is frequently sufficient to crush or mix the sample with a suitable solvent, filter the solution, and inject. Alternatively, some liquid samples can be directly injected without any pretreatment, permitting the development of rapid, routine assays. Examples of this type of sample include body fluids, soft drinks, and chemical reaction mixtures.

Example 2: Analysis of Chemical Reaction Products. Photovoltaic cells are currently being investigated because of their possible use in the conversion of sunlight to electricity. Over an extended period, ultraviolet (UV) light can decompose some of the organic components of these cells (for example, epoxies). Therefore, it is desirable to block UV light from the cell. A "light stabilizer" that would absorb UV (but not visible) light would improve the performance of these devices. A particularly useful design is the direct incorporation of the light stabilizer within the focusing lenses of the cell.

In a recent study, a two-step chemical synthesis of a light stabilizer was attempted (Fig. 12). The objective of the first step was to make the UV-absorbing portion of the stabilizer. The purpose of the second step was to couple the light absorber with iso-

cyanatoethylmethacrylate (IEM). The intention was that the final product be incorporated in a polymeric lens material by covalently bonding the polymer and the IEM half of the product.

The product of the first step was analyzed by liquid chromatography; 0.5 mg of the

Fig. 13 Reversed-phase chromatogram of the product of the first step in the synthesis shown in Fig. 12

t = 14.39 min

Elapsed time, min

Fig. 14 Reversed-phase chromatogram of the product of the second step of the synthesis

16.88 min

14.39 min

Elapsed time, min

product was dissolved in 5 mL of acetonitrile. Because the product is a low molecular weight compound soluble in acetonitrile, reversed-phase chromatography was performed. Figure 13 shows that the product is rather pure, because only one peak (t_R = 14.39 min) is observed in the chromatogram. Eluent leaving the detector was collected at 14 to 15 min, and this fraction was analyzed by mass spectrometry. The mass spectrum showed a molecular ion at m/z = 211, as well as fragment peaks which indicated that the actual product was compound II (MW = 211 amu). The proposed product (I, MW = 241 amu) was estimated to be present at a concentration of only 2% by mass spectrometric analysis of the crude, unchromatographed product.

The synthetic chemist decided to continue the synthesis with compound II. The product of the second step was analyzed by liquid chromatography; 1.4 mg of the product was dissolved in 2 mL of tetrahydrofuran. The reversed-phase chromatogram of the solution is shown in Fig. 14. Several peaks are observed, with the largest having retention times of 14.39 and 16.88 min. Because of the peak at 14.39 min, it was immediately suspected that the product contained a significant amount of compound II. Eluent leaving the detector was collected at 14 to 15 min and at 16.3 to 17.3 min, and these fractions were analyzed by mass spectrometry. The mass spectrum of the first fraction verified that compound II was present in the product. The mass spectrum of the second fraction showed a molecular ion peak at m/z = 366, as well as other peaks that were consistent with the structure of compound II.

In this example, the analytical results provided by the combination of liquid chromatography and mass spectrometry were invaluable in identifying the products of chemical reactions. This approach is applicable to any mixture of compounds if the objective is to unambiguously identify individual components in the mixture. Nuclear magnetic resonance and infrared spectroscopy are also frequently used for structural identification of compounds isolated by liquid chromatography.

ACKNOWLEDGEMENTS

This work performed by Sandia National Laboratories supported by the U.S. Department of Energy under Contract No. DE-AC04-76DP00789.

REFERENCES

1. M.W. Dong and J.L. DiCesare, *J. Chromatog. Sci.*, Vol 20, 1982, p 50
2. *Chromatography Supplies Catalog*, IBM Instruments Inc., Wallingford, CT, 1985
3. J.F.K. Huber and A.M. Van urk-Schoen, *Anal. Chim. Acta*, Vol 58, 1972, p 395
4. J.H. Knox and G.R. Laird, *J. Chromatogr.*, Vol 122, 1976, p 17
5. R.W. Yost, L.S. Ettre, and R.D. Conlon, *Practical Liquid Chromatography: An Introduction*, Perkin-Elmer, Norwalk, CT, 1980

SELECTED REFERENCES

- R.J. Hamilton and P.A. Sewell, *Introduction to High-Performance Liquid Chromatography*, Chapman and Hall, 1978
- E.L. Johnson and R. Stevenson, *Basic Liquid Chromatography*, 2nd ed., Varian, 1978
- J.J. Kirkland, Ed., *Modern Practice of Liquid Chromatography*, Wiley-Interscience, 1971
- C.F. Simpson, Ed., *Practical High-Performance Liquid Chromatography*, Heyden, 1976
- L.R. Snyder and J.J. Kirkland, *Introduction to Modern Liquid Chromatography*, 2nd ed., Wiley-Interscience, 1979

Ion Chromatography

Raymond M. Merrill, Sandia National Laboratories

General Uses

- Qualitative and quantitative analyses of a wide range of inorganic and organic anions and certain cations in aqueous solutions

Examples of Applications

- Aqueous solutions, such as leachates, brines, well waters, and condensates
- Organically bound halides and sulfur following Schöniger flask combustion and adsorption techniques
- Determination of anions on contaminated surfaces
- Plating bath solution analysis

Samples

- *Form*: Solids or aqueous solutions
- *Size*: Minimum of 1 to 5 mg for solids; minimum of 1 mL for solutions; 0.5 µg can be detected on surfaces
- *Materials*: Inorganic and organic materials, geological samples, glasses, ceramics, leachates, explosives, alloys, and pyrotechnics
- *Preparation*: Aqueous solutions can be analyzed as received or after dilution; analysis of solids must follow a sample preparation and dissolution procedure

Limitations

- Detection limits below the part per million level for many ions; part per billion under ideal conditions
- *Cations*: Limited to alkali and alkaline earths, ammonia, and low molecular weight amines if suppressed conductivity detection is used
- Must be ionic in solution
- Must be water soluble
- Limited work has been done in organic solvents

Estimated Analysis Time

- Requires 15 min to 1 h per sample if already in aqueous solutions
- Requires 1 h per sample for organics
- Times for other sample matrices are not well established

Capabilities of Related Techniques

- *Wet analytical chemistry*: Much slower and less sensitive when mixtures of ions are to be analyzed
- *Ion selective electrode*: Less sensitive and limited to one ion at a time
- *Atomic absorption spectroscopy*: Not capable of analyzing anions; more versatile for analysis of cations

Introduction

Ion chromatography is an analytical technique that uses columns packed with ion exchange resins to separate ions in aqueous solutions and dynamically elute them to a detector. Figure 1 shows the components of an ion chromatograph. A pump transfers eluent and sample through the system. A valve provides for the injection of sample solution into the eluent stream, and instrumentation detects the ions after they have been separated. The eluents used are ionic aqueous solutions, and the sample ions are separated by well-established ion exchange principles. The technique was introduced in 1975 and has since developed rapidly in terms of ion exchange resins, types of eluents, and modes of detection. By 1984, the number of ions that could be determined by ion chromatography had grown to more than 100.

Separation Principles. The separation technique known as ion exchange chromatography has been in existence for many years. It is the principle behind household water softeners and laboratory water deionizers. Unwanted ions are exchanged with ions that were originally fixed to a material known as an ion exchange resin. For example, in a water softener, the ions calcium and magnesium, which are responsible for making water hard, are exchanged for sodium ions according to:

$$Ca^{2+} + 2Resin^-Na^+ \rightarrow$$
$$(Resin^-)_2Ca^{2+} + 2Na^+ \quad \text{(Eq 1)}$$

and

$$Mg^{2+} + 2Resin^-Na^+ \rightarrow$$
$$(Resin^-)_2Mg^{2+} + 2Na^+ \quad \text{(Eq 2)}$$

Monovalent (singly charged) sodium occupies one resin site; calcium and magnesium

Fig. 1 Major components of an ion chromatograph

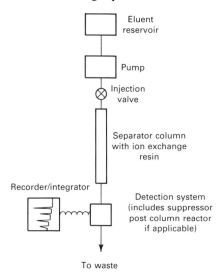

each occupy two resin sites because they are divalent (doubly charged). The number of sites an ion occupies always equals its charge. In Eq 1 and 2, positively charged ions (cations) are being exchanged, and a cation exchange resin is used. When all the active sites are filled with calcium, magnesium, and any other cations capable of exchanging with sodium, the resin must be regenerated, or converted back to the sodium form, by pumping a concentrated sodium chloride solution through it. Negatively charged ions (anions) can be exchanged from solution in the same manner as cations using anion exchange resins.

In ion chromatography, an ionic solution (the eluent) is continuously pumped through a column packed with ion exchange resin having a low capacity. That is, the exchange sites are confined to the surface of the resin; the high-capacity resin used in water softeners have exchange sites throughout the resin. If the column is packed with anion exchange resin, the sites on the resin will be in a state of dynamic equilibrium with the anions in the eluent. That is, all the sites will be occupied by eluent anions, but as the eluent flows through the column, the anions on the resin are continuously exchanging with identical anions in the eluent.

If a small sample of solution containing several different anions is injected into the eluent stream at the head of the column, the sample anions will displace eluent anions from the resin and will in turn be displaced back into the stream by new eluent anions. If each of the different types of sample anions has a different affinity for the resin sites, the eluent will displace the different types at

different rates, and the anions will be separated into distinct bands moving through and out of the column. With the proper selection of eluent solution and resin, the emerging bands of ions are very narrow and well resolved from each other. By providing a means for detecting the bands, they can be recorded as narrow Gaussian peaks whose heights and areas can be related to concentration.

Anions and cations can be routinely determined using ion chromatography, but the technique has been particularly useful in the analysis of anions. Before the development of ion chromatography, anions were determined singly using techniques that were time consuming, lacking in specificity, or hampered by matrix effects. With ion chromatography, the separation of a mixture of fluoride, chloride, nitrite, phosphate, bromide, nitrate, and sulfate anions is so routine that it is used as the standard for checking column resolution.

Modes of Detection

The original method of detection used in ion chromatography involves monitoring the electrical conductivity of the eluent stream after separation of the ions. The conductivity of a solution is a summation of contributions from all the ions present. It is also the reciprocal of the resistivity. Conductivity is a function of both the concentration of the ions and the specific property known as equivalent ionic conductance for each ion in the solution. The original unit of conductance, known as a mho, has been replaced with the siemens (S), which is defined as being equivalent to 1 A/V. The most common unit used in ion chromatography is the microsiemens.

Because conductivity is universal to all ions, it remains the most popular method of detection. The major difficulty in the use of this method of detection arises from the high conductivity of the eluent solution. If the conductivity of the sample ions is measured in the presence of the conductivity from the eluent, their relatively small contribution to the total conductivity is difficult to detect, and because the method is so insensitive, it has limited utility. The novel method of suppressing the eluent conductivity made ion chromatography with conductivity detection feasible.

Eluent-Suppressed Conductivity Detection. The fundamental aspect of this mode of ion chromatography is the suppression reaction, which can be illustrated by considering an anion system. In its simplest case, the eluent contains sodium and hydroxide ions (from sodium hydroxide). The hydroxide ions displace sample anions from the

resin anion exchange sites. The sample ions elute from the separator column in a background of sodium and hydroxide ions. If the column effluent is then passed through a second column containing a cation exchange resin in the hydrogen form, the sodium ions will be exchanged from hydrogen ions, and water will be formed by:

$$Resin^-H^+ + Na^+OH^- \rightarrow$$
$$Resin^-Na^+ + H_2O \qquad (Eq\ 3)$$

Concurrently, sample anions (A^-) passing through the suppressor column will be converted into their acid form:

$$Resin^-H^+ + Na^+A^- \rightarrow$$
$$Resin^-Na^+ + H^+A^- \qquad (Eq\ 4)$$

The eluent emerging from the suppressor column then exhibits the very low conductivity ($<1\ \mu S$) of deionized water, and the the sample anions eluting from the system exhibit the conductivity of their acids. The suppression thus serves two functions. First, by removing sodium ions from the eluent, it minimizes the contribution of the eluent to the detector response. Second, it maximizes detector sensitivity to the analyte anion by converting it to the acid form because the hydrogen ion has the highest of all equivalent ion conductances.

In practice, sodium hydroxide has been found to be a poor choice of eluent; a mixture of sodium bicarbonate and sodium carbonate is more commonly used. The suppression reaction is:

$$2Resin^-H^+ + Na_2^+CO_3^{2-} \rightarrow$$
$$2Resin^-Na^+ + H_2CO_3 \qquad (Eq\ 5)$$

and

$$Resin^-H^+ + Na^+HCO_3^- \rightarrow$$
$$Resin^-Na^+ + H_2CO_3 \qquad (Eq\ 6)$$

The reaction of the analyte anions is the same as in Eq 4. The eluted carbonic acid has a higher conductivity (10 to 20 μS) background than water, but this conductivity is still very low compared with the unsuppressed eluent. In addition, the superior eluting power of the carbonate ion is advantageous.

Suppressed cation chromatography is the opposite of suppressed anion chromatography. The cations are separated with cation exchange resin, and the eluent solution is suppressed with anion exchange resin in the hydroxide form. The eluent is typically a nitric or hydrochloric acid solution, and the suppression reaction is:

$$Resin^+OH^- + H^+Cl^- \rightarrow$$
$$Resin^+Cl^- + H_2O \quad \text{(Eq 7)}$$

The analyte cations (C^+) react with the suppressor:

$$Resin^+OH^- + C^+Cl^- \rightarrow$$
$$Resin^+Cl^- + C^+OH^- \quad \text{(Eq 8)}$$

Equation 7 shows that the effluent background will be that of water. Equation 8 shows that the cations are converted to their hydroxides, a conversion that enhances cation sensitivity because the equivalent ion conductance of hydroxide is second only to hydrogen ion. The eluent suppression technique is limited to ammonia, simple amines, alkali metals, and alkaline earth metals because of the insolubility of most metal hydroxides.

The primary disadvantage of the use of suppressor columns, when the technique was first developed, was that the resin became exhausted and had to be removed periodically from the eluent stream and regenerated to its original hydrogen or hydroxide form, resulting in instrument downtime. Another disadvantage was that the suppressor added a large void volume to the system, which broadened the separated bands of ions and reduced the ability to resolve bands of different sample ions. Further, as the column sites were used, the chemical environment continually changed, causing nonreproducible results for some ions. The introduction of fiber suppressors (Fig. 2) circumvented these problems.

The fibers in these devices are constructed of semipermeable membranes that contain the necessary ion exchange sites and perform the same functions as the packed-bed suppressor. The fiber is continuously regenerated by flowing the regenerant solution over the exterior of the fiber counter to eluent flow; therefore, operation need not be interrupted for periodic regeneration. The fibers have the added advantage of reducing void volume, which lessens band broadening. Because the fiber is always in the same state of regeneration, analytical results are more reproducible. The fibers suffer from two disadvantages: they are very fragile and are easily overloaded by concentrated eluents.

Figure 3 illustrates a recent improvement in suppressors. The use of the sandwiched layers of ion exchange membranes gives the suppressor a stronger configuration, and the further reduction in volume results in sharper peaks with better resolution. The membranes

also have a much larger ion exchange capacity, which provides more range in the selection of eluent strength. Figure 4 shows typical eluent-suppressed ion chromatograms.

Single-Column Ion Chromatography With Conductivity Detection. The success of suppressed ion chromatography spurred development of techniques for nonsuppressed (single-column) ion chromatography to circumvent patents on suppressed ion chromatography and to improve on the disadvantages attributed to the original packed-bed suppressors. Electronically suppressed conductivity detectors were marketed so that laboratories with existing liquid chromatography instrumentation could be modified for ion chromatography, and proprietary ion exchange resins particularly suited to single-column ion chromatography have been developed.

The primary consideration in attempting single-column anion chromatography is decreasing the background conductivity of the eluent. This is accomplished by using resins with very low ion exchange capacity and eluents containing eluting ions with a high resin affinity at low concentration. The most common eluents have been prepared from the salts of benzoic and phthalic acids in the 10^{-3} to 10^{-5} M concentration range. For optimum results, the pH of these eluents should be closely controlled; it is normally adjusted from 4 to 7 with sodium borate or some other low-conductivity species. Figure 5(a) shows a chromatogram of many of the common anions that have been separated using single-column ion chromatography.

Cations can also be determined using nonsuppressed ion chromatography. Dilute nitric acid or nitric acid solutions containing

Fig. 2 Schematic of a hollow fiber anion suppressor

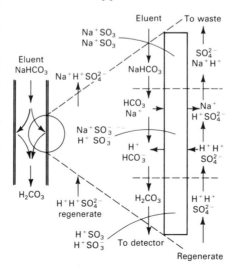

Fig. 3 Schematic of a membrane-type suppressor

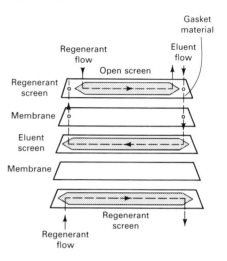

complexing agents are typically used as eluents. Because the eluent is not suppressed, precipitation of hydroxides is not a factor in the analysis of transition metals. Figures 5(b) and (c) show chromatograms for the separation and detection of alkali and several of the transition metals. Alkaline earth metals are also easily determined using these techniques. The peaks shown are in the negative direction (decreasing conductivity). The reason is that the conductance of the sample cations is less than that of the ions present in the eluent; thus, when the sample cations reach the detector a decrease in conductivity is experienced. After the band of sample ions

Fig. 4 Fiber-suppressed ion chromatograms

(a) Anions. (b) Cations

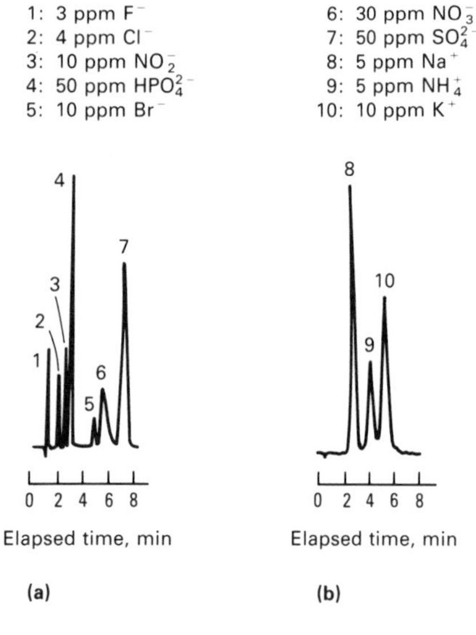

1: 3 ppm F^-
2: 4 ppm Cl^-
3: 10 ppm NO_2^-
4: 50 ppm HPO_4^{2-}
5: 10 ppm Br^-
6: 30 ppm NO_3^-
7: 50 ppm SO_4^{2-}
8: 5 ppm Na^+
9: 5 ppm NH_4^+
10: 10 ppm K^+

Fig. 5 Single-column (nonsuppressed) ion chromatograms obtained using a conductivity detector

(a) Common anions. (b) Alkali metals. (c) Some transition metals

1: $H_2PO_4^-$
2: Cl^-
3: NO_2^-
4: Br^-
5: NO_3^-
6: HCO_3^-
7: SO_4^{2-}
8: I^-
9: 0.5 ppm Li^+
10: 3 ppm Na^+

11: 2 ppm NH_4^+
12: 6 ppm K^+
13: 1 ppm Zn^{2+}
14: 2 ppm Cd^{2+}
15: 5 ppm Pb^{2+}

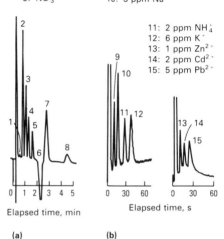

(a)   (b)

Fig. 6 Determination of transition metals using spectrophotometric detection

Wavelength of light used was 520 nm; chromatogram was obtained after a post-column reaction with PAR reagent.

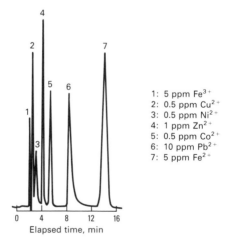

1: 5 ppm Fe^{3+}
2: 0.5 ppm Cu^{2+}
3: 0.5 ppm Ni^{2+}
4: 1 ppm Zn^{2+}
5: 0.5 ppm Co^{2+}
6: 10 ppm Pb^{2+}
7: 5 ppm Fe^{2+}

has passed, the baseline is quickly restored to that obtained with the eluent ions. The normal positive appearance of the peaks illustrated in Fig. 5 is obtained by inverting the polarity of the recording device. The technique of detecting troughs in the baseline rather than a positive response is sometimes referred to as indirect ion chromatography.

Ion Chromatography With Spectrophotometric Detection. The use of a spectrophotometer with a flow-through spectrophotometric cell as a detector broadens the capabilities of ion chromatography. In this mode of detection, the spectrophotometer is set to direct a given wavelength of ultraviolet or visible light through the detecting cell. Any material flowing through the cell that absorbs this wavelength of light will reduce the light by an amount proportional to its concentration. Spectrophotometric detection involves three modes of operation: (1) the ions being detected absorb light at a given wavelength, (2) a reagent that reacts with the eluted ions to form light-absorbing species can be added in a mixing chamber after the separator column and before the spectrophotometer, and (3) the eluent solutions can be the optically active species, with sample ions determined indirectly as valleys in the eluent background.

The direct detection of ions by the spectrophotometric mode is limited to several families of ions, most notably the aromatic ions, which absorb ultraviolet light in a narrow range of wavelengths. Because these ions are difficult to detect by conductivity, spectrophotometric detection is preferred.

Perhaps the widest application of spectrophotometric detection is in conjunction with post-column reactions that convert the eluted ions into light-absorbing species. The technique can be illustrated by its application to the analysis of transition metals. After separation, the metals flow through a post-column reactor, where 4-(2-pyridylazo)-resorcinol (PAR) reagent is added. This reagent complexes with transition metals to form species that absorb light in the region of 520 nm. Figure 6 shows the chromatogram of a mixture of most of the first-row transition metals, along with lead; speciation of Fe^{2+} and Fe^{3+} is evident. Post-column reactions with other reagents have been used to detect polyphosphates, polyphosphonates, ethylenediamine tetraacetic acid (EDTA), and nitriloacetic acid (NTA).

Indirect ion chromatography is becoming more prevalent as a major component assay technique. It is especially well suited to repeated monitoring of similar sample types in a process control or quality control environment. Special columns are available that have both anion and cation exchange capacity (Fig. 7). Because detection is photometrically based, compounds that elute and absorb ultraviolet light lead to interference problems, rendering the technique unsuitable for trace analysis of unknown samples of complex matrices.

Amperometric electrochemical detection can be used to determine some ions that are separated on ion exchange columns

Fig. 7 Indirect analysis of anions and cations using the same column and spectrophotometric detection

(a) Eluent: phthalate buffer; detector set at 280 nm. (b) Eluent: copper ion; detector set at 215 nm.

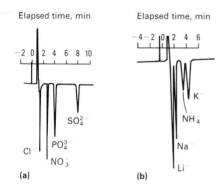

(a)   (b)

Fig. 8 Schematic of a commercial electrochemical detector

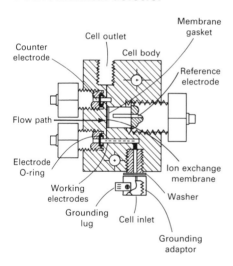

but are too weakly dissociated to be detected by measuring their conductivity. The method is based on the measurement of current generated during the oxidation or reduction of sample species at the surface of the detector working electrode.

A potential is applied between the working and reference electrodes. When an electroactive species with an oxidation/reduction potential approximately equal to this applied potential reaches the working electrode surface, its oxidation or reduction generates a current between the working and counter electrodes. This current is proportional to the concentration of the electroactive species. Because the detector measures the current generated from the analyte ion, eluent suppression is unnecessary, and the detector is

Fig. 9 Sequential electrochemical (top) and conductivity (bottom) detection of anions

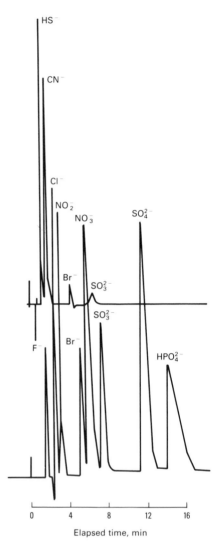

Fig. 10 Illustration of the separation of weak and strong acids by Donnan exclusion

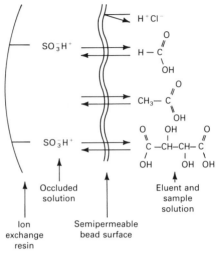

Fig. 11 Separation of carboxylic acids by ion chromatography exclusion

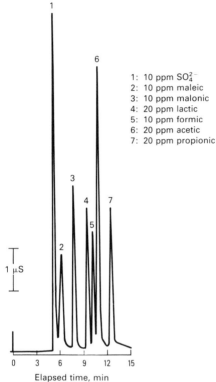

1: 10 ppm SO_4^{2-}
2: 10 ppm maleic
3: 10 ppm malonic
4: 20 ppm lactic
5: 10 ppm formic
6: 20 ppm acetic
7: 20 ppm propionic

often used in conjunction with eluent-suppressed conductivity detection by placing it between the separator column and the suppressor device.

This type of detection has been applied to the analysis of cyanide and sulfide ions, as well as some weakly dissociated but electrochemically active organic ions. Figure 8 shows a diagram of a commercially available electrochemical cell; Fig. 9 illustrates the use of sequential electrochemical and suppressed conductivity detection.

Modes of Separation

The choice of ion exchange material packed into the separator column depends primarily on whether the ions being sepa-

rated are anions or cations. Such factors as the particular chemistry of the analyte ions, the matrix of the sample solution, and the method of detection should also be considered when selecting a separator column.

Standard Ion Chromatography. Most ion chromatography is performed using separator resins with a thin surface layer of ion exchange sites bonded to an inert core of supporting material. Commercial separator columns are packed with resins that have been developed specifically for ion chromatography by minimizing their ion exchange capacities while increasing their ability to separate ions. The core of the resin is made from polystyrene-divinylbenzene or silica. If anions are to be separated, the active site will have a fixed positive charge, and anions will attach and detach from the resin according to their affinities for the active sites. Cations are separated similarly except the resin has active sites with negative charges.

Many columns have been developed, and the chemical characteristics of the particular ions to be analyzed must be known. For example, columns have been developed specifically for the analysis of brine solutions, for the separation of transition metals, and to elute strongly retained anions. If the method of detection is to be nonsuppressed conductivity, very low ion-exchange-capacity silica-base columns have been found to be suitable.

Ion Chromatography Exclusion (ICE). Weakly dissociated anions, such as many of the organic acids, can be separated from strong acid anions using ICE. Although anions are being separated, the separation mode uses cation exchange resins with very

high capacities, and no ion exchange takes place.

Figure 10 illustrates the technique, which implements a phenomenon known as Donnan exclusion to limit the ability of a charged species to move across a semipermeable membrane into the pore volume of the resins. Nonionized species are not subject to Donnan exclusion and may permeate into the pores of the resin. Highly ionized species, such as the strong acid anions, are excluded from the volume within the pores by electrostatic forces, and no retention occurs. The retention of weak acids is primarily a function of their dissociation constants and can be controlled by the pH of the eluent. If the eluent consists of a dilute solution of a strong acid, such as hydrochloric acid, weak acids injected into the stream will become protonated (nonionized). The protonated acids permeate into the pores of the resin and are preferentially retained. With the use of post-separator suppression to convert the eluent to water, separated ions with acid dissociation constants greater than 10^{-7} can be detected using conductivity. Figure 11 shows a chromatogram illustrating the separation of a number of carboxylic acids using this technique.

Reversed-phase ion chromatography uses separator columns packed with polystyrene-divinylbenzene or silica support material to which no ion exchange sites have been attached. The mechanism by which ions are separated is fairly complicated and not well understood; however, separation depends on the partitioning of neutral ion pairs between the hydrophilic mobile phase and the hydrophobic support material. The columns can be used for anion or cation analysis, depending on the choice of pairing reagent. Elution times are controlled by modifying the eluents with varying amounts of water-soluble organic liquids, such as methanol and acetonitrile. The procedure is particularly suited to the analysis of many organic ions and complex inorganic ions that are strongly retained by standard ion chromatographic columns. Any of the various modes of detection is suitable for this technique, but the eluent must be suppressed if conductivity detection is used. Figure 12 illustrates application of reversed-phase ion chromatography to the analysis of cations and anions.

Capabilities

Over 100 ions have been determined using ion chromatography, and the number is increasing. If an unknown exists in solution as an ion or can be made to exist as an ion, it can be separated by ion exchange resins. The limiting factors then become determination of the proper eluent to remove the ion from the column in a reasonable time span and selection of a method to detect it after separation. Table 1 lists some of the inorganic ions that can be routinely determined using ion chromatography. Table 1 also shows that conductivity is by far the most common method of detection.

In addition to the inorganic ions listed in Table 1, ion chromatography has been used to determine many organic species. With the proper selection of columns and detectors, ions from any of the classes of compounds listed in Table 2 can be separated and analyzed.

The sensitivity of ion chromatography for a given ion depends on the sensitivity of a given detection system for that ion. For example, if the ion is to be detected by conductivity, the sensitivity will depend on the specific conductivities of the ion and its counter ion (hydrogen or hydroxide if a suppressor is used). If spectrophotometric detection is used, the sensitivity will depend on the molar absorptivity of the species being detected. Detection limits typically range from low to mid parts per billion and can occasionally be decreased using sample concentration techniques.

Fig. 12 Reversed-phase separation of cations and anions

(a) Cations. (b) Anions

1: 3 ppm NH_4^+
2: 25 ppm monoethanolamine
3: 50 ppm diethanolamine
4: 100 ppm triethanolamine
5: $Au(CN)_2^-$
6: $Fe(CN)_6^{3-}$
7: $Fe(CN)_6^{4-}$
8: $Au(CN)_4^-$

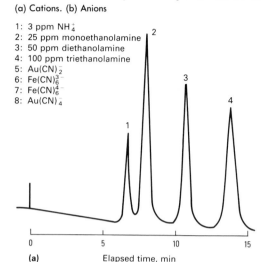
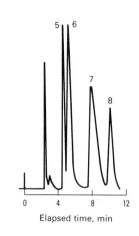

(a) Elapsed time, min

(b) Elapsed time, min

Sample Preparation and Standardization

Samples to be analyzed by ion chromatography must be in aqueous solution or in a solvent system compatible with an aqueous eluent and the ion exchange columns. With the exception of ion chromatography exclusion separation, the analyte species must be ionic while in the eluent. Sample preparation cannot add extraneous ions to the extent that they overwhelm the analytes.

Preparation of Solid Samples. The ideal preparation of a solid sample is dissolution of a known weight in deionized water followed by dilution to known volume. Few samples, however, are water soluble, and other techniques are necessary to assist them into solution. In the determination of some anions, small volumes of mineral acids can be used in dissolution if the acid anion is well resolved from the anion to be determined.

For example, small quantities of hydrochloric or hydrofluoric acid can be used to assist dissolution of samples for sulfate analysis because fluoride and chloride elute soon after injection. If their concentration is low, baseline will be achieved before the sulfate reaches the detector. Judicious use of min-

Table 1   Inorganic ions determined by ion chromatography

Conductivity detection		Spectrophotometric detection		Electrochemical detection
Anions	**Cations**	**Anions**	**Cations**	**Anions**
Arsenate	Ammonium	Phosphite	Cadmium	Bromide
Arsenite	Barium	Pyrophosphate	Cobalt	Chloride
Borate	Calcium	Silicate	Copper	Cyanide
Bromide	Cesium	Tripolyphosphate	Gold	Iodide
Carbonate	Lithium		Iridium	Sulfide
Chlorate	Magnesium		Iron(II,III)	
Chlorite	Rubidium		Lead	
Chromate	Sodium		Mercury	
Dithionite	Strontium		Nickel	
Fluoride			Platinum	
Iodate			Zinc	
Iodide				
Nitrate				
Nitrite				
Perchlorate				
Phosphite				
Phosphate				
Selenite				
Sulfate				
Sulfite				
Tetrafluoroborate				
Thiosulfate				
Tungstate				

Table 2 Organic ions determined by ion chromatography

Class	Examples
Amines	Methyl amine, diethanolamine
Amino acids	Alanine, threonine, tyrosine
Carboxylic acids	Acetate, formate, oxalate, benzoate trichloroacetate
Chelating agents	EDTA, NTA, DTPA
Quaternary ammonium compounds	Tetrabutylammonium, cetylpyridinium
Nucleosides	Adenosine monophosphate, guanidine monophosphate
Phenols	Phenol, chlorophenol
Phosphates	Dimethylphosphate
Phosphonates	Dequest 2000, Dequest 2010
Phosphonium compounds	Tetrabutyl phosphonium ion
Sulfates	Lauryl sulfate
Sulfonates	Linear alkyl benzene sulfonate hexane sulfonate
Sulfonium compounds	Trimethylsulfonium ion
Vitamins	Ascorbic acid

Fig. 13 Schöniger flask apparatus

(a) Flask designed for external ignition. (b) Flask designed for infrared ignition

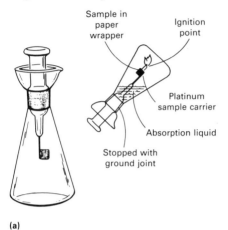

(a)

(b)

eral acids should not affect the analysis of cations. However, hydrochloric acid attacks the stainless steel used in the construction of some columns and the pumps and valves of some chromatographs. Caustic fusion can be used to take glass and mineral samples into aqueous solution. The powdered sample is mixed with a flux, such as sodium carbonate or sodium metaborate, in a porcelain or platinum crucible and heated to the molten state for a suitable period of time. The cooled melt is then taken into solution with hot deionized water. These solutions will have a high ionic background that must be considered when selecting a separation and detection mode for analysis.

Ion chromatography has been used to analyze organic solids for such inorganic elements as the halogens, sulfur, and phosphorus. The sample is prepared by burning it in a closed container and dissolving the combustion products into aqueous solution. Schöniger or oxygen-flask combustion (Fig. 13) is the technique most commonly used to burn organics under controlled conditions. The weighed sample is wrapped in a special paper and placed in a platinum sample carrier to be suspended inside the combustion flask. Immediately before combustion, the flask, containing a small volume of suitable absorbing solution, is swept thoroughly with oxygen.

Figure 13 shows two methods of igniting the sample. In the first method, it is necessary to ignite the sample before inserting it into the flask. In the second method, the sample is sealed into the flask first, and the sample wrapper ignited inside a safety chamber with an infrared lamp. After combustion, the sealed flask is allowed to stand until all the smoke has been absorbed. The liquid is then transferred to a volumetric flask and diluted with deionized water to a known volume. The solution used to absorb the combustion products is adjusted appropriately to ensure that the determined elements

will be converted into stable ions. For example, if sulfur is to be determined, the addition of several drops of hydrogen peroxide to the solution will ensure that all sulfur exists as the stable sulfate ion. Hydrazine can be added as a reducing agent if the sample contains easily oxidized elements, such as iodine or bromine.

Schöniger flask combustion is well suited to assay-type analyses. However, contaminants introduced into the solution by the paper sample wrapper make the procedure unsuitable for most trace-level analyses. Parr oxygen bombs have been used to determine trace levels of inorganics in organic materials. Although more cumbersome, the apparatus can handle larger sample sizes than a Schöniger flask, and high-purity combustion aids are available to minimize sample blanks.

Preparation of Liquid Samples. Aqueous liquids are particularly well suited to analysis by ion chromatography. Dilution with deionized water is often the only sample preparation necessary. In many cases, the as-received sample can be injected directly into the chromatograph. Geological brines and electroplating baths are examples of very complicated solutions that have been analyzed successfully following simple dilutions. If the sample solvent is nonaqueous and incompatible with the eluent solution of chromatographic columns, the analyte ions can occasionally be extracted into water before analysis. An example using this type of sample preparation involves monitoring the degradation of trichloroethylene from a vapor degreaser by extracting the chloride ions released during the degradation reactions. Liquid organics are also amenable to the combustion techniques discussed above.

Removal of Particulates. Particulates will clog separator columns, and it is important to ensure that they are not injected into the chromatograph. Large quantities of undissolved matter should be removed by fil-

tration through an analytical grade filter paper or by high-speed centrifugation. Filters that can be connected directly to the injection syringe are commercially available.

Standardization. Ion chromatography can be used qualitatively to determine which ions are present in a solution and quantitatively to determine the concentrations of the ions. In both cases, the instrument is calibrated by analyzing standard solutions. It is convenient to prepare 1000-ppm stock solutions for each of the ions to be determined. These stock solutions are stable when stored in polyethylene bottles, and standards are easily prepared by mixing and diluting aliquots to known volumes.

Unknown ions are identified by comparing their retention times with those of a solution containing a known mixture of ions analyzed under identical conditions. If the correct identification of an ion is uncertain, the sample can be spiked with a small amount of the ion suspected to be present, then reanalyzed. If the peak is identified correctly, spiking will result in a peak with the same retention time and a greater peak height than the unspiked sample. Otherwise, spiking will cause the appearance of a new peak or a shoulder on the suspect peak.

After identification, the ions can be quantified by comparing peak heights or peak areas to calibration curves constructed from standard solutions. Peak heights are preferable if the chromatographic peaks are symmetrical. They are the simplest to obtain and can be measured using an integrator or a ruler from strip-chart recordings. An integrator is necessary to obtain peak areas when peaks are asymmetrical or there is poor baseline resolution between peaks. Areas can occasionally be used to extend the linearity range of a calibration curve.

The conductivity of the ions is a function of concentration and is linear over a relatively broad range of concentration. The conductivity of strongly dissociated ions is linear to approximately 100 ppm. More weakly dissociated ions, such as carboxylic acids and ammonium, have conductivities that are more concentration dependent, with subsequently narrower ranges of linearity. The linearity of concentration for spectrophotometric detection depends on the extent of deviations from Beer's law, which states that the concentration of a species is a linear function of the amount of light absorbed, the absorptivity of that particular species, and the length of the detector cell path. Such deviations occur most often because of sample-solvent interaction and interactions between sample molecules.

Instrumentation

Most analytical high-performance liquid chromatographs can be upgraded to perform nonsuppressed ion chromatography and are equipped with spectrophotometric detectors. Conductivity detectors have been designed to attach to existing high-performance liquid chromatographs, and columns packed with the proper ion exchange resins are commercially available. An instrument designed solely for single-column ion chromatography is also marketed. Because of patents, instrumentation for suppressed (dual-column) ion chromatography can be purchased from only one manufacturer, which also markets various ion chromatographs, detectors, separator columns tailored for specific applications, suppressor devices (packed bed, fibers, and membrane), and other ion chromatography accessories.

Some method must be provided for recording signals from the detectors. The simplest method is to record the chromatograms using a strip-chart recorder or recording integrator. A high-performance liquid chro-

matograph will be equipped with recording devices, and several companies market integrators specially designed for chromatographic applications. Ion chromatography lends itself to automation, and instrumentation is available that will automatically calibrate, inject samples, record the data, and calculate final results. Several chromatographic software systems are available that allow personal computers to be interfaced with one or more chromatographs to facilitate the collection, reduction, and storage of chromatographic data.

Applications

Example 1: Analysis of Geological Brine. Water was discovered occluded in the wall of a mine shaft excavated into a geological salt formation. Two 3-mL samples were collected. Ion chromatography was used to determine the bromide and sulfate concentrations in the samples. Class A volumetric glassware was used to make all liquid transfers (with the exception of the syringe used to inject samples into the ion chromatograph) and to contain all the diluted solutions. The samples were diluted by pipetting 2-mL aliquots into 25-mL volumetric flasks and filling to the mark with deionized water.

Standards were prepared thus: 100-ppm solutions of bromide and sulfate were made by diluting aliquots of 1000-ppm stock solutions. A 10-ppm bromide solution was prepared by further dilution of the 100-ppm standard. Four calibration standards were prepared by pipetting aliquots of the 100-ppm sulfate solution and the 10-ppm bromide solution into 100-mL volumetric flasks into which 1 g of sodium chloride had been added to match the salt concentration of the unknowns. The concentrations of the standards follow:

Standard	ppm Br⁻	ppm SO₄²⁻
1	0.5	5.0
2	1.0	10.0
3	2.0	15.0
4	3.0	20.0

The diluted samples were injected into an ion chromatograph equipped with a 100-μL injection loop, an anion separator column, and an anion fiber suppressor. The chromatograms were recorded, and peak heights were determined using an integrator. The eluent was a solution consisting of 0.0028 M sodium bicarbonate and 0.003 M sodium carbonate. The fiber suppressor was continuously regenerated by gravity flowing a 0.025 N sulfuric acid solution counter to the eluent flow. The bromide peaks were recorded with the instrument set on the 3-μS

scale. The 30-μS scale was used to record sulfate peaks.

Figure 14 shows the chromatograms for standard 3 and the two samples. The break visible in the baselines is due to the scale change. Table 3 lists the chromatographic peak height data and peak retention times.

The retention times for the known and unknown samples matched well enough that the peaks in the sample solutions could be identified as bromide and sulfate. Calibration curves were constructed by plotting the concentrations of the standard solutions versus peak height (Fig. 15). The peak heights for the unknown solutions were compared to the calibration curves. Sample A was determined to contain 1.21 ppm of bromide and 21.9 ppm of sulfate; sample B, 0.724 ppm of bromide and 11.2 ppm of sulfate. Because the unknown solutions had been obtained by diluting the original samples, the concentration of the as-received samples was calculated using:

$$\text{Original conc} = \frac{\text{ppm (dilute)} \times 25}{2} \quad \text{(Eq 9)}$$

and the original solutions were determined to contain 15.1 ppm of bromide and 274 ppm of sulfate, and 9.05 ppm of bromide and 140 ppm of sulfate in samples A and B, respectively.

The results of the analyses were reported to the requesting organization, which used these and other data to determine whether the solutions resulted from meteorological sources or were occluded in the crystals when the salt bed was formed. This type of analysis is amenable to other complicated solutions, such as electroplating baths.

Example 2: Analysis of Glass Microballoons. Glass microballoons are used as fillers in sealed containers holding electrical components that are stockpiled for long periods of time. When components must be in close contact with foreign materials for extended periods, there is concern that they will become contaminated with corrosive species. A sample of the microballoons was therefore submitted for chemical analysis. Anion chromatography was used to identify potentially corrosive materials and to determine their concentrations.

Samples weighing 0.1 to 0.3 g were mixed with 3.5 g of sodium carbonate in platinum crucibles. The crucibles were covered with platinum lids and placed in a muffle furnace for 30 min at 950 °C (1740 °F). After the melts had cooled, the fused samples were transferred as single buttons to Pyrex beakers, broken with a stirring rod, and dissolved in hot deionized water. Fol-

Fig. 14 Chromatograms for geological brines

(a) Standard 3. (b) Sample A. (c) Sample B

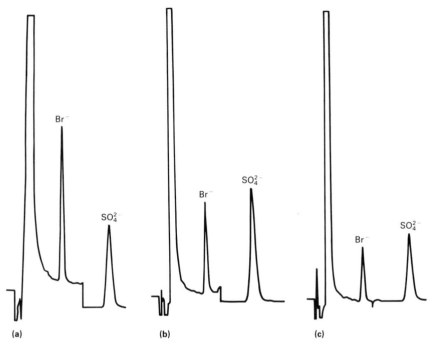

(a)   (b)   (c)

Fig. 15 Calibration curves for bromide and sulfate

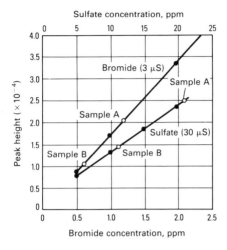

lowing dissolution, the solutions were quantitatively transferred into 200-mL class A volumetric flasks, allowed to cool to room temperature, and diluted to volume.

The samples were analyzed using a chromatograph equipped with a fiber suppressor, a 50-μL injection loop, and a conductivity detector. The eluent, a solution of 0.0028 M sodium bicarbonate and 0.0022 M sodium carbonate, was pumped through the columns at a rate of 2 mL/min. The suppressor was continuously regenerated by gravity flowing 0.025 N sulfuric acid counter to the eluent flow. The chromatograms were recorded, and the data were reduced using a computing integrator. The integrator, which computes the areas and/or heights of the sample peaks, was set to the peak height mode for this analysis. The analyses were performed with the chromatograph set on the 10-μS scale.

The sample solutions contained a high matrix of sodium carbonate, which coeluted

all the other anions. The chromatogram shown in Fig. 16(a) is the result. Aliquots of the sample solutions were then treated with washed analytical grade hydrogen form cation exchange resin. This treatment removed excess sodium carbonate by:

$$2Resin^-H^+ + Na_2^+CO_3^{2-} \rightarrow$$
$$2Resin^-Na^+ + H_2CO_3 \quad \text{(Eq 10)}$$

which makes the solution ideal for analysis by ion chromatography because the sample matrix is the same as the suppressed eluent. The cation exchange resin was added to aliquots of the sample solution until the pH, as determined with paper test strips, was between 4 and 5.

After the reaction was complete, the resin was allowed to settle to the bottom, a sample was drawn into a syringe fitted with a disposable filter, and the solution was injected

through the filter into the ion chromatograph. Figure 16 shows chromatograms of the treated sample; peaks 1 and 3 are artifacts of the sample preparation (they also appear in blanks that were prepared in the same manner as the samples). Peak 2 was identified as ortho phosphate, and peak 4 as sulfate.

The presence of phosphorus was due to the use of a glass in the manufacture of the microballoons to which phosphorus pentoxide, a common glass modifier, had been added. Because the phosphorus is tightly bound in the glass structure, there is little concern that it will cause corrosion in adjacent electrical components. The presence of sulfate is cause for more concern because the balloons are formed by blowing sulfur dioxide gas through the molten glass, and the gas may become entrained inside them and escape by diffusion or when the thin cell walls are broken. Sulfate ion would be formed from sulfur dioxide during sample preparation by:

$$Na_2CO_3 + SO_2 + \frac{1}{2}O_2 \rightarrow$$
$$Na_2SO_4 + CO_2 \quad \text{(Eq 11)}$$

The release of sulfur dioxide into the environment of the components would be very corrosive. Therefore, sulfate was determined quantitatively and converted to SO_2 concentration. Standards containing 5, 10, and 20 ppm of sulfate were prepared by pipetting the appropriate volumes of 1000-ppm sulfate stock into 100-mL volumetric flasks and diluting to volume with deionized water. Table 4 lists the peak height data and sample weights for the standards and the samples.

A calibration curve was constructed by plotting sulfate peak height versus concen-

Table 3 Peak heights and retention times for Example 1

Sample	Br⁻ Retention time, min	Br⁻ Peak height, counts	SO₄²⁻ Retention time, min	SO₄²⁻ Peak height, counts
Std 1	7.20	8505	13.03	7 982
Std 2	7.15	17001	13.02	13 150
Std 3	7.09	33460	13.13	18 305
Std 4	7.16	50214	13.06	23 386
Sample A	7.08	20412	13.03	25 323
Sample B	7.15	12299	13.19	14 346

Fig. 16 Chromatograms for glass microballoons

(a) Before modification. (b) After modification with hydrogen form cation exchange resin

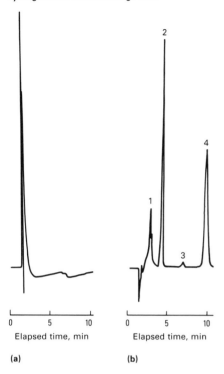

(a)

(b)

Table 4 Peak heights and sample weights for Example 2

Sample	Sample weight, g	Sulfate peak height, counts
1 ppm std		30 980
5 ppm std		143 343
10 ppm std		267 643
20 ppm std		547 136
Sample A..........	0.1046	169 908
Sample B..........	0.2031	275 176
Sample C..........	0.3027	407 015
Blank		32 195
Blank		33 819

where C is the concentration of sulfate (parts per million), B is the blank (parts per million), G.F. is a gravimetric factor to convert SO_4^{2-} to SO_2 (0.6669), and the volume of the sample solutions is 200 mL. The blank averaged 1.08 ppm of sulfate in the sample solutions, and the three samples were determined to have 0.65, 0.59, and 0.61% sulfur dioxide for an average of 0.62 ± 0.03% SO_2. As a result of these analyses, a series of experiments was undertaken to determine the sulfur dioxide content of the atmosphere inside the sealed components. In addition to glasses, caustic fusions have been used to prepare mineral samples for ion chromatographic analysis.

ACKNOWLEDGMENT

This work performed at Sandia National Laboratories supported by the U.S. Department of Energy under Contract No. DE-AC04-DP00789.

SELECTED REFERENCES

- J. Fritz, D. Gjerde, and C. Pohlandt, *Ion Chromatography*, A. Hüthig, 1982

Fig. 17 Sulfate calibration curve for glass microballoons

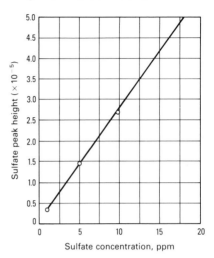

- J.D. Mulik and E. Sawicki, *Ion Chromatographic Analysis of Environmental Pollutants*, Vol 2, Ann Arbor Science Publishers, 1979
- E. Sawicki, J.D. Mulik, and E. Wittgenstein, *Ion Chromatographic Analysis of Environmental Pollutants*, Vol 1, Ann Arbor Science Publishers, 1979
- H. Small, T.S. Stevens, and W.C. Bauman, *Anal. Chem.*, Vol 47, 1975, p 1801
- F.C. Smith, Jr. and R.C. Chang, *The Practice of Ion Chromatography*, John Wiley & Sons, 1983
- R.A. Wetzel, C.A. Pohl, J.M. Riviello, and J.C. MacDonald, in *Inorganic Chromatographic Analysis*, J.C. MacDonald, Ed., John Wiley & Sons, 1985

tration (Fig. 17). The sulfate concentration of each of the sample solutions was determined from the calibration curve, and the percent sulfur dioxide in the microballoons was calculated according to:

$$\% \ SO_2 = \frac{(C - B)(\text{G.F.})(\text{volume})}{10^6 \ (\text{sample weight})} \quad \text{(Eq 12)}$$

Glossary of Terms

A

aberration. In microscopy, any error that results in image degradation. Such errors may be chromatic, spherical, astigmatic, comatic, distortion, or curvature of field and can result from design or execution, or both.

absorbance (A). The logarithm to the base 10 of the reciprocal of the transmittance. The preferred term for photography is optical density.

absorption (of electromagnetic radiation). A decrease in the intensity of the beam (light, x-rays, electrons, and so on) when passing through matter. In many cases specific wavelengths or energies are preferentially absorbed, forming the basis of absorption spectroscopy.

absorption contrast. In transmission electron microscopy, image contrast caused by differences in absorption within a sample due to regions of different mass density and thickness.

absorption edge. The wavelength or energy corresponding to a discontinuity in the plot of absorption coefficient versus wavelength for a specific medium.

absorption spectroscopy. The branch of spectroscopy treating the theory, interpretation, and application of spectra originating in the absorption of electromagnetic radiation by atoms, ions, radicals, and molecules.

absorptivity. A measure of radiant energy from an incident beam as it traverses an absorbing medium, equal to the absorbance of the medium divided by the product of the concentration of the substance and the sample path length. Also known as absorption coefficient.

accelerating voltage. In various electron beam instruments and x-ray generators, the difference in potential between the filament (cathode) and the anode, causing acceleration of the electrons by 2 to 30 keV. See also *depth of penetration, resolution*.

accuracy. The degree of agreement of a measured value with the true or correct value for the quantity being measured.

achromatic. Refers to an optical element that transmits light without dispersing it into its component wavelengths. See also *achromatic lens, apochromatic lens*.

achromatic lens. A lens that is corrected for chromatic aberration so that its tendency to refract light differently as a function of wavelength is minimized. See also *achromatic, apochromatic lens*.

ac noncapacitive arc. A high-voltage electrical discharge used in spectrochemical analysis to vaporize the sample material. See also *dc intermittent noncapacitive arc*.

activation analysis. A method of chemical analysis based on the detection of characteristic radionuclides following nuclear bombardment. See also *neutron activation analysis*.

adsorption chromatography. Chromatography based on differing degrees of adsorption of sample compounds onto a polar stationary phase. See also *liquid-solid chromatography*.

aliquot. A representative sample of a larger quantity.

amorphous solid. A rigid material whose structure lacks crystalline periodicity; that is, the pattern of its constituent atoms or molecules does not repeat periodically in three dimensions. See also *metallic glass*.

amperometry. Chemical analysis by methods that involve measurements of electric currents.

analysis. The ascertainment of the identity or concentration, or both, of the constituents or components of a sample. See also *determination*.

analog-to-digital converter (ADC). A device that converts a continuously variable electrical signal into discrete signals suitable for analysis by a digital computer.

analyte. In any analysis, the substance (element, ion, compound, and so on) being identified or determined.

analytical chemistry. The science of chemical characterization and measurement. Qualitative analysis is concerned with the description of chemical composition in terms of elements, compounds, or structural units; quantitative analysis is concerned with the precise measurement of amount. A variety of physical measurements are used, including methods based on spectroscopic, electrochemical, radiochemical, chromatographic, and nuclear principles.

analytical curve. The graphical representation of a relation between (1) the intensity of the response to measurement (for example, emission, absorbance, and conductivity) and (2) the concentration or mass of the substance being measured. The curve is generated by measuring the responses for standards of known concentration. Also termed standard curve or working curve.

analytical electron microscopy (AEM). The technique of materials analysis in the transmission electron microscope equipped to detect and quantify many different signals from the specimen. The technique usually involves a combination of imaging, chemical analysis, and crystallographic analysis by diffraction at high spatial resolution.

analytical gap. The region between two electrodes in which the sample is excited in the sources used for emission spectroscopy and spark source mass spectrometry.

analytical line. In spectroscopy, the particular spectral line of an element used in the identification or determination of the concentration of that element.

analytical wavelength. In spectroscopy, the particular wavelength used for the identification or determination of the concentration of an element or compound.

analyzer. An optical device, capable of producing plane polarized light, used for detecting the state of polarization.

angle of incidence. The angle between an incident radiant beam and a perpendicular to the interface between two media.

angstrom (Å). A unit of length equal to 10^{-10} m.

anion. An ion that is negatively charged and moves toward the positive pole (anode) during electrolysis. See also *cation, ion*.

anti-Stokes Raman line. A Raman line that has a frequency higher than that of the incident monochromatic radiation.

aplanatic. Corrected for spherical aberration and coma.

apochromatic lens. A lens whose secondary chromatic aberrations have been substantially reduced. See also *achromatic*.

apparent density (of solids and liquids). The mass in air of a unit of volume of a material at a specified temperature.

aromatic. In organic chemistry, pertaining to or characterized by the presence of at least one benzene ring.

assay. Determination of how much of a sample is the material indicated by the name. For example, for an assay of $FeSO_4$ the analyst would determine both iron and SO_4^{2-} in the sample.

atom. The smallest particle of an element that retains the characteristic properties and behavior of the element. See also *atomic structure, isotope, nuclear structure*.

atom probe. An instrument for measuring the mass of a single atom or molecule on a metal surface; it consists of a field ion microscope with a hole in its screen opening into a mass spectrometer; atoms are removed from the specimen by pulsed field evaporation, travel through the hole, and are detected in the mass spectrometer. See also *field-ion microscopy*.

atomic mass unit (amu). An arbitrarily defined unit expressing the masses of individual atoms. One atomic mass unit is defined as exactly $\frac{1}{12}$ of the mass of an atom of the nuclide ^{12}C, the predominant isotope of carbon. See also *atomic weight*.

atomic number (Z). The number of elementary positive charges (protons) contained within the nucleus of an atom. For an electrically neutral atom, the number of planetary electrons is also given by the atomic number. Atoms with the same Z (isotopes) may contain different numbers of neutrons. Also known as nuclear charge. See also *isotope, proton*.

atomic number contrast. See *atomic number imaging*.

atomic number imaging. In scanning electron microscopy, a technique in which contrast is controlled by atomic number

(high atomic number areas appear light, while low atomic number areas appear dark). Usually obtained by imaging based on backscattered electron signal. See also *backscattered electron*.

atomic structure. The arrangement of the parts of an atom, which consists of a positively charged nucleus surrounded by a cloud of electrons arranged in orbits that can be described in terms of quantum mechanics.

atomic weight. A number assigned to each chemical element that specifies the average mass of its atoms. Because an element may consist of two or more isotopes, each having atoms with well-defined but differing masses, the atomic weight of each element is the average of the masses of its naturally occurring isotopes weighted by the relative proportions of those isotopes.

atomization. The subdivision of a compound into individual atoms using heat or chemical reactions. This is a necessary step in atomic spectroscopy. See also *atomizer, nebulizer*.

atomizer. A device that atomizes a sample, for example, a burner, plasma, or hydride reaction chamber. See also *atomization, nebulizer*.

attenuation. Reduction in the amplitude of a signal, including electric currents and light beams.

Auger chemical shift. The displacement in energy of an Auger electron peak for an element due to a change in chemical bonding relative to a specified element or compound.

Auger electron. An electron emitted from an atom with a vacancy in an inner shell. Auger electrons have a characteristic energy detected as peaks in the energy spectra of the secondary electrons generated.

Auger electron spectroscopy (AES). A technique for chemical analysis of surface layers that identifies the atoms present in a layer by measuring the characteristic energies of their Auger electrons.

Auger electron yield. The probability that an atom with a vacancy in a particular inner shell will relax by an Auger process.

Auger map. A two-dimensional image of the specimen surface showing the location of emission of Auger electrons from a particular element. A map is normally produced by rastering the incident electron beam over the specimen surface and simultaneously recording the Auger signal strength for a particular transition as a function of position.

Auger matrix effects. Effects that cause changes in the shape of an Auger electron energy distribution or in the Auger signal strength for an element due to the physical environment of the emitting atom and not due to bonding with other elements or changes in concentration.

Auger process. The radiationless relaxation of an atom, involving a vacancy in an inner electron shell. An electron (known as an Auger electron) is emitted.

Auger transition designations. Transitions are designated by the electron shells involved. The first letter designates the shell containing the initial vacancy; the last two letters designate the shells containing electron vacancies created by Auger emission (for example, KLL and LMN).

automated image analysis. See *image analysis*.

Avogadro's number. The number of molecules (6.02×10^{23}) in a gram-molecular weight of any substance. See also *gram-molecular weight, mole*.

B

background. Any noise in the signal due to instabilities in the system or to environmental interferences. See also *signal-to-noise ratio*.

backscattered electron. An information signal arising from elastic (electron-nucleus) collisions, wherein the incident electron rebounds from the interaction with a small energy loss. The backscattered electron yield is strongly dependent upon atomic number, qualitatively describes the origin of characteristic rays, and reveals compositional and topographic information about the specimen. See also *atomic number imaging*.

barn. A unit of area equal to 10^{-24} cm^2 used in specifying nuclear cross sections. See also *nuclear cross section*.

base-line technique. A method for measurement of absorption peaks for quantitative analysis of chemical compounds in which a base line is drawn tangent to the spectrum background; the distance from the base line to the absorption peak is the absorbance due to the sample under study.

basic NMR frequency. The frequency, measured in hertz, of the oscillating magnetic field applied to induce transitions between nuclear magnetic energy levels. See also *magnetic resonance*.

Beer's law. A relationship in which the optical absorbance of a homogeneous sample containing an absorbing substance is directly proportional to the concentration of the absorbing substance. See also *absorptivity*.

beryllium window. A very thin (~7.5 μm thick), relatively x-ray transparent window separating the x-ray detector from the vacuum chamber, which serves to protect the detector from damage.

bias. A systematic error inherent in a method (such as temperature effects and extraction inefficiencies) or caused by some artifact or idiosyncrasy of the measurement system (such as blanks, contamination, mechanical losses, and calibration errors). Bias may be both positive and negative, and several types can exist concurrently, so that the net bias is all that can be evaluated except under certain conditions. See also *blank*.

birefringent crystal. A crystalline substance that is anisotropic with respect to the velocity of light.

blank. The measured value obtained when a specified component of a sample is not present during the measurement. In such a case, the measured value/signal from the component is believed to be due to artifacts, and thus should be deducted from a measured value to give a net value due to the component contained in a sample. The blank measurement must be made so that the correction process is valid.

blind sample. A sample submitted for analysis whose composition is known to the submitter but unknown to the analyst, used to test the efficiency of a measurement process.

Boltzmann distribution. A function giving the probability that a molecule of a gas in thermal equilibrium will have generalized position and momentum coordinates within a given infinitesimal range of values, assuming that the molecules obey classical mechanics.

bonded-phase chromatography (BPC). Liquid chromatography with a surface-reacted, that is, chemically bonded, organic stationary phase. See also *normal-phase chromatography*, *reversed-phase chromatography*.

Bragg equation. See *Bragg's law*.

Bragg's law. A statement of the conditions under which a crystal will diffract electromagnetic radiation. Bragg's law reads $n\lambda = 2d \sin\theta$, where n is the order of reflection, λ is the wavelength of x-rays, d is the distance between lattice planes, and θ is the Bragg angle, or the angular distance between the incident beam and the lattice planes considered.

bremsstrahlung. See *continuum*.

buffer. A substance which by its addition or presence tends to minimize the physical and chemical effects of one or more of the substances in a mixture. Properties often buffered include pH, oxidation potential, and flame or plasma temperatures.

bulk sample. See *gross sample*.

bulk sampling. Obtaining a portion of a material that is representative of the entire lot.

buret. An instrument used to deliver variable and accurately known volumes of a liquid during titration or volumetric analysis. Burets are usually made from uniform-bore glass tubing in capacities of 5 to 100 mL, the most common being 50 mL. See also *titration, volumetric analysis*.

C

calomel electrode. An electrode widely used as a reference electrode of known potential in electrometric measurements of acidity and alkalinity, corrosion studies, voltammetry, and measurement of the potentials of other electrodes. See also *electrode potential*, *reference electrode*, *saturated calomel electrode*.

carrier. In emission spectrochemical analysis, a material added to a sample to facilitate its controlled vaporization into the analytical gap. See also *analytical gap*.

cathode-ray tube (CRT). An electronic tube that permits the visual display of electronic signals.

cathodoluminescence. A radiative transition wherein low-energy light photons are released during electron irradiation.

cation. A positively charged atom or group of atoms, or a radical that moves to the negative pole (cathode) during electrolysis. See also *anion*.

channeling pattern. A pattern of lines observed in a scanning electron image of a single-crystal surface caused by preferential penetration, or channeling, of the incident beam between rows of atoms at certain orientations. The pattern provides information on the structure and orientation of the crystal.

characteristic electron energy loss phenomena. The inelastic scattering of electrons in solids that produces a discrete energy loss determined by the characteristics of the material. The most probable form is due to excitation of valence electrons.

characteristic radiation. Electromagnetic radiation of a particular set of wave-lengths, produced by and characteristic of a particular element whenever its excitation potential is exceeded. Electromagnetic radiation is emitted as a result of electron transitions between the various energy levels (electron shells) of atoms; the spectrum consists of lines whose wavelengths depend only on the element concerned and the energy levels involved.

chelate. A coordination compound in which a heterocyclic ring is formed by a metal bound to two atoms of the associated ligand. See also *complexation, coordination compound, ligand*.

chemical adsorption. See *chemisorption*.

chemical bonding. The joining together of atoms to form molecules. See also *molecule*.

chemisorption. The binding of an adsorbate to the surface of a solid by forces whose energy levels approximate those of a chemical bond. Contrast with *physisorption*.

chromatic aberration. A defect in a lens or lens system as a result of which the lens possesses different focal lengths for radiations of different wavelengths.

chromatogram. The visual display of the progress of a separation achieved by chromatography. A chromatogram shows the response of a chromatographic detector as a function of time.

chromatography. A separation method based on the distribution of sample compounds between the stationary phase and a mobile phase. See also *gas chromatography, ion chromatography, liquid chromatography*.

cold finger. A liquid-nitrogen-cooled cold trap used to reduce contamination levels in vacuum chambers.

collimate. To make parallel to a certain line or direction.

collimation. The operation of controlling a beam of radiation so that its rays are as nearly parallel as possible.

color center. A point lattice defect that produces optical absorption bands in an otherwise transparent crystal.

coma. A lens aberration occurring in that part of the image field that is some distance from the principal axis of the system. It results from different magnification in the various lens zones. Extra-axial object points appear as short conelike images with the brighter small head toward the center of the field (positive coma) or away from the center (negative coma).

compensating eyepieces. Those designed for use with objectives such as apochromats to correct chromatic aberration.

complexation. The formation of complex chemical species by the coordination of groups of atoms termed ligands to a central ion, commonly a metal ion. Generally, the ligand coordinates by providing a pair of electrons that forms an ionic or covalent bond to the central ion. See also *chelate, coordination compound, ligand.*

composite. A sample composed of two or more increments.

compositional depth profile. The atomic concentration measured as a function of the perpendicular distance from the surface.

Compton scattering. The elastic scattering of photons by electrons. Contrast with *Rayleigh scattering.*

concave grating. A diffraction grating on a concave mirror surface. See also *diffraction grating, plane grating.*

concentration. The mass of a substance contained in a unit volume of sample, for example, grams per liter.

condenser, condenser lens. A term applied to lenses or mirrors designed to collect, control, and concentrate radiation in an illumination system.

conductance. The property of a circuit or its materials of composition that allows the transmission of a current when suitable potential difference exists; the reciprocal of resistance. The usual unit is the siemens. See also *siemens.*

confidence interval. That range of values, calculated from estimates of the mean and standard deviation, which is expected to include the population mean with a stated level of confidence. Confidence intervals in the same context also can be calculated for standard deviations, lines, slopes, and points.

continuum. The noncharacteristic rays emitted upon irradiation of a specimen and caused by deceleration of the incident electrons by interaction with the electrons and nuclei of the specimen. Also termed bremsstrahlung and white radiation.

controlled-potential coulometry. Measurement of the number of coulombs required for an electrochemical reaction occurring under conditions where the working electrode potential is precisely controlled.

convergent-beam electron diffraction (CBED). A technique of impinging a highly convergent electron beam on a crystal to produce a diffraction pattern composed of disks of intensity. In addition to *d*-spacing and crystal orientation information, the technique can provide information on crystallographic point or space group symmetry.

coordination compound. A compound with a central atom or ion bound to a group of ions or molecules surrounding it. Also known as coordination complex. See also *chelate, complexation, ligand.*

coordination number. In coordination compounds, the number of atoms bonded to a central atom or ion. In a space lattice, the number of nearest neighbors of a specific atom or ion.

coulometry. An electrochemical technique in which the total number of coulombs consumed in an electrolysis is used to determine the amount of substance electrolyzed.

counterelectrode. In emission spectroscopy, the electrode that is used opposite to the self-electrode or supporting electrode and that is not composed of the sample to be analyzed. In voltammetry, the current between the working electrode and counterelectrodes is measured. See also *self-electrode, supporting electrode.*

covalent bond. A bond in which two atoms share a pair of electrons. Contrast with *ionic bond.*

critical micelle concentration. The concentration of a micelle at which the rate of increase of electrical conductance with increase in concentration levels off or proceeds at a much slower rate. See also *micelle.*

cryopump. A type of vacuum pump that relies on the condensation of gas molecules and atoms on internal surfaces of the pump, which are maintained at extremely low temperatures.

Curie point. See *Curie temperature.*

Curie temperature. The temperature marking the transition between ferromagnetism and paramagnetism, or between the ferroelectric phase and the paraelectric phase. Also known as Curie point. See also *ferromagnetism, paramagnetism.*

cyclodextrin. Cyclic degradation products of starch that contain six, seven, or eight glucose residues and have the shape of large ring molecules.

D

dc intermittent noncapacitive arc. A low-voltage electrical discharge used in spectrochemical analysis to vaporize the sample material. Each current pulse has the same polarity as the previous one and lasts for less than 0.1 s. See also *ac noncapacitive arc.*

dc plasma excitation. See *plasma-jet excitation.*

dead time. The total time during which the spectrometer is processing information and is unavailable to accept input data.

decay constant (λ). The constant in the radioactive decay law $dN = -\lambda N dt$, where N is the number of radioactive nuclei present at time t. The decay constant is related to half-life $t_{1/2}$ by the expression $t_{1/2} = \ln 2/\lambda$. See also *half-life.*

density (of gases). The mass of a unit volume of gas at a stated temperature and pressure.

density (of solids and liquids). The mass of a unit volume of a material at a specified temperature.

depth of field. The depth or thickness of the object space that is simultaneously in acceptable focus.

depth of penetration. In various analytical techniques, the distance the probing radiation penetrates beneath the surface of a sample. See also *excitation volume.*

detection limit. In an analytical method, the lowest mass or concentration of an analyte that can be measured.

determination. The ascertainment of the quantity or concentration of a specific substance in a sample. See also *analysis.*

deuteron. The nucleus of the atom of heavy hydrogen, deuterium. The deuteron is composed of a proton and a neutron; it is the simplest multinucleon nucleus. Deuterons are used as projectiles in many nuclear bombardment experiments. See also *neutron, proton.*

dewar flask. A vessel having double walls, the space between being evacuated to prevent the transfer of heat and the surfaces facing the vacuum being heat reflective; used to hold liquid gases and to study low-temperature phenomena.

diaphragm. A fixed or adjustable aperture in an optical system. Diaphragms are used to intercept scattered light, to limit field angles, or to limit image-forming bundles or rays.

diffraction contrast. In electron microscopy, contrast produced by intensity differences in Bragg-diffracted beams from a crystalline material. These differences are caused by regions of varying crystal orientation.

diffraction grating. A series of a large number of narrow, close, equally spaced, diffracting slits or grooves capable of dispersing light into its spectrum. See also *concave grating*, *reflection grating*. Compare with *transmission grating*.

diffraction pattern. The spatial arrangement and relative intensities of diffracted beams.

diffuse transmittance. The transmittance value obtained when the measured radiant energy has experienced appreciable scattering in passing from the source to the receiver. See also *transmittance*.

dilution factor. When diluting a sample, the ratio of the final volume or mass after dilution to the volume or mass of the sample before dilution.

dimer. A condensation compound formed from two monomers or molecules.

dimerization. The formation of a dimer. See also *dimer*.

direct injection burner. A burner used in flame emission and atomic absorption spectroscopy in which the fuel and oxidizing gases emerge from separate ports and are mixed in the flame itself. One of the gases, usually the oxidant, is used for nebulizing the sample at the tip of the burner.

disordered structure. The crystal structure of a solid solution in which the atoms of different elements are randomly distributed relative to the available lattice sites. Contrast with *ordered structure*.

Donnan exclusion. The mechanism by which an ion exchange resin can be made to act like a semipermeable membrane between an interstitial liquid and a liquid occluded inside the resin particles. Highly ionized molecules are excluded from the resin particles by electrostatic forces; weakly ionized or nonionized molecules may pass through the membrane.

Doppler effect. The change in the observed frequency of an acoustic or electromagnetic wave due to the relative motion of source and observer. See also *Doppler shift*.

Doppler shift. The amount of change in the observed frequency of a wave due to the Doppler effect, usually expressed in hertz. See also *Doppler effect*.

dosimeter. An instrument that measures the total dose of nuclear radiation received in a given period.

dot map. See *x-ray map*.

duoplasmatron. A type of ion source in which a plasma created by an arc discharge is confined and compressed by a nonuniform magnetic field.

duplicate measurement. A second measurement made on the same (or identical) sample of material to assist in the evaluation of measurement variance.

duplicate sample. A second sample randomly selected from a population to assist in the evaluation of sample variance.

E

elastic constants. The factors of proportionality that relate elastic displacement of a material to applied forces. See also *modulus of elasticity*, *Poisson's ratio*.

elastic scattering. Collisions between particles that are completely described by conservation of energy and momentum. Contrast with *inelastic scattering*.

electric dipole. The result of a distribution of bound charges, that is, separated charges that are bound to their centers of equilibrium by an elastic force; equal numbers of positive and negative charges must be present in an uncharged medium.

electric dipole moment. A quantity characteristic of a distribution of bound charges equal to the vector sum over the charges of the product of the charge and the position vector of the charge.

electric dipole transition. A transition of an atom, molecule, or nucleus from one energy state to another, which results from the interaction of electromagnetic radiation with the dipole moment of the molecule, atom, or nucleus.

electric field effect. See *Stark effect*.

electrode. In emission spectroscopy, either of two terminals between which an electrical discharge occurs. See also *counterelectrode*, *self-electrode*, *supporting electrode*.

electrode potential. Voltage existing between an electrode and the solution or electrolyte in which it is immersed. Electrode potentials are referred to a standard electrode, such as the hydrogen electrode.

electrolysis. A method by which chemical reactions are carried out by passage of electric current through a solution of an electrolyte or through a molten salt. See also *electrolyte*.

electrolyte. A chemical compound or mixture of compounds which when molten or in solution will conduct an electric current.

electromagnetic lens. An electromagnet designed to produce a suitably shaped magnetic field for the focusing and deflection of electrons or other charged particles in electron-optical instrumentation.

electromagnetic radiation. Energy propagated at the speed of light by an electromagnetic field. The electromagnetic spectrum includes the following approximate wavelength regions:

Region	Wavelength, Å (metric)
Gamma-ray	0.005 to 1.40 (0.0005 to 0.14 nm)
X-ray	0.1 to 100 (0.01 to 10 nm)
Far-ultraviolet	100 to 2000 (10 to 200 nm)
Near-ultraviolet	2000 to 3800 (200 to 380 nm)
Visible	3800 to 7800 (380 to 780 nm)
Near-infrared	7800 to 30 000 (0.78 to 3 μm)
Middle-infrared	3×10^4 to 3×10^5 (3 to 30 μm)
Far-infrared	3×10^5 to 3×10^6 (30 to 300 μm)
Microwave	3×10^6 to 1×10^{10} (0.3 mm to 1 m)

electrometric titration. A family of techniques in which the location of the endpoint of a titration involves the measurement of, or observation of changes in, some electrical quantity. Examples of such quantities include potential, current, conductance, frequency, and phase.

electron. A negatively charged particle that resides in specific orbits around the nucleus of an atom. The electron is the lightest known particle that possesses an electric charge. Its rest mass is approximately 9.1×10^{-28} g, about $\frac{1}{1836}$ of the mass of the proton or neutron, which are, respectively, the positively charged and neutral constituents of the atomic nucleus. See also *neutron*, *proton*.

electron diffraction. The phenomenon or the technique of producing diffraction patterns through the incidence of electrons upon crystalline matter.

electron energy loss spectroscopy (EELS). A spectrographic technique in the electron microscope that analyzes the energy distribution of the electrons transmitted through the specimen. The energy loss spectrum is characteristic of the chemical composition of the region being sampled.

electron multiplier phototube. See *photomultiplier tube*.

electron probe x-ray microanalysis (EPMA). A technique in analytical chemistry in which a finely focused beam of electrons is used to excite an x-ray spectrum characteristic of the elements in a small region of the sample.

electron scattering. Any change in the direction of propagation or kinetic energy of an electron as a result of a collision.

emission (of electromagnetic radiation). The creation of radiant energy in matter, resulting in a corresponding decrease in the energy of the emitting system.

emission lines. Spectral lines resulting from emission of electromagnetic radiation by atoms, ions, or molecules during changes from excited states to states of lower energy.

emission spectrometer. An instrument that measures percent concentrations of elements in samples of metals and other materials; when the sample is vaporized by an electric spark or arc, the characteristic wavelengths of light emitted by each element are measured with a diffraction grating and an array of photodetectors or photographic plates.

emission spectroscopy. The branch of spectroscopy treating the theory, interpretation, and application of spectra originating in the emission of electromagnetic radiation by atoms, ions, radicals, and molecules.

emission spectrum. An electromagnetic spectrum produced when radiation from any emitting source, excited by any of various forms of energy, is dispersed.

emulsion calibration curve. The plot of a function of the relative transmittance of the photographic emulsion versus a function of the exposure. The calibration curve is used in spectrographic analysis to calculate the relative intensity of a radiant source from the density of a photographically recorded image.

energy-dispersive spectroscopy (EDS). A method of x-ray analysis that discriminates by energy levels the characteristic x-rays emitted from the sample. Compare with *wavelength-dispersive spectroscopy*.

epitaxy. Oriented growth of a crystalline substance on a crystalline substrate with a fixed orientation between the two crystal lattices.

error. The difference between the true or expected value and the measured value of a quantity or parameter.

escape peak. An artifact observed in x-ray analysis; manifested as a peak at energy 1.74 keV (the silicon Kα peak) less than the major line detected. Escape peaks can be avoided by increasing the accelerating voltage.

Euler angles. Three angular parameters that specify the orientation of a body with respect to reference axes.

excitation index. The ratio of the intensities of two selected spectral lines of an element having widely different excitation energies. This ratio serves to indicate the level of excitation energy in the source.

excitation potential (x-ray). The applied potential on an x-ray tube required to produce characteristic radiation from the target.

excitation volume. The volume within the sample in which data signals originate.

exposure. The product of the intensity of a radiant source and the time of irradiation.

exposure index. The relative transmittance or optical density of a selected spectral line, this value serving to indicate the degree of blackening of the photographic emulsion.

extended x-ray absorption fine structure (EXAFS). The weak oscillatory structure extending for several hundred electron volts away from an absorption edge. The oscillations occur because the electromagnetic wave produced by the ionization of the absorbing atom for some energy E has a wavelength $\lambda = 1.225/(E - E_k)^{1/2}$ nm, where E_k is the energy of the absorption edge. For example, a loss of 100 eV above an edge corresponds to a wavelength of 0.12 nm, which is of the order of atomic spacing. Consequently, the wave can be diffracted from neighboring atoms and return to interfere with the outgoing wave. An analysis of EXAFS data reveals important information about atomic arrangements and bonding. Either synchrotron x-radiation or the electron beam in the analytical transmission electron microscope can be used as the excitation source. See also *analytical electron microscopy, synchrotron radiation*.

eyepiece. The lens system used in an optical instrument for magnification of the image formed by the objective.

F

far-infrared radiation. Infrared radiation in the wavelength range of 30 to 300 μm (3×10^5 to 3×10^6 Å).

ferromagnetic resonance. Magnetic resonance of a ferromagnetic material. See also *ferromagnetism, magnetic resonance*.

ferromagnetism. A property exhibited by certain metals, alloys, and compounds of the transition (iron group), rare-earth, and actinide elements in which, below a certain temperature termed the Curie temperature, the atomic magnetic moments tend to line up in a common direction. Ferromagnetism is characterized by the strong attraction of one magnetized body for another. See also *Curie temperature*. Compare with *paramagnetism*.

field-emission microscopy. An image-forming analytical technique in which a strong electrostatic field causes emission of electrons from a sharply rounded point or from a specimen that has been placed on that point. The electrons are accelerated to a phosphorescent screen, or photographic film, producing a visible picture of the variation of emission over the specimen surface.

field ion microscopy. An analytical technique in which atoms are ionized by an electric field near a sharp specimen tip; the field then forces the ions to a fluorescent screen, which shows an enlarged image of the tip, and individual atoms are made visible. See also *atom probe*.

field ionization. The ionization of gaseous atoms and molecules by an intense electric field, often at the surface of a solid.

filter. A semitransparent optical element capable of absorbing unwanted electromagnetic radiation and transmitting the remainder. A neutral density filter attenuates relatively uniformly from the ultraviolet to the infrared, but in many applications highly wavelength-selective filters are used. See also *neutral filter*.

fluorescence. A type of photoluminescence in which the time interval between the absorption and re-emission of light is very short. Contrast with *phosphorescence*.

fluorometric analysis. A method of chemical analysis that measures the fluorescence intensity of the analyte or a reaction product of the analyte and a chemical reagent.

fluorimetry. See *fluorometric analysis*.

Fourier transform infrared (FT-IR) spectrometry. A form of infrared spectrometry in which data are obtained as an interferogram, which is then Fourier transformed to obtain an amplitude versus wavenumber (or wavelength) spectrum.

Frank-Condon principle. The principle which states that the transition from one energy state to another is so rapid that the nuclei of the atoms involved can be considered stationary during the transition.

free radical. Any molecule or atom that possesses one unpaired electron. In chemical notation, a free radical is symbolized by a single dot (to denote the odd electron) to the right of the chemical symbol.

frequency. The number of cycles per unit time. The recommended unit is the hertz, Hz, which is equal to one cycle per second.

full width at half maximum (FWHM). A measure of resolution of a spectrum or chromatogram determined by measuring the peak width of a spectral or chromatographic peak at half its maximum height.

functional group. A chemical radical or structure that has characteristic properties; examples are hydroxyl and carboxyl groups.

G

gamma ray. A high-energy photon, especially as emitted by a nucleus in a transition between two energy levels.

gamma-ray spectrometry. See *gamma-ray spectroscopy.*

gamma-ray spectroscopy. Determination of the energy distribution of γ-rays emitted by a nucleus. Also known as gamma-ray spectrometry.

gas chromatography. A separation method involving passage of a gaseous mobile phase through a column containing a stationary adsorbent phase; used principally as a quantitative analytical technique for volatile compounds. See also *chromatography, ion chromatography, liquid chromatography.*

gas constant. The constant of proportionality appearing in the equation of state of an ideal gas, equal to the pressure of the gas multiplied by its molar volume divided by its temperature. Also known as universal gas constant.

gas mass spectrometry. An analytical technique that provides quantitative analysis of gas mixtures through the complete range of elemental and molecular gases.

gel-permeation chromatography (GPC). See *size-exclusion chromatography.*

goniometer. An instrument devised for measuring the angle through which a specimen is rotated or for orienting a sample (for example, a single crystal) in a specific way.

gradient elution. A technique for improving the efficiency of separations achieved by liquid chromatography. It refers to a stepwise or continuous change with time in the mobile phase composition.

gram-equivalent weight. The mass in grams of a reactant that contains or reacts with Avogadro's number of hydrogen atoms. See also *Avogadro's number.*

gram-molecular weight. The mass of a compound in grams equal to its molecular weight.

gross sample. One or more increments of material taken from a larger quantity (lot)

of material for assay or record purposes. Also termed bulk sample or lot sample. See also *increment, lot.*

H

half-life ($t_{1/2}$). The time required for one half of an initial (large) number of atoms of a radioactive isotope to decay. Half-life is related to the decay constant λ by the expression $t_{1/2} = \ln 2/\lambda$. See also *decay constant.*

Hall effect. The development of a transverse electric field in a current-carrying conductor placed in a magnetic field.

heterogeneity. The degree of nonuniformity of composition or properties. Contrast with *homogeneity.*

high-temperature combustion. An analytical technique for determining the concentrations of carbon and sulfur in samples. The sample is burned in a graphite crucible in the presence of oxygen, which causes carbon and sulfur to leave the sample as carbon dioxide and sulfur dioxide. These gases are then detected by infrared or thermal conductive means.

homogeneity. The degree of uniformity of composition or properties. Contrast with *heterogeneity.*

homologous pairs. Spectral lines for different elements that respond in the same way to changes in excitation conditions. One line can be used as an interval standard line for the other.

Hooke's law. A generalization applicable to all solid material, which states that stress is directly proportional to strain and is expressed as:

$$\frac{\text{Stress}}{\text{Strain}} = \frac{\sigma}{\epsilon} = \text{constant} = E$$

where E is the modulus of elasticity or Young's modulus. The constant relationship between stress and strain applies only below the proportional limit. See also *modulus of elasticity.*

I

image analysis. Measurement of the size, shape, and distributional parameters of microstructural features by electronic scanning methods, usually automatic or semiautomatic. Image analysis data output can provide individual measurements on each separate feature (feature specific) or field totals for each measured parameter (field specific).

image contrast. A measure of the degree of detectable difference in intensity within an image.

increment. An individual portion of material collected by a single operation of a sampling device from parts of a lot separated in time or space. Increments may be tested individually or combined (composited) and tested as a unit.

index of refraction. See *refractive index.*

individuals. Conceivable constituent parts of a population. See also *population.*

inductively coupled plasma (ICP). An argon plasma excitation source for atomic emission spectroscopy or mass spectroscopy. It is operated at atmospheric pressure and sustained by inductive coupling to a radio-frequency electromagnetic field. See also *radio frequency.*

inelastic scattering. Any collision or interaction that changes the energy of an incident particle. Contrast with *elastic scattering.*

inert gas fusion. An analytical technique for determining the concentrations of oxygen, hydrogen, and nitrogen in a sample. The sample is melted in a graphite crucible in an inert gas atmosphere; individual component concentrations are detected by infrared or thermal conductive methods.

infrared radiation. Electromagnetic radiation in the wavelength range of 0.78 to 300 μm (7800 to 3×10^6 Å). See also *electromagnetic radiation, far-infrared radiation, middle-infrared radiation, near-infrared radiation.*

infrared spectrometer. A device used to measure the amplitude of electromagnetic radiation of wavelengths between visible light and microwaves.

infrared spectroscopy. The study of the interaction of material systems with electromagnetic radiation in the infrared region of the spectrum. The technique is useful for determining the molecular structure of organic and inorganic compounds by identifying the rotational and vibrational energy levels associated with the various molecules.

infrared spectrum. (1) The range of wavelengths of infrared radiation. (2) A display or graph of the intensity of infrared radiation emitted or absorbed by a material as a function of wavelength or some related parameter.

instrument response time. The time required for an indicating or detecting device to attain a defined percentage of its steady-state value following an abrupt change in the quantity being measured.

intensity ratio. The ratio of two (relative) intensities.

interference of waves. The process whereby two or more waves of the same frequency or wavelength combine to form a wave whose amplitude is the sum of the amplitudes of the interfering waves.

interferometer. An instrument in which the light from a source is split into two or more beams, which are subsequently reunited and interfere after traveling over different paths.

internal standard. In spectroscopy, a material present in or added to samples that serves as an intensity reference for measurements; used to compensate for variations in sample excitation and photographic processing in emission spectroscopy.

internal standard line. In spectroscopy, a spectral line of an internal standard, with which the radiant energy of an analytical line is compared.

intersystem crossing. A transition between electronic states that differ in total spin quantum number.

ion. An atom, or group of atoms, which by loss or gain of one or more electrons has acquired an electric charge. If the ion is formed from an atom of hydrogen or an atom of a metal, it is usually positively charged; if the ion is formed from an atom of a nonmetal or from a group of atoms, it is usually negatively charged. The number of electronic charges carried by an ion is termed its electrovalence. The charges are denoted by superscripts that give their sign and number; for example, a sodium ion, which carries one positive charge, is denoted by Na^+; a sulfate ion, which carries two negative charges, by SO_4^{2-}. See also *atomic structure, chemical bonding.*

ion chromatography. An area of high-performance liquid chromatography that uses ion exchange resins to separate various species of ions in solution and elute them to a suitable detector for analysis. See also *chromatography, gas chromatography, liquid chromatography.*

ion exchange. A reversible chemical reaction between a solid (ion exchanger) and a fluid (usually an aqueous solution) by means of which ions may be interchanged.

ion-exchange chromatography (IEC). Liquid chromatography with a stationary phase that possesses charged functional groups. This technique is applicable to the separation of ionic (charged) compounds. See also *ion chromatography.*

ion exchange resin. A synthetic resin containing active groups (usually sulfonic, carboxylic, phenol, or substituted amino groups) that give the resin the property of combining with or exchanging ions between the resin and a solution.

ion neutralization. The generic term for a class of charge-exchange processes in which an ion is neutralized by passage through a gas or by interaction with a material surface.

ion-pair chromatography (IPC). Liquid chromatography with a mobile phase containing an ion that combines with sample ions, creating neutral ion pairs. The ion pairs are typically separated using bonded-phase chromatography. See also *bonded-phase chromatography.*

ion-scattering spectrometry. A technique to elucidate composition and structure of the outermost atomic layers of a solid material, in which principally mono-energetic, singly charged, low-energy (less than 10 keV) probe ions are scattered from the surface and are subsequently detected and recorded as a function of the energy.

ion-scattering spectrum. A plot of scattered ion intensity as a function of the ratio of the scattered ion energy to the incident ion energy.

ion species. Type and charge of an ion. If an isotope is used, it should be specified.

ionic bond. A type of chemical bonding in which one or more electrons are transferred completely from one atom to another, thus converting the neutral atoms into electrically charged ions. These ions are approximately spherical and attract each other because of their opposite charges. Contrast with *covalent bond.*

ionic charge. The positive or negative charge of an ion.

irradiance (of a receiver). The radiant power per unit area incident on a receiver. See also *exposure.*

isobar. In atomic physics, one of two or more atoms that have a common mass number A, but differ in atomic number Z. Thus, although isobars possess approximately equal masses, they differ in chemical properties; they are atoms of different elements. See also *nuclear structure.*

isocratic elution. In liquid chromatography, the use of a mobile phase whose composition is unchanged throughout the course of the separation process.

isotone. One of two or more atoms that display a constant difference $A - Z$ between their mass number A and their atomic number Z. Thus, despite differences in the total number of nuclear constituents, the numbers of neutrons in the nuclei of isotones are the same. See also *nuclear structure.*

isotope. One of two or more nuclidic species of an element having an identical number of protons (Z) in the nucleus, but a different number of neutrons (N). Isotopes differ in mass, but chemically are the same element. See also *nuclear structure.*

J

Johnson noise. See *thermal noise.*

Joule-Thomson effect. A change in temperature in a gas undergoing Joule-Thomson expansion. See also *Joule-Thomson expansion.*

Joule-Thomson expansion. The adiabatic, irreversible expansion of a gas flowing through a porous plug or partially open valve. See also *Joule-Thomson effect.*

K

k-factor. The ratio between the unknown and standard x-ray intensities used in quantitative analyses.

K-radiation. Characteristic x-rays produced by an atom or ion when a vacancy in the K shell is filled by an electron from another shell.

K-series. The set of characteristic x-ray wavelengths making up K-radiation for the various elements.

K shell. The innermost shell of electrons surrounding the atomic nucleus, having electrons characterized by the principal quantum number 1.

Kikuchi lines. Light and dark lines superimposed on the background of a single-crystal electron-diffraction pattern caused by diffraction of diffusely scattered electrons within the crystal; the pattern provides structural information on the crystal.

kinetic energy. The energy that a body possesses because of its motion; in classical mechanics, equal to one half of the body's mass times the square of its speed.

klystron. An evacuated electron-beam tube in which an initial velocity modulation imparted to electrons in the beam subsequently results in density modulation of the beam. This device is used as an amplifier or oscillator in the microwave region.

L

L-radiation. Characteristic x-rays produced by an atom or ion when a vacancy in the L shell is filled by an electron from another shell.

L-series. The set of characteristic x-ray wavelengths making up L-radiation for the various elements.

L shell. The second shell of electrons surrounding the nucleus of an atom, having electrons with principal quantum number 2.

laboratory sample. A sample, intended for testing or analysis, prepared from a gross sample or otherwise obtained; the laboratory sample must retain the composition of the gross sample. Reduction in particle size is often necessary in the course of reducing the quantity.

Larmor frequency. The classical frequency at which a charged body precesses in a uniform magnetic field. $\omega_L = -eB/2mc$, where e is the electron charge, B is the magnetic field intensity, m is mass, and c is the velocity of light. See also *Larmor period*.

Larmor period. The inverse of the Larmor frequency. See also *Larmor frequency*.

lens. A transparent optical element, so constructed that it serves to change the degree of convergence or divergence of the transmitted rays.

ligand. The molecule, ion, or group bound to the central atom in a chelate or a coordination compound. See also *chelate*, *coordination compound*.

light. Radiant energy in a spectral range visible to the normal human eye ($\sim$380 to 780 nm, or 3800 to 7800 Å). See also *electromagnetic radiation*.

line pair. In spectroscopy, an analytical line and the internal standard line with which it is compared. See also *internal standard line*.

linear dispersion. In spectroscopy, the derivative $dx/d\lambda$, where x is the distance along the spectrum and λ is the wavelength. Linear dispersion is usually expressed as mm/Å.

liquid chromatography. A separation method based on the distribution of sample compounds between a stationary phase and a liquid mobile phase. See also *chromatography*, *gas chromatography*, *ion chromatography*.

liquid-liquid chromatography (LLC). Liquid chromatography with a stationary phase composed of a liquid dispersed onto an inert supporting material. Also termed liquid-partition chromatography.

liquid-partition chromatography (LPC). See *liquid-liquid chromatography*.

liquid-solid chromatography (LSC). Liquid chromatography with silica or alumina as the stationary phase. See also *adsorption chromatography*.

lot. A quantity of bulk material of similar composition whose properties are under study.

lot sample. See *gross sample*.

low-energy electron diffraction. A technique for studying the atomic structure of single-crystal surfaces, in which electrons of uniform energy in the approximate range of 5 to 500 eV are scattered from a surface. Those scattered electrons that have lost no energy are selected and accelerated to a fluorescent screen where the diffraction pattern from the surface is observed.

M

M shell. The third layer of electrons surrounding the nucleus of an atom, having electrons characterized by the principal quantum number 3.

macroscopic stress. Residual stress in a material in a distance comparable to the gage length of strain measurement devices (as opposed to stresses within very small, specific regions, such as individual grains). See also *microscopic stress*.

magnetic contrast. In electron microscopy, contrast that arises from the interaction of the electrons in the beam with the magnetic fields of individual magnetic domains in ferromagnetic materials. Special instrumentation is required for this type of work.

magnetic resonance. A phenomenon in which the magnetic spin systems of certain atoms absorb electromagnetic energy at specific (resonant) natural frequencies of the system.

magnetometer. An instrument for measuring the magnitude and sometimes also the direction of a magnetic field, such as the earth's magnetic field. See also *torque-coil magnetometer*.

magneton. A unit of magnetic moment used for atomic, molecular, or nuclear magnets. The Bohr magneton (μ_B), which has the value of the classical magnetic moment of the electron, can theoretically be calculated as:

$$\mu_B = \mu_0 = \frac{e\hbar}{2mc}$$

$$= 9.2741 \times 10^{-2} \text{ erg/G}$$

$$= 9.2741 \times 10^{-24} \text{ J/T}$$

where e and m are the electronic charge and mass, respectively; $\hbar$ is Planck's constant divided by 2π; and c is the velocity of light. See also *Planck's constant*.

magnetostriction. Changes in dimensions of a body resulting from application of a magnetic field.

magnification. A ratio of the size of an image to its corresponding object. This is usually determined by linear measurement.

mass absorption coefficient. The linear absorption coefficient divided by the density of the medium.

mass spectrometry. An analytical technique for identification of chemical structures, analysis of mixtures, and quantitative elemental analysis, based on application of the mass spectrometer.

mass spectrum. A record, graph, or table that shows the relative number of ions of various masses that are produced when a given substance is processed in a mass spectrometer.

matrix. The principal element or elements in a sample.

matrix isolation. A technique for maintaining molecules at low temperature for spectroscopic study; this method is particularly well suited for preserving reactive species in a solid, inert environment.

metallic glass. An alloy having an amorphous or glassy structure. See also *amorphous solid*.

metallography. The study of the structure of metals and alloys by various methods, especially by optical and electron microscopy.

micelle. A submicroscopic unit of structure built up from ions or polymeric molecules.

microanalysis. The analysis of samples smaller than 1 mg.

micrograph. A graphic reproduction of an object as formed by a microscope or equivalent optical instrument.

microscope. An instrument capable of producing a magnified image of a small object.

microscopic stress. Residual stress in a material within a distance comparable to the grain size. See also *macroscopic stress*.

microscopy. The science of the interpretive use and applications of microscopes.

microwave radiation. Electromagnetic radiation in the wavelength range of 0.3 mm to 1 m (3×10^6 to 10^{10} Å). See also *electromagnetic radiation*.

middle-infrared radiation. Infrared radiation in the wavelength range of 3 to 30 μm (3×10^4 to 3×10^5 Å). See also *infrared radiation, electromagnetic radiation*.

mobile phase. In chromatography, the gas or liquid that flows through the chromatographic column. A sample compound in the mobile phase moves through the column and is separated from compounds residing in the stationary phase. See also *stationary phase*.

modulus of elasticity (E). The measure of rigidity or stiffness of a metal; the ratio of stress, below the proportional limit, to the corresponding strain. In terms of the stress-strain diagram, the modulus of elasticity is the slope of the stress-strain curve in the range of linear proportionality of stress to strain. Also known as Young's modulus.

moiety. A portion of a molecule, generally complex, having a characteristic chemical property.

moiré pattern. A pattern developed from interference or light blocking when gratings, screens, or regularly spaced patterns are superimposed on one another.

molality. The number of gram-molecular weights of a compound dissolved in 1 L of solvent. See also *gram-molecular weight*. Compare with *molarity, normality*.

molarity. The number of gram-molecular weights of a compound dissolved in 1 L of solution. See also *gram-molecular weight*. Compare with *molality, normality*.

mole. An amount of substance of a system that contains as many elementary units (6.02×10^{23}) as there are atoms of carbon in 0.012 kg of the pure nuclide ^{12}C; the elementary unit must be specified and may be an atom, molecule, ion, electron, photon, or even a specified group of such units. See also *Avogadro's number*.

molecular fluorescence spectroscopy. An analytical technique that measures the fluorescence emission characteristic of a molecular, as opposed to an atomic, species. The emission results from electronic transitions between molecular states and can be used to detect and/or measure trace amounts of molecular species.

molecular spectrum. The spectrum of electromagnetic radiation emitted or absorbed by a collection of molecules as a function of frequency, wave number, or some related quantity.

molecular structure. The manner in which electrons and nuclei interact to form a molecule, as elucidated by quantum mechanics and the study of molecular spectra.

molecular weight. The sum of the atomic weights of all the atoms in a molecule. Atomic weights (and therefore molecular weights) are relative weights arbitrarily referred to an assigned atomic weight of exactly 12.0000 for the most abundant isotope of carbon, ^{12}C. See also *atomic weight*.

molecule. A molecule may be thought of either as a structure built of atoms bound together by chemical forces or as a structure in which two or more positively charged nuclei are maintained in some definite geometrical configuration by attractive forces from the surrounding cloud of electrons. Besides chemically stable molecules, short-lived molecular fragments termed free radicals can be observed under special circumstances. See also *chemical bonding, free radical, molecular structure*.

monochromatic. Consisting of electromagnetic radiation having a single wavelength or an extremely small range of wavelengths, or particles having a single energy or an extremely small range of energies.

monochromator. A device for isolating monochromatic radiation from a beam of polychromatic radiation. See also *polychromator*.

monomer. A simple molecule capable of combining with a number of like or unlike molecules to form a polymer; a repeating structure unit within a polymer.

Monte Carlo techniques. Calculation of the trajectory of incident electrons within a given matrix and the pathway of the x-rays generated during interaction.

Mössbauer effect. The process in which γ-radiation is emitted or absorbed by nuclei in solid matter without imparting recoil energy to the nucleus and without Doppler broadening of the γ-ray energy.

Mössbauer spectroscopy. An analytical technique that measures recoilless absorption of γ-rays that have been emitted from a radioactive source as a function of the relative velocity between the absorber and the source.

Mössbauer spectrum. A plot of the relative absorption of γ-rays versus the relative velocity between an absorber and a source of γ-rays.

multichannel analyzer (MCA). An instrument that splits an input signal into a number of channels with respect to a particular parameter of the input. See also *energy-dispersive spectroscopy*.

multiple scattering event. A collision process that may be described as a sequence of binary scattering events that may or may not be elastic.

multiplier phototube. See *photomultiplier tube*.

N

N shell. The fourth layer of electrons surrounding the nucleus of an atom, having electrons with the principal quantum number 4.

near-infrared radiation. Infrared radiation in the wavelength range of 0.78 to 3 μm (7800 to 30 000 Å). See also *electromagnetic radiation, infrared radiation*.

nebulizer. A device for converting a sample solution into a gas-liquid aerosol for atomic absorption, emission, and fluorescence analysis. This may be combined with a burner to form a nebulizer burner. See also *atomization, atomizer*.

Neel point. See *Neel temperature*.

Neel temperature. The temperature below which spins in an antiferromagnetic material are ordered antiparallel so that there is zero net magnetic moment. Also known as Neel point.

neutral filter. A filter that attenuates the radiant power reaching the detector by the same factor at all wavelengths within a prescribed wavelength region.

neutron. An elementary particle that has approximately the same mass as the proton, but no electric charge. Rest mass is 1.67495×10^{-27} kg. An unbound (extranuclear) neutron is unstable and β-decays with a half-life of 10.6 min.

neutron absorber. A material in which a significant number of neutrons entering combine with nuclei and are not re-emitted.

neutron absorption. A process in which the collision of a neutron with a nucleus results in the absorption of the neutron into the nucleus with the emission of one or more prompt γ-rays: in certain cases, emission of α-particles, protons, or other neutrons or fission of the nucleus results. Also known as neutron capture.

neutron activation analysis. Activation analysis in which the specimen is bombarded with neutrons; identification is made by measuring the resulting radioisotopes. See also *activation analysis*.

neutron capture. See *neutron absorption*.

neutron cross section. A measure of the probability that an interaction of a given kind will take place between a nucleus and an incident neutron; it is an area such that the number of interactions that occur in a sample exposed to a beam of neutrons is equal to the product of the cross section, the number of nuclei per unit volume in the sample, the thickness of the sample, and the number of neutrons in the beam that would enter the sample if their velocities were perpendicular to it. The usual unit is the barn (10^{-24} cm^2). See also *barn*.

neutron detector. Any device that detects passing neutrons, for example, by observing the charged particles or γ-rays released in nuclear reactions induced by the neutrons or by observing the recoil of charged particles caused by collisions with neutrons.

neutron diffraction. The phenomenon associated with the interference processes that occur when neutrons are scattered by the atoms within solids, liquids, and gases.

neutron flux. The number of neutrons passing through an area in a unit of time.

neutron spectrometry. See *neutron spectroscopy*.

neutron spectroscopy. Determination of the energy distribution of neutrons. Scintillation detectors, proportional counters, activation foils, and proton recoil are used.

neutron spectrum. The distribution by energy of neutrons impinging on a surface, which can be measured by neutron spectroscopy techniques or sometimes from knowledge of the neutron source. See also *dosimeter*.

Nicol prism. A prism made by cementing together with Canada balsam two pieces of a diagonally cut calcite crystal. In such a prism the ordinary ray is totally reflected at the calcite/cement interface while the orthogonally polarized extraordinary ray is transmitted. The prism can thus be used to polarize light or analyze the polarization of light.

noise. Any undesired signal that tends to interfere with the normal reception or processing of a desired signal.

normal-phase chromatography (NPC). This refers to liquid-solid chromatography or to bonded-phase chromatography with a polar stationary phase and a nonpolar mobile phase. See also *bonded-phase chromatography, liquid-solid chromatography*.

normality. A measure of the number of gram-equivalent weights of a compound per liter of solution. Compare with *molarity*.

nuclear charge. See *atomic number*.

nuclear cross section (σ). The probability that a nuclear reaction will occur between a nucleus and a particle, expressed in units of area (usually barns). See also *barn*.

nuclear magnetic resonance (NMR). A phenomenon exhibited by a large number of atomic nuclei that is based on the existence of nuclear magnetic moments associated with quantized nuclear spins. These nuclear moments, when placed in a magnetic field, give rise to distinct nuclear Zeeman energy levels between which spectroscopic transitions can be induced by radio-frequency radiation. Plots of these transition frequencies, termed spectra, furnish important information about molecular structure and sample composition. See also *Zeeman effect*.

nuclear structure. The atomic nucleus at the center of the atom, containing more than 99.975% of the total mass of the atom. Its average density is approximately 3×10^{11} kg/cm^3; its diameter is approximately 10^{-12} cm and thus is much smaller than the diameter of the atom, which is approximately 10^{-8} cm. The nucleus is composed of protons and neutrons. The number of protons is denoted by Z, the number of neutrons by N. The total number of protons and neutrons in a nucleus is termed the mass number and is denoted by $A = N + Z$. See also *atomic structure, electron, neutron, proton, isobar, isotone, isotope*.

nuclide. A species of atom distinguished by the constitution of its nucleus. Nuclear constitution is specified by the number of protons, number of neutrons, and energy content or by atomic number, mass number, and atomic mass.

numerical aperture (of a lens). The product of the lowest index of refraction of the object space multiplied and the sine of the half angle from the object to the edges of the lens.

objective. The primary magnifying system of a microscope. A system, generally of lenses, less frequently of mirrors, forming a real, inverted, and magnified image of the object.

ocular. See *eyepiece*.

optical axis. The line formed by the coinciding principal axes of a series of optical elements comprising an optical system. It is the line passing through the centers of curvature of the optical surfaces.

optical emission spectroscopy. Pertaining to emission spectroscopy in the near-ultraviolet, visible, or near-infrared wavelength regions of the electromagnetic spectrum.

ordered structure. The crystal structure of a solid solution in which the atoms of different elements seek preferred lattice positions. Contrast with *disordered structure*.

outlier. In a set of data, a value so far removed from other values in the distribution that it is probably not a bona fide measurement. There are statistical methods for classifying a data point as an outlier and removing it from a data set.

P

paramagnetism. A property exhibited by substances that, when placed in a magnetic field, are magnetized parallel to the field to an extent proportional to the field (except at very low temperatures or in extremely large magnetic fields). Compare with *ferromagnetism*.

parts per billion. A measure of proportion by weight, equivalent to one unit weight of a material per billion (10^9) unit weights of compound. One part per billion is equivalent to 1 ng/g.

parts per million. A measure of proportion by weight, equivalent to one unit weight of a material per million (10^6) unit weights of compound. One part per million is equivalent to 1 mg/kg.

particle accelerator. A device that raises the velocities of charged atomic or subatomic particles to high values.

particle-induced x-ray emission. A method of trace elemental analysis in which a beam of ions (usually protons) is directed at a thin foil on which the sample to be analyzed has been deposited; the energy spectrum of the resulting x-rays is measured. See also *particle accelerator, proton*.

peak overlap. Formation of a single peak when two closely spaced x-ray peaks cannot be resolved; the energy (or wavelength) of the peak is some average of the characteristic energies (or wavelengths) of the original two peaks. See also *full width at half maximum*.

phase contrast. Contrast in high-resolution TEM images arising from interference effects between the transmitted beam and one or more diffracted beams.

phosphorescence. A type of photoluminescence in which the time period between the absorption and re-emission of light is relatively long (of the order of 10^{-4} to 10 s or longer). See also *photoluminescence*. Contrast with *fluorescence*.

photoelectric effect. The liberation of electrons by electromagnetic radiation incident on a substance.

photoelectric electron-multiplier tube. See *photomultiplier tube*.

photoluminescence. Re-emission of light absorbed by an atom or molecule. The light is emitted in random directions. There are two types of photoluminescence: fluorescence and phosphorescence. See also *fluorescence, phosphorescence*.

photometer. A device so designed that it measures the ratio of the radiant power of two electromagnetic beams.

photomultiplier tube. A device in which incident electromagnetic radiation creates electrons by the photoelectric effect. These electrons are accelerated by a series of electrodes called dynodes, with secondary emission adding electrons to the stream at each dynode. Also known as multiplier phototube, electron multiplier phototube, and photoelectric electron-multiplier tube.

photon. A particle representation of the electromagnetic field. The energy of the photon equals hv, where v is the frequency of the light in hertz, and h is Planck's constant. See also *Planck's constant*.

physical adsorption. See *physisorption*.

physisorption. The binding of an adsorbate to the surface of a solid by forces whose energy levels approximate those of condensation. Contrast with *chemisorption*.

pi bonding. Covalent bonding in which the atomic orbitals overlap along a plane perpendicular to the sigma bond(s) joining the nuclei of two or more atoms. See also *sigma bonding*.

pi electron. An electron that participates in pi bonding. See also *pi bonding*.

pipet. A tube, usually made of glass or plastic, used almost exclusively to deliver accurately known volumes of liquids or solutions during titration or volumetric analysis.

Planck's constant (h). A fundamental physical constant, the elementary quantum of action; the ratio of the energy of a photon to its frequency, it is equal to $6.62620 \pm 0.00005 \times 10^{-34}$ J · s.

plane grating. An optical component used to disperse light into its component wavelengths by diffraction off a series of finely spaced, equidistant ridges. A plane grating has a flat substrate. See also *concave grating, diffraction grating, reflection grating, transmission grating*.

plane strain. The condition in which one of the principal strains is zero.

plane stress. The condition in which one of the principal stresses is zero.

plasma. A gas of sufficient energy so that a large fraction of the species present is ionized and thus conducts electricity. Plasmas may be generated by the passage of a current between electrodes, by induction, or by a combination of these methods.

plasma-jet excitation. The use of a high-temperature plasma jet to excite an element in a sample, for example, for atomic emission spectroscopy. Also known as dc plasma excitation.

plasmon. A quantum of a collective longitudinal wave in the electron gas of a solid.

Poisson's ratio (v). The absolute value of the ratio of transverse (lateral) strain to the corresponding axial strain resulting from uniformly distributed axial stress below the proportional limit of the material.

polarizing element. A general term for a device for producing or analyzing plane-polarized light. It may be a Nicol prism, some other form of calcite prism, a reflecting surface, or a polarizing filter.

polarography. An electroanalytical technique in which the current between a dropping mercury electrode (DME) and a counterelectrode (both of which are immersed in electrolyte) is measured as a function of the potential difference between the DME and a reference electrode.

pole figure. A stereoscopic projection of a polycrystalline aggregate showing the distribution of poles, or plane normals, of a specific crystalline plane, using specimen axes as reference axes. Pole figures are used to characterize preferred orientation in polycrystalline materials.

polychromator. A spectrometer that has many (typically 20 to 50) detectors for simultaneously measuring light from many spectral lines. Polychromators are commonly used in atomic emission spectroscopy. See also *monochromator*.

polymorph. In crystallography, one crystal form of a polymorphic material. See also *polymorphism*.

polymorphism. In crystallography, the property of a chemical substance whereby it crystallizes into two or more forms having different crystallographic structures, such as diamond versus graphite or fcc iron versus bcc iron.

population. In statistics, a generic term denoting any finite or infinite collection of individual samples or data points in the broadest concept; an aggregate determined by some property that distinguishes samples that do and do not belong.

positive eyepiece. An eyepiece in which the real image of the object is formed below the lower lens elements of the eyepiece.

potentiometric membrane electrodes. Electrochemical sensing devices that can be used to quantify cationic and anionic substances and gaseous species in aqueous solutions. These devices are also used for analytical titrations. See also *titration*.

Pourbaix (potential-pH) diagram. A plot of the redox potential of a corroding system versus the pH of the system, compiled using thermodynamic data and the Nernst equation. The diagram shows regions within which the metal itself or some of its compounds are stable.

prearc (or prespark) period. In emission spectroscopy, the time interval after the initiation of an arc (or spark) discharge during which the emitted radiation is not recorded for analytical purposes.

precision. The reproducibility of measurements within a set, that is, the scatter or dispersion of a set of data points about its central axis. Generally expressed as standard deviation or relative standard deviation.

premix burner. A burner used in flame emission and atomic absorption spectroscopy in which the fuel gas is mixed with the oxidizing gas before reaching the combustion zone.

primary x-ray. The emergent beam from the x-ray source.

prism. A transparent optical element whose entrance and exit apertures are polished plane faces. Using refraction and/or internal reflection, prisms are used to change the direction of propagation of monochromatic light and to disperse polychromatic light into its component wavelengths.

probe ion. An ionic species intentionally produced by an ion source and directed onto the specimen surface at a known incident angle and a known energy.

proportional limit. The greatest stress a material is capable of developing without a deviation from straight-line proportionality between stress and strain. See also *Hooke's law*.

proton. A particle that is the positively charged constituent of ordinary matter. Its charge is identical in magnitude but of opposite sign to that of the electron. Its mass equals 1.62726×10^{-24} g. See also *electron, neutron*.

Q

qualitative analysis. An analysis in which some or all of the components of a sample are identified. Contrast with *quantitative analysis*.

quantitative analysis. A measurement in which the amount of one or more components of a sample is determined. Contrast with *qualitative analysis*.

quantitative metallography. See *image analysis*.

quantum mechanics. The modern theory of matter, of electromagnetic radiation, and of the interaction between matter and radiation; also, the mechanics of phenomena to which this theory may be applied. Quantum mechanics, also termed wave mechanics, generalizes and supersedes the older classical mechanics and Maxwell's electromagnetic theory.

quantum number. One of the quantities, usually discrete with integer or half-integer values, needed to characterize a quantum state of a physical system.

quantum theory. See *quantum mechanics*.

R

radial distribution function analysis. Diffraction method that gives the distribution of interatomic distances present in a sample along with information concerning the frequency with which the particular distances occur.

radiant energy. Energy transmitted as electromagnetic radiation.

radiant intensity. The radiant power or flux emitted per unit solid angle expressed, for example, in watts per steradian.

radiant power (flux). The energy emitted by a source or transported in a beam per unit time, expressed, for example, in ergs per second or watts.

radical. See *free radical*.

radioactivity. (1) The property of the nuclei of some isotopes to spontaneously decay (lose energy). Usual mechanisms are emission of α, β, or other particles and splitting (fissioning). Gamma rays are frequently, but not always, given off in the process. (2) A particular component from a radioactive source, such as β radioactivity. See also *isotope, radioisotope*.

radioanalysis. An analytical technique, such as neutron activation analysis, that makes use of the radioactivity of an element or isotope. See also *isotope, radioisotope*.

radio frequency. A frequency at which coherent electromagnetic radiation of energy is useful for communication purposes; roughly the range from 10 kHz to 100 GHz.

radio-frequency spectrometer. An instrument that measures the intensity of radiation emitted or absorbed by atoms or molecules as a function of frequency at frequencies from 10 kHz to 100 GHz.

radio-frequency spectroscopy. The branch of spectroscopy concerned with the measurement of the intervals between atomic or molecular energy levels that are separated by frequencies from about 10^5 to 10^9 Hz as compared to the frequencies that separate optical energy levels of about 6×10^{14} Hz.

radioisotope. An isotope that is radioactive. Also known as a radionuclide. See also *isotope, radioactivity*.

radionuclide. See *radioisotope*.

Raman line (band). A line (band) that is part of a Raman spectrum and corresponds to a characteristic vibrational frequency of the molecule being probed.

Raman shift. The displacement in wave number of a Raman line (band) from the wave number of the incident monochromatic beam. Raman shifts are usually expressed in units of cm^{-1}. They correspond to differences between molecular vibrational, rotational, or electronic energy levels.

Raman spectroscopy. Analysis of the intensity of Raman scattering of monochromatic light as a function of frequency of the scattered light.

Raman spectrum. The spectrum of the modified frequencies resulting from inelastic scattering when matter is irradiated by a monochromatic beam of radiant energy. Raman spectra normally consist of lines (bands) at frequencies higher and lower than that of the incident monochromatic beam.

Rayleigh scattering. Scattering of electromagnetic radiation by independent particles that are smaller than the wavelength of radiation. Contrast with *Compton scattering*.

reagent. A substance, chemical, or solution used in the laboratory to detect, measure, or react with other substances, chemicals, or solutions. See also *reagent chemicals*.

reagent chemicals. High-purity chemicals used for analytical reactions, for testing of new reactions where the effects of impurities are unknown, and for chemical work where impurities must either be absent or at a known concentration.

reciprocal lattice. A lattice of points, each representing a set of planes in the crystal lattice, such that a vector from the origin of the reciprocal lattice to any point is normal to the crystal planes represented by that point and has a length that is the reciprocal of the plane spacing.

reciprocal linear dispersion. The derivative $d\lambda/dx$, where λ is the wavelength and x is the distance along the spectrum. The reciprocal linear dispersion usually is expressed in Å/mm.

red shift. A systematic displacement toward the longer wavelengths of the spectrum.

reduction. In sampling, the process of preparing one or more subsamples from a sample. Reduction may also refer to decreasing the valence of an ion or atom by the addition of electrons.

reference electrode. A nonpolarizable electrode with a known and highly reproducible potential used for potentiometric and voltammetric analyses. See also *calomel electrode*.

reference material. A material of definite composition that closely resembles in chemical and physical nature the material with which an analyst expects to deal; used for calibration or standardization.

reflectance. The ratio of the radiant power or flux reflected by a medium to the radiant power or flux incident on it; generally expressed as a percentage.

reflection grating. A grating that employs reflection off a series of fine, equidistant ridges, rather than transmission through a pattern of slots, to diffract light into its component wavelengths. The gratings used in optical instrumentation are almost exclusively reflection gratings. See also *concave grating, diffraction grating, plane grating, transmission grating*.

reflux. Heating a substance at the boiling temperature and returning the condensed vapors to the vessel to be reheated.

refractive index. The ratio of the phase velocity of monochromatic light in a vacuum to that in a specified medium. Refractive index is generally a function of wavelength and temperature. Also known as index of refraction.

relative standard deviation (RSD). The standard deviation expressed as a percentage of the mean value:

$$RSD = 100 \left(\frac{S}{X}\right) \frac{d^2}{n-1}$$

where S is the standard deviation, d is the difference between individual results and the average, n is the number of individual results, and X is the average of individual results. Also known as coefficient of variation.

relative transmittance. The ratio of the transmittance of the object in question to that of a reference object. For a spectral line on a photographic emulsion, it is the ratio of the transmittance of the photographic image of the spectral line to the transmittance of a clear portion of the photographic emulsion. Relative transmittance may be total, specular, or diffuse. See also *transmittance*.

residual stress. Stresses that remain within a body as the result of plastic deformation. These stresses can be measured using x-ray diffraction residual stress techniques.

resolution. The fineness of detail revealed by an optical device. Resolution is usually specified as the minimum distance by which two lines in the object must be separated before they can be revealed as separate lines in the image.

retention time (t_R). In chromatography, the amount of time a sample compound spends in the chromatographic column.

reversed-phase chromatography (RPC). Bonded-phase chromatography with a nonpolar stationary phase and a polar mobile phase. See also *bonded-phase chromatography*.

rocking curve. A method for determining the degree of imperfection in a crystal by using monochromatic, collimated x-rays reflecting off a ''perfect'' crystal to probe a second test crystal. A rocking curve is obtained by monitoring the x-ray intensity diffracted by the test crystal as it is slowly rocked, or rotated, through the Bragg angle for the reflecting planes.

Rutherford scattering. A general term for the classical elastic scattering of energetic ions by the nuclei of a target material.

S

sample. A portion of a material intended to be representative of the whole. Also known as specimen.

sampling. The obtaining of a portion of a material that is adequate for making the required tests or analyses, and that is representative of that portion of the material from which it is taken.

saturated calomel electrode. A reference electrode composed of mercury, mercurous chloride (calomel), and a saturated aqueous chloride solution.

scanning Auger microscopy (SAM). An analytical technique that measures the lateral distribution of elements on the surface of a material by recording the intensity of their Auger electrons versus the position of the electron beam.

scanning electron microscopy (SEM). An analytical technique in which an image is formed on a cathode-ray tube whose raster is synchronized with the raster of a point beam of electrons scanned over an area of the sample surface. The brightness of the image at any point is proportional to the scattering by or secondary emission from the point on the sample being struck by the electron beam.

scanning transmission electron microscopy (STEM). An analytical technique in which an image is formed on a cathode-ray tube whose raster is synchronized with the raster of a point beam of electrons scanned over an area of the sample. The brightness of the image at any point is proportional to the number of electrons that are transmitted through the sample at the point where it is struck by the beam.

scattering (of radiant energy). The deviations in the direction of propagation of radiant energy.

Schöniger combustion. A method of decomposition of organic materials by combusting them in a sealed flask that contains a solution suitable for absorbing the combustion products. The flask is swept with oxygen before ignition.

secondary electron. A low-energy electron (0 to 50 eV) emitted from a surface that is struck by particles with higher energies.

secondary ion. An ion other than the probe ion that originates from and leaves the specimen surface as a result of bombardment with a beam of primary or probe ions.

secondary ion mass spectroscopy (SIMS). An analytical technique that measures the masses of ions emitted from the surface of a material when exposed to a beam of incident ions. The incident ions are usually monoenergetic and are all of the same species, for example, 5-keV Ne^+ ions. See also *secondary ion*.

secondary x-rays. The x-rays emitted by a specimen following excitation by a primary x-ray beam or an electron beam.

segment. In sampling, a specifically demarked portion of a lot, either actual or hypothetical.

selected-area diffraction (SAD). Electron diffraction from a portion of a sample selected by inserting an aperture into the magnification portion of the lens system of a transmission electron microscope. Areas as small as 0.5 μm in diameter can be examined in this way.

selected-area diffraction pattern (SADP). An electron diffraction pattern obtained from a restricted area of a sample. The sharp spots in the pattern correspond closely to points in the reciprocal lattice of the material being studied. Usually such patterns are taken from a single crystal or a small number of crystals.

selectivity. The ability of a method or instrument to respond to a desired substance or constituent and not to others.

self-absorption. In optical emission spectroscopy, reabsorption of a photon by the same species that emitted it. For example, light emitted by sodium atoms in the center of a flame may be reabsorbed by different sodium atoms near the outer portions of the flame.

self-electrode. An electrode fabricated from the sample material and analyzed by emission spectroscopy.

self-reversal. In optical emission spectroscopy, the extreme case of self-absorption. See also *self-absorption*.

sensitivity. The capability of a method or instrument to discriminate between samples having different concentrations or amounts of the analyte.

siemens (S). A unit of electrical conductivity. One siemens of conductance per cubic meter with a potential of 1 V allows the passage of 1 A/m^2. See also *conductance*.

sigma bonding. Covalent bonding between atoms in which s orbitals or hybrid orbitals between s and p electrons overlap in cylindrical symmetry along the axis joining the nuclei of the atoms. See also *pi bonding*.

signal-to-noise ratio. The ratio of the amplitude of a desired signal at any time to the amplitude of noise signals at the same time. See also *noise*.

single crystal. A material that is completely composed of a regular array of atoms.

size-exclusion chromatography (SEC). Liquid chromatography method that separates molecules on the basis of their physical size. This technique is most often used in the analysis of polymers. Also termed *gel-permeation chromatography*.

solute. The substance dissolved in a solvent.

solution. In chemistry, a homogeneous dispersion of two or more kinds of molecular or ionic species. Solutions may be composed of any combination of liquids, solids, or gases, but they always consist of a single phase.

solvent. The part of a solution present in the largest amount, or the compound that is normally liquid in the pure state (as for solutions of solids or gases in a liquid).

spark. A series of electrical discharges, each of which is oscillatory and has a comparatively high maximum instantaneous current resulting from the breakdown of the analytical gap or the auxiliary gap, or both, by electrical energy stored at high voltage in capacitors. Each discharge is self-initiated and is extinguished when the voltage across the gap, or gaps, is no longer sufficient to maintain it.

spark source mass spectrometry. An analytical technique in which a high-voltage spark in a vacuum is used to produce positive ions of a conductive sample material. The ions are injected into a mass spectrometer, and the resulting spectrum is recorded on a photographic plate or measured using an electronic detector. The position of a particular mass spectral signal determines the element and isotope, and the intensity of the signal is proportional to the concentration.

specific gravity (of gases). The ratio of the density of a gas to the density of dry air at the same temperature and pressure.

specific gravity (of solids and liquids). The ratio of the mass of a unit volume of a material to the mass of the same volume of gas-free distilled water at the same temperature.

specimen. See *sample*.

spectral background. In spectroscopy, a signal obtained when no analyte is being introduced into the instrument, or a signal from a species other than that of the analyte.

spectral distribution curve. The curve showing the absolute or relative radiant power emitted or absorbed by a substance as a function of wavelength, frequency, or any other directly related variable.

spectral line. A wavelength of light with a narrow energy distribution or an image of a slit formed in the focal plane of a spectrometer or photographic plate that has a narrow energy distribution approxi-

mately equal to that formed by monochromatic radiation.

spectral order. The number of the intensity maxima of a given line from the directly transmitted or specularly reflected light from a diffraction grating.

spectrochemical (spectrographic, spectrometric, spectroscopic) analysis. The determination of the chemical elements or compounds in a sample qualitatively, semiquantitatively, or quantitatively by measurements of the wavelengths and intensities of spectral lines produced by suitable excitation procedures and dispersed by a suitable optical device.

spectrogram. A photographic or graphic record of a spectrum.

spectrograph. An optical instrument with an entrance slit and dispersing device that uses photography to record a spectral range. The radiant power passing through the optical system is integrated over time, and the quantity recorded is a function of radiant energy.

spectrometer. An instrument with an entrance slit, a dispersing device, and one or more exit slits, with which measurements are made at selected wavelengths within the spectral range, or by scanning over the range. The quantity detected is a function of the radiant power.

spectrophotometer. A spectrometer that measures the ratio (or a function of the ratio) of the intensity of two different wavelengths of light. These two beams may be separated in terms of time or space, or both.

spectroscope. An instrument that disperses radiation into a spectrum for visual observation.

spectroscopy. The branch of physical science treating the theory, measurement, and interpretation of spectra.

spectrum. The ordered arrangement of electromagnetic radiation according to wavelength, wave number, or frequency.

specular transmittance. The transmittance value obtained when the measured radiant energy in emission spectroscopy has passed from the source to the receiver without appreciable scattering.

spherical aberration. A lens defect in which image-forming rays passing through the outer zones of the lens focus at a distance from the principal plane different from that of the rays passing through the center of the lens.

spin glass. One of a wide variety of materials that contain interacting atomic mag-

netic moments and also possess some form of disorder, in which the temperature variation of the magnetic susceptibility undergoes an abrupt change in slope at a temperature generally referred to as the freezing temperature.

spin wave. A sinusoidal variation, propagating through a crystal lattice, of that angular momentum associated with magnetism (mostly spin angular momentum of the electrons). See also *spin glass*.

standard addition. A method in which small increments of a substance under measurement are added to a sample under test to establish a response function or, by extrapolation, to determine the amount of a constituent originally present in the sample.

standard electrode potential. The reversible or equilibrium potential of an electrode in an environment where reactants and products are at unit activity.

standard reference material. A reference material, the composition or properties of which are certified by a recognized standardizing agency or group.

standardization. In analytical chemistry, the assignment of a compositional value to one standard on the basis of another standard.

Stark effect. A shift in the energy of spectral lines due to an electrical field that is either externally applied or is an internal field caused by the presence of neighboring ions or atoms in a gas, solid, or liquid.

stationary phase. In chromatography, a particulate material packed into the column or a coating on the inner walls of the column. A sample compound in the stationary phase is separated from compounds moving through the column as a result of being in the mobile phase. See also *mobile phase*.

Stokes Raman line. A Raman line that has a frequency lower than that of the incident monochromatic beam.

strata. In sampling, segments of a lot that may vary with respect to the property under study.

stress-strain diagram. A graph in which corresponding values of stress and strain are plotted against each other. Values of stress are usually plotted vertically (ordinate, or y axis) and values of strain horizontally (abscissa, or x axis). Also known as stress-strain curve.

structure factor. A mathematically formulated term that relates the positions and identities of atoms in a crystalline material to the intensities of x-ray or electron beams diffracted from particular crystallographic planes.

subsample. A portion taken from a sample. A laboratory sample may be a subsample of a gross sample; similarly, a test portion may be a subsample of a laboratory sample.

sum peak. An artifact encountered during pulse pileup where two x-rays simultaneously entering the detector are counted as one x-ray, the energy of which is equal to the sum of both x-rays.

superlattice. See *ordered structure*.

supporting electrode. An electrode, other than a self-electrode, on which the sample is supported during spectrochemical analysis.

synchrotron. A device for accelerating charged particles by directing them along a roughly circular path in a magnetic guide field. As the particles pass through accelerating cavities placed along their orbit, their kinetic energy is increased repetitively, multiplying their initial energy by factors of hundreds or thousands. See also *synchrotron radiation*.

synchrotron radiation. Electromagnetic radiation emitted by charged particles in circular motion at relativistic energies.

T

target. That part of an x-ray tube which the electrons strike and from which x-rays are emitted.

texture. A preferential alignment of the crystalline lattice of the various grains in a polycrystalline aggregate.

thermal noise. The electrical noise produced in a resistor by thermally generated currents. These currents average zero, but produce electrical power having a non-zero average, which can affect instrument response. Also known as Johnson noise.

tilt. In electron microscopy, the angle of the specimen relative to the axis of the electron beam; at zero tilt the specimen is perpendicular to the beam axis.

titration. A method of determining the composition of a sample by adding known volumes of a solution of known concentration until a given reaction (color change, precipitation, or conductivity change) is produced. See also *volumetric analysis*.

torque-coil magnetometer. A magnetometer that depends for its operation on the torque developed by a known current in a coil that can turn in the field to be measured. See also *magnetometer*.

total transmittance. The ratio of the radiant energy leaving one side of a region between two parallel planes to the radiant energy entering from the opposite side.

transmission electron microscopy (TEM). An analytical technique in which an image is formed on a cathode-ray tube whose raster is synchronized with the raster of an electron beam over an area of the sample surface. Image contrast is formed by the scattering of electrons out of the beam.

transmission grating. A transparent diffraction grating through which light is transmitted. See also *concave grating, diffraction grating, plane grating, reflection grating*.

transmittance. The ratio of the light intensity transmitted by a material to the light intensity incident upon it. In emission spectrochemical analysis, the transmittance of a developed photographic emulsion, including its film or glass supporting base, is measured by a microphotometer. In absorption spectroscopy, the material is the sample. See also *diffuse transmittance, relative transmittance, specular transmittance, total transmittance*.

triggered capacitor discharge. A high-voltage electrical discharge used in emission spectroscopy for vaporization and excitation of a sample material. The energy for the discharge is obtained from capacitors that are charged from an ac or dc electrical supply. Each discharge may be either oscillatory, critically damped, or overdamped. It is initiated by separate means and is extinguished when the voltage across the analytical gap falls to a value that no longer is sufficient to maintain it.

triton. The nucleus of tritium (^{3}H), the triton is the only known radioactive nuclide belonging to hydrogen and β-decays to ^{3}He with a half-life of 12.4 years.

U

ultraviolet. Pertaining to the region of the electromagnetic spectrum from approximately 10 to 380 nm. The term ultraviolet without further qualification usually refers to the region from 200 to 380 nm.

ultraviolet radiation. Electromagnetic radiation in the wavelength range of 10 to 380 nm. See also *electromagnetic radiation*.

ultraviolet/visible (UV/VIS) absorption spectroscopy. An analytical technique that measures the wavelength-dependent attenuation of ultraviolet, visible, and near-infrared light by an atomic or molecular species; used in the detection, identification, and quantification of numerous atomic and molecular species.

uncertainty. The range of values within which the true value is estimated to lie. It is a best estimate of possible inaccuracy due to both random and systematic error.

unit cell. A parallelepiped element of crystal structure, containing a certain number of atoms, the repetition of which through space will build up the complete crystal.

universal gas constant. See *gas constant*.

uranyl. The chemical name designating the UO_2^{2+} group and compounds containing this group.

V

vidicon. A camera tube in which a charge-density pattern is formed by photoconduction and stored on a photoconductor surface that is scanned by an electron beam.

visible. Pertaining to radiant energy in the electromagnetic spectral range visible to the normal human eye (~380 to 780 nm).

visible radiation. Electromagnetic radiation in the spectral range visible to the human eye (~380 to 780 nm).

voltage contrast. In scanning electron microscopy, additional contrast in an image arising from increased emission of secondary electrons from negatively biased regions of a sample. This type of contrast is often used to advantage in the examination of microelectronic devices.

voltammetry. An electrochemical technique in which the current between working (indicator) electrodes and counter-electrodes immersed in an electrolyte is measured as a function of the potential difference between the indicator electrode and a reference electrode, for example, polarography.

volumetric analysis. Quantitative analysis of solutions of known volume but unknown strength by adding reagents of known concentration until a reaction end point (color change or precipitation) is reached; the most common technique is by titration.

W

wavelength (λ). The distance, measured along the line of propagation of a wave, between two points that are in phase on adjacent waves. The customary units are angstroms, microns, and nanometers.

wavelength-dispersive spectroscopy (WDS). A method of x-ray analysis that employs a crystal spectrometer to discriminate characteristic x-ray wavelengths. Compare with *energy-dispersive spectroscopy*.

wave number. The number of waves per unit length. Commonly used in infrared and Raman spectroscopy, the wave number is expressed as the reciprocal of the wavelength. The usual unit of wave number is the reciprocal centimeter (cm^{-1}).

white radiation. See *continuum*.

X

x-ray diffraction (XRD). An analytical technique in which measurements are made of the angles at which x-rays are preferentially scattered from a sample (as well as of the intensities scattered at various angles) in order to deduce information on the crystalline nature of the sample—its crystal structure, orientations, and so on.

x-ray diffraction residual stress techniques. Diffraction method in which the strain in the crystal lattice is measured, and the residual stress producing the strain is calculated assuming a linear elastic distortion of the crystal lattice. See also *macroscopic stress*, *microscopic stress*, *residual stress*.

x-ray emission spectroscopy. Pertaining to emission spectroscopy in the x-ray wavelength region of the electromagnetic spectrum.

x-ray fluorescence. Emission by a substance of its characteristic x-ray line spectrum on exposure to x-rays.

x-ray map. An intensity map (usually corresponding to an image) in which the intensity in any area is proportional to the concentration of a specific element in that area.

x-ray photoelectron spectroscopy (XPS). An analytical technique that measures the energy spectra of electrons emitted from the surface of a material when exposed to monochromatic x-rays.

x-ray spectrograph. A photographic instrument for x-ray emission analysis. If the instrument for x-ray emission analysis does not employ photography, it is better described as an x-ray spectrometer.

x-ray spectrometry. Measurement of wavelengths of x-rays by observing their diffraction by crystals of known lattice spacing.

Y

Young's modulus. See *modulus of elasticity*.

Z

ZAF corrections. A quantitative x-ray program that corrects for atomic number (Z), absorption (A), and fluorescence (F) effects in a matrix.

Zeeman effect. A splitting of a degenerate electron energy level into states of slightly different energies in the presence of an external magnetic field. This effect is useful for background correction in atomic absorption spectrometers.

REFERENCES

- *Compilation of ASTM Standard Definitions,* 5th ed., ASTM, Philadelphia, 1982
- *Concise Encyclopedia of Science and Technology,* McGraw-Hill, 1984
- *Dictionary of Scientific and Technical Terms,* 2nd ed., McGraw-Hill, 1978
- "Standard Definitions of Terms Relating to Metallography," E 7, *Annual Book of ASTM Standards,* Vol 03.03, ASTM, Philadelphia, 1984, p 12–48
- "Standard Definitions of Terms Relating to Microscopy," E 175, *Annual Book of ASTM Standards,* Vol 14.01, ASTM, Philadelphia, 1984, p 215–219
- "Standard Definitions of Terms Relating to Surface Analysis," E 673, *Annual Book of ASTM Standards,* Vol 03.06, ASTM, Philadelphia, 1984, p 305–309
- "Standard Definitions of Terms, Symbols, Conventions and References Relating to High-Resolution Nuclear Magnetic Resonance (NMR) Spectroscopy," E 386, *Annual Book of ASTM Standards,* Vol 14.01, ASTM, Philadelphia, 1984, p 453–463
- "Standard Definitions of Terms and Symbols Relating to Emission Spectroscopy," E 135, *Annual Book of ASTM Standards,* Vol 03.06, ASTM, Philadelphia, 1984, p 74–80

Metric Conversion Guide

This Section is intended as a guide for expressing weights and measures in the Système International d'Unités (SI). The purpose of SI units, developed and maintained by the General Conference of Weights and Measures, is to provide a basis for world-wide standardization of units and measure. For more information on metric conversions, the reader should consult the following references:

- "Standard for Metric Practice," E 380, *Annual Book of ASTM Standards,* 1985, ASTM, 1916 Race Street, Philadelphia, PA 19103
- "Metric Practice," ANSI/IEEE 268–1982, American National Standards Institute, 1430 Broadway, New York, NY 10018

- *Metric Practice Guide—Units and Conversion Factors for the Steel Industry,* 1978, American Iron and Steel Institute, 1000 16th Street NW, Washington, DC 20036
- *The International System of Units,* SP 330, 1981, National Bureau of Standards. Order from Superintendent of Documents, U.S. Government Printing Office, Washington, DC 20402
- *Metric Editorial Guide,* 4th ed. (revised), 1985. American National Metric Council, 1010 Vermont Avenue NW, Suite 320, Washington, DC 20005-4960
- *ASME Orientation and Guide for Use of SI (Metric) Units,* ASME Guide SI 1, 9th ed., 1982. The American Society of Mechanical Engineers, 345 East 47th Street, New York, NY 10017

Base, supplementary, and derived SI units

Measure	Unit	Symbol	Measure	Unit	Symbol
Base units			Entropy	joule per kelvin	J/K
			Force	newton	N
Amount of substance	mole	mol	Frequency	hertz	Hz
Electric current	ampere	A	Heat capacity	joule per kelvin	J/K
Length	meter	m	Heat flux density	watt per square meter	W/m^2
Luminous intensity	candela	cd	Illuminance	lux	lx
Mass	kilogram	kg	Inductance	henry	H
Thermodynamic temperature	kelvin	K	Irradiance	watt per square meter	W/m^2
Time	second	s	Luminance	candela per square meter	cd/m^2
			Luminous flux	lumen	lm
			Magnetic field strength	ampere per meter	A/m
Supplementary units			Magnetic flux	weber	Wb
Plane angle	radian	rad	Magnetic flux density	tesla	T
Solid angle	steradian	sr	Molar energy	joule per mole	J/mol
			Molar entropy	joule per mole kelvin	J/mol · K
			Molar heat capacity	joule per mole kelvin	J/mol · K
Derived units			Moment of force	newton meter	N · m
Absorbed dose	gray	Gy	Permeability	henry per meter	H/m
Acceleration	meter per second squared	m/s^2	Permittivity	farad per meter	F/m
Activity (of radionuclides)	becquerel	Bq	Power, radiant flux	watt	W
Angular acceleration	radian per second squared	rad/s^2	Pressure, stress	pascal	Pa
Angular velocity	radian per second	rad/s	Quantity of electricity, electric		
Area	square meter	m^2	charge	coulomb	C
Capacitance	farad	F	Radiance	watt per square meter steradian	$W/m^2 · sr$
Concentration (of amount of substance)	mole per cubic meter	mol/m^3	Radiant intensity	watt per steradian	W/sr
Conductance	siemens	S	Specific heat capacity	joule per kilogram kelvin	J/kg · K
Current density	ampere per square meter	A/m^2	Specific energy	joule per kilogram	J/kg
Density, mass	kilogram per cubic meter	kg/m^3	Specific entropy	joule per kilogram kelvin	J/kg · K
Electric charge density	coulomb per cubic meter	C/m^3	Specific volume	cubic meter per kilogram	m^3/kg
Electric field strength	volt per meter	V/m	Surface tension	newton per meter	N/m
Electric flux density	coulomb per square meter	C/m^2	Thermal conductivity	watt per meter kelvin	W/m · K
Electric potential, potential difference, electromotive force	volt	V	Velocity	meter per second	m/s
			Viscosity, dynamic	pascal second	Pa · s
Electric resistance	ohm	Ω	Viscosity, kinematic	square meter per second	m^2/s
Energy, work, quantity of heat	joule	J	Volume	cubic meter	m^3
Energy density	joule per cubic meter	J/m^3	Wavenumber	1 per meter	l/m

Conversion factors

To convert from	to	multiply by
Angle		
degree	rad	1.745 329 E − 02
Area		
in.^{2}	mm^2	6.451 600 E + 02
in.^{2}	cm^2	6.451 600 E + 00
in.^{2}	m^2	6.451 600 E − 04
ft^2	m^2	9.290 304 E − 02
Bending moment or torque		
lbf · in.	N · m	1.129 848 E − 01
lbf · ft	N · m	1.355 818 E + 00
kgf · m	N · m	9.806 650 E + 00
ozf · in.	N · m	7.061 552 E − 03
Bending moment or torque per unit length		
lbf · in./in.	N · m/m	4.448 222 E + 00
lbf · ft/in.	N · m/m	5.337 866 E + 01
Current density		
A/in.^{2}	A/cm^2	1.550 003 E − 01
A/in.^{2}	A/mm^2	1.550 003 E − 03
A/ft^2	A/m^2	1.076 400 E + 01
Electricity and magnetism		
gauss	T	1.000 000 E − 04
maxwell	μWb	1.000 000 E − 02
mho	S	1.000 000 E + 00
Oersted	A/m	7.957 700 E + 01
Ω · cm	Ω · m	1.000 000 E − 02
Ω circular-mil/ft	μΩ · m	1.662 426 E − 03
Energy (impact, other)		
ft · lbf	J	1.355 818 E + 00
Btu (thermochemical)	J	1.054 350 E + 03
cal (thermochemical)	J	4.184 000 E + 00
kW · h	J	3.600 000 E + 06
W · h	J	3.600 000 E + 03
Flow rate		
ft^3/h	L/min	4.719 475 E − 01
ft^3/min	L/min	2.831 000 E + 01
gal/h	L/min	6.309 020 E − 02
gal/min	L/min	3.785 412 E + 00
Force		
lbf	N	4.448 222 E + 00
kip (1000 lbf)	N	4.448 222 E + 03
tonf	kN	8.896 443 E + 00
kgf	N	9.806 650 E + 00
Force per unit length		
lbf/ft	N/m	1.459 390 E + 01
lbf/in.	N/m	1.751 268 E + 02
Fracture toughness		
ksi $\sqrt{\text{in.}}$	MPa$\sqrt{\text{m}}$	1.098 800 E + 00
Heat content		
Btu/lb	kJ/kg	2.326 000 E + 00
cal/g	kJ/kg	4.186 800 E + 00

To convert from	to	multiply by
Heat input		
J/in.	J/m	3.937 008 E + 01
kJ/in.	kJ/m	3.937 008 E + 01
Length		
Å	nm	1.000 000 E − 01
μin.	μm	2.540 000 E − 02
mil	μm	2.540 000 E + 01
in.	mm	2.540 000 E + 01
in.	cm	2.540 000 E + 00
ft	m	3.048 000 E − 01
yd	m	9.144 000 E − 01
mile	km	1.609 300 E + 00
Mass		
oz	kg	2.834 952 E − 02
lb	kg	4.535 924 E − 01
ton (short, 2000 lb)	kg	9.071 847 E + 02
ton (short, 2000 lb)	kg × 10^3(a)	9.071 847 E − 01
ton (long, 2240 lb)	kg	1.016 047 E + 03
Mass per unit area		
oz/in.^{2}	kg/m^2	4.395 000 E + 01
oz/ft^2	kg/m^2	3.051 517 E − 01
oz/yd^2	kg/m^2	3.390 575 E − 02
lb/ft^2	kg/m^2	4.882 428 E + 00
Mass per unit length		
lb/ft	kg/m	1.488 164 E + 00
lb/in.	kg/m	1.785 797 E + 01
Mass per unit time		
lb/h	kg/s	1.259 979 E − 04
lb/min	kg/s	7.559 873 E − 03
lb/s	kg/s	4.535 924 E − 01
Mass per unit volume (includes density)		
g/cm^3	kg/m^3	1.000 000 E + 03
lb/ft^3	g/cm^3	1.601 846 E − 02
lb/ft^3	kg/m^3	1.601 846 E + 01
lb/in.^{3}	g/cm^3	2.767 990 E + 01
lb/in.^{3}	kg/m^3	2.767 990 E + 04
Power		
Btu/s	kW	1.055 056 E + 00
Btu/min	kW	1.758 426 E − 02
Btu/h	W	2.928 751 E − 01
erg/s	W	1.000 000 E − 07
ft · lbf/s	W	1.355 818 E + 00
ft · lbf/min	W	2.259 697 E − 02
ft · lbf/h	W	3.766 161 E − 04
hp (550 ft · lbf/s)	kW	7.456 999 E − 01
hp (electric)	kW	7.460 000 E − 01
Power density		
W/in.^{2}	W/m^2	1.550 003 E + 03
Pressure (fluid)		
atm (standard)	Pa	1.013 250 E + 05
bar	Pa	1.000 000 E + 05
in. Hg (32 °F)	Pa	3.386 380 E + 03
in. Hg (60 °F)	Pa	3.376 850 E + 03
lbf/in.^{2} (psi)	Pa	6.894 757 E + 03
torr (mm Hg, 0 °C)	Pa	1.333 220 E + 02

To convert from	to	multiply by
Specific heat		
Btu/lb · °F	J/kg · K	4.186 800 E + 03
cal/g · °C	J/kg · K	4.186 800 E + 03
Stress (force per unit area)		
tonf/in.^{2}(tsi)	MPa	1.378 951 E + 01
kgf/mm^2	MPa	9.806 650 E + 00
ksi	MPa	6.894 757 E + 00
lbf/in.^{2} (psi)	MPa	6.894 757 E − 03
MN/m^2	MPa	1.000 000 E + 00
Temperature		
°F	°C	5/9 · (°F − 32)
°R	°K	5/9
Temperature interval		
°F	°C	5/9
Thermal conductivity		
Btu · in./s · ft^2 · °F	W/m · K	5.192 204 E + 02
Btu/ft · h · °F	W/m · K	1.730 735 E + 00
Btu · in./h · ft^2 · °F	W/m · K	1.442 279 E − 01
cal/cm · s · °C	W/m · K	4.184 000 E + 02
Thermal expansion		
in./in. · °C	m/m · K	1.000 000 E + 00
in./in. · °F	m/m · K	1.800 000 E + 00
Velocity		
ft/h	m/s	8.466 667 E − 05
ft/min	m/s	5.080 000 E − 03
ft/s	m/s	3.048 000 E − 01
in./s	m/s	2.540 000 E − 02
km/h	m/s	2.777 778 E − 01
mph	km/h	1.609 344 E + 00
Velocity of rotation		
rev/min (rpm)	rad/s	1.047 164 E − 01
rev/s	rad/s	6.283 185 E + 00
Viscosity		
poise	Pa · s	1.000 000 E + 01
strokes	m^2/s	1.000 000 E − 04
ft^2/s	m^2/s	9.290 304 E − 02
in.^{2}/s	mm^2/s	6.451 600 E + 02
Volume		
in.^{3}	m^3	1.638 706 E − 05
ft^3	m^3	2.831 685 E − 02
fluid oz	m^3	2.957 353 E − 05
gal (U.S. liquid)	m^3	3.785 412 E − 03
Volume per unit time		
ft^3/min	m^3/s	4.719 474 E − 04
ft^3/s	m^3/s	2.831 685 E − 02
in.^{3}/min	m^3/s	2.731 177 E − 07
Wavelength		
Å	nm	1.000 000 E − 01

(a) kg × 10^3 = 1 metric ton

SI prefixes—names and symbols

Exponential expression	Multiplication factor	Prefix	Symbol
10^{18}	1 000 000 000 000 000 000	exa	E
10^{15}	1 000 000 000 000 000	peta	P
10^{12}	1 000 000 000 000	tera	T
10^9	1 000 000 000	giga	G
10^6	1 000 000	mega	M
10^3	1 000	kilo	K
10^2	100	hecto(a)	h
10^1	10	deka(a)	da
10^0	1	BASE UNIT	
10^{-1}	0.1	deci(a)	d
10^{-2}	0.01	centi(a)	c
10^{-3}	0.001	milli	m
10^{-6}	0.000 001	micro	μ
10^{-9}	0.000 000 001	nano	n
10^{-12}	0.000 000 000 001	pico	p
10^{-15}	0.000 000 000 000 001	femto	f
10^{-18}	0.000 000 000 000 000 001	atto	a

(a) Nonpreferred. Prefixes should be selected in steps of 10^3 so that the resultant number before the prefix is between 0.1 and 1000. These prefixes should not be used for units of linear measurement, but may be used for higher order units. For example, the linear measurement, decimeter, is nonpreferred, but square decimeter is acceptable.

Periodic Table of the Elements

Metals ← → | Nonmetals ← →

Key to chart

Atomic number → **50** +2 ← Oxidation states
Symbol → **Sn** +4
Atomic weight → 118.69
-18-18-4 ← Electron configuration

Ia	IIa	IIb	IVb	Vb	VIb	VIIb	VIII			Ib	IIb	IIIa	IVa	Va	VIa	VIIa	0	Orbit
1 +1 **H** −1 1.0079 1																	**2** 0 **He** 4.00260 2	K
3 +1 **Li** 6.939 2-1	**4** +2 **Be** 9.0122 2-2											**5** +3 **B** 10.81 2-3	**6** +2 +4 −4 **C** 12.011 2-4	**7** +1 +2 +3 +4 +5 −1 −2 −3 **N** 14.0067 2-5	**8** −2 **O** 15.9994 2-6	**9** −1 **F** 18.998403 2-7	**10** 0 **Ne** 10.17₉ 2-8	K-L
11 +1 **Na** 22.9898 2-8-1	**12** +2 **Mg** 24.312 2-8-2											**13** +3 **Al** 26.98154 2-8-3	**14** +2 +4 −4 **Si** 28.08 2-8-4	**15** +3 +5 −3 **P** 30.97376 2-8-5	**16** +4 +6 −2 **S** 32.06 2-8-6	**17** +1 +5 +7 −1 **Cl** 35.453 2-8-7	**18** 0 **Ar** 39.984 2-8-8	K-L-M
19 +1 **K** 39.09 -8-8-1	**20** +2 **Ca** 40.08 -8-8-2	**21** +3 **Sc** 44.9559 -8-9-2	**22** +2 +3 +4 **Ti** 47.9 -8-10-2	**23** +2 +3 +4 +5 **V** 50.941 -8-11-2	**24** +2 +3 +6 **Cr** 51.996 -8-13-1	**25** +2 +3 +4 +7 **Mn** 54.9380 -8-13-2	**26** +2 +3 **Fe** 55.847 -8-14-2	**27** +2 +3 **Co** 58.9332 -8-15-2	**28** +2 +3 **Ni** 58.71 -8-16-2	**29** +1 +2 **Cu** 63.54 -8-18-1	**30** +2 **Zn** 65.38 -8-18-2	**31** +3 **Ga** 69.72 -8-18-3	**32** +2 +4 **Ge** 72.59 -8-18-4	**33** +3 +5 −3 **As** 74.9216 -8-18-5	**34** +4 +6 −2 **Se** 78.96 -8-18-5	**35** +1 +5 −1 **Br** 79.904 -8-18-7	**36** 0 **Kr** 83.80 -8-18-8	-L-M-N
37 +1 **Rb** 85.467 -18-8-1	**38** +2 **Sr** 87.62 -18-8-2	**39** +3 **Y** 88.9059 -18-9-2	**40** +4 **Zr** 91.22 -18-10-2	**41** +3 +5 **Nb** 92.9064 -18-12-1	**42** +6 **Mo** 95.94 -18-13-1	**43** +4 +6 +7 **Tc** 98.9062 -18-13-2	**44** +3 **Ru** 101.07 -18-15-1	**45** +3 **Rh** 102.905 -18-16-1	**46** +2 +4 **Pd** 106.4 -18-18-0	**47** +1 **Ag** 107.868 -18-18-1	**48** +2 **Cd** 112.40 -18-18-2	**49** +3 **In** 114.82 -18-18-3	**50** +2 +4 **Sn** 118.69 -18-18-4	**51** +3 +5 −1 **Sb** 121.75 -18-18-5	**52** +4 +6 −2 **Te** 127.60 -18-18-6	**53** +1 +5 +7 −3 **I** 126.9045 -18-18-7	**54** 0 **Xe** 131.30 -18-18-8	-M-N-O
55 +1 **Cs** 132.9054 -18-8-1	**56** +2 **Ba** 137.3 -18-8-2	**57*** +3 **La** 138.9055 -18-9-2	**72** +4 **Hf** 178.49 -32-10-2	**73** +5 **Ta** 180.948 -32-11-2	**74** +6 **W** 183.85 -32-12-2	**75** +4 +6 +7 **Re** 186.207 -32-13-2	**76** +3 +4 **Os** 190.2 -32-14-2	**77** +3 +4 **Ir** 192.9 -32-15-2	**78** +2 +4 **Pt** 195.09 -32-16-2	**79** +1 +3 **Au** 196.9665 -32-18-1	**80** +1 +2 **Hg** 200.59 -32-18-2	**81** +1 +3 **Tl** 204.37 -32-19-3	**82** +2 +4 **Pb** 207.19 -32-18-4	**83** +3 +5 **Bi** 208.980 -32-18-5	**84** +2 +4 **Po** (209) -32-18-6	**85** **At** (210) -32-18-7	**86** 0 **Rn** (222) -32-18-8	-N-O-P
87 +1 **Fr** (223) -18-8-1	**88** +2 **Ra** 226.0254 -18-8-2	**89**** +3 **Ac** (227) -18-9-2	**104** +4 **Rf** (261) -32-10-2	**105** **Ha** (262) -32-11-2	**106** (263) -32-12-2													-O-P-Q

Transition elements

*Lanthanides	**58** +3 **Ce** +4 140.12 -20-8-2	**59** +3 **Pr** 140.9077 -21-8-2	**60** +3 **Nd** 144.24 -22-8-2	**61** +3 **Pm** 147 -23-8-2	**62** +2 **Sm** +3 150.4 -24-8-2	**63** +2 **Eu** +3 151.96 -25-8-2	**64** +3 **Gd** 157.25 -25-9-2	**65** +3 **Tb** 158.925 -27-8-2	**66** +3 **Dy** 162.50 -28-8-2	**67** +3 **Ho** 164.9304 -29-8-2	**68** +3 **Er** 167.26 -30-8-2	**69** +3 **Tm** 168.9342 -31-8-2	**70** +2 **Yb** +3 173.04 -32-8-2	**71** +3 **Lu** 174.967 -32-9-2	-N-O-P
**Actinides	**90** +4 **Th** 232.038 -18-10-2	**91** +5 **Pa** +4 231.0359 -20-9-2	**92** +3 **U** +4 +5 +6 238.029 21-9-2	**93** +3 **Np** +4 +5 +6 237.0482 -22-9-2	**94** +3 **Pu** +4 +5 +6 239.052 -24-8-2	**95** +3 **Am** +4 +5 +6 (243) -25-8-2	**96** +3 **Cm** (247) -25-9-2	**97** +3 **Bk** +4 (247) -27-8-2	**98** +3 **Cf** (251) -28-8-2	**99** +3 **Es** (254) -29-8-2	**100** +3 **Fm** (257) -30-8-2	**101** +2 **Md** +3 (258) -31-8-2	**102** +2 **No** +3 (259) -32-8-2	**103** +3 **Lr** (260) -32-9-2	-O-P-Q

Numbers in parentheses are mass numbers of most stable isotope of that element.

Abbreviations and Symbols

Acronyms: Techniques

APM atom probe microanalysis

AAS atomic absorption spectrometry

AEM analytical electron microscopy

AES Auger electron spectroscopy; atomic emission spectrometry

AFS atomic fluorescence spectrometry

ATEM analytical transmission electron microscopy

CBED convergent-beam electron diffraction

DRS diffuse reflectance spectroscopy

EDS energy-dispersive spectroscopy

EELS electron energy loss spectroscopy

ENAA epithermal neutron activation analysis

EPMA electron probe x-ray microanalysis

ESCA electron spectroscopy for chemical analysis

ESR electron spin resonance

EXAFS extended x-ray absorption fine structure

FIM field ion microscopy

FNAA fast neutron activation analysis

FMR ferromagnetic resonance

FT-IR Fourier transform infrared (spectroscopy)

GC gas chromatography

GC-IR gas chromatography-infrared (spectroscopy)

GC/MS gas chromatography/mass spectrometry

GFAAS graphite furnace atomic absorption spectrometry

HPLC high-performance liquid chromatography

IC ion chromatography

ICP-AES inductively coupled plasma atomic emission spectroscopy

ICP-MS inductively coupled plasma mass spectrometry

IR infrared (spectroscopy)

IRRAS infrared reflection absorption spectroscopy

LEED low-energy electron diffraction

LEISS low-energy ion-scattering spectroscopy

MS mass spectrometry

NAA neutron activation analysis

NGR nuclear gamma-ray resonance

NMR nuclear magnetic resonance

NQR nuclear quadrupole resonance

ODMR optical double magnetic resonance

OES optical emission spectroscopy

PAS photoacoustic spectroscopy

PGAA prompt gamma-ray activation analysis

PIXE particle-induced x-ray emission

RBS Rutherford backscattering spectrometry

RDF radial distribution function (analysis)

RHEED reflection high-energy electron diffraction

SAD selected-area diffraction

SANS small-angle neutron scattering

SAM scanning Auger microscopy

SAXS small-angle x-ray scattering

SEM scanning electron microscopy

SERS surface-enhanced Raman spectroscopy

SFC supercritical fluid chromatography

SIMS secondary ion mass spectroscopy

SSMS spark source mass spectrometry

STEM scanning transmission electron microscopy

TEM transmission electron microscopy

TNAA thermal neutron activation analysis

UV/VIS ultraviolet/visible (absorption spectroscopy)

XPS x-ray photoelectron spectroscopy

XRPD x-ray powder diffraction

XRF x-ray fluorescence

XRS x-ray spectrometry

Abbreviations

a crystal lattice length along the *a* axis

ac alternating current

A absorbance

ADC analog-to-digital converter

AFC automatic frequency control

AISI American Iron and Steel Institute

amu atomic mass unit

AOCS American Oil Chemists' Society

AP atom probe

ASM American Society for Metals

ASTM American Society for Testing and Materials

at.% atomic percent

ATR attenuated total reflectance

b Burgers vector

b crystal lattice length along the *b* axis

B magnetic flux density

bal balance or remainder

bcc body-centered cubic

BE backscattered electron

BF bright-field (illumination)

BIV best image voltage

c crystal lattice length along the *c* axis; velocity (speed of light)

CARCA computer-assisted rocking curve analysis

CBEDP convergent-beam electron-diffraction pattern

CDF centered dark-field (image)

CHA concentric hemispherical analyzer

CIRCLE cylindrical internal reflection cell

CL cathodoluminescence

CMA cylindrical mirror analyzer

cmc critical micelle concentration

CN cyanogen

cos cosine

cot cotangent

cps counts per second; cycles per second

CRT cathode-ray tube

CSN conductive solids nebulizer

cw continuous-wave (spectrometer)

d lattice spacing of crystal planes

dc direct current

DCP direct-current plasma

Df dilution factor

DF dark-field (illumination)

diam diameter

DIGM diffusion-induced grain-boundary migration

DME dropping mercury electrode

DNC delayed neutron counting

DSID direct sample insertion device

e electron; natural log base, 2.71828

E energy; modulus of elasticity

E_{cell} measured cell potential

E_{const} constant cell potential

E_p proton energy; primary electron energy

E_x x-ray energy

EBIC electron beam induced current

ECAP energy-compensated atom probe

EDL electroless discharge lamp

EDM electric discharge machining

ELDOR electron-electron double resonance

EMSA Electron Microscopy Society of America

ENDOR electron nuclear double resonance

Eq equation

ESA electrostatic analyzer

et al. and others

ETP electrolytic tough pitch (copper)

F fluorescence

F Faraday constant (96 486 C/mol)

FEG field emission gun

FET field effect transistor

FFT fast Fourier transform

FIA flow injection analysis

Fig. figure

FM ferromagnet

FMAR ferromagnetic antiresonance

FOLZ first-order Laue zone

FTS Fourier transform spectrometer

FWHM full width at half maximum

g diffraction vector

gcp geometrically close-packed

h Planck's constant

H_a applied magnetic field

H_d demagnetizing field

H_k anisotropy field

H_R magnetic resonance field

HB Brinell hardness

HCL hollow cathode lamp

hcp hexagonal close-packed

hfs hyperfine structure

HK Knoop hardness

HMDE hanging mercury drop electrode

HOLZ higher order Laue zone

HOPG highly oriented pyrolytic graphite

HR Rockwell hardness (requires scale designation, such as HRC for Rockwell ''C'' hardness)

HV Vickers hardness (diamond pyramid hardness)

I intensity

I_b background intensity

I_c coherent atomic scattering intensity

I_i incoherent atomic scattering intensity

I_t total diffracted intensity

I_0 initial intensity

ICP inductively coupled plasma

ID inside diameter

IEEE Institute of Electrical and Electronics Engineers

IR infrared

IRE internal-reflection element

ISE ion-selective electrode

JCPDS Joint Committee on Powder Diffraction Standards

K_u uniaxial anisotropy

K-M Kossel Mollenstaedt (diffraction pattern)

L length

ln natural logarithm (base *e*)

log common logarithm (base 10)

LRO long-range order

LTE local thermodynamic equilibrium

m molal solution

M magnetization; magnification; molar solution

M_{eff} effective magnetization

max maximum

MCA multichannel analyzer

MDM minimum detectable mass

ME Mössbauer effect

min minimum

MMF minimum mass fraction

MOCVD metallo-organic chemical vapor deposition

mol% mole percent

MOLE molecular optical laser examiner

n refractive index

N normal solution

NACE National Association of Corrosion Engineers

NASA National Aeronautics and Space Administration

NBS National Bureau of Standards

ND normal direction (of a sheet)

N(E) electron energy distribution

NIR near infrared

NRC Nuclear Regulatory Commission

OD outside diameter

ODF orientation distribution function

OFHC oxygen-free high-conductivity (copper)

ORNL Oak Ridge National Laboratory

p page

P phosphorescence

P polarization (of a molecule); probability

PDA photodiode arrays

PEM photoelastic modulator

pH negative logarithm of hydrogen-ion activity

PH precipitation-hardenable

pixel picture element

PLAP pulsed-laser atom probe

PM paramagnet

P/M powder metallurgy
PMT photomultiplier tube
PSD position-sensitive detector
PST polycrystal scattering topography
R or RE rare earth
R radius of curvature; universal gas constant
RD rolling direction (of a sheet)
REE reentrant
Ref reference
RF radio frequency
RPE rotating platinum microelectrode
RSD relative standard deviation
RSF relative sensitivity factor
SACP selected-area channeling pattern
SADP selected-area diffraction pattern
SAE Society of Automotive Engineers
SCC stress-corrosion cracking
SCE saturated calomel electrode
SE secondary electron
SG spin glass
SI Système International d' Unités
sin sine
SRM Standard Reference Material(s)
SRO short-range order
t thickness; time
T temperature
T_c Curie temperature
tan tangent
tcp topologically close-packed
TD transverse direction (of a sheet)
TE transverse electric
TG transgranular
UHV ultrahigh vacuum
UNS Unified Numbering System (ASTM-SAE)
UTW ultrathin window
UV ultraviolet
v electron velocity
VCD vibrational circular dichroism
VIS visible
VM vacuum melted
vol volume
vol% volume percent

VR vibrational relaxation
VSM vibrating sample magnetometer
WB weak beam
WD working distance
wt% weight percent
XANES x-ray absorption near-edge structure
YAG yttrium-aluminum-garnet
Z atomic number
ZOLZ zero-order Laue zone
ZR zone refined

Units of Measure

A amp
Å angstrom
atm atmosphere (pressure)
b barn
Btu British thermal unit
C coulomb
cm centimeter
cal calorie
d day
eV electron volt
F farad
ft foot
g gram
G gauss
Gy gray
GHz gigahertz
h hour
Hz hertz
in. inch
J joule
K Kelvin
kbar kilobar
keV kiloelectron volt
kg kilogram
kHz kilohertz
kPa kilopascal
ksi kips (1000 lb) per square inch
kV kilovolt
kW kilowatt
L liter
lb pound

m meter
mA milliampere
MeV megaelectron volt
mg milligram
MHz megahertz
min minute
MJ megajoule
mL milliliter
mm millimeter
mo month
MPa megapascal
ms millisecond
mV millivolt
N newton
nC nanocoulomb
ng nanogram
nm nanometer
ns nanosecond
oz ounce
Pa pascal
pm picometer
ppb parts per billion
ppm parts per million
psi pounds per square inch
R roentgen
rad radian
rpm revolutions per minute
s second
S siemens
T tesla
V volt
W watt
wk week
yr year

Symbols

° degree; angular measure
°C degree Celsius (centigrade)
°F degree Fahrenheit
⇌ direction of reaction
÷ divided by
= equals
≈ approximately equals
≠ not equal to

≡ identical with

> greater than

≫ much greater than

≧ greater than or equal to

∫ integral of

∞ infinity

∝ varies as; is proportional to

< less than

≪ much less than

≦ less than or equal to

± maximum deviation

− minus; negative ion charge

× multiplied by; diameters (magnification)

· multiplied by

/ per

% percent

+ plus; in addition to; positive ion charge

√ square root of

~ similar to; approximately

α angle

γ gyromagnetic ratio

Γ magnetic resonance linewidth

Δ change in quantity; an increment; a range

θ diffraction angle

λ wavelength

μ linear absorption coefficient

μA microampere

μin. microinch

μL microliter

μm micron (micrometer)

μM micromolar

μs microsecond

ν Poisson's ratio; frequency

π pi (3.141592)

ρ density

σ scattering cross section; stress

ψ angle between the normal to the diffracting lattice planes and the sample surface

Greek Alphabet

A, α alpha

B, β beta

Γ, γ gamma

Δ, δ delta

E, ε epsilon

Z, ζ zeta

H, η eta

Θ, θ theta

I, ι iota

K, κ kappa

Λ, λ lambda

M, μ mu

N, ν nu

Ξ, ξ xi

O, o omicron

Π, π pi

P, ρ rho

Σ, σ sigma

T, τ tau

Υ, υ upsilon

Φ, φ phi

X, χ chi

Ψ, ψ psi

Ω, ω omega

Index

J

K

L